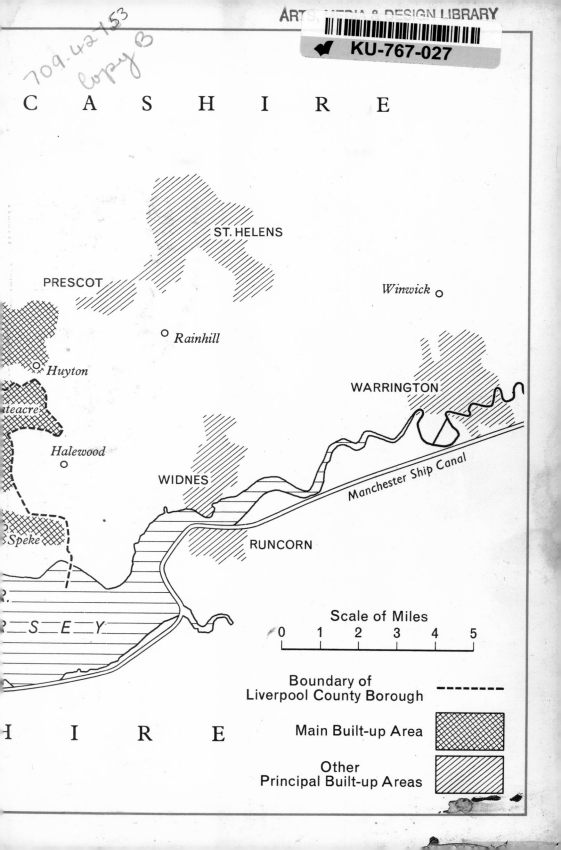

C A S H I R E

ST. HELENS

PRESCOT

Winwick ○

○ *Rainhill*

WARRINGTON

○× *Huyton*

teacre

Halewood
○

WIDNES

Manchester Ship Canal

○? *Speke*

RUNCORN

R.

S   E   Y

Scale of Miles

0   1   2   3   4   5

Boundary of
Liverpool County Borough   - - - - - - - -

Main Built-up Area

Other
Principal Built-up Areas

H I R E

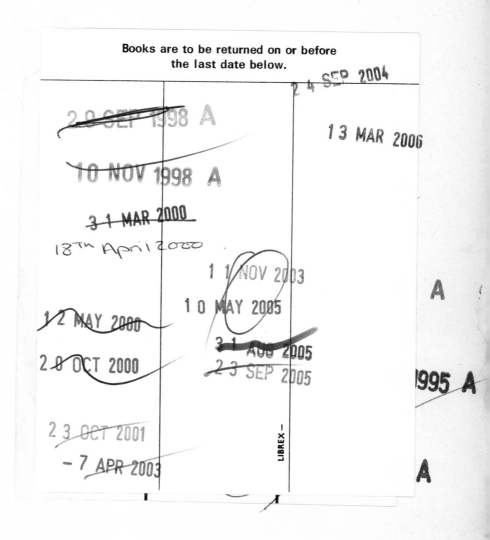

Books are to be returned on or before
the last date below.

24 SEP 2004

2 8 SEP 1998 A

13 MAR 2006

10 NOV 1998 A

3 1 MAR 2000

18Th April 2000

1 1 NOV 2003

1 0 MAY 2005

1 2 MAY 2000

A

2 0 OCT 2000

3 1 AUG 2005

23 SEP 2005

1995 A

2 3 OCT 2001

- 7 APR 2003

A

LIBREX—

BY THE SAME AUTHOR
The Theatre of Bertolt Brecht
and *Popski*. A Life of Vladimir Peniakoff DSO., MC

ART
IN A CITY

John Willett

Published for the Bluecoat Society of Arts by

Methuen & Co Ltd 11 New Fetter Lane London E C 4

First published in 1967
© 1967 by John Willett
Printed in Great Britain by
The Shenval Press
London, Hertford and Harlow

CONTENTS

ILLUSTRATIONS

ACKNOWLEDGMENTS

This book was developed from a report to the Bluecoat Society of Arts, originally presented in autumn 1965 and commissioned thanks to a grant from the Calouste Gulbenkian Foundation. Opinions expressed in it are my own. I am very grateful to both bodies for making its publication possible. The Chairman and Committee of the Bluecoat Society have been helpful, informative, hospitable and patient over a long period. More than anything I hope that it proves of real value to them and to their city.

The city authorities were of the utmost help. Among those who gave me their time were the Lord Mayor (Alderman David J. Lewis), the Town Clerk, the City Architect, the City Planning Officer and the Planning Consultant (both of whom supplied me generously with any material I asked for), the Director of Education and his Art and Crafts Adviser, the City Librarian and the City Public Relations Officer. Alderman H. Macdonald Steward of the Planning Committee and Councillors Shaw, Bessell and Heffer of the (then) Arts Sub-Committee all saw me. The Director of the Walker Art Gallery, his Deputy and his staff co-operated in a great number of ways; my job would have been very much harder without them. The Principal of the College of Art and the heads of the Department of Printing and the Schools of Graphic Design and Teacher Training gave me every facility.

The gallery kindly submitted my questionnaire to its visitors, as did Littlewood's Mail Order Stores to its staff, and Gateacre Comprehensive School to its staff and pupils. I am grateful to all those who answered it so carefully, to Susan Beckett, Paul Eachus, L. M. Green, Susan R. Hasleton and Suzanne Stuart of the College of Art who helped with the interviewing, and to Mr Ainsworth, Mr Baillie, Mr Ellison, Mr Howey, Mr Maskell and Mr Panther on whom I first tested the questions.

Colonel Vere E. Cotton gave me much information from his long experience and lent me valuable papers. Brian Patten, Roger McGough and Adrian Henri generously allowed me to reprint their poems. Dr Joan Evans in London gave me an advance view of her most interesting book on *The Conways*. The editor of the *Liverpool Post* printed three articles in which I aired some of the book's ideas. Mr Bor, Mr Scrutton, Mr Norman, Professor Quentin Bell, Roderick Bisson, John Rees-Jones, Mr Patchin, Sir Emrys Williams and (of the artists) Messrs Horsfield, Ballard, Dooley, Henri, MacKarell and Jardine were kind enough to check relevant sections of the typescript, and a number of amendments of fact are due to them. Sources of photographs have been given separately on page xiii, but I would like here to thank Jürgen Seuss, G. C. Macpherson, Robin Riley, Quentin Hughes, Ralph Fastnedge, Richard Huws, L. Ruscoe, Mr David Wood of Pilkingtons and Roderick Bisson and the Sandon Studios Society for the trouble they took to make prints available.

In a long series of visits to Liverpool so many other people also saw me that I can only try to list them, hoping that omissions will be put down to incompetence rather than ingratitude: Michael Argles (Institute of Education), C. B. Barber (W. R. Jacob and Co.), Leslie Blond, F. C. Boydell, the Headmaster of Breckfield SMS and Messrs Allan, McConkey and Moffat of his staff, Robert Buckley (Stanley Park SMS), Denis Chapman, James Cliffe, Patrick Cohen, Mr Colley of the College of Technology, J. L. Crockatt (Johnson Brothers), Norman Cullen, Mr Davey of J. Davey and Sons, John Eames, the late John Edkins, R. L. Ellis (Dunlops), K. H. Evans, Mrs Featherstone, A. W. Fraser (Rainhill Hospital), Professor and Mrs Fröhlich, the art staff of Gateacre CS (G. C. Drewitt and Messrs Jamieson, Jones, Lewis and Mrs Rooke), E. Gledhill (Kirkby College of Further Education), Mr Godwin of British-American Tobacco, Eric Goldrein, John Gorman, J. A. Haddy (College of Building), the late Neville Hill, Harry Hoodless (Laird School of Art, Birkenhead), C. D. Humphries (Medici Society), the Rev. J. Keir Murren, Dr T. Kelly (University Extra-Mural Department), P. L. Kemp (University Assistant Registrar), G. R. Kennerley, Norman Kingham, Frank Lambert, Sean Leak (St Martin's SMS), the Rev. W. Lockett, R. S. McArthur (Bootle School of Art), W. S. MacCunn, D. M. M'Farquhar (Art High School), the Very Rev. Mgr. McKenna, Dr R. F. McMahon (College of Technology), the Headmaster of Maghull GS, John Metcalfe (Goodlass Wall), G. Moyes (Birkenhead College of Technology), Mr Naylor of Winwick Hospital, the Headmistress of New Heys High School and Miss Monks and Miss Thearle of her staff, Miss M. W. Odell (Mabel Fletcher Technical College), Morton Oliphant, the late S. Pater (Weightman and Bullen), E. C. Roberts (College of Technology), Eric Rowan, John Roxburgh, the Deputy Headmaster of Ruffwood CS, D. R. Scarland (Bluecoat School), E. R. Scott (Lever Brothers), A. Shand (Evans Medical), Professor Lord Simey, Rodger Smith, W. H. Smith's Liverpool Manager, G. J. Stephens (British-American Tobacco), W. L. Stevenson

(Littlewoods), Mrs and Miss Sutcliffe, George Thomas, Sam Walsh, Mr and Mrs Colin Wilson and Professor H. Myles Wright. I would also like to thank Mr and Mrs Roy Burlend for making the visits in question so agreeable, often at very short notice.

Elsewhere I saw the Musêe Royale des Beaux-Arts in Antwerp, the Arts Council, Centre 42, the Civic Trust, the Council of Industrial Design, Alexander Dunbar (North East Association for the Arts), Granada Television, the Hochschule für Bildende Kunst in Hamburg, Astrid Kirchherr, the LCC, Peter Markmann, the Rotterdam City Council (Afd. Kunstzaken), the Royal College of Art (Industrial Design Department) and Mr Sheridan Russell. Others who gave information by letter or telephone included Thomas Agnew and Sons Ltd., the Town Clerk of Antwerp, the Automatic Telephone and Electric Co. Ltd., Sir Gerald Barry, the BBC (Liverpool), the Belgian Ministry of Education, the West Berlin Senator for Bau-und Wohnungswesen, Birkenhead Hospital Management Committee, Blackburn's (Liverpool) Ltd., Arthur Blenkinsop MP, Bootle Technical College, the Mayor of Boston, the Boston Museum of Fine Arts, BICC Further Education Centre, P. J. Broomhall and Partners, Richard Buckle, John M. Caven (Boots), Mrs Joan B. Clarke, Clatterbridge Hospital, the Conway Librarian (Courtauld Institute), William Crawford and Sons Ltd., S. J. Cross (Norwich), the Cunard Steam-Ship Co. Ltd., Deva Hospital Management Committee, Stanley Dumbell, Elder Dempster Lines Ltd., the Estates Officer of Liverpool University, the Ford Motor Co. Ltd., the Town Clerk of Genoa, Alfred Holt Ltd., John A. Hunter Ltd., ICI Paints Division, the International Association of Plastic Arts, Lamport and Holt Line, George Henry Lee and Co. Ltd., the secretary of Littlewoods' Sculptural Design Competition, Liverpool and District Fazackerley Group of Hospitals Management Committee, Liverpool Chamber of Commerce, Liverpool College of Commerce, Liverpool Region Children's Hospital Management Committee, Liverpool Regional Hospital Board, the London Group, London Press Exchange, Market Investigations Ltd., the Mayor and Prefect of Marseilles, Canon Martineau, Mass Observation, N. K. Michael, Ambassador Bowling, the National Gallery, North Liverpool Hospital Management Committee, the North Western Gas Board (Mersey Group), North Wirral Hospital Management Committee, Old Swan Technical College, Owen Owen Ltd., Eduardo Paolozzi, Pilkington Brothers Ltd., Queens Drive Evening Institute, Rainhill Hospital Management Committee, the Royal Academy, the Royal Institute of British Architects, the Royal Society of British Artists, Shaw Street Evening Institute, Sir Alfred Shennan and Partners, South Liverpool Hospital Management Committee, the Tate

Gallery, Mrs Thompson, Peter Walker (Warrington) Ltd, Wallasey Technical College, Walton Technical College, Widnes College of Further Education, Winwick and Newchurch Hospital Management Committee, Andrew McLaren Young, Philip N. Youtz. The getting of information from abroad would have been much harder without the help of HM consular representatives in Antwerp, Boston, Gdynia, Genoa, Marseilles and Rotterdam. I am only sorry that the efforts of Mr D. S. Clarke of the British Council were in vain.

I would like to thank the Bluecoat Society's secretaries, Mr and Mrs Van Mullem, for their many kindnesses, as well as Mrs Cowin and Mrs Ashcroft for help with paperwork. Perhaps my main personal debt is to those who asked me to do the job and to my editor and employers who allowed me to spend so much time on it. Place and people have made it, in all sorts of ways, an unforgettable experience.

Acknowledgments for Illustrations

The author and the publishers would like to thank the following for their kind permission to reproduce illustrations in this book:

Jürgen Seuss for three photographs of Liverpool, on pp. 3, 10 and 11.

The R.I.B.A. for the drawing on p. 35.

Lancashire Life for the photograph of G. W. Jardine on p. 189.

The Liverpool School of Architecture for the photograph of Richard Huws' fountain on p. 109 and David Wrightson's photographs of the Philharmonic and Crown Hotels on pp. 9, 57 and 58.

Gateacre School, Liverpool, for the photographs of pupils' sculpture on p. 154.

The Walker Art Gallery for the illustrations on pp. 21, 39, 44, 69, 70, 72, 74, 80, 116, 117, 118, 135, 170, 171, 192, 264 and 266.

The Trustees of the British Museum for photographs on pp. 33, 45, 52 and 59.

The Bluecoat Society of Arts for the photograph of the Strand-Paradise scheme and a work by Arthur Dooley on pp. 17 and 175.

The Trustees of the Lady Lever Art Gallery for paintings by John Stubbs and Dame Laura Knight on pp. 82 and 263.

Holly Lodge Girls' Grammar School for the photograph on p. 155.

Pilkington Brothers Ltd. for the photograph of Victor Pasmore's mural on p. 99.

The Medici Society Ltd. for the illustration of a painting by Doris Zinkeisen and the Medici Society Ltd. and the artist for the illustration of a painting by Peter Scott on p. 263.

[xiv] *Acknowledgments*

The illustrations on pp. 134, 135, 264, 265, 266 and 267 are included by courtesy of the Trustees of the Tate Gallery, London.

Peggy Mills for the photograph of Peter Startup's entry for Littlewoods Sculptural Design Competition on p. 106.

Peter MacKarell for photographs of his paintings on pp. 186 and 187.

Littlewoods Mail Order Stores Ltd. for the photograph of P. G. Heesom's maquette on p. 106.

The Greater London Council for photographs of Rutherford School and Karin Jonzen's *Mother and Child* on p. 210.

The *Observer* and the Camera Press Ltd. for a photograph of Henri's *Night Blues* on p. 184.

The Architectural Review for the photograph of Peterlee on p. 218.

The Cannon Hill Trust for the photograph of the model of the Midlands Arts Centre for Young People on p. 208.

The Liverpool Regional College of Art for the photographs of the Bluecoat '62 Exhibition on p. 84 and the department's work on pp. 144 and 145.

The Pallas Gallery Ltd. for the reproduction of *The Karlsbrucke in Prague* by Kokoschka on p. 264.

The Gordon Fraser Gallery Ltd. and Eric de Maré for the photograph of a panel in St George's Hall on p. 265 and the Gordon Fraser Gallery Ltd and Hans Wild for the photograph of Epstein's sculpture on p. 267.

Reg Cox for photographs of works by Robin Riley and Adrian Henri on pp. 94, 119 and 181.

The City of Liverpool Corporation for the photograph of the mosaic pavement in St. George's Hall on p. 36 and for the design by Gordon Cullen on p. 104.

The Aberdeen Art Gallery and the artist for the painting by Sir Alfred Munnings, RA on p. 264.

The Radio Times Hulton Picture Library for photographs on pp. 6, 28, 32, 51 and 68.

Hodder and Stoughton Ltd. for the photograph on p. 54.

Frost and Reed Ltd. for works by Tretchikoff and Doyly John on p. 122.

Copyright in *The Balinese Girl* by Tretchikoff is held on behalf of the artist by Frost and Reed Ltd.

SPADEM for the painting by Pablo Picasso on p. 265.

L'Express for the photograph of the Faculté des Sciences on p. 214.

Arthur Tooth and Sons Ltd. for the painting by Augustus John on p. 62.

Stewart Bale Ltd. and The Morris Singer Foundry Ltd. for the photograph on p. 93.

1 : PROBLEM AND PLACE

Art and society: over the past hundred years or so these words have become inseparables, till today their coupling produces an automatic yawn. They are as much of a pair as oil and vinegar, or chalk and cheese; like them they owe their association in our minds largely to the fact that they don't mix. Whose fault this is is open to endless debate: you can blame the present-day artists for talking an unduly private language, or the public for making too little effort to understand them, or the critics and educationalists for failing to reconcile the two groups, or the private or public patron for refusing to support the artists in the meantime or for backing the wrong ones. You can shrug your shoulders and say that the discrepancy is natural to an aimless, fragmented, alienated or godless social system: that it is just a symptom of larger human disasters. The fact itself remains a commonplace: art is cut off from our society by a sizeable gap.

It is remarkable how few constructive ideas this has led to. One would-be scoutmaster after another has rubbed the two terms vigorously together in the hope of producing sparks, but so far there have been clouds of smoke and remarkably little fire. The one or two instances this century where a coherent doctrine of art and society has emerged have been the work of politicians or at best political theorists, who felt entitled to impose their views on the world of art and, as it were, declare the gap closed by decree. Such remedies however are not just superficial and deceptive; they actually make any lasting reconciliation the more remote by discrediting the very word 'society' in the ears of the more independent-minded artists and critics. Except in the field of architecture, with its more obvious social relevance, there is now no vision of the relationship between the two concepts which could act as a stimulus to the visual arts. Though plenty of artists are worried or dissatisfied at their apparent incompatibility there is no inspiring alternative to work for.

But suppose we were to start at the other end. Suppose that instead of theorising from the highest artistic and social principles we were to take a close look, somewhere near ground level, at the situation of the visual arts in a particular community: might this not lead to fresh conclusions, not so much about the ideal relationship in theory but about the network of actual relationships on the ground? Might it not suggest ways in which they could be improved? At least the experiment ought to be worth trying. And yet oddly enough this is just what is never done. In no country is there more than the first rudiments of a sociology of the arts: a tradition of inquiry into all those outside factors – psychological, economic, social, administrative, ideological – on which the practice of art at any given time and place depends. Instead we treat works of art as god-given pieces of inspiration, finding it unnecessary to ask exactly what they do to people, or who paid for them and from what motive, or quite simply how they came to be there. Our instinct is to regard such questions as sacrilege. Our mistake is to feel that wrapping up art in a woolly cocoon of words must enhance it: that analysis can only destroy.

The report which follows is an attempt to show that a quite low-level investigation, based on the experience of a single English city, can not only be reasonably constructive but also suggest conclusions of wider scope. It sets out to see what tasks and possibilities exist for the visual arts in the city; how they have been fulfilled in the past and what the tradition is; how the various sections of a community appear to support art or reject it, together with their apparent tastes and motives; what the resources in local talent are, both actual and potential; and what policy the public authority follows in its schools and galleries. From all this flows a set of specific proposals designed to set the visual arts in a new framework: that of a modern community's interests, plans and needs. Where most proposals for the visual arts, in this country at least, amount to a demand for more of everything – more exhibitions, more artists, more prizes, more pictures for the public collections, more art history, more arts centres, more committees and above all more money – these aim rather to establish a relationship on new lines.

The community under discussion is the city of Liverpool, which not only contains perhaps the best municipal art gallery in England but has long harboured an active body of professional artists. In 1962 the Bluecoat Society of Arts there (a body described in Chapters 2 and 3) decided that its attempts to encourage painting and sculpture locally were not producing results, and that its policy in these matters needed rethinking. Accordingly it looked for an independent outsider who would make a general survey of the visual arts in Liverpool: of needs, demands, openings, and the individuals and institutions available to fulfil them. A Londoner himself, the author is glad that the choice fell on him. Quite apart from the sheer interest of the problem and the sometimes rather unfamiliar directions in which it led, it is difficult to have much to do with Liverpool without developing a special affection for the place. A special affection, because it also embraces exasperation and

1 Liverpool 1965. Looking eastwards towards
the ridge that forms the city's spine

regret at the conditions in which many of its inhabitants have had to live.

There is nowhere like Liverpool, and as it is the background to everything
that follows we had best start with an account of its particular characteristics
and of the situation in which it now finds itself, at least as far as seems relevant to this report. Like Antwerp, Rotterdam and Bremen (with which more
detailed comparisons will be made in Chapter 8) it is a great port of about
three-quarters of a million inhabitants, with all the openness and curiosity
that this implies. But these three-quarters of a million are an unusually
mixed lot, and Liverpool's peculiar scurrying liveliness may well be
due to the fact that its inhabitants are tugged in a number of directions.

B

They represent many races: the Irish – for this is still the cheapest crossing to England from Dublin – the Welsh whose hills one can (with luck) see in the distance, the native English of course, the West Indians and – more noticeable than their actual numbers would suggest – a small but centrally-located colony of Chinese. They are of mixed religion, with Catholic and Protestant more or less balancing one another, though the old fierce hostility has now given way to a keen mutual awareness. Politically they have been unable to relax into the common post-war stupor, for since 1945 power in the city council has passed from Labour to Conservative and back again, and the regular dismissal of the vanquished party's aldermen makes for an unusually quick turnover in municipal life. All this combines to give the Liverpool character its very individual stamp.

One sees it immediately in the children. It is hardly possible to imagine a stronger contrast than that between the children of Hamburg, neatly tucked into their hats, coats and gloves, with their well-ordered ways, their satchels tightly strapped on their backs, and the swarming Liverpool kids, off like small rodents on their own private or collective affairs, remote from grown-up control. Right in the middle of the town you see these anarchic apparitions,

2 Liverpool 7. Children on a
derelict site close to the University

exceedingly startling to the unprepared visitor, but at the same time suggesting a certain profound freedom in which exceptional qualities might be developed. Something of the same outward abandon is visible in their elders, as they convert the main shopping streets into virtual pedestrian precincts on a Saturday afternoon, contemptuously ignoring the power and dignity of the motor-car. It is not surprising that they should as a community be at once open- and independent-minded, quite willing to be influenced by the best Dutch and Viennese models in their prewar housing policy, for instance, or to introduce a French system of prefabricated housing now, yet always loath to be in any way linked with Manchester, only 36 miles away.

Physically the centre of the city is dominated by a long ridge about 150 feet high running parallel to the river Mersey and the 6 miles of docks that line it. On this stand the two cathedrals and the university, and between and around them what used before the middle of the last century to be the elegant residential area: square-cut terraces of dull red brick, interestingly greyed by the old local practice of mixing cinders in the mortar, and sometimes bearing in handsome cast-iron lettering the great Liverpool names of the period; Canning and Huskisson Streets for instance record the city's two most famous early nineteenth-century MPs. Across the edge of this area runs

3 Liverpool 8. Cast-iron; red brick; black mortar; great nineteenth-century names

the deep cutting of the old Liverpool and Manchester Railway, blasted in the solid red sandstone of which Giles Gilbert Scott built his cathedral, but walled off and invisible from above. The docks, though some of the older among them are unforgettably impressive, like the wholly enclosed early nineteenth-century Albert Dock with its arcaded warehouses, are similarly

4 The Customs House (1828) by John Foster, Junior, the best-known Liverpool architect of the early Industrial Revolution. Gibson's statue of Huskisson (see illustration 23) originally stood in front of the building, which was destroyed in the Second World War

shut off from view; the splendid vistas down to the river with its shipping which might be expected from the tilt of the land just don't exist. It is one of the great town-planning mistakes of Liverpool that except for the mis-leadingly-called Pier Head in the middle, with its messy-looking landing-stages, and the Dingle in the south where the ridge actually seems to hang right over the docks, all that can be seen of the waterfront is a high wall with heavy gates in it. As the late City Planning Officer said, Liverpool seems to turn its back on the sea.

Its buildings bear witness to the Industrial Revolution, to the days when, well ahead of the rest of the world, steam brought it prosperity. The tall warehouses with their narrow recesses for hoists set back in the brick facades, the factories and workshops crowding in towards the city centre, the great black commercial buildings, the unmistakeable pubs built by Walker's of Warrington, with a certain comforting opulence, in the domesticated Art Nouveau of the end of the century; these, interwoven with late Georgian back streets containing many small classical details, are the characteristic architecture of the place. Unlike so much of the rest of Lancashire, or indeed

5 The nineteenth-century presence. In front of the St George's Hall portico, with the Prince Consort on horseback, Wellington on his column (right, centre) and (in the distance half-left) the symbolical figure of Commerce on the Walker Art Gallery

of all Victorian England from the Houses of Parliament down, it is not Gothic. It was one of the points of insistence of the leaders of the Liverpool Royal Institution, which dominated the city's artistic and intellectual life after the Napoleonic wars, that a classical revival was the proper architectural expression for a booming mercantile community; and the building of St George's Hall in the 1840s meant that the formal core of the city – library, museum, art gallery, county sessions court and college of technology spreading along the slope to one side of the great public hall – is in a grandly classical style. Even later the dislike of Gothic persisted, most notably when the late Sir Charles Reilly came to be Professor of Architecture at the beginning of this century. The Anglican cathedral constitutes a single massive exception. Otherwise the buildings of central Liverpool seem, consciously or not, to reflect its early leaders' feeling that the Industrial Revolution was a second Renaissance.

At present this is scarcely appreciated except by architectural enthusiasts, for the change in the city's fortunes has been too overwhelming for most of its inhabitants to see the nineteenth-century legacy as anything but a terrible and cramping handicap. As England began to lose her position as the world's leading manufacturer to Germany and the United States – this was something that Conway, the first Liverpool Professor of Fine Art, already saw to be happening at the turn of the century[1] – and far more so after the 1914–18 war, Liverpool became one of the most vulnerable communities in our whole precarious economy. Nobody can forget the unemployment of the 1930s,

6 St George's Hall in 1965. The abominably-designed bus shelter and the fancy lamp standard have since been removed, but there are new and disfiguring signs on gantries over the street

and even today the visitor continually sees, as he does not in London or in comparable foreign ports, the symptoms of a population living close to the margin: too many poorly dressed children and old people; wretched shops in the poorer districts; dockers and labourers who show few outward marks of the social changes of the last twenty years. Today the wealthier citizens have moved away from the city centre, leaving the once elegant terraces to be invaded by a different kind of tenant, Irish, Chinese, coloured, with their children and their clubs and their various street debris. Rateable values have fallen; trees can no longer be planted in public places because of the general destructiveness; people who would once have supported intelligent evening

[1] See his *The Domain of Art;* John Murray, 1901, pp. 85–6.

7 & 8 Apogee of the Liverpool public house. *Above:* In the Philharmonic Hotel, built between 1898 and 1900 with the co-operation of members of the University Appeal Arts department. *Below:* The Crown Hotel in Lime Street, before its defacement by advertising signs. Both these houses belong to Walker's, the firm that gave the city its art gallery.

entertainment and served in local government have in many cases gone to live outside. Even the University is dead at weekends or after working hours.

9 The darker side of a heritage: some of the housing

A recent attempt to keep the senior common room bar open in the evenings drew only two visitors in an entire term.

What so often impresses people about the physical make-up of Liverpool is neither the dingy grandeur of its buildings nor their special power to express its history, but above all the dirt, the poverty and the slums, now seen as a legacy of the 'Victorian' age, even though they are quite equally the result of our own century's inability to cope. These slums run mainly north and south behind the docks, starting almost from the centre of the town; even inland it is not until one reaches the new suburbs built in the 1930s that there are well-planned residential districts other than a few shabby areas of former grandeur. The problem has become overwhelming. In 1963 there were 27,000 dwellings that had been condemned and ought to be demolished and a further 61,000 that had been declared due (which means overdue) for major repair; thus, with an average of 3.32 persons per dwelling in the city as a whole, it could be said that roughly 300,000 of Liverpool's population were living in conditions officially recognized as intolerable. No city council since 1939 has come near to solving this. And even the areas of new housing are hardly attractive by the standards of, say, Bremen or Rotterdam. Kirkby, the brand-new suburb outside the city boundaries to the north-east, is the most commonly criticised for its poor amenities and lack of social coherence; but

10 In the slum belt

Kirkby is still running in, as it were, and seems on every count preferable to the barrack-like district of Speke, built in sub-Georgian style and laid out with grisly symmetry in a treeless waste at the southern tip of the city[1].

It is this burden of poverty and bad planning that has largely decided Merseyside's reputation, not only with the outside world – which is bad enough, as it makes it difficult to attract fresh talent and fresh resources – but, more demoralisingly, with many of its own inhabitants. And yet in spite of every temptation to defeatism there has traditionally been a certain boldness about many of the city's ideas. 'If a thing's big', said Ben Shaw, who was Labour's chairman of the council's Arts Sub-Committee till 1965, 'it'll get big support. If it's little we'll just dodder around.' Two cathedrals are now going up in Liverpool: Scott's Anglican one, started some sixty years ago and still slowly going forward, and Frederick Gibberd's revolutionary Catholic structure, founded on the huge crypt that remains from Lutyens's original plan. The Mersey Tunnel was another great communal effort (which is now being repeated with a second tunnel half a mile further north), while the resources put into the Royal Liverpool Philharmonic Orchestra, the Walker Art Gallery or the two great football teams, Liverpool and Everton, would seem remarkable even in a much more prosperous society. There is a largeness of spirit here which contrasts unexpectedly with the various symptoms of decline.

Partly this is due to the strong tradition of independence and local pride among the heads of the older Liverpool businesses, which such newcomers

11 Liverpool University in its setting, showing the original red stone building by Alfred Waterhouse. In size and seniority it is the fifth English university

as the football pools have tried to emulate. Local government itself may have been weakened by the drift away from the old residential areas, and by the fact that retired people of real ability tend to settle elsewhere; but there is an enlightened Establishment, however small, which has something like a nineteenth century sense of duty. The urge to self-government remains strong, and both this and the sense that Commerce must be the chief cultural patron in the industrial age have long determined the city's attitude to the arts. Wherever these are accepted as a credit to the community and an essential part of its equipment they are generously supported. As will presently be seen, the Art Gallery now not only has one of the biggest annual purchase grants from the rates allowed to any English provincial gallery, but also gets larger sums from local industry and trade than probably any gallery outside the United States.

Under these contradictory impulses there have in the recent history of the town been waves of hope and deep troughs of apathy. There was a remarkable period of reconstruction in the 1930s, when the garden-city-like suburbs were built, with well-lit double carriageway roads running through them: a development that was far ahead of what most English municipalities, including the London County Council, were doing at that time. Then came the war, and with it the destruction of a great part of central Liverpool. For nearly twenty years the opportunity which this presented for a radical replanning of the city was not taken. Planning, as in so many English towns even today, was one of the subsidiary responsibilities of the City Engineer, and the 1947 city plan was hardly a document to fire the imagination. Nor was it put into effect. Two of the principal shopping streets were rebuilt by private enterprise on the old alignments, partly as a result of the well-intentioned views of the late Sir Alfred Shennan, chairman of the city's Post-War Redevelopment Committee and himself the architect of Littlewood's Spinney House, the Pearl Assurance in Lord Street and one or two others of the more deplorable of the new buildings. But where the great bulk of the bombed area was concerned nothing was done at all. No great city outside England, and few inside, have been so slow to set themselves straight after the war, and for a long while the effect on the citizens was, to say the least of it, disheartening. Decline breeds decline. If the centre of a city is allowed to run down the rate income from it drops accordingly; the authorities become less and less able to pay for remedial measures; the richer inhabitants drift off, taking many of the frills of life with them; the attraction offered to new industries and new immigrants grows steadily less. Once this process begins it is difficult to see how it can ever be reversed.

It was against this background that the present inquiry was commissioned, and the past history of the city, from the heady optimism of the post-Napoleonic era to the disillusionments of the 1950s, will be seen to underly much of the eight chapters that follow, as well as some of the positive proposals put forward in the tenth. But cities are always on the move, particularly such mercurial communities as this one, and from the very start of the undertaking Liverpool has been rising on another great wave which has not only  made its name known throughout the world but taken it a good way towards permanent recovery. The public symptoms of this new Merseyside renaissance hardly need reciting: on record and as performers the Beatles were the great world-beaters of 1964; Liverpool won the Association Football Cup in 1965 and the League championship in 1966; Everton won the Cup in 1966; Ken Dodd was the top British entertainer of 1965; Liverpool poets and novelists are beginning to become known, notably with Sean Hignett's *A Picture to Hang on the Wall*, published in autumn 1966; the new Roman Catholic cathedral is about to be consecrated now. At the same time however, though much less conspicuously, a major planning operation has been started which looks like taking Liverpool purposefully and efficiently into the

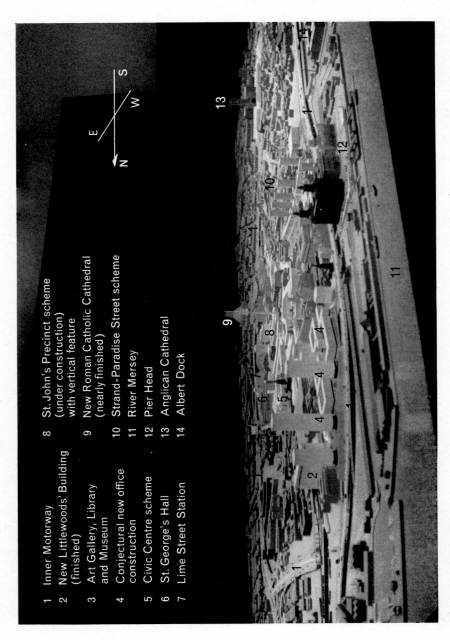

1 Inner Motorway
2 New Littlewoods' Building (finished)
3 Art Gallery, Library and Museum
4 Conjectural new office construction
5 Civic Centre scheme
6 St. George's Hall
7 Lime Street Station
8 St. John's Precinct scheme (under construction) with vertical feature
9 New Roman Catholic Cathedral (nearly finished)
10 Strand-Paradise Street scheme
11 River Mersey
12 Pier Head
13 Anglican Cathedral
14 Albert Dock

12 A new plan for Liverpool. Model showing the city centre, as planned for the corporation by Graeme Shankland and Walter Bor. From the permanent planning exhibit in the Walker Art Gallery

twenty-first century. The result is that there is not only a real spirit of revival in the city but also a new framework, new tasks, new opportunities for the visual artist. It is difficult for the printed word to keep pace with any situation which is developing quite so quickly. The reader must none the less try to bear in mind the probable or projected future. It belongs to the background quite as much as does the Liverpool we know.

What the city did, on the initiative of the former chairman of the Special Redevelopment (1961–2) and Planning Committees (from 1962 to 1963) Harold Macdonald Steward MP, was to appoint two of the leading architect-planners from the London County Council: first Graeme Shankland, who was brought in early 1962 as a consultant to replan the central area, then Walter Bor, who became the first City Planning Officer at the end of the same year, and set up a permanent City Planning Department. These two and their respective teams have worked very closely together and produced a succession of radical reports, proposing a whole new shape for the city; both parties in the Council have backed them, and important parts of the ensuing plan are already being executed or passing through the legislative stage. It really is as if the downward trend were being reversed and Liverpool's long postwar lethargy turned into a source of strength. As the 1965 City Centre Plan puts it, the derelict or underdeveloped areas are so extensive and the proportion of municipally-owned land so high as to

> present redevelopment opportunities unequalled by any other major city in this country and few in the world. Large areas of comprehensive development are therefore feasible and they, in turn, make the creation of a new and attractive urban environment an early possibility in several parts of the city centre.[1]

This could no doubt have been said at any time since the war. The difference now is that action is being taken.

The first outlines of a new city are there for all to study, and they, together with the calibre of the men responsible and their evident power to work as a team, give hope of a transformation such as no other town in England has yet undergone. Its scope is best conveyed by the map overleaf. In the centre three stages are already under way: the remodelling of the Pier Head area, the building of a new seventeen-storey headquarters for Littlewoods' Mail Order Stores and a new St Paul's Square adjoining it, and the construction by developers of a highly original complex of shops, market, car park and hotel straddling the site of the old St John's Market just below

[1] City and County Borough of Liverpool: *Liverpool City Centre Plan*. Liverpool 1965, p. 2. This impressive document follows on the Planning Consultant's eleven reports and is the work of a joint City Centre Planning Group directed by the two planners. There is an account of it by Walter Bor in *The London Magazine;* July 1966, p. 81ff.

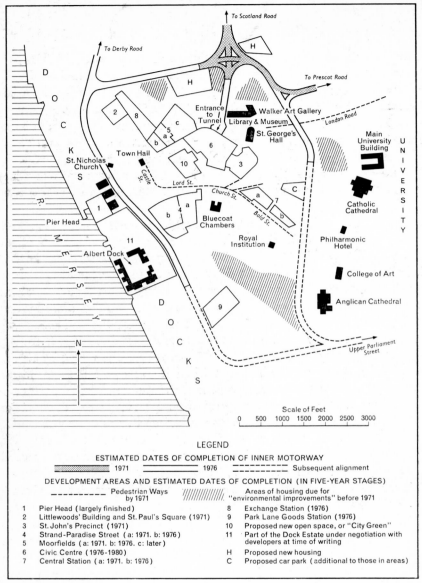

To Scotland Road

To Derby Road

To Prescot Road

Entrance to Tunnel

Walker Art Gallery
Library & Museum
St George's Hall

London Road

Main University Building

UNIVERSITY

St Nicholas Church
Town Hall

Catholic Cathedral

Pier Head

Castle St.
Lord St.
Church St.
Bold St.

Bluecoat Chambers
Royal Institution

Philharmonic Hotel

College of Art

Anglican Cathedral

Albert Dock

DOCKS

Upper Parliament Street

Scale of Feet
0 500 1000 1500 2000 2500 3000

LEGEND

ESTIMATED DATES OF COMPLETION OF INNER MOTORWAY
▒▒▒ 1971   ═══ 1976   ----- Subsequent alignment

DEVELOPMENT AREAS AND ESTIMATED DATES OF COMPLETION (IN FIVE-YEAR STAGES)
---------- Pedestrian Ways by 1971   ////// Areas of housing due for "environmental improvements" before 1971

1   Pier Head (largely finished)
2   Littlewoods' Building and St. Paul's Square (1971)
3   St. John's Precinct (1971)
4   Strand-Paradise Street (a: 1971. b: 1976)
5   Moorfields (a: 1971. b: 1976. c: later)
6   Civic Centre (1976-1980)
7   Central Station (a: 1971. b: 1976)

8   Exchange Station (1976)
9   Park Lane Goods Station (1976)
10 Proposed new open space, or "City Green"
11 Part of the Dock Estate under negotiation with developers at time of writing
H   Proposed new housing
C   Proposed car park (additional to those in areas)

The reconstruction of the city centre. The map above shows the probable stages
of construction of the inner motorway and of the principal redevelopment areas.
(*Top right*) clearing the way for the first of these, the St John's Precinct scheme
(a photograph taken in 1965). It is no 3 on the map. Beneath is a model of the
same project, backed by a perspective drawing of the view from the north (curved)
end of St George's Hall towards the proposed new civic centre (no 6 on the map)
and the Mersey Tunnel entrance. (*Bottom right*) two of the towers in the second
major development area, the Strand-Paradise Street scheme (no 4 on the map),
by two firms of Liverpool architects: Kingham Knight Associates and
Hall, O'Donahue, Wilson

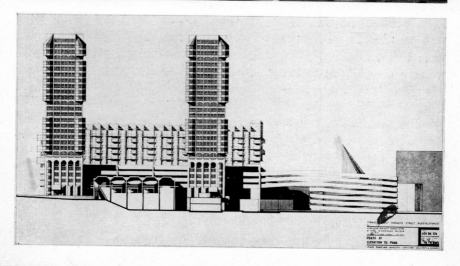

Lime Street. Architects are now working on a rather larger scheme towards the docks, including the five tall towers of flats seen in the model; at the time of writing the council were still negotiating with developers. Beyond this there is (now that Parliament has given its approval) to be an inner motorway circling the centre; a clear segregation of motorway from local traffic, and the establishment of some wholly pedestrian streets; the redevelopment of another large area (Moorfields) on the north side of Dale Street; finally the resiting of the municipal offices and the law courts in a brilliantly-conceived civic centre, masking the Mersey Tunnel entrance and decking over the necropolis-like gardens that at present link it to St George's Hall. The council proposes to build this itself, and it could well become one of the most handsome of Europe's great squares, with the hall itself restored to useful life as a place for national conferences.

In the 'inner residential area' backing the docks and surrounding the centre 50,000 dwellings are to be cleared by 1985, together with all obsolete school buildings. Fringing this area on the east is to be a new north-south motorway bypassing the centre to link eventually with a third Mersey crossing. A new South Lancashire motorway link is to be brought into the city during the same period, joining the inner motorway close to the Anglican cathedral. The aim in all residential areas of the city, as now envisaged, will be to win back pedestrian space from the present street network, to establish a pattern of new parks (10 acres or so, not more than half a mile apart; there will even be new green spaces in the city centre), and to build up District Centres akin to the centres of small towns. In addition the plan calls for four new parks of 200 acres or more on the edges of the city. These are only the guiding lines laid down in the Interim Planning Policy Statement of March 1965; the whole programme which this document sketches is hardly expected to take less than fifty years.

There are also other elements in the picture, particularly a new scheme to use the oldest part of the Dock Estate, some 50 acres centring on Albert Dock, as a vast office centre. The Dock Estate has hitherto been outside the planners' province, and the Dock Board's negotiations with the prospective developers were independently conducted, with the result that the project greatly alters the carefully calculated balances of the plan as a whole, both by crowding the area and by its short-sighted demand that the noble Albert Dock warehouses – one of the city's great historical and architectural assets – should be pulled down. The Ministry of Housing still has to see and rule on the developers' plan, but with these extremely serious reservations (which the local politicians of both parties unfortunately seem keen to waive) the planners are enthusiastic about the scheme in principle, and they also support the other independent plans being worked out for the University and the area round it along the central section of the ridge. This is not only where the Regional College of Art, the Philharmonic Hall and the University Schools of Architecture and Civic Design are situated but also where a number of artists still choose to live. A scheme is at present being examined for the rehabilitation of the early nineteenth-century terraces there as part of a wider experiment in 'urban renewal' sponsored by the Royal Institute of British Architects. The University itself is being developed by a variety of different architects, including some of the best now working in this country, under the general supervision of Myles Wright, the Civic Design (i.e. Town-planning) Professor. And it is worth bearing in mind that a great many eyes are very

17 The new Roman Catholic cathedral seen from Hope Street (December 1965). Right: the Hope Hall, now the Everyman Theatre

soon likely to be turned on Liverpool (just as they are at present turned on Coventry) with the completion and consecration of the new cathedral, right beside the present university area.

Perhaps the case chosen is hardly typical, for both the strongly individual character of Liverpool and the ambitious scale of its plans are remarkable by any standard. But, quite apart from the fact that without such character and such ambitions no inquiry would have been set on foot in the first place, they are still important, if less conspicuous, considerations in the life of any city.

C

Art in a city is not a static affair, concerned only with permanent treasures kept under glass or in air-conditioned rooms; even a museum is likely to be evolving all the time, subtly changing its relationships both with the community that pays for it and with the outside world of art. In other places it might be easy to forget this. The local roots of the arts might be too difficult to spot, or at least to distinguish from those in other parts of England; the future might seem like a hazy and haphazard extension of the past, a matter for pure speculation. In Liverpool they are obvious and urgent.

The chapters that follow are designed to do two things. They are on the one hand a study of the specific situation in Liverpool, as seen between 1963 and 1966 (the date of my last revisions), with certain recommendations for that city which I hope may influence future action there. At the same time they are meant to illuminate the whole relationship between the visual arts and the modern community, in a way which will be helpful outside the area specifically dealt with. This wider setting of the problem is discussed in Chapters 8 and 9, the former giving some account of social-artistic developments in Britain since the Second World War, as well as certain analogous exmples from the Continent, while the latter sketches the background of theoretical debate from the early nineteenth century onward, before focusing yet again on the local scene. These chapters are by no means intended to be skipped by readers concerned with Liverpool's situation, for it seems important that those locally responsible should realize what can be and has been done already, and what ground has already been argued over, to what effect. The tenth chapter however, is an unashamedly parochial one, apart from its ending, and the unconcerned reader has every justification for skimming it quickly. From his point of view what matters here is less the exact detail of the measures recommended than the drawing up of a plan of campaign which can be seen as a whole and will dovetail with the city's reconstruction plans.

I hope that the book points the way to this, though I hope also that it does not overlap too much with the planning documents or with other relevant publications. Liverpool has been the subject of a good deal of outside interest since the Beatles rose to fame, and much else has been written about the city lately, from fan magazines upwards; it may be noticed that photographs by one of the authors of *Beat in Liverpool*,[1] a remarkable study produced by three young Germans and published in Frankfurt, have appeared on previous pages. One such book, Quentin Hughes's *Seaport*,[2] is of the

[1] Jürgen Seuss, Gerold Dommermuth and Hans Maier: *Beat in Liverpool;* Europäische Verlagsanstalt, Frankfurt, 1965.
[2] *Seaport. Architecture and Townscape in Liverpool;* Lund Humphries, London, 1964.

first importance, both for its revelation of Liverpool's very original architectural character, together with the reasons for it, and for its use as a reminder of what in the city is worth preserving. Here again I have tried not to overlap, though I have reproduced one or two photographs from Dr Hughes's collection; readers who feel interested enough in the place to turn to his book will find their reading of the present work greatly enriched. My object where Liverpool's own future is concerned is to supplement *Seaport* and the plans in such a way that all three contribute to the same end: a singularly interesting and enjoyable city. Whether this is so will depend on the action taken. But it should be remembered that everything that follows has likewise got a practical purpose, being written with an eye to that future even where it plunges back into the past.

18 Genius loci. Atkinson Grimshaw (1836-1893): *The Customs House, Liverpool (looking north). Private Collection*

19 Michelangelo looking out from the porch of
the Walker Art Gallery. (St George's Hall is
off the picture to the right)

2 : VIEWS OF THE PAST

Liverpool has a long tradition in the visual arts, and for the best part of two hundred years the city has been the centre for some of our most important provincial exhibitions. It still attracts young artists from all parts of the country by this very fact, though the relative cheapness of living and lodging there is another obvious inducement. In such surroundings the past is much more in evidence than in corresponding ports on the continent, or even in other big British towns. Prosperity came earlier, with its solid monuments in the way of industrial and public buildings; poverty followed quicker, so that there were fewer of those inessential changes of fashion (in shopfronts, signs, offices, public houses) which so drastically transform the urban face. Today the nineteenth century still lies all around the artist: in the facade of the Walker Art Gallery for instance, with Raphael and Michelangelo[1] forbiddingly enthroned either side of the portico and the substantial figure of Commerce on top. None of the major art institutions is less than fifty years old.

Yet something has vanished, as we shall see if we go back over the history of these institutions and the tradition which they represent. For the leading citizens of Liverpool in the nineteenth century were conscious of art as an embodiment and an advancement of their society's aims in a way that is no longer fashionable, and as the century progressed they wanted its benefits to be more and more widely diffused. It was these feelings that provided the motive power of the city's artistic life. Probably it was not so spontaneous a life as now, and none of the artists could be called distinctively Liverpudlian in style, but at least it arose in response to a real demand. Today the most gifted of the local artists remain largely unknown and unbought; the demand is a national and not a specifically local one; and it is for art teachers or art gossip rather than for works of art. The notion that art itself could have a relevance to the community's hopes and ideals, to its work and its leisure, seems to have gone with the Victorian age.

[1] By the sculptor John Warrington Wood, 1839–86, a native of Warrington who studied and worked in Rome.

The rise of art in the city is linked with the figure of William Roscoe (1753–1831), poet, antiquarian, amateur painter, lawyer, biographer of Lorenzo de Medici, self-made merchant banker and Whig MP for Liverpool in 1806–7. Roscoe is now perhaps known primarily for the splendid collection of Primitives which he made and which are now the outstanding feature of the Walker Art Gallery. He bought these, as a former member of the gallery staff has shown,[1] for their historical significance and as curiosities rather than because they were what he liked most; he was an Italophile somewhat of the cast of Samuel Rogers, though one who never left England. He was also a good friend and patron to Fuseli from the 1780s onwards, hanging his dining-room at Allerton Hall (where he moved in 1799) with that painter's works.[2] Fuseli indeed called him 'the man nearest my heart'. In many ways he was pompous and humourless, yet both his sympathies and his interests were ahead of his times; he was opposed to the war with revolutionary France, for instance, and fought long and hard for the abolition of the slave trade on which so many Liverpool fortunes depended. Brougham judged him to be 'in some respects one of the most remarkable persons that have of late years appeared in either the political or the literary world'.[3] Art to Roscoe, and apparently to his friends too, was at once a symbol and a tool for the free, progressive commercial society that they believed in. And it was in this spirit that the forerunners of the present-day College of Art and Liverpool Academy were formed.

Such sentiments were characteristically expressed in the opening of Roscoe's inaugural ode read to the local Society for the Encouragement of Designing, Drawing and Painting on 17 December 1773:

> From climes where Slavery's iron chain
> Has bound to earth the soaring mind,
> Where GRECIA mourns her blasted plain
> To want and indolence resigned;
> From fair ITALIA's once-loved shore,
> (The land of Freedom now no more)
> Disdainful of each former seat,

---

[1] Michael Compton: 'William Roscoe and Early Collectors of Italian Primitives' in *Liverpool Bulletin*, no. 9, 1960–1.

[2] See Hugh Macandrew: 'Henry Fuseli and William Roscoe' in *Liverpool Bulletin*. Vol. 8, 1959–60. This article is largely based on 113 letters from Fuseli to Roscoe now in the Liverpool Libraries, and includes particulars of twenty-seven pictures belonging to Roscoe and other Liverpool collectors.

[3] *Speeches of Henry Lord Brougham;* A. & C. Black, Edinburgh, 1838. Vol. 1, p. 467, in the (retrospective) introduction to his 'Speech at the Liverpool Election 1812'.

The ARTS, a lovely train, retreat:
Still prospering under FREEDOM'S eye,
With her they bloom, with her they fly;
And when the Power transferred her smile
To ALBION'S ever-grateful isle,
The lovely fugitives forgot to roam,
But raised their altars here, and fixed their happier home.

The society thus celebrated was the second of the eventual Liverpool Academy's precursors, the first having been formed at the same premises (30 John Street) in 1769, only a year after the foundation of the Royal Academy in London. In 1774 the society held the first art exhibition ever to be staged in the provinces,[1] a largely amateur affair which included works by Roscoe himself (an ink drawing called *The Mother*, after a French engraving) and his brother-in-law Daniel Daulby. It quickly petered out however, and was again re-founded in 1783, as the Society for Promoting the Arts in Liverpool, which for the first time began to include the work of metropolitan artists in its shows: Paul Sandby and Wright of Derby in 1784; Reynolds, Gainsborough, Fuseli and others in 1787. Its classes were meant to appeal to a wide public. 'It is the aim of the present times,' said the catalogue of the 1784 exhibition,[2] 'to unite beauty with utility; and even the Mechanic who would wish to arrive at eminence, ought not only to cultivate his taste, but to acquire . . . practical knowledge of the art of design. . . .'

Like its predecessors, this attempt failed, and the Liverpool Academy of Arts as we now know it was only founded in 1810. It quickly became incorporated in a larger literary, artistic and scientific body, the Liverpool Royal Institution, with Roscoe, the Liverpool banker B. A. Heywood and Dr T. S. Traill (subsequently Professor of Forensic Medicine at Edinburgh and editor of the eighth edition of the Encyclopedia Britannica) as moving spirits; this had a 'spacious and elegant exhibition room for the use of the members of the Liverpool Academy'[3] and a School of Design 'for instruction in Drawing, as subservient to Professions, Mechanical Employments, or the Study of the Fine Arts.'[4] Apparently the £1,600 bequeathed to the Academy by Henry Blundell of Ince, together with £200 accumulated interest, was

[1] According to the catalogue of the Liverpool Academy of Art's 150th Anniversary Exhibition, Walker Art Gallery Liverpool, 1960.
[2] Reprinted in Joseph Mayer: *Roscoe and the Influence of his Writing on the Fine Arts;* T. Brakell, Liverpool, 1853, p. 12.
[3] *Resolutions, Reports and Bye-Laws of the Liverpool Royal Institution, March 1814–March 1822;* Liverpool, 1822. Report of the Committee 17 July 1817, p. 15.
[4] Ibid. p. 25.

20 Names of early members of the Liverpool Royal Institution, founded in 1814, from the board in its entrance hall. Among those shown here are William Rathbone, William Roscoe, R. V. Yates, John Foster Junior, Andrew Melly and T. Winstanley

handed over to the trustees of this Institution on condition that the Academy should be permanently housed by it.[1] In 1817 the combined bodies moved into the square brick building in Colquitt Street which is still known as the Royal Institution (today it is an adult education centre under the wing of the University Extra-Mural Department and the Academy has no accommodation of its own). Roscoe spoke protractedly at the opening ceremony, giving his own picture of the 'union of the pursuits of literature with the affairs of the world', and preaching the need for a flourishing artistic life as at once obligatory for a self-respecting mercantile community and a welcome means of improvement for the working class. He quoted the Italian states and the Hanseatic towns as proof that 'in every nation where commerce has been cultivated upon great and enlightened principles, a considerable proficiency has always been made in liberal studies and pursuits'. This was no argument for a policy of subsidy however, for 'There is not a greater error, than to think that the arts can subsist upon the generosity of the public' except possibly in their very earliest stages. It was just a matter of intelligent self-interest, where pleasure and utility must necessarily coincide. 'If you will protect the arts, the arts will, and ought to remunerate you.'[2]

---

[1] According to E. R. Dibdin's paper on Liverpool Art History in the *Transactions of the National Association for the Advancement of Art; Liverpool Meeting 1888;* London, 1888, p. 314. He says that 'this right exists to the present day'.

[2] William Roscoe: *On the Origin and Vicissitudes of Literature, Science and Art, and their Influence on the present State of Society.* A Discourse delivered on the opening of the Liverpool Royal Institution, 25 November 1817. Liverpool. Printed by Harris and Co. And sold by Cadell and Davis, London, 1817.

21 Director's room at the Royal Institution,
with original furniture and bust of William
Roscoe, its moving spirit

Views of this kind are to be found in a number of the speeches which Traill and Heywood delivered to the Royal Institution in the 1820s, when the Academy was holding exhibitions nearly every year and the Corporation itself began to give prizes for works of art. It was a moment when peace (and commerce) were being re-established after the Napoleonic wars, and there was something of a local artistic boom. In 1819 the Institution formed the nucleus of its own collection when a group of members presented some thirty-five of Roscoe's pictures which he had sold to help stave off his impending bankruptcy (a quarter of a century later when it opened its own art gallery across Colquitt Street another eighty had been added, mostly through Roscoe's dealer and friend Winstanley). In 1823 Romney's son John presented a group of eighteen cartoons by his father. The outstanding local artist of the time was certainly the sculptor John Gibson (1790–1866, elected RA in 1838), who after 1817 lived in Rome, where Roscoe and Fuseli had put him in touch with Canova; his last work before leaving Liverpool was a mantelpiece for Sir John Gladstone, the future Prime Minister's father.[1] There were however other worthy professionals of less distinction, in men like Samuel Williamson, Charles Towne, Thomas Hargreaves and the head of the School of Design, Alexander Mosses. In 1829 Dr Traill re-

22 The sculptor John Gibson RA (1790-1866), the first eminent Liverpool artist

ported that sales from the last Academy exhibition had totalled £846: 'a decisive proof of an increasing love for the fine arts among our opulent merchants'. Like Roscoe he believed that commerce largely accounted for the cultural achievements of Florence, Genoa and Venice, and he hoped that Liverpool too might now commission works of art for public buildings and churches.[2]

Heywood died in 1828, on the eve of the first Reform Act, Roscoe in 1831. Traill left Liverpool a year or two later, having practised there for about

[1] Gibson left his fortune and a large number of his works to the Royal Academy, which still has some eighty of his sculptures (mostly in the vaults or in the Keeper's House) and some bound volumes of drawings. Among the subjects Venus, Psyche, Cupid, etc, tend to predominate, with Sappho and Queen Victoria also prominent. His portrait by Landseer hangs in the Academy's general assembly room.

[2] *See his Address delivered in February 1829 at the General Meeting of the Members of the Liverpool Royal Institution;* Harris and Co, 1829, pp. 20–1. Roscoe had written to much the same effect to Fuseli in 1803, in a letter quoted on p. 50 of Mr Macandrew's article.

thirty years. By then the Academy had become strongly enough established to make it largely independent of the Institution; in 1830 the Corporation began giving it an annual grant of £200, and in 1831 it moved to its own

23 Gibson's statue of Huskisson (MP for Liverpool from 1823 till his death at the opening of the Liverpool and Manchester Railway in 1830). Formerly on the Customs House site and now, rather inappropriately, in an area of late nineteenth-century development on Prince's Avenue

rooms in Post Office Place, leaving the School of Design where it was. The same group of enthusiasts had meantime made the first moves towards a more widely-based form of adult education, inspired partly by Birkbeck's original London Mechanics' Institute of 1824 and partly, it seems, by the recommendations of M. M. Noah, Sheriff of New York.[1] Originally set up privately in 1821, an Apprentices' and Mechanics' Library, with Roscoe's son as its treasurer, was officially adopted by the town after a public meeting in January 1824 and soon had over 800 readers; according to Brougham's 'Practical Observations upon the Education of the People' it was modelled on the Philadelphia Library Company founded by Franklin a century earlier.[2] The same month Heywood was telling Institution members that Dr Traill (who had been a fellow student of Brougham's at Edinburgh) was involved in 'the meetings of a Mechanics' Institute'; in June 1825 he presided over the foundation of the Liverpool Mechanics' School of Arts from which the present College of Art was to grow. This new body had Huskisson as its first president and Heywood and Sir John Gladstone[3] as chief supporters; its original motto 'Knowledge is power' somewhat alarmed the less enlightened

[1] According to an article in *Kaleidoscope*, Liverpool, 3 February 1824, Vol. IV, p. 255.
[2] *Speeches of Henry Lord Brougham*, Vol. III, p. 140.
[3] President of the Institution in 1828 and 1829. Among the other Liverpool families whose names recur in the list of presidents were the Rathbones, Heyworths and Holts.

members of the Corporation. 'If you go on,' they are supposed to have said, 'in instructing the working classes, they will be so much enlightened that they will be treading on the heels of their superiors.'[1] A painting at the school showed Britannicus crowning Mechanicus. Alas, it seems not to have survived.

During the great reforming decade which followed the new school was put firmly on its feet. In 1832–3 it was reorganized as the Liverpool Mechanics'

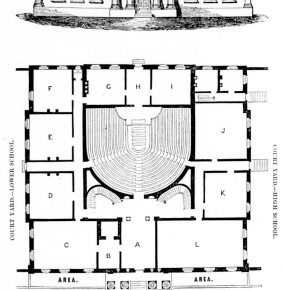

24 The Liverpool Mechanics' Institution. The new building of 1837, still existing as the nucleus of the Liverpool Institute School, a well-known boys' day school in Mount Street, next to the present College of Art

Institution, with classes (*inter alia*) in landscape, mechanical drawing, architectural drawing and 'Drawing the human figure, Ornamental Design and Modelling'; membership rose from 232 before the reorganization to 1,010 in September 1832. In 1835, the year of the Municipal Reform Act, when there were only two Tory members left on the City Council, Brougham came over from Manchester – his first experience of railway locomotion – to lay the foundation stone of its new building. Brougham had been co-founder with

---

[1] See the Mayor's tribute to Dr Traill in the Report of the Liverpool Mechanics' Institution, 15 March, 1836, p. 21. At a soirée in February 1844, Dickens spoke of it ironically as 'an unpopular, dangerous, irreligious and revolutionary establishment'.

Birkbeck of the original Mechanics' Institute in London, and for many years had been associated with Liverpool; he was its counsel in 1808 and stood for Parliament unsuccessfully there against Canning in 1812. 'Today,' he told his listeners at the ceremony, ' . . . all agree in favour of Popular Education' (Cheers).[1] The finished building, to J. A. Picton's design, was opened two years later by another Liberal educationist, Thomas Wyse, a Catholic who was member for Waterford from 1835 to 1847. He called for 'a national school system like a national system of justice, of defence, of protection for our sick and poor . . .'; no class should be cut off from it. For in both France and England education acted as a barrier to crime; it built up the middle class, which is 'essentially the life-principle of society'.[2] Wyse himself was another interesting figure, though largely forgotten today. A governor of the National Gallery and a member of the 1841 Royal Commission on the decoration of the Houses of Parliament, he was also an early advocate of public art galleries, libraries and museums. He was (disastrously) married to Lucien Bonaparte's third daughter Letitia, whose tutor had been a pupil of David; he knew Canova and Thorwaldsen in Rome, yet regarded the classical languages as a luxury and recommended the teaching of music, psychology, history and civics instead.[3]

This was the building where Benjamin Robert Haydon, the great anti-Royal-Academician, came to lecture on a number of occasions between 1836 and 1840, once to an audience he estimated at 1,500. In those days he was the chief propagandist for a national system of art schools, for art professorships in the universities and for the public employment of painters on large decorative tasks. He was also a very strong influence on one member of the building committee, the Liverpool Radical MP William Ewart,[4] who had been chairman of the Select Committee on Arts and Manufactures of 1835–6 which paved the way for the Government Schools of Design, and later

---

[1] *A Full Report of the Speeches delivered by Lord Brougham and Vaux at Liverpool on Monday, 20 July 1835; on laying the first stone of the new Mechanics' Institution, and at the dinner given to his Lordship at the Amphitheatre, James Brancker, Esq, in the Chair.* Liverpool: printed and published by Egerton Smith and Co; Lord-Street, 1835. The speeches can also be found in Vol. III of the *Speeches of Henry Lord Brougham* already quoted.

[2] *Prospectus of the Course of Instruction, Terms and Regulations of the Schools attached to the Liverpool Mechanics' Institution, with a speech by Thomas Wyse, Esq, MP, Chairman of the late Parliamentary Education Committee, delivered at the opening of the New Mechanics' Institution, 15 September 1837;* D. Marples and Co, Lord-Street, Liverpool, 1837.

[3] See Dr J. J. Auchtermuchty: *Sir Thomas Wyse 1791–1862;* P. S. King & Son, Ltd, London, 1939. His own book *Education Reform* was published in 1834. On losing his seat he became British Minister in Athens till his death.

[4] Son of the Liverpool merchant of the same name, after whom Sir John Gladstone, a close friend, called his own son. William Ewart Gladstone followed the second William Ewart to Eton and Christ Church, but the two men seem to have had nothing else in common. None the less Gladstone gave Ewart's portrait by Mosses to the city after his death in 1869.

sponsored the Museums Act of 1845 and the Public Libraries Act of 1850: the two great milestones in the history of official British policy towards the arts. Haydon found the new structure 'a magnificent establishment' and the people lively but rough.

25 William Ewart (1798–1869), MP for Liverpool from 1830–1837, and Chairman of the Select Committee on Arts and Manufactures to which we owe our art school system

The room is too large. You feel pained to fill it. There are too many boys belonging to the schools, and the savage brutality behind is dreadful. No attention or common civility.[1]

In September 1837, through the agency of a Mr Lowndes (with some help from Winstanley) he was commissioned to paint *Christ Blessing the Little Children* for the Asylum of the Blind – a work which had been taken down by 1852[2] and has now vanished – while most of 1839 was spent painting the Wellington portraits now in St George's Hall. 'Liverpool,' he said flatter-

[1] Tom Taylor (editor): *Life of Benjamin Robert Haydon;* Second Edition, London, 1853, Vol. III, p. 99.
[2] Ibid. Footnote to p. 72. The Asylum was where the police headquarters now is in Hardman Street, opposite the Philharmonic Hall.

ingly in one of his lectures there,[1] 'is the only distinguished town since the Reformation which has had the moral courage to employ native historical painters, on the true, thoroughbred principles of patronage, which produced such glorious results in Italy and Greece.' Other cities would surely follow her example, with excellent effects on the country's wealth, taste and manufactures. And this he saw as fulfilling the ambitions of Roscoe, whose 'literature and his love of art have cast a halo round the name of Liverpool, which is felt in conjunction with its commercial power, in every part of the world....'

In March 1842 the secretary reported that the Institution had 3,767 members. By then it seems to have been divided into two boys' schools

THE SCULPTURE GALLERY AND DRAWING-SCHOOL, LIVERPOOL MECHANICS' INSTITUTION.

26 A wood-engraving from *The Illustrated London News* of 2 March 1844, showing what eventually became the College of Art

(High School and Lower School), and an evening school with some twenty-five departments. The attendance at the evening art classes, which had a staff of eight teachers under W. J. Bishop, was over 400; there were also drawing classes in the High School under Charles Barber, a friend of David Cox and president of the Liverpool Academy for 1841–2 and 1847–53. 'At the last exhibition of the Liverpool Academy there were eight paintings by teachers in this Institution, and twenty-one by artists who were formerly pupils within its walls.' Nearly 100,000 visitors (or about double the attendance at the most successful exhibition of our own time, that of Van Gogh

[1] B. R. Haydon: *Lectures on Painting and Design*. London 1846, Vol. II, Lecture X, pp. 115–17.

at the Walker Gallery in 1955) saw an exhibition in the first half of 1840 which had been arranged to raise funds. Here there was sculpture by Gibson and Deare; drawings by the topographical artist W. G. Herdman (another teacher in the evening classes), whose *Pictorial Relics of Ancient Liverpool* was published in 1843; paintings or copies of paintings by various famous names; scientific apparatus, daguerreotypes, and a cap, gloves and shoes worn by Byron in Greece. *The Congress of Science*, an anonymous poem written for the occasion,[1] finishes on a familiar note of cultural optimism:

> Thus forward proceeding, transcendent you'll shine,
> And, trimming the bright lamp of freedom divine,
> Diffuse, while your standard of freedom's unfurled,
> LIGHT, LIBERTY, HAPPINESS over the world.

This whole association of flourishing commerce, radical politics and the neo-classical style in art determined the artistic and intellectual climate of Liverpool in the first half of the century, and it was splendidly commemorated in the building of St George's Hall in the middle of the city. The foundation stone had been hopefully laid in 1837, a year after the building of the new railway terminus the other side of Lime Street; in 1839 and 1840 competitions for its actual design were won by the twenty-five-year-old architect Harvey Lonsdale Elmes; in 1842 work began and in 1854 the hall was opened, after Elmes had prematurely died and C. R. Cockerell had been brought in to finish the work. It was Cockerell who called on the services of the greatest of English classical sculptors, Alfred Stevens, who had worked for him on the doors of the London Geological Museum in Jermyn Street and had already visited Liverpool in 1847 to decorate three rooms for the Blundell family at Deysbrook House, West Derby. The sculpture for the pediment, based on an original design of 1843 by Cockerell which Elmes had seen and admired in the Royal Academy, was actually carried out by W. G. Nicholl, who was also responsible for the four lions in front of the hall, but Stevens saw the half-finished group in Nicholl's studio and suggested changes; its subject, characteristically, was described as 'Commerce and the Arts bearing tribute to Britannia', etc., etc.,[2] though whether that was what

---

[1] *The Congress of Science; A tributary lay on the exhibition at the Liverpool Mechanics' Institute. MDCCCXL.* Printed by D. Marples, Lord-Street, Liverpool 1840. The figures of attendance come from the Institution's annual report of 1842.

[2] See the anonymous notes appended to Stevens's lithograph of the pediment in the Victoria and Albert Museum, also Robert Pepys Cockerell's paper to the Liverpool Architectural Society, printed in *The Architectural Review*, London, October 1902 (especially pp. 139–41). There is an account of the building in Quentin Hughes's *Seaport*; Lund Humphries, London, 1964, pp. 96–104.

27 Harvey Lonsdale Elmes: perspective drawing of St George's
Hall from the north end. (RIBA drawings collection)

Cockerell originally had in mind seems doubtful. The interior pavement was
apparently Stevens's own. This pavement is now normally kept covered
over, while the sculpture has been taken down as dangerously liable to
crumble and is since reported to have been broken up for builders' rubble.[1]
The main part of the building, the Great Hall and the beautiful smaller concert hall, are now hardly used. The citizens, alas, seem not to appreciate
what a marvellous monument this is to the liveliest period of their history.

[1] This was established by Stanley Ashworth in a thesis essay at the Liverpool College of Art.
The decision was taken by the City Engineer's department, unknown to the staff of the Walker
Art Gallery, who at the time of Mr Ashworth's enquiries still believed that the sculptures were
among those stored in the basement of the hall.

D

28 Alfred Stevens: Mosaic pavement inside St George's Hall.
(This is normally kept boarded over)

Since the building of St Paul's no British city has had such an expressive
and grandly conceived central feature.

During the 1840s a decline set in. The Royal Institution had passed its peak;
the chief pioneers of Liverpool culture were dead or departed; the reformers
had lost control of the City Council in 1841. The Mechanics' Institution
ran into financial difficulties and in 1851 had its art department reorganized
on Government School of Design lines; Bishop went over to the new Collegi-
ate Institution in Shaw Street, Everton in 1842 and remained art master
there till the eighties; John Finnie became head of the reformed School of

Design in 1855 and stayed for forty-two years. However, the young artists who had been trained in Liverpool under the older optimistic regime were now beginning to enter the Liverpool Academy, and it was they who around the middle of the century brought a genuine if controversial distinction to Liverpool art. William Huggins became an associate of the academy in 1847 at twenty-seven, W. L. Windus the same year at twenty-five, his brother-in-law Robert Tonge in 1850 at twenty-seven, James Campbell in 1854 at twenty-nine, A. W. Hunt in 1854 at twenty-four. The example of such promising painters, plus the institution of a £50 annual award out of the Corporation's grant, now encouraged some of the most interesting artists in the country to exhibit there: Millais from 1846, Holman Hunt from 1847, Ford Madox Brown from 1848. The second of these came to Liverpool in 1856 and found the Academy 'a homely company' dominated by the merchant John Miller, one of the chief patrons of the Pre-Raphaelites. He went out to Miller's house on Everton Brow, where he found the paintings stacked several deep against the walls, and concluded that Miller was more interested in owning than in looking at them. At that time the merchant was

> a hearty septuagenarian of fresh complexion and boyish temperament, with a cheery word for everybody on the way. His home was super-intended by his daughters, who seated themselves to preside over high tea.[1]

One of these daughters married that shadowy figure P. P. Marshall, who for a time was William Morris's partner. Miller was also a good friend to Windus, whose *Burd Helen* in the 1856 Royal Academy caught Rossetti's attention and then Ruskin's, and was perhaps the best picture to come out of Liverpool in the nineteenth century.

But such developments were no longer in line with the tastes and interests of the city fathers. In 1851 the Academy, largely under Windus's influence, began giving its annual award to the Pre-Raphaelite exhibitors, whom it thus decided to honour well in advance of London. The controversy aroused by this far-sighted policy came to a head in 1857, when the prize went to Millais's *The Blind Girl*. W. G. Herdman, then a man of fifty-two, was expelled from the Academy for the protests which he made in the local press, and took a number of other artists with him to form a new Liverpool Society of Fine

---

[1] Quoted in *John Lea, Citizen and Art Lover*. A sketch by Frank Elias. Philip, Son and Nephew, Liverpool 1928, p. 16. Miller was followed by George Rae of Birkenhead, who bought Madox Brown's *English Autumn Afternoon* (now in Birmingham City Art Gallery) in 1861 and 'became an ardent collector of the later and lusher Rossetti's portraits'. See Mary Bennett: 'The Pre-Raphaelites and the Liverpool Prize' in *Apollo*, London, December 1962, p. 750. The third great local collector of these artists was F. R. Leyland (see pp. 44–6 below), who knew Miller but started collecting slightly later.

Arts. This body had the local Establishment behind it; it was backed by both mayor and bishop, and had the Earl of Sefton as its president.[1] At its first exhibition in 1858 the prize money added up to £200; in 1860 over £4,000 worth of pictures was sold. Worse still for the Academy, the Corporation in 1859 stopped the annual £200 subsidy which it had paid towards the rent of the Post Office Place exhibition room. At A. W. Hunt's request Ruskin wrote a stirring letter of support, which was partly reprinted in the weekly *Liverpool Albion* of 11 January, 1858, calling the Academy's policy 'the first instance on record of the entirely just and beneficial working of academical system'.[2] But by 1861 they were £600 in debt.[3]

There followed a brief period of artistic competition: on the one hand the Pre-Raphaelites, with Miller helping organize their show at Russell Place in London in 1857 and such local artists as Windus, Williamson, Campbell and the Dublin-born William Davis all coming under their influence; on the other, the introduction of foreign painters, notably from Düsseldorf and Brussels, into the rival society's shows.[4] This pace could not be kept up, and in 1861 the council of the new society, again with the mayor's approval, was calling for a fusion of the two bodies. Nothing occurred, so that two years later there was no exhibition by either; the giving of prizes stopped. There were a few makeshift exhibitions by the Academy later in the 1860s, then from 1867 to 1897 there were again none at all. In effect the Academy was defunct, though Ruskin's prophecy proved to be right enough:

[1] The Earls of Sefton and Derby are the two great Liverpool aristocrats, whose estates abut against the city even today. Aintree Racecourse is on land sold by Lord Sefton to Mrs Topham.

[2] *The Works of John Ruskin*. Edited by E. T. Cook and Alexander Wedderburn. George Allen, London, 1904, Vol. XIV, p. 327. The *Albion* appeared between 1827 and 1887.

[3] The prize-winning pictures in the critical years were as follows:

1851 W. Holman Hunt. *Valentine rescuing Sylvia* (Birmingham City Art Gallery). E. R. Dibdin, writing on 26 May 1910 about the Academy centenary, said that this award decided Hunt not to abandon painting.

1852 Millais. *The Huguenot* (private collector, New York)

1853 Holman Hunt. *Claudio and Isabella* (Tate Gallery).

1854 Mark Anthony. *Nature's Mirror* (With Hunt's *The Light of the World* as runner-up).

1855 Augustus Egg. *Life and Death of Buckingham* (Millais's *The Rescue* as runner-up).

1856 Ford Madox Brown. *Jesus Washing Peter's Feet* (Tate Gallery).

1857 Millais. *The Blind Girl* (City of Birmingham Art Gallery). At the time the picture was in Miller's collection.

1858 Ford Madox Brown. *Chaucer reading the Legend of Coustance* (Sydney). Renamed *Chaucer at the Court of King Edward III*. Another version, now in the Tate Gallery, belonged to F. R. Leyland.

1859 William Dyce. *The Good Shepherd*.

[4] In 1860 the exhibitors included Koekkoek, O. Achenbach, Louis and Eugene Verboeckhoven and others; in 1861 several more, plus the interesting French industrial painter Bonhommé who showed *Interior of a Coal Mine* (No. 666) and *Open-Air working of Lapis Calaminaris in the Vieille Montagne, Rhenish Prussia* (No. 755). There were also some Brussels exhibitors in 1859.

29 The most famous
nineteenth-century
Liverpool painting:
W. L. Windus's
Burd Helen, which
was shown in the
1856 Royal Academy,
admired by Ruskin
and owned for a time
by F. R. Leyland. It
is now in the Walker
Art Gallery

Let the Academy be broken up on the quarrel; let the Liverpool people buy whatever rubbish they have a mind to; and when they see, as in time they will, that it *is* rubbish, and find, as find they will, every Pre-Raphaelite picture gradually advance in influence and in value, you will be acknowledged to have borne a witness all the more noble and useful, because it seemed to end in discomfiture; though it will *not* end in discomfiture.[1]

Unhappily Windus, the one really notable painter to come out of so much friction, who, given a different temperament, might have been stimulated to great things by it, seems to have been totally discouraged[2] and to have painted nothing to speak of between 1862 and his death in 1907. 1862 was the year when he left Liverpool, having lost his wife after only four years of marriage: a tragic figure in the history of Liverpool art.

[1] *The Works of John Ruskin.* Vol. XIV, p. 328.
[2] He had also apparently fallen from Ruskin's favour. Ruskin's account of his 1857 Royal Academy picture *Too Late* was one of the harshest he ever wrote.

The 'spirit of self-improvement', as Ramsay Muir called it in his *History of Liverpool*,[1] revived after some thirty years with the Household Suffrage Act of 1867 and Forster's Education Act of 1870. With the Academy in suspense and the Royal Institution too stagnant to attract any public interest, the Corporation itself set up a Fine Arts Committee, sponsored a large Autumn Exhibition annually from 1871 to 1939, and at once began buying works for a permanent collection. Edward Samuelson, Philip Rathbone and J. A. Picton, the principal moving spirits, took matters up much where the earlier generation of reformers had left them, seeing the 'main object' of their exhibition as 'exciting a widespread interest in Art among the masses of the general population', with special reference to the tastes of 'the working man'.[2] To start with it must have seemed that they were brilliantly succeeding. Sales from the first exhibition amounted to £6,395, in 1874 to £9,526, in 1884 to more than £12,000. During the 1872 exhibition, which lasted for three and a half months, 22,894 tickets were sold at 3d, 6d or 1s, plus 332 season tickets; at least 10,000 schoolchildren were reckoned to have been let in free. 242 of the 960 works shown were sold for a total of £6,214, more than a third of it paid by individual members of the Town Council. A year later there was a public meeting at the Town Hall to discuss the provision of a permanent exhibition building, and nearly £7,000 was promised by those present in the room.

That November Andrew Barclay Walker the brewer was elected mayor in succession to Samuelson, and announced that he would give a gallery himself (he also paid for the gallery's extension in 1882). This was the origin of the Walker Art Gallery, which from 1877 onwards housed the Autumn Exhibition and the pictures which the Committee bought from it each year or acquired otherwise. By 1895 there were over 600 of these, including a large proportion of the works from the Royal Institution gallery, which the Corporation took over in July 1892; 103 of the total having been bought out of exhibition profits. As for their quality ' . . . The fact has not been lost sight of,' the Committee is quoted as saying,[3] 'that the public, for whose education and instruction the institution in a great measure exists, delight in subjects of a popular character, and, with this end in view, pictures have

[1] Written when he was Professor of History there and published for the University Press of Liverpool by Williams and Norgate, London. Second Edition 1907.

[2] Corporation of Liverpool: *Report of the Fine Arts Committee upon the second Autumn Exhibition of Pictures 1872*. The Committee felt that a good way to achieve this was to give official prominence to 'a large and striking gallery picture, telling some tale of human action and passion, with simple and effective power'.

[3] In the article by H. M. Cundall, 'Liverpool Walker Art Gallery' in the *Art Journal* for August 1895, p. 250.

he Hanging Committee at an early Autumn Exhibition. Philip Rathbone
irt-sleeves, with Picton on his right and Charles Dyall behind him

from time to time been added which, by appealing to common feelings and sentiments of our daily life, have afforded a fine moral lesson and given great pleasure to the numerous visitors to the Gallery who are uninitiated in

31 Brewer, mayor and patron of the arts: Sir Andrew Barclay Walker's statue in the entrance hall of the gallery he gave

higher forms of Art.' The object was popularization, a continuation of popular education by other means. 'There is, perhaps,' wrote the local antiquarian and dealer Joseph Mayer in 1876, 'no city in the world where the social duty of patronizing Art is now more firmly established than in Liverpool.'[1]

Alas, it now seems to us that few galleries have accumulated a larger number of valueless pictures. A wiser policy by the first two Curators, Charles Dyall (1877–1904), and E. R. Dibdin (1904–18) might have avoided this, for the exhibitions and the interest of the more enlightened patrons attracted the leading English artists and not a few from abroad. But Dyall was not in favour of highbrow or difficult works:

> Art has now taken deep roots in the intelligence of the people. . . . The free air of public opinion will help keep it clear of parasites, and all those enervating influences that prevent its growth and development. It must not be made an intellectual monopoly, nor be so lofty in its aim as to become abstruse and unintelligible.[2]

[1] Joseph Mayer: *Early Exhibitions of Art in Liverpool.* Privately printed. Liverpool 1876, p. 89. The book is dedicted to A. B. Walker. Nine years earlier Mayer had given his own collection to the Liverpool Museum, which had been built in 1856 on a site below that of the gallery.

[2] From his paper to the Art Congress of 1888 (*Transactions*, p. 295). See p. 53 below.

Under these conditions it was hardly surprising that the finest contribution to the city should have occurred outside the gallery, in the fourteen stained glass windows designed by Burne-Jones and executed by Morris for All Hallows' Church, Allerton, which was consecrated in 1876.[1] Yet there were perfectly reputable artists who sent to the autumn exhibitions: Legros, Tissot, Lhermitte, Scholderer and the excellent German realist R. Hirth du Frenes, for instance, in 1878; Sargent and Watts in 1896. There is still in the Walker Gallery a *Study of a Head* which Legros painted there in 1878 'before a large number of art students . . . as a practical lesson in art. Time occupied in painting, one hour and forty minutes'.[2] Herkomer seems to have lectured the same year. In 1881 Hall Caine read a paper on Rossetti's *Dante's Dream*, which the Committee bought from that year's exhibition; this was at an At Home, where the Band of the Liverpool Police Force also played and a Mr Aptommas performed on the harp.

Ruskin was the subject of three enthusiastic articles in the *Liverpool Weekly Albion* in 1872 (on 9, 16 and 23 November), and the next year wrote to an anonymous Liverpool friend suggesting that the Colonna Raphael should be bought for the gallery, the price asked being £40,000.[3] His letter was printed in the *Liverpool Daily Post* of 3 January 1874 and followed four days later by a hostile leading article. But the climate was changing, and only seven years later his secretary W. G. Collingwood, son of the Liverpool water-colourist William Collingwood and father of the philosopher, addressed a meeting of the Art Club with a view to forming a Ruskin Society; Philip Rathbone took the chair. There were also the lampoons – a common nineteenth century form of Liverpool self-expression – and the controversies: Samuelson and Rathbone falling out over the propriety of Alma Tadema's *The Sculptor's Model* in the 1878 exhibition,[4] the Reverend D. B. Hooke damning the gallery as founded on Drink. In a sense it may even have been quite a stimulating time, though only at a low artistic level and within narrow limits. For in the whole history of the Autumn Exhibition the city bought only one reasonably interesting contemporary foreign work: Segantini's strange

[1] G. E. Grayson of Liverpool was the architect. The church was built by John Bibby of Hart Hill in memory of his wife. One window, showing David mourning Saul and Jonathan, is not by Burne-Jones, as he apparently disagreed with Bibby's proposal that it should include portraits of two of the donor's children.

[2] *Walker Art Gallery, Descriptive Catalogue of the Permanent Collection of Pictures.* Compiled by Charles Dyall, Curator. 1890. (No. 179.)

[3] *The Works of John Ruskin*, Vol. XXXIV, pp. 512–13. The picture was on loan to S. Kensington. Pierpont Morgan bought it in 1901 and it is now in the Metropolitan Museum.

[4] Rathbone read a paper at the Social Science Congress that year entitled, 'The Mission of the Undraped Figure in Art'. It is included in the volume of 'Papers on Art' above. A topical ballad in *The Liverpool Lantern* for 23 November of the same year was called 'Nudity and Prudity, or the Battle of the Alma (Tadema). Art Cant – ata'.

allegory *The Punishment of Luxury* in 1893. It is impossible not to accuse the organizers of crass insularity; like most of Britain at that time they simply ignored the great French painters, whose works were not even shown.

32 Giovanni Segantini: *The Punishment of Luxury*. The only modern foreign work of any merit bought by the gallery in its first thirty years

One minor Liverpool mystery is the absence from the gallery of any work by Whistler. For Whistler not only sent to the exhibition but was the principal artist supported – it can hardly be called patronised – by the man he flippantly spoke of as 'the Liverpool Medici': F. R. Leyland (1831–92), who had entered the shipping firm of J. Bibby, Sons and Co from the Mechanics' Institution, risen to be its book-keeper at eighteen and a partner at twenty-eight, and taken it over in 1872 to run it with great brilliance as the Leyland Line.[1] Leyland, a solitary man and a passionate amateur pianist, started collecting Rossetti's work in 1865, having come to know that artist through Miller; his son-in-law Val Prinsep said that 'it was the one real friendship of his life'.[2] He also owned three of Windus's principal paintings and a number of pictures by other relatively enterprising British artists, such as Burne-Jones and Albert Moore. In 1867 he bought Speke Hall, and there Whistler came to stay on a number of occasions, working lengthily on individual portraits (mostly not completed) of his hosts and their three children, and

[1] After his death Pierpont Morgan and Sir John Ellerman shared the ships, and the line ceased to operate around 1930. The present Bibby Steamship Co was a new foundation by the Bibby family in 1891.
[2] Val Prinsep, ARA: 'Rossetti and His Friends', in *The Art Journal*, London, May 1892, p. 134.

33 Whistler and Liverpool.
Speke Hall no. 2. This etching
of 1875 shows the home of his
patron F. R. Leyland (now the
property of the National Trust
and close to the city airport)

34 Whistler: *Shipbuilder's
Yard.* Another Liverpool
etching of 1875

producing some half-dozen etchings of various Liverpool subjects dated between 1867 and 1875. With Mrs Leyland Whistler's relations were reputedly close, certainly jocular; his biographers the Pennells make one improbable reference to an engagement to her sister.[1] Leyland however broke with Whistler after his high-handed behaviour over the decoration of the family's London house – the famous episode of the Peacock Room – and in 1879 figured as the chief creditor at the Whistler bankruptcy, thus earning himself three vicious caricatures.[2]

In 1891, a year before Leyland's death, the artist reappeared in Liverpool to help hang the Autumn Exhibition, staying with Rathbone early in August, apparently in the same room as Ruskin had occupied around the time of their libel action. The centrepiece of his gallery was to be Luke Fildes's *The Doctor*, and from the first he set out to poke fun at such typical Autumn Exhibition works, writing to Mrs Whistler:

> Well a great part of the Academy room is hung – and I fancy that the mischief of the intention is clothed in a certain delicacy – indeed so subtly is it that perhaps after all it will be scarcely perceived – however there it is – As much ridicule and exposure has been brought to bear upon the false sentiment and execrable colour drawing and execution, as one's own nerves could tolerate.[3]

Nor did this story lose anything in the subsequent telling:

> You know, the Academy baby by the dozen had been sent in, and I got them all in my gallery – and in the centre, at one end, I placed the birth of the baby – splendid – and opposite, the baby with the mustard-pot, and opposite that the baby with the puppy – and in the centre, on one side, the baby ill, doctor holding its pulse, mother weeping. On the other, by the door, the baby dead – the baby's funeral – baby from the cradle to the grave – baby in heaven – babies of all kinds and shapes all along the line, not crowded you know, hung with proper respect for the baby. And on varnishing day, in came the artists – each making for his own baby – amazing! his baby on the line – nothing could be better! And they all shook my hand, and thanked me – and went to look – at the other men's babies – and then they saw babies in front of them, babies behind them, babies to the right of them, babies to the

---

[1] Improbable because Mr Andrew McLaren Young tells me there is no mention of her sister, or of any engagement, in Whistler's correspondence with the Leylands, though the story has crept into some of the secondary literature.

[2] See Peter Ferriday: 'The Peacock Room' in *The Architectural Review*, June 1959, Vol. 125, p. 407. Two of these caricatures are lost. *The Gold Scab* is the third.

[3] From an undated letter in the Glasgow University Collection. This and other references to Whistler's 1891 visit were very kindly transcribed for me by Miss Helen Drabble.

left of them. And then – you know – their faces fell – they didn't seem to like it – and – well – ha! ha! they never asked me to hang the pictures again at Liverpool! What![1]

35 Hanging committee for the Autumn Exhibition of 1891. Seated, left to right: Whistler, Philip Rathbone, Arthur Melville, RWS, W. S. Boadle (Liverpool Academy). Behind them, the gallery officials: Alfred H. Frazer, Charles Dyall and John H. Hard

So he told it to the Pennells and D. S. MacColl at breakfast in Paris, as he strolled round the table filling their glasses. His own contribution to the show had been *The Fur Jacket*, but the gallery, not surprisingly perhaps, did not buy, though he had hoped that they might. The portrait of Leyland, which seems to have been all that that gentleman got in return for his advances and commissions, went to the Prinseps. The rest of the Leyland collection, fifty-eight old masters and twenty-nine modern British (including twelve Rossettis but no Whistlers) was sold at Christies on 28 May, 1892, going to swell a total estate of £700,000.

As Leyland for some reason played no part in the gallery's – or indeed the city's – affairs it was Philip Rathbone rather who embodied the spirit of this

[1] E. R. and J. Pennell: *The Life of James McNeill Whistler;* Heinemann, 1908, pp. 192–3.

period in Liverpool, much as Roscoe and Traill had embodied that of the early part of the century. He was however a woollier and less forceful man than they. The slightly absent-minded brother of William Rathbone the Fifth, he came of that remarkable dynasty of Quaker and Unitarian merchants who had initiated such enterprises as the Society for the Abolition of the Slave Trade (in the 1780s), the building of St George's Hall and the setting up of the Domestic Mission in Mill Street. He was chairman of the gallery from 1886 till he died, and was from the first a strong supporter of Ruskin, Morris and the Pre-Raphaelites; it was he who induced subscribers to present the three most important Pre-Raphaelite paintings now in the collection, beside himself giving Legros's *The Pilgrimage* in 1873 and bequeathing six fifteenth-century Italian works on his death in 1895. His portrait was painted for the gallery by Holman Hunt, and he also owned Albert Moore's *The Song of Solomon* and *The Marble Seat*.[1] A young and sceptical newcomer could describe him in 1893 as:

> a queer man, retired now from the Insurance business . . . a man always trying to be epigrammatic and sometimes succeeding (tho' seldom); a lot of common sense loaded with the unpleasant cant of continual posing for effect. He trundles the Art Machine about Liverpool and generally works public galleries and the like; lives in a bit of a house negotiating his way about among all manner of nice things packed together like stars in the Milky Way.[2]

His niece however wrote more charitably that he 'believed in strengthening corporate life and in quickening civic patriotism by appealing to men through their senses and making the visible city a place to be proud of.'[3] He expressed this aim in a number of lectures and papers, both in Liverpool and elsewhere, and tried to put it tangibly into effect by completing the sculptural decoration of St George's Hall.

[1] Whistler, on his visit in 1891, wrote to his wife that this picture was 'very sweet and really most beautiful!'. The letter, dated 3 August, is in the Glasgow University Collection.

[2] W. M. Conway to his future wife's stepfather Manton Marble, quoted in Joan Evans: *The Conways. A History of Three Generations*. Museum Press, London, 1966, p. 85.

[3] Eleanor F. Rathbone: *William Rathbone, A Memoir*; Macmillan, London, 1905, pp. 460-1. The author, who was Liverpool's first woman Councillor and England's first woman Minister, credits her uncle with a liking for 'the most modern schools of impressionism'. But it is clear from his own lectures on 'The English School of Impressionists as illustrated in the Liverpool Autumn Exhibition' (1883) and 'Impressionism in Art' (1890 – both in a mixed collection of his *Papers on Art* in the Liverpool Public Libraries) that this did not mean impressionism as we now understand it so much as the work of men like Stanhope Forbes and Albert Moore. Up to the 1950s the gallery's one French impressionist work was Henri Le Sidaner's *St Paul's from the River*, which was bought from the Autumn Exhibition in 1911 and had a thoroughly British subject.

The history of Stirling Lee's reliefs on the Lime Street side of the hall shows all too depressingly the difference between Liverpool's first and second rounds of 'self-improvement'. The huge building has always cried out to be completed by sculpture – it still does so today – and in 1885 Lee, a product of the Royal Academy Schools and the Paris Beaux-Arts, produced rough designs for five out of the first six panels. The theme, inspired by the

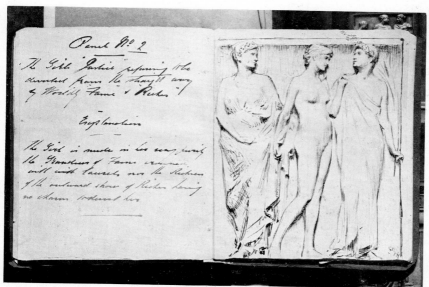

36 The crisis over the St George's Hall reliefs in the 1880s. Pen drawing for the second and, to the corporation, most controversial of Stirling Lee's six sculptures

law courts who are the building's principal users, was Justice: her 'Child-hood, Girlhood, Womanhood, Administration, Result and Final End'. The designs were gently sub-classical, a sculptural counterpart to Albert Moore's style of painting, and as soon as the first panel was completed the Liverpool Architectural Society found that it was 'out of harmony with, and inferior to, the high standard of the architecture'. A move to end the contract was rejected by the corporation by twenty-seven votes to fifteen, but in the summer of 1886 Rathbone was sent up to London to report on the model for the second panel. Here Lee was rash enough to show Justice naked: 'Justice, in her purity' (so runs the inscription), 'refuses to be diverted from the straight path by Wealth and Fame'. Rathbone liked the figure; Armstrong, the director of fine art at South Kensington who went along to Lee's studio with him, 'thought the breasts required stiffening in order to look more monu-

37 The first four of Lee's sculptured panels. With the third a greater rigidity
and formality set in

mental and virginal.'[1] This however was too much for the city Finance and
Estates Committee, who within a fortnight and without waiting to see the
panel broke off the contract by twenty-five votes to three. Rathbone was left
in the minority, and it was not till 1890 that he was allowed personally to
pay for the four remaining panels, and then only on condition that the council
could take them down after five years if it wished.[2]

In 1882, as part of the same great movement for wider education, the
University College was set up. From the first it was intended to found a
Chair of Fine Art there, known as the Roscoe Professorship and endowed by
William Roscoe's admirers, with Rathbone as chief promoter. The Principal,
Gerald Rendall, wanted to appoint William Martin Conway (1856–1937),
the mountaineer, art historian, collector and subsequent member of Parliament. At first the university council havered, so that for three years he came as
an occasional lecturer only. Twenty-eight at the time of his eventual appointment (and by then already tiring of the job), Conway was a man of considerable foresight, who saw 'a new architectural epoch'[3] arising from the use of
steel for building, understood the importance of the *musée imaginaire* some
forty years before André Malraux[4] and tried to get the university to set up a

[1] From Rathbone's report to the council, dated 23 July 1886, in a book of cuttings relating to
St George's Hall in the Liverpool Public Libraries.

[2] Lee later became Honorary Secretary of Whistler's International Society. He is not known to
have executed any other major work, and the remaining panels, looked at with today's eyes, are
noticeably less freely designed and more insipid than the first two. If right eventually triumphed
it was at the cost of being tamed.

[3] Sir W. Martin Conway: *The Domain of Art;* John Murray, London, p. 148.

[4] Ibid, p. 132.

Museum of Photographs. He had no pupils, but was 'used as a kind of free-lance'[1] to give lectures and represent the university on formal occasions; 'the

38 William Martin
Conway, first Roscoe
Professor of Fine Art in
Liverpool University and
one of the instigators of
the Art Congress

function of the professor', so Rendall said, 'was to be to enlighten the public rather than to train artists.[2] . . .' His main Liverpool achievement was to act as secretary (and chief instigator with Rathbone) of a giant Art Congress on the lines of the British Association: the National Association for the Advancement of Art and its Application to Industry. This met annually between 1888 and 1890, the second and third meetings being held in Edinburgh and Birmingham; a further Congress was supposed to be held in 1891 at Nottingham,

[1] Lord Conway of Allington: *Episodes in a Varied Life;* Country Life, London, 1932, p. 84.
[2] Joan Evans: *The Conways;* Museum Press, London, 1966, p. 70. The lecture audiences it seems were often very small. Dr Evans says that on one occasion only eight people were present. However, when Conway first put in in 1886 for the Slade Professorship at Cambridge his Principal and colleagues gave him the most resounding testimonials, Oliver Lodge in particular writing of his 'earnestness and thoroughness worthy of a student of science . . . wholly devoid of that morbid or effeminate sensibility which sometimes accompanies keen artistic perception'. That time it was the architect J. Henry Middleton who got the job. The retiring professor, Sidney Colvin, wrote testimonials for both men.

E

THE GRAPHIC
AN ILLUSTRATED WEEKLY NEWSPAPER

No. 994.—Vol. XXXVIII. | EDITION DE LUXE
Registered as a Newspaper

SATURDAY, DECEMBER 15. 1888

WITH EXTRA SUPPLEMENT

PRICE NINEPENCE
By Post Ninepence Halfpenny

1. Sir Frederick Leighton, P.R.A., President of the Congress, Delivering the Inaugural Address
2. Mr. Walter Crane, President of the Applied Art Section
3. Mr. Alfred Gilbert, A.R.A., President of the Sculpture Section, reads a Communication from Mr. G. F. Watts, R.A.
4. Professor Aitchison, A.R.A., President of the Architectural Section, and Sir F. Leighton
5. The Audience in the Walker Gallery
6. Mr. L. Alma-Tadema, R.A., President of the Painting Section
7. Sir J. Picton proposes a Vote of Thanks
8. Mr. John Brett, A.R.A
9. An Attack on the Royal Academy: Mr. Alma-Tadema in the Chair
10. Mr. Onslow Ford, A.R.A.
11. Mr. Holman Hunt reads a Paper
12. Mr. William Morris in the Rotunda

THE NATIONAL ASSOCIATION FOR THE ADVANCEMENT OF ART AND ITS APPLICATION TO INDUSTRY
SKETCHES AT THE INAUGURAL MEETING AT LIVERPOOL

39 The great Liverpool Art Congress of 1888. A page of sketches showing Lord Leighton (centre). Alma Tadema, Holman Hunt, William Morris and other participants

but apparently never took place. In Conway's eyes, so he explained nearly half a century later, the real purpose of the operation was to obtain the heaviest possible censure of the Corporation's conduct over the St George's Hall panels, which leading sculptors like Alfred Gilbert and Onslow Ford deplored. Once this had been achieved at the second meeting he organized the Birmingham Congress, then resigned 'having determined to undertake the exploration of the great, and till then unpenetrated, mountain region of northern Kashmir. No one else could be found to take on my job as Honorary Secretary of the Art Congress, so the movement came to an end.'[1] He subsequently became Slade Professor at Cambridge, where he had once got a Third in History, and almost at the same time was given a concession for all natural resources in the Acre Territory of Bolivia; in 1895 he was knighted. In 1918 he was elected Conservative Member for the Combined English Universities. His collection of photographs now forms the Conway Library at the Courtauld Institute; his house Allington Castle near Maidstone is attached to Aylesford Priory.

Utterly forgotten now, the Liverpool Art Congress of 1888 must have seemed a historic occasion. Leighton presided, supported by no less than thirteen vice-presidents, and there were sections for Painting (under Alma Tadema), Sculpture (Alfred Gilbert), Architecture (G. Aitchison), Applied Art (Walter Crane), Art History and Museums (Sidney Colvin, who was too ill to come), and National and Municipal Encouragement of Art (under the Edinburgh Professor of Art, Baldwin Brown). The main committee consisted of these six plus eighteen others, including Gosse, Herkomer, Poynter and Philip Rathbone, who was also secretary of the last-named section. About 1,000 people are said to have attended. Holman Hunt, Basil Champneys, Morris and Cobden-Sanderson were among those who read papers, Morris's on 'Art and its Producers' being relatively involved and dull. T. C. Horsfall of Manchester read one on 'How to make Workpeople care for art', Conway on 'Reproductions of Ancient Works of Art for Municipal Museums', Sir Philip Magnus on 'Some Notes on the Training of Industrial Artists', Rathbone on 'Lessons from France as to Imperial and Municipal Encouragement of National Art' – the result of a visit by him to the Paris art schools. Dibdin, Dyall and many others also spoke; Dean Farrar preached the introductory sermon.[2] At Edinburgh a year later Rathbone, now president of his section, chose as his subject 'The Development of Monumental

[1] Ibid, p. 87.
[2] Virtually all the papers are printed in *Transactions of the National Association for the Advancement of Art and its Application to Industry. Liverpool Meeting 1888.* London, 22 Albemarle Street, 1888. There are also volumes for the other two congresses.

Forms of Art, A Political Necessity of Civilisation'. However, Morris, who took over the Applied Art section from Crane, termed the second congress 'on the whole a dull affair' and accused it of 'ignoring . . . the working class except as instruments to be played on.'[1] The only papers of which he approved were those by Sir William Richmond and G. F. Watts.

In September 1888, i.e. before the Liverpool meeting, Conway was succeeded as Professor by R. A. M. Stevenson (1847–1900), Robert Louis Stevenson's cousin, who had worked as a painter at Barbizon and studied with Carolus-Duran in Paris in the 1870s. This very much less extrovert character, a gifted man of limited energies, was pushed into art criticism by R. L. S. and W. E. Henley, and is best known for his book *Velasquez* (1895) which was republished as recently as 1962; Whistler, who knew him, had a copy. More familiar than any other nineteenth-century Liverpool figure with the work of contemporary France, Stevenson attended the Liverpool and

40 The second (and last) Professor of Fine Art. R. A. M. Stevenson with a group at Grez-sur-Loing in 1877, when he was still primarily a painter. Standing, left to right: Anthony Henley, Bentz, Palizzi, Stevenson, Frank O'Meara, Ernest Parton, Willie Simpson

Edinburgh Art Congresses, but was scarcely in tune with the local ideas. 'Art is not life', he wrote, ' . . . sentiment is not imagination', while his American friend W. H. Low reports him commenting on one of Millais's

---

[1] Quoted in J. Bruce Glasier: *William Morris and the Early Days of the Socialist Movement;* Longmans, London, 1921, pp. 86, 89.

pictures in the 1895 Royal Academy: 'Truly British art, a touching anecdote, poetry for the middle class'. There is (or was) a picture by Arthur Lemon for which he posed called *Hard Pressed*, showing an ancient Briton fleeing his enemies, and this became known to his friends as 'The Escape from Liverpool'. 'I thought I might hit it off,' was his account to Low, . . . 'But what I found was that, in addition to my definite work in the College, I was expected to wear a high hat and a carnation in my buttonhole, and talk mild gossip about Botticelli, Burne-Jones and Frith – actually Frith – at garden-parties and afternoon teas. And then there were a lot of pedagogues – duffers who talked about "schools", and attributions to this and that master – and queried about dates, and the *cinque-cento*, and that rot – and their wives, who wished to uplift the working classes by means of art, dear good ladies, of course, but – well, I held out as long as I could and then I simply cut it, for no human being could have stood it any longer.'[1] Stevenson's departure in 1892 seems to have put paid to the Professorship of Fine Art; the job remained vacant, and two years later, by some juggle that has never been explained,[2] it was turned into a Chair of Architecture and the present university School of Architecture took its place, with F. M. Simpson as the first professor.

The new arrangement was that the University College should contribute the Roscoe endowment and the City's Technical Education Committee £1,000 a year, which paid for a Section of Applied Art within the school. This section was a short-lived local offshoot of the wider movement associated with Morris and Walter Crane, and was under the direction of R. Anning Bell, RA, a painter and illustrator in the Pre-Raphaelite wake, with Charles J. Allen as instructor in modelling and Richard Llewelyn Rathbone as metalwork teacher. At the Walker Gallery's spring exhibitions of 1894–8 works by these and other members of the movement were shown, including Art Nouveau book-bindings by D. S. MacColl, so-called Della Robbia ware by Philip Rathbone's son Harold (second cousin of the metal worker) and work by the sculptors Conrad Dressler and Stirling Lee. Lee, Allen and Dressler were together responsible for the second group of six reliefs on St George's Hall (symbolizing National Prosperity and now suitably draped); R. Ll. B. Rathbone for the metal doors to the Unitarian Church in Ullet

---

[1] Will H. Low: *A Chronicle of Friendships, 1873–1900;* Hodder and Stoughton, London, 1908, p. 467. Low says Lemon's picture is in the Tate Gallery, but it cannot be traced there. For the fullest account of Stevenson see Denys Sutton's biographical study in the *Velasquez* reprint, Bell, London 1962.

[2] According to Lionel B. Budden (ed.): *The Book of the Liverpool School of Architecture;* Liverpool and London 1932, the idea originated with the Liverpool Architectural Society. On the other hand Roderick Bisson in *The Sandon Studios Society and the Arts;* Liverpool 1965, p. 4, says it was Stevenson's own suggestion.

Road. A third Rathbone, Harold's architect brother Edmund, meanwhile ran
The City Beautiful Wayside Café, 'a home from home for aesthetes'[1] near

41 Liverpool Art Nouveau.
Richard Llewelyn Rathbone's
metal doors to the Unitarian
church in Ullet Road

where The Cavern now is. The Applied Art Section's real monument,
however, (as Dr Hughes has shown in *Seaport*) was the Philharmonic Hotel,
built during the Walker brewery's late nineteenth-century spate of pub
construction, between 1898 and 1900. The Philharmonic's metal gates by
H. Blomfield Barr are one of the sights of Liverpool.

The section had some bright recruits, notably J. Herbert MacNair, who
was Charles Rennie Mackintosh's brother-in-law, and in 1901 Augustus
John. The 1902 Education Act however forced the Corporation to take over
the School of Design, which since 1883 had been in a new building in
Mount Street next the old Mechanics' Institution; and it seemed logical to
detach the Applied Art Section from the university and fuse both to make a
new city School of Art. Executed in 1905, this decision pleased neither the
Applied Art teachers nor their students, and that year a number of them
broke off to form an independent art school at 9 Sandon Terrace under
MacNair and the newly-arrived painter Gerard Chowne. They had the

---

[1] Roderick Bisson: *The Sandon Studios Society and the Arts;* Parry Books, Liverpool, 1965, p. 66.
Mr Bisson's book contains much relevant information about the old Applied Arts Section, together
with the society which was shortly to emerge from it and the artists associated with both.

42 Liverpool Art Nouveau. Brass door furniture in the
Philharmonic Hotel

support of the livelier teachers at the University (which got independent
status as such in 1903 and was full of a new self-confidence), and John
painted some of his best early portraits of such men as J. M. Mackay, E. K.
Muspratt, Sir John Brunner and Kuno Meyer. 'Liverpool,' he recalled half

43 Liverpool Art Nouveau. H. Bloomfield Barr's metal gates to the
Philharmonic Hotel, drawn by a student at the School of
Architecture

a century later, 'commonly considered a dull, ugly and commercial city, for me abounded in interest and surprise.'[1] He had in fact given up teaching two or three years before the split, but he remained working close by in Chatham Street. Outside the Sandon group he was less appreciated. In 1902[2] the Liverpool Academy rejected his application for membership, and when that year a group of subscribers gave his portrait by Rothenstein to the Walker Gallery it was catalogued simply as *Portrait of a Young Man.*

44 & 45 Augustus John's Liverpool period.
Above: *The Mulatto.* An etching of 1910, first state. According to Campbell Dodgson,' The man was a man from Barbados, etched at Liverpool.' Left: *Old Man of Liverpool.* An etching of 1902

The brief Art Nouveau movement seems to have fizzled out as soon as the Applied Art section parted company with the architects. But the result was for the first time in Liverpool to create an organized group of artists outside and in opposition to the recognized art establishment. When Sandon Terrace was pulled down in 1907 to make a playground behind the Mechanics' Institution the new school moved down the hill to the Bluecoat School buildings (where the University School of Architecture, now under C. H. Reilly, joined it two years later.) There it transformed itself into the Sandon Studios Society, a mixed group of practising artists and amateurs with John,

---

[1] Augustus John: *Chiaroscuro;* Cape, London, 1952, p. 59. After leaving the city he painted further portraits of Reilly, Oliver Elton and Sir Charles Sherrington.
[2] *Not* 1905, as suggested by the Academy's 150th Anniversary Catalogue. Roderick Bisson established the correct date from the Academy minutes.

Steer, Lavery and Mackintosh as honorary members and Chowne and Mac-
Nair as teachers. The Liverpool Academy was at that time a dead body,
though it had begun holding exhibitions again in 1897; the Autumn Exhi-

46 Teachers of the Applied Art Department with the Professor of
Architecture. Left to right: Gerald Chowne, Charles J. Allen,
J. Herbert MacNair and Charles Reilly

bition was largely controlled by the London artists, the Royal Academy
having at one point threatened a boycott when the Liverpool influence
seemed to be getting too great. The coal merchant (and total abstainer) John
Lea, who had succeeded Rathbone as chairman, was 'slow to push out into
new deeps' according to his biographer; 'he had certain intellectual and
spiritual limitations'.[1] Dibdin took over at the Walker Gallery in 1904, and
began the unhappy but not uncommon policy of taking members of his committee up to London each year for a tour of the studios. According to Sir
W. B. Forwood[2] they would visit 200 in ten days, and always had the same
cab-driver. He also wrote regular unsigned articles on art for the *Liverpool
Post*, where he can be found calling Oscar Wilde an 'unhappy victim of

[1] *John Lea. Citizen and Art Lover.* A sketch by Frank Elias. Philip, Son and Nephew, Liverpool
n.d. (1928), p. 25. Lea stood as a Liberal for East Toxteth in 1909 and was beaten by Sir Edward
Marshall Hall; he became Lord Mayor in 1914. Frank Elias wrote several books for the Religious
Tract Society and was a contributor to *The Boy's Own Paper*. His biography is generally eulogious.
[2] Cited by Elias (p. 34).

diseased propensities',[1] and writing of 'the jejune El Greco' and of Goya as being 'singularly ill-regulated as regards his life or his art'.[2]

So the irreconcilable gap was no longer between the art-lovers and the Corporation, as it had been at the time of the St George's Hall panels, but between the official bodies and the unofficial one. On the one hand there was the NEAC show organized by Chowne at the Royal Institution building in 1905 and attended by Steer and Tonks. There was the Sandon Society's spring exhibition of 1908, which included a Monet (*Etretat*) and twenty-one works by Augustus John. Above all there were the two Post-Impressionist shows, one in March 1911 and the other in February 1913, drawn from the famous exhibitions organized by Roger Fry at the Grafton Gallery in London and accompanied in each case by a section of Sandon artists. Against these enterprising ventures the Walker Gallery could set a belated show of the Barbizon school, including Corot, and of etchings from Georges Petit's Paris gallery in March 1908, while a batch of NEAC painters was admitted to the Autumn Exhibition of that year. In 1911 the Le Sidaner was bought. This lagging shift of taste however was hardly enough to excite the informed art lover, and there was no longer the old concern with the uninformed. Attendance at the gallery had been falling since the beginning of the century – 'doubtless due,' said Dibdin in his 1912 report to the city council, 'to the inducements offered in other directions, notably the attractions of numerous picture palaces and the tendency of many to spend their leisure time motoring'.[3] And Dibdin himself still reacted to modern art with a now all too familiar philistinism, comparing Vlaminck's *Pontoise* in the second Post-Impressionist show with 'Master Tommy's results with his first paint-box' and ridiculing van Gogh for the thickness of his paint.[4]

Opposition to the Sandon Society and its works reached a climax in 1909, when a lawyer friend of Augustus John's called H. Chaloner Dowdall was the retiring Lord Mayor and asked John to paint his presentation portrait, on the grounds that 'you will have the biggest gate the Autumn Exhibition has ever had, and I shall have a picture worth 500 guineas within five years' time'.[5] The painting, with Dowdall as a heavily dramatized civic Don Quixote and a rubicund footman called Smith as his Sancho Panza, took little account

[1] 'Art and Degeneracy', 29 December 1912.
[2] In a book review on 14 January 1914. These articles, together with two remarkable patriotic poems of autumn 1914 and other interesting items, are in a cuttings book 'Articles by E. R. Dibdin 1907–14' in the Liverpool Public Libraries.
[3] Quoted in Frank Lambert: 'The Walker Art Gallery. Growth of a Policy (2)' in *Liverpool Bulletin*. February 1952, Vol. I, no. 3, p. 3.
[4] Article of 15 February 1913, in the same cuttings book.
[5] Letter from Dowdall to Vere E. Cotton, 6 November 1945, in a book of cuttings and letters relating to the portrait, no. Hq. 759/2 JOH in the Liverpool Public Libraries.

of municipal dignity and affronted many of the citizens. Coming on it among the more congenial Autumn Exhibition pictures by Alma Tadema, Leighton, Luke Fildes and Solomon J. Solomon, the *Liverpool Post* critic called it:

> either an extremely bad practical joke or else the grossest exhibition of bad and inartistic taste we have ever seen on the walls of the gallery.[1]

47 Another object of controversy: John's portrait of Lord Mayor Dowdall, 1909, now in the National Gallery of Victoria at Melbourne

Four days later the same writer was contrasting the 'hubbub among the long-haired gentry', which this verdict not unnaturally provoked, with the more laudable attitude of 'healthy-minded students of art'. Similarly 'Bent Briar' in the satirical *Porcupine* referred to 'long-haired neurotic commentators', arguing that

> If to coax Dicky Sam and his wife through our turnstiles we have to rely upon 'freak' pictures, the sooner we go out of the business, the better.[2]

John himself seems to have been taken aback by the venom of such attacks, which he found 'stupid, disgusting and unnecessary'.[3] Dowdall as ex-mayor defended him in a lecture at the gallery, but within ten years had sold the picture to a private buyer in Sussex who offered him £1,400 for it, or four-

[1] 18 September 1909.
[2] *Porcupine*, Liverpool, 25 September 1909.
[3] Interview in the *Dispatch* of 4 October 1909

teen times John's original fee.[1] It never found a home in Liverpool at all, and in 1938 went off to the National Gallery of Victoria – the year the Walker Gallery bought the *Two Jamaican Girls*, its first example of John's work.

The tensions of 1909 stimulated the Sandon group to produce a pamphlet called *The Sport of Civic Life, or Art and the Municipality*,[2] which set out to attack the official art policies all along the line. In this Henry Carr the Liverpool painter wrote on the Autumn Exhibition; the stage designer G. W. Harris, an ex-pupil of John's, on the Liverpool Academy, whose centenary was then impending ('When you hear the drums banging for the Liverpool Academy don't get up, it's not worth it. . . .'); Charles W. Sharpe on the commissioning of a London artist to paint four lunettes in the Town Hall vestibule; Frank Rutter on the cleaning of the Roscoe pictures and the building up of the permanent collection. There is also an amusing lampoon on John Lea, who is made to say:

> Now, this is a canvas we cannot well sky,
> It teaches a moral and catches the eye,
> If I say the word the City will buy [then a refrain].

> ART'S a fine thing and it's all very well,
> But COMMERCE is greater – it's harder to spell,
> So we'll hang up the works that are likely to sell.

> Lea, – lie – low!

[1] Dowdall was under some criticism for selling a picture in which Liverpool, despite its behaviour in 1909, still felt a proprietary right – especially as he at the same time bought a house and three acres of ground on Boars Hill near Oxford, to which he retired. He explained the circumstances in the letter to Cotton already quoted:

. . . . a little later I was being good naturedly chaffed at the round table of The Conservative Club where the party leaders lunched. So I retaliated 'Well you may not like it, but you are businessmen, and I will bet I could get £1,000 for it.' Alderman Oulton was on my left and said 'Sell it', and it went right round the table everyone saying 'Sell it'. Sir Charles Petrie, Alderman Savage, Sir William Forwood (less confiden:ly), and I think Sir Thomas Royden and others. Anyhow when I came here and had nowhere to hang it I wrote to Sir Charles Petrie who was then leader of the Council, reminded him of the joke and asking him if it would be generally agreeable if I took the joke seriously. . . .

Probably (as Colonel Cotton points out), Sir Charles and the other lunchers had been the chief donors of the portrait, which in those days was commissioned not by the Corporation but by a group of the sitter's friends. Then a month after Dowdall had had the offer of £1,400 from Mr Warren of Lewes House he got a letter from the Tate Gallery offering him £200 or £300 for the picture. This letter too is in the book of cuttings and bears a pencilled note:

I asked my wife if she thought my son, who was then 10, would rather have his father in the Tate and a nominal price or the full market price and she said 'Don't be a fool'. H.C.D.

In the 1950s the Walker Gallery borrowed the picture from Melbourne, and Dowdall, now an old man, spoke about the circumstances of its painting.

[2] Edited and published by Charles W. Sharpe, Liverpool 1909. A successor appeared in 1912 under the title *A Bushell of Chaff*. Roderick Bisson says John Lea asked the School of Art and the local booksellers to boycott it.

The main item in the pamphlet however was an essay by William Rothenstein called 'Art and the Municipality', which no doubt related to the
lectures given by him in Liverpool in early 1908 (on 'The Artist and the City')
and at a Walker Gallery soirée presided over by Dowdall in October 1909;
it may also reflect his discussions at Ditchling with Eric Gill. He was all in
favour of making use of the local artist. 'I hold it to be more important,' he
said, 'that such culture as is native in any city should be tended, developed,
and ultimately employed than that a hundred masterpieces adorn the walls
of the public gallery.' What should have been done was:

> to encourage a man of energy and discernment to settle in the growing
> city, capable of co-operating together in planning spaces and buildings,
> whether private or public, and of inspiring a circle of eager local crafts-
> men of every kind, who would thus have laid foundations for a living
> school of art.

He suggested that the Corporation should induce 'one or two men of tried
character and attainment' to settle in Liverpool 'to advise and organize the
collective efforts' of gallery, museum and theatre, which would remain under
their existing management. 'Thus might be founded as it were a University
of the Arts', with its students 'decorating schools, mission houses, chapels,
halls, of any kind and however humble.'

> The necessary elements are there already – money *is* spent and work of
> various sorts is required, and local students, and enthusiasm, and latent
> talent. What is needed is to bring these elements into relation, and under
> modern conditions this can only be brought about by the devotion and
> energy of an enthusiast, working – and paid to work – for that end.

This would be much better than the prevailing situation, where the artist
seemed 'little more than a parasite, waiting on the caprices of the rich rather
than expressing the essential culture of his own time.'[1]

Simpson's successor C. H. Reilly invited Rothenstein to be his lecturer in
art at the School of Architecture. The invitation (which was refused) and
many of the ideas which Rothenstein outlined are part of a larger scheme
described in Reilly's memoirs,[2] by which a powerful group would have moved
into Liverpool cultural life under the wing of the university. The idea was to
create a chair of Aesthetics for MacColl, who would also have become
director of the Walker Gallery; John, Epstein and Elgar would then have
been asked to become respectively professors of painting, sculpture and
music. The Corporation were not keen, arguing that painting was their responsibility rather than the university's; but something of the plan seems to

[1] Ibid, pp. 5–9.
[2] *Scaffolding in the Sky;* Routledge, London, 1938, pp. 124–5.

have filtered into the 1914 project for a Lancashire Society of Arts centred on the Bluecoat School. This eighteenth century group of buildings now housing the Sandon Society was rented in 1909 by W. H. Lever (the subsequent Lord Leverhulme) for the benefit of the University School of Architecture and at Reilly's request. When it proved necessary to secure the freehold if the school was to be saved from redevelopment, Lever was persuaded to put up the money on behalf of the friends and tenants of the buildings. The idea was that the proposed society of arts should in due course take them over from Lever and run them as an arts centre. Part of its function as outlined was to give fellowships to eminent creative artists which might induce them to work in Liverpool for limited periods. Every year two fellows each in painting, decorative painting and design, sculpture, architecture and civic design, music, and literature and drama were to be appointed and lent rooms in the school on condition that they spent at least two months in Liverpool and discussed their work with other members of the society. In the event Lever changed his mind, and turned the scheme down flat when the Great War ended. But it remains the emasculated ancestor of the present Bluecoat Society of Arts.[1]

With that we have the main framework of the Liverpool art organizations as we know them today: the gallery, with the Roscoe collection of old masters; the Regional College of Art centred on its buildings of 1883 and 1905; the Liverpool Academy; the Sandon Studios Society; the Bluecoat Chambers and its studios; and the disappearance of any kind of art or art historical department at the university. Each of these phenomena was founded on a set of ideas which has not necessarily ever been fulfilled, yet arose from the local situation and the growth of the city and is still somehow hanging in the air like a very old radioactive cloud, even though few people are conscious of it now. It is almost as if there were a pattern in these things: a fresh social or philosophical approach to the problem leading each time to a small burst of activity as first the Royal Institution, then the Mechanics' Institution, then the Liverpool Academy, then the official Autumn Exhibition and finally the Sandon Society found new energies and an interested public. Each time it took some years for the word to get around and for the artists, local or metropolitan, to absorb the stimulus and produce their main works. By then the original approach had been forgotten or discarded, for the one man with the persistence and perhaps blindness to go on hammering away at the same

---

[1] The history of this society is given in W. S. MacCunn: *Bluecoat Chambers;* Liverpool University Press, 1956.

points from start to finish had been Roscoe, who came too early in the story for his achievement to take a very tangible form. His monument is in his collection; it is not in the structure of art in Liverpool.

Over and above this there was also a much larger shift of attitude which was not confined to Liverpool or even to this country. The social, educational, almost philanthropic view of the arts which evolved in the nineteenth century only appealed to the brighter spirits so long as it was not bureaucratized. As soon as it became official corporation policy there was a reaction against it in the name of artistic exclusiveness and good taste: that new emphasis on personality and technique which appeared in R. A. M. Stevenson's book. The Sandon Society, for instance, accepted the idea of the artist as gypsy, as gentleman or as scholar. It was more than doubtful about his role in civic life.

It is worth thinking how far this might have been avoided by a more intelligent corporation; certainly Philip Rathbone's death in 1895 seems to mark a turning point. For the real question in the arts in a city like Liverpool is how far the shift of patronage and policy-making into municipal hands can be used to stimulate rather than merely alienate the artist. Can the old concern with art's social function survive without turning him in on himself? All we can do here is try to show how history raises such questions; a far more detailed study would be necessary if they were to be answered. But the ideas and the events of those years are still there to be thought about, and so are the major monuments and many of the works which the local artists produced. A wider consciousness of these things would certainly help in the development of any new pattern for art in English provincial cities.

3 : ESTABLISHED INSTITUTIONS

Such is the background to the present art 'establishment' in the city, and the extension of central authority and central grants in the educational and cultural field has only confirmed it. Only the Liverpool Academy, of the institutions which we have mentioned, can today be considered as a purely local enterprise. The Walker Gallery is one of the four provincial galleries (the others being Glasgow and the university collections at Oxford and Cambridge) which the Standing Commission on Museums and Galleries regards as having been 'built up to national standard';[1] in 1960 it became the first provincial gallery to be substantially helped by the government to buy a picture it needed. The College of Art, the University and also the Public Libraries (with their Art Library and collection of prints) are geared into the national educational and library system, while the Bluecoat and Sandon Societies are seen as part of an embryo network of arts centres such as the present government, the Arts Council and the Gulbenkian Foundation all in their various ways wish to encourage. Bodies like these have changed in many respects since the nineteenth century, but broadly speaking they have not lost in importance. More than most English cities, Liverpool provides a strong and active structure for the visual arts.

The great transformation in the Walker Art Gallery dates from 2 April 1931, when Vere E. Cotton, Philip Rathbone's grandson-in-law, wrote a letter to the *Liverpool Post* denouncing its collection as 'utterly unworthy' of the place. He organized a petition of eighty leading citizens to complain that the gallery was failing to fulfil its purpose, which he proposed should be the formation of a balanced collection of British painting. This was true in that both attendances and sales at the Autumn Exhibitions had been falling off ever since 1904,[2] but whether the purpose had ever been quite what it now became is doubtful. Up to the time of Cotton's assault the gallery more or less rotated round the Autumn Exhibition, and the large collection of pictures which had been formed was mainly purchased thence; only the Roscoe

[1] Standing Commission on Museums and Galleries: *Survey of Provincial Museums and Galleries;* HMSO 1963, paragraph 22.

[2] Frank Lambert: 'The Arts – Painting' in *Liverpool Echo,* Centenary Edition, 1955, pp. 77–8. See also his two articles 'The Walker Art Gallery – Growth of a Policy' in *Liverpool Bulletin,* Vol. I. nos. 2 and 3, October 1951 and February 1952.

48 The Walker Art Gallery. An early photograph

pictures lent by the Royal Institution and the occasional legacy (like Rathbone's) provided a striking exception, actively disliked by the more philistine members of the public.[1] The only income for purchases up to 1929, apart from a bequest of £2,000 by Lord Derby in 1892, was the annual profit on the Autumn Exhibition, which dwindled over the years almost to the point of disappearance; it was in that year that the corporation first made a purchase grant: £750. Frank Lambert, however, who took over as director in 1932, with Hugh Scrutton as his successor in 1952 and Cotton himself as chairman of the city's Libraries, Museums and Arts committee almost uninterruptedly from 1939 to 1955, between them turned it into a place that artist and scholars all over the world have to take seriously. In 1931 it was near the bottom of the larger English provincial galleries. Today it is one of the small group at the top.

It normally shows a good representative collection of English painting from the seventeenth century to the present day, an outstanding group of Flemish and Italian primitives, a sprinkling of works by other great European painters, from Rubens through Rembrandt and Courbet to Seurat and

[1] See the unsigned article in *The Liverpool Review* 'A Chamber of Horrors' of 5 March 1887, when Roscoe's pictures were still hanging in the Royal Institution. 'The climax of horror is reached ... when you come to the end wall, where the examples of the Byzantine school are hung which formed the main portion of the Roscoe bequest. Anything more terrible than this Byzantine chamber of horrors it would be impossible to imagine except it might be a nightmare.'

Matisse, and a few modern foreign paintings, not however of the first rank. It also attracts important loans; Christ Church, Oxford, for instance deposited its pictures in the gallery while its own new gallery building was being built, and twenty-four of Lt-Col A. Heywood-Lonsdale's pictures, including a Rembrandt and a Chardin, have been on loan since 1959. There is no Autumn Exhibition. Instead there is the annual show of the much revived Liverpool Academy, which has been held in the gallery since its postwar reopening in 1951, and, every two years since 1957, the John Moores Liverpool Exhibition, which has for young British painters become a biennale nearly as stimulating as those of Venice, São Paulo and Paris, and in every way more accessible. All this is a great achievement; it means that in thirty years the city has began to catch up with the main international current of taste and interest in pictures (instead of, as before, lagging thirty years behind it).[1] and that it is now known for its gallery to many people elsewhere who take no interest in shipping, football or pop music. It means too that within the new network of

49 Simone Martini: *Christ discovered in the temple.* One of the outstanding masterpieces of William Roscoe's collection now in the Walker Gallery

[1] Dibdin's Barbizon show was in 1908. The Barbizon painters were internationally famous (and selling for high prices) thirty years earlier. They were painting their best works some thirty years before that.

50 Lucas Cranach: *The Nymph of the Fountain*. Another of the
Walker Gallery's Roscoe pictures

centralized art patronage and management – both official and private –
Liverpool carries considerable weight. The remarkable thing is that all this
is not more widely appreciated in Liverpool itself.

At least until very recently, the driving force in the gallery's development
has come neither from the 150,000-odd visitors who are counted through its
doors in an average year[1] nor from their elected representatives who govern it,
but from a group of Liverpool's business leaders, with Cotton at their head.
Until 1956 the purchase grant from the rates never exceeded £1,000 a year,
and it was only six years later that it began to compare favourably with that
available to other big provincial galleries; it now stands at £10,000 for 1964–5,
which reflects the much greater interest recently taken by the council. The
main burden however of those purchases which have so transformed the
gallery's status has been borne by certain local firms, who have either individually paid for works the gallery has asked for or, more recently, subscribed
to special funds in its support. Eleven major acquisitions in the past fifteen
years, including the Rembrandt and the Rubens, have come about in this
way, while some twenty of the most modern English paintings have been

[1] Attendance figures are not at all a reliable clue to the impact made by such an institution on the
public, though they can be a reasonable guide to the success of a particular exhibition. For what
they are worth, here are the attendances at the gallery for the period 1958–65:

1958/9	127,000	1962/3	125,427
1959/60	188,959	1963/4	125,427
1960/1	177,985	1964/5	127,596
1961/2	155,987	1965/6	213,191

given by the sponsors of the John Moores exhibitions. The kernel of the collection is still the Roscoe and other pictures from the Royal Institution, which were finally made over to the city in 1948; most of the 5,000 or so odd works in the cellars or out on loan come from the old pre-1931 purchasing policy; the seventeenth, eighteenth and early twentieth century English works added since come largely from a legacy of £20,000 from Lord Wavertree, a member of the Walker family who was deputy chairman of the Arts Sub-Committee and died in 1932. The development of the foreign collection and the extension of the English school into our own time have been due to the public spirit of industry, shipping, stores, insurance and banks.[1]

[1] This patronage can be analysed as follows:

(a) Seven works given individually by firms.
   Gainsborough: *Sir Robert Clayton* (1950). The Liverpool Post and Echo.
   Crome: *Landscape* (1950–1). Owen Owen and Co Ltd.
   Stubbs: *Molly Longlegs* and *Three Brood Mares at Grass* (1951–2). Lewis's Ltd.
   Flemish Tapestry: *Fortitude* (1952–3). Martins Bank Ltd.
   Rembrandt: *Self-Portrait* (1953–4). Alfred Holt and Co (P. H. Holt Trust).
   Van Dyck: *Portrait of the Infanta Isabella-Clara-Eugenia* (1954–5). The Royal Insurance Company Ltd.

(b) Given by Mr John Moores from the exhibition bearing his name:
   1957–8: Paintings by Jack Smith, Ceri Richards, Victor Pasmore, John Bratby and Sheila Fell.
   1959–60: Paintings by Robin Philipson, William Scott and Terry Frost.
   1961–2: Paintings by Sandra Blow, William Crozier, R. B. Kitaj, Joseph Tilson and David Tindle.
   1963–4: Paintings by Roger Hilton, Stephen McKenna and Christopher Paice.
   1965–6: Paintings by Michael Kidner and Michael Tyzack.

(c) Firms subscribing to the purchase of Rubens: *The Virgin and Child with St Elizabeth and the Child Baptist*. (1959–60):
   Alfred Holt and Co (P. H. Holt Trust)   Tillotsons (Liverpool) Ltd
   Pilkington Brothers Ltd (of St Helens)   Continental Cinema, Wallasey
   Peter Walker (Warrington) Ltd   Sing White and Co
   J. Bibby and Sons Ltd   Tilney, Parr and Rae
                                             Blackledge and Broughton

(d) Contributors of £1,000 and more to the Special Picture Purchase Fund Appeal (mainly seven-year covenants from 1960):
   Peter Walker (Warrington) Ltd   Topham's Ltd
   Martins Bank Ltd   The Vernons Organization
   Royal Insurance Co Ltd   Granada TV Network Ltd (of Manchester)
   Alfred Holt and Co (P. H. Holt Trust)   ICI
   John Holt (Overseas) Ltd   Liverpool Daily Post and Echo
   Lewis's Ltd   Tate and Lyle Ltd
   Owen Owen Ltd   British-American Tobacco Co Ltd

There have also been outstanding contributions by Mr C. F. J. Beausire and the Misses Beausire, members of a Liverpool business family, who between them have given P. de Loutherbourg's *Landscape with Figures* (1953–4) and £7,000 to the Appeal.
   The above list is intended only to illustrate the argument of the text, not to give an exhaustive account of benefactions to the gallery.

Common enough in America, such support of a city gallery is more rare in England, and because central grants (from the Treasury, from the Arts Council, from the National Art-Collections Fund or from the foundations) are often made conditional on a comparable local effort it is apt to snowball, bringing in two or three times the amount locally subscribed. Moreover it impels the city to take something of the same interest and keep up its own contribution if it is not to let the business oligarchy become predominant in the gallery's affairs. So far this has worked well in Liverpool, and the purchase of the Rubens *Virgin and Child* in 1960 is a good example. Here the

51 Rubens: *Virgin and Child, with St Elizabeth and child Baptist.* Bought by the Walker Gallery in 1960. Its most expensive acquisition yet, marking an important change in official policy towards the provincial galleries

subscriptions from private and business contributors and locally-administered trusts totalled about £10,000; the city matched this with £10,000 from the rates; £5,000 more came from the foundations and the National Art-Collections Fund; thus there was a total of £25,000 raised by the gallery which the government matched with another £25,000 to reach the purchase price of £50,000. Perhaps only 10 per cent of this sum came strictly from business, but without it the rest would not have been forthcoming. And the Rubens operation was doubly important as a demonstration both because it marked a change in government policy towards the provincial galleries (for which Cotton had been pressing since 1952; it was later formally set out in the 1963 Report of the Standing Commission on Museums) and because it provided a pattern for the gallery's subsequent Special Picture Purchase Fund Appeal. This fund, which passed £62,000 by May 1962 and has been used to buy the gallery's Courbet, Seurat, Monet and Cézanne, took advantage of the system of seven-year covenants under which any sum given is increased by tax concessions.[1] It was raised by a Labour Sub-Committee chairman, Ben Shaw.

I tried in conversation with one or two of the leading contributors to the gallery to discover just what it is that makes Liverpool business people willing to act in this disinterested way. Several of them are themselves collectors – Mr G. R. Kennerley of Vernons Pools, Mr Morton Oliphant of Tate and Lyle, Colonel Cotton (a former director of Martins Bank), Mrs Bibby, Mr S. Samuels, Mr John Moores of Littlewoods;[2] Mr Moores and Mr Kennerley indeed are also painters – and the obvious wish to pass on the pleasure they have derived from pictures certainly plays its part. There is also quite simply local pride, strongest with firms whose headquarters are in the area, though a branch of some larger concern is liable to contribute if it is autonomous enough. One director suggested that a firm should contribute as a duty to its employees, particularly if the gallery kept them in touch with its activities; another feared that the old family firms might soon become too impersonal for well-wishers like himself to be able to sway the board of directors, though much depended on the personal feelings of the chairman, who would often be allowed his own way over such commercial non-essentials. Whether these are so much motives, however, as explanations is more problematic, and it may well be that precedent and example are what really matters. The Liverpool business community is a close-knit one, whose most influential members are liable to find themselves meeting in a number of different capacities on different committees. When one of them in the

---

[1] Courbet's *Marée basse à Trouville* and Seurat's *Maisons Blanches, Ville d'Avray* were bought from Mr A. Chester Beatty for £22,500. This sum was met as follows:

£12,000 from the Special Picture Purchase Fund
£5,000 from the National Art-Collections Fund
£2,500 from the fund administered by Victoria and Albert Museum on behalf of the government.
£2,000 remitted as a gift by Mr Chester Beatty
£1,000 from the annual purchase grant

Cézanne's *The Murder* cost £32,400, of which £5,000 came from the National Art-Collections Fund and the rest from the Appeal.

[2] Mr Kennerley for instance owns paintings by Jawlensky, Soutine, Matisse, de Stael. Mr Oliphant has two Courbet landscapes, two early Fantin-Latours, a Gauguin landscape of 1884, several Sickerts, etc. The Samuels collection includes among much else a number of works by Pasmore, Sutherland, Eric Gill and Matthew Smith.

shape of Cotton made a really determined assault on his colleagues' generosity in the 1950s he created that most important of Anglo-Saxon attitudes, a tradition.

The building-up of the collection by these means has proceeded mainly on the lines of 'filling gaps'. That is to say that the gallery has aimed at showing

52 Seurat: *Maisons blanches, Ville d'Avray*. Bought by the gallery in 1961 as one of its first purchases from the new Special Picture Purchase Fund to which local businesses contribute

the work of certain schools and certain artists, and has bought its pictures not so much on individual merit as to fill in missing links in the intended chain. In 1951, when the gallery was reopened after its wartime occupation by the Ministry of Food, the director's intention was 'to provide an orderly survey of the whole course of British painting from Tudor times to the present day.'[1] The chief gaps he then saw were Hogarth, Constable and the Norwich school, and the 'younger and more advanced contemporaries', this latter being the result of Cotton's deliberate policy of not buying any picture until at least twenty years after it had been painted. The reopening coincided with the 1951 Festival of Britain, which the gallery celebrated with the first major

[1] City of Liverpool Libraries, Museums and Art Committee Annual Reports for the year ended 31 March 1952, p. 39.

exhibition since 1885 to be devoted to the work of George Stubbs. Three years later in his annual report the new director redefined the gaps as being

> in English painting of the sixteenth and seventeenth centuries, and in the continental schools from the seventeenth century onwards. The most urgent need of all is for a proper representation of modern art.[1]

From 1957 on this need for modern pictures has been met almost entirely from the John Moores exhibitions, so that there has been little occasion for those embarrassing conflicts which happen when a director who is accustomed to looking at modern works has to justify a purchase to a committee who are not. But this embraces modern English painting only. Where the continental schools are concerned most of the outstanding modern figures – Picasso, for instance, Braque, Klee, Bonnard, Léger – are still missing. They could have been bought cheaply enough in the 1930s, but where its own purchases were concerned the gallery virtually disregarded all foreign painting from its foundation until about ten years ago. This is its one real weakness.[2] 'Though the collection must be mainly British', wrote the retiring director in 1952;

> a group of French impressionist work would be most welcome, to demonstrate its influence on the New English Art Club and to illustrate the fundamental truth that art does not work in a social and historical vacuum. Their prices, however, are beyond the Gallery's resources. . . .[3]

This was over three-quarters of a century since the First Impressionist Exhibition and some forty years after the Liverpool impressionist shows, and although the Gallery's main purchasing effort has subsequently been turned in this direction it is a very late starter in the field.

It has held some important loan exhibitions. The chief in public appeal was the Van Gogh exhibition at the end of 1955, which was organized by the Arts Council and was essentially the exhibition shown that year in London; it had 44,209 visitors in six weeks. The most interesting as pieces of local enterprise were the Le Corbusier show of winter 1958/9,[4] which was partly

---

[1] Ditto for the year ended 31 March 1954, p. 43.

[2] A universal weakness in this country however. See Ronald Alley's devastating article 'The Representation of Twentieth-Century Foreign Art in British Public Collections' in *The Museums Journal*, London, Vol. 61, No. 1, June 1961. Mr Alley took fifty-six leading British galleries, excluding only the Tate, and found that they owned between them four Matisses, three small early Picassos, two Braques, two Légers and *no* paintings by Klee, Gris, Chagall, Miró, Kandinsky and other key figures.

[3] Frank Lambert: 'The Walker Art Gallery – Growth of a Policy' (2) in *Liverpool Bulletin*, February 1952, Vol. I, No. 3, p. 17.

[4] With 17,200 visitors in seven weeks this exhibition made a profit of £360. Local grants amounted to £475, those from the RIBA and the Arts Council to £900, admission fees to £840. It was subsequently shown at the Building Centre in London.

paid for by local architects and builders and was very largely initiated by the gallery and members of its committee, and the Ford Madox Brown exhibition for which Miss Mary Bennett was responsible in 1964. It has organized (as opposed to taking over ready-made) one-man shows for a very few contemporary artists: Uli Nimptsch (1957), John Napper (1959), George Mayer-Marton (memorial exhibition 1960), and Stuart Sutcliffe (memorial exhibition May 1964).[1] A great part of its effort has also in recent years gone to the proper listing and storage of the less presentable part of its collection, and to the overhaul of the loan scheme by which unwanted or specially purchased pictures can be borrowed at an annual charge of £1 per picture by public offices, schools and other bodies. It receives, shows and helps to judge the entries for the annual Topham Trophy competition for designs or models for a steeplechase trophy to be raced for at Aintree; in 1962 and 1963 this was won by two quite original small pieces of sculpture by John W. Mills of the College of Art at St Albans; in 1964 by N. Harding and in 1965 by Valerie Cooke. But the activity for which it has become most widely known is the holding of the biennial John Moores competitions, which in the last seven years have not only started drawing the London art critics to Liverpool but given the younger generation there that basis of familiarity with modern art which their elders lacked.

The objects of the Moores competition have remained virtually the same since 1957, and they are defined as

1 To give Merseyside the chance to see an exhibition of painting and sculpture embracing the best and most vital work being done today throughout the country;

2 to encourage living artists, particularly the young and progressive.

The exact conditions, the treatment of invited artists and the relative encouragement to be given to young and old, have varied each year, though the total prizes provided by Mr Moores have remained fairly constant at £4,000. Attendance rose from 10,000 at the first show (or about a third of that at the 1872 Autumn Exhibition) to 16,500 in 1961, when £3,915 worth of pictures were sold over and above the prize purchases. In 1959 there was an experiment, and a French section and a French judge (Professor André Chastel) were included; in 1963 there was no sculpture as Moores sponsored a separate competition in connection with the new Littlewoods building (discussed on p. 105 below). Broadly speaking the initial sorting of the 2,000 or so entries has been done by the gallery staff and the judging by a jury drawn mainly from the London art world (who also see the whole lot). The result has been verdicts which have sometimes anticipated, sometimes

[1] See pp. 164–7. This exhibition had 10,661 visitors.

confirmed those of London and are close enough to current international taste to be respected abroad. Such names as Jack Smith, for instance (1957), John Bratby (Junior, 1957), Souza, Joseph Tilson (both minor prizes the same year), Hubert Dalwood (sculpture, 1959), those of all the major prize-winners in 1961 – Henry Mundy, Sandra Blow, Leon Kossoff and R. B. Kitaj – as well as Peter Blake and David Hockney of that year's juniors and Antony Donaldson, Harold Cohen, Michael Kidner and Bridget Riley in 1963 were, if not wholly unknown in the London galleries, by no means recognized as they since became. Whether this alignment with the newest fashions is the best thing either for the artists or for the galleries who acquire their pictures is more debatable; some of these young artists' reputations have already started to slump again; others will no doubt follow. But such for the moment is the way in which the liveliest modern art progresses, and the exhibition of 150 or so selected entries in the Walker Gallery has each time

53 Modern pictures acquired from the Moores shows. Left to right: R. B. Kitaj, Alan Welsford, Allen Jones, Sam Walsh (a Liverpool painter). Beyond the door: Arthur Ballard (ditto) and Roger Hilton

been charged with a sense of discovery and surprise that makes it worth travelling a long way to see.

Liverpool's own artists are hardly prominent in the Moores exhibitions, though of course they are well placed to compete. Only four have been included in more than a single show; only nineteen have ever reached this stage at all, though Sam Walsh had a picture bought for the gallery at the 1963 show while John Edkins and (in the junior section) George Moore won minor prizes in 1965.[1] The gallery indeed is determined not to lower its carefully built-up standards just in order to give encouragement to local art, which the director feels is not part of its job, though it has a nucleus of works by leading Liverpool artists of the past which it will occasionally add to; thus it bought Windus's *Burd Helen* some seven years ago, and has also acquired a number of works and objects for their associations with William Roscoe. It has however developed a working arrangement with the Liverpool Academy, whose annual exhibitions have since 1951 been held in its rooms, and the president of the Liverpool Academy is ex-officio an advisory member of the Arts Sub-Committee by which the gallery is governed. It was in fact partly due to the director that the academy instituted an open section in 1955, which has since then been selected by two gallery and one academy representatives and one outsider. As a result of this move the academy now gets some 900 works sent in by non-members each year, and this has given it a new lease of life.

Unlike the gallery the academy has had to make do with its own resources, and if its progress in the 1950s and 60s has accordingly been a good deal more modest and parochial it matters no less to the artists. It is now one of the most flourishing provincial societies of professional artists, with some eighty members; in contrast with the tradition of the neighbouring academy at Manchester its exhibitions now include no London men; and altogether its position is better than at any time in the past 100 years. Admittedly things were better still immediately before that; for its sales before 1860 were said normally to total more than £1,000, with £2,500 in one record year,[2] whereas the average sales in the three years 1962–4 were only £185. But it is to some extent now caught between two forces larger than itself: the rising tide of amateurism and the steadily increasing attraction of the metropolitan (or even the international) art market for collectors and artists alike. This might be expected to deprive it of character; the insistence on professional standards,

[1] Edward Atkinson (1957), Arthur Ballard (1959, 1961), Martin Bell (1957), Sidney Bonner (1963), John Chadwick (1963), Austin Davies (1957), John Edkins (1965), Alfred Edwards (1965), Henry Graham (1957), John Hart (1957, 1959), Adrian Henri (1961, 1965), Nicholas Horsfield (1959, 1961), James Howie (1957), G. W. Jardine (1957), Noel McCready (1959), George Mayer-Marton (1959), George Moore (1965), Robin Riley (1959), W. L. Stevenson (1957), Stuart Sutcliffe 1959), Sam Walsh (1963), J. Coburn Witherop (1957).
[2] According to B. H. Grindley: *History and Work of the Liverpool Academy of Arts.* Lecture delivered at the Free Public Library, Museum and Gallery of Art, Liverpool, 9 February 1875. For earlier years Henry Lacey's *Pictorial Liverpool*, Liverpool 1844, gives the following figures: 1824 £10, 1825 £30, 1827 £489 and 1843 £840.

as quite rigorously maintained by the present committee, means that it depends largely on the professional teachers of art at the College of Art and elsewhere, most of whom have their eyes half-turned to London as the one centre where an artist can live by his work; the College itself moreover, under the new system recommended in 1960 by the National Advisory Council on Art Education, is drawing more of its students as well as its teachers from other parts of the country. Even in the 1840s and 50s however the academy had no very pronounced local flavour, to judge from those works of the time which have survived. With one or two isolated exceptions all the artists of

54 The conclusion of the 1965 Liverpool Academy, with Nicholas Horsfield, the retiring president

merit in the area now send to its exhibitions. As a result these are not only liable to contain the occasional work of what might be called national calibre – i.e., which would not disgrace a British Council show abroad – but are unique in modern England as the expression of a sizeable professional community of artists somehow surviving, without external grants, in a big provincial city. In 1965 it even began once more to find buyers for the pictures, selling £1,128 worth, or more than in any year since the Second World War. In 1966 the sales amounted to £774.

Not all the city's collection is in the gallery, for the engravings and etchings left by H. F. Hornby in 1906 were placed in the public library, and since then they have been added to, theoretically in consultation with the gallery; Goya's *Tauromaquia*, for instance was bought some four years ago with the aid of the Friends of the National Libraries and the National Art-Collections Fund, and altogether the City Librarian has about £1,000 a year to spend on purchases for the Hornby Library, which also contains rare books and manuscripts. £100 or £200 a year are additionally spent on the city's topographical collection of printed and watercolours by local artists, including

55 From the gallery at Sudley: William Dyce's *Gethsemane*

the commissioning of new works, and these two collections, totalling about 10,000 items in all, are drawn on for exhibitions both in the Central Public Libraries next door to the Walker Gallery and in branch libraries all over the city. There is also the Art Library, which comes under the City Librarian; owing to the peculiarities of the Dewey classification system it contains not only art books but books on sports and pastimes. It was opened in 1955 in a ground-floor room of the gallery so that it could be reached either from the gallery or from the library buildings next door. With the rebuilding of the Brown Library however, which now provides admirable new reading rooms at the other end of the buildings, it was removed and the way through blocked up.

There are a number of other public galleries on Merseyside, starting with

Sudley, an agreeable early nineteenth-century house in the suburbs of Liverpool which has been attached to the Walker Gallery since 1944 and contains Victorian furniture from the Melly family and a number of pictures formerly belonging to the shipping merchant George Holt (1825–96), notably a late Corot, Gainsborough's *Viscountess Folkestone*, three Turners and Dyce's strange *Gethsemane*. The most interesting of these galleries is the Lady Lever Art Gallery at Port Sunlight, built in Imperial-Classical style between 1914 and 1922 by the first Lord Leverhulme in memory of his wife and situated in the heart of this pioneer garden-city close to the very odd non-denominational Unilever church that is also the family mausoleum. At one end in the place of honour is Queen Victoria, flanked by portraits of Lord and Lady Leverhulme; at the other a large marble statue of Ferdinando de' Medici, no doubt symbolizing commercial munificence. In between it contains a good collection of furniture together with major works by the Pre-Raphaelites, Burne-Jones and Herkomer, plus other Victoriana, a Fantin-Latour, two good country scenes by Stubbs, Gainsborough's *Mrs Freer*, Raeburn's portrait of Telford, Turner's *The Falls of the Clyde*, several Richard Wilsons and some Spanish primitives. It is run by trustees and its Curator is the former deputy director of the Walker Gallery. Birkenhead itself has a well-designed gallery building of the mid-1920s, the gift of the Williamson family, which is chiefly remarkable for its paintings by Wilson Steer, who was born in that city though he never worked there. This and the single room at Bootle are looked after by the respective municipal librarians. All these bodies are quite independent of one another, though in accordance with the suggestion of the Standing Commission on Museums and Art Galleries they now form part of an area museum service for the North-West, which sees to the care and conservation of items from nine-tenths of the museums in the area. In the Walker Gallery's view the structure of committees which this calls for is too cumbrous, and the result not very inspiring. The director feels that a better solution would have been for the gallery to take some overall responsibility for Birkenhead, Bootle and others that are part of the Merseyside agglomeration.

The revival of the Liverpool Academy has taken place largely at the expense of the Sandon Studios Society, whose exhibitions are now very secondary to the annual academy shows. With the passage of time the society has seen many of its ideas accepted by the old establishment, until it too has become an establishment offshoot, and not one of the more important ones. Though its music and drama groups are active enough, people concerned with the visual arts now treat it primarily as a social club – its subscription is three times that of the academy, which keeps the younger artists at a distance – and

56 & 57 From the Lady Lever Art Gallery at Port Sunlight:
George Stubbs's *Haymaking* and *Haycarting*

because its rooms are located in the Bluecoat Chambers it acts as restaurant, meeting and drinking place for the artists and organizations that centre on that early eighteenth century building. Its relations with the Bluecoat Society proper are not always very clear even to its members. In a sense however the Bluecoat was an offshoot of the Sandon, having been formed to manage the property after it was bought by public appeal in 1927, and consisting originally of twenty-four members actively connected with the Sandon Society or otherwise prominent in the appeal. These people constituted themselves into twelve committee members and six trustees, and have continued to function ever since by co-option, so that membership is not open to the outside world and no facilities are offered. Their purpose from the first has been to run the building 'as an Institution for the purposes and within the meaning of the Literary and Scientific Institutions Act, 1854, for the promotion of the fine arts, literature and science for adult instruction and the diffusion of useful knowledge generally.'[1] Tenants have been selected accordingly. A subsidiary intention was to organize lectures, concerts, plays and 'kinematic demonstrations' for the same educational objects. Mr W. S. MacCunn's history of the society however shows that major financial worries prevented it from thinking about any positive policy of this sort until after the Second World War. In 1961 it established the Bluecoat Forum as a co-ordinating committee to link the various other societies – artistic, architectural, musical, literary, photographic, cinematic, etc. – who now have rooms in the building (there are also a number of artists and architects who have studios there). The Sandon retains a special place as the largest and most sociable of these; it is the oldest tenant, and without the energies of its members (and specifically of the late Mrs Calder), the building would long since have been lost to commercial redevelopment.

The Arts Enquiry sponsored by the Dartington Trustees, in its report of 1946 on *The Visual Arts*,[2] spoke of the society as 'an arts centre to which there is no parallel in England', and with the increasing interest in the arts centre principle a certain amount of attention has been focused on the Bluecoat Chambers by those concerned with helping the arts. Under the new pattern of art patronage in England the Bluecoat Society can appeal for help to the Arts Council or the foundations and be sure that its claims will be given weight; the Arts Council in fact made it grants totalling over £5,000 in the period of postwar repair and reconstruction. It is only since about 1955 however that the society has been able to feel sure enough about the future of the building to think what the policy of an arts centre in Liverpool

---

[1] Deed of 28 January 1927.
[2] Oxford University Press, 1946, p. 56. See pp. 197–8 below.

G

58 'Bluecoat 63'. The open-air sculpture exhibition in the front courtyard of the Bluecoat Chambers

might be and to wonder whether it is organized to provide it. This has always been the order of priorities, and it is reflected in the hierarchy of societies, for here the very concept of an arts centre, as defined in the 1914 proposal for a Lancashire Society of Arts and again in 1920, was devised as a means of guaranteeing the building's security against redevelopment, rather than vice versa. In 1955, however, the then secretary W. S. MacCunn suggested[1] that it might be time to put some of 1914's less ambitious principles into effect:

> Painters of distinction could be induced to visit and work in Liverpool; exhibitions and musical recitals could be sponsored; new works could be commissioned; a lectureship that, in time, might do for the arts what the Gifford lectures do for philosophy could be founded; the publication of books dealing with one or the other of the arts could be undertaken; and research could be helped.

Further ideas followed: scholarships for painters, a club for young artists, subsidized exhibitions for them, Merseyside exhibitions in a London gallery, the lobbying of Merseyside business people to buy more local works, Bluecoat fellowships and free studios for a year for promising artists, and, once again, public lectures on art. Some of this has been realized; the system of

[1] In his *Bluecoat Chambers;* Liverpool University Press, 1956, p. 68.

scholarships has been tried and (apparently failed), but two rooms in the building now make a slightly makeshift exhibition gallery, and the society is prepared to subsidize suitable shows there, with increasing success; indeed those of the early part of 1966 were of a consistently good standard, featuring work by John Edkins (one-man show), Margaret Dean, Frederick Bushe and Sean Rice. The main actions otherwise have concerned the two spring festivals organized by the Bluecoat Forum – Bluecoat 63, which brought large crowds to see (or hear) work by the building's tenants, and the equally popular Shakespeare celebrations in 1964. Another was to commission the present report.

I have cited these organizations as making up the Liverpool art establishment, and that is how they are spoken of by the younger artists and their friends. It is a loosely used word, and since a London journalist first coined it in the 1950s it has become charged with a certain envy and resentment which often vanishes once the user becomes a member of the establishment himself. None the less there is a sense in which institutions do become established, and that is when they are so generally accepted that they go on running without anybody having a very clear idea what their purpose is. In Liverpool as much as anywhere there is a reluctance to think clearly about these matters; thus the Town Clerk's report of June 1958 on the Cultural Life of the City speaks as if we were living in Roscoe's day:

> The happy relationship of commercial success and cultural encouragement is marked to a degree in this City, but that in itself is in no way unusual for it was common in the Italian towns of the Renaissance period, and indeed culture can only thrive where there is patronage to give it freedom of perception and development.

'Education' is still put forward as the aim of art, partly out of habit no doubt but partly because it is only for what the Bluecoat Society's 1953 Declaration of Trust calls

> the promotion and advancement of aesthetic education and the cultivation and improvement of public taste. . . .

that our present laws allow artistic enterprises exemption from tax. The only difference from the 1880s here is that, where once it was essentially self-education that was meant, the term now suggests an oligarchic condescension which some people, including some artists, much dislike.

'The public as a whole', wrote a correspondent to the *Liverpool Post* in 1956, does not ask for masterpieces: it just wants good paintings which can delight the eye, not pictures which conform to some obscure standard of technical perfection appreciated only by a group of art critics.[1]

This problem of creating a sense of participation, of common enjoyment and mutual respect, must strike all these organizations the more keenly their standards go up, and the gallery at least has already felt it, for both the director and those committee members with whom I talked have spoken emphatically of the need for a publicity drive to make Liverpool people more conscious of the treasures they own. It is a doubly difficult task, for not only does any nationally important institution often need to be impervious to un-informed local criticism but the means for informing the public is nowadays outside the local establishment's control. On the one hand the success of a gallery like the Walker is judged increasingly by the impression it makes in the wider field of art scholarship, international exhibitions and so forth – a field to which more and more attention is being paid by government, uni-versities and the Press – rather than by any evidence of the satisfaction which it gives to the citizens. On the other the public no longer gets its taste for art from lectures and conducted tours such as the gallery itself can organize, or even from the local Press (though the daily *Liverpool Daily Post* has done a great deal to help[2]); but more from television and the illustrated Sunday magazines.[3] Even there any kind of 'educational' flavour is distasteful to most adults now that so many of us have undergone art education at school.

So long as an institution is confident of its purpose it can pursue it blindly and trust to the rapid evolution of our society's taste for pictures to support it sooner or later. Elsewhere however it is a matter of somehow capturing the local public's interest, or of giving it a sense of pride in the institution, or of getting it to identify itself with the latter's activities. These are in a way admissions of weakness; the very fact that a distinction is being drawn between institution and 'public' suggests that there is a cleft that can only be repaired by special measures. One such measure was the scheme put forward by a Labour Arts Sub-Committee member, Eric Heffer MP, for a special show, initially of working-class art. On the grounds that, as he put it,

[1] G. N. Ridley of Wallasey, on 9 October.

[2] In 1958 and early 1959, for instance, it ran a weekly series of quite large reproductions of the gallery's best pictures, together with short notes on them. In Roderick Bisson it has an unusually shrewd and well-informed critic; it has also published articles by the director and had helpful comments and leading articles on the gallery's problems. It was incidentally the first Liverpool firm to buy a picture for it.

[3] Radio and television programmes featuring the gallery have included the BBC television 'Animal, Vegetable, Mineral' on 6 October, 1955, a visit to the 1957 John Moores Exhibition by the BBC 'Critics', a programme on Granada TV on 9 May 1956, followed by 'One Hour in the Walker Gallery' on 21 November of the same year, and a thirty-minute tour of the gallery in BBC television's 'Looking North' programme on 6 March 1959.

art has largely become divorced from society. The mass of the people are little interested in it, and certain modern trends have not helped.

  – he proposed an exhibition, possibly to become a regular event, of artists who because they work in industry or have lived or live in the environment of industry, reflect clearly the life around them, and in this sense marry art genuinely with society.[1]

The idea met with considerable criticism, both for its class bias and because in England now most realistic painting of working-class themes is likely to be amateur and to look it. It materialized however in somewhat different form in March 1965 as a small exhibition held under the title 'Industry and the Artist'. This included not only more or less realistic studies and actual industrial diagrams or working drawings but also sections of abstract, pop, optical and kinetic art which were held in one way or another to reflect the artist's view of the industrialized world. It was not a special public success, and it does not seem to have brought new visitors into the gallery.

[1] Letter to the *Liverpool Post*, 2 July 1963.

59 Art in public. Monuments to Liverpudlian and other worthies look out from below St George's Hall over the tunnel entrance towards the Municipal Offices (centre) and the twin towers of the Liver Building (left).

4 : ART IN PUBLIC

There is no 'establishment' to determine what we see around us in streets and buildings and in our places of work, for the visual arts no longer count as part of ordinary life. Ninety-nine per cent of what passes before our eyes has no conscious tradition or organization behind it, and in those few cases where it does rank as art, design or decoration, it cannot be attributed to any identifiable policy but at best to something vague, to a trend. This is the rule in our country, and Liverpool is no exception. That identification of art with the interests and ethos of the community which led to the building of St George's Hall largely vanished in the second half of the nineteenth century; the arts and crafts movement of the nineties was too weak there to produce more than isolated models and experiments; Rothenstein's rousing appeal for the embellishment of the city remained the rhetoric of an outsider. The legacy of public or deliberately socially-directed art that the present inhabitants were left with was a small one, so small that most of them would scarcely recognize its existence. Attempts to extend it have as a result been few; there is only one recent piece of public statuary that has made an impression on most people's consciousness, and that for rather special reasons. But at least the field can be surveyed as a whole, and because its pattern is not untypical of this country it is more worth studying than at first appears.

What *does* at first appear? A good deal can be seen from the steps of the Walker Art Gallery, for the main concentration of public sculpture in Liverpool stands around St George's Hall and the Mersey Tunnel entrance, with a second cluster a quarter of a mile away down Dale Street at Pier Head. Much of the siting of these worthy but largely boring monuments seems to have been decided piecemeal and almost by accident; thus in March 1927 Charles Bell Birch's Disraeli was shifted back into the St George's Hall portico, where it looks badly out of scale, to make room for the 1914–18 war memorial, while Sir Goscombe John's Edward VII at Pier Head was originally meant for the other side of the hall, but was banished on the insistence of Reilly and others.[1] The ruining of St John's Gardens, the open space that sweeps down from the hall to Herbert Rowse's Wembley-style tunnel entrance, by what Reilly called 'that forest of statues and unnecessary

[1] See C. H. Reilly: *Scaffolding in the Sky;* Routledge, 1938, p. 139. It looks no better where it is.

60 Art in mid-air. The Disraeli monument in front of St George's
Hall being shifted backwards up the steps to make way for the
War Memorial

stone piers'[1] was an unhappy series of concessions to our passion for com-
memorating not only national but local figures. The effect has been to bring
monumental sculpture as such into disrepute. As we shall see later, it is now
either ignored or actively resented. There has been no public critical discussion of it since Reilly's shrewd and amusing article with its description of
Birch's Major-General William Earle (born in Liverpool in 1833 and killed
in the Sudan in 1885) 'leading a charge from the safe retreat of the portico'
and of Charles J. Allen's 'frieze of figures explanatory of insurance' on the

[1] C. H. Reilly: 'Some Liverpool Monuments' in *The Liverpool Review*, February 1927, Vol. 2,
no. 1, p. 3.

Royal Insurance building. There cannot be more than a tiny handful of people in Liverpool who either know or care who such statues are by.[1]

And yet there are a number of monuments that do not disgrace the city or make it look in any way ridiculous. Gibson's statue of Huskisson in Prince's Avenue (illustrated on p. 29) is the outstanding instance,[2] though it was obviously not meant to stand where it now is; he was likewise respon-

61 More meaningless figures. Sir W. B. Forwood, with the Picton Library in the distance and the western facade of St George's Hall

sible for a less visible figure inside the Huskisson Memorial below the Cathedral and a good statue of George Stephenson in St George's Hall. The unhappy fate of the sculpture for the hall's pediment we have already seen.

[1] They are here identified from an album *City of Liverpool. Photographs of Statues, Monuments and Memorials*, which was prepared in 1922 and is to be found in the Local History Library. The most sought after sculptors for such purposes seem to have been Sir Goscombe John (who also did King George V and Queen Mary above the tunnel entrance, and the Engine Room Heroes' Memorial at Pier Head), Sir George Frampton, RA (statues of Canon T. Major Lester and Sir W. B. Forwood in St John's Gardens and of Sir Alfred L. Jones at Pier Head), and Charles J. Allen RBS (bronze groups of Education, Industry, Commerce and Agriculture on the Victoria Memorial; two reliefs on St George's Hall; Florence Nightingale at the junction of Upper Parliament Street and Prince's Road; panels on the Rt Hon Samuel Smith memorial in Sefton Park).

[2] Gibson insisted on presenting his figures in classical draperies. His biographer in the *Dictionary of National Biography*, Cosmo Monkhouse, quotes him as saying that 'The human figure concealed under a frock coat and trousers is not a fit subject for sculpture. I would rather avoid contemplating such objects.'

But in the Nelson memorial behind the town hall and the equestrian George III in London Road (which is almost a straight copy of that of Marcus Aurelius on the Capitol in Rome) there are worthy works by a slightly earlier classical sculptor, Sir Richard Westmacott. This nineteenth century classicism was of course very much the style of Liverpool's early intellectual leaders. There are however also twentieth century works of merit in Herbert Tyson Smith's two war memorials, the one in the Post Office and the bronze frieze on the rather clumsily-shaped and-placed town memorial for which Disraeli had to be moved. The black basalt sculptures on the ventilating shaft at Pier Head are likewise excellent of their (1920-ish) kind, though they are rather lost at the back of a building which in itself is a large and deplorable architectural sham.

Nearly all such works of art – if that is the right word for some of them – are designed to commemorate rather than to beautify, and the generally funereal associations which have grown up around public art in Liverpool seem to have discouraged subsequent city councils from commissioning anything more. The great programme of municipal housing carried out in the 1930s under Sir Lancelot Keay was almost bare of extraneous decoration; about the only exception is Gerrard Gardens, a vast block of flats not far from the gallery (and innocent of course, of any vestige of garden), where there are two competent but tame sub-Meunier reliefs of idealized workers, much too small for the scale of the building. Since the war there has been just one such venture, a long abstract pattern in polystyrene by Antony Hollaway for some municipal flats at Primrose Drive, Huyton; otherwise works of art have been confined to new school buildings, mainly to those not built by Liverpool corporation. Even there they are less frequent than in London.

There was an obvious chance for the city to commemorate its return to life after the bombing, much as was done with Zadkine's statue on the waterfront at Rotterdam; however it was seized not by the municipality but by the firm of Lewis's, whose director the late George Breeze was an admirer and patron of Epstein's. The ensuing *Spirit of Liverpool Resurgent*, a male bronze figure on a prow jutting out of Lewis's exceedingly undistinguished new building, would have been badly placed for such a grandiose gesture even if the failure to rebuild the city's centre had not made it a rather premature boast. As it was not only was it one of Epstein's less successful works but the immediate focusing of the spectator's attention on the figure's genitals has remained distracting to the citizens, so that the three smaller but more impressive relief panels beneath it go largely unobserved. Yet all the same the commissioning of the Epstein was a bold effort, and a decade later the example still seems to nag at the corporation. Dr Ronald Bradbury, for instance,

62 A post-war gesture by Liverpool, or rather by Lewis's stores. Epstein's figure *Spirit of Liverpool Resurgent* (photographed before the trams were abolished). It should be compared with Zadkine's *The Destroyed City* in illustration no. 139. Note particularly the three panels over the doors, which passers-by are apt to over-look

the present City Architect, told me that he had made tentative enquiries to find out if Henry Moore could undertake a work for the remodelled Pier Head area, only to be told that the artist was too heavily booked. More recently Eric Heffer has again proposed that there should be some major piece of sculpture on this site, symbolizing the new spirit of Liverpool as the Epstein is now felt not to do.

There has been no coherent policy for using artists in conjunction with the official building and planning schemes, and even in the new school buildings the occasional use of sculpture and (more rarely) murals has been on the initiative of the architect rather than on that of the Education Committee or its director. There are one or two quite striking pieces of work in the Liverpool area, but about the only schemes to have been carried out under the municipality have been Childwall County College, with its sculpture by Mitzi Solomon Cunliffe (then of Manchester), Anfield Technical College, which has a relief by the London artist William Mitchell, Herbert Thearle's Sandfield Park Special School, with decorations by Roderick Bisson, and Springfield Park Comprehensive School, with its rather forlorn small figure by Stanley English standing in a pool; these last two are local artists. The Lancashire County Education Committee and their architects seem to be more enterprising; certainly Ruffwood Drive Comprehensive School in the new suburb of Kirkby is well above Liverpool standards both archi-tecturally and in it use of mosaics to symbolize the figures (Telford, Darwin, etc), after whom the 'houses' are named. Over at Birkenhead the Technical college building by Willinck and Dod has a cluttered and somewhat stereotyped mural by Eric Kennington – a kind of Birkenhead pot-pourri – but the newer and more important Liverpool College of Technology has nothing. The late city director of education told me that there have just not been the funds available for that sort of thing.

This is where the Roman Catholic schools differ. Built in many cases by the same architects as the new Catholic churches and subject to the same overriding concept (which the diocesan authorities themselves plainly hold) of art as a testimony to the glory of God, they have been a good deal less austere in their use of artists. These are mainly local, and not always of the first quality, but there seems to be a certain harmony of effort between artist and

63 The Roman Catholic church as patron. Relief by the Liverpool sculptor Robin Riley on St Kevin's School, Kirkby

architect which surely helps the former's work, and in Robin Riley's long abstract relief on L. A. G. Prichard's St Kevin's School, Kirkby, the Catholic system has produced the most striking new public work of art in the area. The policy is the same for both schools and churches. Thus Weightman and Bullen, a Liverpool firm now specializing in this work who have built fifteen to twenty churches and over 100 church schools since 1949, told me that they try to convince the responsible priest in each case that work by an individual artist means more than, say, mass-produced Stations of the Cross from West Germany. Their principle might be defined as 'little and decent'; for instance, they will use clear glass rather than bad stained glass which they feel might never be removed. They pick the artists, discuss the exact number and nature of the works with the client, and decide their placing and probable cost before any building starts. They cannot afford Moore or Sutherland, but they have commissioned works by such local artists as Riley, George Thomas and Arthur Dooley (for sculpture), Robin Magee (for church furnishing) and the late George Mayer-Marton (for mosaics). The results are not spectacular; no art-lover's breath is going to be taken away, certainly, on entering one of these churches. They do however

64 A typical church of the 1950s. Weightman and Bullen's Holy Ghost Church at Bootle, with mosaic by the late George Mayer-Marton

represent a considerable raising of the standard of Catholic church furnishing in the north of England and an unusual instance of local talent purposefully used.

In 1967 the new Roman Catholic cathedral will be consecrated. With its novel circular plan, like a vast upturned funnel, its windows by John Piper and Patrick Reyntiens and its sculptures by William Mitchell, Frederick Gibberd's great building quite possibly *will* take the breath away, and seems likely to provide for some years a religious-artistic sensation to rival Coventry. Scott's Anglican cathedral further along the same ridge is still slowly expanding and completing itself, but in a traditional style which made its impact many years ago and can add little fresh to the visual life of the city. Through its extra-mural department and the Reverend William Lockett, who is in charge of the art teaching there, the university has organized conferences on 'The Modern Architectural Setting of the Liturgy' (September 1962) and 'New Church Architecture' (September 1963), the first of which was attended by both Bishops of Liverpool and included a lecture by Gibberd on the new cathedral. At the same time there was an exhibition of modern church art at the Bluecoat Display Centre. In all these ways it can be said not only that the churches on Merseyside are conscious of the architectural use of the other arts as the lay authorities are not, but that they are specifically taking pains to learn about modern artists.

The university, which will incidentally have Gibberd's cathedral on its doorstep, is if anything even more ambitious in its commissioning of works of art for its buildings. Not only does it pursue a fairly consistent policy of spending roughly $\frac{1}{2}$ per cent of the cost of each new building in this way but it has bypassed the local artists in favour of men with something of a national reputation. Thus there is a group of three vertical hammer-shaped objects by Hubert Dalwood outside the Physics Building and a mosaic by Geoffrey

Clarke inside it; there is a mural by the late Peter Lanyon in the Civil Engineering Building, and a set of terracotta plaques by John McCarthy in the Mathematics Building showing 'the growth of mathematical ideas'. The same building has an iron screen and gate by this artist, and there are a rather dim horse and cow in brick relief on Maxwell Fry's Veterinary Building and a sculpture and a door handle by Mitzi Solomon Cunliffe in the Department of Civic Design. There are also a number of buildings still under construction or to come, each with a university committee in charge, though it has so far been the architects who have nominated the artists to be used. The object of this apparently progressive scheme of patronage, as the Professor of Civic Design explained it to me in his capacity as planning consultant to the university, is that students who will form the future leaders of the nation need to be brought into contact with works of art, and all the more so if these have been lacking in the environment from which they come. Unfortunately it largely breaks down on the quality of the works commissioned, which have turned out at best unmemorable. Why this should be so will be discussed later, but its bearing on the possible use of prominent but not top-rank modern artists for public tasks in Liverpool is obvious. It is an example to be learnt from rather than followed.

Occasionally a business in the town will buy interesting pictures for its own premises or commission work specially. Walker's the brewers first set the example, perhaps, with the nineteenth-century paintings which they bought for decorating their pubs; there are some fine Frith-like scenes hanging in the magnificent back room of The Vines in Lime Street. The chief case recently was Leonard Rosoman's forty-foot mural of the Liverpool waterfront for Barclays Bank in Water Street; an efficient but not very inspired compromise between the *genius loci* and the natural talent of the artist. But for his death this job would have gone to the local artist Mayer-Marton, who had done a quite successful smaller mural for the passenger department of Coast Lines. There is also a panel by another local painter, John Heritage, in the RAC office, and a mural of 1960 by a former Liverpool couple, F. H. and C. V. Lyle, in the self-service restaurant of Littlewoods Stores. British Railways likewise have good modern paintings hanging in the dining-room of the Exchange Station Hotel, though probably not as the result of any decision taken locally. But none of this is perhaps so promising for the future as one or two rather more inconspicuous instances: the metal panel representing a printed circuit which Arthur Ballard made for Johnson's TV shop in Lord Street at the suggestion of Quentin Hughes the architect; the paintings by Sam Walsh and Peter MacKarell in the bar of Dick Egerton's Royal Court Hotel, bought from them when they were com-

A successful commission by the University:
hn McCarthy's metal gate to the Mathematics Building

66 The best modern Liverpool mural: Arthur Ballard's metal relief in Johnson's T.V. shop, Lord Street

parative beginners; or the paintings by Walsh and Adrian Henri which Reg Mason has installed, to the apparent mystification of the customers, in some of his betting shops. Ballard's panel is the best mural work in Liverpool (in my knowledge and judgment), while the others seem to show a spontaneous taste for the livelier kinds of art, free from self-conscious feelings of patronage.

Wherever the visual arts are brought into the open like this it becomes hard to draw a line between art in the strict sense and civic and industrial design. The arts are no longer segregated in a gallery, to be looked at with specially-conditioned eyes; often they are stripped even of the largely reverential aura that accompanies their religious or educational use. They become woven into quite other activities, where they may be noticed or not according to their merits (and the observer's visual alertness) and must harmonize or compete with a thousand different sights, most of them man-made. This is a complex field for the art-lover to enter, and many of those supporters who helped to put the Walker Art Gallery so firmly on its feet have preferred not to explore it at all. It may be that their feeling for pictures is still in part an aristocratic one, and that they feel there is a risk here of art being profaned; moreover so far as their own business establishments and their own manufactures go they find that aesthetic judgments are subject not only to technical and commercial considerations but to the views of colleagues and the maintenance of smooth labour relations. This can make the redecoration of a factory a much more difficult business than the giving of a picture to the gallery, and the contrast between a firm's supposed taste (as judged

67 Outside Liverpool. Victor Pasmore's mural in the refectory of the new Pilkington buildings at St Helens

from its gifts and from the personal tastes of its chiefs) and the actual appearance of its premises and its products is often a little surprising. One eminent local cultural benefactor taxed with inconsistencies of this sort is reported to have replied: 'That's quite different. That's business.'

None the less there are some who have made considerable efforts to improve the look of their offices and factories, while others have acquired pictures of varying merits for their decoration. Admittedly as yet only two of them can be seen as a major visual asset to the area, and neither is strictly on Merseyside: Pilkington Brothers' new buildings at St Helens have a big mural by Victor Pasmore in the refectory, while in Ralph Tubbs's excellent Granada Television buildings over in Manchester – which are perhaps mentionable in this report because Granada covers Liverpool from there – a good collection of paintings has been formed on the recommendation of Sir Gerald Barry and a panel of advisors. These are outstanding in

H

that both represent the development of a bold visual arts policy[1] within the daily affairs of a major organization; the similar attempt now being made by Littlewoods will be dealt with a little later.

With Lever Brothers' vast factory (5,000 workers) at Port Sunlight it was more a matter of the late chairman G. A. S. Nairn wishing to remedy the visual squalor of the place, which E. R. Scott the Civil Engineer then re-painted according to new and most attractive colour schemes.[2] Part of the object was to reduce fatigue and sickness, but it cannot be proved that production has been affected, though the workers appreciate it. At Jacobs Biscuits at Aintree, a group of airy but architecturally undistinguished factory buildings with about 3,000 workers, the firm's architects in 1961 worked out a set of selected 'standards and finishes' for the offices which is followed and gives an impression of cleanliness and coherence. The directors here are convinced of the importance of environment. 'I am afraid,' writes Mr C. B. Barber,

> I cannot offer evidence on the importance of decor in factory working conditions. I am sure it is true that good design and pleasant appearance have their unconscious effect. I should add, we are fortunate in having at this factory a Sports Field and garden, and we pay great attention to the outside appearance and general surroundings.

This firm is glad to draw its labour force from a 1930s suburb rather than from the gloom and squalor nearer the centre or from a still unsettled area like Kirkby. At British-American Tobacco's factory (1,200 employees; the company chairman is also chairman of the Council of Industrial Design in London) redecoration is the responsibility of the engineer. The offices are fairly light and agreeable; in the canteens and dining-rooms, which are considerably less so, there are a few smallish reproductions by artists like Seago and Doyly John.

Pictures or murals in such places of work are a rarity.[3] Under its loans-out scheme the Walker Gallery lends works to English Electric and the Blue

---

[1] Though on no scientific basis. Thus the Group Welfare Advisor of Pilkingtons wrote to me that 'As one who is personally influenced by the appearance of the premises in which I work, I feel sure that many people are influenced in this way. However, we have done no research in this field, and therefore it is not possible to give any reliable information on this subject.' The directors wished to support modern art and asked the architect of the new buildings to recommend an artist. The firm also buys prints for its canteens.

[2] The operation is described by Mr Scott in an article in *Personnel Management* for October 1950.

[3] I circularized a number of firms with 1,000 or more employees, mainly those recommended by the Chamber of Commerce as likeliest to show interest. Here is a fairly characteristic reply:

> We do not have any policy for commissioning Works of Art for decoration, etc, in our communal rooms or canteens and with regard to colour schemes, these are usually taken care of by our own Architects Department who very often obtain complete colour schemes from Paint Manufacturers.

Funnel Line and for public display at Martins Bank and Holt's Arcade (i.e. to four commercial firms as against fifty schools and seventeen assorted municipal establishments to whom it lends); the Colour Print Gallery in London, which hires out sets of reproductions, has only one Liverpool industrial customer, R. Silcock and Sons (as against nine in Manchester, and six Liverpool schools). The late Sir Ben Johnson, however, whose dyeworks at Bootle started early this century on paternalistic lines and had one of the first industrial welfare departments in the country, owned a large collection of pictures which overflowed his own house and was hung all round the works; apart from a few watercolours of the works itself by Herbert J. Finn his trustees sold it through J. Davey the Liverpool dealer, 'without, so far as we know, comment or protest from the employees'[1]. Johnson was incidentally one of the founders of the Bluecoat Society.

Likewise J. Bibby and Sons, the cattle food business, had a collection which was auctioned by Outhwaite and Litherland on 15 November 1961. This was mainly 1930s British royal academic, though it included Maximilien Luce's *La Pleine* (sic) *de Bagneaux* and a painting by Maufra; in addition the same firm used to produce a publication for their rural customers called *Bibby's Annual* for which they commissioned original works, including many by a *Punch* artist and Royal Academy exhibitor (from 1880 on) called Gunning King, whose most famous work was *Come Along, Baby*. It would be true to say that art in the strict sense is less widely accepted in Liverpool industry than is the use of colour, whose managerial value is now more or less recognized. At Goodlass Wall, the Speke paint manufacturers, there is a Colour Advisory Service whose manager told me that colour photography, foreign travel, and the Civic Trust's 'facelift' schemes[2] have all helped sharpen

---

[1] Letter of 17 April 1963 to the author from J. L. Crockatt, the present managing director. Mr Crockatt's views on the whole problem are worth quoting further:

> The writer believes strongly that a high standard of painting and decoration is of psychological value in a factory. We think that regular re-decoration and freshening up is of greater importance than choice of colours. The question of colour choice has not had much attention in this factory, but was a matter with which the writer experimented to a considerable extent in a factory he managed before coming here just over two years ago. The practice there, which is now beginning to be felt here, was to select two or three colour schemes for a particular department using, generally speaking, the British Standards Institution colour card for factories. The employees in the department would then be consulted and allowed to choose which of the two or three available schemes they wanted.
>
> There is no way of proving that this technique has any commercial value, but as we have said above, we believe there is a psychological effect, particularly among female employees.
>
> A comparable effect is sometimes obtained and clearly seen in shops. We are all the time taking our oldest branches and modernizing them. We have often noticed that the staff, who may have been dowdy and not sufficiently careful of their appearance, suddenly take a new lease of life and become smart and well turned out when we give them a bright up-to-date shop.

[2] See p. 205. Goodlass Wall worked on the Holyhead 'facelift' and helped prepare the scheme for Ormskirk.

people's awareness of colour. It was interesting however to learn from him that an inquiry about murals from the Dunlop works there had led them to consider founding a mural prize for art schools. One of this service's young designers (themselves all art-school trained) produced a largeish abstract wall construction which his fellow-employees in the factory have come to accept, though many of them are said to have disliked it at first.

Much of what we have been discussing has been on a pretty low level, and it is no good pretending that the visual climate of modern Liverpool is exciting. The Walker Art Gallery may pursue a high standard, but too few Liverpudlians identify themselves with it; the nineteenth-century buildings may have a unique massive splendour, but despite the recent formation of a branch of the Victorian Society not enough people yet appreciate it for there to be any real certainty of its being respected or preserved. The visual results of the old industrial paternalism moreover, at places like Port Sunlight and Johnson's Dyeworks, may nowadays seem slightly absurd, but no newer and more intelligent attitude has come to replace it. Dominating everything is a twofold handicap which it would be wrong to pass over in silence: the shortage of inspiration among recent generations of Liverpool-based architects, and the willing acceptance by most sections of society of a very poor standard of design. Although first-rate architects cost no more than bad ones there is as yet scarcely a single modern building on Merseyside that is really worth looking at; in the centre office blocks like the new State House in Dale Street or competent-looking shops like Hendersons in Church Street or Walker and Hall in Lord Street are startling exceptions, while further out there are all too few new buildings to compare with Gerald Beech's sports pavilion at Wyncote, Nelson and Parker's Hamilton House at Blundellsands or the Ruffwood Drive school. To a great extent the revolution in English design since 1951 passed Liverpool by; there were fourteen Merseyside names on the Council of Industrial Design's 1963 register of designers and three in the 1965–6 membership list of the Design and Industries Association, for instance, as against forty and sixty-four respectively from Manchester; nor would anybody guess that Liverpool was a great printing centre from the design of the average local brochure or poster. This does not mean that progress even at a low level is unimportant, least of all from the point of view of the community concerned. But it does make for a distinction between those who are trying to apply the arts more constructively within these limitations and the smaller number who want to see a change of level as well as a more widespread use of art.

The issue has been raised above all by the new plans for the centre and subsequently for the whole of the city. The extent of the proposed rebuilding,
the likely predominance of the modern architectural idiom with its absence
of decoration, the new types of structure called for and the number of open
spaces and pedestrian ways to be made visually interesting: all this is likely
to pose some very large problems of commissioning and cooperation. It is
not entirely easy to switch one's mind to the new scale; indeed the great risk,
given the existing background, is that even those most familiar with the future
picture of Liverpool may set their sights too low where the artist's contribution is concerned. The assumptions from which the planners are setting
out, certainly, and the new 'overall conceptual framework' which they have
outlined could hardly be bettered; the aim is not just to remedy the years of
neglect and once again produce an efficient city but to shape what Walter
Bor's Interim Planning Policy Statement repeatedly calls the 'total environment', that complex network of urban factors that at once expresses and
influences the personality of the citizens. The approach is humane and far-
sighted, taking account of the essential character of the place (whose coherence and exceptional 'city scale' both planners have emphasized) and of
the need to retain a nucleus of those massive nineteenth-century buildings,
industrial as well as civic, to which this is due.[1] Liverpool is to be a town,
writes the present chairman of the Planning Committee, 'in which visitors
will find visual pleasure, colour, excitement, activity and recreation,'[2] while
Shankland cites the example of certain historic city centres, which he calls
'great collective works of art where the skill, care and love of the community
has been most concentrated.'[3] Two concepts are accordingly emphasized in
the City Centre Plan: 'The city as Art' and 'The city as Entertainment'. 'One
of the basic objectives of the Plan,' says the same document, 'must therefore
be to make Liverpool more beautiful.'[4]

If this is really to be so then the tasks for the visual artist – who can come
from any part of the world, it should be remembered – will be very important
indeed. As yet however they have not been elaborated except in the form of a

[1] This is made clear (and has been accepted by both parties in the City Council) in Section 2.19
of the *Liverpool City Centre Plan*, though to my mind the policy laid down there is too rigid and
pays too little attention to areas like Nelson Street (the Chinese quarter) which are essential to the
city's character though not architecturally distinguished. It is a bad sign however that the report on
'Preservation of Historic Buildings in Central Liverpool' which Dr Quentin Hughes prepared for
the planners has now been shelved by the Council without discussion, possibly because of its
emphasis on the merits of Albert Dock.
[2] W. H. Sefton's foreword to *Liverpool City Centre Plan;* City and County Borough of Liverpool, 1965, p. 1. Alderman Sefton is the leader of the present Labour majority in the council.
[3] *City and County Borough of Liverpool Planning Consultant's Report No. 10. Draft City Centre
Map;* Graeme Shankland, 28 Bedford Square, London WC1., 1963, p. 19.
[4] *Liverpool City Centre Plan*, pp. 67–8.

few rather random suggestions thrown out by the planning documents. These have been more generally concerned with the importance of 'Townscape', of outdoor space and its handling, right down to such matters as improving the dismal Liverpool street furniture and planting more trees. Thus the two sections of the City Centre Plan dealing with 'Culture and Entertainment' (§2.5) and 'Advertisement and Display' (§2.21) call for the

68 The possible shape of things to come. A drawing by Gordon Cullen for one of Graeme Shankland's planning reports

use of 'well designed illuminated signs and displays' to enliven the place at night; the former also for 'the generous use of sculpture and fountains', (thus tacitly by-passing other forms of art).[1] In Shankland's Draft City Centre Map the dispiriting title of 'Civic Husbandry' is given to a mixed bag of suggested measures including 'planting of trees, choice of pavings, design of light fittings and street signs, commissioning of works of art, building fountains'.[2] Fountains indeed are a favourite if rather damp hobby-horse for both planners, possibly because of the presence in Liverpool of a highly original artist in that genre. The *City Centre Plan*, once again, suggests that

> Water features strategically located throughout the pedestrian areas of the city could provide a unifying theme of a unique character for the new Liverpool.

'Water and fountains,' it suggests, 'will have a great role to play.'[3]

It is plain that these rather sketchily-thought-out propositions conceal a widespread will to see artists of all branches made use of. Bor for instance was responsible when at the LCC for commissioning the first sculpture for a

[1] *Liverpool City Centre Plan*, p. 68.
[2] *Draft City Centre Map*, p. 54.
[3] *Liverpool City Centre Plan*, pp. 87, 90. (From section 2.18, on 'Urban Form'.)

council housing estate – a figure by Trevor Tennant in Stepney (St Anne's) – and would evidently be prepared to take responsibility for such commissions in Liverpool. Dr Ronald Bradbury the City Architect is also in principle keen to cooperate with artists, though he lays more emphasis on the practical problems involved, arguing that so far he has had neither the staff nor the money to pay much attention to such things. At the University both the Professor of Architecture and the Professor of Civic Design are anxious to promote this alliance of the arts, while there is evident good will at the Walker Gallery, among the best Liverpool private architects (including notably the two firms working on the Strand-Paradise Street scheme) and in other influential quarters. How far this feeling is shared by the local politicians is slightly less clear. There is however a conscious feeling among leading councillors of both parties that it would help the city in many ways if it could earn a reputation for being visually more interesting and agreeable. This, in Eric Heffer's view, would not directly decide any firm to set up a factory in Liverpool perhaps, but it would be bound to have some influence on key members of its staff.[1] Talking to me, he quoted the example of Pittsburgh, where he had been told that the slum clearance and smoke abatement scuemes had brought executives to live in the centre of the city.

Under the new planning regime the most remarkable step taken so far has been by Littlewoods Mail Order Stores, John Moores's firm, which when building its tall new headquarters in the central area behind Exchange Station held a competition with prizes of £9,500 for a 'sculpture or three-dimensional design' to go in the high space under it. It was an important precedent both as representing an extension of the principle of the Moores Exhibitions into the field of public art – i.e. an attempt to open out the scheme of patronage in the city – and also as part of an all-round effort to raise design levels in a big firm, whose results can already be seen in smaller instances such as the company's printed matter and the signposting and layout of its Church Street

[1] The Public Affairs Officer at Ford's new Liverpool factory at Halewood (near Speke) wrote as follows (letter of 25 July 1963):

> On the subject of the effect of Liverpool environment on the recruiting of personnel, the Halewood factory is of course a fine example of what has been achieved to put the Merseyside image into its proper perspective. To launch the Halewood plant it was necessary to transfer 200 key personnel from Dagenham and other Ford locations to Merseyside. Many of these men and their families had false conceptions about life and conditions on Merseyside, and so we set ourselves the task of eradicating these impressions.
>
> Firstly we produced a film of life on Merseyside showing the beautiful countryside, fine shopping centres and housing developments, and this was shown to all the potential key men and their families at special social evenings at Dagenham. During these functions welfare officers answered questions on the important subjects of education and housing.
>
> The result of this social experiment was that we had 200 volunteers eager to start a new life in the North, and every one of them has settled down on Merseyside.

store. Already Littlewoods has an art society with about 800 members, and Moores lends pictures from his own collection for display in the two main office buildings; W. L. Stevenson, the former head of the College of Art, is in charge of the Department of Architecture and Planning. Perhaps the sculpture competition has not brought quite the results the firm hoped for, since none of the accepted big names in modern British sculpture chose to enter; the 2,000 employees in the new building are not going to be sitting over a masterpiece. None the less it stimulated a number of highly original designs – notably Peter Startup's brightly-coloured wooden 'maritime forms' and the 'hydromobile' by C. L. Crickmay of Liverpool, neither of which got

69 A subsidiary prizewinner in the Littlewoods Sculptural Design Competition (1964): Peter Startup's two changeable wooden structures

70 A John Moores prize for public art. Maquette by P. G. Heesom, first prizewinner in the Littlewoods Sculptural Design Competition for that firm's new building

prizes, as well as some good drawings by P. G. Heesom of Rhyl whose design was chosen to be carried out – and by making so many bright young sculptors think about the problem of public art in Liverpool and showing both their failures and their successes it may have done some very valuable spadework.[1] Its lessons need to be considered together with those of the university scheme.

As part of the 'Bluecoat 63' display at the Bluecoat Chambers a group of local artists and architects[2] set out to show how they too could contribute to the new city. The original idea evidently was to show collaborative schemes for particular Liverpool sites and buildings, in the hope of stimulating private and official interest in commissioning such work. In a modest way this succeeded; thus the WEBA group formed by Weston, Edkins, Ballard and Arnatt, four teachers at the College of Art, was subsequently asked to produce a work for a new building being put up by the Thames Investment Society behind the Liver Building, while at one time it looked as if ATV's new bowling alley in Wavertree Road might get a metal sculpture by Frederick Bushe for its façade, largely at the suggestion of Stephenson, Young and Partners, the architects.[3] Neither of these projects in fact materialized, and although the show itself was well attended it consisted either of completed works – including besides those already mentioned a good crucifix by Arthur Ballard for a chapel in North Wales designed by Quentin Hughes and Gerald

[1] The prizewinners in the first stage of the competition were divided into two sections. J. C. Dougill, Heesom, D. Troostwyk, J. M. Whiskerd, M. Kenny and R. M. Jones got £500 each and a commission to develop their designs further for final judging. H. V. Gregory, C. Sanderson, Miss F. A. M. Jardine, Roger Dean, Startup and F. L. Kenatt got £250 travelling scholarships. Kenny and Dean are Liverpool sculptors; Heesom is from Rhyl. At the second stage Heesom's model was selected for the main award of £5,000. The judges at both stages were Sir William Coldstream, Milner Gray and Peter Chamberlain.

[2] The committee, under the chairmanship of Dr Quentin Hughes of the School of Architecture, consisted of Arthur Ballard, Roderick Bisson, Nicholas Horsfield (painters); George MacPherson (sculptor); James O'Donahue and Roy Parker (architects); Graham Ashworth (of Shankland's town-planning team), John Patterson, Lucjan Pietka, and the Professor of Architecture, Robert Gardner-Medwin. The catalogue introduction spoke of the happier days when 'there was a welding of all visual arts under the leadership of architecture', and named the Constructivists as a modern school aiming at the same sort of synthesis. It listed twenty-eight local artists (six of them with studios in the Bluecoat Chambers) 'who have either had experience in producing murals, sculptural panels or other architectural features or have shown an interest in participating in this sort of work'.

[3] The client's first reaction to the idea is interesting for its realistic attitude to the problems involved. Mr L. S. Michael of Ambassador Bowling, ATV's subsidiary, told the architects that:
> It is of course an extremely dangerous thing to do, because there is a tendency for sculpture of this nature to 'date' very rapidly in appearance. One would obviously be looking for something as abstract as possible, without completely losing the bowling implication.
>
> A completely abstract piece of sculpture while having excellent decorative qualities would convey nothing to our prospective clients. . . . On the other hand a straightforward replica of bowling pins and balls might be extremely boring and inappropriate as part of the permanent decorations of the building.

Beech – or of purely hypothetical schemes by artists alone, sometimes without much architectural relevance. They were small-scale affairs when considered in relation to the immensity of the tasks which the new city plans might provide, and the only revelation of the show was the panels by G. W. Jardine, made by photographic enlargement from some of his collages; they were however hardly architectural.

The other body to concern itself with these problems is the Merseyside Civic Society, which has become active over the past four or five years in all matters affecting Liverpool's appearance and design standards and is now sometimes consulted by the corporation; it has about 500 members and is run by a mixture of architects and laymen. It has been concentrating of late on the appearance of the streets. Thus it has designed flowersellers' and newsvendors' stands as prototypes to raise the miserable level of the street furniture; it has pressed for a change in the Brunswick green colour of the buses; and it initiated a 'facelift' operation for Williamson Square, a process which normally brings economic as well as aesthetic benefits to the chosen area, but has in this case been held up largely as a result of the square's probable early redevelopment. Besides this it has started a move to encourage the main Liverpool stores to improve their fashion standards (as Browns of Chester are held to have done); and has taken part in various negotiations concerning the proposed municipal tidying-up of the neglected but highly romantic cemetery around and beneath the Anglican cathedral. Its boldest step was to commission the Denbighshire sculptor Richard Huws[1] to design a fountain, originally to be erected outside Liverpool, then switched to the city itself to commemorate the starting of work on the city centre. This cleverly-conceived hydraulic contraption, as striking in design as anything in the Littlewoods competition, long had no site allotted to it, but the corporation has now arranged with one of the developers for it to be put up above a new car park near Pier Head, and the Arts Council has given £750 towards the cost.

Such, in outline, is the present position of public art in Liverpool, and it is worth reflecting on it if anything further is to be done. For the unfortunate thing about the public use of works of art in this way is that although it is sometimes recommended as a self-evident desideratum the people who would have to put it into effect are left to act more or less in the dark. The subject is

---

[1] Huws, once a shipbuilding apprentice at Cammell Laird's Birkenhead yard and now lecturer in engineering at the School of Architecture, was responsible for the very successful water sculpture at the 1951 South Bank Exhibition.

71 Fountain by the local sculptor-engineer Richard Huws, commissioned by the Merseyside Civic Society and now being erected near Pier Head

astonishingly neglected by critics and historians of art; there is (to my knowledge) *no* book in any country that even gives illustrations of the outstanding examples of such work in the world today, let alone an account of how they come to have been commissioned or their effect on the public for whom they were designed. The result is that potential patrons and officials in our cities, and artists and architects too, not only are often hamstrung by ignorance of the possible methods and mistakes, but are largely unaware of those achievements which justify public art today. In the circumstances if they have a sense of responsibility they may well refuse to act. If they have not then they are likely to act wrong.

This is why it has been worth looking at public art in Liverpool in this sometimes rather pedestrian manner. No doubt it has been a disheartening experience for readers accustomed to the grand sensations and technicolor scandals of books on modern art, but at least it allows art, architecture, design and other often disregarded elements of our visual environment to be brought into some sort of common perspective, and it raises problems which anybody who hopes to operate in this field has got to bear in mind. For who, to begin with, decides the commissioning of a public work of art? Segregate a picture or piece of sculpture in a gallery, and the role of the expert is at once admitted; the gallery's director, within certain limits, will have his way. Not so once art gets outside the ghetto walls; it is then normal for any councillor, company director or other patron to act on his own judgment, and the only question is whether it is he or his architect who will pick the artist, and site and specify the work. If there is no reason why the new type of patron should necessarily be the best person to decide this there is little more why the architect should, for although architects know well enough what is going to fit their own buildings they are not bound to have God-given qualifications to distinguish between good art and bad. Those Baroque artists who accepted 'the leadership of architecture' were sometimes pedestrian practitioners within their own particular fields, and the modern (post-Corbusier) architect's affection for artists whose geometric gifts outweigh their colour sense can easily be disastrous as soon as those gifts drop below the top (i.e. Arp-Nicholson-Gabo-Vasarely-late Pasmore) level.

All the signs in Liverpool are that the architect considers the nomination of an artist to be his province. And in a sense this is understandable, for the Liverpool artists evidently feel that public design issues are not their affair; they have, for instance, done nothing to support the new city plans and they play no part in the Civic Society. Moreover most artists (and not only in Liverpool) have to come a long way if they are to work with an architect at all. There is, in the City Architect's view, a new type of artist now evolving who is interested in structural details and what can be done with them; Mitchell or Hollaway, for instance, can see the possible sculptural implications of a plan at an early stage and agree them with the architect so that their work becomes part of the actual building process; but Liverpool has nobody trained in this way. The result, so Dr Bradbury feels, is that there is a gap between artist and architect which can only be remedied by quite small-scale experiments in collaboration. Similarly the late Stanisław Pater, the Polish-born architect who was mainly responsible for churches at Weightman and Bullen, found that artists tend to have a poor sense of scale unless they have done architectural work before, so that in most cases he would ask them to make a full-size maquette to be tried out on the proposed site. Not that it is necessarily the most efficient collaborators from the architects' point of view who will produce the best answer. Too much of the 'built-in' decoration on recent buildings – the Liverpool Building Centre is a characteristic example – is a humdrum regurgitation of modern art conventions which has no real identity of its own and could date disastrously as soon as the fashion supporting it has collapsed. Certainly the architect's assumed primacy in this field is subject to more qualifications than he normally admits.

Frequently, in the instances which we have been looking at, there has been an almost total divorce of the work of art from its site. This was ludicrous enough with the statues of Huskisson, Disraeli and Edward VII being shifted around like enlarged chessmen, but the case of the Huws fountain shows that sculpture can be commissioned without a site at all; (other possible homes suggested for it included Pier Head and Williamson Square, with a proposed public lavatory contending for the latter). This is the real weakness both of the works commissioned by the university and of the competitors in the Littlewoods scheme; they bear less relation to their background than to that of the artist. Dalwood's sculpture outside the Physics Building, for in-

72 The danger of cliché: cast sculpture by William Mitchell on the new Building Centre in Hope Street, near the splendid Philharmonic Hotel. This is the kind of decoration that now tends to be appreciated by architects, since it is conceived and executed as part of the building.

stance, besides being blankly uninteresting in itself from too many angles, was out of scale with the building and out of character with the relics of nineteenth century Liverpool around it. Geoffrey Clarke's indoor mosaic, again, might well look good in a gallery, but it depends on a highflown written explanation alongside it to explain its symbolism, and unfortunately the light is too bad for the main symbol to be distinguishable. These artists are the choice of the architects, but they have not necessarily been brought in at an early enough stage; the fact that twenty-four different architects are being used makes for a certain disjointedness, while although they include some of the country's leading men (Lasdun, for instance, Spence, Fry), the buildings so far finished have hardly shown them at the top of their form. There has

73 A new development in the University's art policy. Paintings hanging in the Electrical Engineering Building, seen from the street through a window reflecting the new cathedral

been a different policy in the case of Yorke, Mardell and Rosenberg's Electrical Engineering Building, where £3,000 was spent on original paintings and prints (of the architect's choosing) to be hung in corridors, common rooms and so forth; a number of the paintings – non-figurative works of no special distinction – are in a glass-walled basement corridor which can be inspected from the street. The prints are by leading contemporary English artists and mostly look very well. And most recently some £2,500-worth of paintings, half of them by Liverpool artists, have been bought for the new Social Studies and Modern Languages Building, this time under the chairmanship of Professor Ridley (himself a collector) and with the architect as a member of the selecting committee.[1]

It would be a mistake to blinker ourselves to the failures because of a commitment to the kind of modern artists concerned in them, or even a sense that failure on this level is better and more exciting than success in purely local terms. It would be a greater one to decide on this evidence that modern art is unfitted for public tasks or that the honest northern artist is preferable to the over-publicized Londoner. The lessons are surely more than the commission-

[1] The Science Lecture Theatres building subsequently built to the design of Professor Robert Gardner-Medwin in association with James and Bywaters includes work by two local artists: a tapestry by Geraldine Carmichael and concrete reliefs by Frederick Bushe.

74 Out of place and out of scale. The three sculptural figures
outside Sir Basil Spence's Physics Building. In the distance, the
massive brick ventilating shaft to the railway tunnel

ing of public art is at present undertaken too amateurishly, without enough
sense of site and purpose; that symbolizing pious sentiments like the resur-
gence of Liverpool is merely laughable unless they correspond to a strong
public feeling; that the architect needs advice and the artist some awareness
of scale and materials if their arts are to combine effectively; above all that
once art gets out into the open the pseudo-philosophizing and the display
of personal temperament which impress gallery-goers or magazine readers
matter less than a real feeling for the background – the background not only
of the building in question but also of the city's climate and architecture and
the hopes and needs of the people who live there. This is something which to
my mind emerged strongly from the exhibits in the Littlewoods competition;
that attitude of 'take it or leave it' which the self-respecting artist now adopts
towards patrons and dealers is likely to seem merely insulting to the public
who find his work impinging all uninvited on their everyday lives. It must
speak to them in some other terms if it is to become rooted there.

Moreover there is no system of change and exchange as within the segregated world of the gallery; there is no cellar for the dumping of unwanted
works. Perhaps in due course public art will go off like fireworks or be
stripped down like posters, but this is not how it operates at present. For
better or worse it is there for good.

5 : QUESTIONS OF TASTE

In the years since the war this once philistine country has got caught up on a wave of interest in art, and particularly in the development of modern art over the past century. The booming prices in the saleroom, the establishment of art history as an academic subject in our universities, the vast increase in art books, the crowds packing the modern art exhibitions: all these are evidence of a great change in our attitude. Today art, even of the most seemingly outrageous avant-garde kind, is acceptable in smart English society; a topic for conversation, a good capital-gains investment, a subject for theses, a hobby for retired major-generals, an occupation for debutantes, it has become very nearly a reputable pursuit. The professional artist has altered; he is no longer expected to be a gentleman, like the painters of Bloomsbury or Camden Town or the fashionable artists between the wars; he is now accepted as a man of a race apart, a visual entertainer whose main function is to surprise. A whole generation of more or less classless painters and sculptors has come out of the art schools to meet the demand for short-lived sensations; they come often from ordinary provincial families and local art schools, then pass into the London machine, where the rewards are great so long as they are in fashion. The pace is hot in this world, which is very different from the one most civic and industrial patrons were brought up in. It is not easy to keep track of the movements of taste.

Yet each of the last two chapters has finally come down to this question, for both the public gallery and the unconfined art of streets and open spaces have got to mean something to the ordinary citizen if they are to justify themselves. How far then can the patrons and potential patrons of art in Liverpool count on this rapid rate of development being maintained on Merseyside too? Obviously there is a time-lag in such matters between Liverpool and London, and much that is accepted by a wide public in the capital is still disliked and viewed with mistrust in the provinces; it may indeed only be seen at all in Liverpool because of a certain itch to check up on the latest London craze. None the less it is clear that the general evolution is infectious. The figures for attendances at the Walker Art Gallery have improved, as we saw on p. 70; the increase in the sale of postcard reproductions shows that interest in the pictures is becoming less casual; the Bluecoat gallery is establishing itself; while use of the art library seems to have gone up very rapidly at first.[1] The books most in demand are monographs on particular artists and schools and the semi-popular (*haute vulgarisation*) illustrated books produced by such publishers as Skira, Thames and Hudson, Weidenfeld, and Oldbourne, typical results of the new international system of 'co-production' by which the expense of printing and block making is shared between a number of different countries. Admittedly these are only small straws to show which way the wind blows, but it would be wise to regard Liverpool taste too as changing, even if its development has so far been slower and more idiosyncratic than that of England as a whole.

There has been nothing in recent times to compare with the three great Liverpool art arguments of the past: the cases respectively of the Pre-Raphaelite prizewinners, the St George's Hall reliefs, and the Lord Mayor's portrait. Yet even with a gallery of the reputation of the Walker the elected representatives still intermittently dig in their toes and oppose the purchase of a work which they do not 'understand'. This has not happened often, first because under the Cotton-Lambert regime there was a practice of buying no very modern work;[2] more recently because the Moores gifts have created a strong modern department without much need for controversial spending of public money. Nor should it be taken too seriously when it does, for quite apart from the fact that a democratic opposition exists precisely to raise objections there is also a school of thought both in and out of the council which feels that controversy is an effective way of stimulating interest in the gallery. The first important case was in 1958, when the Arts Sub-Committee refused to allow the director to spend £247 on a painting by William Scott. 'I feel that this is an insult,' councillors were quoted as saying;[3] 'If we tell the City Council we have bought that we won't get any more money'; 'I cannot see any merit'; 'A monstrosity'; 'I would rather have Winston Churchill's *Still Life*'. Before the end of that year the picture had been bought by the

---

[1] The figures for postcards sold are: (year ending) 1958, 16,729; 1959, 17,518; 1960, 18,119; 1961, 24,151; 1962, 28,065; 1963, 22,138; 1964, 23,873; 1965, 22,924; 1966, 28,822.
  The City Librarian's annual reports give the following details: 1958, an increase of almost 5,000 readers (on a previous total of about 15,000); 1959, no mention; 1960, lending issues up by 40 per cent, reference issues by 38 per cent; 1961, both up by about 15 per cent; 1962, lending up by 25 per cent and reference by 75 per cent. Since then there has been some falling-off, owing partly to rebuilding operations, partly to the provision of more art books in branch libraries.
[2] In Cotton's view there should be a distinction between what the gallery ought to show – which should be extremely catholic so that visitors can see as much as possible of what is going on in art – and what it should buy and keep.
[3] *Liverpool Evening Express*, 21 February 1958.

I

Musée de l'Art Moderne in Paris; it is now worth about three times the sum asked. Three years later the opposition objected to the purchase of the Henry Moore *Falling Warrior* in comparable terms: 'a phoney pot-boiler', for instance, 'Just a blob of metal', and 'Where is its face?'[1] In 1963 however the

75 A purchase by the gallery that was opposed in committee: Henry Moore's *Falling Warrior*

city's first modern American painting – a smooth (and to my mind) superficial abstract work by Paul Jenkins called *Phenomena Votive* – was bought thanks largely to the enthusiasm of the Sub-Committee chairman, Robert Bessell, and it is possible that the tide may be changing.

Councillors do not necessarily sit on the Arts Sub-Committee because they wish to; 'the average councillor', so one of them told me, 'just couldn't care less about the gallery'. This attitude, slightly overstated perhaps, seems to many a fair enough representation of that of the public, and at one time it may have been so. Whether the same holds good today is more doubtful. Despite the director's complaints in his annual reports (of 1953–4, 1954–5, 1958–9, 1962–3) that the city is largely unaware of the treasures it owns a surprising number of the people whom I myself questioned, either directly or on paper, at least knew that the gallery was a proper subject for interest, even for pride. A feeling of this sort is perfectly compatible with a failure ever to visit the place, and what people get out of the collection and what it actually contains are two very different matters. The best-liked (or best remembered) pictures are a curious mixture; among the postcard reproductions Lowry's *The Fever Van* is a best-seller; while my own enquiries in 1963 put Daguerre's

[1] See the *Liverpool Daily Post* of 13 and 14 January 1961 for the sub-committee and of 2 February for the council meeting.

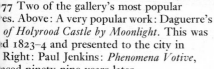

77 Two of the gallery's most popular
es. Above: A very popular work: Daguerre's
of Holyrood Castle by Moonlight. This was
d 1823–4 and presented to the city in
Right: Paul Jenkins: *Phenomena Votive*,
ased ninety-nine years later

romantic *Holyrood Castle* and the new Jenkins abstract (both at that time
hanging conspicuously on the stairs up to the main collection) as the main
favourites. The primitives found few supporters: one or two for the Simone
Martini; none for the Ercole de' Roberti *Pietà*, which is surely one of the most
beautiful pictures in England. One boy even suggested that all the old
pictures ought to be put in a 'museum': an interesting indication that galleries are coming to be seen as places for new visual experiences, to which the
study of earlier masterpieces is a positive obstacle.

A certain licence is allowed in a gallery, which is withdrawn as soon as art
gets out into the streets. The difficulty facing public art in Liverpool is that
when it is more or less traditional in style, nobody will notice it, while when
it is not it is noticed all right, but is liable to be taken as a personal affront by
the public. Most of the existing public statues simply are not looked at; the
Liverpool citizens I questioned had only the vaguest idea of what was round
St George's Hall, that great conglomeration of statuary in the heart of the
city, and apart from the four Landseerish lions (which were no doubt im-
printed on their memories as children) dismissed it as a display of militarism
and royalty: something to which they automatically shut their eyes. This
situation they are used to and accept. It was a different matter however when
the Bold Street Association, representing the smartest and architecturally
least disagreeable shopping street in Liverpool (which Shankland has sug-

78 *Not* a public favourite: Ercole de' Roberti's *Pietà*, from the Roscoe collection in the Walker Gallery

gested glassing-over and turning into a pedestrian way), put a bombed corner site at the disposal of a local modern sculptor. This well-intentioned act proved a model flop. It started happily enough with a small unveiling cere-mony at which the association's vice-president expressed his hopes 'that the public of Liverpool will recognize this work of art as an asset to the city and respect it. I personally think we should encourage young artists to create works like this and give them every opportunity to display them in Liverpool.'[1]

[1] *Liverpool Daily Post*, 19 September 1960.

Then, wrote the *Liverpool Daily Post*'s reporter:

> The draperies fell . . . and there was the sort of silence in which everyone is wondering to say . . . A child let out a howl. Then twenty-seven-year-old sculptor Robin Riley, of Catherine Street, Liverpool, tried to answer all those questions from the baffled and bewildered.

'I was primarily concerned in making a figure as a piece of sculpture,' Riley was quoted as saying. 'It was sculpturally unnecessary for it to have arms. I wanted to create the impression of the power in human beings, in humanity and in life itself.' Again. 'The figure is the reflection of my own personal awareness and it cannot be explained. It is just a figure. You either have a purely personal emotional reaction or you have not.'

There is an emergency meeting of the Bold Street Association; the statue itself is given police protection. Next Arthur Maiden Ltd, the poster hoarding firm who control the site, insist that it should be removed, on the pretext of 'reported public reaction against it, which might be directed against us when we are in no way responsible for it.' No, their managing director tells the *Liverpool Post*,[2] it wasn't that it was indecent,

> although people had said it was offensive and vulgar. Yes, it might be art, but they didn't think so. They were merely exercising their right to have it taken away.

79 (*above*) Public art and public taste. Robin Riley's *Standing Figure* after its removal from the Bold Street site. **80** (*right*) Arbiters of this taste: Arthur Maiden Ltd's Liverpool headquarters

[1] *Liverpool Daily Post*, 19 September 1960.
[2] Ibid., 20 September 1960.

A crowd gather; the statue is lowered to the ground. The vice-president rather wistfully says they had 'hoped that this site might become a showplace for many of our young artists'. Riley accuses his critics of being ashamed of humanity.

A man with a beard said: 'Dreary old Liverpool strikes again.'

An old man with a flat cap said: 'Get away, mate. We've got enough of that kind of thing with old Herbert on top of Lewis's.'

'Hardly anyone,' commented the *Post*'s reporter, 'could describe their objections to it. It's back to front, it's a prostitution, it looks as though it's got a nasty mind, it's revolting, they said. And, plaintively, what does it mean?' The statue was later given asylum in a Liverpool private garden, though Councillor Maguire of Crosby would have liked it put on the Blundellsands sea front. 'I think,' he explained, 'it typifies the struggle of our merchant seamen during the war.'

In the use and choice of works of art for homes the population of Liverpool lag not only behind London but behind their own past. So far as original works are concerned, there are now only two established picture dealers in central Liverpool – Boydell, and J. Davey and Son (who is also one of the principal frame-makers) – as against some twenty half a century ago. Davey told me too that in his father's time there used to be 240 gilders in the union in Liverpool and as many again who were not members; today there is one. Agnews had a Liverpool branch from 1873 to 1909 and there was also in those days a good market for local painters; thus in 1876 the *Porcupine*'s London correspondent was writing of the resentment felt by the London exhibitors at the Autumn Exhibition who suspected that 'the bulk of the twelve thousand and odd pounds resulting from the sales in William Brown Street found its way into the pockets of the local men.'[1]

Today this is all very much changed. Not only do the few noteworthy Liverpool collectors (such as Mrs Bibby and Messrs Oliphant, Kennerley and Samuels) do their buying in London – Boydell told me that he had never been asked for a work by any of the great French painters – but the Liverpool artist finds it difficult to sell. Though old Liverpool pictures, especially of a topographical nature, are in considerable demand, both Boydell and Davey feel there is practically no market for the present generation of artists. Of those whom I myself have talked with, certainly, only the sculptor Herbert Tyson Smith and, with considerable difficulty, Dooley, George Thomas and James Cliffe have been able to live without relying mainly on a teaching job. It was considered exceptional by his confrères when Nicholas Horsfield, by-

[1] *The Porcupine*, Liverpool, 5 February 1876, p. 708.

passing the dealers, sold some £750 worth of pictures in 1963 from a one-man show at the Bluecoat Chambers that represented the cream of two years' work, though in spring 1966 Sean Rice the sculptor also sold nearly all his works from a two-man exhibition in the same gallery. Generally speaking the uncertain income from local sales can only represent pocket-money to the artist, nothing more.

Both Davey and Boydell say that business has much improved in the past few years; the growing interest in pictures has affected people's furnishing habits, especially when setting up a new home, and the fashion for bare walls is disappearing. None the less there is no gallery in Liverpool such as artists and students would like to visit, or the leading painters to show in, or the chief patrons to support. Of the two survivors Davey finds that the market is for old pictures, including nineteenth century works, for which there is a demand in America. Boydell's is rather more interesting; it has dignified

81 The Boydell Gallery, at the corner of Castle Street and Dale Street, the principal Liverpool picture dealers

premises and a good stock of early nineteenth century and the more con-servative modern watercolours, and although many of the oils are stereo-typed landscapes by unknown continental painters, imported in batches and selling for only £10–£30, Boydell himself commissions competent small paintings of Liverpool scenes by Gordon Ellis, an artist living in Scotland. He is beginning now to sell more abstract work, but only when, like that of the French artist Michel Mouly, it has already become familiar through reproductions, the pace-setters here being the Bristol print firm Frost and Reed. There is nothing in the activities of either of these establishments to replace the gallery run by Eric Rowan (lately of the College staff) for the New Shakespeare Theatre Club which the American actor-director Sam Wana-maker managed between November 1957 and January 1959. Here there were shows of Klee, Francis Bacon and Joseph Herman that are still talked about in Liverpool. Unfortunately the gallery was badly placed to catch the ordinary theatregoer, and had little success in selling pictures. It was doing a public gallery's work rather than that of a dealer.[1]

The main market in Liverpool is for coloured prints, and these are often by artists of whom the right-thinking art-lover rests in happy ignorance: painters of colourful landscapes like Doyly John, Deakins and George Hann, and above all the South African Tretchikoff, whose pictures show expressionless girls with huge smooth faces in a strange green and purple glow, exotically dressed against a flat wall-paper-like background. A few years ago when the Medici Society branch in Bold Street put one of these in the shop window it drew so many admirers that the police rang up to know what was wrong. Such works, which are stocked also by Boots's Art Department and by Owen

◀ **82** Best selling prints: (1) Tretchikoff's *The Balinese Girl* **83** ▲ (2) Doyly John's *A Bridge in Venice*. Both these artists are published by Messrs Frost and Reed

Owen,[2] sell for about £4 or £5; Boots furthermore have an interesting device called Craft Master, 'the original painting-by-numbers set' which is a do-it-yourself version of similar subjects in similar colours: Loch Lomond, for instance, Mountain Châlet, Spanish Dancers, Wild Stallions, St Tropez,

---

[1] I have not seen the gallery run by the painter Ray Fields at Bebington near Port Sunlight. This is combined with a working studio.

[2] The Central Buyer for Owen Owen told me in May 1963 that 'The fashion at the moment is for Spanish subjects, Harbour scenes, Mountain and Swiss-type scenes, and a colourful range of Italian Lakes. . . . Old Masters are not popular with the exception of Constable's *Haywain* and *Flatford Mill*.' He attributed this to the increase in foreign travel.

Mademoiselle and The Charm of Paris (showing the Sacré-Coeur).[1] Lewis's sell much cheaper so-called 'Canvatex' reproductions of Cézanne, Picasso, Matisse and Utrillo; I saw a reproduction of the de Stael footballers in the window of the Times Furnishing Co, and in Lewis's Show House, when I visited it, there was a really good selection of prints on the walls (including not only Braque and Dufy but the Uccello *Rout of San Romano*), for which the salesman in charge had had 'quite a few orders'. Once again it seems that the climate is changing. The Medici Society, which has had a Liverpool branch since before the 1914 war, held its first exhibition of truly modern prints, organized in conjunction with the Redfern Gallery in London and

[1] The following detailed report from Mr John M. Caven of Boots's picture department is dated 30 April 1963.

In the last few years there have been two or three definite fashions in our customers' demands. First of all there was the period when only the large colourful bird pictures by Peter Scott, Vernon Ward and Hugh Monahan would be sold. We sold at that time about seven of these to any one other subject. Then we had D'Oyly John, and other painters of that kind, with their gay continental prints. These were very popular, and it is still very common to see them in people's homes. We still sell this kind of print, but nothing like the sales of a few years ago.

Meanwhile the craze for two or three small pictures on a wall was in, mostly subjects of birds or flowers. The demand lasted quite a long time, and ended, as it had to, with the large pictures coming back.

For a short while the V. Ward Flower prints sold very well, then Tretchikoff came onto the scene with his very colourful Chinese Girl, Lost Orchid, Weeping Rose, and many others. For the last two years his have been the best all round selling reproductions, and we are still doing quite well with them.

Nevertheless the fashion is beginning to change once again, but this time there doesn't seem to be any definite subject or artist that our customers are following, but copies of the old masters, and French impressionists, seem to be selling better than ever. This however has been made easier for the public with the very exceptional value colour prints which 'Prints for Pleasure' of London have been introducing, also the Brush Stroke Mounted Prints at 19s. 11d.

The 'Facsimile Reproductions' of Bristol, are very good, but are more expensive, and most people do not want to spend a lot of money on a picture when it may only be up a year or so at the most.

The following have been our most popular prints in the last few months:

'Saw Ohn Nyun'	By Sir Gerald Kelly
'Moonlit Sea'	By R. De La Corbiene
'Balinese Girl'	By Tretchikoff
'Amanda and Harriet'	By Strevens
'Chinese Girl'	By Tretchikoff
'Red Skirt'	By R. Clemente
'Tumbling Waves'	By E. Mandon
'Freedom of the Plains'	By M. Bordi
'The Haywain'	By J. Constable.

In closing I would like to say that, in the buying of pictures, we have found that the Liverpool public are about a year behind what is being sold in the South and London, and even longer in some cases. For instance pictures without glass were being sold in London in the larger shops two or three years ago, but are only now taking on in Liverpool.

Since then, Mr Caven tells me, there has been little change in the type of print that sells best. Customers have, however, been buying more in the £8–£12 range, and there is a new demand for original continental oils.

84 The Medici Galleries' Liverpool branch in Bold Street

including works by Kandinsky, Feininger, Chagall etc., in the summer of 1963, and its somewhat unexpected success led to its becoming an annual affair. Seven copies of the most 'difficult' picture, for instance, the Kandinsky *Accord Réciproque*, sold at ten guineas. The wishy-washy devotional pictures of Margaret Tarrant seem to be losing some of their old appeal; Vlaminck sells well, also Lowry and the Picasso child with the dove. Intellectuals, on the whole, tend to choose Brueghel, professional people Canaletto; Dali's Crucifixion does well with Catholics; Constable is the most popular of all. At the same time a rather indifferent abstract by a French painter called Jean Jacus, entitled *Ships of Thought*, has done well with schools. The title makes such a good essay subject.

None of these prints originates in Liverpool, of course, any more than do the best-selling modern oil paintings, so that even if the choices made are significant it cannot be said that the works themselves exactly reflect local taste. They do however to some extent determine it, to judge from the pictures exhibited in amateur art shows. *Bettwys-y-Coed, Rarin' to Go, Nr Matterdale, Late Roses, Sunset and Smoke, Call of the Sea, The Langdales, Spanish Fountains, Highland Cattle*: these opening titles in the Merseyside Artists' Association's 1964 Spring Exhibition give a good idea of the sort of themes prevailing among such part-time painters. There are other amateur societies besides this one, of course; the Liverpool Artists Club has become essentially a business men's club, but there are also the Liver Sketching Club and the Wirral Artists from across the Mersey, whose standard is rather higher. But both the Merseyside Artists and the Childwall Art Group, an energetic amateur outfit based on the Childwall Evening Institute, seem impregnated with the gaudy escapism of the print shops; there are colourful landscapes, scenes from the sunny south, exotic portraits like bad bible illustrations, and more recently a sprinkling of fearful abstract or 'symbolic' works. It is rare to find anything that tries to reflect the Liverpool scene or the experiences of everyday life; and though the Childwall group's 1963 show did have one quite original small painting its theme, a lowering bison, was as remote as any. There were also (besides idealized portraits of cats, and other horrors), a number of pictures by a student at the Walton prison art classes, mostly imaginary landscapes such as one might find in a furniture shop, but including one abstract. The Paul Jenkins in the Walker Gallery, the shows at the Medici and now this. . . . Half a century after its origins, some twenty years since the millionaires began to accept it, the battle for abstract art is being won in Liverpool too.

On this popular, amateur level there is a great deal of copying, sometimes of style and subject, sometimes of actual works. If there is any degree of self-expression here it lies simply in a choice of more or less conventional, prede-termined themes (which change gradually with fashion), and in the actual craftsmanship of handling paint. This, certainly, is how it appears in the big mental hospitals round Liverpool – Deva, Winwick and Rainhill – where the therapeutic value of art is now accepted but the actual practice amounts to little more than a time-occupying hobby, to be ranked with old-time dancing, wool rug-making and occupational therapy in general. Sometimes childish, sometimes reaching a fair amateur standard, the pictures produced in these huge cut-off communities (of which Winwick and Rainhill in particular were unforgettably depressing) are not treated as guide to diagnosis; at Winwick copying prevails, often from travel brochures or from Walt Disneyish draw-ings, at Deva there is a proportion of original art of a kind, but much copying too.[1] The only truly personal works of art that I saw had been produced at

---

[1] A report by the art teacher in the Deva Group of Hospitals in 1963 said that a teacher was then visiting Deva Hospital twice a week for three hours, and Moston once. Patients with artistic talents and/or some previous training were given courses in drawing and painting, including abstract or imaginative painting in oils. The others, if amenable to being taught, were instructed in perspective and water-colour. The patients worked to music, particularly to that of composers unfamiliar to them, like Delius, Sibelius and Wagner. In good weather they were encouraged to work out of doors.

The most withdrawn patients were left to draw or paint on their own and tended, from a medical standpoint, to do the most interesting work. There was some clay modelling, that by an epileptic and certain subnormal patients being of special interest. Some of the patients showed great original-ity, one of them having a gift for 'caricature in abstract form'. Many were good at posters, and these were used on notice boards and elsewhere in the hospitals.

For special occasions the teacher might organize groups of patients to produce large paintings. One of these was used for the Christmas decorations in 1962.

Some patients were destructive, using sharp instruments to attack an image. The classes were of up to about twenty.

Rainhill (a building designed by the architect of St George's Hall, with 2,400 inmates and a main corridor a quarter of a mile long), where the education officer A. W. Fraser himself owns a picture of Arthur Ballard's and has decorated his recreation room and library with good prints. Here one patient had sculpted two quite original heads in stone, while another produced over a period of years drawings and paintings of extreme interest, pictures which not only progress through a steadily increasing competence and complexity towards abstraction and simplification but have a range of imaginative reference which nobody would have guessed to lie in the power of the uneducated and totally uncommunicative artist. Though this man gave up three or more years ago – he is still a patient, alas – his work deserves to be known for its own sake, quite apart from any bearing which it might have on his case. It is a remarkable instance of spontaneous gifts, and it makes one wonder what the Liverpool amateur artist might not be able to do if he used his own eyes and imagination rather more, and got away from the painting-by-numbers frame of mind.

So far in Liverpool there has not been much to suggest the emergence of any naturally self-expressive local talent in the visual arts which would match the astonishing outbursts of popular music over the last few years. As will appear later, however, there are local artists like Ballard and Arthur Dooley

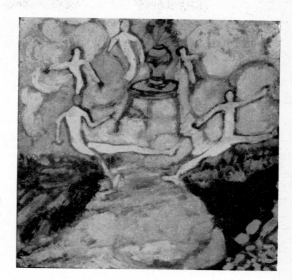

85-89 Art as expression: five pictures from a sequence by an untutored patient in Rainhill mental hospital. They are in chronological order, and after the last of them he stopped painting

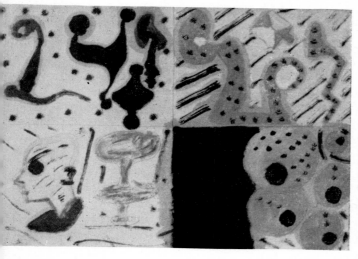

the sculptor who believe that the talent and the possibility of its expression are there, and that it is only a matter of time before it will break out. Whether this is so is a large question, bound up not only with the whole system of art education in the city but with the achievements and potentialities of the professional local artists themselves, two subjects which will be considered in later chapters. It is encouraging however that there should recently have been a couple of attempts to organize Liverpool arts festivals, of a quite non-establishment kind, that have set out to express the spirit of the place. The first of these, the South Liverpool Festival of Art, was originally held in 1960 and based on the Domestic Mission, a late nineteenth century Unitarian foundation in Liverpool 8; in 1964 it developed offshoots in Garston, Vauxhall and Speke and a selection from them all was shown at the Walker Gallery under the title 'Liverpool: People and Places'; in 1966 it spread to several other areas, which held their own District Festivals of Art, and the Walker Art Gallery's final selection ('Liverpool Today and Tomorrow') drew 15,410 visitors in a month.

The idea behind the South Liverpool Festival was the conviction of the Rev. J. Keir Murren of the Domestic Mission that art was at once a means of recording the life and character of the neighbourhood and a socially cohesive force. He had discussed at various club and committee meetings what forces of this kind could be found to set against those that up till then had been helping drag down that section of Liverpool and, he said, 'it was coming away from a John Moores art exhibition that art clicked with me.' He had when I saw him two Picasso postcards in his own small and rather dingy room, and there was a Picasso mother and child hanging in the chapel along with Della Robbia plaques made by Harold Rathbone in the 1890s; none the less he told me that he was 'not art mad at all', but just 'using art in this very real social sense'. The first two of the festivals, as eventually organized by Murren jointly with the neighbouring David Lewis Settlement, contained respectively about 450 and about 700 pictures, mainly by children, showing scenes, episodes and people of the neighbourhood; more recently the project has become part of a larger Community Council, which is concerning itself with a wide range of social problems, from housing and street improvement to the relations between residents and local industry. Though both exhibitions gave expression to a good deal of liveliness and amusing observation the artistic talent revealed was not at first very striking, but the cream of the later shows included works that were genuinely beautiful, as well as directing attention to the everyday environment and the hope of improving it. As an apparently successful example of a new kind of collective (or neighbourhood) art therapy they are a most interesting precedent, suggesting that a similar but wider sense of new artistic curiosity and vitality will be of very practical benefit to the city as a whole.

The two Merseyside Arts Festivals organized in August 1962 and May 1963 by John Gorman were held in the Hope Hall near the new Catholic Cathedral, with the support of Leslie Blond, cinema proprietor, property owner and patron-cum-landlord of the arts. They were the work of the younger professional or would-be professional artists and poets, though of such as the establishment has hitherto rather ignored. This group of people, which includes the poets Roger McGough and Brian Patten (editor of the

90 A poem by one of the participants in the Merseyside Arts Festivals and Hope Hall Events

MOTHER, THE WARDROBE IS FULL OF INFANTRYMEN

Mother, the wardrobe is full of infantrymen
i did, i asked them,
but they snarled saying it was a mans life

Mother there is a centurion tank in the parlour
i did, i asked the officer
but he laughed saying Queens regulations,
and it was out of tune anyway.

Mother polish your identity bracelet
there is a mushroom cloud in the backgarden
i did, i tried to bring in the cat
but it simply came to pieces in my hand.
i did, i tried to whitewash the windows
but there weren't any
i did, i tried to hide under the stairs
but i couldn't get in for the civil defence leaders
i did, i tried ringing Candid Camera
but they crossed their hearts.

i went for a policeman but they were looting the town
i went for a fire engine but they were all upside down
i went for a priest but they were all on their knees
Mother don't just lie there say something please
Mother don't just lie there say something please

Roger McGough

Liverpool poetry magazine *Underdog*) and the painters Walsh and Henri, contains, to my mind, a number of the brightest talents in Liverpool, though it was handicapped by lack of funds and organization and also by the dinginess of the Hope Hall, then a cinema and subsequently given over to the Everyman Theatre. The club in the basement of this hall – supposedly the scene of some remarkable Love Feasts in the last century[1] – was till recently the real meeting point for Liverpool popular music and the other arts. In the hall itself Blond has shown, besides local painters, an exhibition of paintings by Bomberg and mixed shows from the Waddington and St George's galleries in London; although neither the architecture nor the patrons have been ideal for such a scheme he evidently hoped it might fill the place of Wanamaker's New Shakespeare. For the 1963 festival Henri organized the exhibition in the hall; there was another in the Friends' Meeting House and an amateur show in Stanley House, where a number of coloured people live. There were poetry readings by McGough and Pete Brown (of London), also an international folk music concert, folk dancing at Pier Head, and a debate with Mrs Bessie Braddock. It seems characteristic of Liverpool, and perhaps of England, that there should have been no contact between Gorman and Keir Murren of the Domestic Mission, though both were based on Liverpool 8, and that although I was in Liverpool at the time of this festival, and seeing a number of people in the art world, I never heard about it. The establishment, it is not unfair to say, did not approve of the Hope Hall.

My own attempts to gauge Liverpool's natural tastes and needs and its degree of familiarity with art began with the questionnaires already referred to in connection with the Walker Gallery's pictures. As the detailed analysis of the results in Appendix A will make plain, they were worded so as to discover the recipient's awareness of art not only in the gallery but as a human activity, a possible environment at home and in public places, a means of embellishing the city; and then to establish by means of a series of twenty postcard reproductions how he reacted to different styles of painting and sculpture of our own day, ranging from conservative to 'advanced'. The original aim was to have these questions put verbally to samples in different quarters of Liverpool, but in the event the vast majority of interviewees filled in their own forms, and almost half of them came from a single school. The

---

[1] According to James Stonehouse's History of the Streets of Liverpool in James Boardman: *Liverpool Table Talk a Hundred Years Ago*. Liverpool 1882, p. 149. He says that Samuel Warren reported them in *Blackwood's Magazine*. The hall, then a dissenting chapel, subsequently became the church of St John the Evangelist.

final composition of the 368 replies – 84 from visitors to the Walker Art Gallery, 172 from children and 27 from staff at Gateacre Comprehensive School, 31 from employees at Littlewoods Spinney House offices and 54 from interviewees – was certainly anything but scientific. None the less I did find this a useful and suggestive way of communicating with a large variety of people – it is remarkable what an impression of personality a filled-in questionnaire can in fact give, and how much it says that is anyway not statistically analysable – and enough of the evidence which it provided seemed to tally with other impressions for its main pointers to be significant. In this odd mixture the conservatism of the children, taking similar directions to that of the non-Art Gallery adults but going rather further, offset the more 'aesthetic' tendencies of the art gallery visitors; both, for instance, agreed in preferring Peter Scott to all the other postcards, whereas the gallery visitors put him near the bottom. I would disregard the children however when it comes to questions not of taste but of knowledge; asked to identify a monument or name a Liverpool artist they clearly consulted one another as they did not where personal preferences were involved.

The first thing that struck me about the answers was the relatively high degree of what might be called accessibility and the small evidence of any total alienation from art. Roughly two-thirds of those questioned were in personal contact with some kind of artist (amateur or professional in the proportion of nearly three to one); about 40 per cent of all adults, or 25 per cent if you exclude the gallery visitors as unrepresentative on this point, indulged in some kind of visual art themselves; less than a fifth disliked the idea of one of their children going to art school. This was evidence more of open-mindedness than of any very active interest. Not more than one adult in six took part in any art group or art class, and although the vast majority had seen art programmes on the television – largely *Monitor*, but above all the programmes on Michelangelo – it was evidently in many cases as passive consumers, since only one in three of the total admitted to looking out for them. As for the proportion who confessed to having no pictures in their houses it was strikingly high for this visually-conscious age. Roughly a third of those who answered (and the same proportion of the non-gallery adults) said that they had none. The percentage among the children was higher, but that may be because some of them saw the question as referring only to their own personal possessions.

The local artists are largely unknown. Of my 368 informants thirty had heard of Arthur Dooley, no doubt because of his personality and his appearances on television rather than on account of his actual sculpture. Twenty-four named Stubbs and nineteen Arthur Ballard, the present Academy presi-

K

dent, but all except eight of the former and six of the latter were form-mates at Gateacre School who were clearly helping one another. Adrian Henri got four mentions – this being before he too was the subject of a television programme – and, among others, Herdman two and Huggins one; but artists like Gibson and Windus from Liverpool's past and Horsfield, Jardine, Hart and Tyson Smith from the present all went unmentioned. Roughly two-thirds of the 368 and three-quarters of the non-gallery adults were unable to name anybody – an astonishingly high proportion for a city that used to pride itself on its achievements in the arts. Nor do the citizens notice at all clearly the statuary that is around them out of doors. Of the adult total roughly a quarter had no idea what was in front of St George's Hall; one half ignored the relief and figures above the main Mersey Tunnel entrance (which nearly 22,000 cars pass under daily); an eighth did not even know exactly what was above the entrance to Lewis's, while only one in ten was at all conscious of the reliefs below. Outside St George's Hall two in five knew the lions (though with some uncertainty as to their number); one in five knew the war memorial, one could identify Victoria and Albert, and another one had a vague notion of equestrian figures ('prancing horses with staid horsemen', as one informant descriptively called them). Very few mentioned the retiring Disraeli or the gallant General Earle.

Through these answers a picture builds up of a community which accepts the idea of art as something desirable, but largely shuts its eyes to its actual manifestations. This is so to some extent even with the Walker Art Gallery, though there seemed to be less indifference here than is often alleged. Very few indeed – only three adults out of 196 – condemned the gallery as a waste of money; the answers from the gallery visitors were naturally more enthusiastic, but of the remaining adults only about a quarter expressed indifference, as against 45 per cent who wanted the collection to be added to and a fifth who felt pride in it. Admittedly about a tenth of these adults (and, more surprisingly, a quarter of the Gateacre schoolchildren) had never yet set foot inside the gallery, but nearly 44 per cent had visited it within the previous two years, which is more than might have been expected. My invitation to 'name a picture you liked' however brought evidence of certain blindness, not so much because of the actual choices expressed – though the apparent absence of interest in the Roscoe collection and, to a great extent, in the Rembrandt and Rubens and other recently-acquired masters is disconcerting – as in the frequent failure to make any choice at all. Less than half those questioned were able to name a picture; some of them, thanks perhaps to the unclear wording of the question – it ought to have specified 'a picture you liked *there*' – named works which are not in the collection – and often I got the impression that the respondent was not expressing a preference so much as scratching his head for the name of any picture in the world he could remember. Much the same blankness occurred with the respondents who said that they did have pictures in their home; a substantial minority were unable to identify them in any way.

And yet these same informants seemed to show an overwhelming appetite for more art in their lives. Was this just the way the questions were worded? I don't think so, as I felt exactly this odd combination of tolerance, apparent blindness yet longing for beauty when trying the questionnaire on a group of mainly working class hospital patients (whom I have excluded from the results as the questions were subsequently slightly altered). There were two groups of questions widely separated: first 'what do you feel about the idea of seeing paintings, sculpture and so on at your place of work?', then the same *inside* public buildings, then the same outside such buildings and in open spaces. Here four-fifths of all adults said they liked it at their place of work, over 96 per cent inside public buildings and four-fifths out of doors (the children's trend throughout was similar, though the resistance was higher, especially among the lower forms). The second group asked if it was 'a good thing that the Council should spend money on works of art for (a) improving the look of the city? (b) the city collection in the Walker Gallery?', then went on to ask if the informant would be willing to see an extra halfpenny rate – a purely hypothetical figure, equivalent to over £50,000 a year – devoted to these purposes. It attempted to eliminate non-ratepayers from the answers and to make certain that any ratepayer knew what such expenditure would mean to his own annual rates. The result here was naturally to damp first enthusiasms, but less than I would have expected. Again, four-fifths of the adults said 'yes' to (a) and to (b); three-quarters in each case said 'yes' to the extra halfpenny rate. Eliminating the non-ratepayers made no change to the proportion willing to accept extra rate (a), and actually sent that for (b) (extra expenditure on purchases for the gallery) up once more to four-fifths. Only between 10 and 15 per cent of these fell off when they actually realized what they themselves would have to pay. About two-thirds of the eighty ratepayers approved the (conjectural) extra charges.

It is quite a striking succession of sweeping votes for a more active public art policy, though it is anybody's guess how far they represent Liverpool opinion as a whole. No doubt it would be rash to assume that four-fifths of the local electorate want these things. All the same I am convinced that the opinions being voiced were by no means those of a special stratum of art-lovers but would be widely repeated; and that the potential support for such a policy could be stronger than even the keenest advocates of the arts in

91 & 92 Germaine Richier's frightening figure, *Water* (black and white postcard), was predictably disliked, as was Victor Pasmore's *Square Motif* (coloured postcard). Both from the Tate Gallery

Liverpool at present think. But exactly what sort of art is it that they have in mind? The object of getting people's reactions to the twenty postcards presented at the end of the questionnaire was to see not merely what art was most congenial to them but where they drew the line between the modern art they could tolerate and that which they found jarred on them. These pictures fell into five main groups: the traditional, print-dealers' type represented by Peter Scott, Laura Knight, Doris Zinkeisen and Munnings; the modern figurative painting of Derain, Kokoschka (whose picture I expected to provide the highest common factor of Liverpool taste), Vlaminck and Augustus John; the more 'extreme' modernism of Picasso, Appel, Ben Nicholson and the abstract Pasmore; the impressionist sculpture of Renoir and Epstein; finally the modern sculpture of Henry Moore, Picasso again, Pevsner and Germaine Richier. There was also a Lowry (drawn, like the John, Vlaminck and Renoir, from the Walker Gallery's own collection) and, as an odd shot, one of the second batch of reliefs from outside St George's Hall. The point was not so much to conduct a democratic vote – which could be a deadly mistake in the arts – as to find out where we stood. If I was going in due course to make recommendations that flouted accepted tastes I wanted to know what I was doing.

This was where the opinions of the different sections – school children, gallery visitors and other adults – varied most widely; indeed, the element of unpredictability and variation between individual forms was far higher than for any of the earlier questions. It is impossible to tell, moreover, what weight

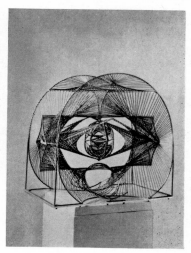

93 & 94 L. S. Lowry's *The Fever Van*
was very popular and Antoine Pevsner's
construction, was liked by a surprising
number of people who had no use for other
abstract work

of like or dislike attaches to any single opinion, or how much thought has
gone into it, or how far certain condemnations, like the gallery visitors'
verdict on Munnings and Laura Knight, are based on a sense of rivalry –
a need to disapprove of certain names, or certain *kinds* of painting – rather
than a pure aesthetic judgment. But that is after all how taste is made up,
and certain conclusions did stand out. Thus I expected that the figures by
Moore and (above all) Richier would be widely disliked since so many
people seem to feel an empathetic pain when the human form is in any way
maltreated by a sculptor (this, surely, was the real trouble with Riley's arm-
less figure in Bold Street). Indeed they were, but it seemed most odd that
on the one hand Pevsner's far more abstract sculpture should be viewed so
very differently, while on the other Pasmore's beautiful and – I would have
thought – wholly inoffensive abstract painting of 1950 was rejected, getting the
largest score of 'dislikes' from the gallery visitors and having altogether
192 out of 338 voices definitely against it, a majority larger than that cast
for any 'like' except the Peter Scott. Perhaps abstraction of a more or less
'machine' kind can be judged without the usual suspicion that the viewer is
being hoaxed or insulted; it was remarkable that the Pevsner was liked by at
least two people who otherwise only liked Munnings, Scott or Laura Knight;
and it also has that element of intricate workmanship which matters to
people who themselves work with their hands. That does not explain however
why the Ben Nicholson and the Appel should be ranked by all sections well
above the Pasmore, or why half the gallery-goers should dislike it.

The main likes are not surprising. Peter Scott came easily top, supported by 74 per cent of the children and 72 per cent of the non-gallery adults; the pictures which the gallery visitors and the rest could agree in liking were indeed the Kokoschka, but even more the Lowry, the Vlaminck (which showed a boat, a popular subject in a port), and the Augustus John. The significant point here was perhaps the general popularity of the Lowry, which came equal top (with the Picasso girl) in the gallery list, and fourth for the other adults and the children; this is partly no doubt because it is a thoroughly Lancashire picture, partly because it mixes the childish and the adult, partly because it is a popular picture in the gallery's own collection; familiarity is certainly an important factor in determining taste. It was also far the least disliked of all the cards, scoring thirty-seven dislikes only as against forty-six for the next-comer, the Vlaminck. The highest degree of indifference ('don't care') was shown – quite rightly, in my view – for Dressler's tame relief from St George's Hall, though the *fauve* Derain also scored highly (except with the children, a lot of whom disliked it), while the Ben Nicholson got roughly a third of 'don't care's from all sections. A minor oddity was the liking of many gallery visitors for Doris Zinkeisen's piece of impressionist pastiche, which comes out a particularly bilious green in the postcard. I can't help suspecting that this was a perverse tribute to Manet or to the general prestige of impressionism rather than to the picture itself.

After looking through all these it does seem that it is those who have had least education who are quickest to dislike works of art. Three of the Gateacre children, for instance, registered fifty-eight dislikes between them (out of sixty possible expressions of opinion); another, making up his own form as there were not enough to go round, put the 'dislike' column first in red ink (he had nine dislikes to six likes); while a young insurance employee who had left school at sixteen disliked all but three of the cards. The gallery visitors were certainly more tolerant; there was no card that more than half of them disliked, whereas for the children there were four (Richier, the Picasso sculpture, Pasmore and Henry Moore) and for the non-gallery adults five (the same plus Appel). The gallery-goers expressed slightly more likes per head than the rest and only four dislikes, as opposed to 6.17 dislikes per head for the other adults and 6.22 for the school children. The average ratio of dislikes to likes in each case suggests that for every eight cards they disliked the gallery visitors liked fourteen, but the other two groups only nine. Of course this is once again largely a matter of familiarity; when people actively dislike a work of art it is usually not because they judge it a bad one but because they find it strange. At the same time I suspect that there may be a broader element of resentment about it: that those who feel educationally handicapped in any way are hostile to what they cannot understand, where others would either try to puzzle it out or feel secure enough to suspend judgment. If this is true it could be an important consideration in planning the city's future art policy, though it should be noted that there is no such distinction where the general urge for more art is concerned, which seems to seize all alike.

I quoted the Bold Street fiasco at some length earlier because it so vividly illustrates the danger of meeting this urge in the wrong way. Despite the enormous increase in interest in art matters, despite the visual stimulus given by television and colour photography, there is still a great gulf between modern art and the public which is ignored only at the cost of pain to all concerned. Such art is not easily accepted; it contains, for many people, causes of offence which can only be cancelled out by the power of conviction of the work itself and of the manner in which it is presented to them – two things that were perhaps lacking in the Bold Street case. But that is only one of the hazards. It is all too easy to compromise on excessively tepid works, like the bulk of the existing Liverpool monumental statuary, which are just as likely to discredit public art by boring people until they no longer look at, or even notice them; indeed the difference between my informants' great desire for art inside public places and the somewhat reduced enthusiasm (often among the more knowledgeable of them) for open-air works is, I suspect, mainly due to the dismal example set so far. It is really a very difficult dilemma, for even the most intelligent (and often the most socially-minded) of modern artists tend to skate over these problems – which are not normally talked about except by hostile critics – while the public authorities responsible feel uncertain of their standards and ignorant of the precedents that might help them. Much could be done in Liverpool, perhaps, if the city had a policy for the visual arts which people could identify with the gallery. Many of the resentments and resistances we have been discussing might be overcome by local pride.

So far however the signs of any real identification of art with the city or with the people's lives there have not been encouraging. There is obviously no particular sense of association with the Liverpool artists, and although there is an active amateur art movement there it bears no distinctive local flavour; too much of it is a rehash of the very lowest level of accepted themes and styles, like many of the prints in Liverpool's under-pictured homes. Vaguely the citizens look to art as a benefit which they would like to have, but this may only mean that they are expecting too much of it. Despite the admirable intentions of the South Liverpool Festival the attempt there to knit the visual arts more closely into people's daily lives has still not done much to stimulate an indigenous visual tradition. It may well be that both things will have to go together: that a genuine basis of acceptance – and tolerance – for a more go-ahead official policy will only be created when Liverpool begins to feel that she can assert herself visually as she has already asserted herself in sound and in sport. This of course does not mean that a lot of Merseyside Lowrys have to be produced and put to work decorating the city, but that the sense of individual self-expression and of collective self-expression might turn out to be linked. It is not enough just to develop in the wake of London. If Liverpool really wants more public art she will have to strike out on her own.

6 : EDUCATING THE EYE

'The great need of the present day, from the point of view of the production of Fine Art, is the Education of the Amateur, the purchaser.'[1] Thus Conway, writing in 1901, some years after his Liverpool experience. But that is only one aspect of the problem. If we leave aside the subtle but surely very strong influence of a sense of educational deprivation there are still a number of different ways in which art education of one kind of another can affect the visual scene. There is not only the education of the amateur, who nowadays has to be seen as ratepayer, industrial administrator and local politician as well as mere private purchaser of Kandinskys and Tretchikoffs, and is catered for under the discouraging-sounding heading of Art Appreciation. There is also the more professional and academic field of Art History, which produces the experts to educate others: a subject which has enormously expanded since 1945. There is practical instruction in art, where the handling of visual ideas and the materials to express them with is taught to three main groups: children, future professionals (chiefly teachers and designers for industry) and the amateurs for whom art is anything from a time-filling hobby to a frustrated passion. Finally there is the teaching or preaching of design as an application of visual judgment and three-dimensional common sense to everything that we build, make or buy.

In an increasingly specialized world these different aspects of art teaching are rarely seen as parts of a single process. Our society has its accepted ideas about each kind – art appreciation, art history, child art, art schools, painting as a pastime and the preaching of good design – but everywhere they seem to be governed by different committees and pursued along individual channels; whether conservative or 'progressive' they are, as a rule, not brought into relation with one another. Yet you need only look at a city like Liverpool to see how they all bear on the situation which we have been discussing in the last two chapters. The enjoyment of the real treasures of the Walker Art Gallery (as opposed to *The Death of Nelson* or the latest subject of controversy), a keener interest in the work of local living artists, the understanding of the city's own architecture and the considered judgment of any works of public art: it all depends on some kind of 'art appreciation'. Simi-

[1] *The Domain of Art.* p. 24.

larly evolution of anything like a distinctive Liverpool style in art depends not only on the practical teaching given in schools and art schools but on the facilities offered to the talented individual to express himself, whether or not he is making art his job. And the whole visual level of life in the city depends on the half-instinctive adoption of decent design standards in what the people of the place buy in the shops, have around at home or in public places, and, above all, actually make. All four types of teaching are ultimately concerned with the same thing: with the sense of arrangement, balance and colour, with the eye and with visual curiosity. They act on one another; any progress made in the one must stimulate the rest.

At the time when Conway wrote this close interconnection was still taken for granted, so that the Walker Gallery, the University with its Roscoe professorship, the Workers' Educational Association – even the institution of drawing as a compulsory subject in schools – were parts of a general educational movement to which the Arts and Crafts exhibitions also belonged. Since then the whole concept of adult education has very much altered. It is no longer a matter of making up for the deficiencies of a man's formal education, which in those days ended at thirteen or even at ten, so much as helping to occupy his increased leisure. The old notion of works of art as a means of improving the ignorant mechanic's mind, based as it was on an association of goodness with beauty which few would make so confidently today, has given way to a less condescending but also a much less ambitious approach. In Liverpool at least the WEA has become virtually a part of the university's extra-mural department; both are concerned to teach their now much better-educated adult pupils what happens to interest them rather than what some higher policy considers they ought to learn. Art, in our leisure-haunted age, is certainly part of this. The politics, economics and current affairs that preoccupied classes in the 1930s have largely lost their audience; art and archaeology, sociology and psychology, even subjects like travel and jazz and 'preparation for retirement' have moved into the centre of the programme. This of course reflects the generally increased interest in art throughout the country. In England, Wales and Scotland there were thirty-nine extra-mural courses in the visual arts in 1945/6 and 518 in 1961/2; in the Liverpool extra-mural area the comparable figures were one (for 1946/7) and twenty-nine. Out of the thirty-nine WEA classes held in Liverpool itself in 1965/6 five dealt with the visual arts, and there were further classes in Birkenhead, Wallasey and other parts of the agglomeration.

The decline of the missionary spirit means that much of this apparently increased interest is now a more or less idle one. The classes are held in the university buildings or the Royal Institution or in middle-class suburbs; the Friday art-appreciation classes at the Institution are attended above all by housewives; only about one in twenty of the WEA students are manual workers; over four-fifths of the university extension students left school after fifteen. The Deputy Director of the gallery, who takes the chief Liverpool WEA class on the history of art, told me that there were not more than half-a-dozen males in that class. His attempt to stimulate greater keenness by describing something of the sheer detective work, both scientific and critical, involved in the history of art was discouraged by a Ministry inspector who thought that he should concentrate on 'appreciation'. And this purely passive appreciation seems to be the main objective of very nearly all the courses organized. Only now and again is there an attempt to relate the study of art to any constructive aim; thus the extra-mural department's staff tutor in art, whose conferences on modern church architecture have already been referred to, has also conducted courses on this subject in Preston and West Kirby, while in the 1963/4 session there was a class at Crosby on 'Merseyside Architecture: Old and New' taken by F. M. Jones of the School of Architecture: a subject vitally connected with the replanning of the city. Generally the system is geared to the production of consumers for whom art is a leisure-time luxury, a kind of holiday. The association of art with summer travel, already evident enough from the paintings in amateur art shows, is rammed home by the successful art tours which the extra-mural department has organized. These have taken bodies of mainly professional people and teachers to visit the Spanish or Italian museums for a fortnight at between £45 and £65 a head; in 1965 the department organized a Hellenic cruise, costing about three times as much.

For seven years between 1954 and 1960 the Walker Art Gallery and the extra-mural department together organized lectures of an altogether higher standard. They were held in the gallery's lecture theatre, whose 180 seats they usually filled; at those on twentieth century art indeed the audience was too big, so that they had to move to the university. For the first five years they consisted of a course in the history of art from the Renaissance to the present day, and they were lifted out of the normal sphere of adult education both by the setting and by the inclusion of such lecturers as Professor E. F. Jacob and Sir Kenneth Clark. There was also during this period one rather exceptional university extension course, where Victor Pasmore, Keith Vaughan, the late Stanley Spencer, Alan Davie, Joseph Herman, Robert Clatworthy and Arthur Ballard spoke on contemporary art; one or two members of the then audiences told me that they regretted the gallery's decision to break off the association. A modified form of this scheme was restored in 1964, with a series of lectures chiefly by outside authorities on the gallery's own pictures. In the interim the gallery had been turning its attention to the Liverpool schoolchildren, who since 1957 have had their own Schools Officer giving conducted lectures to some 5,000 or 6,000 of them every year. Ben Shaw the late sub-committee chairman would have liked there to be a special children's room, but the problem so far has rather been to attract the sixth-formers. A coffee and sandwich party was held for them in conjunction with the show of Miss Sonia Henje's collection of modern pictures (organized by the Arts Council and also seen at the Tate Gallery) in the autumn of 1962, and this was very successful. Otherwise the keenest visitors have been the primary schools.

As a means of exciting enthusiasm for art, lectures have lost much of their old importance, despite the new attractions of the coloured transparency – a dangerous instrument which can come to seem more attractive than the picture itself. Parties can bring people to a gallery and draw attention to an exhibition, but they make serious viewing of the works almost impossible and it is open to doubt whether they really further the interests of art by turning it into a social event. It is rather television and to a lesser extent the coloured magazines that give most people their impetus and their new ideas about the visual arts today, and this is true even of many artists (it was suggested to me that some embryo art historian ought to establish how much of current iconography is traceable to the *Sunday Times* colour supplement). Here the programmes organized for schools by Granada Television in Manchester set an admirably high standard,[1] but despite their Lancashire origin they are designed for broadcasting throughout the country, and neither they nor John Berger's Granada series *Drawn from Life* of autumn 1961, with its attempt to relate people's occupations and preoccupations to the work of great artists, had any special bearing on the problems of Merseyside. This inevitable squeezing out of purely local concerns, even from regional television, might be expected to have two effects on art education in Liverpool: to lead those responsible to make closer contact with the programme organizers on the one hand, and at the same time to make them use the traditional

---

[1] The series, each of ten weekly programmes designed for the 15–18 age group, have been:
  Autumn 1961. *Design.* (Reyner Banham, Misha Black, Sir Hugh Casson, Nikolaus Pevsner, Paul Reilly, etc.)
  Spring 1962. *Context.* Art in Life since Time Began. (Banham, M. I. Finley, Jacquetta Hawkes, George Lehmann, Bryan Robertson, Sir John Summerson, etc.)
  Autumn 1962. *Art in the Making.* (Robertson interviewing Ralph Brown, Denys Lasdun, Colin MacInnes, Bernard Meadows, Keith Vaughan, Vicky, etc.)
  Spring 1963. *Word and Image.* (Ten talks by the Rev Moelwyn Merchant.)
In 1963 three schools in Liverpool and three in other parts of the agglomeration were known to be watching.

media for matters of local importance rather than for the general encouragement of art. But this does not seem to have happened, and for better or worse
the apparatus that exists is used to teach appreciation of almost anything
except Liverpool's own assets, background and possibilities.

The principal art school, the Regional College of Art in Hope Street, is
administered by the city and still lives next door to the Liverpool Institute
School from which it separated in 1905. It has however become far more
closely geared into the national art educational pattern, and its local character
is reflected less in the direction of its teaching than in the fact that many of
the local artists have jobs there. It is not merely, as its name implies, a
school for the whole region, including Preston, Blackpool and North Wales;
since the 1960 report of the National Advisory Council on Art Education
under Sir William Coldstream it has become one of those art schools of
quasi-university status that train for the new Diploma in Art and Design,
with the result that standards in those departments whose work I have seen
have risen rapidly even as the present book was being written.[1] Under this
scheme, which came into operation in 1963 with the admission of the first
Dip AD students, the composition of the student body was bound to change,
for not only have the higher general educational qualifications demanded
(five 'O' levels, including at least three in academic subjects) meant that art
students from all over the country now compete for places, but the more
general education provided makes this a possible university substitute for
some who would not otherwise have become art specialists. The so called pre-
Diploma course, or first year basic course for all students, can still be planned
on the College's own lines, but is now virtually in the position of a lesser art
school whose students must pass the new requirements if they are to continue; it is at present physically separated from the College proper. The
Teacher Training Department, which trains for the Art Teachers' Diploma
and is the main source of art staff for Liverpool's primary and secondary
schools, is also outside the Coldstream recommendations; it is run in conjunction with the university Institute of Education. Otherwise where art is
concerned – that is Fine Art (including sculpture since 1965), Graphic
Design and Textiles and Fashion, but not Three-Dimensional Design, for
which the College has not yet been recognized by the National Advisory
Council – the College is the regional instrument of a national system.

There is thus nothing very distinctively Liverpool about the College,
though both John Moores and Leslie Blond have helped it by giving scholar-

[1] That is to say in the Fine Art (including sculpture) and Graphic Design Schools. The school of
Textiles and Fashion provided nearly all the prizewinning entries in a competition held by the
Cotton Board in October 1965, when all but two of the art schools training for the new diploma in
this subject competed.

ships, nor has it any other specially remarkable characteristic on the art side;
it is, from the national point of view, simply the best art school in a hitherto
somewhat uninspired area, whose most famous postwar product, John
Lennon of the Beatles, is not exactly an artist and was far from appreciated in
his student days. Yet it has one unique asset in its printing school, which
since 1960 has occupied a large and well-equipped new building adjoining
the main part of the College. Liverpool is among the main centres of the
printing industry in the country, and vocational training as a whole is a field
which the National Advisory Council left 'for local initiative and organization by schools and colleges in consultation with industry and commerce.'[1]
The Department of Printing accordingly continues to be guided by a special
Printing and Allied Trades Advisory Committee and runs not only independently of the new Dip AD system but to a great extent independently of
the rest of the college; except in the basement there is not even a communicating door between the two buildings. No doubt there are advantages
in the freedom from interruption and distraction which this means for the
700 or so part-time printing students, who outnumber the full-timers next
door by about two to one. All the same, one need only look at the lack of new
graphic and typographic ideas in Liverpool printing – on poster hoardings, in
locally-designed brochures, and in the Liverpool papers, despite all their
purely technical pioneering – or at the graphic design work done in the College to feel that an opportunity is being missed. Far more than the Royal
College of Art in London, whose designers have few chances to make personal
contact with printers or study their machines, Liverpool has the equipment

[1] Ministry of Education: *Vocational Courses in Colleges and Schools of Art*. Second Report of the
National Advisory Council on Art Education. HMSO 1962, paragraph 2.

and the technical skill to become the country's main source of visual ideas in printing and book production. Yet both Ballard and MacKarell, of the livelier painters among the College staff, seemed to see it as entirely natural that they should never have done any work with the splendid apparatus next door, while conversely it was depressing to find one of the new colour offset machines in the printing department being used to produce pictures of the crudest calendar-illustration sort.

The part of the College which does seem to be generating new ideas is the Teacher Training department, which is interested less in the Bauhaus-like exercises in use of materials practised in the pre-Diploma course than in finding fresh ways of relating visual expression to interests and experience within a child's range. Some of the ideas tried out here or in schools co-operating with the department have been the plotting of movements (of the ball in football or of customers to and from a Wigan pub) as the basis for a picture; the use of plans, real or imaginary, for the same purpose; variations on everyday objects – just what, for instance, can be done with a chair –; the use of subjects like transport which command a wide interest and technical knowledge that can be expressed in drawing; the use of engineers' drawings as models; the making of some sort of construction by the pupil, which he then makes a picture of; development of micro-sections of plants, etc; imaginative variations of relative size, such as a flowerbed seen by a three-inch dwarf; or the putting of verbal and numerical structures (like a crossword puzzle or a list of engine numbers) into pictorial form. What the College is in effect doing here in a small way is to revive the Renaissance spirit of curiosity, of using visual creation as a means of understanding how our environment works, but to extend it both by calling on the visual discoveries of modern art

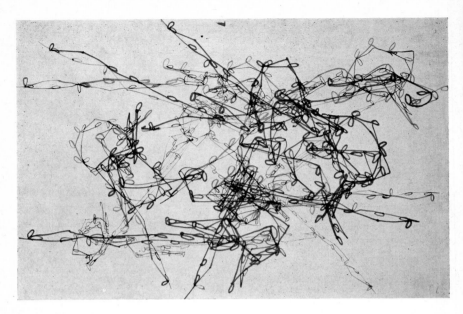

Children's work under the auspices of the teacher training department.
Above: *Gavotte*. Below: *Juke Box*

and by considering processes, movements and other relationships as well as immediately visible reality. It is an interesting direction in which to be experimenting, and it could easily prove a fruitful one in a wider sphere than that of art education. For there are the germs here of an approach to art which would be aligned with, and not merely to one side of, the modern technological world.

The Coldstream recommendations left the lesser art schools – which on Merseyside means those at Birkenhead, Wallasey and Bootle – to conduct vocational training according to the needs of local industry, to run preparatory courses for those hoping to go to a diploma course elsewhere, and to teach art under their own arrangements to part-time students. There was also a suggestion that they should try to become 'focal points for all those in their neighbourhood who are interested in the visual arts and that they should try to increase public interest in these arts by such means as lectures, exhibitions, etc.'[1], something that for the College would mean wasteful competition with the gallery and the Bluecoat Society but could well be of relevance for the lesser art schools. Birkenhead indeed would like to develop along these lines, if only it had more space. So far as the fine arts are concerned these have become overwhelmingly (and in the case of Bootle exclusively) schools for the part-timer, which in effect means the amateur; Birkenhead's prospectus for instance offers 'development of skill by those who enjoy art as a spare-time activity' and says that 'Beginners are specially welcome'. When I went to Bootle the school was living under rather makeshift conditions in a house formerly used as a salvage dump, pending removal to a proposed new College of Further Education; some of the painting and pottery students had been attending ever since 1945 and there had evidently been little turnover in the classes for some years. At Birkenhead the school is crammed into a solid brick building of the 1870s, with a forlorn looking area of terrace houses behind it; there are over 100 part-time painters of all ages, some retired and some just out of school. There are also part-time fine art students at the Regional College, but the Birkenhead Principal told me that there is an unsatisfied Liverpool demand for part-time painting and that there are many additional applicants whom he could take if he had the room, given the necessary permits from the Liverpool Corporation. These permits are a means of settling accounts between the different local authorities; in 1963 students over 21 were normally paying 37s 6d a year to come once a week, plus £1 for additional evenings; at Bootle they paid between 22s and 33s a year to come for three evenings a week.

[1] Ministry of Education: *First Report of the National Advisory Council on Art Education*; HMSO 1960, paragraph 60.

L

99 Boys at Breckfield Secondary Modern School, in old-fashioned buildings not far from Anfield football ground

100 An art class at Gateacre Comprehensive, one of the newer and larger Liverpool schools

There has also in Liverpool been an institution called the Art High School, with about 100 pupils. This was once a preparatory school for all departments of the College of Art, living under the same roof with it: one of a small number of such schools all over the country which were intended to fill the time between the school-leaving age of 14 and entry to art school proper. With the raising of the school-leaving age in 1947 its original *raison d'être* vanished; it moved to separate (supposedly temporary) premises in houses in Gambier Terrace that year and in 1960 broke off from the College altogether. Perhaps because of the name, perhaps because the headmaster was a trained artist, it tended to get boys and girls wanting to make art their main subject, and the head certainly wished art to be the backbone of the teaching. But the school no longer figured as prominently as it had among those gaining places at the College, and it became something of an unresolved oddity in Liverpool education: a niche for unorthodox pupils or for those who would like a straight academic education but were unable to get into a Grammar or a Secondary Modern School. It was closed in 1966 and the pupils were transferred to one of the comprehensive schools; the buildings reverted to the College of Art.

Besides these art schools I visited a number of secondary schools, some under Liverpool, some under Lancashire County Council, in order to get an idea of the native talent for art and the measures taken to bring it out. All of these were schools where I had been advised, from one direction or another, that the art department was of particular interest; thus although they varied very widely quâ schools (academically, socially and architecturally), they cannot

be taken as wholly representative of Merseyside art teaching. They were none the less extremely encouraging; indeed the real problem they raised was why the often quite original self-expressive energy found there was not found, in more developed form, in the art schools – a problem by no means unique to Liverpool. Where Liverpool differs is that this talent, contrary to the general conception of children's art – and in contrast with all the illustrations in Sir Herbert Read's well-known *Education through Art*, for instance – is not primarily pictorial but sculptural; it cannot have been sheer coincidence that all the most interesting work I saw was three-dimensional, whether in pottery, sculpture, wood and metal constructions or cut paper. The best drawings and paintings came from schools in poor areas – Breckfield Secondary Modern School in Everton and St Martin's SMS in Liverpool 8 – but they were also the most naive and conventional ones. In the former there were vivid pictures of daily life (including an episode at the dentist's and one at the police station) as well as bright geometrical designs and perspective exercises, (perspective being taught less as an aid to representation than because it interests the children for its own sake). At St Martin's, where there was at that time only one art teacher and the whole school did art because there was a shortage of staff for other subjects, the boys were sent out into the shabby streets and waste areas to pick up subjects (and objects too, which can be used as improvised stencils or stamps to print with or build into con-structions and mosaics). The result was that their work reflected the Liver-pool scene more closely and literally than any other I saw; it has figured largely in the South Liverpool Festival exhibitions at the nearby Domestic Mission.

101 & **102** Pottery figures by boys at Breckfield SMS

103 Drawings by boys at Breckfield SMS

BEFORE THE KICK-OFF

What a crowd,
Rattles buzzing like aggravated bees.
Policemen pulling kids out of the ground.
Flashes of light bursting out everywhere.
Children running onto the pitch for autographs.
The crowd swaying to and fro,
Like a piece of silk held into the wind.
The bright green pitch,
Clashing with the red and white of scarves and rosettes.
The men squabbling with each other about teams and players.
The Kop lets up a mighty roar,
Shouting the Liverpool chant,
As the teams come out.

Alan Jones. 2A

---

104 A poem from the *Breckfield Broadsheet*, Summer Term 1963

The methods of the Preliminary Course evolved by Itten and Moholy-Nagy at the Bauhaus in the 1920s are often reflected in these schools. Thus it is common to find experiments with materials of a more or less abstract kind, or prints made from embossed wall-papers, cigarette packets or whatever else comes to hand. At the Bluecoat School however – the boys' school that once occupied the present building of the Bluecoat Society but is now in a solid Edwardian scholastic edifice further out – there was a whole-hearted incursion into constructivism after the sixth form had been taken to see the Arts Council exhibition *Construction England* at the Walker Gallery in the spring of 1963. Within the (to my mind somewhat cramping) limitations of non-figurative art the work done here in scrap wood, bent metal, cane and string, and also in one or two instances in stone, was most impressive, and all the more noteworthy because the training is directed towards encouragement of a general visual awareness rather than particular proficiency in art. The other remarkable development was at Gateacre CS, one of the biggest (1,600 pupils) and newest schools, situated in one of the newer south-western suburbs and with a full-time art staff of six. Here one teacher in the metal-work department – nominally a craft teacher in the technical wing, and accordingly not included in the six – happened to be a Camberwell-trained

105-107
Constructions by
boys at Liverpool
Bluecoat School

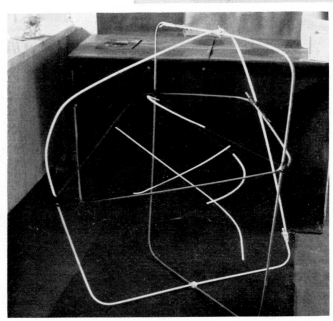

sculptor, who taught foundry and welding by getting the children to make metal constructions or figures out of scrap. These and related exercises have produced surprisingly expressive results; even examinations can be conducted on these lines, as is shown by the following paper which was given to one of the bottom forms:

Metal Constructions – Answer Question 1 and three others, four in all. Paper marked out of 40.

1 Name ten objects you can use in making a construction.
2 Draw, in line only, a construction it would be possible to make using a chair as a starting point.
3 Draw, in line only, a design using a H type TV aerial.
4 Draw, in line only, a construction you could make out of straws or wire. Base this on any objects you have seen on the way to school (the street lamps for example).
5 Draw in solid form (shade on one side only), a wooden model of this school as seen from the top.
6 Draw, in line only, as many different roof shapes and chimney stacks as you have seen.

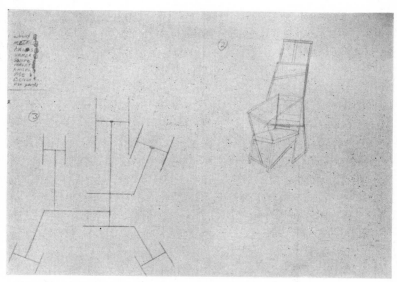

108 Gateacre CS. A page of answers to the questions above

Gateacre is one of several schools producing lively pottery figures and groups – Breckfield being another – and the former pottery teacher wrote a thesis for Manchester University on the apparent tendency for some of the

109 Scrap metal sculpture by three fourteen-year-old boys at Gateacre CS

110 & 111 Other sculptural work done in the metalwork class at Gateacre CS

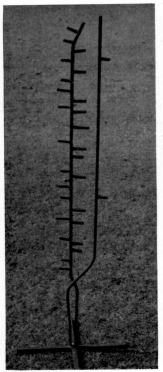

best work to come from the lower streams, a tendency also mentioned by other teachers, and one which conflicts with the new conditions for admission to the College.[1] At Stanley Park SMS, in an undistinguished building of 1938 by the cemetery in Anfield – it has subsequently been transformed into a girls' Comprehensive – I saw some entertaining mosaics made of lino and other more or less fortuitous (or *Merz*) materials; at Ruffwood CS (1,900 pupils), the Lancashire County Council school at Kirkby whose buildings were discussed earlier, there was fabric printing and a plan to do ordinary printing; at New Heys Girls' GS, another of the best and best-sited new school buildings in the area (designed by Herbert Thearle), the girls' paintings are framed and used to decorate staircases and corridors. I also saw a collective exhibition put on in the College entrance hall by Holly Lodge High

112 Part of an exhibition of work by girls at Holly Lodge Girls' Grammar School

School for Girls, which was interesting above all for the use of letters in some of the pictures, one of them a large collaboration by the bottom form. The best academic drawing I saw was one from Wade Deacon GS. Generally however the most striking work that I saw outside Gateacre and the Bluecoat was at Maghull GS (680 pupils), another of the Lancashire schools in the new

[1] Though it is sometimes forgotten that paragraph 5 of the first Coldstream Report specified that 'students of outstanding artistic promise' should be admitted to the diploma courses even without the required 'O' level qualifications.

northern suburbs, where every year the whole mixed school contributes to a big group exhibition on a single theme – a bullfight, a circus, the life of Lord Nelson – which demands a term's preparation and involves not only a wide variety of media but some costume study and historical and geographical research. The bullfight material included work by students who subsequently went to the College – a plaster head of a matador, a bull's head on bicycle handlebars – and a big tempera painting of a bullfight by three sixth-formers.

The struggle in the schools, it seems, is to get art recognized as something more than a suitable occupation for lower forms and a special subject among

113 Breckfield SMS tries to teach awareness of design

'O' level candidates. It depends entirely on the headmaster (and on the degree of confidence existing between him and his art staff) whether sixth-formers are allowed to take art up again, as was happening in only about a quarter of the Liverpool selective schools at the time when I began my enquiries. The main question here is whether art is to be regarded as a matter of basic education, a field where any civilized man should feel at home, or to be treated as a speciality, even a sideline. So far the prevailing view in the Education Committee seems to have been the latter. This no doubt accounts for the iron curtain which has dropped down somewhere between the evident talent and interest visible in the schools and the rather uninspired amateurs and aimless lecture audiences mentioned earlier. Some schools try to avoid this by encouraging a few pupils to come back and work after they have left the school; thus Maghull has old pupils attending its senior art club and at

Ruffwood the headmaster hopes to act as a local community centre with evening activities for boys and girls who have left; similarly the Prescot Further Education Centre (run by Callendar Cables) in 1962 started an evening art class so that ex-secondary school boys could carry on work which they had been doing with a particular teacher. Both at Stanley Park and at St Martin's (360 pupils) however – two schools in poor areas – the art masters spoke of the difficulty of finding suitable jobs for their talented pupils and helping them to work further. Two from Stanley Park were then painting part-time at the Childwall College of Further Education; one was employed by Dollond and Aitchison the opticians, who were teaching him photography; one had a job in a library and was painting in his spare time. Two from St Martin's had gone to the Art High School; one clever potter was now making shoes; Robert Dooley (no relation to the sculptor) who got the first award at the South Liverpool Festival did a year at the Art High School, working in a butcher's shop at weekends, then became a manual labourer.

The teaching of the principles of good design, which is rare enough in the schools – I only saw evidence of it at Breckfield SMS and the Bluecoat School – seemed on the whole to be unheard of and unthought of at the technical colleges and Colleges of Further Education to which other pupils go on. 'No aspect of aesthetic design is dealt with', 'No element of art or design training', 'Have no call to introduce design training in any way'; these were typical phrases in reply to an enquiry to various Merseyside Further Education establishments, and even a new and apparently go-ahead place like the Kirkby College of Further Education had no use for the idea. Indeed the late Director of Education for Liverpool gave me the impression that my (quite hypothetical) suggestion of introducing teaching of industrial design into the College of Technology was something that he had never considered. This treatment of design as a subject apart, an intrusion of aesthetics into a domain where it has no business, as something no more essential to the grown-up than art itself, springs partly from misunderstanding. At least that is what I concluded both from Birkenhead Technical College and from the fine (and very stimulating) new College of Technology down the hill from the Walker Gallery. At Birkenhead, where (besides the Kennington mural) the students' union has bought good reproductions to hang on the walls, the Mechanical Engineering department seemed to be unaware of the connection between the beautifully-finished tools and measuring instruments made there and any wider concept of good design; 'design', to judge from an unflattering comparison made between two lathes, one with a mock-streamlined casing and one without, is thought of as a kind of coating of good taste put on after the job is complete.

In 1962 the Ministry of Education instituted a short annual course on Aesthetics and Engineering Design at Loughborough, where the main theme – stressed at the first course by the Chief Research Engineer for BMC and the Chief Designer for British Transport – was the need for co-operation between Art and Technical Colleges, the work of the Pre-Diploma course at Leicester being used to show how much closer the two vocabularies can be than is often imagined. Among others at the College of Technology I saw John Rees Jones, an engineering lecturer who had been on this course. He had since introduced a lecture on industrial design into the College's course on Engineering Design and Stress Analysis, but felt that there were two difficulties: that it was hard to get students to create instead of just working to pattern, and that there were no exploratory exercises in the use of materials as at the Bauhaus. In his view students would not feel the need to 'build in' good design from the start unless education on these lines began already at school. A fundamental trouble also is that engineers are attracted to management rather than to design, at least in the sense in which they understand it. Apart from this the only kind of visual teaching at the College was in the Department of Food Technology (an elegant term covering the training of bakers and pastrycooks), which is relegated to the basement of the college's old building. Here there was some drawing and painting and colour theory – much of it on a Walt Disney-cum-Mabel Lucy Attwell level, to judge from the resulting designs – with a view to the decoration of cakes.[1] And this was not untypical of the attitude of the other vocational colleges. Except in the Mabel Fletcher Technical College in Liverpool 15, where the student nurses who are its main raison d'être do art as part of their general education, the subject is only taught to those whose work demands an extra element of daintiness – not exactly an approach to appeal to the engineers.

Industrial design is however taught as part of the first year course in the Department of Architecture and Surveying at the Liverpool College of Building, a former section of the College of Technology which now takes part-time students in its own building just below the university and the College of Art. Here the students do experiments with materials and with mechanical principles – I saw for instance a harmonograph which one of them had devised for making rhythmical pen patterns – and they also learn letter-carving in stone. In 1958 they designed and built a sculptural-looking

---

[1] The best cake designs I saw were gingerbreads stamped from a plasticine mould, which had something of the quality of the modelling in the schools. They are said to be commercially unsuccessful.

crawling and climbing structure in concrete for an adventure playground run by the University Settlement below the Cathedral, using begged materials and borrowed equipment; unfortunately it is now in a sadly derelict state. More recently they were consulted by the Sales Manager of Bayco, one of Meccano's subsidiaries, who wanted to devise modern structures that could be made from Bayco toy building parts; designing these gave considerable entertainment to a group of students who had just taken the intermediate exam. This college, which is little known to those of the College of Art staff I mentioned it to, also produced one of the most original designs in the Liverpool Architectural Society's exhibition held as part of Bluecoat 63.

At the university there has been a move to institute a new chair of Fine Art. Nobody to whom I talked there seemed to have a very clear idea what a Professor of Fine Art would actually do, nor is it now known by what constitutional or unconstitutional process the original Roscoe Professorship of Fine Art became diverted to architecture: a question which it might be relevant to examine. The university however put the proposal before the University Grants Commission in its 1962–7 quinquennial estimates, which were cut; and since then it has been suggested that there should be a new Professor of Visual Arts as a kind of roving propagandist. There is already a small basis for fine art study there, in addition to the school of architecture and the department of Civic Design (which dates from 1909), in the provisions made by the late Sir Sydney Jones, a director of Alfred Holt's who was Treasurer and Pro-Chancellor of the university and also Lord Mayor. Thus there is a Sydney Jones Collection in the Tate Hall where university receptions are held – it proved to be locked when I was shown round it, and to consist of a very average lot of English watercolours – there are legacies for making additions to it, and three annual Sydney Jones Lectures on art or architecture. In 1961–2 these lectures were given by Sir Anthony Blunt, Alistair Smart of Nottingham University and Victor Pasmore, representing the three categories from which the planned chair might be filled: art scholar, university lecturer-cum-gallery curator (as Professor Smart then was), and practising artist.[1] This last is a type of appointment recommended by the Bridges Report of 1959,[2] but it meets with some scepticism in Liverpool as

[1] In 1962–3 they were given by Ian Nairn; in 1963–4 by Alan Bowness, Adrian Heath and Hugh Scrutton on different aspects of the John Moores competition. In 1964–5 they were devoted to the theatre. In 1966 John Hart spoke about art education.
[2] *Help for the Arts*. A Report to the Calouste Gulbenkian Foundation 1959. Paragraph 111. 'At very little additional cost universities could provide valuable encouragement to artists by employing them on short-term contracts. In return the artist could give occasional lectures and arrange exhibitions, and by being accessible so that students can see him at work in his studio he can show how in fact an artist paints...'

encouraging the artist to develop a flamboyant 'personality' rather than work. The Professor of Civic Design feels that as it is also unlikely that a first-rate art historian could be lured away from the London libraries and collections except perhaps in order to found an honours school of art history (which is no part of the plan) the best solution would be a professorship of industrial design. This is something that at present exists in no other English university, though industrial design is taught in the engineering departments of a number of universities[1] and there is a move on foot to found a chair at the new university of Warwick. At Liverpool however the current idea is only that there should be a new Department of Building Production, with an Industrial Design section included. The Director of the Council of Industrial Design, who is C. H. Reilly's son, thinks there should be an industrial design department in any university where engineering is an important subject.

Taken as a whole then, Liverpool's system of visual education seems to be lacking in purpose, consistency and continuity. There is too little evidence of co-ordination or common thinking even between neighbouring institutions whose age groups and subjects of study overlap; there is not even much contact. Everywhere there seem to be barriers, though nothing solid and outward such as could be demolished by order; more an unquestioned tradition of boundaries, sometimes drawn so constrictingly that a kind of no-man's land is left all round: the dead ground into which the visually alert child slips after the age of sixteen. Art, with which visual design is generally included, is still seen as unnecessary for adults unless they are to make a career of it; at best it is something for leisure, holidays and retirement, a way of making dull realities palatable, an aid to selling them – the decoration on the cake. Given such an attitude (and of course there are exceptions) it is not surprising that Liverpool's people's taste in art, whether as consumers or as amateurs, should so often be essentially escapist and exotic, or that art and manufacture, even that handsome Victorian couple Art and Commerce, should so often be strangers.

The local relevance of such education is as a rule not seen. Yet there is surely a connection between this failure to carry visual training into higher

---

[1] Glasgow, Newcastle, Manchester (Department of Building), Leeds and Leicester. The Royal College of Art has an industrial design department which has about thirty students and a staff of four; the course lasts four years. I was told there that the disadvantage of industrial design as a full-time subject is that there are not many jobs to be filled annually – perhaps fifty in the whole country – and to the university-trained engineer they seem like the bottom of those open to him. For Manchester's rather different approach see p. 206.

education, to 'build in' the visual element at all stages, and the actual level of design and decoration in shops and streets. People who had learnt to look about them more critically in everyday life would still find it a huge task to make Liverpool a beautiful city, but at least they would sweep away unnecessary horrors like the present bus shelters, and they would better appreciate what is good in the Liverpool scene. The same is true of any possibility of a visual self-expression to match the city's fierce vitality; the necessary sense of identity through art – even an awareness of the present Liverpool artists, their strengths and weaknesses, – can hardly be developed unless art seems actual and accessible, nor can promising beginnings like those of the Teacher Training department and the best secondary schools lead far if the talents they have found get no chance to develop after school. The interest in art among the population is undeniable. But unless the system develops clearer objectives the danger is that it will degenerate into a superficial concern with art fashions, with sensations and talking points and checking up on what was in the Sunday paper or on television. There is more to be got out of art than that.

114 Linocut from Gateacre CS

Any plan for the future must depend largely on the presence or absence of notable local artistic talent on Merseyside. At the moment this is not an easy point to resolve, for not only are judgments of living art a highly subjective business but in this case we have to apply two separate sets of criteria at once. There is, as we have seen, a body of professional artists in and around Liverpool who must, as such, be judged by the same standards as the viewer would apply to professionals anywhere else in the world. They have also to be considered in terms of the jobs waiting to be done, many of which, given the state of modern communications, could as well be tackled by artists from London or from abroad. At the same time it is impossible to ignore the quite different problem of establishing a distinctive local spirit and tradition. We have already had small symptoms of this in work done in the schools and in the Teacher Training department of the College and at Rainhill hospital (though oddly enough not by the local amateur societies), and any signs of it among the professionals must be interesting almost irrespective of merit. Thus we have to look at these artists against a double background: first that of the city's plans, needs and tastes; secondly its character, both visual and social. Indeed art itself is a double business, as we are coming increasingly to recognize, where not only the finished work has to be judged but also the excitement and the social impact of its creation. Today nobody can view art as consumption or production alone.

This second aspect of the Liverpool scene has become widely familiar over the past three years. With its boxers, its comedians and its two great football teams (not to mention the Grand National) the place has always had its own clear identity in the public mind, but it has never been so well known as now. Television began it, perhaps, with the Z-cars serial and Alun Owen's plays and the very moving Liverpool television documentary by Denis Mitchell called *Morning in the Streets*; then the folk-song revival popularized Stan Kelly's performances of the old Liverpool songs.[1] But what took Liverpool's name around the globe was the so-called Mersey Sound and its most famous exponents, the Beatles. Commercialized as it quickly became, this

---

[1] His record of sea songs *Liverpool Packet* is Topic no. 27. The same firm publish a record by The Spinners called *Songs spun in Liverpool* (TOP 69).

was a spontaneous form of popular music that developed in clubs and cellars all over Liverpool at the end of the 1950s: small groups of very young, very un-slick and apparently un-professional musicians shouting and pounding out their tunes on electric guitars. The four Beatles were at first only one of the wildest and toughest of these; they came together in 1960, were top of the local popularity poll in 1961, started recording for EMI in 1962, then became a national institution the next year and a world-wide craze during 1964. Since then they have been pushed out of the top place in the national popularity charts by groups from other parts of the country, but they still stand in many people's minds for a special kind of Liverpool vitality, so that the artist who used once to say evasively to his southern friends 'Oh, I'm from Cheshire' now finds it is more creditable to admit he is a Liverpool man. 'The Beatles are the best thing that has happened to Liverpool,' the painter Adrian Henri told me. He was not thinking only of the noise they make.

For the particular creative ferment which threw up the Beatles and dozens of other rhythm and blues groups was more than a clever exploitation of old musical clichés and new techniques of amplification. Under the ballyhoo and the apparent banalities it was a fresh wave of young Liverpudlians, bright products of the post-war state school system, who had found their own way of expressing themselves without any noticeable advice or encouragement from anybody else. With their special brand of anarchy, aggressive yet human, they were just one jump ahead of their contemporaries in other British cities, and there is no real reason why their energies should not have found other channels. There is indeed enough of a link between the Liverpool pop movement and other forms of art to show that we are dealing with something bigger than sceptical critics think. Henri, for instance, whose pictures are discussed below, has worked with pop groups in presenting his 'events' (loosely organized stage performances akin to Happenings) at the Hope Hall or the home of the Mersey beat, the Cavern Club. Brian Patten and Roger McGough, the poets who have helped provide his texts, are associated with two of the country's most promising local poetry magazines: *Underdog* and *Phoenix*. Patten's poems are to be published by Allen and Unwin, McGough's novel by Michael Joseph; with Henri they are to feature in a Penguin Modern Poets volume and in Edward Lucie-Smith's anthology *Liverpool Scene*. McGough has formed a cabaret-type group called The Scaffold with John Gorman and Mike McGear, the latter being brother to Paul McCartney of the Beatles; they have made two records and under Brian Epstein's management are gradually winning an audience outside Liverpool. Lennon of the Beatles was a student at the College of Art; his Thurber-like drawings

M

decorate his short books of Joycean prose and nonsense verse, *John Lennon In His Own Write* and *A Spaniard In The Works*.

It is only recently that these people's undoubtedly lively minds have been applied to raising the popular song lyric above the bottom level of banality. But Bill Harry, the founder-editor of *Merseybeat* (subsequently renamed *Music Echo*, a local equivalent of the *Melody Maker*), is another ex-student of the College; he has printed unusually interesting photographs of the groups by the Liverpool photographers Peter Kaye and Graham Spencer, while the Beatles' own photographer Robert Freeman, besides supervising the excellent colour effects of their rather poor second film, designed Lennon's books, of which the first was one of the most elegant and original pieces of British book production in 1964. All these may seem straws in a lot of wind: small matters compared with the stupefying boom of the music and its more commercial accompaniments, or even with the main tradition of visual art in Liverpool. But they do show the possibility of generating visual and poetic counterparts to this music in the autonomous cultural life of Merseyside, and there are other artists besides Henri who are aware of it. Arthur Dooley the sculptor, for instance, told me that he had talked to the young members in clubs and cellars where the groups perform (he reckons that there may be 300 such groups in Liverpool altogether, while the City Centre Plan estimates some eighty beat clubs in the centre alone) and tried to show them that there were analogies between his sculpture and their own means of self-expression in music and dancing. They have become interested in his sculpture as a result, he says; they have come down to his studio and have bought or commissioned pieces. He and other artists have been financed and befriended by Alan Williams, owner of the Jacaranda and Blue Angel clubs and original manager of the Beatles before Brian Epstein (himself a picture collector) took them over.

The most striking instance however is that of the painter Stuart Sutcliffe, who died of a brain tumour in Hamburg in 1962 at the age of twenty-one. Sutcliffe, a Scot by birth – his father came to Liverpool as a ship's engineer – went to Prescot Grammar School and the College of Art, where he was a friend and contemporary of John Lennon. He had a picture in the John Moores exhibition in 1959 while still a student, and the College gave him considerable freedom to work on his own, though it refused to accept him for teacher training after he had passed his diploma as a painter. He became a founder-member of the Beatles, playing bass guitar with them on their Hamburg trip in 1960, staying on to attend the State High School for Art there, but playing again on their second Hamburg visit the following summer. At first he was totally disillusioned with painting after having been turned down (for a mixture of good and bad reasons)[1] by the College, where his works seem to have reflected the influences mainly of Bratby and Bomberg. But at Hamburg two artist friends encouraged him to come and work under Eduardo Paolozzi, then the visiting professor there, and this un-

115 Stuart Sutcliffe, the fifth Beatle, in his Hamburg studio, with two of his black paintings

leashed a remarkable burst of creative activity in a much more personal and original style. Probably no recent Liverpool painter has worked with anything resembling this intensity, and the range, variety and colour of his last few months' works made a very strong impression when they were shown

[1] Among other things it was felt, understandably, that he was a painter and not a teacher.

116–117 Hamburg drawings by Stuart Sutcliffe

at the Walker Gallery in May 1964. 'A very perceptive and sensitive person, and very restless', Paolozzi called him in an interview, and again:

> There is that sort of marvellously desperate thing about the whole Liverpool business now. I always felt there was a desperate thing about Stuart in his life. . . . I was afraid of it.

He was an outstanding loss to Liverpool and quite possibly to English painting. And over and above the merit of his pictures he has a special significance as somebody whose burning creativity switched from art into pop music and then back again. He showed the way.

Not that Sutcliffe himself, by all accounts, saw any particular connection between his music and his painting; he seems rather to have treated them as two distinct channels. But the very existence of this alternative is important in a community where the one medium has so far utterly overshadowed the other, and the simple fact that he was a Beatle immediately makes painting accessible to those of his own and younger generations who might otherwise be put off by the heavy curtain of cash, plush and gloss surrounding so much of modern art. Outwardly one would not think of him as a specifically local painter; though some of his Hamburg drawings seem to identify him as a pupil of Paolozzi's they give little clue to his nationality, let alone his Liverpool background. Yet undoubtedly in the Liverpool context he means something quite special. He was not only a small, tragic, self-consuming figure in the tradition of Jackson Pollock and the actor James Dean (with both of whom he seems to have felt some affinity) but a link in something larger: the shadowy chain relating a pretty low form of music to the most high-brow brands of modern art.

Considerations like this perhaps seem remote from conventional art criticism, but in Liverpool the city's particular self-awareness and the aggressive energy of its young people are both socially and culturally important. It becomes impossible to overlook them, so that although my first acquaintance with the art of the area was made without any great knowledge of such factors I have thought it best to outline them before moving on to discuss individual artists. For they did in fact largely alter my view of modern Merseyside art as I was getting to know it; familiarity for once bred interest and hope rather than the more usual contempt. To give some idea of my quite sceptical starting-point, here is my first introduction to Merseyside art en masse at the Liverpool Academy Exhibition of 1963:

> It has been hung so as to feature a large wall of the more with-it painters which faces you at the end of the big room. And you feel that everyone

118 In the 1963 Liverpool Academy show. The four large pictures hanging at the top are by John Edkins. Extreme left and right are by Adrian Henri. The two women are in front of a painting by Sam Walsh. The remaining four are by Philip Meeson

is rather striving to keep up, though in fact they are a long way down the line. The less the striving, in most cases, the better the picture: the two *Still Life with Guitars* by G. Gwyn Evans (Birkenhead) and Sylvia F. Forster (Heswall) are un-modern but good, and there are excellent straight pencil drawings of domestic subjects by Margaret Hughes. But clearly these are fish out of water nowadays. It's all tagging after other movements; thus on the large end wall the hard-edged abstracts of Edkins and the pop pictures of Adrian Henri are really would-be London pictures. Henri at least is below London standard for the kind of thing he's trying to do. And nowhere in the whole shooting-match is there any kind of flicker which one can say is specifically Liverpool.

The best are indeed on this end wall: one of Edkins's (*Nomex*) and *Restricted Area* by Philip Meeson. But it's something done years ago in Germany and France. Nicholas Horsfield's (half way on one side wall) I know too well to judge in this context – it just looks out of place to me. A good pinkish Arthur Ballard opposite fighting with the red of the wall; A. says it's the only painting he's done for ages (is dated '62). Peter MacKarell's (derived from battleship construction sets) were all right in design but spoilt by black-green and orange colouring which I found strident. Martin Bell was unexciting but professional, and again moving with the times in square patches of colour. John Heritage, a big black-on-white like a blown-up drawing, which seemed rather good to me but called forth a snort from N.H. I understand better why after seeing one or two other things by him – notably a horror in the Sandon dining room.

Also quite a pretty, Mundy-ish painting by David Breese and professional-looking etchings by John Roberts. Christopher Leyne's painting also professional in a cubist style. And then of course two of Jardine's surrealities, but not up to his best. Good piece of sculpture (skull) in steel by B. S. L. Rice.

In the months that followed my opinions of Henri and MacKarell changed a good deal; the Edkins picture was bought by the Walker Gallery and came to look rather impressive among paintings by much better-known modern British artists, some of them acquisitions from the John Moores shows. It would be wrong to disguise such changes by trying to give only final verdicts, and I propose to quote largely from my notes and set down my impressions as they came.

At that time I knew Nicholas Horsfield, the then academy president, and his pictures extremely well; I had some slight acquaintance with his successor Arthur Ballard and had seen his work at Roland, Browse and Delbanco's gallery in London; I had seen the odd picture by Martin Bell, G. W. Jardine and John Hart in mixed exhibitions outside Liverpool. All these were (and are) on the staff of the College. Ballard, I knew, had spent several months

119 Sculpture by Sean Rice

painting in Paris in 1957 under an admirable Liverpool Corporation scheme which allows teachers an occasional spell of paid work or study abroad; the works of his I had seen were subdued, often earthy in colour, and non-representational in a rather negative way. He used to give the impression of forcing himself into abstraction not because it came naturally to him but out of some misplaced sense of obligation – to the spirit of the time, perhaps, or to the prevailing critical trend – and something of the same sense threatened his friend and colleague Horsfield: a sense which can be dangerous in an art community like Liverpool's, where there is not the same plethora of styles to choose from as in the great art capitals and it is easy to feel out of the swim.

Within his own conventions, which are those of a post-Sickertian impressionism combined with a Fauve colour sense, Horsfield is an outstanding artist whose best works – nearly all of them landscapes remote from Liverpool – could hang in a national collection. Extremely well-equipped technically, he is however not at all a facile painter, and in the Liverpool atmosphere of self-doubt he is apt on occasion to worry himself and his pictures to

120 Nicholas Horsfield: *Mount Street* (Walker Art Gallery)

a virtual standstill. He feels that today the real revolution in art, and one which he dislikes and rejects, is the turning of the artist into an exhibitionist. The conflict, he writes

> seems to me to lie not, as formerly, in the rather tame squabble between so-called 'abstract' and figurative painting, but between acts of public declamation and private sensitivity.

In this climate, with its extraordinarily rapid consumption of artistic personalities,

> I begin to feel left on the shelf and sometimes doubt the values which have guided me without question for twenty-five years. Perhaps others of the middle generation, those whose ideas were formed, say, in the last years before the war (a bad time) may feel similarly.

He and Ballard spring from utterly different backgrounds, Horsfield being a southerner trained at Charterhouse and the Royal College of Art who fell in love with Liverpool when working as an Arts Council regional official in the North-West, while Ballard is a native Liverpudlian, son of an artisan, and an ex-student of the College. But Ballard too, I noted after my first visit to him in 1963, was

121 Arthur Ballard:
*Non-figurative
painting* (Walker Art
Gallery)

uncertain of his values, or of the very existence of meaning of values, and hesitant about his own motives for doing almost anything he does. In the last two or three years he has painted very little, and what he has painted has been in no consistent style. The picture in the 1963 academy was the last of his characteristic abstract works I saw; since then he has experimented rather unenthusiastically with pop art and in the 1965 academy showed two very different but equally elegantly-painted boxing pictures, recalling the Liverpool heroes of his youth. He has been more interested in commissions of an almost sculptural kind, such as the 'printed circuit' panel and the chapel cross referred to earlier. But both he and Horsfield could be doing a good deal more, and although they have revolutionized the academy their influence on the painting at the College is now only indirect, the one being head of the pre-Diploma course there and the other jointly directing[1] the department of General Studies. It is a real criticism of Liverpool as a community that it does little to induce such highly gifted people to paint.

Horsfield had a one-man show at the Bluecoat Chambers in 1963, Ballard one at the New Shakespeare gallery in 1958. Horsfield sold nearly all his

[1] With Jack Bevan, translator of the poems of Salvatore Quasimodo.

pictures, Ballard two. Otherwise Ballard has shown locally only in the academy, selling roughly a picture a year except in 1956, when one of his works was hung upside down and the ensuing Press controversy brought him six purchasers. From the first Moores show his picture was sold to George Holt the shipowner, who presented it to the university via the P. H. Holt Trust; it was last heard of hanging in the metallurgical department. From the second show W. L. Stevenson bought the picture for John Moores, in whose office it now hangs. Nor can it be said that any of this has been

122 Arthur Ballard:
An original Liverpool Group. (Nel Tarleton,
Stan Rowan, Ike Bradley, Stan Clayton)

particularly rewarding. He made some £250 a year from sales through his London dealers while they were still taking his pictures, but they have not given him a show now since 1959. His two commissions in the TV shop and the school brought him about £40 each; neither he nor any other Liverpool artist I talked to has had commissions from the shipping lines,[1] though Holt bought one of his boxing pictures to put in a training establishment. The most he has made altogether from painting in any year has been some £400. He is certainly the best-known living Liverpool painter and, as he himself says, 'I could have worked as a charwoman and earned more money.' And yet (I noted)

> He very strongly supports Liverpool art, or rather its possibility. He has great faith in Liverpool individuality, which he thinks will assert itself in art sooner or later; we'll see something 'better than the Beatles'. He's proud of the efforts he's made to support individualists in the College, e.g., precisely, Lennon of the Beatles, whom the Graphic Design department were reluctant to accept. The boy was no good as an artist, he claims, and an intolerable rebellious nuisance. But he had character.

> Ballard thinks that the distinctive Liverpool art will come, and for that reason he's very much against the Moores show, which he regards

[1] I wrote to all the local shipping firms who might employ artists for the embellishment of their passenger vessels, and of the four that replied at all none used artists from Liverpool. Cunard, for instance, leave such matters to the 'design consultants' for the ship in question, who are unlikely to have the same local roots as the company itself.

as too broadly national. He argued that Moores ought not to 'bring this bloody great umbrella to cover us up' and that Biennale towns like São Paulo and Venice have failed to develop any art of their own. At the same time as all this I'm sure he himself minds very much about succeeding on the wider scale.

At the Hope Hall one night he and Arthur Dooley the sculptor came to blows over the question of working-class children and their chance of getting into the College, Dooley claiming that the system favoured what he called 'doctors' daughters'. To Dooley it seems that there is too much teaching either for commercial ends or to produce further teachers in a kind of self-perpetuating circle. Like Ballard he is a native of Liverpool of considerable physical toughness; his father is a docker and he himself served nine years with the Irish Guards and worked in Dunlop's Speke factory before establishing himself as a self-taught sculptor in 1961. Now well-known locally, he works in bronze, and his figures of men and animals, at once religious and revolutionary in conception, have considerable strength and feeling for their material and in their clumsier way belong to the same tradition as those of Henry Moore (despite his professed dislike for that artist and his contempt on finding that Moore's massive compositions are less solid than they look). Here are notes of three meetings with him:

1 James Cliffe took me round to see Dooley, but we didn't find him. A side street off Seel Street, with small old specialized shops and artisan-like outfits: goldbeaters across the street and a signwriter in the front room. Above the door a carved wooden sign saying A DOOLEY SCULPTOR. A black dirty entrance passage leading through to a padlocked door on the left: at the end a collection apparently of junk metal. A dark and poky courtyard glimpsed beyond.

We were just leaving again when Dooley's mate came in, a very pleasant sober and respectable-looking chap in specs, who is a wood-carver and shares the room. He opened the padlock easily enough without a key. Inside, a dark jumble of carvings, 18-inch high Moore-like figures in draperies, architects' drawings for a church at Leyland, rather a good watercolour drawing by Dooley's friend John Watts, a big expressionist-style painting by another friend now doing time in Walton for housebreaking. And, taking up quite a slice of the room, the enormous bed in which a fellow-sculptor had assured me D. would be reposing.

He had in fact gone off to the foundry, apparently re these figures which he is doing for the Leyland church. His friend described Dooley's visit to Faczinski the architect to ask him for £400. F. told him architects didn't do business quite like that. Dooley: 'All right then; give us five pounds.'

No hesitation about what he says, evidently. A TV interview for *Tonight* couldn't be broadcast owing to his language.[1] And on art schools and the jobs people get there: 'Three thousand a year and as much crumpet as you can eat.'

2 I managed to catch him rather briefly in the coffee bar. A big, dirty, sad-looking chap humped over a tiny coffee table, with two apparent acolytes in jeans, one each side of him. Conversation punctuated regularly (and no doubt automatically) with swearwords. Utter contempt for the College, for the Walker Gallery, for pretty well everything. Obviously thinks it's more important that anyone who wants to should be free to pursue art than that the art produced should be any good, or should find a home.

He approves strongly of the Rev. J. K. Murren, some respect for A. Ballard, much for this chap Watts. Thinks kids in school have all the natural art stifled in them; no idea of what the Teacher Training department does, or of the effect of such teaching methods. He and his friends were in favour of Berger's TV programmes, which the pale-faced, red-headed one (quondam Liverpool University, evidently) had certainly seen.

3 Again I found Dooley in the cafe over the Jacaranda Club, staring sadly out of his big face with one arm round a pale, silent girl in trousers and a light blue pullover. He offered me tea; the girl slipped off, evidently operating as a waitress. After talking for the best part of two hours I finished up feeling that he was genuine and likeable in his complaints against our society and in his sense that social and artistic activities must be linked; that he was wholly cynical about the art set-up and about exploiting the publicity which he sees as the key to it; that as an artist he *could* be personal, if a bit unskilled still, but is perhaps coming to take the easy way out of problems, even when it is work he genuinely cares about. I am sure he could do quite a bit for art in Liverpool, but whether he will do it through his work I'm not so certain.

He's obsessed with education. Nobody leaves school knowing how to *think*; they're just fed facts, and thinking comes (if it comes at all) at university. The practice of art, he feels, can change this, though he despises art teaching in Liverpool schools, which he evidently judges from his own experience, not knowing how it has improved since. The teddy-boy type, for instance, has been turned out with no thinking equipment, no relation to anything larger, simply with his self, and all

[1] Dooley himself denies this. 'That bad language is a fable'.

123 Arthur Dooley: one of the Stations of the Cross for St Mary's, Leyland

he can do is look after that self and dress it up. And this he sees as deliberate, quoting one schoolmistress down in Toxteth speaking of some child's educational handicaps: 'Well, it isn't going to matter. He's only a docker's son.' Thus (a) he wants wholesale revolution; (b) he feels there's a class barrier round the College; and (c) he sees art as something which can and should provoke thinking, and also self-fulfilment. This is because of his own experience: obviously his sculpture has been immensely liberating to him, and has enormously stimulated his ideas on all kinds of subjects.

He himself went to school in Upper Park Street, still a slum school today, where there was then no art teacher, only plasticine (or modelling clay?) and pans of paint set out on the desks. His conversion – it clearly was that, by his account – took place in the army in the Middle East. There he was appalled by the conditions in which people lived, and felt at first that orthodox Catholic charity and redemption was the answer. He sold Catholic papers on coming home, throwing himself into his religion and (I think he said) writing sometimes about it. Then, he said, he wondered if he couldn't express his ideas about these things better by making them. I saw what he says is the first piece of sculpture he made: a small, very abstract and rudimentary, knife-edged bronze figure: rather good, and from an autodidact remarkable. He is now a communist, he says, though he is a Catholic too, if not a very good one. In a sense he does think with his hands: he was not only no good at maths at school but even abhors the sight of a ruler. Like a French carpenter, if he has to measure something he'll just mark it off on an odd bit of wood.

Dooley has shown in Liverpool University, at the St Martin's Gallery, London (1962), at Blythes' Stores, Edinburgh (1963, during the Festival) and at the Bluecoat Chambers in 1964. On the recommendation of Lucjan Pietka of the School of Architecture he was commissioned to produce the Stations of the Cross for Weightman and Bullen's Church of St Mary at Leyland. Besides the young pop group supporters referred to earlier he has sold his work to London television commentators like Michelmore and Allsop, and to Professor and Mrs Frederick Ridley of the university, who own six of his pieces and were at one time coming to the studio almost weekly. He has also sold a figure to the Walker Art Gallery. Altogether he reckons that in his first two years of whole-time work as a sculptor he sold 150 items, which is probably more than any other Liverpool artist could say.[1]

The other man who has made a slight dint in local awareness is Adrian Henri, though in his case it is probably the 'events' and the poetry readings with which he is associated that have made his name known outside the art community, rather than his actual pictures; he was the subject of a short film in the BBC's *New Release* programme in June 1966. At the time when I first heard of him he was living in the early nineteenth-century residential area behind the Cathedral and the university but teaching part-time in the Manchester College of Art; he later joined the staff of the pre-diploma course at Liverpool. Born in 1932, he was educated at St Asaph Grammar

---

[1] Messrs. Tinlings, the printers and owners of the *Liverpool Post*, illustrated their well-produced engagement diary for 1966 with photographs of Dooley's work, annotated by the artist, and gave it the title *A.D. 65*.

School and trained at Kings College, Newcastle, notably under Richard Hamilton, and this together with his considerable literary interests has made

124 Adrian Henri with some of his work in the area of his Falkner Square house

him unusually at home (for an English painter, and even more so for a provincial one) in the Dada and 'pataphysical traditions of the continental avant-garde and among the modern American works that reflect them. His special contribution has been to sense the relevance of these and other apparently rarefied manifestations of the modern movement to the particular climate of Liverpool, for which he has great feeling and affection. 'The neo-Dada artist of today may use shock tactics', he has written,[1] ' . . . but the shock tactics are used to make a positive affirmation, events dedicated to cities "with love and squalor".' As a poet he has been able to put the key figures in his mythology, from T. S. Eliot[2] to the film *Ashes and Diamonds*, into a Liverpool context and make them seem at home there; it was he, for instance, who organized a Père Ubu procession to Falkner Square on Alfred Jarry's ninety-first birthday. As a painter he has shown inter alia at the

[1] In an article 'Events are Happening' in *The New University*, Oxford, number 12, 1963, p. 17.
[2] See his 'In Memoriam T. S. Eliot' in *The Times Literary Supplement*, 11 February, 1965.

THE NEW 'OUR TIMES'

(For Felix Fénéon)*

At 3 p.m. yesterday, a Mr Adolphus Edwards, a Jamaican immigrant, was pecked to death by a large bronze Eagle in Upper Parliament St. A U.S. State Dept. spokesman said later, 'We have no statement to make as of this time.'

2
Police-constable George Williams, who was partially blinded by a 15-lb jellybaby thrown at a passing pop singer, is to be retired on half-pension.

3
Bearded Liverpool couple put out of misery in night by drip oil heater, court told.

4
A certain Mrs Elspeth Clout, of Huyton, was killed by an unidentified falling object. It was thought to be a particularly hard stool evacuated from the toilet of a passing aeroplane.

5
2 chip-shop proprietors were today accused of selling human ears fried in batter. One of them said, 'We believe there is room for innovation in the trade.'

6
Fatality in Kardomah bomb outrage: Waitress buried Alive under two thousand Danish pastries.

7
At the inquest of Paul McCartney, aged 21, described as a popular singer and guitarist, P.C. Smith said, in evidence, that he saw one of the accused, Miss Jones, standing waving bloodstained hands shouting 'I got a bit of his liver.'

Adrian Henri, Jan. 1964

(a free 1960s Liverpool version of Fénéon's great 'Our Times')

125 A characteristic Liverpool poem by Henri. Fénéon was the late nineteenth-century art critic and anarchist

1961 and 1965 John Moores shows, at the Portal Gallery in London (two-man show with Sam Walsh), at the British Pop Art Show at Nottingham in 1963 and at the Northern Ireland Arts Council painting competition in Belfast in 1964, where his *Père Ubu in Liverpool* won the third prize of £200. But above all, perhaps, he is a showman, for he has worked six or seven summers in a fairground at Rhyl (for which he has painted decorative panels), and he has the rare gift in an age of exhibitionists of being able and anxious to present other people's work besides his own.

The address I had been given proved to be:

A mysterious, virtually abandoned house in the corner of Falkner Square. No bell, no names on the door; push in and up anonymous stairs and there's nothing but shut doors on every landing. No sound or sign of life. I think I called out in the brown hall, but no movement. Then as an afterthought I tried the area steps and found a bell by the basement door and pushed it. That was Henri's, and on about my third visit his wife asked me in to wait for him in a room with books, sofa, cast-iron nine-teenth century fireplace, some own painting and some (as it turned out) Walsh's, where I took up a Calendrier Pataphysique which some friend had sent them. No Henri that time, but Mrs told me there would be some form of Event, plus a bar extension, in the Hope Hall that night. Adrian was chasing around in connection with it.

So in due course I went there. People were crammed smokily into the further room in the basement, waiting agog for something unknown to start. A broad, mildly Turkish-looking figure with beard and glasses came up from behind: this was Henri. Then a mixed programme: sketches, chap reading poems, two nice young girls singing folksily to guitars. Some of it rather good; most of it inaudible. No kind of décor, but the spare performers, or perhaps initiate onlookers, sitting round at the back. Not enough effort made to keep up the tempo, and interest rather slackened off. But altogether a good and lively atmosphere.

Next day Henri at home with the gramophone playing Shostakovitch violin concerto while his wife tried to sleep. He teaches at Manchester but likes living in Liverpool; about to move somewhere else in the same quarter, which is plainly congenial, with its streets full of dirty ragged kids playing, black and white mixed, and its slumping Georgian houses. He himself comes from Birkenhead, but the family settled there from Mauritius; hence the name, which is pronounced Henry but no affecta-tion. Has worked with Pete Brown, so knows of Michael Horovitz and his lot; is patronized by George Melly, who has three of his pictures and

N

POPILUDE for the artist Adrian Henri

America your stars have been eaten by reindeers.
I can almost smell the scent of the pines on the canvas.
I knocked on the pink cottage but no one answered.

Colourblind artists protesting against the nylon stocking.
Camp journalists protesting against the blood.
In the handbag secret gaschambers are being prepared for the
extermination of the few remaining poets.

On the obscure snowscape
lyrical mice nibble poems. You can almost hear the crippled musicians
playing sad tunes in damp green gardens, you can almost hear
the spastic lovers weeping straight bones beneath the trees.

A delicate moth struck by polio. I can see the sad skulls
of bleak artists studying me through many years of night.

The painting has a hole in its corset
through which drop atomic grandparents with strange and terrible ideals.
With sizzling faces. And the sun rocking itself to sleep in the living room.

In the white distance Ubu stands alert.
I'm an ant lost in the vast brylcream jar. I am the weird eggshell
whispering in the blue lakes, he tells the hidden reporters disguised as mirrors.

Adrian. There's a mutilated chinaman in your breadtin.
On some mornings I hear him screaming/wailing sad things/trying to find
the yellow prince who cried to Africa.

But now we are too late. My bedroom has been invaded by 8 pregnant birds.
And many other secret things rode jeeps across the landing.
Midnight. I wait in the dark corridor for england to come out of the w.c.

The birds were screaming in the wrong canvas.
The desert invaded by tulips/by the fantastic virgins
by the gunslingers from distant planets/O
merciful Dada limping across the asylum on a rocking horse.

Brian Patten

126 A poem by Brian Patten, who works with
Henri and McGough

one of Walsh's.[1] Enjoys the matière and sheer luscious technique of painting, as well as having this strong literary-dramatic bent. Themes: Ubu in Liverpool; birds in the big brutal city; the ordinary pop imagery of Omo packets and so on. His 'events' have been televised, so he is not entirely shy of putting himself across, but I thought him genuine none the less, and the pictures were in many cases better than his exhibits in the academy show. But was rather repelled by a thing with a bloody pillow stuck in it and some ironic title. Henri himself quite pleased with.

Unfinished: a big painting on unusually coarse-textured canvas of the Entry of Christ into Liverpool. Modelled on Ensor, who figures in it

127 Adrian Henri: *The Entry of Christ into Liverpool*

along with Dooley, Melly, Pete Brown, Ubu, Charlie Mingus and other such. He and Walsh, who made his appearance nowabouts, had a 2-man show at the Portal Gallery in June 1962, and also one more recently in the Hope Hall on the cinema walls. Do local people buy their pictures?

[1] Melly, member of a well-known Liverpool family – George Melly, MP's furniture is in Sudley, and there is a plaque in the Cathedral to an uncle who fell serving with the Red Cross on the last day of the Italo-Abyssinian War – is the blues singer and co-author of the *Flook* cartoon in the *Daily Mail*. Brown is a London poet who does a good deal of public reading; his collaborator Horovitz is editor of *New Departures* and organizer of the 'Live New Departures' shows at the Institute of Contemporary Arts and elsewhere.

Not much, it seems, though they have sold one or two to an economics lecturer [Frederick Ridley, now a professor]. Walsh has had the occasional commission: he has a painting (no good, I fear) in The Crack and

128 Painting by Sam Walsh, a Dublin artist working in Liverpool

one in the Royal Court pub, and he has done three for betting offices for Reg Mason, one of them in Ivy Leigh, West Derby, next Mason's house. Dick Egerton, son of Ma Egerton at the Royal Court, accosted him: 'You look like a painter. Will you paint a portrait?'

Walsh, some three years younger than Henri, is an Irishman, who studied painting at the Dublin College of Art, and came to England in 1955 to lead 'a double life as a portrait painter for money and an abstract painter for love'. From this uneasy compromise he moved, under the combined influence of Larry Rivers and Francis Bacon, to a kind of pop art based on huge blown-up faces (like his Bacon portrait in the 1963 Moores show, which the Walker Gallery bought), on advertising and the cinema and on the satirizing of sexual jinks in high society. 'For long,' wrote Henri in an article on him,[1] 'the man who painted was not the man who read Galaxy and likes monster movies'; but now he is. He also, as is evident from his latest pictures, finds the obsessive disgust of W. S. Burroughs's books congenial, though his own

[1] In the Liverpool undergraduate paper *Sphinx* for spring 1962, p. 24. The same issue contains a note on Henri by Walsh, a joint manifesto (Point 6: 'We would like children to find our pictures at the bottom of cereal packets') a d some illustrations.

reflection of it seems at once more modish and more sardonic than the writer's. No Liverpool painter has developed faster in the past three or four years, and his paintings are in increasing demand. Of the six works which he showed in

129 Sam Walsh: *Three Figures in a Warm Climate* (Walker Art Gallery)

the very successful 1965 academy five were sold, two of them to the Walker Gallery. The following year he sold four.

Recently Henri has twice put on his Events to the authentic pop music fans in the Cavern Club, apparently with great success. I saw the first show which he organized in autumn 1963 in the Hope Hall cinema (as against the basement room); despite total lack of publicity it drew an audience of about 350, which was better than many of the films:

> It also included some really good things, especially by Roger McGough, and was accompanied by an electric-guitar group called the Road-runners: the first time I've heard poetry-and-jazz that really came off. There were two good poems by McG – the second called 'Summer with Monika', describing his stay-at-home, kitchen-sink holiday in the sum-mer of the Profumo scandal – and also a very effective turn with all three poets, Gorman, him and Brian Patten, reading verses to a pet tune of the group's, which then let its own vocalist loose. A piece of pure knock-about: two mysterious men breaking up an elaborate structure like an oversized hatstand, which Henri had now and again been hanging some

130 *Night Blues*, one of Henri's 'Events', with the artist (centre) and Brian Patten (at table on right)

object on. And a really very funny, originally-conceived and-written sketch by McG with a nuclear disarmer in a bomb-proof suit being questioned: this acted by Gorman and himself. A girl dancer from Oldham (I think) who capered around in the outer aisles – there being very little room on the stage. Occasional interruptions from the balcony. Henri as compère. Patten now and again disclosed by the curtain, typing away at a great epic poem which finally he never read. Large pictures by a painter called Don McKinlay who used to work with Walsh and Henri and went off to live near Bury, propped against the proscenium. A finale with all the company running round and round the cinema, waving flags; I later found out that this signified 'Roadrunners'.

There really was something there. Staging was poor, owing partly to amateurishness, partly to unsuitability of the stage; but there were no awkward lulls. And it was spontaneous, unpretentious, I thought, and above all indigenous. It seemed to meet the demands of a young and attractive audience, who later packed out the club downstairs. So presumably it was a success from the Hope Hall's point of view too.

A very different kind of artist is Peter MacKarell, who took part in Henri's exhibition 'New Images from the North' at the second Merseyside Arts Festival. The son of a Liverpool charge hand shipwright, he was a pupil at the College and is now on the staff of the Teacher Training department there; physically he is of much the same type as John Lennon. He too is writer as well as artist; he is a regular contributor of articles and drawings to *The Times Educational Supplement*, and he has written two unpublished novels that are sometimes untidy and undisciplined but contain excellent comic passages based on his own experience of teaching and his highly critical view of various aspects of modern art. I had admired a large battle picture of his which I saw

DEATH OF A BIRD IN THE CITY

You should never have said that
Now
Your smiles are whiteelephants
and your face a photograph
to be comeacross
some slow brown Sunday

You should never have said that
Your tongue is a mother without pity
Now love is gone
and anonymous
like the death of a bird in the city

Roger McGough

131 Poem by Roger
McGough for another
Henri 'Event'

in the College: a work that bypassed the whole modern movement, including
the formalism of his own 1963 academy pictures, and went back to nineteenth
century romanticism of a most vivid sort. He and a colleague, I found,

are making a kind of sand-table model on which they propose to fight the
American Civil War as a game of 'L'Attaque'.

He lives on the ground floor of one of a group of early nineteenth
century houses at the cathedral end of Huskisson Street. A sympathetic
place, with not much furniture (but that solid) and nothing but Mac-
Karell's pictures on the walls. Curtains etc. good modern design. The
odd wall in a strong colour. Plenty of books.

Immediately inside, a striking picture with little white circular labels,
some rimmed in red, some in blue – both these lots numbered – and a
third lot blank, dotted around on a glowing green ground through which
a brown base shows streakily. This is Liverpool v. Everton, the product
of MacKarell's interest in plotting moves; there is some connection with
a sort of tiddley-wink soccer game which I don't quite understand. Also
in the same passage, early pictures of grotesque heads, built up to some
extent three-dimensionally, which he did as a student and now dislikes
but his wife won't throw away. A bathroom with wall made into a scrap-
book from colour photos, ads and God knows what else. In kitchen, one
or two other such pictures, with an old bus on one. In front room, paint-

ings developed from drawings of boats, etc., somewhat in the vein of his academy ones: one of them in fact, over the mantlepiece, having been rejected much to his annoyance.

In the bedroom MacKarell showed me a set of photos of tugs etc. in docks, and the model of the Prinz Eugen. A group of outline drawings from this and from the Hood: drawing silhouette of shadow with light at different angles so as to give umpteen different (slowly varying) outlines of the ship. Then pen and wash drawings done at Birkenhead docks, basis of some of the paintings in the front room: decent but not spectacular. Out in the passage the big battle picture. A smaller but

132 Peter MacKarell: *The Charge of the Texas Dragoons at Bandoleer Crossing* (detail) (Social Studies building, Liverpool University)

similar Civil War painting above his desk in the bedroom; in honour of it he put on a United States Seventh Cavalry cap given by a student. Also hanging there: a watercolour of Singapore docks done when he was in the army, and one of a shored-up yacht at Pwllheli. Besides ships – he is rare, incidentally, in finding a genuine Liverpool subject - he has another source in maps and charts. Throw-out admiralty charts on one wall; some earlier drawings in folder, not very good, based on map ideas.

I asked him re showing and selling. Mostly to friends or friends' friends, who will come up after the Academy and offer him £20 less than he's asking for a picture there. He once had a portrait of his wife in the academy, and as a result several people asked him to paint portraits. But he had done it because he wanted to, he says, and had little wish to paint other people. The New Vision Centre in London took some of his pictures, but he doesn't know what they did with them; he has also shown twice in the theatre at Lincoln, where one of the people responsible is a friend of his. Besides that he gives his pictures away: to Alun Owen the playwright (and script-writer of the first Beatles film), to Budd Schulberg (author of *On the Waterfront*), to Ben Johnson the eminent cowboy and others such. One is destined for the present commander of the Confederate forces in this country, who lives somewhere like Henley-on-Thames. He says he enjoys doing this: these people have given him pleasure (or more), and how else can he show it? Plainly he is someone who loses interest in his work once he's done it. He doesn't seem to be discontented with his outlets, and hasn't tried to do very much about improving them.

133 Peter MacKarell: '*You know we French stormed Ratisbon a mile or two away*'

Since then MacKarell has done further battle pictures and a striking *Dante and Beatrice in Liverpool*, part parody, part social realism; and moved house. He himself feels that his work as an illustrator is in some ways more important and more rewarding to him than his painting. 'Highly descriptive graphic drawing is integral to my work as an artist,' he writes; but although his drawings are perhaps more disciplined than his paintings, they also seem stiffer and less spontaneous. The great merit of his work as a painter, to my mind, is that it arises from an absolutely genuine *interest* each time. If the result is near-pop – something he hotly denies – it's not because pop is the fashion but because this subject (football, e.g.) is what he happens to be immersed in. If it is different (as with the American Civil War) then the approach can be quite different too. In this he is himself putting into practice the methods he and John Hart have devised in the Teacher Training Department for canalizing the ordinary Liverpool child's curiosity and observation into various kinds of art. His considerable aggressiveness and effervescence have been set purposefully to work.

The complete contrast is Jardine, who is a romantic rooted in the English nineteenth century and in the international surrealism of the 1930s, and works steadily away in his studio on the top floor of the Bluecoat Chambers, paying little apparent attention to other people's fashions. Born in Liverpool in 1920, he went to Wallasey Art School at a time when it consisted of six students and one master, he says; then in 1939 got a scholarship to the Royal College of Art, where he won the Travelling Scholarship for graphic design and studied mural painting under E. W. Tristram. 'The murals painted on wall-sized sheets of board,' he has written of his work there,[1]

> I found could be successfully sawn up into little bits and the bigger lumps discarded. This way I could get down to a nice little head or composition as small as four inches square. Even now if I am not satisfied with the composition of one of my pictures I saw it up into smaller ones.

Now he is a lecturer at the College of Art, and at the moment is probably of all these local painters the one who sells best in London. There he has had three successful one-man shows at the Portal Gallery, whose director Lionel Levy was formerly a student of dress design at the College. He has also had shows in Brussels (Galerie Vendôme, 1961) and Chicago (Callard Gallery, 1962). I myself (to return to immediate impressions) first saw his pictures –

> two of them, if I remember right – around 1950, when Nicholas Horsfield got up his Arts Council exhibition of Lancs painters. That, he now says, is about when he started to become known, and his work hasn't really changed much since. He is a strange-looking chap: a broad face with bright eyes, sticking-out ears and little motion in it: a slightly ungainly and awkward figure, though it would be difficult to say why. He gives an extremely self-contained impression, an air of living within himself, knowing his limitations and calmly going on pursuing his own aims. Of all the painters here he seems the least restless, though he says he lives here primarily because he has a job at the College; unlike John Hart, with his intense affection for the place, he says he'd sooner work anywhere than where he was born and bred.

At the College he teaches in the graphic design school, which has its

---

[1] George Wallace Jardine: 'Another World', in *The Painter and Sculptor*, London, spring 1962, Vol. 4, number 4, pp. 18–23.

134 George Wallace Jardine, in his studio in the Bluecoat Chambers

own presses for woodcuts and lithographs. Some time ago he introduced a class of apprentice lithographers from the Printing School to the notion of collage, and says they were hopeless at it; instead of juxtaposing the incongruous or unexpected they tried to stick things in their right place, putting a bus against the background of a street, and so on. This concept of collage he derives consciously from Max Ernst, and the other artist he mentions as affecting him is Klee. [More lately he has become interested in Klimt and Schiele.]

The painting of his I liked best (on this first visit) was a shell collage over the fireplace, and obviously he likes it too. Otherwise his recent pictures are a bit more preraphaelitey than they used to be: partly because he is including very literally painted nudes, girls painted sometimes from the imagination, sometimes from one of the College models,

135 Shell collage by G. W. Jardine

and partly also because he finds himself putting in more and more arabesques of foliage etc. in a way that seems to link up with the art nouveau revival.

This kind of picture, with its overtones of Moreau, Watts, Böcklin, isn't my cup of tea, but they are personal and pretty genuine, and they are often very well painted. Colour is not impressive, the flesh especially having the air of pastry; they are now sweet where they used to be quirky in a rather primitive way, a kind of Lancs surrealist H. Rousseau. Nor is there much to their composition. There is a real poetry about them, however.

What I liked much better were the small portrait heads, of girl students apparently, which I don't think he shows. These are quite straightforward, carefully literal paintings of matt texture, which have been painted with love and have a quite personal flavour even though the element of fantasy has been deliberately kept out of them. They are certainly the best portraits I've seen in Liverpool, apart perhaps from Nicholas Horsfield's of Eric Goldrein the barrister.

The blown-up collages shown in Bluecoat 63 were an afterthought almost, a development from his albums which he is showing in his next Portal Gallery exhibition. At these shows – the first was in 1960 – he sells quite well, evidently. An American dealer bought all the leftovers from the first two: 20 out of the 60 pictures he had sent. Local buyers: Melville Curlender – six. Peter Rockliff – some. O'Donahue, Kingham, English.[1] But he doesn't sell from the academy for some reason. And the Walker have never bought. In fact he doesn't particularly need to sell here. He has not had commissions because he didn't want them; he was asked to do murals but turned it down.

The collage albums were remarkable: worthy successors to Ernst's *La Femme 100 têtes*. And Jardine has been steadily producing both paintings and collages since that date, notably a fair-sized mosaic on the subject of *Midsummer Night's Dream*. Perhaps he is more of a Liverpudlian than one might think; certainly his stubborn, almost pig-headed imaginativeness has something in common with the tenacity of his fellow-Lancastrian L. S. Lowry, and although he rarely exhibits in the north of England the fact that he is admired and respected by such a very different younger artist as Henri indicates that he is an ineradicable part of the Liverpool scene.

These are just the handful of artists whose work I chose, arbitrarily perhaps or accidentally, to study. There are many others. John Hart, for instance, a slight spectacled figure of buzzing energy, not only runs an outstanding department at the College but produces a steady output of non-figurative paintings; the last batch I saw were brownish abstractions on hardboard with much deep scratching. Like Charles Burton, the head of the department of painting, he no longer sends to the academy, but his work is in a number of Liverpool collections, including the students' common room at the School of Architecture. I have already mentioned John Edkins, then at the College, a hard-edge abstractionist from London who before coming up to Liverpool had not exhibited since his student days; the picture which the Walker Gallery bought in 1963 was the first he sold in Liverpool, though he was offered (and turned down) a commission to do a church mural for Weightman and Bullen,

[1] Melville Curlender is a successful Liverpool builder, who gave the Walker Gallery its new coffee bar. Rockliff, a prominent amateur musician and chairman of the Bluecoat Forum, works in the family printing firm. James O'Donahue and Norman Kingham are architects, with offices in the Bluecoat Chambers; their two firms are collaborating on the new Strand-Paradise scheme. Stanley English is the sculptor and a member of the Liverpool Academy.

136 An artist revealed by Liverpool:
the late John Edkins's *Fortification*

137 John Edkins: *Seven Answers*. Bought by the Walker
Art Gallery from the 1965 Liverpool Academy

apparently because he felt unable to make any aesthetic compromises. Long plagued by illness, he died on 20 August 1966, only a few months after his first one-man show at the Bluecoat Chambers. He was an artist of unmistakably high quality who found Liverpool stimulating and felt that the academy had given his pictures their first external contracts; his colleagues quite rightly had a high respect for him and are sure that sooner or later he would have achieved major success.

Among the others there is Robin Riley the sculptor, who lives in Liverpool 8 though he teaches at Preston; he was responsible for the excellent relief at St Kevin's School, Kirkby and for the recumbent Christ in one of Weightman and Bullen's churches at Blackley near Manchester (St Clare's, Victoria Avenue), as well as for the unhappy Bold Street figure. There is Don McKinlay, now making very sensitive and original wooden sculptures

138 Two wood sculptures by Don McKinlay

in a strange patchwork style. There is Sean Rice, already mentioned, and Fred Bushe, two good sculptors in metal. There is Herbert Tyson Smith, still working at all kinds of stone carving jobs at the age of 82 in the back yard of the Bluecoat Chambers, and other long-standing pillars of the Sandon Society in Edgar Grosvenor, a clever caricaturist slightly in the Beerbohm tradition, J. Coburn Witherop the Walker Gallery's restorer and Roderick Bisson, a pioneer of the modern movement generally in Liverpool, who was exhibiting abstract work as long ago as 1936 and recently had the pleasure of seeing one of his prewar paintings in a respected London dealer's, priced at £400 and attributed to Albert Gleizes.

They and a number of other more or less wholetime artists (there are about eighty members and associates of the Liverpool Academy alone, all but six of them local and few of them amateurs) play a considerable part on the local art scene: probably as much as some of those singled out for discussion above. There are also those now working outside Liverpool, like Gordon Fazakerley, a former student of the College, who became interested in the Situationist movement and went to live in Copenhagen. Likewise Fanchon Fröhlich the engraver does much of her work at Hayter's studio in Paris. But it seemed better to concentrate on a few varied figures, in the hope that not only their work itself but their very different temperaments and circumstances, their beliefs and doubts, their attitudes to art and their contacts (or otherwise) with their fellow-artists and with the Liverpool public, would throw some light on our very complicated subject. For it is not just a matter of who are the 'good' artists in the area. Public art and private art each demand different qualities in an artist; moreover a man may have a local importance which the outsider might never guess from seeing his actual work, either as a source of pride and encouragement to other artists or as a reminder (discouraging to some, certainly) that the highest standards can and must be pursued even in a provincial community, or again (as happened with Augustus John at the beginning of this century) by the sheer infectiousness of his energy and brilliance. People's interest in art; the uses they find for it; the relations between ephemeral and permanent, act and product, personality and its sublimation: the whole business is changing, in a state of flux. And on top of that we have the particular Liverpool situation and climate, and the possibility of its spontaneous expression in art.

I don't think myself that any artist in the area, though Edkins might have been the exception, could be trusted to make a success of a major public work of art; there are a few (by no means as many as Bluecoat 63's 'Artist works with Architect' show hoped to suggest) who could produce smaller public works that would not actually disgrace the city; there are perhaps half a dozen whose work on a more private scale might attract a knowledgeable collector or gallery director from any part of the Western world, including Liverpool itself. There are one or two artists who matter to the city also because of the standards they represent, or because they have shown the Liverpool flag (as it were) in galleries elsewhere or on the television screen, or because they form a small focus of creativity for their fellows. It is not a tremendous score if one thinks about it in relation to the city's reconstruction plans, to the public appetite for art there, or to other art centres in Europe and the USA. All the same it is a good deal more than most English provincial cities can boast, and if there is also the beginning of a distinctively Liverpool approach to artistic creation it could be important.

In my view there are signs of this, though so far it emerges more in the character of the artists concerned and in their closeness to the city's other media of expression (not excluding soccer and verbal argument) than in anything that could be called a recognizable style. But there is just a possibility that some spark might be struck in the visual arts which would lead the gifted schoolchild to turn to them again after leaving school, and attack them with the same passion as he has been attacking his drums or his electric guitar. The impetus of course need not come from Liverpool itself; familiarity with modern art and a certain active curiosity about it are growing throughout the country; the old snobberies have to contend with a new feeling that 'anyone can do it'; in short, for better or worse, art is opening up. But there are these local links with pop music and poetry and popular mythology, and any sense that things were really beginning to move in the Liverpool art world might provoke surprising reactions. Excitement stimulates excitement, especially in such a temperamental community, and there are many factors which might contribute: more signs of local interest, for instance, or a greater consciousness of Liverpool art on the part of other centres, or any purposeful involvement of artists in the city's reconstruction. Once a distinctive movement started it might be almost as hard to hold back as the Mersey Sound.

At the same time depression does breed depression, and Liverpool artists are vulnerable to discouragement, very much like the Liverpudlians as a whole. They are not yet a confident community, for all the advances of the past few years, nor are they a very cohesive one. It is a question of striking the right balance, for of course an artist who has no doubts of himself at all is likely to be rhetorical and boring; moreover, if group activities (with their -isms, manifestos and the rest) are good for publicity, solitude perhaps makes for more serious and more truly original work. But the rather poor support which the artists seem to have got from local collectors cannot help matters much. The very existence of a body of professional artists in Liverpool is a bit of a sham, for there are only two or three in the whole city who do not rely on teaching or some other primary employment, treating the sale of their works as a more or less irregular windfall. It is an unhappy fact that the average Liverpool patron no longer buys Liverpool work. In 1965, as we have seen, the academy sold thirty out of 137 exhibits for a total of £1,128: as

o

against an average total of £185 for the three preceding years. In present-day terms this is a remarkable achievement, but it seems pathetic when set against the nineteenth-century figures quoted on page 78, just as the sales from (and attendances at) the Moores shows have been pathetic by comparison with the early days of the Autumn Exhibition. Pathetic, that is, even when matching pound for pound; but in those days a pound meant rather more – to both patron and artist – then it does now.

Under such conditions the position of a painter without a teaching job to fall back on is bound to be extremely exposed. I only met one man in this category; nor did I hear of any other, though the sculptors can sometimes struggle through. He is James Cliffe, a portrait painter and decorative artist who has a studio in the Bluecoat building and did rather a good unsolicited portrait of Dooley for the 1963 academy show. His independence is not exactly an advantage to him. Thus he is not only frustrated and upset by the concessions to clients' taste which he sometimes has to make – a form of guilt which has held him back from applying for academy membership – but dreadfully vulnerable to any illness or disability. He told me that he feels outside the circle of Liverpool artists; very conscious that he cannot paint as he wishes, and anxious to break free from this bondage. But alas, if it isn't one kind of bondage it's another, and those who are free to paint as they want are tied to teaching jobs and to the place itself. This is the artist's dilemma, not only in Liverpool but in any other community which treats him primarily as entertainer or self-exhibitor, and has nothing it specially wants him to do.

8 : THE WIDER SCENE

In England as a whole the great change in the situation of the arts dates from the 1939–45 war. Four things seem then to have coincided to bring about an entirely new policy of state patronage, encouragement and diffusion. There

139 A successful public symbol. Zadkine's *The Destroyed City* on the Rotterdam waterfront

was a new public interest in the arts (and also in serious reading), brought about by the stress and boredoms of war. There was the general upheaval and destruction which forced people to innovate and extemporise without much regard for accepted tradition; thus there were concerts in music-halls, plays in factory canteens, art shows in pubs. There was a widespread concern with planning a new Britain, from the Beveridge Report down to those city plans so many of which seem to have remained on paper. And there were at the Treasury a group of officials and advisers genuinely anxious to promote the arts, the best-known being that brilliant member of the Bloomsbury circle, J. M. Keynes.

From this combination sprang first such wartime devices as the War Artists Advisory Committee and the Council for the Encouragement of Music and the Arts (CEMA): the first two bodies in this country designed to give systematic state patronage to the arts. At the same time an Arts Enquiry was set up by the Dartington Hall Trustees which, with a good deal of ministerial support, produced four reports almost equivalent to official Blue Books on the Visual Arts, Music, Drama and the Factual Film; the Visual Arts volume,[1] by a committee of fourteen under Dr Julian Huxley's chairmanship, being published in 1946. The position as set out in this extremely competent study was different in many essential ways from what it is now. The new rich had not yet begun buying modern pictures; prices were generally low. There was no municipal gallery approaching metropolitan standard; the Phaidon Press were the only publishers of art books worth mentioning; there were few instances of notable artists being commissioned to embellish churches or public places, and such as they were they dated from the war. But the Enquiry's ruling concept of 'State assistance to the visual arts' (p. 34) still dominates official and 'establishment' thinking on the subject, and its eight pages of suggestions (first formulated in November 1944) outline the system and many of the still unrealized objectives that have governed policy in this field for the past twenty years. Thus it proposed the setting up of an Arts Council and a Council of Industrial Design, which was put into effect before the report came out, and simultaneously a 'corresponding increase in the responsibility of local authorities', which was not. It favoured the grouping together of galleries, concert halls, civic theatres etc. to make cultural centres in large towns, and the establishment of Arts Centres in smaller ones.

Rising on the ashes of CEMA, the Arts Council was formed with a double task: in the terms of its Royal Charter,

> to increase the accessibility of the fine arts to the public throughout Our Realm, to improve the standard of execution of the fine arts . . .

At the same time its main financial effort was quietly directed to a third objective, the building up of a national opera: something that was passionately desired by a number of influential enthusiasts but was not specified in the charter at all. These three aims are not necessarily incompatible, but it can hardly be said that the Council has pursued them all equally – thus in the year 1963–4 out of a total budget of £2,751,676, £1,215,000 went to subsidize Covent Garden and the Sadler's Wells Trust and £117,007 on other operatic and ballet ventures, as against £55,199 for the visual arts for the whole of England (excluding the North East) – and since the closing down of its regional offices accessibility has taken very much third place. It is not that the Council is reluctant to support local initiatives for restoring the balance, as the case of the North East will show when we come to it, but it has largely abandoned the effort to think such initiatives out for itself. As far

[1] *The Arts Enquiry. The Visual Arts.* A Report sponsored by the Dartington Hall Trustees, Oxford University Press 1946.

as the visual arts in Liverpool go, for example, it plays no real role apart from the rare despatch of an important exhibition to the Walker Gallery and the still rarer purchase of a local artist's work. Intermittently the Director of that gallery sits as a member of the council's Art Panel (twenty-four strong), but its composition is mainly metropolitan, and most of the Council's work for the visual arts consists of organizing exhibitions without specific regional interests in mind, though it is prepared to make small grants to artists' societies and to non-profit-making commercial galleries. Its local influence is an indirect and intangible one, springing from the general stimulus which it has given the arts in this country, from the exhibitions which it circulates,[1] and the effect of its big London exhibitions in promoting the greater visual curiosity to which we have already referred.

In 1958 the Calouste Gulbenkian Foundation, an international philanthropic body set up under the will of the oil millionaire, formed a committee under the chairmanship of the former permanent head of the Treasury, Lord Bridges, to review the needs of the arts in Britain. The committee quickly decided that it was in the provinces rather than in London that the arts particularly needed help,[2] and Liverpool was one of the six cities where they went to gather evidence. Like the founders of the Arts Council, they wished both to pursue high (but undefined) standards and to further accessibility; at the same time they called for 'more scope for experiment' in the arts and a greater effort to promote their appreciation among the young.[3] They criticized the existing system of state patronage on three main grounds: that it operated through existing bodies instead of helping new needs; that it was weighted against experimental art (a contention which could hardly be put forward today); and that it did 'far too little' for the provinces.[4] To remedy this they made a number of proposals, of which the most original was the grouping together of local authorities (on the analogy of the Area Museum Council for the South West) to work with an arts officer paid, initially, by the Foundation: a scheme subsequently put into effect in Newcastle and the North East. They supported the provision of more Arts Centres, the institution of picture loan schemes by universities and colleges and the appointment by the former of artists on short-term contracts. They were concerned at the dropping of art

---

[1] In the year 1962–3 five of the temporary exhibitions in the Walker Art Gallery were organized through the Arts Council.

[2] *Help for the Arts.* A Report to the Calouste Gulbenkian Foundation 1959. United Kingdom and British Commonwealth Branch, the Calouste Gulbenkian Foundation, London 1959, paragraph 4.

[3] Ibid. paragraph 16.

[4] Ibid. paragraph 43.

by many schoolchildren after the age of fourteen, and hoped that both private and public patrons could be induced to include works of art in plans for new buildings. What exactly could be done about these matters they did not say, but they pointed out that a trust or foundation had great advantages over bodies like the Arts Council: it could back individuals, and it could afford to make mistakes.

Such examples of comprehensive thinking have been infectious. In 1958 the chief provincial art galleries banded together at Sheffield to press for greater state recognition, both in the matter of sharing new accessions to the national heritage (such as works given to the state in lieu of death duties) and in that of direct government grants. This move, in which Cotton of Liverpool was prominent, resulted first in the special grant for the Walker Gallery's Rubens, the first ever made to a provincial gallery, then in the stepping up of the purchase funds made available through the Victoria and Albert Museum from £2,000 to £25,000 a year (for 1960–1), and finally to a full *Survey of Provincial Museums and Galleries*[1] by the Standing Commission on Museums and Galleries originally set up in the 1930s. The Commission, whose members included the chairman of the Arts Council's Art Panel and one of the Bridges Committee – indeed the views expressed by these bodies are often close to the extent of overlapping – recommended the organization of further Area Councils on the lines of that in the South West, an increase in School Museum Services (i.e. organized visits to galleries, and loans to schools from them), greater co-operation between cities and their universities, and, among much else, the further increase of the purchase funds from £25,000 to at least £200,000 a year. They now stand at half that sum.

Private industry and organized labour have been caught up in the process. In 1963 the Institute of Directors, after Sir Kenneth Clark had addressed their annual conference, set up their own Arts Advisory Council under the general direction of the Arts Council's retiring secretary, Sir W. E. Williams. This will advise businesses about buying works of art, developing amateur activities and choosing worthwhile artistic enterprises to support; and it is clear from its composition[2] that its judgments will not differ greatly from the Arts Council's own. Patronage of this sort has of course been exercised independently by individual industrialists with a personal or professional interest in the arts, notably John Moores and Sidney Bernstein, whose Granada Television has not only built up the excellent collection of pictures and sculpture already referred to but formed a Northern Arts and Sciences Foundation to support the arts in the provinces. Granada has its own adviser

[1] Her Majesty's Stationery Office, 1963.
[2] Given in *Investing in the Arts*, Institute of Directors, London 1964.

in these matters – Sir Gerald Barry, the director of the 1951 Festival of Britain, which set new standards for the public use of modern works of art – and it specifically hopes to revive the individualism of the regions and make our provincial cities comparable with those of Italy and Germany. Its first measures have been in Manchester, where it has endowed a chair of Drama at the university and set up a school of acting. It has made grants to Sheffield and Lincoln repertory theatres and founded fellowships at York University and Manchester College of Art. In 1962 it bought Epstein's *Genesis* and *Jacob Wrestling with the Angel* for public exhibition.

The Trade Union movement has so far confined itself to gestures. At its 1955 congress it pressed the government to increase the Arts Council grant, in 1959 it called for a comprehensive review of state and municipal patronage; which the Prime Minister declined. Then in 1960, on the motion of Ralph Bond of the Association of Cinematograph, Television and Allied Technicians, it passed a resolution (number 42 on the paper) headed 'Promotion and Encouragement of the Arts':

Congress recognizes the importance of the arts in the life of the community especially now when many unions are securing a shorter working week and greater leisure time for their members.

It notes that the trade union movement has participated only to a small extent in the direct promotion and encouragement of plays, films, music, literature and other forms of expression including those of value to its beliefs and principles.

Congress considers that much more could be done and accordingly requests the General Council to conduct a special examination and to make proposals to a further Congress to ensure a greater participation by the trade union movement in all cultural activities.[1]

As a result of this vote the TUC general council's statement to the next year's congress included a carefully-reasoned twelve pages accepting that 'public support for the arts is at present totally inadequate' but rejecting all idea of direct promotion by the movement as unnecessary and liable to encourage propaganda art and 'sectarian "workers'" cultural activities'.[2] In the council's view it would not help attract working class audiences any better if works of art were to deal more with working class experiences and aspirations, nor was there any reason to distinguish between workers' tastes and other people's. Local trade union bodies ought certainly to become more closely associated with the available cultural enterprises – by organizing visits by trade union parties, for instance, and keeping members informed about

[1] *Report of Proceedings at the 92nd Annual Trades Union Congress;* TUC, London 1960, p. 506.
[2] *Report of Proceedings at the 93rd Annual Trades Union Congress;* TUC, London 1961, p. 197.

cultural events – and trades councils should 'initiate or support'[1] anything that might promote a wider trade union interest. But the criteria must simply be those of 'integrity and of a respect for the highest standards'. In short, said the council,

> They do not wish the trade union movement to seek to exploit the arts for narrowly trade union purposes; nor do they wish, or intend, to commit the trade union movement to uncritical support of any particular cultural interest. But they are convinced of the need for closer relationships at every level between the trade union movement and those concerned directly with the arts . . .[2]

None the less on the strength of the 1960 resolution the playwright Arnold Wesker launched his Centre 42 with a number of eminent trade unionists on its council and the double aim of taking good art, both highbrow and low to trade union branches throughout the country, and at the same time stimulating local creativity. This interesting scheme was more radical than anything else since 1945 – it was the only one to look like developing new art forms, for instance – and in 1962 six 'trade union festivals' in provincial towns were staged whose visual component consisted of a nine foot high triptych by John Bratby and exhibitions of work by schoolchildren and local artists. Receipts however only covered a tenth of the expenses; the TUC's Trades Councils' Joint Consultative Committee got alarmed at so many unauthorized costs; the audiences were not, it seems, fired; and the local art was bad. Liverpool Trades Council was among those which Wesker visited, but it showed no enthusiasm for such a festival; Henri and Gorman called on the centre in London, but felt that it would not combine with their own ideas. The connection with the unions seems thereafter to have become more tenuous, the element of social pioneering less. Apart from the General Council's complaint about costs, nothing more has been said about art and culture at the TUC's annual congresses. On its side, Centre 42 is now concentrating almost entirely on raising funds from other sources to build a threatre-cum-arts-centre in the splendid Victorian ex-engine shed which has been given it in Camden Town, from which teams can be sent to any provincial communities that ask for them. Provincial centres are to follow; the ultimate ideal is that all artistic work should be presented to the public free.

In 1964 when the Labour party was returned to power – with the Liverpool constituencies leading the swing and Huyton returning the new Prime Minister – Miss Jenny Lee became an Under-Secretary responsible for the Arts: initially in the Ministry of Works but later transferring (as from 1

---

[1] *Report of Proceedings at the 93rd Annual Trades Union Congress*, TUC, London, 1961, p. 202.
[2] Ibid., p. 203.

March 1965) to that of Education. It was the first time a British Government had made such an appointment, though it had in fact been proposed two years earlier in a Conservative Political Centre pamphlet called *Government and the Arts*.[1] There is not really much difference between the parties in this field; thus the Conservative pamphlet dealt in the now accepted way with problems of patronage, the need for an increased contribution to local authorities, and the filling of gaps in public collections; and when in February 1965 Miss Lee produced her own White Paper *A Policy for the Arts. First Steps* (Cmd. 2601) it represented above all an attempt to accelerate the whole existing process. According to her paper the Arts Council in 1965–6 was to get nearly £500,000 more than it expected (for 1966–7 the grant went up another £1,800,000); the purchase funds allotted to local galleries and museums through the V and A were to go up to £104,000; arts centres and regional associations were to be specially encouraged; in the words of paragraph 43, 'A network of this kind should be developed to cover the whole country.' The work done for the arts in the schools was praised, though concern was felt that after school 'the impetus seems to weaken' (paragraph 60); it was hoped that local authorities and other public bodies would take to including works of art in their new buildings and displaying good pictures in their old ones; the government undertook to set an example. At the same time there is by implication in this same paper a certain criticism of existing assumptions; thus responsibility for the Arts Council has now been removed from the Treasury to the Ministry of Education, and when the paper was debated in the House of Commons on 27 April 1965 Miss Lee spoke of the danger of the Council's becoming a clique, and promised to bring in more regional representatives. Nor is she a member of Centre 42's council for nothing. For her paper may pay the usual tributes to high artistic standards, but it also states that:

> It is partly a question of bridging the gap between what have come to be called the 'higher' forms of entertainment and the traditional sources – the brass band, the amateur concert party, the entertainer, the music hall and pop group – and to challenge the fact that a gap exists.

– a sentiment, and a sentence, that has clearly not come from a civil service pen.

Such have been the main developments in the country as a whole, and they project a continually moving picture behind the Liverpool scene. For we now live in a land whose policy-makers recognize an obligation to see that the

[1] *Government and the Arts;* Conservative Political Centre, 1962.

arts flourish. This is partly the charitable approach of the helping hand, partly a genuine concern with high artistic standards, which private patronage alone would not be able to maintain. What actually constitutes high standards in the visual arts is decided neither by academic (or other) principles nor by public feeling but by taste: the taste prevailing among dealers and critics and virtually the whole of the official art world outside a few bodies labelled Royal. The maintenance of these consequently rather volatile standards matters more to the policy-makers than the satisfaction of local demands for art; but they recognize this as an obligation too and are increasingly uneasy about their relative neglect of it. Like all administrators they have a tendency towards formal simplification, seeing virtue in arts centres and regional or area associations rather than a confusion of different cities and individual artistic enterprises. They are apt to applaud reflections of their own taste – witness the *Survey of Provincial Museums and Galleries*'s criticism of purchases from the Royal Academy and enthusiasm over the penetration to the smaller galleries of more acceptable modern artists (paragraphs 25–7) – not perhaps realizing how easily this can lead to a tasteful uniformity. But they have fired a growing number of industrialists with their view that the arts must be supported, and now that it has become accepted orthodoxy the local authorities are increasingly following suit.

Thus if Liverpool wishes to pursue a more active visual arts policy it can call for support from several quarters, with good hope of getting it. And there are a number of lesser bodies and schemes, some of them dating from long before the developments of the past twenty years, which are also there to help. It is worth briefly noting these, as it is surprising how often they are ignored or the subject of misunderstanding. On the exhibition side, to start with, there are the travelling exhibits available to schools, training colleges, etc., from the Victoria and Albert Museum Circulation Department and the Council of Industrial Design. On the public art side there is the Society of Mural Painters, which is a professional body including such well-known artists as Ivon Hitchens and Leonard Rosoman and able to guarantee a workmanlike job at a set scale of fees; there is also a register now being maintained for the RIBA by the International Association of Plastic Arts, which lists more than 100 artists capable of working in collaboration with architects and gives photographs of their work. On the design side the Council of Industrial Design already in 1960 mounted a show in the Bluecoat Chambers which was seen by 37,000 people in fifteen days and linked with specially-selected displays in certain shops. On the civic design side there is an RIBA scheme for studying 'urban renewal' – i.e. methods for the more or less economic rescue of declining streets and districts which might

otherwise be pulled down – and there is also the Civic Trust, which was started in 1957. Besides offering an annual prize to stimulate schemes of local self-improvement this industrially-supported body has successfully propagated the idea of street 'face-lifts' where shopkeepers and property owners carry out a co-ordinated plan of redecoration and redesign under a single architect. Such efforts have been found to pay in terms of increased trading, though the first examples have tended to reduce interesting visual idiosyncrasies to pastel shades, Festival of Britain plastic lettering, and a common level of accepted good taste.

Many of the measures that a provincial city might adopt, some of them blessed by the senior policy-makers, have already been put into effect in one place or another. The biggest and in some ways the most interesting of such schemes is the North East Association for the Arts, which was founded in Newcastle at the end of 1961 with Arthur Blenkinsop, now the Labour Member for South Shields, as its first secretary. This is a joint enterprise of some fifty local authorities stretching from Berwick-on-Tweed to the North Riding, who have set up what is in effect an Arts Council for the region, based on Newcastle. It is supported by the proceeds of $\frac{1}{8}$d rate (more or less) all round; by private industry to the extent of about £6,000 in 1964–5 (three-quarters of it from ICI, Procter & Gamble and Tyne Tees Television); and, rather more symbolically, by trades unions and working men's clubs, who together contributed just over £100 for the same period. It also administers the Arts Council's subsidies for most of the enterprises in its area (£22,000 in 1964–5), while the Gulbenkian Foundation pays the salary of its full-time arts officer as the Bridges Committee suggested. So far the federation has not been able to do much for the visual arts apart from subsidizing certain galleries and exhibitions, notably in Billingham, where a shop has been turned into an outpost of one of England's finest and most oddly-situated provincial museums, the Bowes Museum at Barnard Castle. It aims however to treble its effort in this direction, giving direct help to artists, supplying transport and catalogues for travelling exhibitions from the public galleries, and possibly sponsoring a big competition on the lines of the Moores shows. Both its last two annual reports have asked for showings of the major exhibitions normally confined to Edinburgh and London. The association would also like to see more patronage of the arts by industry, commerce, hotel owners and the unions, and has mooted the idea of 'a service of advice and contacts'. As yet however, it has only been able to illustrate the odd item of public sculpture[1] in the *North East Arts Review*, a magazine

[1] The sculptures illustrated are by Colin Davidson (stylised Vikings on the central parade at Jarrow), Kenneth Ford (abstract work outside Scotswood Road housing development, Newcastle),

which it published as a means of generating interest and giving an outlet to local writers. The magazine itself, a good idea in principle, seems to have fallen slightly flat and has now been replaced by adapting the existing poetry magazine *Stand*, edited by Jon Silkin and previously published from Leeds.

Likewise in the provinces there are a number of redbrick or new universities which have some sort of art department. Newcastle and Reading are special cases, for there the split that occurred in Liverpool never took place, and the university has remained responsible for the local college of art; that at Newcastle now being one of the best in the country, with its own gallery, the Hatton Gallery. But Bristol and Hull have lecturers in art history attached to their history department; Birmingham has the Barber Institute 'for the cultural benefit of all students', with some fine paintings in its collection; Aberystwyth has an arts and crafts section in its education department. Three such universities in England have actual departments of art history: Leeds, Manchester and Nottingham. So, in Scotland, do Edinburgh and Glasgow. The latter also has the Hunterian Museum, which includes a marvellous Rembrandt *Entombment* and an outstanding group of Whistlers, while Manchester, helped by a £10,000 grant from the Gulbenkian foundation, has taken responsibility for the Whitworth Gallery, previously an independent foundation devoted mainly to drawings and watercolours. In these cities, as in Birmingham, the university collection has been established in a place which already has a good gallery of its own.

In Manchester there are courses in Industrial Design Technology within the College of Science and Technology, now a part of the university. They are run by two lecturers in Industrial Design in the Department of Building, but are intended also for engineers and industrial designers proper, and in fact bear on much wider problems of management and modernization. Aesthetics has little place in this teaching. Ergonomics, or the study of working conditions, the handling of design information, statistics, computer programming, the design of systems: the subjects taught there have a much more scientific slant, with 'exercises in visual appreciation' only appearing at the end of the list.

Other universities have adopted the American system of short-term appointments for 'resident artists': an idea first introduced into this country some twenty years ago at Leeds, where the late E. C. Gregory founded fellowships for a sculptor, a painter and a poet, to be held in each case for three years. Nottingham followed suit, then York, where the Granada fellow-

Edwin Hawking (relief outside police headquarters, Middlesbrough), and Geoffrey Dudley (*Fertility* outside entrance to ICI main offices, Billingham). Mr Dudley is the late lecturer in sculpture at King's College, Newcastle; Mr Hawking teaches at Middlesbrough College of Art.

ship has been held in turn by a composer, a novelist and an artist; the latest to adopt this practice is Trinity College, Cambridge. Brighton is going considerably further by setting up its own arts centre, supported by the Gulbenkian Foundation to the tune of some £50,000 (spread over three years), with (it is hoped) studios, music rooms, gallery and theatre, as well as a number of resident practitioners. The object of such attachments, as has often been said, is at once to give the artist an agreeable atmosphere to work in and to let other members of the university see him in action and learn something of his point of view. Whether in the case of the visual arts the object is actually attained is another matter, which is much less often discussed.

Outside the universities there is a wide variety of other relevant schemes. Thus Manchester now has not only an industrial design exhibit as part of its Building Centre, but also its own Civic Trust for the North West which is run by a committee of local industrialists and guaranteed by thirty firms subscribing £500 a year apiece; its present director was formerly a member of Graeme Shankland's planning team. Coventry has the only new municipal art gallery to be completed since the 1930s, besides Basil Spence's cathedral and some rather melancholy sculpture in the shopping centre. Leeds runs a picture loan service from its art gallery; Birmingham has a privately-sponsored kiosk called the Ikon Gallery now showing modern art in one of the open spaces of the Bull Ring shopping centre, and is building an ambitious Midland Arts Centre for Young People with theatres, cinema, a 'visual arts pavilion' and other facilities for the under-26s grouped together in a park; while, to come back to the capital, there is a very successful scheme for providing works of living art for London hospitals. This was started by the Almoner of the National Hospital for Nervous Diseases, who some ten years ago began borrowing pictures from artists for hanging in waiting-rooms, wards and corridors that had remained bare ever since the hospital was built. The Nuffield Foundation then allotted £2,000 (later increased to £3,000) a year so that pictures could be bought, and lent to other hospitals too; a committee was formed which appoints two buyers every year; and today there are twenty-seven hospitals co-operating and eleven more on the waiting list, while forty of the borrowed pictures have been sold to impressed visitors, to the not unnatural satisfaction of the artists. There is also one rather different London venture that is worth mention because of its bearing on the problems of urban renewal. Areas of previously down-at-heel Georgian housing, notably on the Northampton Estate in Canonbury and at Kennington, have been improved and redecorated since 1948, with the result that rents approximately trebled over fifteen years and individual houses sold at a profit of about £5,000 apiece. This indicates that such areas can be made to attract the better-off; preserving them can be not only aesthetically right but also economically rewarding.

140 One of the best-known of recent English schemes: the Midlands Arts Centre for Young People, now under construction at Cannon Hill Park, Birmingham

Above all, London has progressed faster and faster than any provincial city in the public use of works of art. The sculptures, murals and mosaics that have gone up in the last twenty years or so, from the big Morley College murals by Keith Vaughan and Robert Medley to the Barbara Hepworth sculpture on John Lewis's Oxford Street store, are beyond counting, so that it is difficult now to go into any new office building without finding some example of modern art: not understood perhaps, and no doubt not liked, but accepted none the less, and indubitably there. The problem was well expressed by J. M. Richards in a survey of the new sculptures for the *Design and Industries Association Year Book* 1962–3, which incidentally illustrated

Geoffrey Clarke's big works on Thorn House and in the entrance to the Castrol building. He denied that the old aristocratic patrons

> always had a well-trained eye. It was often no more so than that of the modern businessman, the difference being that there used to be accepted standards to conform to. Now there are none, and the patron is thrown on his own resources. If he is sensible enough to know his own limitations he will seek advice – but whose advice?

The Greater London Council (ex-LCC) has been infinitely more enterprising than the Liverpool Corporation in commissioning works of art as part of new housing schemes and schools, and it has its own Advisory Committee on Art Acquisition (Patronage of the Arts). This body has existed since 1958 and is composed of equal numbers of Council members and members of the Arts Council's art panel, plus the Chief Architect and the art inspector from the Education Department who seems to have been the moving spirit. It plans schemes and nominates artists – normally to the Architect's, Housing or Education Committees, who may reject them – and has an allocation of £20,000 a year. Most of the works commissioned or bought have been for schools.[1] Mr Maurice Wheatley, the art inspector in question, told me that the resistance to purely abstract works is stronger among secondary than among primary schools, evidently because the former are at once more observant and more opinionated. In his view artists often work better for existing schools than in new buildings, where they deal only with the architects and make no contact with the people who are going to be in daily relations with the finished work. At the same time Mr Wheatley himself is responsible for buying prints and pictures for circulation round the schools; there is a library of art films, some of them made by teachers and financed by the Council; and about seventy schools are now taking circulating showcases from the Council of Industrial Design.

The great shift to public patronage, the new popularity of the arts among the young and the official acceptance of the modern idiom have all been paralleled elsewhere. What we are seeing in England is only part of a much wider movement which exists in all highly industrialized countries and spreads out from them as part of their influence on the rest of the world. Traditionally

---

[1] Artists commissioned in 1961 included Victor Pasmore (mural in Barnsbury Boys' Secondary School and mobile for Fairlawn School, Lewisham); Bernard Meadows, Ralph Brown, Karin Jonzen, George Ehrlich (all sculpture) and Robyn Denny (mosaic). Work was in progress by William Turnbull, Keith Vaughan, Robert Clatworthy, Uli Nimptsch and others. Details and locations are given in E. Lidbetter: 'An Experiment in Patronage', *Museums Journal*, London, June 1961, Vol. 61, no. 1, pp. 30–38.

we have been apt to lag behind the neighbours where the practice and enjoyment of the visual arts is concerned, but today this is hardly so, and the situation in a number of towns roughly comparable with Liverpool suggests,

141 The London County Council art patronage scheme. A conservative work: Karin Jonzen's *Mother and Child* on the Sydenham Hill housing estate

142 More advanced: the Rutherford school in Marylebone. Sculptural shapes by the architect, Leonard Manasseh

perhaps surprisingly, that the latter's effort and resources are now relatively good. Of course such comparisons cannot be exact; city finances, museum and art school administration, even the basis for reckoning art gallery attendance figures, all differ from one country to another, and much depends on the age of the town in question and its particular national status. None the less the details for such ports as Rotterdam, Marseilles, Boston and Genoa, all of which also have a population of about three-quarters of a million, as well as the smaller but still comparable Antwerp, do not wholly disgrace Liverpool. The galleries in Antwerp and Rotterdam are world-famous; they are older and better endowed than the Walker Gallery; yet they had fewer visitors over a comparable period. Only the privately-supported Boston Museum of Fine Arts, with six times the number of visitors and about twenty times the purchase money, implies a substantially different attitude to art. To quote the director of the Walker Art Gallery, who went there with his Chairman in the autumn of 1963: 'The fundamental impression is of a society using its art galleries far more intensively than we do.' Yet public art in Boston seems to be as neglected as in Liverpool, and there is no evidence of any strong local creative tradition.

In both Rotterdam and Antwerp however there has since the war been a development of public art, and particularly public sculpture, that makes even London's performance look trivial. In the former case this resulted naturally from the city's reconstruction after the bombing of 1940, and from the provision that sets aside 1 per cent of the cost of any public building for its decoration by works of art. At the beginning of 1963, for instance, there were eighty-two works listed there as commissioned or bought for new municipal buildings, mostly schools; the artists being all Dutch, though not necessarily local, and the average price in the £200–£600 range. A section of the art department (or *afd. Kunstzaken*) in the municipal offices is devoted to such projects, and where whole areas are concerned, as in a housing scheme, the percentage can be spent on the open spaces rather than the buildings themselves. This system however might not have caught the public imagination if it had not been for certain outstanding works, the two most important of which, Zadkine's *The Destroyed City* on the waterfront and Gabo's great abstract construction outside the Bijenkorf store, were due to private commissions. They and other sculptures by major international artists – Henry Moore's brick relief on the building centre and Marini's horseman on the Zuidplein – helped to stimulate a whole tradition of including sculpture or other forms of decoration in any new building whether official or not: the post office, insurance buildings, the new Unilever headquarters and so on. Undoubtedly Rotterdam is proud of the results. And as if that were not enough there is the municipally-financed Rotterdamse Kunststichting, which sets out to bring the public into contact with the arts by means of its own theatres and small galleries. There is the Kunstkring, an art club with about 1,000 members and a municipal subsidy of some 8,000 florins a year. On top of everything else the Ministry of Education will subsidize private purchases from certain approved exhibitions to the extent of 35 per cent of the price of the work.

At Antwerp, only sixty miles away and lying like Rotterdam (and Liverpool, for that matter), on a river estuary, there is a historic town with a great artistic tradition, a national gallery and comparatively little new building. Here in 1950 the first great open-air sculpture show was held in the Middelheim municipal park, some distance from the centre. This exhibition, which was the model for that at Battersea in London, has become a regular biennial event, and in 1958 it blossomed out experimentally into '*Het Beeld in de*

P

143 The example of Rotterdam, another bombed port.
Wessel Couzijn's *Unity Embodied* outside the Unilever building

144 Oscar Wenckebach's
Jacques. A popular public figure

Stad', an exhibition of similar works of modern sculpture scattered in streets, open places and other more or less suitable sites throughout the town. Simultaneously, starting in 1950, the municipality has built up the Middelheim park into an immense permanent open-air sculpture museum, with representative works by all the internationally best-known figures, including Moore, Hepworth, Reg Butler, Kenneth Armitage and others from this country. It is the only enterprise of its kind in the world, and the city spends some £10,000 a year adding to it. Leaving aside drawings and projects, it now contains over 200 works.

The closest to Liverpool of these continental ports is Hamburg, despite its much greater size, longer history and greater autonomy, and in recent years there has been a lively interchange of pop musicians between the two cities; it was indeed thanks to this that Stuart Sutcliffe was working there. The main art gallery, the Kunsthalle, is marvellously well off for nineteenth-century French paintings and modern works, mostly acquired when they were still quite cheap. There are good examples of the major impressionists, two particularly beautiful Corots, good Légers, Gris, Picasso, Munchs, Kokoschkas, Klee's *Der goldene Fisch*, a splendid Ensor still-life of 1896 and much else that no English provincial gallery could now hope to match. Similarly Bremen, with less than a third of the population, has two world-famous pictures in Monet's *Camille* and Manet's portrait of Zacharie Astruc; it also has a small museum devoted to Paula Modersohn-Becker, still little known in this country but a unique early twentieth-century painter and the outstanding artist of the local Worpswede school. But from our point of view the most remarkable thing in these two Hanseatic cities is Hamburg's collection of local scenes and subjects by distinguished modern artists. There are portraits and landscapes by Bonnard and Vuillard dating from 1913, a good Marquet and two slight but perfect Liebermanns of the Elbe. There is also a recent view of the city by Kokoschka and a portrait of Herr Brauer, its socialist president. (He is not a Lord Mayor, since Hamburg is not merely a city but a constituent province of the German Federal State.)

In Western Germany it is up to 2 per cent of public building costs, whether Federal or local, that has to be spent on decorative works of art, though there are many anomalies and variations as between provincial governments. In Hamburg, where there is a nine-man 'Art Commission' consisting of artists and officials, over 1,500 works have been commissioned in this way since the system began in 1951; the sum spent is now more than 1 million marks a year, and something like 130 local artists have recently benefited, with the lion's share going to about twenty-five. Likewise in France there have been regulations since 1951 laying down that 1 per cent

145 The example of Antwerp. The Middelheim sculpture park.
(The work on the left is by Duchamp-Villon)

of the cost of any school or university building above a certain size must be applied to 'un ensemble de travaux de décoration', the artist responsible being nominated by the architect and approved by a special committee at the Ministry of Culture. It is said that there have been long delays in clinching such commissions[1] there, and that some two-fifths of the funds theoretically available have not in fact been used. None the less 6 million (new) francs were spent in 1962 – about £450,000 – and by the end of that year 467 schools had been dealt with and nine out of ten French sculptors were thought to be dependent on such jobs for their living.

Neither in France nor in Germany however, have the results been satisfactory, and on 19 January 1963 the French Minister of Culture made a statement in the Assembly proposing that the system should be changed. Instead of the frequently wretched works of art by living sculptors that had been more or less gummed on to so many new buildings he suggested concentrating on a few first-rate artists and using the rest of the money to provide schools with good reproductions of the (national) classics – works

[1] See the report in *L'Express*, Paris, 14 February 1963.

146 The French example. One result of the 1 per cent law; jazz decorations on the new science buildings for Paris University

specifically 'qui ont fait la gloire de la France'.[1] And true enough even an alleged 'ville d'art' like Barentin in the Seine-Maritime, which had the former Minister of Education André Marie as its member and accordingly contains public statues by Rodin and Bourdelle, a vast mosaic by Gromaire and much else, appears as a hotch-potch of largely irrelevant objects, dotted among ugly buildings. But intelligible as Malraux's suggestion was, it met fierce opposition from the artists, Zadkine (for one) arguing that 1 per cent was already too little, and did no more than cover the cost of a preliminary maquette.[2] And if the French had erred by putting their bad art on public show the opposite policy in Germany evidently worked no better. For part of the objection, according to a report by the Hamburg Rechnungshof (or committee on public expenditure) for 1962[3] was that

> so far the public has hardly had a chance to become aware of all these works, as they are mainly situated in places or buildings to which few people have access.

147 The example of Hamburg and the 2 per cent rule. The right art in the wrong place

[1] *Journal Officiel.* 19 January 1963. *Not* 'la gloire de l'humanité', note.
[2] This and twenty-five other individual or collective protests are quoted in *Arts* (Paris), 20–26 February 1963.
[3] Quoted by Gottfried Sello in *Die Zeit*, Hamburg, 24 November 1964.

Thus situated they might well be even less appreciated than they would be out in the open: a nude statue by the excellent sculptor Gustav Seitz, for instance, seemed hardly appropriate to a police station, where it was liable to be thought to portray a naked policeman. As a result of such anomalies the 2 per cent rule (or *Verwaltungsanordnung über Kunst am Bau*) was amended by the city senate early in 1966 to allow the pooling of the sums allotted, more concentration on the more important (or more suitable) buildings and – a complete innovation in Federal Germany, this – the employment of non-local and even foreign artists.[1] It will be for the Art Commission to decide whether a given building is to be embellished or the money put aside, though they are still not empowered to commission work for existing buildings or for open spaces.

Such instances are a warning that the mere multiplication of works of art is not enough; nor is greater generosity with public money. Even the employment of the most eminent artists, as insisted on by M. Malraux, is a much more precarious business than enthusiasts seem to imagine; the UNESCO building in Paris, for instance, includes big works by Moore and Picasso, Arp and Miró, but none of them seems to have been designed with much awareness of the site, the building or its probable atmosphere (a function of the people using it, their interests and activities) and once the prestige of such names has worn off a bit the works themselves are going to look misconceived.[2] This lesson is driven home by the experience of Rotterdam and Antwerp. On the face of it theirs sound like astonishingly enlightened projects, examples to be quoted wherever the question of public art is under discussion. That does not stop the realization from being in many ways depressing. The Middelheim sculpture park is a solemn place, and there is something aimlessly funereal about the discreet placing of the statues among lawns, shrubberies and trees; sculptures conceived *in vacuo* and designed for galleries or competition juries look sadly out of place in so elegiac a setting. In Rotterdam the Zadkine is, like much romantic sculpture, a rather dated work, but at least it is a successful public symbol in the way that the Epstein at Liverpool should be but is not. The Gabo, if the spectator can forget the pretentious explanations that get tangled around such structures, is a sheer delight. But there is also a frightful lot of mediocre work on mediocre buildings, and the creative excitement, the new ideas and interests that ought to spring up as a result of so huge a scheme, are not in evidence.

[1] See Herr Sello's article 'Keine Angst vor Henry Moore' in the same paper of 29 April 1966.

[2] Already pointed out in Professor Edgar Wind's *Art and Anarchy*; Faber, London, 1963, pp. 94–5. 'In this building devoted to the cultural work of the United Nations the arts loiter about the place without function, distracted and disunited.'

148 Rotterdam's masterpiece. Naum Gabo's great construction outside the Bijenkorf store. (The derrick beyond, like the sheds, was connected with the building of the underground railway)

If Rotterdam were a success the Dutch artists would once again be the liveliest in the world. The fact that they are not shows that something has gone wrong.

Perhaps there has been too much tendency since 1945 to think simply in terms of patronage: to treat the problem as one of finding new patrons in the state, the local authorities and the great industrial and social institutions, to take the place of the self-glorifying monarch and the rich private collector. Abroad, provisions like the percentage rule have been thought up less because there is a real public demand for embellishment, or a school of artists whom it would be criminal not to employ on it, than as a means of giving people jobs. Too little distinction is made between those whose style and talents are suited to such work and those who are not. This applies whether the public patron chooses, like the French Ministry of Culture, to go only for the most eminent artists, or prefers to distribute his funds more evenly and thinly. The great lesson of the Baroque has not been learned: that it is not necessarily the best individual works of art that fit best into an architectural scheme. It is still common, even among architects, to think of decoration as something to be glued on to the building once finished; neither the kind of integration practised at Peterlee (where Victor Pasmore was a con-

149 A building at Peterlee in County Durham, where Victor Pasmore helped with the visual planning

sultant from the first, helping to decide even the siting of the houses), nor the possibility of shorter-lived, more changeable and adaptable forms of decoration have yet been much explored. In this country concepts like 'arts centre' and 'regional federation'[1] have passed into our cultural shopping lists without any very precise definition of what they involve. It is not clear, for instance, whether an arts centre is a centre primarily for creating the arts or simply for consuming them. Creation, as opposed to interpretation, does not benefit from having the audience on the spot; the studio and the gallery are best kept separate. Nor indeed is there any reason why the consumer institutions should all be centralized, unless this simplifies their introduction to cities which (unlike Liverpool) lack them. Ideas like the arts centre now seem to be bounced by our cultural planners like a football for rival players to tussle for and hope to kick in a particular direction;[2] there is no

[1] On 20 June 1966 a meeting of interested groups under the chairmanship of the Lord Mayor of Liverpool decided to set up a Liverpool Arts Association which would act as such a federation, and a working party was formed to plan it. The visual acts were not at first represented. One object of a federation is to permit the state to distribute funds which it is not allowed to give to individual organizations or groups. What the others are remains slightly unclear. It is apparently less difficult to set up new cultural administrative bodies than to remove such restrictions on the existing ones.

[2] Thus in Liverpool the Bluecoat Society would like to be regarded as an arts centre, while an independent claim for an arts centre of a primarily theatrical nature has been put forward from a

knowing where they may end up. Above all, the immense problems of the public's remoteness from much modern art and the artists' frequent indifference to its views have been left to solve themselves. The new patrons seem to think that they have a duty to be passive – as if patrons in the great ages of art had ever been that – and that there is nothing incongruous in introducing gallery-, even Biennale-type art into a lay public's daily lives. Such failure to face obvious difficulties, though not bound to be disastrous, is fair neither to the public nor to the artists, and generates among both parties an unfortunate sense that the whole position is false and slightly ridiculous. Getting the money and establishing the administrative framework are only the start of it. The development of a stimulating climate depends on other things.

Merseyside Arts Centre Association organized by the Royal Institution and Merseyside Unity Theatre. The Town Clerk has suggested the formation of a number of smaller centres to serve outlying areas as well. The City Centre Plan proposes a new arts centre building behind the Bluecoat Chambers to meet various currently unsatisfied needs. In my view it might be better if the magic words 'arts centre' were left out of such discussions.

9 : POINTS OF DOCTRINE

The weakness of the policy of the last twenty years is that it rests on assumptions which are very seldom discussed. Admittedly this saves a great deal of argument, and to those who feel that the assumptions are on the whole the right ones it may seem safer to establish them on grounds of authority, snobbery, faith and (strongest of all) custom than to thrash them out before a possibly unsympathetic public. None the less it is wrong, because under the surface they become widely and uneasily doubted, above all at a certain distance from our taste-making metropolis. 'The visual arts are integral to a civilization'[1]; 'in any civilized community the arts and associated amenities . . . must occupy a central place';[2] 'support for the living arts';[3] 'the needs of the arts';[4] 'the maintenance, improvement and development of artistic taste';[5] 'the healthy progress of artistic practice and appreciation':[6] phrases like these from the basic scriptures of the previous chapter obviously beg enormous questions. We are taking too much for granted, and artists and public alike know that we are, and once we start doing so it is difficult to know where to stop. The tacit assumptions breed an equally tacit[7] suspicion that the whole edifice is founded on make-believe; it becomes a castle in the air with no visible connection to our individual problems and hopes.

The rethinking of the relationships between art and the rest of life seems to go in waves, usually in response to the stimulus of great political events. Thus the French Revolution, taking up certain ideas of Rousseau's and Diderot's, evolved the notion of giant popular festivals and made the Louvre into the first great public gallery. The early nineteenth-century reformers in England saw art philanthropically, as a popular educational force; it was also they who most strongly pressed for a proper system of training in design for utilitarian ends. 1848, with its second, abortive outbreak of revolutions

[1] *The Arts Enquiry. The Visual Arts*, p. 42.
[2] *A Policy for the Arts. First Steps*, paragraph 14.
[3] Ibid, paragraph 25.
[4] *Help for the Arts*. Paragraph 1.
[5] Constitution for the North-Eastern Association for the Arts. Clause 2(a).
[6] *The Arts Council of Great Britain. The 19th Annual Report*. 1963–4, p. 13.
[7] It may be starting to find its tongue. See Marghanita Laski's radio talk 'Why spend public money on art?' in *The Listener*, London 8 April 1965, pp. 507–9. Miss Laski's point is that before we spend public money on anything we should know as far as possible what we are doing and why we are doing it.

throughout Europe, brought the triumph of Realism in French art: that more truthful and down-to-earth attitude to real-life subjects, which was oddly (and so far as we know unconsciously) reflected in the rise of the Pre-Raphaelites here. Something of the same interaction of aesthetics and politics could be seen again after the First World War, in the immediate artistic impact of the German and Russian revolutions, and, by a sharp but not wholly unnatural reaction, in the disastrous Nazi and Stalinist art policies that followed in the 1930s. The Second World War too had its repercussions in the shape both of the organizational developments outlined in the last chapter and of the doctrine of 'commitment' associated with Jean-Paul Sartre. But the longest and in many ways the most interesting of these periods of narrowing of the gap between art and society was that which followed the establishment of popular education in England and the Third Republic in France. Between about 1870 and 1905 a great new movement developed for the dissemination of the arts; both the arts and crafts movement and the new approach to design preached by Morris contained an element of social philosophy, while posters, coloured reproductions, photographic block-making and the first half-tone art books sprang up as new methods of popularization. It was then that bodies like the WEA, the Universités Populaires and the Russian Proletkult were started and the European Socialist parties turned into mass organizations, and as a result the social and artistic ideas of those years are still a part of traditional left-wing and popular educational thinking. All these waves are fairly distinct. What each threw up can be clearly recognized among the strange mixture of deadwood and treasure that now lies on the beach.

The oldest and commonest social use for art, once the magic and the sanctity had gone out of it, was to symbolize and celebrate: a religious figure or idea, a ruler, a military victory or, with Jacques-Louis David after 1789, a popular revolution. This concept was extended to apply not only to the individual work of art but to everything to do with the art of a given period. Thus the artists' committee of the Paris Commune voted on 15 April 1871 to set up 'vast rooms' for teaching and to circulate reproductions of masterpieces and 'images of morality and intelligence' to town halls as a contribution 'to the splendours of the future and the universal Republic'. 'Just as one says "le style c'est l'homme",' so Courbet's uncle is supposed to have told him many years earlier, "one ought to be able to say 'l'art c'est la société".'[1] This identification of the two familiar concepts was a new idea in the nine-

[1] Quoted in Champfleury's *Souvenirs et portraits de jeunesse*. Paris 1872, p. 182.

teenth century, though it is much the same notion as underlies Roscoe's doctrine of art in a mercantile city. The people who followed Roscoe however were more concerned with the purely economic arguments for cultivating the visual arts. In France this was taken for granted: by 1836 there were eighty provincial art schools there, and the connection between artistic training and a high standard of manufacture and workmanship had been clearly seen ever since Colbert's time. The English agitation for something of the same sort was associated with Radicals like Joseph Hume, Ewart and Wyse, and particularly with the great northern cities: Haydon in 1839 was clearly thinking of Liverpool and Manchester when he mooted 'a confederation of the leading towns to join in a petition for Schools of Design and State patronage for Art'.[1] The English art schools were subsequently set up, but the problem remained. More than half a century later Conway gave one of his Slade lectures on the subject of 'The Practical Value of Art':

> The plain hard-headed man-of-business in England may some day, possibly, begin to entertain a suspicion that the question, how to improve the artistic quality of our manufactures, is a practical question of the most solid importance.[2]

During the nineteenth century the idea of art as celebration became inextricably bound up with that of art as a moral force, as Dean Farrar put it, 'to refine, to elevate, to brighten, not only the palace of the noble but the cottage of the poor'.[3] This is a concept which has caused great trouble and suffering in the wrong hands, and to some extent it is still with us. We in this country associate it above all with Ruskin, to whom the Divine, the Good and the Beautiful seemed almost interchangeable, so that a fine work of art was at once a revelation of the deity and an encouragement to the good life. Morris, Watts and other enlightened art proselytizers of the end of the century took it over from him; thus Morris in 1879:

> in my mind, it is not possible to dissociate art from morality, politics and religion. Truth in these great matters of principle is one.[4]

In France the identification was made a great deal earlier; witness Diderot's judgment of the (to us often cloyingly sentimental) pictures of Greuze – the 'Jeune fille qui pleure son oiseau mort' in the 1765 Salon, for instance. It reappears in the admonition of the French revolutionary Société Populaire et Républicaine des Arts to the artists that their job was:

[1] *Life of Benjamin Robert Haydon.* 2nd edition. Longmans, London 1853, vol. III, p. 106.

[2] In his *The Domain of Art*; John Murray, London 1901, p. 87.

[3] From his sermon to the Liverpool congress of the National Association for the Advancement of Art in 1888, printed as a preface to its *Transactions*.

[4] From his lecture 'The Art of the People' in Birmingham Town Hall, published as a pamphlet in Birmingham that year and reprinted in G. D. H. Cole's centenary volume *William Morris*, Nonesuch Press, London 1948, pp. 534–5.

to choose subjects tending to instruct, to bring about a moral recognition, to inspire love of the country and enthusiasm for liberty.
– though this advice seems in the event to have carried little weight. And it fitted well with the strange republican utopianism that preceded and overlapped the mainly non-moralising realism of the mid-nineteenth century. Thus the left-wing Abbé Lamennais in his *Esquisse d'une philosophie* of 1841 saw art as expressing the ideology and social forms of its period and argued that it should now become the prophet of 'the religion of the future'. This part symbolic, part educative or even propagandist view of art found echoes in the great dissemination movement around 1900, just as the French Second Republic's moral-symbolic decorative projects by Chenavard found their successors in the Third Republic and Puvis de Chavannes. It underlay that early socialist mirage of the perfect society glimpsed in Morris's *News from Nowhere* and the Belgian Emile Vandervelde's references to 'la cité future': the 'cathedral of Socialism' which was the symbol of the Bauhaus in its first years. It was inherent in the arts and crafts movement, in the work of men like Walter Crane and Eric Gill, and in the readiness of Bonnard and Vuillard and the Nabis, unlike their Impressionist predecessors, to turn to decorative art. It was also the very essence of Tolstoy's artistic theories.

At the same time it was wide open to use or abuse by men whose primary interests were not artistic at all but political or religious. Under Napoleon III, for instance, the new realism in the arts was seen as subversive and immoral: 'for him,' wrote one of the Imperial cultural officials, Arsène Houssaye, 'everything was a means of governing'.[1] Although it was the emperor's policy outwardly to encourage the arts (the great exhibitions being of particular importance in speeding up European cross-fertilization) his art adviser Count Nieuwekerke was determined to stop 'eccentricity' and 'false vocations'. 'France is fertile,' he said at the opening of the 1863 Salon – the year of mass rejections and the Salon des Refusés – 'and her artists are the first in the world, just like her soldiers.'[2] Flaubert may have been acquitted of blasphemy in *Madame Bovary*, but the court that tried him took good care to denounce any idea of Realism,

> which would be the negation of the good and the beautiful and, by giving rise to works offensive to eye and mind alike, would commit continual offences against public morality and right living.[3]

The whole realist trend was subversive, and when Millet was rejected in

[1] Houssaye: *Confessions* II, p. 428.
[2] Quoted from *Le Moniteur* for 7 July 1863 in Fernand Desnoyers: *Le Salon des Refusés;* Azur Dutil, Paris 1863, p. 85.
[3] *Gazette des Tribunaux*, 9 February 1857, quoted on p. 435 of the Editions de Cluny edition of *Madame Bovary*. Paris 1936.

1863 he assumed that it was as a socialist[1], which in fact he was not. A similar but exactly contrary distortion of art in that period can be seen in the socialist philosopher Proudhon, whose *Du principe de l'art* of 1865 treats art as essentially propaganda. Where the existing state was using it as an instrument of repression, he argued, it ought rather to become the embodiment of society's aims, 'an idealist representation of ourselves and of nature, with a view to the moral and physical perfecting of our species'.[2] In both views what mattered was first the message, the subject, secondly the artist's respectful or critical approach to it.

At the end of the century Max Nordau evolved his unfortunate concept of *Entartung*[3] or 'degeneration': the notion that artistic movements could be psychologically healthy or sick. This was all that was needed to give the moral interpretation of art that final twist which we find in the reactionary doctrines of the 1930s. Both in Soviet Russia and in Nazi Germany a decade of officially-supported utopianism, experiment and flirtation with abstractionism and machine art was followed by its equally official condemnation as a symptom of social disease. Modern art was 'unhealthy'; depending on whether Zhdanov or Hitler was speaking it was seen as a symptom of Western bourgeois decadence or as 'art Bolshevism'; in other words it was identified with the regime's bogey-man, whatever colour he might be. In both cases alike it was clearly the politician's duty to stop it, to promote art with a 'content' or obviously intelligible subject and message, and to set the artists, as a disciplined task force, to glorifying what he saw as society's proper ethics and ideals. These naturally proved to be the historical forces he himself represented, the policies of which he was spokesman and, by an all too easy extension, the spokesman's own person. Duration apart, there was only one real difference between the two repressive and authoritarian aesthetic systems: the Nordic, racial, anti-semitic element which was present in Nazi but not in Soviet art. Even this was only a perversion of Proudhon's principle of representing idealized human specimens; the Nazis wanted blond heroes, and that is what the artists had to depict.

The abuses invited by the socio-ethical view of art have led at one time and another to its total rejection. Already in the 1850s Champfleury was protesting that

---

[1] Letter from Millet to Sensier, quoted in Moreau-Nelaton: *Millet raconté par lui-même*, Paris 1921, II, p. 129.

[2] Proudhon: *Du principe de l'art;* Garnier, Paris 1865, p. 198.

[3] *Degeneration;* Heinemann, London 1895. Nordau's principal degenerates were the Pre-Raphaelites, the French symbolists, Tolstoy, Wagner, Maeterlinck, Ibsen, Zola and Nietzsche. Since he finds symptoms of serious psychological abnormality in these and many other outstanding figures of the period it becomes difficult to see who, apart from Turgenev, he approves of.

It's neither painting's nor music's function to expound social systems; as soon as painting turns to education it ceases to be painting. It becomes a pulpit which is depressing and disagreeable to look at, for it is a pulpit without a preacher in it.[1]

And Zola, writing a year after Proudhon's book had appeared:

His *rational art*, his brand of realism, is really just the negation of art, the tedious illustration of philosophical clichés. My kind of art on the other hand is a negation of society, an affirmation of the individual, divorced from all rules and social obligations.[2]

Yet Zola was the outstanding social novelist of his time[3] and Champfleury was not only one of the founders of realism and the leader of the Diderot revival but also the first systematic student of the popular arts. There is an apparent inconsistency here which we find also in the position of Sir Herbert Read, who argues that art is purely autonomous; that its symbols symbolize nothing outside the artist himself; that it

is not and never has been subordinate to moral values. Moral values are social values; aesthetic values are human values.[4]

– yet feels that it is a great social force none the less. Art in his view does lead to moral improvement, even if it is fatal to judge it by that; it does effect changes in the texture and quality of a society; and although Tolstoy is wrong in thinking that it reduces violence it could none the less fulfil humanity's needs for 'a principle of strife or rivalry which is not mutually destructive . . . but which nevertheless gives the moral equivalent, the *courageous tone* of war'.[5] Thinkers whose prime concern is with the arts, it is perhaps fair to say, will fight any moralist or politician for art's right to be independent, while admitting to themselves that it is not.

Art as a form of education for all citizens was one of the basic principles of Plato's Republic, but for the greater part of the nineteenth century the practical, economic view of the matter prevailed; indeed in 1852 art schools in this country were put under a new section of the Board of Trade called 'the Department of Practical Art'. In the art education of that time, writes Professor Quentin Bell,

[1] Champfleury: *Grandes figures d'hier et d'aujourd'hui*. Paris 1861, pp. 236–7. From the section on Courbet.

[2] Zola: *Mes Haines*. Nouvelle édition. Charpentier, Paris 1879, p. 39.

[3] Not however to the author of *Eric, or Little by Little*, who in his sermon to the Liverpool Art Congress spoke of him as having 'prostituted the gift of genius to the service of corruption'.

[4] From his essay on 'Society and Culture' (Lecture delivered at York in 1946) in *The Grass Roots of Art*, New edition, Faber, London 1955, p. 93.

[5] Ibid., p. 44.

> The curriculum had nothing to do with aesthetic feeling, nothing to do with nature or the imagination; it was established not for the benefit of the pupils but for that of their prospective employers.[1]

To those who associated art with wider human concerns, whether social or religious, this was an impossibly stunting attitude: harmful not only to the art students but to education in general. It was Ruskin above all who changed it, with his constant flow of noble prose in favour of a less mundane approach. 'Art,' wrote G. F. Watts in 1880, 'pressed into the service of general education, as once it was of religion, might again be great;' and in 1885 Ebenezer Cooke published the two articles on child art which Read sees as the first symptoms of the modern outlook.[2] This was the period of the foundation of the Roscoe Chair and the Walker Gallery, of the move of the Liverpool College of Art into its present building and of the pictures for schools scheme sponsored by T. C. Horsfall and the Manchester Museums. In 1876 the Kyrle Society was founded 'to bring beauty home to the people' by providing works of art for hospitals, workmen's clubs and parish rooms; by 1888 it had eight or nine provincial branches.[3] Nor was it all just a great educational movement in which art was, as it were, getting caught up. There was also a feeling that the arts might be 'healthful influences'[4] for the industrial proletariat (as against drink); that they might be a 'graceful source of recreation': a hope which had already been implicit in the founding of the Mechanics' Institutes half a century earlier. Views to this effect were expressed by Watts in his paper for the Edinburgh Art Congress of 1889, where he begged 'the heads of firms, often themselves men of culture, lovers and collectors of art', to start 'encouraging their workmen to be artistic.'[5]

For all his agreement with Watts, this was much what Morris at the same Congress called 'a kind of mumbo-jumbo fetishism for the working class. . . . Just the sort of tommy rot that curates talk about religion at mothers' meetings, and Oxford professors say about education at Cutlers' Feasts.'[6] Influenced more by Ruskin's social and political writings than by his ideas of art, Morris began lecturing in 1878, and from the first he spoke as a practising craftsman and in the name not of paternalism but of the working man. From

---

[1] Quentin Bell: *The Schools of Design;* Routledge, London 1963, p. 261.

[2] Quoted in part in Read: *Education Through Art;* Faber, London 1943, pp. 167–8, and originally published in the *Journal of Education*, December 1885, pp. 462–5, and January 1886, pp. 12–15.

[3] According to its statement in the *Transactions of the National Association for the Advancement of Art* for that year.

[4] *George Frederic Watts*. Vol. III, 'His Writings', Macmillan, London 1912, p. 264.

[5] Ibid., p. 265.

[6] Quoted from Bruce Glasier in E. P. Thompson: *William Morris Romantic to Revolutionary;* Lawrence and Wishart, London, 1955, p. 647.

Ruskin's *The Stones of Venice* he took the picture of the workman in the hey-day of Gothic architecture, happily and unselfconsciously contributing his best to a great work of art, and he saw a revival of 'the decorative arts' as a means of bringing back this lost pleasure in the things we use and the things we make. Leisure, to Morris, was not so much a gap to be filled by the consumption of art as an impending stimulus to its production. What he cared about was the barrier that had grown up between artist and craftsman – a point that can be found again in Walter Gropius's original Bauhaus programme of 1919 – and the need for what he called 'intelligent popular art'.[1] By this however, he meant something a good deal more remote than had Champfleury, whose *Histoire de l'imagerie populaire*, his *Chansons populaires des provinces de France* and *Histoire de la caricature moderne* all appeared in the 1860s; for to Morris the Renaissance was 'the fruit of the five centuries of free and popular art which preceded it, and not of the rise of commercialism which was contemporaneous with it':[2] an opinion that incidentally shows how far he was from the Roscoe doctrine that had prevailed in Liverpool. 'The absence of popular art,' he told the readers of the *Manchester Examiner* in 1883

> from modern times is more disquieting and grievous to hear from this reason than for any other, that it betokens that fatal division of men into the cultivated and the degraded classes which competitive commerce has bred and fosters.[3]

Unfortunately he let his understanding of that division become swamped in his 'hatred of modern civilization',[4] thus unwittingly making a further division in the decorative arts between industry and craft. It was not really healed until the Bauhaus began its collaboration with industry in the 1920s.

'In theory', said a leading article in *The Times* of 26 November 1889, 'we all acknowledge that it is desirable to bring art home to the masses of the people'. The movement for the diffusion of art which spread out from England towards the end of the century was immense; its manifestations followed one another thick and fast. None the less it was compounded of

[1] Morris: *Selected Writings and Designs;* Pelican, London 1962, p. 93. From the lecture on 'The Lesser Arts', delivered in 1878.

[2] From 'Gothic Architecture', a lecture to the Arts and Crafts Exhibition Society. Morris: *Stories in Prose. Stories in Verse. Shorter Poems. Lectures and Essays.* Edited by G. D. H. Cole. Nonesuch Press, London 1948, p. 25.

[3] *The Letters of William Morris to his Family and Friends.* Edited by Philip Henderson, Longmans, London 1950, pp. 165–6.

[4] *Selected Writings and Designs*, p. 36. From 'How I Became a Socialist', originally published in *Justice*, 16 January, 1894. Morris's admirers today tend to play this hatred down, but I think it has to be admitted. See also the lecture on 'Gothic Architecture' quoted above.

Q

some very contradictory elements. There is all the difference in the world between the improving effects of looking at art and the self-realization of creative work; between instruction and fun; between the charitable distribution of the arts as a good social influence (ranging from therapeutic tonic to political propaganda) and their conscious annexation by groups who have been denied them. Morris in particular treated art not as a mere social benefit but as a basic right which ought to be 'felt to be as necessary to man as his daily bread,[1] and a number of continental socialists followed him in this: Steinlen's teacher Georges Renard in Switzerland, for instance, and Emile Vandervelde, the Belgian Socialist leader.[2] In 1896 Edgar Steiger, editor of the party illustrated weekly *Neue Welt*, told the German Socialist conference at Gotha that

> We want to take all that's good and beautiful from former social systems, plus the whole capacity to enjoy it, and lay it before the working people. . . . So that we may all become complete men.[3]

Against that there was the French *Art pour Tous* society visiting London on 14 July 1904 and being received at establishments like Buckingham Palace, the Westminster Deanery, and the Association of Conservative Clubs; there were wealthy art philanthropists like Philip Rathbone and the Earl of Carlisle; there were for that matter R. A. M. Stevenson's uplifting Liverpool ladies. A very successful society was formed at the Mannheim Kunsthalle a few years later which organized lectures in the gallery (seventy-eight in the winter of 1913–14, with an average attendance of 455), bought works of art and ran an annual lottery whose winners could have them at a tenth of the price. Aimed at 'the moulding of a New Man',[4] it was called the 'Freie Bund zur Einbürgerung der Kunst': the association 'for giving citizenship to art'.

Part of this whole movement to tighten the links between art and society has always been the idea of public art, which would get out of the museums

---

[1] *Selected Writings and Designs*, p. 37.

[2] Renard's article 'L'Art et la vie de tous les jours' in *L'Art pour tous*, Paris, vol. II (1904), p. 343, cites Ruskin and Morris as originators of the notion of beauty as a fundamental human right. Vandervelde's lecture of the same year on 'Le Socialisme et les artistes', reprinted in his *Essais socialistes; Alcan*, Paris 1906, likewise quotes Morris and complains that 'art doesn't exist for the great mass of the workers'. Being harder-headed than Morris, he argued that it was more important to concentrate on socialized industry rather than the artist-artisan with his rich clients, and he recognized that the workers tend to like conventional and second-hand forms. (See his p. 362.)

[3] *Protokoll über die Verhandlungen des Parteitages*. Berlin 1896, first day.

[4] *Die Kunstmuseen und das deutsche Volk;* Kurt Wolff, Munich 1919, p. 31. From Fritz Wichert's essay 'Die bildende Kunst als Mittel zur Selbstgestaltung des Volkes', which describes the Mannheim system.

and make its appearance, whether independently or under the wing of architecture, in our everyday life. Thus when David was a member of the Convention he proposed a Palace of Equality, which would be decorated with
frescoes and sculptures, while in England Haydon, that enthusiastic admirer
of Liverpool, spent much of his time and energy in campaigning for great
public decorative schemes. Listening to the Prince Regent opening parliament in the old House of Lords in November 1812, he 'conceived a grand
series of designs to adorn the ample sides of the house . . . the horrors of
anarchy – then the injustice of democracy – then the cruelty of despotism –
the infamies of revolution – then the beauty of justice – and to conclude with
the limited monarchy and its blessings'.[1] It was his barely disinterested keenness to execute this plan – first for the proposed Waterloo monument in
1815, then for the new Houses of Parliament after the fire of 1831 – that led
him to lobby continually for 'moderate and judicious'[2] public art patronage
of a kind previously unknown in this country, and he seized with delight
on the report of the Committee for the Purchase of the Elgin Marbles as the
first official admission of how the fine arts

> had contributed to the reputation, character and dignity of every
> Government by which they had been encouraged, and how intimately
> they were connected with the advancement of everything valuable in
> science, literature and art.[3]

He had hopes of Brougham, but Wellington in his common-sense way told
him that 'No minister could go to parliament with a proposition for a
vote for a picture to be painted, and there can therefore be no such encouragement here as there is in other countries. . . .'[4] Haydon of course was interested
in British artists, and primarily in British historical artists (which meant
himself), but the example in most men's minds at that time was Munich,
where between 1819 and 1840 King Ludwig employed the Nazarene artists
Schnorr and Cornelius on large-scale frescoes.[5] The Ewart Committee of
1835–6 held that the use of sculpture and painting in great public buildings was worthy of a civilized nation; a Select Committee was appointed in
1841 to 'take into consideration the promotion of the fine arts in this country
in connection with the rebuilding of the Houses of Parliament',[6] and began

---

[1] *Life of Benjamin Robert Haydon*. Second edition. Longmans, London 1853, Vol. I, p. 207.
[2] Ibid. Vol. II, p. 60.
[3] Ibid. Vol. II, p. 57. This passage was included in Haydon's petition to the House of Commons
which Brougham presented in 1823.
[4] Ibid. Vol. II, pp. 287–8. Entry for 12 October 1830.
[5] Illustrated and discussed in Keith Andrews: *The Nazarenes;* Clarendon Press, Oxford 1964.
Chapter V.
[6] Samuel and Richard Redgrave: *A Century of Painters of the English School.* London 1866,
Vol. II. p. 515. From Chapter XV, on 'Fresco-Painting and State Patronage.'

by flirting with the idea of using the Germans. Promoted to the status of Royal Commission, this committee pottered on for about twenty years, issuing thirteen reports and holding four public competitions; and the final results, including the suicide of the bitterly disappointed Haydon, were not happy. It is interesting that Schnorr, who felt that German artists would do the job better, was none the less in favour of restricting it to Englishmen. He argued that this would both express our particular 'artistic national culture' and at the same time have a more stimulating influence on the younger artists here.[1]

In an appendix to Haydon's posthumous memoirs Watts, one of the Westminster prize winners, commented that it would further 'public instruction and artistic training' if the State undertook to decorate all public buildings, including 'town halls, national schools and even railway stations'.[2] He suggested that art students might take Flaxman's designs and enlarge them (e.g. on the walls of Eton College) and he himself volunteered to paint the great hall at Euston; 'the architect expressed great alarm about it'.[3] This echoes a scheme which makes fleeting appearances in the history of nineteenth-century French art, for the provision of murals in stations and other non-official buildings. The originator of this is supposed to have been the utopian socialist (Fourierist) Victor Considérant who put it forward in his paper *Démocratie Pacifique* during the 1848 revolution; he also appealed to the artists to make his proposed 'phalansteries' (or pre-Corbusier communal blocks housing 2,000 people) into something finer than the cathedrals, and hoped that every man would become an artist.[4] Apparently there were actual negotiations about this time for Delacroix and Decamps to decorate the side walls of a Paris terminus.[5] Courbet and Champfleury both seem to have been aware of the idea, which from our present point of view is more interesting than either the vast symbolic projects of Chenavard or the real mural masterpiece of the period: Delacroix's frescoes in the Paris church of S. Sulpice. For Champfleury saw very early on that 'the nineteenth century has nowhere found an architectural style except in its building of market or exhibition halls and railways',[6] and pointed out that 'industry . . . has more space at its disposal than have the cathedrals, and it is waiting for an artist capable of

---

[1] Letter to Eastlake of 23 February, 1842, quoted in *The Nazarenes*, p. 85.

[2] *Life of Benjamin Robert Haydon*. Second edition 1853. Appendix by Watts on the public employment of artists. Vol. III, pp. 375, 372. Watts was a friend of Tom Taylor, the book's editor. Taylor was Thackeray's successor as editor of *Punch*.

[3] *George Frederick Watts*. His Writings. Macmillan, London 1912, Vol. III, pp. 120-1. From his statement to the 1863 Commission on the Royal Academy.

[4] Victor Considérant: *Destinée sociale*. Second edition, Paris 1848, pp. 318, 321.

[5] See Paul Mantz's article in the *Gazette des Beaux-Arts*. Paris 1878, Vol. I, p. 29.

[6] *Grandes figures d'hier et d'aujourd'hui*, p. 259.

covering the empty walls of its temples'.[1] Here is the same realistic attitude to the new technology as can be seen in the themes proposed by Manet in 1879 for murals in the new Paris Hôtel de Ville: 'Paris – markets, Paris – railways, Paris – bridges, Paris – underground, Paris – gardens and racing'. This scheme, alas, was not accepted, but unlike the murals painted by Morris and his friends in the Oxford Union or by Ford Madox Brown in Manchester Town Hall it did deal with the contemporary world.

The official art policy of the Third Republic favoured the commissioning of grand public art schemes, but of a celebratory and ennobling kind, as seen in the dreamlike costume pieces of Puvis de Chavannes. The Belgians had paved the way here, allotting part of their budget to murals as early as 1860; it was also in Belgium that the trimestrial review *L'Art public* (with the architect Victor Horta and the socialist deputy Jules Destrée on its committee) was started in 1907, following three international congresses on the subject (in 1898, 1900 and 1905). By then the conception of public art was broadening out, and *L'Art public* aimed to improve the standard not only of monumental art but of telegraph poles, street lamps and street furniture in general. Posters and cheap reproductions had also become relevant with the development of new printing techniques; thus the Medici Society was founded by Sir Eustace Gurney in 1908 to import old master prints for working-class homes, while an essay of 1905 by the poet Gustave Kahn described Jules Chéret, the first of the great poster artists, as more important even than Morris because he recognized the realities of industrial life:

> The pleasure palaces of future cities such as Zola conjures up in *Travail* and Morris in *News from Nowhere* are likely to find these works constructed strictly on the basis of immediate reality preferable to any other form of decoration.[2]

This was only too true. The Russian revolution of 1917 brought a short-lived wave of 'propaganda by monuments', as Lenin called it, with his visions of Campanella's ideal city – statues of revolutionary heroes, including a particularly controversial abstract Bakunin by L. Korol'ev – and there were also decorated propaganda trains, pageants and temporary decoration of whole streets before the withdrawal of the more socially-minded artists into industrial design. But generally the great monumental schemes had come to seem boringly rhetorical, and they have been out of favour with art critics ever since.

'Any *official* direction of the arts,' says an essay on 'artistic sociology' published in 1892, 'whatever the government in power, is really only a

---

[1] *Histoire de l'imagerie populaire*, p. 289.
[2] In Louis Lumet: *L'Art sur tous*; Edouard Cornély, Paris 1905, p. 305. Also p. 307.

charitable organization which uses everybody's money to manufacture objects that nobody wants and no-one knows what to do with.'[1] And the critic Gustave Geffroy in 1905:

> Present-day bourgeois society cannot have a good influence on public art.[2]

This was perhaps only an easy way of rationalizing in class terms what was really a much more awkward problem, but it was largely on class grounds that the social-aesthetic theorists of this period were divided. Those like Morris and Vandervelde, Franz Mehring in Germany and Plekhanov from Russia, who hoped that the working man would seize art in the same way as he was going to seize political power, were confident that he would evolve his own new styles and that the decline of 'bourgeois' art did not much matter. The Marxist interpretation of art, of which they were early exponents, could (and still can) set art movements very illuminatingly against their social background, but too few learnt from Marx himself not to identify those movements with the supposed virtues or vices of the society producing them, and in any case neither Marx's views nor theirs helped much in the choice of a constructive policy. The real difference between them and other supporters of the same social-artistic causes appeared over the question of levels of taste. Thus Watts believed that 'all great and generous reforms must originate with the upper class',[3] while Lucien Pissarro told the anarchist paper to which he used to contribute that it was better to produce for a minority than for the aesthetically backward masses.[4] It was exactly this minority that Morris, who after all did most of his work for it, claimed to mistrust; he felt that it was ineffective.

> I do not believe in the possibility of keeping art vigorously alive by the action, however energetic, of a few groups of specially gifted men and their small circle of admirers among a general public incapable of understanding and enjoying their work. I hold firmly to the opinion that all worthy schools of art must be in the future, as they have been in the past, the outcome of the aspirations of the people towards the beauty and true pleasure of life.[5]

[1] J. Maret-Leriche in *L'Art social*, Paris, March 1892, p. 114. The political tone of this paper was socialist.

[2] *L'Art pour tous*. Paris 1905, Vol. III, p. 203. Louis Lumet, the editor of this magazine and prime founder of its parent society, had two months earlier been made secretary of a committee set up by the Ministry of Education and Fine Arts to buy from the two main salons. In 1906 he was appointed to the new Conseil Supérieur des Arts Décoratifs.

[3] *George Frederic Watts. His Writings*. Macmillan, London 1912, Vol. III, p. 314.

[4] Letter to *Les Temps nouveaux*. Paris, 7 December 1895.

[5] *The Letters of William Morris to his Family and Friends*. Edited by Philip Henderson. Longmans, London 1950, pp. 355–6. Letter of 10 November 1893 to the *Daily Chronicle*.

A resounding statement, but it has two unfortunate limitations. There is no historical evidence for it, and its practical conclusion must surely be that all non-political action is a mistake.

Many of these diverse threads have reappeared in the last twenty years and in the plans and policies discussed in the previous chapter. Much of what was previously put forward as an ideal has been converted into actual administrative machinery. The underlying philosophy was summed up thus by Lord Bridges in 1958 in a lecture on 'The State and the Arts':

> First, that it is the duty of the state to provide something of the best in each of the arts as an example of inspiration to the whole country. Secondly, that the state has also a duty to see that those who can derive satisfaction from the arts have the opportunity to do so. . . .[1]

There is implicit in this system a sometimes conflicting mixture of principles: art must be good for a society and a good representative of it, yet the state must avoid imposing an aesthetic orthodoxy; art must circulate to those who need it, but without departing from a trained minority's conception of 'the best'; art helps the community, yet its public administrators speak only of helping art. Much of the recent talk about patronage indeed makes it sound as if art were an indigent old gentleman for whom a subscription were being got up.

Over on the left Morris's spirit still flickers; thus when Ralph Bond moved the famous Resolution 42 in 1960 he spoke scornfully of

> the idea that culture should be the preserve of an enlightened intelligentsia and that any old rubbish is good enough for the masses.[2]

But there are now virtually no differences between the parties in these matters; the notion of 'working-class art' has become unpopular even in Centre 42; and Arnold Wesker has recently complained to his architect that 'in the document we are forced to submit to official bodies for their help we often fall into the trap of talking about "Moral Responsibilities" and "the pattern that men's lives should take"'.[3] The social mission of the movement seems in effect to have been shelved in favour of a purely artistic one, even as far to the left as that.

A good deal of the discussion about 'culture' by writers such as Raymond Williams and Richard Wollheim[4] is about culture in the sense of general

---

[1] Bridges: *The State and the Arts*. The Romanes Lecture, Clarendon Press, Oxford 1958, p. 16.
[2] *Report of Proceedings at the 92nd Annual Trades Union Congress;* TUC, London, 1960, p. 436.
[3] Centre 42: *Brief to René Allio*. (Duplicated.)
[4] Williams: *Culture and Society 1780–1950;* Chatto and Windus 1958. Penguin 1961.
Wollheim: *Socialism and Culture;* Fabian Tract 331. London 1961.

education, based largely on the study of English literature: i.e. culture as conceived by Arnold and F. R. Leavis. But there have also in the last few years been signs of a quickening interest in the social usefulness of the arts proper. Their direct relevance to manufacture, in the form of industrial design, is more and more widely acknowledged, even in Eastern Europe; they are caught up, however ignominiously at times, in the advance of advertising and commercial television; and in England at least the treatment of art in schools as expression rather than discipline has led to a complete change in the importance attached to the subject. Admittedly an investigation conducted in 1964 with the public of twenty-one representative French art galleries led its authors to conclude that the frequenting of museums and the development of a taste for pictures are functions of a man's education, and that without wider access to certain educational levels (approximating to our 'A' levels and above) any attempt to popularize such pursuits must fail.[1] On the other hand we have recently heard a new appeal for 'embellishing public buildings with sculpture and paintings'[2] and seen new emphasis placed on the need for firms to promote amateur art as part of their welfare service, on industry's duty to support the cultural facilities of the towns where it is located, and on the practical advantages of having educated and cultivated employees.[3]

'Up-to-date corporations', wrote a reviewer in the *New York Times* at the end of 1964,

> eager to attract young executives to their outlying plants, frequently stress, and sometimes create, appropriate esthetic amenities.[4]

There is also, with the spread of automation, a much more urgent concern with the problem of leisure. This is a main theme of the book by one of the late President Kennedy's cultural advisers, which sets out from the alienation and lack of sense of direction attributed to modern American society and concludes with an appeal for 'art as a common enjoyment, a focus for the pleasures and delights of the citizenry'.[5] It proposes the carrying out of communal public works – roads, parks, fine buildings – as a means of lifting men's noses above their immediate private concerns. It calls for the improvement of street furniture, the bolder handling of space in the city and the

---

[1] See Pierre Bourdieu and Alain Darbel: *L'Amour de l'art*, les musées et leur public; Editions de Minuit, Paris 1966. A parallel investigation was conducted in a number of other European countries, but its results have not yet been published. England was not among them.

[2] G. R. Strauss, MP in the debate of 27 April 1965 on Government Support for the Arts.

[3] Points made by Sir W. E. Williams in *Investing in the Arts;* Institute of Directors, London 1964. See pp. 10, 13 and 21; also the article by Mr Miki Sekers in *The Director* for February 1964.

[4] Robert Lekachman, reviewing Alvin Toffler's *The Culture Consumers* in the *New York Times Book Review*, 13 December, 1964.

[5] August Heckscher: *The Public Happiness;* Hutchinson, London 1963, p. 277.

official sponsoring of art as 'the expression of order and the embodiment of inward values'.[1] Art, as the director of the York art gallery has said

> has almost been cast for the role of a substitute for faith and religion, and we expect 'Art' to satisfy all the higher aspirations of mankind.[2]

There are even now artists who are concerned above all with the idea of public art; thus Victor Vasarely's exhibition of 1963 at the Musée des Arts Décoratifs showed him to have worked out interesting and original schemes for coloured geometrical units to be incorporated in varying patterns in architecture, and he lays a fresh emphasis on the importance of teamwork and the use of mechanically-reproducible elements. But what seems largely new today is the widespread interest in popular art. Such 'sociology of the arts' as has sprung up since the 1950s in a number of Western countries – it is, as Richard Wollheim has pointed out, 'one of the most primitive reaches of the social sciences'[3] – has been mainly concerned with this. Men like Richard Hoggart and Stuart Hall at Birmingham University, where their Centre for Contemporary Cultural Studies is partly financed by a grant from Penguin Books; like Robert Escarpit at the University of Bordeaux, with his Centre de Sociologie des Faits Littéraires;[4] like the French critics Edgar Morin and Roland Barthes; like Umberto Eco in Milan and Karl Markus Michel in Frankfurt am Main: people like these are systematically investigating the ground opened up by such pioneers as Walter Benjamin and Mrs Leavis (*Fiction and the Reading Public*, 1932): that is, approaching the arts from the consumer's end and at the same time relating its production to major technological and social changes. They are not much concerned with the popular art of a remote golden age (even if Morris's images still seem to float at the back of one or two English minds), nor do they deal with the 'proletarian' culture preached by the Communists in the 1920s: art on working–class themes which somehow could earn this title without necessarily being either produced or consumed by the working class. Because it is mass consumption and mass production with which they are dealing they treat popular taste seriously, without condescension, and they have helped us all to realize that meeting it calls for more skill and organizing ability, and more artistry even, than we have in the past been prepared to allow. As a result the old barrier

[1] *The Public Happiness*, p. 267.

[2] Hans Hess: *The Artist in an Industrial Society;* Department of Adult Education, The University of Hull, n.d. 1964, p. 7. A paper read at the York conference on The Place of the Visual Arts in an Industrial Society in April 1964.

[3] *Socialism and Culture*, p. 38.

[4] His *Sociologie de la littérature* was published by the Presses Universitaires de France, Paris, in their 'Que sais-je?' series in 1958. With Nicole Robine he is the author of a report on local reading habits, *Atlas de la lecture à Bordeaux*, Faculté des Lettres et Sciences Humaines, Bordeaux, 1963. His study for UNESCO of *The Book Revolution* was published by Harrap in 1966.

between highbrow and lowbrow art is being slowly demolished: films, jazz, crime stories, comics are now quite commonly analysed by reputable critics; majority educational standards are rising, and the concept of minority culture has become eroded rather faster than its guardians think. The whole process seems unconsciously symbolized in the rise of a so-called pop art combining the use of directly accessible imagery, often drawn from our mass-produced culture, with spatial and colour conceptions that have not in the past been widely understood.

All this is more relevant to the case of Liverpool than may at first sight appear. For what we have been discussing in this sketchy tour of the vast and complex area of social-artistic interrelations is not just the background of ideas underlying the present British system of official art patronage but also the changing mental climate in which Liverpool's own tradition has been formed. The development of art teaching in the Mechanics' Institute, for instance, as encouraging useful skills and reputable habits was only part of the nation-wide campaign for art schools of which Haydon considered Liverpool to be one of the leaders. B. A. Heywood as early as 1820 saw 'the luxury and refinement of commercial employment' as replacing 'the patronage and encouragement of the arts, which were induced by the religion, patriotism and private luxury of the ancients';[1] Ewart was member for the city at the time when he inspired the Select Committee on Arts and Manufacturers whose chairman he became; even after the petering out of the Reform Age, the Liverpool Academy, by supporting the Pre-Raphaelites, was in advance both of its town and of its time. The great dissemination movement at the end of the century saw the foundation of the Walker Gallery, the 1888 Art Congress and the Art Nouveau group at the university, again as part of the new attitude to art, crafts and public enlightenment which dominated official art policies everywhere up to 1914. Philip Rathbone, like August Hecksher and Raymond Williams in our own period, hoped to strengthen social coherence, to enable the individual to realize that he is a requisite element in a living organic whole;[2] Rothenstein thought that public works and the presence of great artists might create a living school of art. Advanced German architects in the early twentieth century came to know Port Sunlight as an example of paternalist garden city-type housing; a correspondingly paternalist dissemination of art was responsible for the pictures in Johnson's Dye-

[1] Chairman's Report, 14 March 1820, p. 13, from *Resolutions, Reports and Bye-Laws of the Liverpool Royal Institution*, March 1814–March 1822.

[2] Philip H. Rathbone: *The Political Value of Art in the Municipal Life of a Nation*. A lecture delivered at the Free Library, Liverpool, Liverpool 1875.

works and in due course for the Lady Lever Gallery, though the latter arrived some twenty years too late. Almost anything that matters in Liverpool's relationship with the visual arts can be related in this way to a wider school of thought, so that the doctrines we have been discussing are doubly connected with our immediate subject. They act directly on the people who think about such matters. They shaped the institutions about which they have to think.

The ideas now floating in the Liverpool air seem to bear only an indirect relation to the old nineteenth century radioactivity. They may be summarized as follows. The Walker Gallery is perhaps fully appreciated only by a small minority, but it is worth the city's paying generously to keep it up to standard both as a great educational force[1] and as a heritage for the citizens: something they can be proud of and show off. Extreme modern art may be difficult for them and for many of the local politicians to stomach; none the less it is part of our world, and one cannot simply try to ignore it without risking spiritual stagnation. Generally speaking money spent on the visual arts is felt to be well spent; you must see it this way, a severely ill patient in the Royal Infirmary told me, 'if you've any thought at all for your city; without these things you become fourth-, fifth-, sixth-rate'. Similarly the firms who support the gallery's appeals feel that they have a stake in the city – a large one if they are large employers of labour –, that they must back anything of major civic importance, and that if the decline of the individual private patron has left a gap they must try to fill it. In doing so they are conscious that they are helping to make the city more attractive; the immediately discouraging impression which the sight of Liverpool has often made on those arriving there is present to many minds. There is a feeling among some of them that improvements and cultural amenities may help bring qualified employees and possibly even entire new firms to the area. The director of one big Aintree factory for instance was sure that better housing and a pleasant atmosphere improved the quality of the labour force, while the Engineer at Port Sunlight told me that his firm had previously found it difficult to get research staff for its old laboratories on account of the gloomy outlook from them, but that the construction of new laboratories had changed this.

The South Liverpool Festivals came about because the Domestic Mission wanted to stimulate the social forces which would raise the neighbourhood and counteract those pulling it down; art seemed to be the answer. In the university the inclusion of works of art in the new buildings was undertaken,

[1] Cotton's memorandum on the occasion of the visit of a deputation from the Sheffield conference of provincial galleries to the Chancellor of the Exchequer in 1958 spoke of the bigger galleries as the vital instruments of art education in this country.

as we saw earlier, out of a sense of obligation to students who represent the potential leaders of the nation, at a critical stage in their lives. In the new Catholic churches the visual arts are included as expressing the glory of God. One of the chief football pool promoters pointed out to me the new popularity of Coventry and its attraction for visitors. Any comparable scheme in Liverpool ought to be based on the use of the leading British artists – he instanced Moore, Nicholson, Scott and Pasmore – as an initial core. The right method was to get something started: 'give it a kick, then you've got something to talk about'; national publicity would follow. The effect would be to make Liverpool the art centre of the North West and draw people into it.

None of these arguments made a greater impression on me than the overriding principle put forward by Ben Shaw, then the chairman of the city's Arts Sub-Committee. He was talking about the success of the Van Gogh exhibition in 1955, which had led him to the conclusion that the Gallery must try to concentrate on showing really first-rate work. 'Particularly to those that don't know,' he said, 'only the best will do.' He is absolutely right. People who are not used to painting or sculpture can still be swept off their feet by the sheer force and quality of something which they do not yet 'understand'. The initiated can afford to be interested in the second- or third-rate artist; they may learn from him in all sorts of ways, and the echoes or allusions which they recognize in his work may seem quite beautiful. This escapes anybody who has no background of looking at such things and simply lacks the initial impetus to hunt for such refinements. The moral should be written out in letters of gold for all those concerned with disseminating and administering the arts.

10 : A PLAN OF CAMPAIGN

In making positive proposals for Liverpool I would like to ignore the idea of art as education, or even as a civilizing force. It is true that we judge a nation's degree of civilization partly by its art, but that is because the concept of civilization has long presupposed a condition in which the arts flourish. It would be much harder to prove that the practice or enjoyment of art makes people better individuals or even better citizens; Greek art, as Marx pointed out to those who identify art's virtues with those of society, was bound up with Greek slavery; the marvellous Roman amphitheatres were not exactly built for youth festivals; and in our own time nobody placed art on a higher pedestal than an amateur artist called Adolf Hitler.[1] No: if people need art it is not to bolster up their claim to be civilized but because it is an age-old human activity, a continual delight to practise, study or simply sit back and gape at; full of jokes, problems, explosions, sudden breath-taking beauties; something unpredictable that can be set against modern life's mechanisms and routines. 'Even when people speak of higher and lower degrees of pleasure,' wrote Brecht,

> art stares impassively back at them; for it wishes to fly high and low and to be left in peace, so long as it can give pleasure to people.[2]

Whether we take art to be a key to things beyond this world or as a marvellously refined man-made contrivance it is this that people want when they claim art as one of the basic rights of man. It is not a loud claim, though it is becoming more so. But it can easily be stifled and distorted if the art-conscious minority appears in the guise of Lady Bountiful, patronizing the artists and improving the public mind; for nobody likes being condescended to, and rightly or wrongly the suspicion is bound to arise that the guardians of art are only trying to find takers for the kind of art that they themselves enjoy.

---

[1] I have just read a description by a dead painter friend, whose judgments I respected, of the late Professor Klaus Schilling, a specialist in tropical diseases then (1941–2) working in Florence. He was a passionate and discriminating art lover, fascinated particularly by Giorgione: 'his conversation about painting was always fruitful and rewarding'. He was hanged for the experiments which he carried out on human beings in Dachau concentration camp. (Kurt Craemer: *Mein Panoptikum;* Hoffman und Campe, Hamburg 1965, pp. 128–34.)

[2] *Brecht on Theatre;* Methuen, London, 1964 p. 181 (Paragraph 5 of his 'Kleines Organon für das Theater'.) The last qualifying phrase could have been left out.

What the public would, on the other hand, appreciate is to see art associated with the general drive for better living: to see it as a hope rather than an implied reproach. For this reason in a city like Liverpool it should above all be linked firmly to the great schemes for replanning and redevelopment. If people are certain not to want it in that context, then it should not be forced down their throats. Morris saw further than our official patrons when he maintained that art might just as well die out as develop on a false footing. For of course art does not die; it is an indelible human habit. But if in the long run it is going to be wanted, then the corporation should make it available, and it would be wise for them to start planning for this right away.

So let us return to the city scale, and sum up the problem. Art has got itself in a false position because we have come to treat the visual arts as something set apart from other human concerns. Industrialists and business people, for instance, who are generous in their patronage of the visual arts, often have no use for them in their own works or offices. Similarly in the colleges of technology and elsewhere design seems to be treated as a dispensable extra, a luxury embellishment added to objects once the serious business of making them is over, rather than a sense of arrangement, elegance and logic that ought to guide it from the outset: something that is shared with intellectual disciplines such as mathematics, and is more fundamental than either craft or techniques. Art is accepted as a stimulating and psychologically liberating exercise for school children, particularly in lower forms, but unless he decides to make it his profession even the most gifted child finds no encouragement (and often no chance) to pursue it after he has left school. A barrier falls between it and the serious business of living; the one is shunted off into the art gallery, the other is left to get along with hideously-made goods and often with bare walls. The chance of any spontaneous visual self-expression outside the group of professional artists is needlessly lessened.

There is another major question, and I should define my attitude to it before going further. That is the frequent incompatibility of minority judgments and the tastes of many members of the public. In a gallery that the majority hardly ever visit the problem is not really acute; sharp disputes about matters of taste are in fact likelier to arise in committee than among those who come to look at the pictures. But as soon as art gets out into the street the matter is very different, not least because it is so difficult to rectify mistakes. None the less, if Liverpool is to incorporate public works of art in its great replanning projects, then it would be wise to include some that will be outstanding in our time and bring credit to the city among the scattered but in some ways surprisingly coherent minority of art lovers throughout the

world. This means works of possibly 'extreme' modern art which are bound
to cause hot controversy in the city itself.

Two things are important here: first of all Shaw's Law, as we may call
the principle put forward at the end of the last chapter; secondly the rapidity
with which the taste for modern art is developing in this country, and its
association with classes and interests far removed from the old nucleus of
connoisseurs. Intolerance of the unfamiliar, as we saw earlier, is not a mark of
education, and its importance is dwindling as educational benefits spread;
moreover as people come to see art as fun rather than as a high Ruskinian
cocktail of the Beautiful and the Good they will be less worried by the new
forms it takes. Already a great work, however extreme, is likely to be accepted
even if it still puzzles and occasionally irritates the older citizens. But with
lesser works the situation is different. There is no point in authority's
fighting aesthetic battles for the sake of inferior modern public art; the
waverers will not be convinced, and if they were it would just mean a lowering of standards. Minor examples of public art ought not gratuitously to run
against strong popular feelings, though whether these are aroused or not
depends to some extent on how the work is presented; a high degree of
abstraction may, for instance, be accepted in the guise of decoration or
advertisement or some kind of superior toy, yet arouse immediate opposition
if put forward as Art.

The immediate recipient of the proposals that follow is the Bluecoat
Society of Arts. Much that I suggest is quite outside the society's scope, but
I am putting it forward none the less in the hope that this report will also be
read by others who are concerned about the future of Liverpool, its buildings
and its educational system, its reputation and the general sense of life in
the city. It seems to me important that the problem should be treated as a
whole: that if it is to be tackled at all there must be an overall plan of campaign into which the smaller proposals fit. The plan which I outline therefore
is intended to be seen as itself part of the city's plan for reconstruction and
redevelopment, and to be presentable to the public as such. It should not be
treated just as a string of disjointed proposals to be carried out individually;
for some of them are only worth executing within the overall campaign and
might otherwise do more harm than good. In short, although there are many
things here that the Bluecoat Society can do on its own I would ask it first
to father the whole plan, to sponsor discussion of it and to make it a Bluecoat Plan for the future of the visual arts in Liverpool. This need not prevent
the society from also taking smaller steps, but it must be very certain, and

be able to convince both artists and public, that they are steps towards an agreed goal.

THE GOALS I suggest are: (1) to humanize and beautify the reconstruction of the city; (2) to strengthen its identity, both to its own citizens and to outsiders; (3) to stimulate a distinctive Liverpool art, particularly among the younger generation, and to remove obstacles to visual self-expression; (4) to break down the barriers which isolate art and design as supposed inessentials; and finally (5) to create an exciting atmosphere for persons and institutions concerned with art.

Accordingly, the first thing I would propose is that a PUBLIC ART ADVISER be appointed to make a plan for the use of works of art in conjunction with any new schemes for building development, housing, street furniture and open spaces. He or she would need to have had administrative experience, to command the confidence of artists and to have a good knowledge of the best living artists both at home and abroad; he would also need a genuine understanding and appreciation of Liverpool as a place. He would have to work closely with planners, architects and private developers, and should, I think, be responsible to the Corporation rather than to the Bluecoat Society or to an outside body. He should however be much higher-powered than the corresponding municipal department in Rotterdam or the Art Commission in Hamburg; to avoid compromises with mediocrity the initiative must lie with one man. He would not be required to make proposals for each new building, but for entire areas of the city where building was going on: for the comprehensive development areas of the city centre and the 'action areas' established further out.

The works which he would commission would as a rule best be FINANCED by adding up to 2 per cent to building costs, though whether private developers would comply with this practice would depend on his powers of persuasion and on the force of the example set by the corporation. This addition would not however be automatic, and although no work would be commissioned except with a specific site in mind there would be no rigid need to apportion works to buildings. The aim rather should be to PLAN BY AREAS, corresponding broadly to areas of major development or rehabilitation within the city plan. It might also be possible to interest COLLECTIVE PATRONS (firms, the university, the nationalized industries, the trusts) in underwriting a given area. A newspaper or a television company, for instance, could do this and get an interesting story to report, from preliminary sketch projects to final public reaction.

The CHOICE OF ARTISTS would be made by the adviser, but would have to be approved by the patron and his architect, planner or engineer. It ought also to be ratified on behalf of the Corporation, preferably by a special expert committee which might contain the Director of the Walker Art Gallery, the Chief Planning Officer, a representative of the Civic Society and a representative of the Liverpool Academy, with a chairman from the majority party. In my view the important commissions should be given to the best artists for the job, irrespective of nationality; there should be no special sense of obligation to give work to English, let alone Liverpool artists, or to share the jobs out fairly; the object should rather be to create really impressive works which would stimulate the private demand for art locally and infect any artist within range. The great influence that can be wielded by an OUTSTANDING INTERNATIONAL ARTIST working in the city, if only for a few months, should not be forgotten; the example of Augustus John's brief Liverpool period should be borne in mind. Every effort should be made to attract one or more of the major figures to work in Liverpool, and if possible to make use of local collaborators. It is too late to ask Picasso, but that is the level at which Liverpool should aim.

Special measures would have to be taken to introduce each artist not only to the site(s) he is to design his work for but also to the city itself and the inhabitants for whom he is working. Any artist who is not prepared to accept this, and simply wishes to paint or sculpt as for a gallery but larger, is likely to be unsuited to public commissions. It should also be taken for granted at all levels that art, architecture and mundane matters of design such as street furniture are not independent of one another but contribute to a common scene and must be judged as a whole. One way of stressing this would be to encourage the expert committee, including the adviser, to comment on all visual aspects of the area under consideration. Another idea which might be considered is that of getting a geometrically-minded abstract sculptor at an early stage to advise on the detailing of the proposed new inner motorway and the three-dimensional shape of its junctions. This could have been a job for the late Hans Arp.

The second major proposal I would like to make is that the whole SYSTEM OF ART TEACHING in Merseyside (not Liverpool only) schools and colleges should be overhauled with a view to breaking the barrier (a) between art and adult life and (b) between design and manufacture. The first problem here is how to make it easier for the artistically gifted child who is not going on to a full-time art school to keep his hand and eye in none the less. One way of doing this would be to DIVIDE PART-TIME TRAINING in the fine arts into two categories so as to separate the younger pupils who still want to develop their techniques and their personalities from older people who simply use art schools as a cheap way of pursuing their hobby as amateurs. The smaller

R

art schools, whose function in the new national pattern seems very unclear, might be turned over to the latter, possibly with increased fees, while part-time training under teachers from the College of Art could then be reserved for those who need to learn rather than primarily to occupy themselves.

The design barrier can only be broken by persuading teachers, especially of technical subjects, that good design is itself a discipline, where the visual sense helps to secure logical arrangement, economy and control: something that should be thought of as relating to consumer research, for instance, quite as much as to aesthetics. But it would be a great help if the university would set up a DEPARTMENT OF INDUSTRIAL DESIGN, as has been suggested, and preferably one that could serve other higher educational establishments in the city. What is needed is a small unit capable of conducting research and of supplying an element of design teaching not only to the university's own engineering faculty but to any course in the city colleges whose students are likely, by manufacture, planning, management, or simple buying and selling, to influence the appearance of our daily surroundings. Design would have to be taught not as a speciality, but as an essential component of these people's training, whether or not they themselves are ever likely to design anything. This is a field where there are many people with the missionary spirit, and some of them should be spreading it in Liverpool.

Another aid to a better-co-ordinated system of visual teaching in the city would be more exchange of information. This could be organized through some form of STANDING CONFERENCE ON ART EDUCATION, with representatives drawn from the University, the Walker Gallery, the Colleges of Art, Building and Technology, the City Libraries and the Directorate of Education, and possibly from the neighbouring boroughs too. Its function would be to advise and help art teachers in the area, and to keep itself informed about their work. It might be worth trying a preliminary meeting of such a group with a few dozen local art teachers. If it seemed to raise useful questions and even to settle a few of them, then such meetings should be made a regular institution.

There are a number of lesser measures which could be taken within the framework of a general visual arts campaign, though they might well be ineffective on their own. There is, for instance, the problem of a COMMERCIAL GALLERY FOR MODERN ART. At present this does not exist in Liverpool; the Bluecoat Society's rooms are a makeshift. In my view a lively and well-informed dealer in modern art will establish himself in the city as soon as there seems to be a stimulating artistic climate there and a keen public interest; to devise special inducements to lure one to Liverpool before then would be to put the cart before the horse. In the interval however, more might be done to advise and encourage the dealers who are already there. If the Bluecoat Society, or the Academy for that matter, were occasionally to organize an exhibition for them they might not only be pleased to show it but be able to sell the exhibits. The experience of the Medici Society with modern prints is a pointer; good modern work *can* be sold through the existing channels. The answer, in my view, is more liaison, and I would recommend an exploratory meeting at the Bluecoat Chambers with representatives of the Medici, the Boydell Gallery, Lewis's, the Academy and the Bluecoat, and if possible somebody who knows about the activities of the London dealers.

The Bluecoat Society could well sponsor a scheme for PICTURES IN HOSPITALS on the lines of that run in London. I suggest that it tries to get the support of a number of leading doctors and hospital committee members known to be interested in the visual arts, then organize an exhibition of works by local artists in a suitable hospital. Some of the artists might be willing to come and meet patients and hospital staff, and talk about the works. A report should then be prepared on the venture, with photographs, and circulated to the initial supporters, to hospital management committees and individual hospital secretaries in the area, and subsequently to the Press. Individual hospitals would be asked if they wished to come in on the scheme, whose scale would depend on the response. Up to this point the scheme would have to finance itself; it could hardly ask for outside support before it was running. The pictures would at first be borrowed from the artists, though they would be for sale (to staffs and patients as well as to institutions). The scheme could continue on this basis or could go over to the London system of itself actually buying the pictures; this is something that could be decided later.

The Society, together with the Trades Council if it were interested, could evolve a similar scheme for circulating works by local artists to FACTORY COR-RIDORS, CANTEENS AND RECREATION ROOMS, and also trade union offices. Again, it should try to enlist the support of managers and directors, and start with a pilot scheme and borrowed works. Again, personal visits by some of the artists would be a help. Once the pilot scheme had been concluded and reported on, the Society and its supporters would have to choose how the use of the works was to be paid for in future; they could be hired from the artists (who might at the same time offer them for sale if they wished) or they could be purchased so as to form a central circulating collection, with the participating firms paying an annual subscription, based perhaps on the number of their employees.

Much the same principle could be applied with LOANS TO SCHOOLS. Instead of second-rate reproductions on the walls they should be encouraged to have the work of local artists, especially if these were prepared to come along and discuss it with the pupils. The Walker Gallery has already been buying works for lending, some of them by local painters. It might however be worth consulting a few interested teachers - there are some who are already members of the Academy or the Sandon Studios Society – and the TeacherTraining Department at the College. A pilot scheme with borrowed works and personal visits could be tried out at a few selected schools, and the results then reported to the Director of Education. If they seemed worth while he or the individual schools might be able to make a small annual allocation to finance hire and transport of pictures.

If a plan could then be drawn up in collaboration with the gallery all three of these projects – hospitals, industry and schools – could be run together and supplied from a single store of works of art.[1] The Society and the gallery would have to decide whether the problems of administration and storage space would permit this. The cause of Liverpool art in general would also benefit greatly from a more systematic attempt to acquaint Liverpool people with their local artists. To this end the Society should recruit a panel of artists and other experts who would be willing to give ILLUSTRATED TALKS ON LIVERPOOL ART, ancient and/or modern, or specifically on their own work, and should build or borrow a suitable collection of slides. They could then offer these talks to schools, factory art clubs, local art groups and any other audiences likely to be interested.

Awareness of Liverpool's own visual tradition is vitally important, especially at a time when so much reconstruction is planned. I would like to support the RECOMMENDATIONS OF THE PLANNING DEPARTMENT'S REPORT ON THE PRESERVATION OF HISTORIC BUILDINGS IN CENTRAL LIVERPOOL, which include the revision of the existing lists, the publication of a pamphlet on the subject, the fixing of plaques on outstanding buildings and the foundation of a 'history of Liverpool' museum. This report should be debated by the council; both it and the book *Seaport* by the same author deserve wide study, particularly in the context of the threat to Albert Dock. The local architectural research conducted at the University, to which some of Dr Hughes's many interesting discoveries are due, ought now to be matched

---

[1] Within six months of the presentation of this report, but quite independently of it, a North West Medical Arts Society had been founded by a group of doctors and their wives. Its inaugural exhibition was held at Rainhill Hospital on 12 May, 1966. Membership, entailing the right to hire pictures at a basic rate of one guinea per six months, is open not only to hospitals, but also to other entities and individuals. The Bluecoat Forum is now helping with the practical administration.

I have left my recommendation as it stood, in order to show its place in the general plan of campaign. Whether it will actually fill that place depends on Liverpool's willingness to see its problems as a whole rather than tackle them piecemeal.

by similar RESEARCHES INTO LOCAL HISTORY AND LOCAL ART. Any encouragement which can be given to these, whether in the University or at the
College of Art, would be helpful in strengthening the city's identity. In Germany or Italy there would be local publishers to disseminate their results, but
this is unfortunately rare in England, and even a great printing centre like
Liverpool is no exception. Only poetry magazines like *Underdog* and *Phoenix*
and the occasional issue of the student magazine *Sphinx* have at least tried to
convey the visual character of the place; the Society should see that they continue to appear, and note their appearance and contents in its Arts Forum
Bulletin. It might also be worth making contact with *Music Echo*, which
could influence a large young audience by devoting an occasional column to
the visual arts.

There is, however, a lack of any CENTRAL REVIEW OR NEWS SHEET for those
concerned with the visual arts in the area. They need a small monthly publication, if possible illustrated, which would keep them in touch with one
another and with what is going on locally. This is something that the Society
could well provide, either by developing the present bulletin and giving it a
less cumbersome title or by starting a new organ. Such a publication should
aim in the first instance to be informative, though it might in due course
become more ambitious and even solicit contributions from outside Liverpool. Its core would be news of exhibitions, projects, commissions, jobs,
official purchases, gallery activities, the art schools and the various art
societies, together with reports, interviews and reproductions of current work.
It might delegate responsibility for certain departments to the Walker Gallery,
the Civic Society and the School of Architecture, possibly also reporting the
results of the type of research mentioned in the previous paragraph. It
should not be over-ambitious in presentation: e.g. it could be typewriter-set.

If it is to tackle these tasks, and above all if it is to play an influential
part in the suggested campaign, the BLUECOAT SOCIETY ITSELF will have to
undergo some changes. At the moment it consists (trustees apart) of a committee originally instituted to manage the buildings, plus a Forum to coordinate the activities of tenants and other cultural societies; it has no
acknowledged responsibilities outside this, and it is not really equipped for
planning and new organization. In my view it ought now to be reconstituted
as a buildings and finance committee, plus an arts committee, with the chairman of the Forum as a member of the latter. The arts committee would be
responsible not only for the use of the society's hall and gallery but for
actively furthering the arts in Liverpool, both on and off the premises. For
this it would need a more or less full-time organizer, and it might well consider whether it could not meet some of the cost involved by inviting

membership of the society, individual and collective. Among the inducements to members might be participation in the picture loan schemes proposed above and receipt of any publications; other benefits would transpire as soon as there was somebody systematically devoting himself to planning. They would also be supporting the campaign outlined here.

There are two other preliminary steps which ought to be taken before the main operation starts. First, it would help to arouse public interest and clarify the ideas both of the artists and of their potential patrons if there were a COMPREHENSIVE EXHIBITION DEVOTED TO PUBLIC ART at the Walker Art Gallery. Such an exhibition has not, to my knowledge, been held in this country, and many people outside Liverpool might find it a good occasion for discussing a little-understood subject; thus it would attract publicity, particularly if the Corporation could at the same time announce something like the present plan. It might be usefully be linked with a congress of experts from outside Liverpool: a revival on a more modest and less exclusively National scale of Conway's Association. The exhibits would need to include pictures, models and plans of outstanding examples throughout the world, as well as actual works of art and ideas for their siting. Some of them could be displayed in suitable places in the city, as was done in Antwerp.

Secondly, the corporation ought to mount A TRAVELLING EXHIBITION which would convey the city's particular flavour and character, above all by visual means. This should be shown not only in Liverpool itself but in London and overseas, in the many centres which have become curious about Liverpool since the rise of the Beatles. Adequately prepared, it would at the same time be a first-rate advertisement for the city, a good way of helping its citizens to discover their own assets, and a great fillip for Liverpool art. A project for a 'Look at Liverpool' exhibition on these lines which I worked out in consultation with Henri, Ballard and MacKarell is given as an appendix. We planned it to answer an objection from the Director of the Walker Gallery (at a discussion of some of the points raised in this chapter) that art with a distinctive Liverpool flavour did not exist.

To sum up this plan of campaign briefly, in rough chronological order and with indication of responsibility (in brackets), what I am proposing is:

Adoption of a plan for the visual arts.

Modification of the Bluecoat Society's committees.

Start of visual arts news sheet (Bluecoat).

Discussion of schools loan scheme with teachers (B).

Recruitment of speakers on Liverpool art and collection of slides (B).

Standing Conference on art education (Liverpool Corporation and B).

Consultation with Liverpool commercial galleries (B).

'LOOK AT LIVERPOOL' EXHIBITION (LC, with B and Liverpool Academy).

Setting-up of Department of Industrial Design (University and LC).

Reorganization of part-time art school teaching (LC and Ministry of Education).

Preliminary support for loan schemes for hospitals and factories (B, with Liverpool Trades Council).

Trial runs for loan schemes for hospitals, factories and schools, using borrowed works of art (B, with LTC).

EXHIBITION OF PUBLIC ART, possibly with conference (LC, with assistance of the Arts Council).

Appointment of Public Art adviser (LC).

Ditto expert committee on visual aspects of the city (LC).

Institution of loan schemes for hospitals (B). (See note on p. 246 above.)

Ditto factories (B, with LTC).

Ditto schools (B, with LC).

DESIGNATION OF FIRST AREAS AND ARTISTS for public works of art (LC).

Allotment of subsidiary tasks in these areas (LC).

If the operation could unfold in this way as a linked plan it would have powerful effects. It would stimulate national and international interest in Liverpool and reinforce the picture of a genuinely resurgent city. It would arouse a mixture of controversy, pride and delight in the city itself. It would help to attract lively-minded people to Liverpool, as visitors or as citizens. It would encourage the younger generation to express itself visually as well as through pop music. It would give work to Liverpool artists and strengthen their position as a distinctive school. It would breathe new life into the existing art institutions: the gallery, the College of Art, the Academy. It would also be a comprehensive operation such as had never been launched before, and it could have historic results for the visual arts.

Is this scheme a model for the development and use of art in the city? Not, I hope, on the surface. The aim has been throughout to derive the proposed measures from the specific situation of Liverpool: from a low-level look at its history, resources and tastes. They are meant to reflect the character of the place, using the experience of other cities and other theories of art as background material, but not necessarily as patterns to conform with. Nor should the scheme be used as a pattern itself. All the same I hope that the general line of approach will be found to be a helpful one, usable elsewhere under different conditions. Seen in this light it ought to serve the cause of decentralization and local cultural differentiation, as against the prevailing trend towards uniformity of methods and above all of taste, created in the name of high artistic standards and determined ultimately by a network of closely linked committees and advisory bodies, based on the capital.

For elsewhere too the need is to plan in terms of the actual situation on the ground and to take into account people's real feelings about art, rather than go only by the ideals of a minority, however admirable, or accept the largely negative public relationships that artists have come to treat as normal and even necessary. It is not that minority taste and the artist's wish for isolation should be wholly disregarded, nor is it the city's job where the arts are concerned to give the public what it says it wants. But the community's state of artistic education is a limiting factor that can only be overridden with a full knowledge of what is involved. In Germany and Russia after the First World War it was overridden too far unthinkingly, so that despite the liveliness and lasting importance of the movements that flourished then the reaction which followed did even more damage to art and (quite literally) to artists than the popular pandering of the later Victorians.

What matters for the future of art is not 'help' and 'support' so much as the straightening out of relationships and their uninhibited development in the future. It is this that has emerged as the main concern of the present enquiry. The citizens as a whole need to see that the visual arts are a source of endless fun, discovery, fascination: one of our great resources to set against aimlessness and boredom. They should learn not only to respect but to use them. The adolescent in particular must come to treat art as a natural and creditable pursuit: a potential outlet for him even if he is not making it his profession. Manufacturers and consumers – anybody who fabricates objects or uses them – must learn that art is not only decoration but the actual art of making: that there are visual means of asserting and arriving at common sense. As for the artist himself he has to feel that he is part of a community, however much he may be forced to disagree with its inexperienced criticisms and to resist its claims. None of these are new relationships. But in the modern city they have been distorted and blocked.

However local circumstances may differ, the barriers and distortions are of much the same kind whatever city we look at. The main objective for those concerned about the pattern of art there must be to clear them away and hope that the great increase in interest, understanding and activity in the visual arts will resolve many subsidiary problems. This objective is certainly being pursued in other places, but it has to be pursued locally, in terms of the local situation. In a world where communication has become so rapid and so relatively cheap, and geographical frontiers in art have been very largely swept away, this is the one hope of avoiding an ultimately cramping monotony. I hope that whether or not they accept its reasoning other cities will be moved by the present study to embark on their own. It is not just the supply of art to the city that matters. It is bringing their relationship to life.

Questionnaire: The Visual Arts in Liverpool

There were 368 replies to the questionnaire discussed on pp. 130-7. Of these fifty-four were the result of interviews in different districts of Liverpool by five students at the College of Art. In the other cases the respondents filled the forms in themselves without an interviewer. Eighty-four came from visitors to the Walker Art Gallery, thirty-one from employees (mainly clerical staff) at Littlewoods' Spinney House, 172 from pupils at Gateacre Comprehensive School and twenty-seven from the staff there.

Excluding the school children the age distribution was:

Between 15–20	58 respondents
21–35	73
35–60	52
over 60	6

There were more than ten respondents from four (variegated) Liverpool postal districts – 8, 15, 16 and 23 – and from Wallasey; the vast majority of the schoolchildren came from Liverpool 25. There were between two and nine respondents from each of the other districts apart from 1, 2, 5 and 10 (i.e., the business district, the Scotland Road area and Aintree, all of which had none), and four apiece from Birkenhead, Huyton and Formby.

Age on ending full-time education (excluding the school children):

16 or under	73
17–20	36
21 and over	33
Still at school	8
At university	20
At other colleges	13

The following shows the division of responses between the Walker Art Gallery visitors (WAG), the interviewees (Int) Littlewoods' employees (L), the Gateacre school staff (GS(s)) and the Gateacre pupils (GS). Totals in each group are shown in brackets.

Question 1

	WAG (84)	Int (54)	L (31)	GS(s) (27)	GS (172)
Are you interested in painting and sculpture?					
Yes	82	34	14	25	112
No	2	20	13	1	58

Do you ever do anything of the sort yourself?

	WAG	Int	L	GS(s)	GS
Yes	53	14	7	7	106
No	29	36	11	19	58

Do you have any of your own work hanging or showing in your house?

	WAG	Int	L	GS(s)	GS
Yes	39	7	3	6	54*
No	15	7	3	1	59

* *Of whom six had answered 'No' immediately above.*

Question 2

Do you go to public art galleries and art exhibitions?

	WAG	Int	L	GS(s)	GS
Yes	74	22	4	16	34
No	1	11	6	1	53
Sometimes	9	19	16	11	76

How long is it since you were in the Walker Art Gallery?

	WAG	Int	L	GS(s)	GS
Month or less	58	5	0	3	5
1–3 months	13	2	0	3	20
3–6 months	2	1	2	3	29
$\frac{1}{2}$–1 year	3	7	4	4	23
1–2 years	4	9	2	4	22
2–5 years	0	7	5	4	10
Over 5 years	1	13	5	2	7
Never	0	8	4	0	43

Name a picture you liked:

Daguerre's Holyrood Chapel	11 votes
Henry VIII (School of Holbein)	11 (including 7 GS)
The Death of Nelson (Maclise)	10 (including 9 GS)
Paul Jenkins's Phenomena Votive	7
Lowry's The Fever Van	7
Faithful unto Death (Poynter)	7 (including 5 GS)
Murillo's The Virgin and Child	5
Scott's Blue Abstract	4
The Beehive (? Zobel's To the Hive)	4
Rubens's The Virgin and Child	3
Rembrandt's Self-Portrait	3
Simone Martini	2
When did you last see your father? (Yeames)	2

There were also a number of pictures which got a single vote. One respondent said 'none', another said 'all'. Altogether there were 170 named choices, of which some were not in the gallery.

What other art gallery or exhibition do you visit?

None	43
National Gallery	26
Tate Gallery	25
Lady Lever	15
Louvre	13
Birkenhead	12
Bluecoat } Manchester }	11
Southport	10
Sudley } Warrington } Edinburgh }	4
Others	36

Question 3

How long is it since you bought any sort of picture?

	WAG	Int	L	GS(s)	GS
A year or less	34	13	7	10	41
1–5 years	14	11	2	9	12
Over 5 years	2	4	2	5	2
Never	25	25	19	3	65

What was it and how much?

Thirty-four of the above were postcards. The rest fell into the following categories:

(i) Original paintings: 15 (£131 10s+); including a gouache by Peter Lanyon, Adrian Henri's *Ubu on Rhyl Sands* and a copy after Constable.

(ii) Prints and watercolours: 8 (£19 6s+); including Brangwyn, David Roberts and 'a pupil of Buffet'.

(iii) Reproductions of recognized modern artists: 17 (£15 17s+); including 5 Utrillo, 2 Picasso and one each of Marc, Monet, Renoir, Buffet, Bonnard, Cézanne, van Gogh, Modigliani, Braque and Dali.

(iv) Classical reproductions: 10 (£22+); 3 Mona Lisas, Constable's *Hay Wain*, Dürer's *Praying Hands* and pictures by Goye, Duccio, Canaletto, Vermeer and Stubbs.

(v) Popular reproductions: 45 (£57+) (may include some photographs); 4 or 5 Peter Scott, 3 Vernon Ward, 1 to 3 Tretchikoff, 9 unidentified landscapes, 6 unidentified seascape, 3 Spanish, 2 each horses, flowers and ballet.

(vi) Unidentifiable reproductions: 13 (£13 11s+).

NB Expenditure shown is below actual amounts, as about a third of respondents did not give prices.

Question 4

Have you seen films or television shows about art and artists?

	WAG	Int	L	GS(s)	GS
Yes	67	41	11	25	108
Blank	3	2	4	0	24
No	10*	12	9	2	34

One of these commented 'They will spoil your own idea of painting.'

Do you look out for programmes of this sort?

Yes	51	21	3	12	40
Blank (or ambiguous)	7	5	4	6	35
No	12	27	11	7	81

Three of the 'no's' said they had no TV.

Question 5

Have you any friend or relative who does drawing or painting of that sort of thing?

	WAG	Int	L	GS(s)	GS
Yes	62	43	13	17	99
No	19	12	14	9	68

The GS responses are valueless here, as art is taught in the school.

Professional or amateur?

Professional	27	20	2	4	10
Amateur	36	23	10	14	87

Question 6

Name a Liverpool artist

	WAG	Int	L	GS(s)	GS
No answer	35	41	23	16	117
Irrelevant (e.g. Constable, Sir G. Scott, Paul McCartney, etc.)	2	0	0	1	10
Arthur Dooley	12	8	2	5	3
Arthur Ballard	4	2	0	0	13*
Stubbs	5	0	0	1	18†
Adrian Henri	3	0	1	0	0
Edward Halliday	1	2	0	0	0
A. P. Tankard	2	0	0	0	0
Trevor Hughes	2	0	0	0	0
Will C. Penn	1	0	0	0	1

All these are from one form (LM).
†*Sixteen of these are from one form (4Y).*

The following got one mention each:

(i) By GS pupils: Peter MacKarell, Fred O'Brien. (I have disregarded four GS pupils' mentions of their own teachers).

(ii) By W A G: Mayer-Marton, Mollie Garland, Austin, Perceval, Don McKinlay, Davis, Cris Wood, Sam Walsh, Lowry, William Huggins, George Thomas, Brian Burgess, Stanley Hill, Max Eden, Stanley English, R. P. Richards, Mavis Blackburn.

(iii) By GS staff: A. Butler, Stanley Reid, E. Carter Preston.

(iv) By Littlewoods' employees: W. L. Stevenson, Sean Rice, Griffin.

(v) By interviewees: Gordon Ellis, John Heritage.

Question 7

What do you feel about the idea of seeing paintings, sculpture and so on at your place of work?

	WAG	Int	L	GS(s)	GS
Like	68*	41†	24†	28	116
Dislike	3	9	2	0	12
No fixed place of work	10	5	2	0	43

* Three expressed qualifications: (i) 'not sculpture'. (ii) 'except female faces.' (iii) that context, environment, etc., must be right.

† One 'with qualifications'. One said 'but not too much – consider visual art expressions are not really appreciated by majority of "passers-by"'.

‡ One depending on quality. One 'painting only, dislike sculpture'.

Question 8

What do you feel about the idea of seeing it *inside* public buildings - libraries, hospitals, stations and so on?

	WAG	Int	L	GS(s)	GS
Like	81*	52	29	27	141
Dislike	3	1	1	0	26

* Four with qualifications: (i) except hospitals, (ii) except hospitals and stations, (iii) as 7 (ii) above, (iv) 'Depends on building situation, etc.'

Question 9

What about seeing it on the *outside* of public buildings, or in squares, parks and open spaces?

	WAG	Int	L	GS(s)	GS
Like	67*	36†	23†	25	116
Dislike	16	17	7	2	48††

* Five qualifications: (i) sculpture only, (ii) 'but not

paintings', (iii) as 7(ii) above, (iv) as 8(iv) above, (v) 'but
sparingly'.
† *One said 'but not too much', as for question 7.*
‡ *One specified 'decent architecture, not modern'. Another
was impressed by Birmingham and Coventry.*
†† *It is possible that some of the younger children thought
questions 8 and 9 mutually exclusive.*

Question 10

Have you any pictures in your home?

	WAG	Int	L	GS(s)	GS
Yes	71	40	14	18	90
No	10	14	16	8	76

What are they and who are the artists?

It is not worth listing the answers in detail, as they follow the pattern of those to question 3.
In addition to those mentioned there the paintings included work by William Huggins,
Alexander Nasmyth, S. Lamorna Birch and (of local artists) Stuart Sutcliffe, Don
McKinlay, Sam Walsh and Peter MacKarell. The prints, watercolours and drawings
included work by Birket Foster, Orovida, Paul Nash, Mark Gertler, Nina Hamnett,
Gaudier-Brzeska, Kathleen Major (of Wigan) and Edgar Grosvenor. This was of course at
one end of the scale only; at the other were calendars, photos of pop stars, paintings by
the physically handicapped, and 'mural wallpaper'.

Question 11

What do you feel about the city's collection of pictures in the Walker Gallery?

	WAG	Int	L	GS(s)	GS
Proud	29*	21†	1	3	30
Should be added to	62‡	15	13††	20	47
Indifferent	5	14	10	3	25
Should stay as it is	2	3	1	0	14
Waste of money	2§	2	1	0	18

* *One says 'fairly'.*
† *One: 'A lot should be weeded out and replaced.'*
‡ *One: 'Could be greatly improved. Collection of classical
Italian paintings should be diminished (could be put in
museums where they belong) to make way for more pro-
gressive art of today.' Next respondent concurred.*
†† *Includes one respondent who has never been there.*
§ *Two schoolboys from Widnes.*

Question 12

Do you belong to any art society or attend any art appreciation class?

	WAG	Int	L	GS(s)	GS
Yes	25	3	0	0	—
No	52	49	30	26	—

What?

Extramural and WEA	5
Wallasey School of Art or art society	4
Bootle School of Art	2
Birkenhead School of Art	1
Southport School of Art	1
Regional College of Art	1
Liver Sketching Club	1
Chester College of Further Education	1
Warrington Art School and art group	1

The art school figures here are likely only to refer to part-time students. The Gateacre pupils have been omitted.

Question 13

Would you like to see any child of yours go to art school?

	WAG	Int	L	GS(s)	GS
Yes	45	13†	9*	14‡	81
Blank or ambiguous	16**	7	11	11	53
No	12††	13§	5	2	22

* *One says : 'if genuinely talented'.*
‡ *One : 'if so inclined'.*
† *One : 'if it wanted to', one 'if good enough', two 'would mind'.*
** *One says 'daughter yes, son no'.*
†† *One : 'unless he wanted to'.*
§ *One : 'only if exceptionally talented'. One says 'other plans'.*

Question 14

What statues are there on the Lime Street side of St George's Hall?

	WAG	Int	L	GS(s)	GS
No answer, don't know, or wrong	24	10	10	9	30
LIONS*	24	33	17	14	122

S

	WAG	Int	L	GS(s)	GS
(of which Four lions	*1*	*17*	*1*	*1*	*4)*
HORSEMEN†	16	13	7	4	70
Victoria	23	18	1	2	8
Albert	18	17	1	4	4
other royalty	7	1	4	0	16‡
DISRAELI	10§	11**	0	5	0
GENERAL					
EARLE††	5	2	0	0	0
WAR MEMORIAL	12‡‡	22	2	1	19
DOLPHINS (*on*					
lamps)	3	1	0	0	0
RELIEFS	0	4	0	1§§	0

*Other suggestions include Walpole, Birkenhead, Gladstone,
'various Victorians', 'Local philanthropists', 'historic men
of battle' and 'Victorian stuff'. A student at Bangor said
'I do not consider them statues'.*

* *Quantities given from 1 to 5. Descriptions include 'Land-
seer', 'Queen's Beasts', 'Albert and the Lions' (2–3 times)*
† *Identified as Wellington, St George, King George IV, V
or VI, etc.*
‡ *Usually named as one of the Georges.*
§ *Once identified as Shakespeare, once not at all.*
** *Twice described as 'man'.*
†† *Only once identified correctly. Also called Gordon,
Kitchener and (very accurately). 'somebody brandishing a
sword sunhelmeted'.*
‡‡ *Includes one mention of the sculptor, Tyson Smith.
This is the only time the sculptor of any of these objects is
named.*
§§ *Termed 'Greek reproductions'.*

*I have omitted mentions of the Wellington monument, as its
position is ambiguous in terms of the question.*

Question 15

What is over the entrance to Lewis's?

	WAG	Int	L	GS(s)	GS
No answer, or don't					
know	10	6	8	1	16
SPIRIT OF LIVERPOOL					
RESURGENT *or*					
*something near**	13	6	7	15	27
EPSTEIN	27†	23	7	21‡	9
MAN, *statue or figure*	41	40	11	6	125
specifically NAKED	19	9	9	2	57

specifically on PROW	3	3	2	0	22
RELIEFS	11	7	1	1	0

* *Such as Spirit of Freedom, Spirit of Youth, The New Life of Liverpool, Upsurgence of Liverpool, Liverpool Rejuvenate.*
† *Twice identified as 'Adam', once as Apollo.*
‡ *Once identified as 'David'.*
Other suggestions included Commerce and 'Spirit of Lewis's'. There were also some ten derogatory remarks such as 'Cooo!', 'not nice', 'monstrocity' (sic) and 'vulgar looking man'.

Question 16

What is over the main Mersey Tunnel entrance?

	WAG	Int	L	GS(s)	GS
No answer, don't know, wrong or hopelessly vague	45*	23	13	13	68
KING & QUEEN†	25	24	10	10	58‡
(of which George and Mary	20	19	8	8**	34§)
One monarch only	3	3	3	1	10
WINGED RELIEF††	8	10	5	4	25

* *'Too familiar with it to know', said a member of Crosby Borough Engineer's Department.*
† *Among monarchs suggested, in various improbable couplings, were Edward VI, Queen Anne and George IIV (sic).*
‡ *Including two descriptions just as 'man and woman' and 'two statues'.*
§ *Five of these suggest that the statues are busts or heads only.*
** *Includes one description of the pair as seated.*
†† *Only one exact description. Often described as Liverpool coat of arms.*

Question 17

Is it a good thing that the Council should spend money on works of art for:

(a) *improving the look of the city?*
(b) *the city collection in the Walker Gallery?*

		WAG	Int	L	GS(s)	GS
(a)	Yes	68*	39†	22	25	120
	Indifferent	3	2‡	1	0	18
	No	10§	13	3	1	16

(b) *Yes*	77	40	13	24	80
Indifferent	4	4	7**	2	39
No	3†††	10	6	1	34††

* One : 'But not to the detriment of vital social services'.
† One : 'When slum clearance has been completed'.
‡ Includes a visitor from Solihull, who says 'No – if monuments. Yes – if like Gabriel at Coventry'.
§ One : 'It would be useless'.
** One : 'Within strict limits'.
†† Includes seven who under question 11 said that the gallery should be added to.
††† Includes one who under question 11 said that the gallery should be added to.

Would you be willing to see an extra halfpenny rate devoted to:

(a) *works of art on new buildings or in conjunction with the new planning schemes?*
(b) *improving the city's collection?*

		WAG	Int	L	GS(s)	GS
(a)	*Yes*	59	38	18	23	—
	(*of whom actual Liverpool rate-payers*	*19*	*22*	*8*	*19*	—)
	Indifferent	9	4	3	1	—
	(*of whom actual Liverpool rate-payers*	*1*	*3*	*1*	*1*	—)
	No	10	11	5	1	—
	(*of whom actual Liverpool rate-payers*	*6*	*6*	*2*	*1*	—)
(b)	*Yes*	70	33	10	23	—
	(*of whom actual Liverpool rate-payers*	*24*	*22*	*4*	*19*	—)
	Indifferent	5	6	6	2	—
	(*of whom actual Liverpool rate-payers*	*1*	*3*	*4*	*2*	—)
	No	3*	13	9	1	—
	(*of whom actual Liverpool rate-payers*	*0*	*5*	*1*	*1*	—)
	Rates included in rent	19	2	4	12	—

* Includes one who said Walker Gallery should be added to, under 11 above.

The Gateacre pupils have been omitted as not having enough experience of the rate burden.

What is the rateable value of your house or business?
Would you personally be willing to spend (½d rate on this sum) a year extra on your rates?

	WAG	Int	L	GS(s)	GS
Yes	18	20*	4	14	—
Blank	0	0	2	1	—
No	2†	7	5‡	0	—

* Two specified 'Walker Art, not outside.'
† One states: 'Rates far too high already'. The other appears to be a schoolboy and not a ratepayer.
‡ Includes two who said Yes to (a) and (b) above.

Question 18

Would you look through the set of cards and sort out which you definitely like, which you don't care about, and which you definitely dislike?

	WAG	Int	L	GS(s)	GS

1 Peter Scott: Brent Geese Flighting under a Mackerel Sky. *Medici Society* PC 1213

	WAG	Int	L	GS(s)	GS
Like	24	40	24	11	124
Don't care	19	7	0	8	29
Dislike	27	6	1	8	12

2 Doris Zinkeisen: The Picnic. *Medici Society* PC 1333

	WAG	Int	L	GS(s)	GS
Like	34	29	7	8	70
Don't care	18	12	15	12	57
Dislike	18	14	3	5	30

3 Dame Laura Knight, DBE, RA: Ballet. *In the Lady Lever Art Gallery. Medici Society* PC 957

	WAG	Int	L	GS(s)	GS
Like	18	28	13	6	99
Don't care	23	7	9	11	30
Dislike	25	18	2	8	36

4 André Derain: The Pool of London 1906. *Tate Gallery* (6030)

	WAG	Int	L	GS(s)	GS
Like	24	21	7	7	33
Don't care	27	12	15	14	54
Dislike	17	21	3	6	76

5 Oskar Kokoschka: The Karlsbrücke in Prague. *National Gallery, Prague. Pallas Postcard* 1251.

Like	35	31	11	11	65
Don't care	21	18	9	13	47
Dislike	8	7	5	3	45

6 Augustus John, OM, RA: Two Jamaican Girls. *Walker Art Gallery.*

Like	38	36	8	14	57
Don't care	19	7	11	11	65
Dislike	7	10	5	0	37

7 Maurice de Vlaminck: Environs de Rouen. *Walker Art Gallery.*

Like	39	34	10	14	78
Don't care	20	13	14	10	54
Dislike	8	7	1	2	28

8 Sir Alfred Munnings, PPRA: Gipsy Life. *Aberdeen Art Gallery. Medici Society* PC 1215

Like	18	23	8	3	112
Don't care	23	20	12	15	43
Dislike	24	11	3	5	8

9 Ben Nicholson: Painting 1937. *Tate Gallery* (*T* 50)

	WAG	Int	L	GS(s)	GS
Like	22	6	7	9	35
Don't care	22	13	8	12	57
Dislike	25	32	11	6	71

10 St George's Hall, Liverpool: Carved Panel (by Conrad Dressler). *Photograph by Eric de Maré. A Gordon Fraser Card.* BKO 2–15.

Like	18	29	8	8	56
Don't care	31	12	13	14	72
Dislike	11	12	3	3	31

11 Pablo Picasso: Portrait of a Young Woman. Version III. *Collection of the Artist. Soho Card* 371.

Like	44	20	8	16	67
Don't care	9	9	5	9	48
Dislike	16	26	13	2	45

See illustration 92 on p. 134

12 Victor Pasmore: Square Motif, Blue and Gold: The Eclipse 1950. *Tate Gallery* (5974).

Like	24	3	2	5	29
Don't care	10	12	6	10	45
Dislike	34	37	18	11	92

13 Karel Appel: Amorous Dance 1955. *Tate Gallery* (*T.* 212).

	WAG	Int	L	GS(s)	GS
Like	25	15	6	10	44
Don't care	20	5	4	8	46
Dislike	19	34	16	8	76

14 Pierre Auguste Renoir: The Little Blacksmith. *Walker Art Gallery. English Life Publications, Derby.* 6753***

Like	41	27	10	11	52
Don't care	14	13	10	12	65
Dislike	6	13	4	1	39

See illustration 94 on p. 135

15 Antoine Pevsner: Maquette of a Monument Symbolizing the Liberation of the Spirit, 1952. *The Tate Gallery.*

Like	38	19	11	5	78
Don't care	6	8	8	18	46
Dislike	19	25	8	4	39

16 Pablo Picasso: Cock 1932. *The Tate Gallery.*

Like	19	6	4	6	23
Don't care	19	7	5	10	34
Dislike	25	40	14	11	101

See illustration 91 on p. 134

17 Germaine Richier: Water, 1953-4. *The Tate Gallery.*

Like	27	3	1	1	17
Don't care	13	6	6	4	30
Dislike	29	44	17	22	117

18 L. S. Lowry: The Fever Van. *Walker Art Gallery.*

	WAG	Int	L	GS(s)	GS
Like	44	11	6	17	87
Don't care	22	12	12	9	51
Dislike	3	8	6	0	20

See illustration
93 on p. 135

19 Henry Moore: Project for the Family, 1944. *Tate Gallery.*

Like	38	8	2	7	22
Don't care	10	5	6	11	54
Dislike	18	42	16	9	79

20 Sir Jacob Epstein, KBE: Mrs Epstein, 1918. *Sir Alec Martin. Photograph by Hans Wild. A Gordon Fraser card.* SKEJ–7

Like	31	27	11	12	56
Don't care	23	11	9	10	52
Dislike	8	13	3	4	47

NB The seven cards of sculpture (10, 14, 15, 16, 17, 19 and 20) were black-and-white, the remainder coloured. Special points to note are the subjects of 3 (ballet), 4 and 7 (ships), and 6 (coloured people). Also the controversial names: Munnings (8), Picasso (11 and 16) and Epstein (20). Four cards were of works in the Walker Gallery (6, 7, 14, 18), one in the Lady Lever (8) and one of a St George's Hall sculpture (10). All these represent factors affecting judgment.

APPENDIX B Comparative data for five cities

	Genoa	Marseilles	Antwerp	Rotterdam	Boston	Liverpool
1 Population	802,991 (1961)	783,738 (1962)	251,419 (1962)	731,500 (1963)	697,938 (1962)	747,490 (1961)
2 Revenue from taxation	£3,923,600 (1962) (6,834,934,519 lire)	£10,000,000 local taxes (137,601,038 fr.)	£2,762,000 (1962) (382,230,762 FB)	£15,800,000 from taxation and 'Municipal Fund' (fl. 158,160,000)	£54,725,000 (1962) ($152,230,470)	£12,946,508 (1962-3)
3 Annual average tonnage through port 1958–62 (net registered tons)	23,714,976	51,024,604	36,051,740	63,746,000 (1962)	19,642,517	28,896,996
4 Main Public Art Galleries	1 Palazzo Rosso 2 Palazzo Bianco 3 Galleria d' arte moderna (and seven museums)	1 Musée de Beaux-Arts 2 Musée Cantini 3 Musée Grober –Labadie	1 Royal Gallery of Fine Arts 2 Rubens's house 3 Middelheim sculpture park 4 Mayer van den Bergh museum 5 Ridder Smid van Gelder museum	Boymans/van Beuningen Musem	Museum of Fine Arts	1 Walker Art Gallery 2 Sudley Art Gallery and Museum
5 Expenditure on principal art gallery	£87,350 (1962) (152,159,027 lire)	£21,400 (1963 est.) (292,856 fr.)	1 £61,640 (1958) paid half by city half by state 2 £62,360 (1961)	no data	£528,600 (1961) from private sources only	£112,595 (1959-60)
6 Amount devoted to purchase of pictures out of municipal funds	No allocation. Decided ad hoc	£1,240	1 State grant of £25,300. No municipal contributions	£27,500 (1963)	(Income from private sources available: £200,000 in 1961)	£10,000

	Genoa	Marseilles	Antwerp	Rotterdam	Boston	Liverpool
7 *Number of visitors per year at principal gallery*	121,533 (1962)	17,830 (1962) excluding free admissions and school visits	2 £16,000 of which c. £10,000 for sculpture park 140,576 (1962)	94,000 (1962)	750,000 (1962)	125,427 (1962/3)
8 *Art schools*	Liceo artistico Nicolò Barabino	Ecole des Beaux-Arts	Royal Academy of Arts City pays 44 per cent	Academy for Plastic Arts 30 per cent municipal	1 Massachussetts College of Art 2 Boston Museum School Both private (Also 8 others)	Regional College of Art
9 *Number of students*	452 (1962–3)	c.1000	c.1000	c.550	2 1000 including part-time	335 full-time 1,751 part-time (1962)
10 *Expenditure on art school(s)*	£35,241 (1962)	£286,000 (1963 budget)	£25,810 city contribution (1958)	no data	None from public funds	£213,575
11 *Private and commercial galleries*	7	5 plus	5	5	? 17	4
12 *University departments concerned with the visual arts*	Institute of Art history		National Higher Institute of Art	None	Boston University School of Applied and Fine Arts (also departments at Harvard, Brandeis, etc.)	School of Architecture, Department of Civic Design
13 *Expenditure on publicly commissioned murals, mosaics, sculptures, etc.*	None	£6960 from state funds (1 per cent of school building costs)	£7200 from city funds £36,000 from state funds	£35,000 (1962)	c. £3500 (maintenance and upkeep only)	

The cities supplying these details were also invited to name any notable painters and sculptors living in or near the city. The best known seemed to be Floris Jespers and Baron Opsomer (Antwerp), Bernard Buffet (near Marseilles), G. Romijn and L. van Roode (Rotterdam). Boston grandly claims at least 300 recognized practising artists.

They were asked if they gave preferential treatment to local artists. Rotterdam did not answer, Antwerp said not, Genoa gives a scholarship of about £300 a year to a local artist. Genoa, Antwerp, Rotterdam and Boston all said that there were no distinctions between their political parties in art matters. Asked for instances of business or trade union patronage, Antwerp said that two Zadkine sculptures had been presented by the Agence Maritime Internationale and the Banque de Paris et des Pays-Bas; Rotterdam cited the support given to art by firms who put works of art in or near their buildings or present works to the city. No city reported any case of trade union patronage.

Unfortunately it proved impossible to get comparable details from Bremen, Valencia and San Francisco. Some incomplete information came however from the Polish port of Gdansk. The estimated population there is 300,000, the port traffic (for 1962) 3,199,377 tons. The public gallery is part of the Pomeranian Museum; there is also a School of Fine Arts. There has been much reconstruction and restoration of the city's historic buildings since 1945, and the artists and the school have taken an active part in this. A report says that 'the guiding principle in decoration of the historic reconstructed buildings seems to have been the reproduction of traditional designs while using modern techniques with colouring and materials'.

APPENDIX C

Project for a 'Look at Liverpool' Exhibition

This project was worked out by me in consultation with the Liverpool painters Adrian Henri, Arthur Ballard and Peter MacKarell.

Objects are:

1 To exploit the current interest in Liverpool. To show that the city's vitality is not confined to its singers and guitarists, but that these are part of a larger pattern.

2 To convey the place's visual impact, which is like nothing else in Europe and contains much that is of unique architectural and historical interest.

3 To show off its peculiar artistic talents, both latent (in the schoolchildren, etc.) and professional; to set them tasks and to make Liverpool people as well as others more aware of them.

4 To show them in combination with the new plans and with the best of the old heritage, and in this way to suggest a possible visual climate for the future.

Scheme is for a travelling exhibition which could be sent to London, Hamburg, Paris, Rotterdam, Antwerp and anywhere else where the name of Liverpool now arouses interest. It would not be primarily an art exhibition. Pictures and sculptures would be included on the same footing as photos, models or anything else: i.e. as so many means of contributing to a total Liverpool impression.

Method of achieving this:

1 Collection of relevant photographic and documentary materials, models, poems, recordings, etc.

2 Selection of works of art from nominated artists. Further selection from certain schools and from outstanding amateurs. (All these would have been asked to put forward work and given an outline of the scheme.)

3 Writing of a script – the basis for arrangement of material and writing of captions.

4 Engagement of a first-rate professional exhibition designer, to mount the exhibition so that it can be shown in a variety of halls and spaces.

5 Artists to add further embellishments and diversions as the show takes shape.

6 Arrangement and rehearsal of any 'live' events.

Finance would have to be by the Corporation or by interested Liverpool industries, or by a combination of the two. (Industry might take advertising space on the free surfaces of the exhibition, or might care to offer prizes for participating artists.) The cost of the major project (A) might, I understand from an experienced designer, be anything from £5,000 to £15,000, plus the designer's fees which are standard at 10 per cent on £5,000, increasing 1 per cent for every £500 less. Project (B) is a much reduced version.

The absolute essential is perfection of finish in the mounting. Well-presented, the show could make a forceful and original impression, extending and consolidating the territory won for Liverpool in people's minds by the success of the music groups and the footballers. But a complicated mixed exhibition like this cannot afford the least mediocrity in mounting, captioning or lighting.

Look at Liverpool : Project A

Entrance – through a mock-up of the Lime Street cutting, showing texture of its sides.
Floor – railway lines.
In the cutting: The Gibson statue of Huskisson with material about him, the Liverpool and Manchester railway and his death, possibly models of that railway.
Ceiling: blue sky, or night sky.

Space 1   **First Impressions**
Liverpool children
St George's Hall
The Library – Walker Gallery group of buildings
Other Victorian architecture
Statesmen associated with Liverpool: Canning, Gladstone, Brougham, Creevey, etc.
Roscoe and the anti-slavers
The docks
Ships and ship models
Nineteenth-century trade (labels, advertisements, documents, etc.)
The mixed population
Paintings conveying spirit of the place
Poems

Space 2   **The churches**
Scott's cathedral
Gibberd's cathedral
Lutyens plans
Designs related to any of these (for windows, etc.)
Dooley sculptures
Orange Lodge banners
Photos of processions and of eminent clergy

Space 3   **The arts**
Liverpool paintings from Stubbs, Windus to now
Sculpture
Coloured projections of further paintings (to be changed)
Roscoe and his collection
The Moores competition: story and examples
The Royal Liverpool Philharmonic: documents and photos
Facilities for hearing its recordings

Musica Viva
Fritz Spiegl
Liverpool Theatres, actors and comedians

Space 4   **Grotto by G. W. Jardine** (if agreeable)

Space 5   **Football**
Footballers and the two teams
Football crowds
Historic moments
The pools: how they work
Historic cheques (transfer fees, pools winnings)
Nets, goalposts, etc.
Paintings relating to football and sport

Space 6   **Redevelopment**
The slums
The City Centre Plan, drawings, model etc
Plans for remainder of the city
Gordon Cullen drawings
New housing
Comparable schemes actually executed
Paintings: anything that fits the rebuilding theme or conveys the slums
Any new architecture of merit
Composite work on this theme by Maghull Grammar School pupils (if agree-
able)

Space 7   **Pop Music**
A Cavern-type space. Also to be used for actual performances
Documents and other souvenirs of the Beatles
Documents and other souvenirs of other groups
Photographs from *Merseybeat* (now *Music Echo*)
Facilities for listening to records
Record sleeves
Lennon's drawings and any others by musicians
Paintings: Stuart Sutcliffe and any others relevant to the theme.

Space 8   **Natural talent**
Remarkable sequence of paintings by patient at Rainhill
Works of art by schoolchildren
Pottery and metal sculpture from Gateacre Comprehensive School
Projections from Teacher Training Departments at College of Art
Constructions from Bluecoat School
Children's poems
Photographs of school buildings, old and new
Pictures by amateurs

These spaces to be formed of adjustable units, so that they can be connected to fit the total space available, whether elongated or compact. If necessary one or more can be omitted. Projection of slides to be done by back projection; the slides to be changeable. There should be facilities for showing films (*Morning in the Streets* and other TV features on Liverpool). Recordings to be played in the spaces: Stan Kelly songs, children's songs, other Liverpool music, performances by Beatles and other groups, poetry. Individual listening to be possible too (? by earphones). Listeners to be able to pick their own records for earphone listening, as in a record shop.

Painting and sculpture. Besides what is specified above, anything else that fits in.

The ubiquitousness of children. To be conveyed by the occasional blown-up photograph.

Look at Liverpool : Project B

Section 1 **The place as it is**

        Photographs of Victorian architecture (Graham Smith, etc.)

        Designs for St George's Hall (Cockerell, Stevens)

        The Docks. (Eric de Maré photos. Detailed drawings)

        Scott's cathedral designs

        Nineteenth-century trade. (Documents, bills, etc.)

        The slums (Graham Smith's photos)

        Walker's pubs

        Liverpool children (photos)

        The mixture of populations (statistics and photos)

        Religious banners and processions

        Stills from *Z-cars*

        Paintings, etc.: Topographical

                    Henri's Liverpool 8 pictures

                    Jardine collages

                    Horsfield view of Mount Street

                    School drawings (Breckfield, St Martin's)

        Music: Stan Kelly songs. Liverpool music picked by Fritz Spiegl. *Z-cars* march

        Poetry: from Henri, McGough, Patten, schoolchildren, etc.

Section 2 **Sport and entertainment**

        The two football teams. Photos and documents

        Football crowds (Photos)

        The pools. Facts and statistics

        The Topham Trophy (designs and history)

        Documents and souvenirs of the Beatles and other groups

        Photos from *Merseybeat* (Peter Kaye)

        Listening booths with earphones for hearing records

        Record sleeves

        Drawings by John Lennon and other musicians

        Paintings: MacKarell (football)

                Walsh (racing, etc.)

                Sutcliffe (and his associations with Beatles)

        Poems read to jazz (Patten, McGough, Gorman)

Section 3 **The arts**
  The Moores show (facts, and photos of prizewinners)
  The Walker Gallery (with photos of some pictures)
  The Royal Liverpool Philharmonic (Documents, photos and recordings, again
    with listening booths)
  The Liverpool Playhouse: its productions and actors
  The Everyman Theatre
  Paintings: (a) Historical. Windus, John, Henry Carr, Steer
          (b) Present day: Artists already mentioned, plus Ballard, Sidney
            Bonner, Edkins, McKinlay
          (c) Sequence by a patient at Rainhill
  Sculpture: Dooley
        Riley
  School work: Gateacre Comprehensive School, Bluecoat School, examples from
        Teacher Training Department at College of Art

Section 4 **The future**
  Model of the City Centre Plan
  Exhibit from the Planning Department
  New City housing (Plans, photos, etc.)
  Gordon Cullen drawings
  Gibberd's Catholic Cathedral (With designs for windows, etc.)
  Sculpture for the Littlewoods building
  New architecture of note
  Paintings: Henri after Ensor
        Schoolchildren's pictures on the reconstruction theme
  Composite feature (pictures, paper, sculpture, figures and so on) by pupils of
        Maghull Grammar School on this theme
  Poems
  Photographs of Liverpool children

These four sections are for planning purposes only. They should not be given the titles
or divided into water-tight compartments but allowed to run into each other. In this
version the exhibition could be mounted on screens which could then be set up to form
different flow patterns according to the varying space available, in no predetermined
sequence.

At some points they could be joined together to form larger surfaces. All other elements,
such as lighting, loudspeaker system, floor coverings and any suspended exhibits, would
then be fixed to suit the pattern chosen.

T

INDEX

L202, 484/F

LEABHARLANN CHONTAE LONGFOIRT
Longford County Library & Arts Services

This book should be returned on or before the latest
date shown below. Fines on overdue books will
accrue on a weekly basis or part thereof.

LD)

06. MAR 12

12 III. 11   18/12/2013   26/9/2016

21. JUL 11

06. AUG 12   25 NOV 2016   – 8 AUG 2017

01. NOV 11
03. JAN 12   29 AUG 2017

2 2 FEB 2019   12 NOV

1 6 APR 2019

1 2 MAR 2019

RP13555

Hollywood Hills

ALSO BY JOSEPH WAMBAUGH

FICTION

Hollywood Moon
Hollywood Crows
Hollywood Station
Floaters
Finnegan's Week
Fugitive Nights
The Golden Orange
The Secrets of Harry Bright
The Delta Star
The Glitter Dome
The Black Marble
The Choirboys
The Blue Knight
The New Centurions

NONFICTION

Fire Lover
The Blooding
Echoes in the Darkness
Lines and Shadows
The Onion Field

JOSEPH
WAMBAUGH
Hollywood Hills

CORVUS

First published in the United States of America in 2010
by Little, Brown and Company.

This edition first published in Great Britain in 2011
by Corvus, an imprint of Atlantic Books Ltd.

Copyright © Joseph Wambaugh 2010.

The moral right of Joseph Wambaugh to be identified as the author
of this work has been asserted in accordance with the
Copyright, Designs and Patents Act of 1988.

9 8 7 6 5 4 3 2 1

A CIP catalogue record for this book is available from
the British Library.

ISBN: 978-1-84887-876-1 (hardback)
ISBN: 978-1-84887-877-8 (trade paperback)

Printed in Great Britain by TJ International Ltd, Padstow, Cornwall

Corvus
An imprint of Atlantic Books Ltd
Ormond House
26-27 Boswell Street
London WC1N 3JZ

www.corvus-books.co.uk

ACKNOWLEDGMENTS

As ever, special thanks for the terrific anecdotes and great cop talk goes to officers of the Los Angeles Police Department:

Art Arguirre, Randy Barr, Kevan Beard, Charles Bennett, Vicki Bynum, Don Deming (ret.), Nicole Garner, Brett Goodkin, Mike Gray, Richard Guzman, Tracy Hauter, Craig Herron, Jack Herron (ret.), Don Hrycyk, Oscar Ibanez, Bart Landsman (ret.), Al Lopez, Kathy McAnany, Alfred Morales, Dan Myers, Bruce Nelson, Jeff Nolte, Thomas Onyshko, Al Pesanti (ret.), John Robertson (ret.), Sunny Sasajima, Tom Small, Mark Stainbrook, John Thacker, Geraldine Thomsen, Obie Vaughn, Jeff Von Lutzow, Carl Worrell

And to officers of the San Diego Police Department:

Brigitta Belz, Meryl Bernstein, Cindy Brady, Sarah Creighton, Jessie Holt, Ron Ladd (ret.), Joe Lehr, Lynda Oberlies, Mo Parga, Jesus Puente, Tony Puente (ret.), Donna Williams

And to officers of the Lompoc Police Department:

Jon Bailey, Jason Flint, Ron Hutchins, Joe Rapozo (jailer/dispatcher)

And to officers of the Chula Vista Police Department:

Greg Puente, Brian Treuel

Hollywood Hills

★ ONE ★

THE BUTT-FLOSS BUNNY'S busted, bro," said the alliteration-loving, sunbaked blond surfer. He was already in his black wet suit, lying on the sand and ogling the photo shoot thirty yards farther south on Malibu Beach on a late summer day that made Southern California's kahunas wonder why the rest of the world lived anywhere else.

"They can't jam her, dude," his taller surfing partner said, hair darker blond and also streaked with highlights, as he squirmed into his own black wet suit. "The ordinance says no nude sunbathing. Well, she ain't sunbathing and she's wearing a gold eye patch over her cookie and a pair of Dr. Scholl's corn pads over her nibs. So she ain't technically unclothed, even though she is, like, hormonally speaking, as naked as Minnie the mermaid who haunts my dreams."

"Anyways, everybody can see she ain't no surf bunny," said the shorter surfer. "Even her toenails are way jeweled up and all perfectamundo. So if chocka chicks wanna go denuded for a professional photo op, they deserve a pass."

"She deserves more than that for putting up with that met-sex woffie, for sure," the tall surfer said, referring to the skeletal metrosexual photographer in a tight pink T-shirt, with a fall of *so* casual highlighted hair draped over his non-camera eye. The photographer

3

was yapping orders to his perspiring young male assistant, whose gelled hair was combed up from the sides in a faux-hawk 'do, almost as fast as he clicked photos of the redhead.

"If she gets a ticket, it should be for littering a public beach with those two hodads in rainbow rubber, not for displaying her fabuloso physique," the shorter surfer replied, alluding to the two male models sharing the photo session as mere backdrop.

One was wearing a cherry-red wet suit with a white stripe up one leg, and the other a lemon-yellow wet suit equally offensive to the observing ring of sneering water enforcers who claimed this part of Malibu as kahuna turf. They viewed anyone wearing anything but a solid black or navy wet suit as dissing surfing traditions, and as a legitimate target to be surfboard-speared if they dared enter the water to claim a wave.

That lip-curling judgment was further confirmed by the leashes attached to the spanking-new longboards being used as props, surfboard leashes being almost as objectionable as colored wet suits to the gathering group of surfing purists watching the goings-on. The longboards, one turquoise, one violet, were positioned directly behind the magnificent redhead, who kept changing poses for the photographer. He was carefully framing provocative body shots fore and aft, unfazed by the L.A. Sheriff's Department black-and-white pulling into a parking space reserved for emergency vehicles.

"Here comes five-oh," said the taller surfer to his partner when two uniformed deputies, a young man and an older woman, got out and strode across the sand toward the photo shoot.

"Never a cop when you need one, bro," the shorter surfer noted. "And we don't need one now. The last time the little scallywag jiggled, one of her corn pads popped loose, which was like, too cool for school."

The taller surfer said, "Roger that. She is fully hot. Fully! But personally, right now I'm all dialed in to see what happens if the pair of rainbow donks actually hit the briny on their unwaxed logs.

4

The surf Nazis're gonna go all return-of-*Jaws* berserk when they smell that kooker blood in the water."

"Get your happy on, bro," his partner said. "Forget the two squids. Just wax up and enjoy the gymnosophical gyrations of that slammin' spanker."

"Gymno...?" said the tall surfer. Then, "Dude, I hate it when you take community college classes and go all vocabu-lyrical instead of speaking everyday American English."

Just then, the woman deputy, a tall Asian veteran with her black hair pulled into a tight bun, moved ahead of her burly young Latino partner to confront the photographer, who reluctantly stopped shooting and faced her.

"This is attracting an unruly crowd," she said. "It's not the time or place for a photo session of this nature on Malibu Beach. I'd like you to shut it down and take it to a more private location."

As the deputy said this, the redhead was performing splits on the yellow surfboard that one of the male models had placed flat on the sand as a pedestal for the next flurry of shots. But when the redhead got into the splits position, she lost control of her eye patch thong, attached by a string that rode over her hips and disappeared between the cheeks of her liquid-tanned buttocks. When the eye patch got crumpled against her upper thigh, her shaved genitalia were exposed, and a cheer went up from the raucous ring of twenty young men, most of them in wet suits, now completely surrounding the photo shoot. A salvo of lascivious commentary followed as the young men pushed in closer.

"See what I mean?" said the woman deputy to the photographer. "Shut this down now."

"About her thong," the photographer said. "If she puts one on that's made of wider material, will we be all right? I mean, I've been told that if there's a patch over her tulips and enough material in back so that her cheeks don't touch each other, it cannot be considered nudity on a public beach."

The giggling redhead, seemingly aroused by the male effluvium enveloping her like funky smoke, said to her boss, "You mean it'll make my costume legal if my cheeks don't touch?"

And with that, she arched her back, grabbed a buttock in each hand, and spread them slightly, all the while winking at her play-surfer colleagues in rainbow suits. Both of them had declined her offer to whiff a few lines just before the photo shoot and now looked unnerved by her coke-driven behavior.

The one in the lemon-yellow wet suit whispered in her ear, "Gloria, this is not risqué, this is fucking risky. We're surrounded by testosterone-crazed animals."

"That's it," said the woman deputy as the model rearranged her thong. "You're in violation of the law. Get off this beach and stand by our car. Do it now."

The photographer sighed in disgust, hands on his narrow hips, and gazed up, muttering to the vast cloudless sky over Malibu and the Pacific Ocean before reluctantly saying, "Okay, kids, it's a fucking wrap."

"I was just getting into it!" the redhead cried, snatching a towel from a folding chair.

And though alcohol consumption was prohibited on the beach, the grungiest of the nonsurfers were hammered, and an open can of beer was thrown from the back of the crowd. It soared over the heads of the nearest surfers, striking the deputy on the back of the head just above her bun of hair, splashing beer onto her tan uniform shirt.

"Owwww!" she yelped, whirling toward the mob.

"I saw which one did it!" her partner said, barging through the ring of wet suits, running down the beach after a fleeing teen in a torn T-shirt. As a result of having sloshed down two 40s of Olde English and a six-pack of Corona, the teen tripped over an obese, snoring tourist in plaid golf pants who was tits up and turning bubblegum-pink under the late afternoon sun.

The deputy wrestled the kid to the sand, looking as though he were trying to decide whether to grab handcuffs or pepper spray, when his partner, blood droplets wetting the collar of her uniform shirt, ran up and pounced on the thrashing teen, who yelled, "I didn't mean to hit nobody! It was just a lucky shot!"

"Unlucky for you, asshole," the Latino deputy said.

"I can hook him up," the woman deputy said to her partner as they grappled, "if you'll get his goddamn arm twisted back."

"I'm suing you!" the kid hollered. Then to the milling crowd of onlookers, "You people are witnessing police brutality! Give me your names and phone numbers!"

After their prisoner was handcuffed, they jerked him upright and started dragging him toward the parking lot.

Then another of the grungier beach creatures, in board shorts, inked-out from his neck to his knees with full-sleeve tatts on both arms and missing an incisor and two bicuspids in his upper grille, yelled, "Let him go. He didn't do nothing. Some nigger threw the beer and ran off."

He drunkenly slouched toward the deputies, full of booze and bravado, holding the neck of an empty beer bottle like a hammer, and the young deputy drew his Taser and pointed it at him. The female deputy immediately talked into her rover and requested backup while she kept her eyes on the increasingly rowdy mob, at the same time trying to decide which of the half dozen nonsurfing sand maggots could be a real threat.

She didn't realize that backup was much closer than she thought, and it arrived in a violent explosion of energy that stunned everybody. The tall blond surfer and his shorter partner issued no warnings, but running full speed, the taller one surged in low like a blitzing linebacker and slammed his shoulder into the lower spine of the guy with the beer bottle, who sailed forward, back bowed, and crashed hard against two surfers, knocking both of them flat on the sand. One of the other sleazed-out beach lice in ragged jeans

instantly leaped on the back of the tall surfer as he was getting to his feet and tried for a stranglehold. He let go when the shorter surfer grabbed his hair, jerked his head back, and dug three piston punches into the guy's kidneys, which made him drop to the sand, howling louder than his wounded mate.

"Get him to your car fast!" the tall surfer yelled to the deputies.

He picked up and brandished the beer bottle, standing shoulder to shoulder with his partner, facing off the jeering gaggle of now-hesitant surfers as the deputies continued dragging their hand-cuffed prisoner across the warm white sand of Malibu Beach.

The remainder of the surfing crowd suddenly had to rethink the whole business after seeing the two beach rats get cranked by the dynamic duo, whoever the fuck they were. And besides, since the wicked wahini and her crew were scampering to their SUV, the sexy rush was over. They figured that pretty soon there'd be more cops.

And anyway, they'd been out of the water too long. Adrenaline started gushing and synapses snapping when they saw half a dozen other surfers digging through the breakers. The surf was peaky and a young ripper came slicing in on a hugangus juicy while other surfers hooted him on. So what the fuck were they doing on dry land dicking around with these cops anyway?

Suddenly, as though on command, they all turned and began scrambling toward the ocean like a raft of clumsy sea lions, but once in the water and on their boards, they were transformed, and they darted, sleek as otters, through the shore break, with cops and even the redhead utterly forgotten. Their only concern was not get-ting cut off as they paddled from break to break in waves punchy and raw, waiting for a big one because this...*this* was what it was all about. They had discovered the meaning of life.

After the deputies got their handcuffed prisoner strapped into the backseat of the caged patrol unit, the tall surfer and his shorter partner heard the yelp of sirens as the LASD black-and-white units came roaring into the parking lot.

"Dude, I mighta rearranged a few disks in that sand maggot's back," the tall surfer said to his partner. "If we don't wanna get bogged to the ass in paperwork and lawsuits and shit, I think we should, like, fade out at this point and maybe frequent Bolsa Chica Beach for the next few weeks."

"I hear ya, bro," his partner said. "The sleazed-out surf rat that I nailed is gonna be pissing blood for a few days, so I ain't ready to answer a bunch of questions about why we didn't ID ourselves and advise them of their rights and give them all a chance to kick the shit outta the deputies and us, too. I say, let's bounce."

The younger, Latino deputy was busy corralling the photo crew as witnesses for his reports, and the older, female deputy was gingerly touching her injured head and scanning the growing crowd of looky-loos, but she couldn't find the surfing pair who'd decked the beach rats. She definitely needed them for the arrest and crime reports now that they were going to book their prisoner for the felony assault on a peace officer, but the arriving backup units caused a traffic snarl and she had to direct cars out of their way. This allowed the tall blond surfer and his shorter blond partner, hiding behind the throngs of beachgoers, to slip away, collect their boards, and scurry unobserved to their pickup truck in the parking lot.

They drove off and headed for the closest In-N-Out Burger, where they each devoured two cheeseburgers and fries. They arrived at work in time for a shower, a shave, an allowable application of hair gel, and a quick change into uniforms, ready for the 5:15 P.M. midwatch roll call.

All of the other police officers at Hollywood Station referred to this team of surfer cops as Flotsam and Jetsam.

TWO

FOR YEARS, HE had been dubbed "Hollywood Nate" because he carried a Screen Actors Guild card and was forever seeking stardom, as were thousands of Los Angeles bartenders, waiters, parking attendants, receptionists, window washers, dog walkers, and even people with vocations and professions, all nurturing similar hopes and dreams. Hollywood Nate's mother and older sister had always maintained that if only he had not been cast in a couple of TV movies early in his police career—back when Hollywood still made TV movies—the bug might not have bitten him so hard. Lots of cops from Hollywood and other police divisions worked the red carpet events or were hired as off-duty technical advisers on feature movies or TV shows, and that was the end of their emotional involvement with show business. But Nate was different.

Hollywood Nate's handsome hawkish profile and wavy dark hair, now going gray at the temples, along with his penetrating liquid brown eyes and iron-pumping build, had gotten him more than just sleepovers from below-the-line female employees on nearly every production he'd worked. Nate had also been given lots of paying jobs as an on-camera extra, and he'd even gotten those few speaking parts in TV productions, soon gathering enough credits

to get a SAG card, which he proudly kept in his badge wallet beneath his police ID card. The "Hollywood" moniker would be his for the rest of his police days because the LAPD had always loved having a "Hollywood Lou" or a "Hollywood Bill" among its ranks, and since the seventeen-year LAPD veteran "Hollywood Nate" even had a SAG card, that made it better.

The thirty-eight-year-old cop had been somewhat indulged for a few months by his fellow coppers on the midwatch during a time of deep sadness for all of them. It came after Nate's partner, Dana Vaughn, had been shot dead by a thief whom Nate then killed with return fire. Nate had grieved intensely for Dana Vaughn and had needed to surmount overwhelming feelings of survivor guilt and deep regret for never having told her certain intimate things, like how she had touched his heart and what she had meant to him in the short time they had worked together as patrol partners. Now he had recurring dreams of telling her those things, and in the dreams, she never answered him but would smile and chuckle in that special way of hers that always made him think of wind chimes.

It was during that mournful and restless period that Hollywood Nate had been offered an audition that came from working the red carpet on a warm summer night at the Kodak Theatre on Hollywood Boulevard. There were thirty cops there that night, all happily drawing overtime pay. Rudy Ressler, a second-rate director and producer who once had coproduced an Oscar-nominated movie, attended that affair with an up-and-coming pair of young beauties known only to people who spent their lives watching nighttime TV designed for Gen X-ers. Ressler's personal escort that evening was a UCLA theater major skinnier than Victoria Beckham and younger than his own daughter. When the event ended and the Kodak was disgorging the multitudes, Nate had occasion to apply some muscle to the stampeding paparazzi that had crowded in on the foursome as they walked to the director's rented limo.

It wasn't that the aggressive paparazzi were interested in shooting photos of the director, but Brangelina, moving fast, had emerged from the crowd right behind the Ressler foursome. Things got very unruly very quickly, and the frightened UCLA coed began whimpering when an obese paparazzo with a camera hanging from a strap around his neck and a Styrofoam cup in his hand backed against her, mashing her into Ressler's hired limousine.

Nate had stepped in then with pap pressing on all sides and hooked a low elbow very hard into the belly of the fat guy, causing him to let out a *woooo,* double over, and spew Jamba Juice all over other paparazzi. Nobody in that crush of nighttime fans, including other pap, had seen the surreptitious elbow chop, and even the groaning paparazzo didn't know what had hit him. But Rudy Ressler saw it, as did one of the security aides of the LAPD chief of police. The aide waited by the chief's ominous-looking SUV with its dark-tinted windows.

When the Ressler party got into their limo, the director turned and said to Nate, "Thank you for helping us, Officer. If there's anything I can ever do for you..." And he handed Nate a business card.

Hollywood Nate said, "You may regret that rash remark, sir." And he took the badge wallet from his pocket to show Rudy Ressler his SAG card, and said, "At the station they call me Hollywood Nate because of this."

"I'll be damned," the director said. He laughed out loud, turning to his companions and saying, "This officer is a SAG member. Only in Hollywood!"

"Have a good evening, sir," Nate said with a hopeful smile.

"Call me when you get a chance, Officer. I'm serious," the director replied, looking at Hollywood Nate appraisingly this time.

Before the limousine pulled away, Nate heard Rudy Ressler say to the driver, "We're dropping Ms. Franchon at her sorority house

and then you can take the rest of us to Mrs. Brueger's home in the Hollywood Hills. Do you remember where it is from last time?"

"Yes, sir, Mr. Ressler," the driver said.

The limousine drove off, leaving the other cars blowing horns and flashing their high beams at the inevitable traffic jam, and the paparazzi still snapping pictures. Hollywood Nate decided to take a better look at the chief's SUV and at the LAPD security aide standing beside it, who looked familiar. When he got closer, he recognized the wide-bodied, balding, mustachioed Latino cop in the dark three-piece business suit. It was Lorenzo "Snuffy" Salcedo, an old friend and classmate who had served with Nate in 77th Street Division when they were boots fresh out of the police academy, as well as later, when Snuffy had worked patrol at Hollywood Station for two years.

Snuffy had served nine years in the navy before becoming a cop and was ten years older than Nate. But he wasn't showing the effects of his forty-eight years. He had competed in power lifting in the Police Olympics and had a chest like a buffalo. Snuffy had acquired his nickname from his habit of tucking a pinch of Red Man chewing tobacco inside his lower lip and spitting tobacco juice into a Styrofoam cup. Some cops mistakenly thought that he was dipping snuff. Nate remembered that their training officers at 77th had threatened to make Snuffy drink the contents of his cup if they caught him, but at Hollywood Station, once he was off probation, he'd kept his lip loaded most of the time. He was always the division champ when it came to chatter and gossip, in a profession where gossip was coin of the realm.

Back then, their late sergeant, whom they'd called the Oracle, was often tasked by the watch commander to deal with Snuffy's droopy 'stash. But the Oracle would simply say to him, "Zapata is dead, Snuffy. Trim the tips off that feather duster next time you're clipping your nails."

Snuffy seldom did and the Oracle didn't really care. Then Nate thought of how much he missed the Oracle, who'd died of a massive heart attack on the Walk of Fame in front of Hollywood Station. The stars in marble and brass on that part of Wilcox Avenue were not there to commemorate movie stars but as memorials to the Hollywood Division coppers who had been killed in the line of duty.

Nate's reminiscing stopped when Snuffy Salcedo left the LAPD chief's SUV at the curb and jogged toward the red carpet parking area, arms outstretched. Under the mustache his toothy grin was glinting arctic white from all the lights on Hollywood Boulevard.

Nate said, "Snuffy Salcedo, I presume?"

Snuffy said, "Hollywood Nate Weiss! Where the fuck you been and how are you? *Abrazos, 'mano!*"

He gave Nate a rib-crushing embrace, and up close Nate saw that bulge under Snuffy's lower lip.

Snuffy said, "I saw you spear that chubby pap, you rascal. Glad to see you still got the chops you learned back in the day with me." Then he did an Elvis impression and sang, "Down in the ghet-to!"

Nate said, "I see you still got that revolting wad of manure inside your lip. Does the big boss let you drive with a cup of tobacco juice in the cup holder?"

"It disappears when Mister shows up," Snuffy said.

Many of the veteran LAPD cops had never accepted this chief of police, the second one to be imported from the East Coast since the Rodney King riots. This chief had come seven years ago, and when the coppers referred to him privately, it was not with "Chief" before his surname but with "Mister," the ultimate invective, meaning that he was just another imported civilian politician and could never be a real LAPD copper.

"So how do you like driving for this one?" Nate asked.

"Have you ever had a colonoscopy?" Snuffy said.

"Why've you stayed in Metro all these years, Snuffy?" Nate asked. "Aren't you sick of it yet?"

14

"The overtime money driving for this one has been keeping me where I am," Snuffy said. "Mister is the first LAPD chief to need security aides everywhere but in his bathtub. You'd think a guy that's been married as many times as he has woulda picked a babe that cooks this time around, but there's no food in their house and they go out every night to eat. On his weekend days off, he even needs us with him. We're a full-service detail with this one. There's five of us security aides and we're all getting richer than Bruce Springsteen and the E Street Band."

"I had a feeling his Irish twinkle might mask a gloomy Celtic interior," said Nate.

Snuffy Salcedo said, "In addition to an ego that makes him think the MetLife blimp should have his face on it instead of Snoopy's, I think Mister's got something like OCD. He has a thing about stoplights and he counts them. I might get yelled at if I take a route with too many of them. And he's obsessed with wiping his face with Kleenex. If there was even half the oil coming out of Mister's pores that he thinks there is, we wouldn't need any more imports from Saudi Arabia. Since I don't have a degree in abnormal psychology, I just concentrate on the overtime money when he's like that. By the way, did you get married again?"

"Not a chance," Nate said. "And no kids."

"You were so lucky her casabas never got to producing dairy products. Me, I'll be paying for our kids till Jesus returns."

"Even without kids I know what divorce costs," Nate said, nodding. "Twelve months of eating Hungry-Man nukeable food until I could afford an occasional lamb chop."

"I used to call mine RK," Snuffy said, "because during sex she was about as active as roadkill. Yet she talked me into paying for a boob job for both her and her sister, and she went wild after that. Four new mammaries and I had no access to any of them. I was the boob."

Nate said, "Me, I'm not gonna marry another Jewish woman

no matter what my mother wants. My ex turned scary mean the minute her blood sugar rose with morning orange juice. It took a while after the divorce till she stopped breaking eggs on my car."

"Guys like you and me should mix 'n' match," Snuffy said. "And always marry outside our tribes."

"I'd sure like to see you transfer back to Watch Five at Hollywood Station," Nate said sincerely. "It'd be like old times. We could partner up. I'd even let you keep your spittoon in the cup holder and try not to puke all over myself when you used it."

"What!" Snuffy said incredulously. "You haven't heard?"

"Heard?"

"I've finally had enough of this driving gig. I'm transferring back to Hollywood in time for the next deployment period. I thought there'd be notices on the bulletin boards by now, and pictures of me in the roll call room right next to the Oracle's."

"Fantastic!" Nate said. "Wait'll I spread the word. Snuffy Salcedo's turning in his chauffeur's cap and coming home to roost."

"Long overdue," Snuffy said. "I've driven for three chiefs. The only one I liked was the first one that City Hall imported from the East Coast. I wish the mayor hadn't gotten rid of him when he found out the dude wouldn't trade his Las Vegas jaunts for eternal youth. I grew fond of him. Basically he was just a harmless old porch Negro."

Nate was about to ask Snuffy if he'd heard from any of their classmates lately, when the burly Latino cop stopped chattering long enough to turn toward the herd of people emerging onto the red carpet, and said, "Holy shit! He's already out!"

Hollywood Nate turned and saw the chief of police, his wife, and another elegantly dressed couple standing on the curb in front of the Kodak Theatre, and the chief wasn't twinkling. All of the bonhomie that he'd shown to the paparazzi was gone.

Snuffy Salcedo scampered to the SUV, jumped in, and zoomed

to the pickup area, where he leaped out and ran around to open the rear door for Mrs. Chief. Nate saw the chief jawing at Snuffy and neither looked very happy.

On the next transfer list, P2 Snuffy Salcedo did return to Hollywood Station, where he could no longer get as rich as the E Street Band.

THREE

LEONA BRUEGER HAD always referred to her home located high in the Hollywood Hills, almost to Woodrow Wilson Drive, as a mini-estate. Three residential lots had been bought and cleared of aging houses and tied together to make it the largest parcel in that part of the Hills, with a splendid view almost to the ocean. Her late husband, Sammy Brueger, had made most of his early money by buying into three wholesale meat distributors at a time when people said you couldn't make real money in that business.

Sammy Brueger proved them wrong and did it with a slogan that his first wife dreamed up: "You can't beat Sammy's meat." And then, early in the presidency of Richard Nixon, Sammy started following the New York Stock Exchange and became interested in a stock for no other reason than that its NASDAQ symbol, POND, was the maiden name of his wife. He was a born gambler, and when he learned that POND stood for Ponderosa Steak House in Dayton, Ohio, he thought that Lady Luck was calling him. The stock symbol bore his wife's name, and the product was something that he bought and sold every day—meat! So Sammy plowed everything he had into that stock and it zoomed upward an astounding 10,000 percent and he became very rich. He divorced the wife named Pond and married a failed actress whose surname never helped him, and neither did she. Because of the prenuptial, the second one wasn't so expensive to unload.

His third and final wife, Leona, thirty-two years younger than Sammy, told other trophy wives at her Pilates class that the meat slogan had certainly been true in the last ten years of the old man's life, and she thanked God for it. She still shuddered when she thought of him in his old age crawling over her at night like a centipede.

Leona Brueger was still a size two, and was trainer-firm, with expressive brown eyes, delicate facial bones, and a Mediterranean skin tone that bore no evidence of the considerable work she had bought in order to stay looking so good at the age of sixty. Her last birthday had been devastating, no matter how much she had tried to prepare for it psychologically. Leona Brueger's natural hair color had been milk chocolate brown at one time, and she hated to think what color it would be now if she ever stopped the monthly color and highlights.

On a summer afternoon while sitting by the pool skimming *Elle* and *Vogue* and reading *Wine Spectator* cover to cover, she happened to see a mention of a Beverly Hills art gallery where Sammy had bought three very expensive pieces of Impressionist art, two by French artists and one by a Swede. Leona couldn't remember much about the artists and hardly noticed the paintings back when Sammy was alive, opining to girlfriends that trees and flowers should look as though they were living things distinct from the land that nourished them. And the nearly nude body of a peasant woman feeding a kitten in one of the paintings depressed her. She feared that she would look like that when, despite Pilates and a weekly game of tennis on the Brueger tennis court with her Pilates partners, her ass finally gave up and collapsed from boredom and fatigue.

But the article she was reading made her wonder why it had taken her so long to have the paintings appraised after Sammy died, trusting him that they were of "museum quality." He'd always said that the very pricey pieces should hang exactly where he'd placed

them: in their great room, the dining room, and along the main corridor of "Casa Brueger."

She strolled inside from the pool, sipping an iced tea, wishing it were late enough for a nice glass of cool Fumé Blanc, and studied the three oldest pieces to try to see why anyone would think they were so valuable. She stood before the largest, the one of a woman squatting beside what looked to Leona like a pond or a lagoon. She decided to call the Wickland Gallery on Wilshire Boulevard to ask Nigel Wickland when he'd be coming back for the appraisal. The art dealer had stopped by a week earlier at her request and taken a preliminary look, but he'd said he needed to "research the provenance" before he could give her accurate information. It was hard for her to think about appraisals or any other business when she was about to embark on one of the great adventures of her life.

She'd leased a villa in Tuscany for three months and was going there with Rudy Ressler, the movie director/producer she'd been dating off and on for more than a year. Rudy was amusing and had lots of show-business anecdotes that he could relate by mimicking the voices of the players involved. He wasn't as young as she would like if she decided to marry again, but he was controllable and an amazingly unselfish lover, even though that didn't matter as much as it used to. And he still knew enough people very active in show business to ensure that they'd always have interesting dining partners. His one Oscar-nominated film had kept him on the A-list for the past twenty years. If they ever married, she figured she'd end up supporting him, but what the hell, she was bucks-up rich. Sammy had left her more than she could ever spend in her lifetime. And that reminded her again that she was now sixty years old. How much of a life *did* she have left?

For a moment Leona couldn't remember what she was about to do, but then she remembered: call the Wickland Gallery. She got Nigel Wickland on the phone and made an appointment for the following afternoon, when he would have a closer look at the

thirteen pieces of art. She'd have to make a note to ask the gallery owner if he thought her security system was adequate to protect the artwork while she was in Tuscany. But then she thought, screw it. Sammy had the art so heavily insured that she almost hoped someone would steal all of it. Then she could buy some paintings that were vibrant and alive. It was time for Leona Brueger to get out and *really* live, away from her palatial cocoon in the Hollywood Hills. She might finally take the risk and buy a vineyard and winery up in Napa Valley.

Raleigh L. Dibble was in his third-floor apartment in east Hollywood, getting ready for the part-time job he was doing that evening on the only day off from his regular work. It paid chump change, but it helped with the rent and the car payment on his nine-year-old Toyota Corolla, which needed tires and a tune-up. He stood before the mirror and adjusted his black bow tie, a real one, not one of those crappy clip-ons that everyone wore nowadays. He fastened the black cummerbund over his starched dress shirt and slipped into his tuxedo jacket for a big dinner party in the Hollywood Hills celebrating the release of a third-rate movie by some hack he had never heard of.

All Raleigh knew about the homeowner tonight was that the guy was a junior partner in a Century City law firm who needed an experienced man like Raleigh to augment his hired caterers and make sure that things ran smoothly. Raleigh's past life as the owner of a West Los Angeles catering business had qualified him for these quasi-butler jobs where nouveaus could pretend they knew their ass from corned beef. Raleigh had met a lot of wealthy people and earned a good reputation, which brought him a small but steady income and had kept him from drinking the Kool-Aid after his business had gone belly-up.

He thought he didn't look too bad in the tux. Mother Nature, the pitiless cunt, had put macaroni-and-cheese handles around his

middle, and it was getting scary. At only five foot seven he wasn't tall enough to carry the blubber overload. Though he didn't have much hair left, what he had was nutmeg brown with the help of Grecian Formula. And his jawline was holding up, but only because the extra fat had puffed his cheeks like a goddamn woodchuck. Now he had a double chin—no, make it a triple. If he could ever earn enough money, he hoped to get a quarter of his body siphoned into the garbage can by one of the zillion cosmetic surgeons plying their trade on the west side of Los Angeles. Then maybe a hair transplant and even an eye lift to complete the overhaul, because his eyes, the color of faded denim, were shrinking from the encroachment of the upper lids. Enough money could rectify all of that.

Before he left the apartment for that night's gig, he figured he'd better call Julius Hampton, his full-time boss for the past six months. The old man had just turned eighty-nine years of age when he'd hired Raleigh, who was thirty-one years younger almost to the day. Raleigh had been hired the month after Barack Obama took office, and it was an okay job being a live-in butler/chef and all-around caretaker six days a week for the old coot. He was being paid by a downtown lawyer who administered the Hampton trust fund, but the lawyer was a tight ass who acted like it was his money, and Raleigh had had to practically beg for a wage increase in early summer.

Julius Hampton had been an indefatigable and flamboyant cruiser of Santa Monica Boulevard in his day, but he'd never made any kind of pass at Raleigh even before learning that his new employee was straight. Raleigh figured that gay or straight, it wouldn't matter to the old man anyway, since Raleigh was no George Clooney, and the geezer was through with sex. Julius Hampton was left only with fantasies stoked by their weekly visits to west Hollywood gay bars, more out of nostalgia than anything else.

This boss had been a longtime friend of a lot of other rich old

men on the west side, not all of them gay by any means. Raleigh had driven Julius Hampton to many dinner parties where Raleigh would hang around the kitchen with the other help until the party was over or his boss got tired. On nights when the old man's phlebitis was bothering him, Raleigh would bring the collapsible wheelchair from the car and wheel him out to the old Cadillac sedan that his boss loved and Raleigh hated. Raleigh figured that in his day, Julius Hampton probably had a lot of boy sex in that Cadillac, back when his plumbing still worked. Maybe sitting on those beat-up leather seats brought him delicious memories. In any case, his boss had dismissed the suggestion every time Raleigh urged him to junk the Cadillac and buy a new car.

Raleigh L. Dibble had been in the catering business almost continually since his high school days in San Pedro, the third child and only son of a longshoreman and a hairdresser. As a young man he'd begun concentrating on using good diction while he was on a job, any job. He'd read a self-improvement book stressing that good diction could trump a poor education, and Raleigh had never gone to college. All he'd ever known was working for inadequate wages in food service until he went into business as a working partner with Nellie Foster of Culver City, who made the best hors d'oeuvres and gave the best blow jobs he'd ever known. They'd done pretty well in the catering business when times were good, working out of a storefront on Pico Boulevard. But they'd gotten into some "difficulties," as he always described his fall from grace.

Raleigh had been forced by circumstance to write several NSF checks, and after that was straightened out, the IRS got on them like a swarm of leeches, sucking their blood and tormenting them for over a year until a criminal case for fraud and tax evasion was filed in federal court. Raleigh had done the manly thing at that time and taken the bullet for both himself and Nellie, claiming to authorities that she knew nothing about the "edgy paperwork" that had helped to keep them afloat temporarily.

23

He'd been sentenced to one year in prison to be served at the Federal Correctional Complex in Lompoc, California, and the night before he had to report to federal marshals, Nellie gave him a tearful good-bye and thanked him for saving her ass. She promised to write and to visit him often. But she'd seldom written and never visited, and she married a house painter two months after Raleigh was behind bars. And he didn't even get a farewell blow job.

Raleigh had served eight months of his sentence, gotten paroled, rented a cheap apartment in a risky gang neighborhood in east Hollywood, and lived by hiring out as a waiter to various caterers he'd known when he was in the business. Then he'd stumbled into the position with Julius Hampton as what the old man called his "gentleman's gentleman." Julius had seen too many English movies, Raleigh figured, but he made sure his diction was always up to par when he was in his boss's presence.

The dinner party in the Hollywood Hills that night turned out to be disastrous because the lawyer homeowner had hired a Mexican caterer to serve what was supposed to be Asian fusion. As far as Raleigh was concerned, there was nothing more dangerous than a Mexican with a saltshaker, and everything tasted of sea salt. Raleigh played his role to the hilt, but Stephen Fry as Jeeves the butler couldn't have saved this one. His feet and knees were killing him when the night finally ended and he could get home to bed.

The next morning Raleigh was up early and on his way to pick up Julius Hampton to take him to Cedars-Sinai for a checkup with his cardiologist. After that, they went back to the Hampton house, where the old man had his afternoon nap, and he was raring to go again when he woke up and remembered that it was the night for his weekly lobster dinner at the Palm. Raleigh had never been crazy about lobster but he could have a rib eye and a couple of Jack Daniel's to get him through the rest of the evening at one of the west Hollywood gay bars that the old man still liked to frequent at least one night a week.

By the time they'd finished dining and arrived at the gay bar, it was filling up with other customers also arriving after dinner, and they were lucky to get a small table. The sweating waiters couldn't deliver drinks to the customers fast enough. Raleigh and his elderly boss were sipping martinis close enough to the three-deep bar patrons for the old letch to gawk at all the muscular buns in tight pants, some of which Raleigh figured were butt-pad inserts. Many of the younger hustlers wore tight Ralph Lauren jerseys with jeans or shorts, and the old boy gazed at them with melancholy. Raleigh was certain that their crotch mounds were from stuffing socks in their Calvins. He figured the youthful hustlers must buy socks by the gross at Costco.

Julius Hampton recognized Nigel Wickland before the Beverly Hills art dealer recognized him. "Nigel!" he said as the art dealer was passing their table on his way back from the restroom.

At first Raleigh thought that Nigel Wickland was about sixty years old, but up close, he looked more like sixty-five. He was tall and fashionably thin, with a prominent chin, heavy dark eyebrows, and a full head of hair so white that it looked mauve under the mood lighting. He wore a tailor-made, double-breasted navy blazer, a pale blue Oxford cotton shirt, and an honest-to-god blue ascot impeccably folded against his throat. Raleigh wondered if the blazer was Hugo Boss or maybe Valentino, or was it a Men's Wearhouse copy? And how about the shoes? Were they O.J. Simpson Bruno Maglis or knockoffs? Nigel Wickland wore his clothes so well that you couldn't tell if they were the real things.

Then Raleigh's attention was drawn to the man's exquisite hands. The fingers were long and tapered, the nails beautifully manicured, and there were no prominent veins to be seen, which there should have been on a man his age. Raleigh wondered if guys even had cosmetic surgeons do their hands around here, and if so, whether they called it a hand job.

The art dealer stroked his chin and seemed nonplussed for a

moment, probably thinking that Julius was just another dotty old queen who frequented the west Hollywood clubs, until the octogenarian said, "It's me, Julius Hampton. Remember? We played bridge at the Bruegers' a couple of times before Sammy passed away."

"Julius!" Nigel Wickland said. "Of course I remember. How *are* you?"

As they shook hands, Julius Hampton said, "Still upright, more or less, with the help of my man here. I'd like you to meet Raleigh Dibble. I don't know what I'd do without him. Sit down and join us."

The art dealer extended his graceful hand to Raleigh and said, "Nigel Wickland. Pleased to meet you."

"Same here, Mr. Wickland," Raleigh said.

"Nigel, please," the art dealer said to him. "And may I call you Raleigh?"

"Of course," Raleigh said.

Raleigh wondered if the toffee-nosed accent was legit or something the art dealer affected for L.A.'s west-side nouveau. Raleigh had spent nearly six months bumming around Europe as a young man and had lived in London for a summer, waiting tables at a bistro. He'd even considered affecting an Oxbridge accent like Nigel Wickland's when he'd been in the catering business but decided that it could backfire if his customers found him out. They liked their phonies to be less obvious phonies around these parts.

"What'll you have?" Julius Hampton said to the art dealer, and Raleigh noticed that the old man's bony hands were trembling most of the time. It was hard for him to hold a martini glass anymore without spilling it.

Nigel Wickland ordered a banana daiquiri and chatted with Julius Hampton about the bargains now available at the Wickland Gallery. Raleigh Dibble figured he knew the Nigel Wickland type well enough. The west side of L.A. was full of them. Given the art

dealer's obvious ego, the gallery would of course bear his name. And even though a man as old as Julius Hampton would be an unlikely prospect for a sale, Nigel Wickland seemed compelled to chat him up about the treasures to be had just a few blocks away on Wilshire Boulevard. Raleigh figured that the art dealer was constantly chumming the waters in case any of Julius Hampton's less grizzled friends or neighbors was ever tempted to take the bait.

"The bloody recession is forcing people to sell for indecently low prices," Nigel told them, and signaled to the waiter for another round when his glass was still half full.

Boozer, Raleigh thought, but then reminded himself that in the gay bars everyone seemed to drink more to bolster their courage for encounters that were often risky.

It was then that Nigel Wickland said, "Have you been to the Brueger house since Sammy passed? I sometimes wonder how Leona is really holding up."

Old Julius Hampton cackled and said, "The merriest of widows is dear Leona. I understand she sometimes dates a filmmaker named Rudy Ressler when he's not molesting children at UCLA, where he lectures at the film school. He's one of those people who make cheap indie films that probably go straight to DVD."

Raleigh had been impressed many times by his employer's knowledge of the movie business as well as any other business that was peculiarly relevant to Angelenos. Like his father before him, Julius Hampton had made his fortune as a real-estate developer, and the Hampton brokers bought and sold to real Hollywood names on a regular basis, not to second-raters like Rudy Ressler. As Julius Hampton and Nigel Wickland chatted about people they knew in common, Raleigh excused himself and went the restroom.

While Raleigh was gone, Nigel Wickland said, "Nice chap. Seems competent."

"Very," Julius Hampton said, with just enough drink in him to

gossip. "His catering business failed some time ago and he's eking out a living now. He's basically very honest but he got in some tax trouble with Uncle Sam back then. Had to spend some time locked up in federal prison. I have a PI do a background on everyone I hire. I've never questioned Raleigh about his past even though I know a lot about it. I can tell you that he cooks like Julia Child."

"The poor fellow," Nigel Wickland said. "That is certainly a spot of bother to live down, isn't it? Still, many people around here have had similar problems with the IRS. That doesn't make him a criminal."

When Raleigh returned from the restroom, Nigel Wickland started paying more attention to him than to Julius Hampton. Raleigh didn't sense that it was a gay thing. It just seemed that Nigel Wickland wanted to learn about his work history. Nigel asked if this was his first job as a butler/chef. And he seemed very interested in Raleigh's former catering business, saying he thought he remembered Raleigh's employees catering some soirees at the Wickland Gallery. Raleigh thought that was just bullshit until he remembered that Nellie *had* catered a fancy gig at a Beverly Hills art gallery. They'd lost money on it when she'd failed to anticipate the amount of champagne needed, and she'd had to quickly run to the nearest liquor store and buy cases at retail. Was that the Wickland Gallery? He couldn't remember.

Then Nigel Wickland started to wheeze. He took a few short deep breaths that didn't seem to help him. He muttered, "Please forgive me," and took an inhaler from his trousers pocket, turning away from Raleigh and Julius Hampton. He put the inhaler in his mouth and pressed the canister, simultaneously inhaling deeply, holding the steroid in his lungs as long as possible.

When he exhaled, he turned back to them and said, "I'm sorry. Adult-onset asthma. It started three years ago. Part of the indignities of advancing age."

Julius Hampton said, "You think you're old? Like Willie Nelson

said, I've outlived my dick. I wouldn't want to outlive my liver. Without a decent martini, what's the point in any of it?"

Nigel Wickland then said to Raleigh, "Did you ever think about starting up your catering business again? I don't mean in the middle of this recession but later."

"It takes starter money to get a business like that going," Raleigh said. "I'd have to win the lottery or something."

"Still, there's nothing like the feeling of independence that being one's own boss can give. Especially with men of a certain age, like you and me."

Julius Hampton said, "What it all boils down to is relevancy. All the elderly understand that. You will, too, sooner than you think. Marty Brueger always talks about it. He says when he started feeling irrelevant, he knew he was through with living. That's what he's doing in Leona's guesthouse — waiting to die."

"Well, you're not irrelevant, Mr. Hampton," Raleigh said quickly.

Nigel Wickland said, "Hear me, god. Save us all from irrelevance."

As Nigel returned to pumping the chubby butler about his work history, Julius Hampton began getting restless at being left out of the conversation. After the second martini, the old man said, "Well, Raleigh, is it time to go home and see what's on TV tonight?"

Then Nigel Wickland said quickly, "Raleigh, here's my card. Give me a ring and I'll show you around the gallery. Any time at all. I think you'd enjoy it."

When they were driving home, Julius Hampton said, "Well, well, Nigel Wickland seemed smitten with you, Raleigh. What's the secret of your attraction?"

"Unless he likes Pillsbury Doughboys, it couldn't be physical," Raleigh said, patting his belly. "I've got so much flab spilling over my belt that my hips look like a muffin top. I think he was just being friendly, Mr. Hampton."

"Nigel doesn't strike me as the overly friendly type," Julius

Hampton said, looking at Raleigh as though he certainly couldn't figure out Nigel's interest.

The next afternoon before taking his nap, Raleigh's employer told him he could take the afternoon off. Raleigh couldn't decide whether or not to visit Sharon, his older sister in San Pedro. His other sister had died of lung cancer when he was in prison, and both parents were gone, so Sharon was the only close relative he had left. But she was an Evangelical Christian who always spent at least half of every visit trying to bring him to Jesus. He decided he didn't feel up to it today.

He thought about going to a movie in Westwood, or maybe visiting an old friend who used to work for him and Nellie in the catering business. She was a busty Brazilian in her midforties. Alma was hopelessly clumsy and had broken more glasses than the Sylmar earthquake, but she'd sleep with him if she was in the mood, and he loved to kid her that she had tits from here to paternity. Raleigh couldn't remember the last time he got laid and was almost horny enough to buy a knobber from one of those Asian masseuses on Hollywood Boulevard. He phoned Alma but the number was no longer in service, so on a whim he drove his Toyota to the Wickland Gallery and popped in unannounced.

A prim young woman in a jacket and skirt and very sensible heels said, "Good afternoon, my name's Ruth Langley. Is there anything I can help you with today or would you just care to have a look around?"

"Mr. Wickland's invited me to stop in for a personal tour of the gallery," he said. "The name's Raleigh Dibble."

When she escorted him to Nigel Wickland's office, the art dealer stood up, came around his massive mahogany desk, and shook hands energetically.

"So glad you came. You're just in time to come and have a drink with me," Nigel Wickland said, donning his linen blazer, the color of a martini olive.

Raleigh figured the ascot must be for evenings in gay bars, because the art dealer was wearing a white shirt with a forest-green silk necktie. He made Raleigh feel shabby in his off-the-rack rusty brown sport jacket worn over chinos, with black leather loafers that needed the heels replaced.

They went to the bar at the Ivy and took a table. Just as before, Nigel Wickland ordered a banana daiquiri, and a second one before he'd finished the first. In the light of day Raleigh could see that the art dealer's eyes were watery and there were broken veins on the sides of his nose. A juicehead for sure, he figured. Still, he was buying the drinks and Raleigh's curiosity was killing him, so he ordered a Jack on the rocks.

After he was half finished with the second drink, Nigel Wickland said, "If you don't mind my asking, Raleigh, did you actually sell your catering business or . . ."

"It tanked," Raleigh said with a wry grin, starting to feel the Jack Daniel's already. "I got nothing out of it. So here I am, a domestic servant."

"Hardly that," Nigel Wickland said. "I'm sure you're a valued employee to Julius. But I can't imagine that the pay is very good."

"A living," Raleigh said. "Sort of. But the food's great because I buy and cook it for both of us. Mr. Hampton still has a young man's appetite." Raleigh drained the glass, and Nigel Wickland immediately signaled for another.

"I'd like to rely on you to be discreet, Raleigh," the art dealer said. "I know you've been with Julius a relatively short time, but I might be able to offer you a better position."

"With you?" Raleigh said. "I'm an art Neanderthal."

"I don't mean in my gallery," Nigel Wickland said. "After meeting you the other night I realized that you have exactly the qualifications that a client of mine needs at this time. You heard Julius and me mention her name. Leona Brueger?"

"I vaguely remember that," Raleigh said, getting into the second

Jack, a delicious golden burn sliding down his throat and making him feel the glow coming on.

"I've recently learned that Leona Brueger is deeply involved with Rudy Ressler, the filmmaker that Julius mentioned."

"The child molester?" Raleigh said. "That's what Mr. Hampton called him."

Nigel Wickland smiled and said, " He doesn't try to entice children with a kitten and chocolate bars, believe me. College coeds, his targets of choice, are not exactly children, even if they do behave that way. But Rudy's changing his ways and has been getting increasingly serious about mature women, especially the widow Brueger."

"It sounds like you know them pretty well," Raleigh said.

Nigel said, "I've come to know more than a little about Leona Brueger after having been contacted to appraise the late Sammy Brueger's formidable art collection. I've been led by her to believe that she's going to sell it all, along with the house, perhaps to marry Ressler and move to Napa, where she'll grow grapes or whatever people do when they have more money than good sense."

"Nigel," Raleigh said finally, "this is all very interesting, but I don't see how I could possibly fit in here."

Nigel said, "Leona Brueger has been saddled with Sammy's brother Marty, who is eighty-seven years old and ailing. Marty spends most of his time in Leona's guesthouse, but occasionally he likes to get out and about. She needs the services of a butler/driver/companion who can cook three meals a day for him. Just as you do for Julius. Leona Brueger also likes an occasional little dinner party at home, but the people she's hired have been unsatisfactory. It's not so easy for her to find a man who can cook and manage a dinner party as well as do the rest of it for her brother-in-law. After we met, I realized that with your background and experience, you're just what she's been looking for. You're a perfect fit, Raleigh."

"But I've got a job," Raleigh said. "And it's permanent, not temporary."

"If you're happy where you are, forget I mentioned it," Nigel Wickland said. "But Leona told me she'd pay seven thousand dollars a month to the right man, and of course you'd have luxury quarters to live in and meals you'd prepared yourself. You can buy anything you'd like from the markets and bill it to your employer's account. You'd have no living expenses. The job would probably end around the first of next year. After that, she's going to arrange for a luxurious retirement home for Marty Brueger when she sells the house. She'd do it now, but he refuses to go, and his lifetime care and contentment are prominently mentioned in Sammy's will, so she must accommodate him. But by year's end, his growing dementia will probably take care of things. The urgency here and now is that she wants to leave for a long holiday in Tuscany and she's in need of the right man ASAP."

Raleigh was quiet for a moment and then said, "Of course that's a whole lot more than I make, but my job's permanent. I don't know about quitting Mr. Hampton for a temporary job."

"How permanent is any job with a boss who's eighty-nine years old?" Nigel Wickland asked. "Do think about it and let me know if you're interested. I'm just doing this as a favor to my client Leona Brueger. It's nothing to me one way or the other."

Raleigh thought there was something not quite right, and he said, "I remember that when you and Mr. Hampton talked about Leona Brueger, you wondered if she was holding up well since her husband's death. It seemed like you didn't know all that much about her."

Then it was Nigel Wickland's turn to pause. He finally said, "Frankly, since I've been involved in the appraisal of her artwork, I've come to know her well enough that I've learned about her plans. Naturally I couldn't mention to Julius that I thought you'd be so much better off working for my client. If it weren't that you're just so perfect for this job, I wouldn't be bringing it up to you at all. So whatever you decide, mum's the word, Raleigh."

"I've got to think about this," Raleigh said.

"Yes, do have a think," Nigel said.

When Raleigh left Nigel Wickland, he decided that the prospect of earning that kind of easy money was tempting, but after the job ended, what would he do? He'd successfully completed his parole, but memories of prison had kept him superstraight. He'd even been afraid to tell lies on job résumés, and it was no cinch for an ex-con to get decent employment after mentioning a prison record. Yet it was true that with an eighty-nine-year-old boss, how permanent could his current job be? And he was sick of having to plead with the shyster who managed the Hampton trust fund to give him the pay he deserved.

Raleigh Dibble hardly slept that night. The next morning he phoned Nigel Wickland, and when he reached the art dealer, he said, "Nigel, it's Raleigh Dibble here. When can I have an interview with Mrs. Brueger?"

FOUR

An extraordinary number of celebrity names turned up in crime stories during the first full year of the Great Recession. Many of them ended up on reports passing across the desks of Hollywood Division detectives. The police station in which the detectives were housed was an unusual place, perhaps the world's only police facility where framed one-sheet movie posters decorated the walls. In the geographic territory of the station the bizarre was commonplace, and if something eerie or outlandish could not be explained or even understood, more often than not, the cops would just shrug and say, "This is fucking Hollywood." After that, nothing more needed to be said.

During that last year of the eight-year federal consent decree, which finally ended in July, only about a dozen detectives remained at Hollywood Station, when there should have been three times that many. The LAPD had labored under the oversight of federally mandated watchdogs since the Rodney King riots, as well as the so-called Rampart Division scandal, an ignominy that turned out to involve exactly two felonious cops. But it was enough for the critics who had been lying in wait to bring down the proud, some would say arrogant, police department.

After charter amendment F stripped the LAPD chiefs of civil service protection, politicians began calling the shots, and hundreds

of LAPD investigators were diverted to serve the monitors of that consent decree in "reforming" a police department that no LAPD police officer thought needed to be reformed. For years the plaintive refrain heard all around the Department was, "Charter amendment F changed our world." And what with budget shortfalls and the fact that the state of California was itself on the brink of bankruptcy, all the street cops and detectives who were still doing actual crime suppression were overwhelmed.

There had been a rash of burglaries in Los Angeles that targeted young celebrities. Two of the main suspects among a group of seven were a young man and young woman in their late teens from Calabasas, a rather affluent suburb in the San Fernando Valley. They'd met in a remedial school, a kind of last-chance high school. Another of the young women involved in the burglary and fencing ring would boost celebrity magazines from newsstands and supermarkets, and pick out targets that would be researched on the Internet. Celebrity homesites were Googled and satellite maps of their homes were obtained, and their schedules could be followed online in celebrity blogs. Another one of the young women in the group of burglars had been part of a TV reality show that at first purported to show an ex-Playmate raising three wild kids.

The burglary victims included actors Orlando Bloom, Lindsay Lohan, Audrina Patridge, Rachel Bilson, Megan Fox, and famous person Paris Hilton. Some of the homes had security cameras, and on one video, a youthful man and woman were photographed during the crime. On the video from another of the celebrity homes, four of the young burglars could be seen parking their car on Outpost Drive and walking about a hundred yards, arm in arm *backward* until they were safely past the surveillance camera, at which point they turned around and tended to business.

They made several stops at residences they were casing before being satisfied, and they did not wear hoodies, trying not to look like the public's conception of a typical burglar. They entered

through unlocked doors, open windows, and doggie doors. Only occasionally would they have to pry open a window. There were even a few hot-prowl burglaries, committed with people at home, in the county area policed by the Los Angeles Sheriff's Department.

The burglary ring stole clothing, jewelry, purses, some electronics, and cash. They burglarized Paris Hilton's home a few times, but she knew about only one. When the police cracked the case, they called her at 3 A.M. and she came in to identify her stolen property, seeming delighted to have the loot returned. She claimed that its value was well into seven figures, but detectives, who lived in a more mundane world, had their doubts. Orlando Bloom, whom detectives referred to as "a gentleman," was always helpful when called upon, and had there been such a thing, would have gotten the detectives' favorite victim award.

Search warrants were served as far away as Las Vegas on one of the teenage females and on their fence, a twenty-eight-year-old who called himself a nightclub promoter. He handled the stolen goods and was charged with receiving stolen property and other related crimes. LAPD and LASD detectives believed that perhaps two dozen burglaries were committed during a two-year period.

Defense lawyers negotiated, offering to discuss the return of missing property if new felony counts were not filed, but it all ended in what detectives said was akin to "a failed hostage negotiation" after one of the attorneys walked out, saying, "I'm not in the property business."

Another defense attorney, whose young client claimed to be working for a Christian organization that assisted people in need of housing, seemed to believe every word that his sobbing client told him. A detective said of the lawyer, "He's the kind of guy who goes to a strip club and believes that the lap dancer really loves him."

None of the young people were hard-core junkies but some of them smoked OxyContin, the equivalent of synthetic heroin, the

drug du jour of countless young Americans and a powerhouse opioid that had even addicted America's leading conservative talk-show host, Rush Limbaugh. The news photos of the pretty, female suspects in their low-rise jeans, hiding their faces but not their firm bare bellies, provided weeks of entertainment for TV and tabloids. They were dubbed "The Burglar Bunch" and "The Hollywood Hills Burglars" and, even more provocatively, "The Bling Ring."

Local and national media described their antics as cautionary tales of the dangers to young people posed by the Hollywood celebrity lifestyle. The rationale was that it was constantly in their faces thanks to websites that detailed the shenanigans of celebutantes, along with reality shows that portrayed people their age living the life in Hollywood nightclubs. According to celebrity commentators who never eschewed a cliché, an abundance of danger to young people was out there on those "boulevards of dreams."

There were a number of boulevard dreamers who couldn't get enough of the Bling Ring, one of whom was twenty-two-year-old Jonas Claymore. He was a dropout from Hollywood High School who'd smoked way too much crystal meth during his final year of school and had never gone on to community college or done much of anything that his working-class parents had expected of him. The meth eventually led to terrifying attacks of paranoia where he became convinced that he was under twenty-four-hour surveillance by LAPD narks, and on one unforgettable evening, two of his former schoolmates decided to wean him off methamphetamines by introducing him to the wonders of 80 mg green tablets of OxyContin and other oxycodone drugs like Percocet, Percodan, and Tylox.

His current housemate, Megan Burke, was a twenty-year-old high school graduate from Bend, Oregon, who had been a good student, popular, and college-bound, before she'd developed a yen to "experience Hollywood," as had so many thousands before her. She could not have specifically defined what that meant. Of course,

she would have been embarrassed to admit that there were vague fantasies involving the movie business, and even then, she was too mature to think that she would be "discovered." Yet it was always there at age eighteen, the notion that where life moves at twenty-four frames per second, anything is possible.

She had persuaded her mother to let her come to Los Angeles for the summer before college with a list of places in Southern California that she wanted to visit. She had explained to her mother that this was her "odyssey," the journey of self-discovery that she and many of her classmates believed was essential for self-fulfillment. The original plan was to stay for two months working at the Gap for a former Bend neighbor who had moved to Los Angeles and managed the store. The woman had even arranged for Megan to share an apartment with two other girls, and the money she earned selling clothing had allowed Megan to support herself. She had hoped to send part of her earnings to her mother, who had raised Megan and her younger brother, Terry, after their father had deserted the family when the children were still in elementary school.

Experiencing Hollywood wasn't anything like Megan thought it would be, especially after she learned how expensive everything was in L.A., but things went well enough until she was persuaded by her roommates to experiment with some of their trendy pharmaceuticals, like Xanax and Percocet. Those drugs led her to Vicodin and finally to OxyContin, by far the most addictive and powerful of the prescription drugs available to her, and OxyContin led her to Jonas Claymore, whom she met through a girlfriend at work.

Jonas was a valet parking attendant at upscale restaurants and he made good tips. He was tall, rail-thin, cute, and goofy, with a bush of cinnamon hair and a gap-toothed grin. He made her laugh easily and sold her OxyContin twice a week when he'd come by her apartment.

When they got high together for the first time, he said, "You won't be offended if I drop trou and show you something, will ya?"

"Show me what?" she said uneasily.

"This," he said, turning away from her and lowering his jeans and underwear. On one buttock was tattooed *what*. On the other buttock was tattooed *ever*. When he pulled his pants up he said, "Most of the girls I know think it's kinda funny."

After several drug experiences they became sexually involved, but it was never satisfactory for either of them because of Jonas's drug-induced ED problems. Megan liked the other oxycodone products, like Vicodin, referred to as "norcos" or "watsons," and she liked the Percocet, aka "perks," but nothing could beat the 80 mg OxyContin, called "OC" or "ox" or "80s" or "beans." Soon, Megan Burke fell passionately in love, not with Jonas Claymore, but with smoking ox. He loved it even more than she did and always seemed to have it in abundance. Then her life quickly fell apart. She lost her job at the Gap and got a part-time job at Denny's as a waitress, but she lost that, too, and came to dread the desperate phone calls from her mother when the college plans were abandoned.

Megan finally sold her old Hyundai when money ran out, after she had been living with Jonas for nearly a year in a cheap apartment in Thai Town, but not with the knowledge of his landlord or her despairing mother in Oregon. By then, Megan had begun avoiding most of her mother's phone calls and would not reveal her address or anything about Jonas Claymore, not wanting her worried parent to know how far she had fallen and how fast had been the descent.

After reading and seeing TV reports that members of the Bling Ring smoked ox, it had made Jonas Claymore proud that it was also his drug of choice. Ox was far more expensive than the crystal meth he'd formerly adored, and more than other pharmaceuticals that he'd use when he didn't have enough money for the OCs. He

was barely hanging on to his current job of parking cars at two of the newest Melrose Avenue restaurants.

It wasn't often that Jonas actually read the *L.A. Times* or anything else, but when he thought there might be something in the paper about the Bling Ring, he'd run to the supermarket and buy or steal one. He adored reading about the designer wardrobes that the Bling Ring coveted and plundered, and especially the Chanel merchandise, Louis Vuitton purses, and Rolex watches they'd looted during their crime spree. They'd even stolen underwear that they could wear themselves while they dreamed. Jonas couldn't get enough of the stories and searched for more on television and especially in the tabloids.

One summer evening, Jonas was sitting in the front seat of a BMW 535i that he'd parked, engrossed in juicy Bling Ring coverage. At the same time, his boss, a chesty and bossy Russian lesbian who ran the valet parking concession for both restaurants, was looking for her young employee in the parking lot. The lanky lad was disappointed that there was no photo of Paris Hilton in this particular story, and he was only halfway through the article when his boss came up from behind and jerked open the door of the Beemer.

"What the fock you do-ink, Jonas?" she demanded in that Russki accent that he had come to hate.

"Sorry, Ludmila," he said, folding the paper and jumping out of the car. "Just taking a two-minute break."

"That is shit!" she said. "I am look-ink everywhere for you. I am all ate up with you."

"Fed," Jonas Claymore said.

"What?"

"Fed. You're all *fed* up."

She stood glaring up at the gangly young man and said, "Do not laugh at me, Jonas."

"I'm not laughing, Ludmila," he said. "How about letting me get back to work, okay?"

"You do not know how to work. You do not know shit," she said, and gave him an impulsive shove with her open hand.

"Hey!" Jonas yelled. "You just put your fucking hand on me. There's a law about employers harassing employees."

Two young women paused on their way to the nearest of the restaurants when they heard the raised voices in the parking lot. In what was left of twilight they saw a skinny, long-necked valet parking guy with a wiry thatch of cinnamon hair that was wind-tunnel wild from parking the cars with windows down. He wore a long-sleeved white shirt, black bow tie, and black pants, and was shouting at a burly woman identically clad, whose dark hair was cut as short as the guy's.

"Do not do threats with me!" Ludmila yelled. "You no good, worth-noth-ink shit!"

"You can shove your job up your fat ass, you lesbo freakazoid!" Jonas Claymore yelled back, his bobbing Adam's apple the size of a hen's egg. He ripped off his clip-on tie and flipped it at her, catching her right in the eye.

She responded with a blow. Not a bitch slap. A real punch. A straight right-handed corker with a lot of hefty shoulder behind it, and Jonas Claymore's upturned nose exploded in a blood spray and he fell back against the BMW, dropping to his knee for a second.

Then he leaped up, screaming, "I'm gonna tear your throat out, you commie cunt!"

One of the two women watching from the sidewalk took her cell phone from her purse and dialed 9-1-1.

By the time 6-X-32 of the midwatch showed up, both combatants were down on the pavement exhausted from having wrestled and punched and bitten and clawed for several minutes. Jonas Claymore clearly had gotten the worst of it. His face bore scratches and contusions, and his buttonless shirt was hanging out and blood-spattered. His breath came in short rasps and his hairless

concave chest heaved as he pawed at his right ear where a tiny snippet of the lobe had been bitten off. His former boss had a purple mouse under one eye and a bruised lower lip and her left shirtsleeve was completely ripped away.

The black-and-white squealed into the parking lot and two blue-uniformed cops got out, the shorter one carrying a side-handle baton.

Jetsam said to his partner, "I'll take the female, bro."

"Roger that," Flotsam said, walking toward Jonas Claymore, who was standing, hands on his knees, bent over and trying to catch his breath.

Before the tall cop could speak, Jonas said, "That Russki douche bag started it! She pushed me and then she slugged me. I was just defending myself."

"You didn't do too good a job of it," Flotsam noted.

"She suckered me!" Jonas hollered, loud enough for gawking passersby to hear.

"Keep your voice down," Flotsam said. "And tell me what happened."

Meanwhile Ludmila was trying to tie her white shirt together in order to cover her size 46 E cup bra, and she said to Jetsam, "He is no-good bum. I hire him. I pay him good. He never share tip with nobody. He is worth-noth-ink shit!"

"How did the fight start?" Jetsam asked.

"He is say-ink rude things to me. He use his dirty mouth and make me fight."

"Are you saying that you got physical before he did?"

"What?"

"Did you hit him first?"

"Well . . . ," Ludmila said, as though she were contemplating an exceedingly difficult question. "Is depend-ink how you see si-too-ation."

"Uh-huh," Jetsam said. "I had to be there, right?"

Flotsam suggested that Jonas tip his head back and press the remnants of his shirt to his nose and hold it there.

"Are you really interested in making a battery report?" Flotsam asked. "And a private person's arrest?"

"Wouldn't you?" Jonas pulled the balled-up shirt away from his face for a moment.

"I'd have to think about it," Flotsam said. "She's a woman."

Jonas said, "She's a slit-licking lizzy warthog! She ain't no woman."

"According to the law she is," Flotsam said. "We'll do what you want. You could make a private person's arrest and we'll be glad to transport, but then we'll expect you to follow through all the way. Think about going to court and telling in public how that babe clocked you. It could be way embarrassing, dude. Up to you, though."

That stopped Jonas cold. He thought about it a moment, about the humiliation and all the hassle, and he said, "Well, what if we forget about it, the both of us? Can we do that?"

"Okay with us," Flotsam said. "But I don't wanna get another call about you two duking it out again."

"You won't. I'm going home," Jonas said. Then he yelled to Ludmila, "You can't fire me! I quit, you goddamn commie carpet muncher!"

"Fock you, stupid head!" his former employer said and flipped him the bird.

That afternoon when Jonas Claymore got back to his apartment that he shared with Megan Burke in Thai Town, she was lying on the couch watching an old TCM movie in a Percocet fog.

She was shocked when she saw him, and said, "Jonas! What happened to you?"

"I got in a fight at work," he said, "with some fucking Russian. Hollywood's full of commie trash. There ain't no Americans in charge of anything these days."

Megan said. "You're hurt."

She was wearing a baggy T-shirt and cutoffs and her legs looked even knobbier and paler than the last time Jonas paid any attention to them. When he'd met her, she had healthy dark brown hair in a stylish bob that ended a couple of inches below her ears and looked like a dark hoodie. She liked to wear those cute tights from Target then, but now the tights and most of her clothes were gone, and her hair was longer, dull, and frizzy. He figured that pretty soon it would be bleached out and falling to her shoulders with bangs reaching to her eyes like Lady Gaga's. A lot of the girls he knew did that to themselves, trying to look like the singer, but they ended up looking like shot-out skeezers, all sunken-eyed, pruned, and shriveled. There were dark circles under Megan's nervous violet eyes and altogether he thought she looked like shit.

"Just get me a damp washcloth and a towel," he said. "I gotta lay down."

When he was lying on the couch, she returned and started dabbing at his wounds, causing him to yelp when she touched his damaged earlobe.

"Jonas," she said. "You've lost a chunk of meat from your ear! How did that happen?"

"A bite," he said.

"He bit you?" she said, shocked.

"Fucking Russians shoulda been nuked to the Stone Age," he said to the ceiling.

She said, "He hurt you pretty bad."

Then Jonas said, "You shoulda seen the damage I did. It wasn't one-way."

She dabbed at his ear with a soiled dishtowel, saying, "I'm sure you kicked his butt."

"I knocked the shit outta that Russian pus bucket," Jonas said to the wall. "Then I almost get busted by the cops for defending myself. Me, the victimized American."

Megan said, "Just rest now and don't think about it."

"This is why my grandpa killed communists in Vietnam?" Jonas said to the coffee table littered with fan magazines, candy wrappers, and pizza boxes, as well as OC paraphernalia, including a 6 × 10 inch piece of tinfoil creased in half, a cigarette lighter, and a ballpoint pen with the ink tube removed lying beside it.

"Try to calm yourself," Megan said.

"So a commie dirtbag could come to Hollywood and sucker me when I wasn't looking?"

Megan said, "Your nose'll start bleeding again. We've got half an eighty left. Do you want to chase the dragon?"

"A half of one bean?" Jonas said. "But I gave you a Ben Franklin yesterday!"

"It was three days ago, and Wilbur's charging us eighty-five per ox. And we smoked a piece of it when we did those watsons and perks. You're having a brownout. Don't you remember any of it?"

He vaguely recalled the Vicodins and Perocets, but he couldn't recall smoking half of an 80 mg OxyContin tablet. "It's that goddamn screw-top wine," he said. "It fucks up my memory. Can't you go boost a better bottle somewhere? I'd even settle for a couple forties of OE."

"I'm not a thief," Megan said.

Jonas was getting heart palpitations and was sweating cold. His knee joints and right shoulder were aching, which he blamed on the fight. But when he looked more closely at Megan he saw that she had broken into a sweat as well, and she couldn't stop yawning and scratching herself. That is, when she wasn't coughing.

"Goddamnit, Megan, look at us," he said. "We're jonesing. I gotta chase the dragon and I mean right now!"

She jumped up, ran to the bedroom, and got the last piece of the OC tablet, bringing it to the coffee table and placing it in the crease of the foil.

"This ain't a complete half," Jonas accused. "You smoked a bite off it, didn't you?"

Megan didn't reply and he was too desperate to press her.

"Just hurry up," he said.

Megan placed the flame of the lighter underneath the foil and heated the OxyContin tablet. Jonas picked up the empty ink tube, which, unlike a drinking straw, would not burn easily, and put it in his mouth. Megan tilted the foil, and as the heated fragment slid down the crease propelled by gravity and heated from beneath the foil, Jonas hungrily inhaled, and even swallowed as much rising smoke as he could, chasing that smoking ox down the crease before it burned up completely.

"You're not worried about me, are you, Jonas?" Megan said. "Don't you think I need a taste, too?"

Jonas said to her, "You call this chasing the dragon? All you left me was a crumb. There ain't enough ox here to chase a fucking lizard."

He waited for the rush, but all he got was an anemic feeling of lethargy. They were developing such a tolerance that for weeks neither of them had felt the warm flush of the skin or the wonderful drowsy euphoria that they used to get when there was enough for them both. When they weren't so addicted.

"Wilbur only deals in cash, no credit," Megan said between coughs. "I tried hard to talk a couple of OCs out of him when he came on to me, but he smells awful. I wouldn't ever let him so much as touch me for anything, Jonas. There're some things I won't do." She gulped back a sob and said, "I don't want to ever come to that!" She threw herself facedown on the sofa then and wept.

He looked at her, thinking, yeah, pretty soon she'd have the Lady Gaga hair and a tramp stamp or two, like the last woman he'd let live with him. She'd probably end up peddling her ass on Sunset Boulevard. Then he tried to remember the girl he'd met when she was selling clothes at the Gap. Why was it that every girl he met turned into a degenerate?

"Goddamnit," Jonas said, "we need enough bank for that

fucking quack over in Echo Park. He'll write us scrips for anything we want if the money's right."

Then Jonas felt a deep depression envelop him and he stopped looking at Megan and said, "I got fired," to Cuddles, her calico cat, who was squatting on a kitchen chair sleepily watching all the human drama unfolding.

The calico cat just yawned, lifted a back leg, and licked her ass, but Megan sat up and said, "You what? Oh, Jonas, what're we going to do?"

"Don't worry," Jonas said. "For quite a while I been thinking a lot about the Bling Ring. They only fucked up and got caught 'cause they didn't stay focused. I think they had a cool idea, though. You and me, we could do it right."

"Do what right?"

"Walk into the houses of celebrities and other rich people and take what we want. And make enough to live decent and stop slaving for all the foreign shitbags that're taking over the whole town."

"You're not making sense," Megan said. Then she started coughing again and her sweating increased.

"I'm making sense for the first time in a long time," Jonas insisted.

"Let's talk about it tomorrow," Megan said, wiping her face on her T-shirt. "It's stressful to talk like this when you're all beat-up and not thinking."

"Baby, it's easy," he said, "and the Bling Ring had a blast doing it."

"It's not like running out and boosting from department stores," Megan said. "Breaking into houses? That's very different and very scary."

"Whadda you mean 'breaking'?" Jonas said. "Those rich morons up in the Hollywood Hills, they leave their houses wide open. Know where Paris Hilton kept her house key? Under the fucking doormat. And they leave their windows unlocked. And you're get-

ting so skinny these days, you could crawl through a doggie door too small for a fucking Chihuahua. Nothing could stop us from getting into any house we want."

Megan Burke suddenly flashed on how it had been in the beginning with Jonas Claymore, back when she was someone else and so was he. At first, they'd smoked pot on dates before doing zannies and benzos. It was carefree and it was fun at first. Then came the perks and norcos. And then they'd started smoking OxyContin, and after riding the ox for all these months, they had become unrecognizable people. Megan didn't know this Jonas, and in fact, she didn't even know this Megan that she had become.

"Can we please talk tomorrow, Jonas?" Megan pleaded. "This is nerve-racking and it's making me burbly."

"Jesus fucking Christ," Jonas moaned, eyes rolling back, not wanting to be reminded that he, too, was experiencing bouts of diarrhea since the jonesing episodes started. "I ain't got enough tribulations in life, I gotta hook up with a chick with irritable bowel syndrome? Why can't I catch a break just for once?"

"Sorry. Gotta do number two," Megan said, getting up and running to the bathroom.

"Go ahead, jingle bowels," he said. "Drop a deuce for me while you're at it."

FIVE

TWO WEEKS AFTER the red carpet event at the Kodak Theatre, Hollywood Nate Weiss was lying on the sofa in his North Hollywood apartment, where he lived alone, considering the business card he'd received from the director Rudy Ressler. For years, while working red carpet events and taking every opportunity to chat up the rich and famous, he'd been given plenty of business cards by virtue of being an LAPD cop from people who hoped he could fix a ticket or do other things for them that were equally impossible. He'd tried and mostly failed to meet the kind of people who could get him real work. No one was more aware than Nate that the clock was not on his side.

The last job where he'd had a speaking role was three years ago in an indie production that had vanished and not even gone to DVD. He'd been a day player on that one and of course had been typecast as an LAPD cop. His scripted line was "Put your hands on your head and grab the wall."

When he'd tried to tell the director, a no-talent bully ten years younger, that it was impossible to grab a wall or anything else when your hands were on your head, the director said, "And what're your qualifications in such matters?"

The assistant director then whispered to the director that Nate was an LAPD police officer in his other life, and the director

grumbled something and then said to Nate, "Just go, 'Up against the wall.' And try to act excited because you've collared a perp you've been looking for." Then he turned to the assistant director and said, "Or maybe we should have the lieutenant say that?"

"Say what?" the AD asked.

"We just collared a perp we've been looking for," the annoyed director said.

"Excuse me," Nate interrupted. "The words *perp* and *collar* are terms used in the East, and though they're very popular on TV shows, we don't use either of them at LAPD. Would you like me to give you some substitute words that we use out here in the West?"

The director had dead-stared him for a moment and said, "Just say 'Up against the wall' and let it go at that. So okay, Officer... whatever your name is, let's try to get it right in one take and move the fuck on!"

Nate figured he must've gotten it right in one take. Either that or the little putz simply had had enough of him, because he growled, "Cut," two seconds after Nate delivered the line. Then he said, "Print it."

Nate was out of costume and on his way within the hour. If he could do it over again, he'd do or say whatever was asked of him without comment. It had been so hard to get work even as a day player that he hadn't done anything lately except take jobs as an extra a few times a year. And at age thirty-eight, time was surely of the essence.

Remembering his humiliation at the hands of that director caused him to get up and find the business card of Rudy Ressler. He opened his cell and dialed the number.

A young man answered, saying, "Rudy Ressler's office."

"This is Officer Nate Weiss, LAPD," he said. "Mr. Ressler asked me to call."

The young man said, "Just a moment," and put Nate on hold.

Nate almost gave up, but after nearly five minutes, the director

came on the line and said, "Officer Weiss. I'm glad to hear from you!"

"You asked me to call you, Mr. Ressler," Nate said.

"I certainly did," Rudy Ressler said. "I owe you. Let's do lunch today. How about two o'clock?"

"You don't owe me anything," Nate said, disappointed. He'd hoped for more than lunch from this man.

"I certainly do," the director said. "And I'd like to discuss the possibility of you reading for me. I'll be starting a movie for cable a few months after I get back from Europe."

A job! That perked him up, and Nate said, "I'd love to have—do lunch with you. I don't have to go on duty till five fifteen. Where and what time?"

After they finished talking, Nate got dressed. He started to put on a Tommy Hilfiger jersey but decided instead to wear a red tapered Polo shirt to reveal his biceps in case the part was for a buff-looking guy. And then he had to settle on gray cargo pants from Banana Republic because they were the only pair he had that was clean other than jeans. He figured the cargos would be okay because he wanted to look younger. He wondered if he should tell Rudy Ressler that gray temples were *very* premature in his family and offer to dye them dark if the director preferred. He hated to think about the fortieth birthday about to befall him in just eighteen months.

Nate showered and got to feeling upbeat because this was the first night he'd be working with Hollywood Station's new arrival, Snuffy Salcedo. Of course, all cops were notorious gossips, and a police station secret was as hard to keep as a first marriage, but Snuffy was surely in a class of his own. Hollywood Nate figured he'd get an earful about the chief and Snuffy's life among all the police brass and the drones at City Hall. But for now, Nate had big game to hunt.

*   *   *

At 1:50 P.M., Hollywood Nate pulled into the parking lot of a hot restaurant in west Hollywood. It was one of the new Italian places he'd read about that charged exorbitant prices to paint the food on the plate. They featured bite-size morsels of "imaginative" pasta and unrecognizable tidbits of sea creatures that wouldn't fill the belly of the baby opossums that raided the trash cans near Nate's apartment in North Hollywood. But he wasn't there for the food.

He spotted Rudy Ressler sitting at a patio table shaded by potted palms with an attractive woman who Nate figured was probably Ressler's age, though she looked younger. Nate understood the magic that was performed every day in the offices of plastic surgeons and dermatologists who almost outnumbered Realtors on the west side of Los Angeles. She was dressed for summer in a champagne-colored button-front sleeveless linen dress, and her highlighted chestnut hair was cupped just below her tiny ears.

Next to her was a younger man about Nate's age in a Calvin Klein multistripe gray suit, a crisp white shirt, and a necktie that cost more than everything on Nate's body. He had been around Hollywood types long enough to recognize the uniform of the day for agents from ICM and CAA.

Rudy Ressler was dressed supercool in a wrinkled cotton shirt, a black T-shirt beneath it, loose-fitting, acid-washed jeans, and retro black tennis shoes. In short, he took pains to dress as he had when he was in middle school, as did most of the above-the-line people on any shoot that Nate had ever worked. In the light of day the director looked older than he had on the red carpet. His rusty thinning hair was growing out at the roots, and his skin was getting blotchy. The director's eye job wasn't great either, and when Nate got close he could see the surgical scars by Ressler's ear. Nate thought the director ought to sue the quack who remodeled him.

At first Rudy Ressler didn't recognize Nate, but when he did, he jumped to his feet. "Officer Weiss!" he said, loudly enough for

others at nearby tables to hear, obviously thinking it exotic and cool to be doing lunch with a cop.

Nate smiled and they shook hands. Rudy Ressler said, "I'd like you to meet my fiancée, Leona Brueger. And this is my agent, Todd Bachman."

Leona Brueger gave Nate a dazzling smile, held out her hand palm down, so that he didn't know whether to shake it or kiss it, and said, "Well, this is a treat. A real cop. Or should I say police officer?"

"Cop's fine," Nate said. "In fact, it's my favorite word."

He shook her hand, and it was quite cool for such a hot afternoon. The agent gave him a vigorous sweaty handshake and said, "Rudy tells me they call you Hollywood Nate, but I'm not sure why."

"He works at Hollywood Station," Rudy Ressler said. "And get this. He has a SAG card!"

"You're an actor as well as a cop?" Todd Bachman said.

"When I can get work," Nate said.

Rudy Ressler said to Nate, "Todd's with CAA."

"Would I have seen you in anything?" the agent asked Nate.

"I'm not sure," Nate said self-consciously. "But I'm always available if you need my type in a production you may be packaging."

Nate thought that everyone laughed too hard at that. He was trying to be amusing but he was also being very serious here.

"Are you represented?" Rudy Ressler asked.

"Well, not exactly," Nate said, getting stoked over the possibility of being represented by CAA.

Leona Brueger chuckled and said, "He's got a great look for anyone casting a cop character, doesn't he, Todd? The camera would love him."

When she said it, her lashes fluttered subtly, and Nate thought, An older chick batting her eyes at me? But then he noticed that her eyes were a bit heavy-lidded and there was an empty wine bottle in an ice bucket beside her, but neither the agent nor Rudy Ressler had

a wineglass in front of him. So then he realized that Ms. Brueger liked to get her drink on.

The agent looked at his watch, and Nate saw that it was a Swiss Army watch like the one he wore. The absence of at least a Rolex made Nate conclude that the guy's client list probably included a lot of B-listers like Rudy Ressler.

The agent said, "Rudy, Leona, must go. More tomorrow. Will loop you in as soon as I hear more from A&E. Good to meet you, Officer."

He kissed the air in Leona's direction, rose, and departed. And Nate was disheartened that the agent hadn't even offered him a business card.

When he was gone, Leona Brueger stood wobbling for an instant and said to Rudy, "Damn these new Jimmy Choos. Too sky-high for me."

Nate looked down and thought that the double ankle straps looked very smart around her shapely ankles, but the leather resembled snakeskin, and he was not fond of reptiles. She took a little step sideways before righting herself and heading for the ladies' room. Sure, Nate thought, it's just the shoes.

When she was gone, Rudy Ressler said, "Leona and me, we're going to Tuscany for three months. At least that's the idea, but I don't think I can stay away that long. We plan to get married before the end of the year and move up to Napa. Leona's got a yen to own a vineyard and make wine." He pulled a sour expression and said sotto, "I don't know how long her fantasy will last, but you know how women are."

Nate said, "And, uh, how about the cable movie you mentioned? When do you think you might start prepping it?"

"Right after the first of the year," Rudy Ressler said. "I'd like you to read for the part of a police detective. It's not a big part but it does involve a couple of pages of dialogue and a big action sequence. Would you be interested?"

Nate's breath caught and he said, "Absolutely."

"Of course, I can't promise you the part right now. First you'll have to read for us. But if you do an acceptable job, it would be fun to have you in the role. The r-e-a-l cop playing the r-e-e-l cop. The publicists could have fun with it, too."

Nate took an LAPD business card from his wallet with his cell number on the back and said, "I'll be honored to read for you, Mr. Ressler."

"That's fine, Nate," Ressler said. "Just fine."

When Leona Brueger returned, she said, "Ready to go, Rudy?"

"I'll get the car," he said and headed toward the entrance.

Leona Brueger put her arm through Nate's and he walked her to the door, where a stunning young hostess who Nate figured for another aspiring thespian said, "Good day, Mrs. Brueger. Hope to see you soon."

Before Nate pushed open the door, Leona Brueger reached up with her free hand and squeezed his biceps, saying, "You've got impressive arms, young man."

"I have to work extra hard in the gym to keep them," Nate said. "It's hell getting older."

"You don't know older," Leona said wistfully, looking up at him. "Sometime you should drive up to my house and I'll pour you a drink and tell you sad stories about older."

When they got outside, Rudy Ressler's Aston Martin was waiting and he was standing beside it with a cell phone to his ear. He said to Leona Bruger, "Damn! Leona, I'm terribly sorry. I just got a call from our editor, who's practically in a fistfight with the director over the final cut. Can you possibly catch a cab?"

Nate said, "I can take Mrs. Brueger home."

"Could you, Nate? That's great," Ressler said. "Okay with you, Leona?"

"Go referee the fight," she said. "See you this evening."

Before he got in his car, Rudy Ressler said, "I just had a thought,

Leona. While we're in Europe, maybe Nate here could drive by in his patrol car once in a while and check in on the house and the new man. What's his name?"

"Raleigh Dibble," she said.

Ressler said, "Yeah, Raleigh. Would you mind, Nate? There's some valuable art in that house and that's a lotta responsibility for a new guy."

"Be glad to," Nate said, realizing that he did not get to do lunch.

When Rudy Ressler had pulled away and Nate was waiting for the parking attendant to retrieve his car, he smiled apologetically and said to Leona Brueger, "When was the last time you rode in a seven-year-old Corvette?"

"At one time in my life I drove an eighteen-year-old bathtub Nash," she said. "I was only slightly older than my mode of transportation but I loved that beast. I was driving it when I met my first husband, who I came to love a lot less than my old car, but through him I eventually came to meet Sammy Brueger. Now how about the story of *your* life, Nathan? Do they call you Nathan?"

"My mother and father do," he said. "But everybody else calls me Nate."

"Nathan Weiss." When she said his name, she gave his biceps another squeeze and hung on to him unsteadily. "How is it that a nice Irish-Italian girl like me ends up being attracted to gorgeous Jewish men?"

He smiled self-consciously and said, "Must be the circles you travel in. I haven't run into all that many gorgeous Jewish men. But I'm not much of a Jew anyway. Haven't even gone to temple since I was a kid." Then he paused and said, "Except a couple of times when somebody died."

"Relatives?"

"Cops."

"Jewish cops?"

"No, but I still felt compelled to go and pray for them, even though I know it's all mumbo jumbo."

She looked up at him and said, "Revealing that personal information to me just made you even more attractive. But I'll bet you're used to compliments from women, aren't you, Nathan?"

Nate was relieved when the parking kid arrived, and he drew the Vette up beside a Ferrari 599 that he'd read in *Motor Trend* was selling for more than $300,000. Another kid delivered an Audi R8 that Nate had read sold for a paltry $150,000.

The kid held the door open for Leona Brueger, and Nate tipped him $10, the most he had ever tipped for car service.

After he got behind the wheel, Nate said, "I do apologize for my car."

She smiled and said, "You really are too cute for words, Nathan." Then she took off her right shoe and said, "These goddamn things're killing me."

She removed the left shoe and held it in her hand while Nate drove north in heavy traffic. He looked over and touched the shoe, saying, "Is it really snakeskin?"

"Damned if I know," she said. "I'm not a shoe whore. I'm one of those broads that just buys the brand and hopes for the best." She yawned and leaned back, slurring her words slightly and said, "Go ahead and ask me."

"Ask you what?"

"How much I paid for them."

"I wasn't thinking that," Nate said, but he was.

"Come on, Nathan," she said. "I've had lots of cops in my extended family. The price of things was always on their minds. I understand you. I grew up poorer than you can imagine. I was a regular little Scarlett O'Hara when I came to this town, vowing never to be poor again. It didn't take me long to learn that everything in Hollywood is for sale if you know how to shop."

"Okay, how much do those shoes cost?" Nate asked.

Leona yawned again and said, "I think they were thirteen hundred and change."

That impressed him for sure. He looked down at the shoes again but didn't touch them this time.

Trying to make conversation to keep her awake, he said, "It sounds like you and Mr. Ressler have a wonderful vacation coming up. Two months in Tuscany sounds great."

Her eyes were closed when she spoke. "Tuscany again. A different villa this time. Rudy's never been there. Rudy's never been many places outside of Hollywood, Beverly Hills, Malibu, and the San Fernando Valley, where he can run his production company on the cheap."

"And you're getting married when you get back? Congratulations."

She opened her eyes and said, "My, my. Rudy shared a lot when I went to the ladies' room. It must be the badge you carry. He's very impressed with authority figures. When he has dinner with the chief of police he almost wets his pants." Then she told him her address in the Hollywood Hills and closed her eyes.

Nate wondered if a bottle of wine always made her so chatty. And he wondered if an innocent flirtation with Leona Brueger might give him more juice with Rudy Ressler. Then he remembered what an assistant director had said to him on one of the last jobs he'd worked. The AD had observed the producer's wife, a woman twenty years older than Nate, flirting with him. It made him say to Nate, "Officer, if you want to get work in this business, don't pet the cougars. Not when they belong to the boss."

She actually began dozing by the time they reached the foot of the Hollywood Hills and the Corvette began climbing up Outpost Drive to Mulholland. Nate had always enjoyed driving in the Hills in a black-and-white, admiring the view homes, fantasizing about that one break that could make it all possible for him, too.

When he got to the address she'd given him, he pulled up to the

gate and stopped. It was easily the largest residential property in this part of the Hollywood Hills and Nate had to admit he'd love to be shown around.

He said gently, "Uh, Mrs. Brueger, we're here."

She opened her eyes and rummaged in her purse until she found a key ring that had a small remote device on it. She pressed it and the gate swung open. He drove in on a long, curving, faux-cobblestone driveway. He made the circle around a bubbling fountain so that the front of his car was facing the gate and she was on the side in front of the huge tiled arch over the main door.

He jumped out and ran around to open the door for her but she was already out, holding her $1,300 shoes in one hand and her purse in the other.

"Come in for a minute, Nathan," she said.

"Okay, Mrs. Brueger," he said.

This was a first. He'd been inside many homes in the Hollywood Hills over the years but as a cop, almost never as a guest.

She unlocked the door and pushed it open, walking to a nearby computer panel on the wall to punch in her code and deactivate the high-pitched alarm warning.

"Follow me," she said.

He did that, crossing a foyer of Mexican tile until he was looking down two steps into the great room. It was very large and it seemed that almost every square foot of the white plaster walls contained paintings: oils, watercolors, and numbered lithographs.

Leona Brueger tossed her shoes on a massive glass coffee table, knocking over some pricey-looking knickknacks.

She said, "Have a seat. I'll be right back. What're you drinking?"

The entire interior was done in cream and custard colors: the walls, the drapes, the carpet, the side tables, and even the twin sofas, with accent pillows in subtle pastels. It all spelled comfort to Hollywood Nate. There was none of that minimalist crap he was constantly seeing in magazines and in the *L.A. Times* home section.

This all looked stuffed and overstuffed. He had the impression of being enveloped by a giant voluptuous marshmallow.

And then there was the view. It was Hollywood, but not his Hollywood down there at asphalt level. This was Hollywood as seen by God, if there was one. The smog from this elevation was not ugly, not a dingy gray blanket of dangerous gases settling over the L.A. basin in late summer. No, this was a blaze of vivid primary colors propelled by offshore breezes and later would be lit by a last solar gasp before the sun fell into the Pacific. It was astonishing how beautiful and even delicious the L.A. smog could look from a $15 million home in the Hollywood Hills.

She paused on the top step and said, "Do you like the view?"

Nate said, "Up here the smog is the color of a cabernet and over-ripe plums and purple grapes with a spray of peach juice flowing through it. But somehow I don't think this is what they mean when they say that Hollywood is just a big fruit bowl."

Leona Brueger said, "Why, Officer Weiss, you do surprise me. Not only do you carry a SAG card but you have a touch of the poet in you. I wonder what other surprises you might be keeping hidden."

Nate looked at his watch and said, "I have to be at work and in uniform by seventeen fifteen—I mean, five fifteen. I better not have a drink."

She turned and said, "How about diet soda? You look like the healthy diet soda type."

"Fine," he said. "Thanks."

The coffee table between the two sofas was piled with art books that looked as though they'd never been opened, and women's magazines that looked well perused. When she returned with his diet soda in a crystal goblet, she had a goblet of white wine for herself. She held her glass up to his and said, "Chin-chin," which a makeup artist that Nate used to date said was "the cry of the Hills birds," meaning the women of the Hollywood Hills.

She sat down two feet away from him on the sofa and said, "I

gave the butler the afternoon off. He won't be back until seventeen hundred—I mean, five o'clock."

That made Nate chuckle, and then he said, "Would he be Raleigh, the guy I'm supposed to see when I check on your property after you're gone?"

"That's him," Leona Brueger said. "Some of my friends say I shouldn't leave all this"—she waved in the general direction of the paintings—"with a man who's only worked here such a short time, but he's also worked for a friend of ours and comes highly recommended. Besides, I don't give a rat's eyeball for all this. It was my late husband's passion, not mine. It's well insured anyway, so que será, será."

"I don't know very much about art," Nate said, sipping his soda and thinking, Yes, this lady really does like to get her drink on.

"Neither do I," she said. "And I'm too old to learn. And speaking of old, how old did you say you are?"

"I'm thirty-eight," he said. "I know I'm getting a bit long in the tooth to make it in the movie business. I've been a cop since I was a baby of twenty-one."

"Hah!" she said. "Old. Thirty-eight is old, is it?"

She took a long pull from the wineglass and put it down on the coffee table. She scooted close to him and said, "I'll bet I could help your career a little bit. As far as the part in whatever the thing is that Rudy's doing, you've got it. I'll see to that. But it's only a couple of days' work. I know other people in the business. People with real topspin. I could introduce you around. Some evening when you're off duty, would you like to come here to a dinner party and meet a few of my friends?"

"You bet I would," Nate said, wondering if a chemical peel gave her that buttery skin.

"I have to warn you, though," she said, "all they talk about is diets, drugs that facilitate diets, and box-office grosses."

"Fine with me," he said.

"Can you really act?"

"Well, I'm not one of those who go through life imagining how everything would look through the lens of a Steadicam, but I've taken some classes," he said. "And I've had a couple of speaking parts, but not in a feature film yet. And I can't count the number of times I've been an extra." He stopped when he saw her lips curve up in a little smile, and he felt like a kid bragging to a wealthy aunt. Then he said, "So, yes, I think I can act. But so can thousands—no, make it tens of thousands—of other people trying for the same breaks. I know what I'm up against."

"Rudy Ressler is no Martin Scorcese," she said, "but I'm sure you're aware of that. Is that how you see yourself? In a crime movie directed by Scorcese or maybe by Clint Eastwood?"

"In my fantasies?"

"Yeah, let's hear your fantasies."

"To be honest, in my fantasies I'm not playing a cop. I see myself in a Woody Allen movie."

He watched her burst into laughter, and he wasn't sure how to interpret it until she stopped and said, "You are adorable, Nathan Weiss. I think I could like you a lot."

"I like you, too," he said, not knowing what else to say. And then it occurred to him that what was making him feel so uncomfortable and awkward was not just the fact that she was Rudy Ressler's fiancée and he wanted the job. And it wasn't just her age. She was a fit, hot-looking woman, even if she was as old as his mother. It was that she was *rich*. This was the first time in his life that Nate Weiss was playing a flirtation scene with a seriously wealthy woman.

"Meanwhile, you do have a job that you like, yes?" Leona said.

Nate said, "At Hollywood Station we used to have a sergeant we called the Oracle. He said that doing good police work was the most fun we'd ever have in our entire lives. And I've found that to be true." Then he thought of his former partner, Dana Vaughn, of

her lying dead in his arms, and he said, "For the most part it's been fun."

"Where does acting come into it, then?" she asked.

Nate said, "I thought acting would be what I could do full-time after my pension is vested. I'll reach that in three more years, but if I retire at that time, I still won't be able to draw the pension until I'm fifty years old. I figure I could be a full-time actor in the interim. But I need a break. Don't we all?"

"So that's your dream, is it?" she said.

Nate said, "My dreams aren't complicated. Any one of the Kardashians could interpret them."

She said, "I'm surprised that when you serve twenty years as a cop you aren't able to receive any pension money yet."

"I'll still be too young then," Nate said.

"Too young," she said with a look of melancholy. Then her eyes narrowed and she said, "Me, I'm old enough to have my cop and eat him, too."

Talk about a cougar! This man-eater looked like she truly could come at him, fang and claw. While he was contemplating that troubling catamount image, she said, "I'm old enough for anything. *Any* damn thing at all."

With that she leaned over abruptly and kissed him on the cheek and then on the mouth. Her kiss was open-mouthed and warm, with lots of tongue.

When she pulled away, she looked at him, sloe-eyed, and he figured there was no way out, not if he wanted to be in Ressler's movie. This menopausal momma was about to debauch him right here in this goddamn marshmallow palace!

Leona stood up and unbuttoned her dress and let it hang open. He saw a lace-trimmed white bra that held breasts he guessed were helped by silicone, and a flat belly that she'd earned, and shapely thighs the color of burnished copper, compliments of a tanning bed, he supposed.

As though reading his thoughts, she said, "The tawny color is mostly mine even without tanning, compliments of my Italian old man. But my ma was Irish, so I can hold a grudge with the best of them. Don't ever cross me, gorgeous."

Nate watched her let the dress fall to the floor and he thought that she might be his mother's age but that's all they had in common. Then it occurred to him that he had actually flashed on a flittering image of his mother, and he thought, What the hell's this, Oedipus time? Was Hollywood Nate Weiss just another Jewish momma's boy? But no, that cliché was just too ridiculous.

Leona said, "We should behave like grown-ups and go to my bedroom for this first-timer, shouldn't we? Yet somehow, being with a lovely lad like you I don't want to behave like a grown-up. Do you?"

She unhooked her bra and let it fall to the floor with the linen dress, and he thought, Silicone for sure, but understated and very acceptable. Then it was his turn to give a command performance, so he put his glass on the table beside the sofa and stood. Just then another image flared, as hot and blinding as a red carpet spotlight. His mother still used those same words on him at least once a month: "Behave like a grown-up and find a nice woman, Nathan." Goddamnit! If he couldn't sweep away the terrifying notion that he was about to shtup his own mother, he'd never even get it up!

Nate started feeling feverish and not in a good way. If ever he needed the tips he'd learned in that UCLA film class . . . Maybe if he were a method actor, he could go all Tom Jones sensuous and imagine something decadent, like a bathtub full of cherries jubilee or something. He had a sudden sensation of flop sweat, and he hadn't even flopped yet. Then he heard the sound of a car clattering down the axle-cracking, fake-cobblestone driveway, and it didn't sound like Rudy Ressler's purring Aston Martin.

"Shit!" she said. "That's Raleigh's car. What the hell's he doing back here after I gave him the fucking afternoon off? Jesus Christ!"

"I'd better get going," Nate said with more than a small measure of relief. "Does he come in through the main door?"

"No, the kitchen door, damn him. But you don't have to slink away, Nathan." She picked up her clothes hastily and said, "Let me run to the bedroom and change. We can still sit and chat."

"I'd better go," Nate said, moving quickly to the front door, thinking that he definitely didn't want the butler to gossip about him to Rudy Ressler. "You can tell him that I dropped you off and came in to use the bathroom for a minute so he doesn't wonder about my Vette in the driveway, okay?"

She stood with her crumpled dress in her arms and said, "When we get back from Europe, I want you here for dinner parties, yes? And other things?"

"Yes, ma'am," Nate said with a grin, handing her a business card bearing his private cell number.

"Yes, Leona," she prompted.

"Yes, Leona," he said.

"Don't ever call me ma'am or Mrs. Brueger," she said. "Never again."

"Never again, Leona," he said, with an even bigger grin that required more acting skill.

When Nate was in his Corvette and driving out through her gate, he thought once more of the assistant director who'd said, "Don't pet the cougar." It wasn't until he was motoring down Mulholland Drive that he began to understand his conflicted feelings in that house. Sure, it was her money, and her age, that triggered those childish thoughts of his mother, but there was something else. It was the first time in his entire life that he'd been put in the position of actually living the ultimate Hollywood cliché. She had challenged him to man-up and sell his ass for a movie role, and he had waffled like a teenage ingenue on a casting couch. She had been every inch a man-eating cougar, and Hollywood Nate Weiss had been nothing but a twitchy fucking rabbit.

SIX

As THAT SUMMER was winding down, most of the dozen working detectives at Hollywood Station had to wonder what else could happen. It wasn't just the antics of the Bling Ring by any means. Another crime spree involved the "BMW Bandits," who had attacked more than fifty BMWs, mostly on the west side and Wilshire district. They were discriminating thieves who often ignored personal articles such as laptops and other pricey items that owners left in their cars. What they were after were replaceable air bags and high-tech headlights, costing nearly $3,000 to replace in BMW 3 and 5 series cars. Other traditionally valuable and vulnerable car parts, like wheel rims, were being ignored, and the thieves were able to access and remove the air bags very quickly. Hollywood was expected to be next on their list of favorite areas of attack.

But the wave of home and auto burglaries was nothing compared with the strange and disturbing serial murders that occupied some of the detectives at Hollywood Station. One of the most bizarre involved the stabbing of homeless people. The first murder took place midday on a lovely Hollywood afternoon near Sunset Boulevard and Western Avenue. A homeless man managed to put in a call to police, saying, "I think I've been shot," before falling over dead. He had not been shot but stabbed, and he died of a lethal puncture wound to the chest.

Another murder occurred on Hollywood Boulevard by the Music Box Theater. A homeless man was found dead on the ground, where he'd been lying for hours. The initial patrol officers to arrive saw no blood trail and at first did not think he'd been stabbed. After detectives arrived, they learned that one of the nearby commercial buildings had a security camera on which their suspect, another homeless man, was recorded watching his intended victim. The killer would approach the sleeping man, and whenever a pedestrian passed by, he would walk away. At one point he even seemed to spot the video camera watching him, but he was undeterred.

He'd taped a steak knife to his forearm inside two pieces of cardboard that acted as a sheath. When he felt it was safe, he simply walked over to the sleeping man and seemed to poke him. There was no slashing, no overkill. Just the chest puncture, and it was enough.

A third attack occurred at Yucca and Wilcox Avenues. A homeless man awoke with pain in his chest. When he got up, blood gushed from a chest wound and he found that he could not walk. He was rushed to the hospital in time to save his life.

The killer turned out to be a former inmate of a state mental facility. Random beatings and even the senseless killing of vulnerable homeless people were certainly not rare, but this was Hollywood's first serial attacker of homeless people who was himself a homeless person. The detectives referred to him as "the ultimate self-hating bum."

Clearly, the most heinous case in the Hollywood detectives' murder books in the first year of the Obama presidency involved Michael Thomas Gargiulo, who was awaiting trial for serial murder. Gargiulo, a thirty-two-year-old air conditioner and furnace repairman, originally from the Chicago suburb of Glenview, Illinois, was initially linked in a peripheral way to a Hollywood actor.

Long before coming to Los Angeles from Illinois, Michael Gargiulo had been questioned as a teenager in the murder of his high

school classmate Tricia Pacaccio. She was stabbed to death in what detectives called a "blitz attack" on her doorstep in August 1993, a week before the eighteen-year-old was to report to Purdue University as a freshman with an interest in environmental issues. In her high school yearbook, the bright and popular girl said she "wanted to save the world," but as it turned out, she couldn't save herself. Her murder went unsolved, although DNA material was found under the fingernails of the victim. Years later, Hollywood detectives became intimately acquainted with that case, following a terrible murder in the Hollywood Hills.

On February 22, 2001, actor Ashton Kutcher had driven to the Hollywood Hills bungalow of his girlfriend, Ashley Ellerin, to take her to a Grammy Awards party. She was a stunning twenty-two-year-old fashion student, a model, and an occasional Las Vegas dancer. The young actor knocked and rang the bell but got no answer. He looked through a rear window and saw what he thought were wine stains on the carpet. He left the bungalow, and Ashley Ellerin's body was found the next day by her housemate. The first detective to arrive called the crime scene "a massacre."

Every window in the bungalow had bars on it, and there was even a steel door. The doors were in good repair, all freshly painted with no sign of forced entry. Inside, from the front entry down a long passage, were spatter and drops of blood. Beyond that, there was a lot more blood all the way to the body lying on the top landing, described by detectives as "a bloody pulp." Her hair looked as though she'd just washed it and was fresh from a shower at the time of attack. She wore a terry-cloth robe and pajamas. Her throat had been sawed and ripped open and her head was knocked off the brain stem. Only mangled ribbons of tissue connected her head to her body. The medical examiner stopped counting stab wounds at forty-eight.

Criminalists tried to get latent prints and DNA evidence, but all of the fingerprints in the bungalow belonged to the victim or her

housemate. Later, after searching his memory for any possible suspect whom she might have let into their home, the housemate of Ashley Ellerin mentioned "Mike the furnace guy" to police. He said that Ashley and a friend had met Mike when he'd walked out of the nearby dog park one day. Mike was described as being six two, 180 pounds, and having a "dark demeanor. " He had stopped by the bungalow one afternoon when Ashley was not at home, telling the housemate that he wanted to work on her furnace, and he had been spotted driving his truck slowly past the bungalow on another occasion.

That crime resulted in a seven-year investigation that eventually led Hollywood Division detectives to Illinois and the Pacaccio murder, as well as to other blitz attacks in the Los Angeles area in 2005 and 2007. A detective with the L.A. Sheriff's Homicide Bureau described one of them as "the most violent murder I ever saw, bar none." The attacker had done horrible "staging" with body parts on that one, and it looked as though the victim had been ravaged by a pack of sharks.

And finally, in 2008, a Santa Monica woman was attacked in her home but managed to fight off her assailant and survive, despite serious stab wounds. DNA evidence was collected and coordinated and it brought everything together. Michael Gargiulo was at last in custody, awaiting trial in 2010. And Hollywood paparazzi would be ready for Ashton Kutcher if he should be required to testify, drooling over the possibility that his wife, Demi Moore, might accompany him to court.

So there was no dearth of violence and other serial crimes for the dozen overworked detectives at Hollywood Station to deal with, and the detectives at the Major Assault Crimes table got their share of domestic violence cases in that first year of the recession. The MAC detectives who responded late on a blistering hot afternoon to an unusual domestic violence call from a woman in an apartment building in Little Armenia were both cops with more

than twenty years on the Job. Gina Villegas, a forty-three-year-old energetic Mexican American, and Carl Cheng, a forty-two-year-old laconic Taiwanese American, were both children of immigrants who got to use their language skills frequently in the polyglot community that was Hollywood.

They hadn't needed their foreign-language skills when they got ordered to Little Armenia. They were responding to a telephonic plea made to their D3 supervisor by a terrified woman who said that she had been stalked and threatened by an ex-lover who was father to the baby she had given birth to only five weeks prior. Thelma Barker, their detective supervisor, was a bootstraps-up black veteran with thirty-one years on the Job. She was born and raised in Compton and had been a victim of domestic violence herself during a brief marriage at the age of nineteen.

The old three-story building in Little Armenia, consisting of twenty-eight rental units, was a rectangular block of gray stucco, and was possibly the most protected apartment building in that part of east Hollywood. Because of episodes of tagging by street gangs in the area, the owner had taken the extraordinary step of hiring local pensioners as watchmen. The geezers took turns sitting in a tiny office off the lobby from 9 P.M. to 6 A.M. seven days a week, when vandalism was a threat. There were no fire escapes or any exterior balconies that could be easily accessed.

The detectives rang the manager and were buzzed inside by a retired plumber who also did handyman jobs in the building. When he learned who the detectives were looking for, he said, "Confidentially, I don't like it when the owner of this property gets so charitable. The girl in three-ten is his niece, or so he claims. She's behind two months in the rent and still he lets her stay. Don't tell her I told you, but she leaves her two babies alone sometimes. I've felt like calling you when she does it, but she's the boss's special tenant, if you know what I mean, and I don't wanna lose this job."

Gina Villegas thanked him, and when they got to the one-bedroom

apartment on the third floor, a dangerously thin woman met them at the door. She was a twenty-five-year-old strawberry blonde with frightened, darting eyes, trembling hands, and suspiciously stained teeth.

Carl Cheng's glance toward his partner said, Tweaker.

Before either cop could say anything to her, the woman said, "I'm the one who called your office. My name's Cindy Kroll. My ex-boyfriend is threatening me. I think he wants to kill me."

"And why would you think that?" Gina Villegas asked while Carl Cheng glanced around the little apartment.

There were two chairs at the small Formica table in the kitchen. And in the living room, if you could call it that, was a sofa, a shabby overstuffed chair, an infant's crib, and a playpen, all crowded together around a big-screen Sony TV.

Carl Cheng smirked subtly in his partner's direction as if to say, No matter how crappy they live, they always have a better TV than I do.

Cindy Kroll said, "Sorry there's no place to sit down." She pointed to a thirteen-month-old in the playpen. Then she said, "My five-week-old baby boy's asleep in my bedroom. We don't have much room here."

Gina Villegas said, "A thirteen-month-old and a five-week-old? You're not wasting time starting a family, are you?"

"My baby boy was an accident, and that's what's causing the problem," Cindy Kroll said. "His father wants me dead for demanding child support."

"Are you married to him?" the detective asked.

"No," she said. "After my first baby was born, my husband, Ralphie, took off and left us. I had a tough time and could only make a few bucks cleaning houses. I had a job cleaning the apartment of Louis Dryden every week for four months. He lives up on Franklin Avenue and has a pretty good job at a real-estate company in Santa Monica, selling vacation rentals. He's maybe ten

years older than me, and, well, we started getting intimate while I was working for him and pretty soon I got pregnant."

"Pregnant by *him?*" Gina Villegas said.

"Of course by *him.*" Cindy Kroll's darting eyes flashed. "I'm no slut."

"No, I didn't mean that you were. But you also have a husband, right?"

"He's outta my life. I got pregnant by Louis and nobody else."

"Go on," Gina Villegas said.

"He gave me some cash to get an abortion but I didn't do it. I decided to have the baby and hire a lawyer. For the past couple of months my lawyer's been calling him, but Louis says the baby isn't his. He says he's engaged to a terrific woman now and I'm ruining his life with my lies."

"How about a paternity test?" Gina Villegas said. "That should settle the matter."

"That's what my lawyer's working on now. We're gonna take him to court."

Carl Cheng spoke for the first time and said, "Why're we here, ma'am?"

"He stalked me today," Cindy Kroll said. "He caught me at the Seven-Eleven store I always go to and told me this is my last chance. He said he'd give me five thousand dollars to leave him alone and quit saying the baby's his."

"And what'd you say?" Carl Cheng asked.

"I told him to talk to my lawyer."

"And when you were at the store, where were your babies?" Gina Villegas asked.

After a long pause, Cindy Kroll said, "I was only gone for a few minutes."

"You can't leave babies alone like that. It's child endangering and it's against the law," Gina Villegas said.

Cindy Kroll said, "I asked the woman in the next apartment to

look in on them every few minutes. Don't you wanna hear what I got to say? This man threatened me!"

This time Gina Villegas glanced at her partner. A woman next door? Sure.

"Of course we want to hear," Carl Cheng said. "What did he say exactly?"

Cindy Kroll now addressed all answers to the male detective and said, "He told me his entire life and career were on the line. He said his fiancée was not like me. When I asked him what he meant, he goes, 'She's a lady, not a whore like you.' And then he threatened me."

"Use his exact words if you can remember," Carl Cheng said.

"Okay, he said to me, 'Whatever happens is on your head, not mine. You're forcing me to do whatever I gotta do to stop your blackmail from wrecking my whole life.' That's exactly what he said."

Carl Cheng said, "Did you ask him what he meant by that?"

"I knew what he meant," Cindy Kroll said. "I'm not stupid!"

Gina Villegas said, "What you know or think you know about the implication of his words will not satisfy the District Attorney's Office. Did he say more than that? Anything specific by way of a violent threat?"

Cindy Kroll directed her answer to Carl Cheng and said, "Then he goes, 'I'll make it ten thousand dollars but no more. Take the extortion money and get outta my life.' That's exactly what he said."

"What did you say?" Gina Villegas asked.

Cindy Kroll looked at her this time and said, "The same thing. That he should talk to my lawyer."

"It doesn't constitute a threat of violence," Carl Cheng said.

"Look, Detective," she said to him, "I had sex with that man lotsa times. All I want is a reasonable amount of child support to raise his baby boy." Then she paused and said, "*Our* baby boy."

"There're limits to what we can do," Gina Villegas said.

"You gotta do something now!" Cindy Kroll said. "The man's been smoking a lotta crystal meth. Way more since our troubles started, and it makes him totally paranoid. He had an insane look in his eyes today when he threatened me. Do you know what it's like to get all paranoid from smoking crystal?"

Carl Cheng's look said, No, but I'll bet you do.

"Do you know if he has a police record?" Gina Villegas asked.

"Not that I know of."

"Have you done crystal meth with him?" Gina Villegas asked.

"Oh, fuck!" Cindy Kroll said, and stifled a sob. "You don't care if he kills me! I need protection. Tonight is when he likes to go out and score enough crystal for the weekend. I'm in danger tonight."

Gina Villegas sat down at the kitchen table, pushed some baby debris aside, and opened her notebook and said, "Okay, give us his address and phone number. We'll try to have a talk with him."

"What if he's not home?" Cindy Kroll said. "I need protection at least for tonight."

"There are domestic violence shelters," Gina Villegas said. "And restraining orders. Have you talked to your lawyer about all that?"

"I don't wanna go to a fucking shelter!" Cindy Kroll said. "I want police protection here in my home."

Carl Cheng said, "We can't camp out here based on what you've told us. But we'll ask the radio car in this area to drive by tonight and keep an eye on the place. I gotta tell you, though, this building's like a fortress. I noticed that the rear fire door is steel-reinforced with no handle on the outside. And you have a watchman in the lobby, right? Does Louis Dryden have a key, either to the main door or to your apartment?"

"No," she admitted. "He only came in here a few times after he drove me home."

"Well, there you go," Carl Cheng said. "You're safe here. But just to put your mind at rest, a black-and-white will do drive-bys tonight. Okay?"

After returning to the station, the MAC team tried to reach Louis Dryden by phone but got no answer, and no answering machine picked up. They ran a record check using the description supplied to them by Cindy Kroll but came back with nothing that fit Louis Dryden on Franklin Avenue. They were already into overtime by then and so were five other detectives, busy in their tiny cubicles, making phone calls and working computers.

The MAC team told D3 Thelma Barker about the vague implied threat that Louis Dryden had allegedly made. They said that Cindy Kroll's boyfriend was a tweaker and they were sure she was, too.

"The mother of the year, she ain't," Carl Cheng finally told his D3. "Our read is that she gave birth to a baby she doesn't want just to trap the guy into marriage or blackmail him into a nice cash settlement, or maybe both."

"Tell you what," their D3 said. "I know it's getting late and you'd like to get started on your weekend, but just to be on the safe side, let's ask a patrol unit to drop one of your business cards with a phone-me message on Louis Dryden's doorstep. That'll put the fear of God in him if he's thinking of doing something stupid." She looked at her watch and said, "The midwatch is about finished with roll call. Why don't you tell the sergeant what this is all about and also ask that a radio car drive by the place a few times tonight for a quick look-see. You never know with tweakers when they're amped up."

"If she's a tweaker, too, maybe she's the one that's paranoid," Carl Cheng said. "That's what tweakers do, get all paranoid."

"It'll make me feel better if you do it my way," his D3 said with a look that ended the discussion.

"Okay, boss," Carl Cheng said with a sigh of fatigue. "Anything you say."

★ SEVEN ★

THE NEW WATCH commander, Lieutenant O'Reilly, conducted roll call that afternoon for Watch 5, the midwatch. He was a thirty-year-old lieutenant who so far the troops didn't much like. He'd tested well on promotion exams and was recently appointed to his rank with only nine years on the Department and sent to Hollywood Division for his probation. He gave them a condescending lecture that was so boring it couldn't have been enlivened with hand puppets. It was all about treating the citizens of Hollywood with the utmost respect, even those who were as crazy as rabid squirrels. And in Hollywood that included a lot of folks.

On the wall behind the long tables where his captive audience sat were framed movie posters, including ones for *Sunset Boulevard* and *L.A. Confidential,* an indication that the officers of Hollywood Station were very aware of their unique geography. Finally, the lieutenant ran out of things to lecture them about and said, "Let's go to work." The cops gathered their gear, but before leaving the room, each of them touched for luck the framed photo of their late sergeant whom they'd called the Oracle. They had loved their old supervisor, and he had thought of them as his children.

The framed photo, which was affixed to the wall beside the doorway, bore a brass plate that said:

The Oracle
Appointed: Feb 1960
End-of-Watch: Aug 2006
Semper Cop

The assistant watch commander, Sergeant Lee Murillo, a calm and bookish Mexican American with hair the color of stainless steel and the knotty rawboned body of a long-distance runner, had fifteen years of LAPD experience and was a supervisor they did happen to like. He was downstairs in the detective squad room talking to the MAC team about Cindy Kroll and Louis Dryden, and he gave the Little Armenia drive-by job to 6-X-76 when Lieutenant O'Reilly was finished with them.

All five patrol units, including 6-X-32, manned by Flotsam and Jetsam, and 6-X-66, with Hollywood Nate driving and Snuffy Salcedo riding shotgun, left the kit room with their gear and headed for the parking lot at 6 P.M. They toted black nylon war bags full of gear, as well as Remington shotguns, Ithaca beanbag shotguns, helmets, Tasers, pepper spray, and rovers. During the prior several years that the LAPD had suffered under the federal consent decree, they had also been required to draw from the kit room devices to record superfluous data about people they stopped or arrested. None of that data collecting had ever provided police critics with information that they'd hoped would prove claims of racial profiling. As hard as they tried, the disgruntled critics of the LAPD were not able to wave the race flag when it came to traffic and pedestrian stops.

P2 Vivien Daley, one of three female officers working the midwatch that evening, was the driver of the shop belonging to 6-X-76, so called because of the shop numbers on the roof and doors of their Crown Vics. Those numbers allowed a unit to be easily identified by citizens and by the LAPD helicopters, called airships by the troops.

The late summer sun was still high enough that Viv Daley put on her sunglasses when she got behind the wheel. The thirty-year-old cop was born and raised in Long Beach and had played varsity basketball at Long Beach State, but she had disappointed her parents, who wanted her to become a teacher. She always said she'd applied at the LAPD "on a whim" but had never regretted it in the eight years that she'd served. Viv loved to quote the Oracle to her parents, especially his often-repeated mantra: "Doing good police work is the most fun you'll ever have in your entire lives." She found that to be true.

Viv Daley had scrubbed good looks, and the only makeup she carried was a pencil to darken her sandy eyebrows and a subtle pale lipstick, a shade approved by the Department. She kept her auburn hair pinned up above the collar of her uniform shirt, as was required of all female patrol officers. At end-of-watch, when she'd changed into her jersey and jeans and three-inch wedges, she stood taller than almost every male officer on the watch, but Flotsam could still look down at her, wedges or not.

Her passenger partner "keeping books," or "taking paper," which simply meant being the report writer, was twenty-nine-year-old Georgie Adams, who had seven years on the Job. He wore his raven hair slicked back, and with his black irises and chiseled features, he was as dark and exotic-looking as Viv Daley was fair and freckled. The dissimilarity extended to their stature as well. At a wiry five foot eight, he was the shortest male officer on the midwatch, a full five inches shorter than his gym-fit partner, and though he was well muscled, he didn't outweigh her by much due to her large-boned frame. He referred to Viv as "tall sister" and often called her "sis."

Because of his Anglo-Saxon surname but swarthy appearance, questions about his ethnicity came up immediately with new partners, and when it did, Georgie Adams was quick to display his sinister smile and say, "I'm a Gypsy boy. A distant cousin to the late George Adams, California's 'King of the Gypsies.'"

Nobody ever knew if Georgie's claim was true, and nobody had been able to pry much more of his history from him. He'd served in Iraq with the Marines and had been wounded by a roadside bomb, that much was known for sure. He was born and raised in San Bernardino, California, and sometimes he told what everyone figured was a preposterous story of having been bought from a Gypsy clan passing through town by a Syrian carpet importer and his wife, who raised him and let him keep his noble Gypsy surname. Yet whenever he was called to the home of an Arabic-speaking crime victim in Hollywood, it was clear that he could not speak the language of the Syrians. The next guess was that he was of Latino descent, but he could not speak Spanish either. All bets were off at Hollywood Station as to Georgie Adams's true ethnicity.

His personnel package downtown didn't reveal much, as one of the curious Hollywood Division supervisors who had taken a look at it learned. The supervisor even contacted the civilian employee who had conducted Georgie's background check. He was told that the applicant's parents, Jean and Theodore Adams, were third-generation San Bernardino residents whose forebears were Okies from the great migration of the 1930s. And further, the background investigator said, Georgie had come to them through a county adoption with almost nothing known about his birth mother, a teenage drifter, and nothing at all about his biological father.

The only certainties were that, immediately after graduating from high school in San Bernardino, Georgie Adams had joined the Marines and after his discharge had enrolled at a community college, which he left to join the LAPD. And that was it. The other cops referred to him as "the Gypsy," and he seemed to like the handle.

Georgie's partner, Viv Daley, never questioned him about his ethnicity or asked anything about his shadowy past. She simply said, "It's none of my business. And anyway, I love a mystery."

The surfer cops were attracted to Viv Daley and had tried many

times to take her surfing, saying they'd turn her into a "quantum quebee," which she learned from Jetsam was a compliment, meaning a hot surfer chick. But so far Viv had resisted their many invitations to attend the nighttime ragers on the sand, including one that was scheduled for Sunday night at Bolsa Chica Beach, where many firefighters and cops liked to surf.

When she told her partner about the invitation, and her concern that a bunch of boozy surfers might get a bit too aggressive and handsy with any women present, Georgie offered to go with her as chaperone.

He said, "Sis, if any drunken surfer trash put their paws on my bosom buddy, I'll cut out their fucking hearts and feed them to the seagulls."

"'Bosom buddy,'" Viv said. "That's charming, but I don't think I'll be needing a Gypsy assassin as a chaperone."

When Jetsam heard from Viv about Georgie's offer, he informed Flotsam, who said, "Dude, maybe we oughtta like, rethink our rager invite to Viv. The Gypsy might spoil the party if he goes all aggro and starts carving up kahunas."

There'd been persistent rumors ever since he arrived at Hollywood Station that Georgie Adams carried a buck knife on duty in an ankle rig. There had been two known cases in LAPD history of unarmed undercover officers killing assailants with a knife when they were trapped in a deadly situation. The Gypsy was known for his mordant sense of humor, but when he showed his baleful smile and let it be known that he was looking for a chance to be the first *uniformed* LAPD copper to do it, the others tended to believe he might be serious.

The first time the rumor about the buck knife reached young Lieutenant O'Reilly, he ordered Sergeant Murillo to check it out, and if it was true, to put a stop to it immediately.

"Tell Adams he isn't playing a role in a spaghetti western here," Lieutenant O'Reilly said to his sergeant.

But the desk officer overheard the watch commander's order, and LAPD's jungle wireless went to work immediately. By the time Sergeant Murillo got around to asking Georgie Adams to accompany him to the locker room, the young cop didn't look at all surprised, nor did he question his supervisor about his reason.

"I'm sorry, Adams," Sergeant Murillo said when they were alone in the locker room, "but I've been tasked to find out if you carry a buck knife in an ankle rig, and if you do, to order you to stop doing it."

Silently, Georgie reached down and pulled up both pant legs all the way to his knees. Sergeant Murillo saw no buck knife. What he did see was mottled scar tissue from third-degree burns, and grafts that looked like scorched lumpy egg white, wrapped around Georgie's shins and calves from the top of his six-inch zip-up boots to just below his knees.

"Okay, thanks," Sergeant Murillo said, and left him in the locker room.

When he returned to the watch commander's office, Sergeant Murillo said, "I've spoken with Adams and checked for a buck knife."

"What did you find out?" asked Lieutenant O'Reilley.

"That he *earned* his Purple Heart," said Sergeant Murillo. "And I'm gonna invite him and his partner to meet me at Hamburger Hamlet for code seven tonight. Where I'll buy them any goddamn thing they want."

Lieutenant O'Reilley never asked Sergeant Murillo about the buck knife again.

Back when Viv Daley and Georgie Adams had first been partnered, Sergeant Murillo had taken her aside in the sergeants' room and said, "I know that Adams is an acquired taste. I was wondering if you're happy working with him?"

Viv Daley said, "Sarge, I wouldn't trade him for anybody at Hollywood Station. When the Gypsy's got your back, a girl couldn't

be more safe at a sleepover in the Lincoln Bedroom." Then she added, "Except for when Bill Clinton lived there."

Viv and Georgie drove to Louis Dryden's apartment building on Franklin Avenue and slid the detective's business card in the jamb of Dryden's front door where he couldn't miss it, then began patrol and cleared for calls. While driving eastbound on Hollywood Boulevard on the way to their area, they saw that the Street Characters were out in force in front of Grauman's Chinese Theatre. The recession had brought hard times to even some of the costumed performers, who posed for photos with tourists and received voluntary tips for it. They were not allowed by law to panhandle or make demands of the tourists.

Newscasters gleefully reported to their audiences whenever tensions arose around the Grauman's forecourt, where the handprints and footprints of famous movie stars were set in the cement pavement. On a recent occasion, Elmo the Muppet had been arrested for aggressive panhandling, and so had the dark-hooded character from *Scream*. Street Character Freddy Krueger was also busted for taking his role too seriously and allegedly stabbing someone. Mr. Incredible had been jailed, as had Batman and Chewbacca from *Star Wars*. So far, the several Darth Vaders had behaved themselves, but Spider-Man, or rather one of several using that costume, got popped by Hollywood cops for slugging somebody.

As 6-X-76 passed Grauman's, Georgie Adams said, "I'm gonna be real disappointed if SpongeBob SquarePants ever gets busted for something. I always liked him on TV."

"I never much liked Spider-Man," Viv said. "Too creepy. Crawling around like an insect and all that."

"Let's make a pass by that apartment house we're supposed to check," Georgie said. "Then I can log it and get it over with. Sounds like it's just a PR job the detectives are foisting off on us poor overworked bluesuits."

In the last of the daylight, when the summer sun was settling down behind the Pacific Ocean, giving Hollywood its special rosy glow, the old apartment building in Little Armenia looked impregnable to the officers of 6-X-76.

"This is bullshit," Georgie Adams said. "Real-estate guys like Dryden don't kill their squeezes themselves. They hire it done. He'd just find an Eighteenth Streeter or some other local crusier and put a ticket on her."

"The detectives said he's supposed to be into crystal meth," Viv reminded him. "A desperate guy on ice might do anything when he gets all spun out."

"Anyways," Georgie said, "even Spider-Man himself couldn't get in there."

"Spider-Man," Viv said, mulling it over. She then drove around to the alley behind the building and parked by the attached carport.

"What're you looking for, sis?" Georgie wanted to know.

"Any sign of a trail from his web-shooter," Viv said with a sly smile. "I think old sticky foot *could* get into her apartment."

"How?"

"There," she said, pointing to the neighboring apartment building.

The building was in the process of being renovated and reroofed before the winter rains came. An eight-foot temporary chain-link fence was all that secured the construction site. Rolls of tar paper and shingles were visible inside the fence where workers had left them, along with two aluminum extension ladders.

"So?" Georgie said.

Viv said, "He could climb over the fence and borrow one of those extension ladders."

"So?" Georgie said. "She's on the third floor. Most ladders don't go that high unless you're a firefighter on a truck."

Viv said, "He could use the ladder to get onto the carport roof and then pull it up and extend it high enough to do the job."

"You got some imagination, sis," Georgie said. "But there's no accessible window over the carports."

"But from that point he could get clear to the roof of the building."

"Then what?" Georgie said. "He goes down her chimney? News flash, sis. There ain't no chimneys."

"I noticed the small window on the south side," Viv said. "She keeps it wide open. I'll bet there's no AC in that little place and she needs ventilation. He could scoot to the edge of that flat roof on his belly, lower his legs down in front of the open window, and swing right into her apartment."

"Like a spider?" Georgie said mischievously.

"Like a meth-crazed, desperate tweaker," Viv said. "With all those paranoid tweaker thoughts spinning through his head."

"That's probably the kitchen window there on the south side," Georgie said. "I'll bet it's over the sink. If he went in there, he'd land in her garbage disposal and she could just turn it on and flush that fucking spider right down the drain."

"You are *such* an asshole, Gypsy," Viv said, poking him in the shoulder when her partner showed her his wicked little grin.

Despite Georgie's protests, Viv managed to find time to drive by the apartment building and check out the alley two more times.

On their last check of the evening, Georgie Adams shined the spotlight on the graffiti sprayed on the stucco wall of the building on the alley side. There were gang slogans and the letters *AP* for "Armenian Power" written large.

Georgie said, "At least the Armenian cruisers respect education. All their graffiti is spelled right."

At 9:15 P.M. on that moonless night, when the smog and overcast blowing in from the ocean hung low over the Los Angeles basin, there was a ruckus on Hollywood Boulevard that brought four of the midwatch units responding. Catwoman, who had tried in vain to

look like Halle Berry, head-butted Superman for muscling in on her tourist tips and knocked him right on his ass in Grauman's forecourt. The boozy superhero ended up dazed on John Wayne's boot prints and yelled to everyone that he was going to murder Catwoman.

This Superman was not one of the younger Street Characters and didn't much resemble the movie version's. He had a nose full of broken veins, and a double chin, and was starting to get a middle-aged paunch that his costume with all the built-in muscles couldn't hide. When he got to his feet, he lurched at the plucky Catwoman, who held her ground with claws extended. But then Marilyn Monroe, who was actually a forty-year-old transvestite named Melvin Pickett, came to Catwoman's aid.

Superman grabbed Catwoman, who fought back and tried to kick him in the groin. When Superman drew back a fist, Marilyn Monroe stepped in and belted Superman across the mouth with her leather purse, which was heavy with rolls of quarters she'd collected for the Sunset Strip Beautification Project. There was a major donnybrook going on by the time the first black-and-whites arrived.

Six-A-Fifteen from Watch 3 showed up before any of the midwatch units, and that turned out to be unfortunate for Superman. The cop driving 6-A-15 was Preston Lilly, who'd served thirty-five years with the LAPD, twenty-two of them at Hollywood Station. He was a large, square-shouldered man with a massive shaved skull the color of old ivory. His eyes were gray and spaced too far apart, making them seem out of sync when aimed in your direction. Some people said that looking into the face of Preston Lilly was like looking at an enormous pale eel. He had already decided to retire before the end of the year, and he was sick of working 6-A-15 because he was always getting bullshit calls to the rich whiners in the Hollywood Hills.

"You can never make them Hills dwellers happy," Preston Lilly complained to his partner, a Cuban immigrant named Mario Delgado. "A bunch of guys with too much money and a bunch of

trophy wives with too much time on their hands. They like to bitch just for the sake of bitching."

The phlegmatic Cuban just shrugged and said, "Better than working down in Watts, *'mano*." He had recently transferred to Hollywood Division from Southeast Division. Then he added, "We got to take some shit from the *jotos* in the Hills. They might be friends of the chief. Or maybe the mayor. That's the way life is."

"I own my own pink slip," Preston Lilly said. "My pension's vested. I could commit murder and they'd still have to send my pension checks to me at San Quentin. And I already filed my retirement papers, so nobody better fuck with me, in the Hills or in the flats. I got nothing to lose, *compadre*."

Superman found that out when Preston Lilly stepped in to break up the tussle. Because Marilyn Monroe was sober, she'd been able to get a good choke hold on the larger Street Character, and Superman was sitting on Grauman's forecourt with his back to Marilyn, who had him in not only a choke hold but also a scissors grip, with her shaved legs around his waist. The Incredible Hulk, a gentle soul who hated violence of any kind, had picked up Marilyn Monroe's purse and was guarding it and pleading in vain for the combatants to stop fighting.

Marilyn Monroe's platinum blond wig got twisted askew at the start of the fight and the hair was hanging in her face like a sheepdog's. Her white dress was ripped open all the way down the side and had been torn off one shoulder. A large falsie had popped up out of her bra and was resting on Superman's shoulder like an inverted cereal bowl. The panty hose on both of Marilyn's legs was shredded, and her open-toed three-inch spikes were now without heels. And while Superman sat helpless, Catwoman pounded his face with relatively ineffectual blows that nevertheless made him howl in drunken rage.

"You're dead!" he screamed. "When I get up, I'm killing you, you nigger cunt!"

"You gotta get up first, peckerwood!" she yelled back, and socked him in the eye with her little fist.

The first thing that Officer Preston Lilly did was grab Catwoman by the arm and flick her away from the brawlers. Then he said, "Cease and desist, Ms. Monroe! And you, too, Man of Steel!"

Meanwhile, there were hundreds of tourists watching, whistling, howling like coyotes, and it seemed like every single one of them was snapping photos.

Marilyn Monroe released her scissors hold as well as the choke hold and she stumbled to her feet with one shoe missing now. When Preston Lilly took Superman by the arm to drag him to his feet, the still boozy Street Character said, "Take your hands off me, you bald-headed pig fucker!"

"I don't like your mouth," Preston Lilly said. "You better lock it up."

Superman answered that by spitting on Preston Lilly.

The big cop looked down and saw the spittle dripping from his LAPD badge onto the blue uniform shirt pocket and running down to the pewter pocket button.

Mario Delgado saw Preston Lilly instinctively ball his huge right fist, but the little Cuban stepped in fast and said, "Whoa, partner! You're being watched by three hundred witnesses and about a hundred of them might be hostile."

That made the Cuban cop take charge of things and grab one of Superman's arms, and then both cops got Superman's hands cuffed behind his back.

Marilyn Monroe held up a heel-less shoe and yelled to Superman in her natural baritone voice, "I paid three hundred bucks for my Louis Vuitton's and that was a sale price, you sleazy turd! I'm suing your sorry ass!"

The arriving midwatch units got things under control, and after making the milling throngs move along, they began interviewing the other Street Characters who had witnessed the fracas. Preston

Lilly walked Superman to their shop and strapped him in the backseat, then got behind the wheel to await his partner.

Mario Delgado was busy talking to Flotsam and Jetsam, who were trying to help Marilyn Monroe get what was left of her white dress pinned up enough to cover her pantie girdle. It was then that Superman, bitching that he was the real victim and that Preston Lilly was a fascist swine, hacked up a big loogie and spit it through the caged partition of the police car right onto the shaved skull of Officer Preston Lilly.

Mario Delgado was shocked when he turned and saw Preston Lilly suddenly start up the engine of the black-and-white and heard him yell, "Catch a ride back to the station, partner! I gotta get Superman outta here!"

The black-and-white squealed away from the curb and was gone. Just like that.

"What the hell?" the baffled Cuban cop said to Flotsam, who replied, "Dude, I think Preston don't want any witnesses."

Nearly forty minutes later, Mario Delgado paced anxiously in the parking lot of Hollywood Station, but still his partner and Superman had not appeared. He went inside and up to the lunchroom, where he bought a soda from the machine and then joined Hollywood Nate and Snuffy Salcedo in the report room.

The Cuban cop was not finished with his soda when they all heard yammering coming from the passageway leading from the parking lot door. Mario Delgado and Nate and Snuffy all ran out of the report room and found Preston Lilly walking the handcuffed superhero to the holding tank, where he put him inside, removed the handcuffs, and pushed him down onto the bench. He closed the door, but everyone could still see Superman through the shatterproof window, and he kept hollering. They could also see that there wasn't a mark on his very flushed face other than the small abrasions he'd received in the fight.

Sergeant Murillo left the sergeants' room to come and see what

the yelling was all about, and when Superman saw the chevrons on his sleeves, he hollered, "Sergeant, I demand to make a citizen's complaint! I've been tortured! It was worse than waterboarding!"

Preston Lilly looked at Sergeant Murillo and said, "That's preposterous."

Superman jumped up from the bench and ran to the glass window, yelling, "That skinhead Nazi took me to the Hollywood Freeway on-ramp and got out and grabbed my hair and pulled my head through the open window. And he rolled it up until I was trapped by the neck. There I was with my hands cuffed behind my back and my head hanging out, and he drove a hundred goddamn miles an hour for I don't know how long and I was screaming the whole time for him to stop! It woulda been better if he'd just tied me to the hood like a fucking road-killed deer!"

Sergeant Murillo looked at Preston Lilly, who said, "Go ahead and cut paper, Sarge. I'm at the end of my career, where I can take the safety off and tell the captain what I think. Or the bureau commander. Or the fucking chief of police, for that matter. I'm bulletproof now. But as far as what Superman says? It's preposterous."

Superman said, "Sergeant, I swear to you. When I begged for mercy, all he did was drive faster. I could hardly breathe. And do you know what he said? He floored it all the way and he yells to me, 'Nobody's whupping on you, Superman. I'm just letting your own lips beat you to death.' That's what he said."

Preston Lilly looked at Superman and at Sergeant Murillo and said, "That's preposterous."

Sergeant Murillo said to the big cop, "Preston, do what you can to move up your retirement date. And until you go, please leave the safety on."

EIGHT

JUST AFTER MIDNIGHT Cindy Kroll heard a scraping sound on the roof. Her first thought was that some crows were up there pecking at the composite material that was designed to look like wood. She had fed her baby daughter some applesauce and bottle-fed her infant son before lying down on the bed in her T-shirt and underpants. It was so hot, she was just trying to catch some breeze from the open windows, and she had not intended to go to sleep yet, but she had dozed. The wine she'd had earlier while watching TV had done it.

She reminded herself that she had to cut down on the wine and she was dying to smoke some crystal, but she knew she had to kick it. Then she remembered that her daughter had fallen asleep in the playpen and that she had to get up and put her in her crib. Her son was lying beside her asleep, and she looked at him. She thought he resembled his father, Louis Dryden. She didn't mind that. Louis was a good-looking man even if he—

Her thoughts were interrupted when she heard more scraping on the roof above her apartment. And then a cup fell from the sink in her kitchen and broke on the floor. And then all the dishes from the drainboard crashed to the floor, and her first thought was, Earthquake! Then she heard footsteps coming toward her bedroom.

*   *   *

The code 3 call came after the three warning beeps over the police radio. Then the RTO at Communications Division said, "All units in the vicinity and Six-A-Forty-nine, a woman screaming."

When they heard the address of the call that was given to a Watch 3 unit, Viv Daley said, "That's the Kroll address!"

Six-X-Seventy-six was very close to the location and jumped the call, arriving in less than three minutes. Georgie was out before Viv even brought the Crown Vic to a stop, and they both ran to the front door, standing in a wash of illumination from the security lights overhead.

The front entrance was well secured by a set of heavy wooden doors that opened out, and there was a small panel of double-glazed window in each door. The lobby inside was lit but there was no sign of the watchman that they were told would be there. They could see a door inside the lobby with a sign that said "Manager," but it was closed.

And then they saw Cindy Kroll. She was staggering down the staircase toward the lobby, wearing only the T-shirt and cotton underwear. The T-shirt was blood-drenched and ripped open, and her chest bones glistened in the light. She reached the lobby floor, lurched from side to side, and dropped to her knees. A man wearing a black hoodie sweatshirt and black jeans ran down the stairs, a knife raised high over his head, yelling something unintelligible at the fallen woman as he tried to stab her again.

He may never have seen the orange fireballs coming at him or heard the explosions, but Viv Daley and Georgie Adams fired a total of thirteen rounds from their .40 caliber Glocks through the glass panels in the doors. Two of Georgie's rounds hit Louis Dryden, one in the hip and one under the left eye. Three of Viv's rounds got him in the shoulder and chest.

Lights went on all over the apartment building and in the building next door, as well as in a private residence across the street.

Viv Daley yelled through the broken glass, "Open this door! Somebody come open this door!"

"Police!" Georgie Adams yelled, kicking the double doors twice. Open it!"

Then through the broken window panels they saw an elderly man emerge in terror from the manager's office. He stepped over the body of Cindy Kroll and yelled to the police, "Don't shoot! I'm the watchman!"

He opened the door and began babbling. When he became intelligible, he said, "I heard her scream once and I called you right away! But you got here so fast, somebody on the third floor must've called first! And a few minutes later I heard her screaming again but this time it sounded like she was coming down the stairs and a man was also screaming curses and he was coming down and I got scared and locked my door!"

Georgie Adams shined his streamlight onto Louis Dryden's face and saw the entry wound clearly. He holstered his pistol and grabbed his rover, calling for a rescue ambulance for Cindy Kroll. He also reported the officer-involved shooting that would bring dozens of people to the apartment building before the night ended.

Viv Daley turned Cindy Kroll onto her back in case CPR was possible. But the young woman's chest was slashed wide open, exposing her breastbone. When Viv saw that Cindy Kroll's eyes were open and her mouth was twisted into a rictus of violent death, she didn't bother to feel for a pulse.

Viv looked at her partner, who averted his eyes from hers, and he said to her, "You better check on the babies. I'll secure the scene here."

Viv's heart was hammering when she got to the landing of the third floor. She felt dry-mouthed and light-headed, and she could hardly believe that she had just fired her weapon outside the police pistol range. Though it was her first time, it had happened so fast

and there had been such an adrenaline surge that she hadn't had time to feel much fright. But she was feeling it now.

She held up her hand, and in the light from the third-floor hallway the hand looked palsied. She had a streamlight in her other hand, and when she got to the door, she found it wide open. There was no sound from within and she was suddenly more afraid than she'd ever been in her life.

Viv put her hand on her pistol grip, but it wasn't for personal safety. The hand was acting reflexively, doing what a cop's hand does in moments of fear. Any personal threat to her was past, yet she was weak and feeling nausea from the overwhelming fright sweeping over her, from dread of what she might find in there.

Viv Daley crept into the apartment. She stepped gingerly into the cluttered living room and was so instantly relieved that her legs almost buckled. The thirteen-month-old was safe in her playpen, her face tear-streaked but she wasn't crying now. She wore a white jersey with a pink duck on the front, and a diaper, and she was sitting and staring at a brown teddy bear on the floor of the playpen as though in a daze.

"Hello, sweetie," Viv said to the little girl, who turned and looked at her in confusion.

Then Viv rushed hopefully into the bedroom and found the baby boy. He was wearing only a diaper and was dangling from the upper rail of the crib from a cord to a cell phone charger that had been tied around his neck. His face was purple and his eyes were shut tight.

"No!" Viv shouted, not even aware that she'd spoken.

She jerked the cord from the crib and her fingers slipped twice before she untied it from where it was digging into the soft flesh of the infant's neck, and she said, "I knew it! I knew it!"

And then she thought, This baby's dead. What am I doing? This is a crime scene and this baby's dead!

Still, she lifted the infant, thinking, He's so light. He's so small. She put the baby into the crib, and for no reason she could later

fathom, she covered him to his wounded neck with his cotton blanket.

Viv stared at the dead baby and thought, All evening I imagined this. I knew Dryden could get in from the roof. I knew it. Why didn't I act on it? Why didn't I push the boss for a stakeout? What kind of cop am I?

The baby girl in the next room started crying then and was standing, holding on to the playpen rail. Viv went to her and picked her up, and she looked at Viv in shock and confusion and said, "Mommy."

The toddler wrapped her arms around Viv's neck, and Viv felt the silky blond hair against her cheek, and the child said it again: "Mommy."

Viv said, "Hush, baby, hush." And she began rocking her back and forth and didn't hear Sergeant Murillo, who appeared behind her along with Snuffy Salcedo and Hollywood Nate, who remained in the hallway, looking in through the open door.

Viv was a lot calmer now and she said in a monotone to her sergeant, "In there. I found the baby hanging by the neck from the crib rail. I hoped he might still be alive so I took him down. But of course he wasn't. I put him to bed."

Sergeant Murillo looked at her and entered the bedroom for only a moment before he returned.

He said quietly to Viv, "Don't touch anything else. A homicide team and SID will be here very soon to process the scene, and FID's also on the way. They'll separate you and Adams and it'll be a very long night of questions, from FID especially, but this is obviously an in-policy shooting, so I don't want you to stress over it. Just tell them exactly how it went down."

"I knew this might happen," Viv said quietly to Sergeant Murillo. "It's almost like I could see him coming in from the roof."

After hesitating, Sergeant Murillo looked at his officer and said in an even quieter voice, "Adams told me all about that, and yes,

the ladder's still in place on the carport roof where the dead man left it. But you didn't know this would happen. It was just what-if speculation on your part. The place looked perfectly secure. You don't have a crystal ball. Nobody could've anticipated this, Viv. You can't blame yourself. The dead guy's to blame. Nobody else."

Viv Daley put the tot in the playpen and she immediately began crying and held her arms out to Viv saying, "Mommy, Mommy."

"She thinks you're her mommy," Sergeant Murillo said. "Dear lord."

Snuffy Salcedo, still in the common hallway with Hollywood Nate, said, "Jesus Christ. This is too awful."

Nate said nothing and Snuffy turned and went downstairs.

"I gotta get outta here," Viv said to Sergeant Murillo.

"Viv," he said. "You and your partner will have to be separated while you wait for FID. We're gonna see a lot of people around here in a little while. We'll transport the little girl."

When Viv got to the doorway, Hollywood Nate stood aside for her. She turned once to look back at the child in the playpen who held out her arms to Viv and between sobs said more urgently, "Mommy!"

Viv descended the stairwell to the lobby floor and found four cops from Watch 3 keeping neighbors away from the crime scene tape. Snuffy Salcedo was talking to Flotsam and Jetsam, who were in the street directing traffic and waving the criminalists' van from SID into a parking space. Several of the uniformed cops whispered to one another, an indication that word had spread quickly about what Viv Daley had found in the third-floor apartment.

Flotsam said somberly to Jetsam, "Dude, remember how the Oracle always told us that doing good police work was the most fun we'd ever have in our entire lives?"

Jetsam said, "Yeah, and Viv and Georgie did *real* good police work when they lit up that fucking maniac."

"True," Flotsam said, "but I don't think this night's going on their desktop in the category of fun."

Georgie was standing on the sidewalk outside the tape with the watch commander, Lieutenant O'Reilly, who was awaiting the imminent arrival of homicide detectives and the administrative team from Force Investigation Division, as well as the coroner's body snatchers. But when he saw Viv emerge from the building, he left the lieutenant and approached her.

She looked at her partner, at the anxiety in his eyes, and Georgie said to her, "I never thought it could happen, sis. Honest to god, I never thought for a second that anything like this could happen."

"Please, Gypsy, shut the fuck up," Viv Daley said.

NINE

RALEIGH DIBBLE WENT to work for the Bruegers two weeks after his employment interview, and Leona Brueger was so pleased with him that she decided to leave with Rudy Ressler for Tuscany the following week. Julius Hampton did not attempt to sabotage the job for his employee despite his disappointment and irritation at losing Raleigh on such short notice. When Leona's attorney phoned Julius Hampton for a reference, the old man truthfully said that Raleigh had been a splendid butler, cook, driver, and companion. He added that he hated to lose Raleigh but he could not compete with the money that Leona was offering.

The thing that clinched it with Leona Brueger was Raleigh's work in the kitchen. He demonstrated what he could do during an impromptu luncheon for Leona and a few friends, including Rudy Ressler. Raleigh prepared a simple coq au vin, minus the diced pork in case anyone had religious dietary issues. Leona Brueger's Guatemalan housekeeper and cook, Marta Sandoval, was sixty-six years old and planning to retire anyway, since the house was going to be put on the market. She told Leona Brueger that she was not jealous of the new man and was delighted to receive three months' severance pay. She planned on moving to the home of her eldest daughter in East Los Angeles.

Raleigh decided during that impromptu luncheon that Julius

Hampton had been right about Rudy Ressler. The schmuck actually complained that Raleigh's quiche appetizer had a "pinch" too much salt in it.

Pinch this, you phony, Raleigh thought, but replied, "I'm so sorry, sir. Can I get you anything else? A fruit and cheese plate, perhaps? A few sips of delicate Chablis with a hint of strawberry will cleanse any salt from your palate. May I get you a glass?"

Raleigh went to the butler's pantry and poured the director a glass of screw-top Chardonnay that he used for cooking and placed it before the director, saying, "It's an amusing little Chablis, sir. The hint of strawberry is balanced by an essence of mint, I believe."

Rudy Ressler passed the glass under his nose, sampled a tiny sip, and said, "Yes, I can taste the strawberry and the mint, but it's not overpowering." He sipped again and said, "That's a fine choice, Raleigh. Thank you."

Raleigh Dibble was willing to put up with just about anything in that house, especially after Leona Breuger promised him an unspecified bonus when she returned from Tuscany. She told him that she would then begin preparing the house for what she called "the big fall sale of Casa Brueger." Nigel Wickland told Raleigh that when she felt the urge, Leona Brueger could be "crazily generous" and that the bonus might be substantial.

Raleigh didn't even mind Leona Brueger's eighty-seven-year-old brother-in-law, Marty Brueger, who stayed in the guest cottage almost all of the time, watching the E! network with his dentures in a glass beside his chair grinning at him. The wizened old coot never so much as entered the main house unless he was looking for whiskey, so Raleigh tried to make sure that the liquor cabinet in the cottage was well stocked.

Marty Brueger was shrunken from age and spinal stenosis, and he spent most of his time in his chair with his legs elevated on a pillow. Marty had a nest of wiry hair with some surprising sprouts of black growing among the dull gray strands. He wore thick glasses

that made his brown eyes appear enormous and he looked like an ancient frazzled parrot. Leona Brueger told Raleigh that her brother-in-law had been an energetic skirt chaser until recent years, and his uncontrolled libido had been the cause of expensive paternity lawsuits when he was a young man, and sexual harassment lawsuits when he got old.

She said to Raleigh, "Just make sure Marty has some T and A videos to look at and good whiskey to drink, and he'll be no trouble."

One of the first things the old man said to Raleigh was "Can you make good chili? Since Chasen's closed down, nobody in this goddamn town can make a decent bowl of chili. I miss Dave and Maud Chasen like I miss my prostate."

"Mr. Brueger," Raleigh said, "you're in luck. Back when I was in college, I worked one summer as a busboy at Chasen's. I kept my eyes open and my palate on high alert. My chili won't disappoint you."

Of course it was a complete lie, but Raleigh had made enough chili in his day that he figured he could please the geezer, and he did.

Raleigh had everything well under control by the time Leona Brueger and Rudy Ressler actually left for Italy. Marta Sandoval stayed on for only two days after her employer was gone, which was just long enough to tidy up the house and change all the towels and bed linens. With the help of two grandsons, she moved all of her clothes and belongings from the housekeeper's quarters to a rented van, and she was gone. And then, with Marty Brueger tucked away in the cottage most of the time, Raleigh Dibble had the entire Brueger estate to himself, and it was sweet.

The security system was sophisticated but Raleigh learned it easily enough. The outside lights and video cameras were elaborate and took a bit of practice. He only had to take Marty Brueger to dinner two times in the first two weeks, once to Musso and Frank,

of course, and then to the Formosa Café. The elderly Hollywood rich still loved the few old hangouts remaining. Raleigh was sure that the Polo Lounge at the Beverly Hills Hotel would be on the itinerary as soon as the old boy remembered clearly that he'd once loved their Neil McCarthy salad.

Marty bored Raleigh with personal anecdotes about all the celebrities in the caricature drawings on the walls of the Formosa Café, but Raleigh figured they were lies. He deduced that Marty Brueger was just the slacker sibling of an older brother who had made sure his kid brother was taken care of in old age. Still, Marty Brueger was even less trouble to care for than Julius Hampton had been, so Raleigh had no complaints, and he indulged the old man as much as possible.

Raleigh lived contentedly for nearly a month, and then one evening he got a call from Nigel Wickland. Nigel asked if Raleigh could meet him in Beverly Hills at Nic's on North Canon Drive for some "filet mignon with blueberries."

When Raleigh responded, "Puh-leeeze, Nigel, are you serious?" the art dealer said, "All right, never mind the trendy food. We'll just have a martini or two and a plate of their crispy onions. Meet me there at five thirty."

The guy was a mystery, Raleigh thought, and just about impossible to predict. Nigel had gotten him this great gig with the Bruegers, yet he hadn't wanted any thanks or favors in return. Now there was clearly a sense of urgency in the art dealer's latest invitation. Before he left for the meeting, Raleigh walked out of the main house to the cottage and made sure that Marty Brueger was contentedly watching his big-screen TV.

"I'm going grocery shopping," he said to the old man. "I'll make you a nice supper when I get back."

"Before you go, take the video out and put in the one on the shelf," Marty Brueger croaked. "I think I like *Keeping Up With the Kardashians* even more than *The Girls Next Door,* don't you? And

stop at the liquor store and pick up a bottle of Jameson's Irish whiskey. Get me the rare stuff that costs two hundred bucks a bottle. Just tell them to bill it to Leona."

"Certainly, Mr. Brueger," Raleigh said. "I won't be long."

Raleigh made sure that every door in the main house was locked and then set the alarm and video cameras. He had permission to drive the Mercedes SL550, which Leona Brueger called her "run-around town" car, so he decided to take it instead of his old Toyota. He liked the way the car hugged the road as he drove down from the Hollywood Hills on his way to Nic's on North Canon Drive.

Raleigh found Nigel Wickland waiting in the Martini Lounge and he looked agitated. There was a busy late-afternoon crowd, and Nigel was sitting at a table sipping a vodka martini instead of his usual daiquiri. The art dealer's bonhomie wasn't on display this time when he motioned Raleigh to sit.

"Did you get caught in traffic?" Nigel asked, as though annoyed.

"No, but I had to lock up and see that Mr. Brueger was okay," Raleigh said. "I'm only twenty minutes late."

"Perfectly all right, "Nigel said quickly.

For once, he wasn't sartorially turned out like the Savile Row snobs that Raleigh had despised during his London days. Nigel was wearing a gray seersucker jacket that needed cleaning and a slightly wrinkled white dress shirt open at the throat.

After Raleigh's drink arrived Nigel said, "How old are you, Raleigh?"

Raleigh sipped and said, "What's this all about?"

"I'm older than I look," Nigel Wickland said. "I'm sixty-four years old."

No, you look it, Raleigh thought. The art dealer had a faint scar running behind his ear that Raleigh hadn't noticed before. He's had work done, but he still looks his age, Raleigh thought. Then he said to Nigel, "I'm fifty-eight."

"It's hell when you know you're growing old and can't afford it," Nigel said. "It's frightening, isn't it?"

"What do you mean, 'can't afford it'?"

Nigel said, "You're making a good wage with the Bruegers, but, Raleigh, it's going to end in a few months. They're not taking you with them when they move to their vineyard in Napa. You'll be out of work again."

"No, I didn't see myself as a grape picker in Napa," Raleigh said, a bit insulted. "I expect I'll get by in life without sitting at a stoplight with a sign saying, 'Will Butler for Food.' I'll find another position. I'll get by."

"Aren't you tired of just getting by?" Nigel Wickland was so intense that Raleigh hesitated.

Then Raleigh said, "Maybe I'll find me a Leona Brueger and marry her like that weasel Rudy Ressler is doing. Or maybe I'll win a big lottery."

Nigel Wickland showed Raleigh a patronizing smile, ran his fingers nervously through his mane of white hair, and said, "Be realistic, Raleigh."

Raleigh drained his glass and said, "You be realistic, Nigel. Or more to the point, be straightforward. What're you getting at?"

Nigel Wickland picked up his cocktail napkin and dabbed at his mouth, at the bead of sweat that had popped out above his upper lip. In fact, Raleigh saw, there was sweat forming on his brow as well. Then he said, "I'm in financial trouble, Raleigh. This fucking recession is killing my business. I may have to let Ruth go and I don't know how long I can keep the bloody doors open."

"Sorry to hear that," Raleigh said as Nigel signaled for a round of fresh drinks.

"You and I," Nigel said, "we could help each other. We could form a ... partnership and help each other."

"What kind of partnership?"

"You could make more money than you've ever imagined," Nigel Wickland said.

"I tried that," Raleigh said. "And did eight months at Lompoc in a room with lots of guys you wouldn't care for at all."

Then, with a burst of words spoken so fast that it took Raleigh a moment to comprehend, Nigel Wickland said, "I just want you to let me into the house some afternoon for an hour or two. I'll need you to turn off the video cameras and let me in unseen. And you can help me for a few minutes and then go tend to Marty Brueger in his cottage until I'm ready to go."

After digesting the import of the art dealer's words, Raleigh said, "For this I'm going to make more money than I've ever dreamed of? And what do I tell the police when you steal her jewelry or whatever it is that you have in mind, Nigel? Do I tell them that a home invader came in with guns blazing, or what?"

Nigel Wickland said, "I just want to photograph two of her paintings."

"Photograph her paintings?"

"Yes, I've had some experience with photography and I think I can do it. All I'll have to do is return one more time two weeks later for about another hour, and that's it."

"I think you've been drinking too many of those martinis, Nigel," Raleigh said. "You're not making sense."

"It's about a painting switch," Nigel said. "I know of a custom lab owned by a sweet young man with whom I once had an understanding. He has mild Asperger's syndrome and can hardly manage to shake hands whenever we meet, but he's a marvel at what he does in a photo laboratory. I can shoot two of the Brueger paintings with a digital camera and get the proportions exactly correct. Then I can take the disc to him, and I guarantee you that he will produce an enlargement on poster board to the precise measurement of the paintings in Leona Brueger's house. It will cost me three thousand dollars but he's already promised that if he gets his

money up front, he can get the work done in a fortnight, no questions asked." Then Nigel added, "That's two weeks."

"I know what a fortnight is, Nigel," Raleigh said. "I had the misfortune of working one summer in London at a bistro near the King's Cross tube station, and it was a misery. But I still don't know what you're talking about."

"We must have a chin-wag about dear old London town sometime," Nigel said. "Anyway, I shall have to return to the Brueger house another time after that."

"I don't like that next part," Raleigh said. "The part I now see coming."

"I'll need access again to replace the paintings with my photocopies on poster board, fitting them into the existing frames. And then I'll be on my way with the originals. No harm, no foul, as your basketball fans love to say."

"You're talking like a wack job," Raleigh said. "Whadda you mean, no harm?" Realizing that his diction was slipping, Raleigh lowered his voice and said, "You're talking about entering her house and stealing her paintings!"

"She's an ignorant arriviste, like most of my clients," Nigel retorted. "She cares nothing about Sammy Brueger's art or *any* art. She told me that she wouldn't mind if the house burned to the ground with all the paintings in it. Everything is insured to the hilt."

"And what the hell happens to me when she figures it all out and calls the police?"

"She won't figure it out, Raleigh," Nigel Wickland said. "She's culturally ignorant. She barely looks at any of her art, and I can promise you that only a close inspection by an expert could detect the switch. That may happen a few years from now when she bothers to take the paintings from the storage facility where they're going. She's told me they'll all be stored when she moves away from the house, and I guarantee you that's where they'll stay for a very

long time because she doesn't care about any of them. In fact, she's commissioning me to box each piece and personally supervise the trucking transfer to her preferred storage facility."

"Hellooo!" Raleigh said. "So what happens when she does get around to collecting them and maybe putting them up for auction with some art dealer like you? Somebody'll spot the switch for sure!"

"That's the beauty of my idea," Nigel Wickland said. "After they're crated and ready to leave Casa Brueger, I'm going to make sure that the crate containing the switched paintings is a different manufacture from all the other crates, and that the crate shows subtle signs of having been tampered with. The people who transfer these things are just ordinary truckers who will notice nothing. When the switch is finally discovered years from now, the theft will be blamed on someone who works at, or has access to, the storage facility. Leona will collect from the insurance policy and nobody will be harmed except for the insurer, and when has anyone felt sorry for insurance carriers? It's foolproof, Raleigh."

Raleigh was silent for a moment and then said, "How much money could the paintings bring? Realistically."

"They could be sold easily in Copenhagen, Stockholm, Bern, or even Berlin. I've personally contacted a discreet European auctioneer who believes he can get at least six hundred thousand U.S. dollars for *The Woman by the Water*. The other piece of Impressionist art that I have my eye on is called *Flowers on the Hillside,* and he assured me that it should bring an equal amount. Raleigh, you and I will be dividing at least a million dollars after expenses. Tax-free! No more tending to dotty old men for you. And enough money for me that I can perhaps keep my gallery open until this goddamn recession ends. Plus there's a special bonus for me in that these two wonderful pieces of art will end up with someone who truly appreciates them and not with some vulgarians in the Hollywood Hills."

"Half a million," Raleigh said, and the sound of it brought a

catch in his throat. When he spoke again he said, "When did you find out about me, Nigel?"

"Find out what?"

"That I'm an ex-convict. Someone who might seriously listen to your 'foolproof plan'?"

"The first night we met," Nigel Wickland admitted. "When you were gone to the gents, Julius Hampton talked about you. He said that you'd had a bit of difficulty with the law and had been in prison. You see, Raleigh, he had a background investigation done by a private investigator when he hired you. Perhaps you didn't know that."

Raleigh was quiet for a long moment, and then he said, "Nobody accepts an ex-con at face value. They all have to dig, and distrust you, and pay you less than they'd pay somebody who's ten times worse but never got caught. Someone who's done lots worse things than not paying enough of the taxes that the government gouges you with."

"I know how ex-convicts get shat on," Nigel Wickland said, putting his manicured fingers on the back of Raleigh's hand and patting sympathetically. "So yes, I confess that I did think you might be more amenable to my idea than the average person would be. But I could also see immediately that you were a man with imagination and ambition."

"Now you're going too far, Nigel," Raleigh said. "Quit while you're ahead."

"You look a bit peaky," Nigel Wickland said, eyes widening. "Are you in, then?"

"If this goes sideways and I get busted, I'm ratting you out to the police and making the best deal I can for myself," Raleigh Dibble warned. "You better understand that up front."

"Fair enough," said Nigel Wickland. "I'm not worried, Raleigh. Not at all."

"You will be if you end up inside with lots of other guys who

had foolproof plans," Raleigh said. "And state prison, where we'll go, is a lot worse than Club Fed, where I did my time. In a state lockup you'll learn to sleep on your back with one eye open." Looking at Nigel Wickland, he added, "But maybe you're not so scared of that part."

"That was unnecessary, Raleigh," Nigel Wickland said. "Homophobic humor is beneath you."

TEN

"Up, up. get the fuck up!" Jonas Claymore said to Megan Burke, who had been awake most of the night, vomiting.

It was 10:30 A.M. and she was exhausted, and still suffering from withdrawal aches even though Jonas had taken the last $100 from his checking account and bought them half an ox. They divided and smoked it late in the evening after dining on a Fatburger that neither of them really wanted.

"I don't feel well," Megan said, lying on the double bed they shared, her makeup from last night smeared all over her face.

She looked like a blow-up doll that somebody had let the air out of, he thought. She looked like the corpse in one of those slasher movies, where the guy with the knife likes to paint their dead faces. Jesus! How did he get himself into this relationship?

"We gotta do some work today," he said. "We're dead broke."

Megan dragged herself into a sitting position, feet on the floor, and said, "I'll get another waitress job as soon as I feel better."

"Don't try to clown me," he said. "You ain't gonna feel better till you stop jonesing. And you ain't gonna stop jonesing till you give up the beans and norcos and perks. Because you can't handle any of it."

She yawned twice and said, "And you can, I suppose."

"I'm a recreational user," Jonas said. "I know my limits. But you? You're all smoked out."

"Sure," Megan said, shuffling across the bedroom to the bathroom. She sat down and continued, "You're always in control, aren't you?"

"That's disgusting," Jonas said. "Can't you close the door when you piss?"

She answered by slamming the door without getting off the toilet. Then she said, "You're the one that got fired. Get mad at yourself, not at me."

"I didn't get fired. I quit."

Megan didn't answer. She was nauseous and started dry heaving.

"Why can't I catch a break?" Jonas said to her impassive calico cat.

Then he dressed in a Warner Bros. sweatshirt that he thought made him look like a studio employee, along with relatively clean jeans and tennis shoes.

When Megan started to dress in another T-shirt and shorts, he said, "Why can't you call one of your old cock-blocking roommates and borrow some share wear? And for chrissake, brush the moss off your teeth. Any more, it'll look like you invented a tooth sweater."

By noon on a hot Los Angeles day, they were cruising in Jonas's fifteen-year-old VW bug in the Birds, those streets on the western side of the Hollywood Hills named for feathered friends, like Nightingale, Robin, and Oriole.

"Do you know that Harrison Ford don't even know how many airplanes he owns?" Jonas said as they drove up into the Hills. "I read this interview where he said he owns six or eight. He don't even know for sure how many."

Megan, who was wearing a passably clean yellow jersey, jeans, and flip-flops, slouched in her seat and stared out at the multimillion-dollar homes. "How long do we have to do this?" she said. "I'm getting carsick."

Ignoring her complaints as usual, he said, "And then there's Nicolas Cage. He's in financial trouble because it takes mega-millions for him to survive each year. Do you know he has a collection of comic books that's probably worth more than a few of Harrison Ford's airplanes?"

"Uh-huh," Megan said. "That's intriguing."

Any response at all from her these days encouraged him, and he said, "He had an Action One Superman comic book worth who knows how much. One like it sold recently for three hundred grand. And he didn't even know the comic books were stolen until months passed. Think of it, Meg, three hundred thou for one comic book. And they don't even miss them till somebody gooses them and says, 'Where's the fucking comic book?' That's the kind of stuff you find laying around celebrity cribs all the time. And the best thing is, you're not hurting anyone when you take it. Half the time they don't even know it's gone."

Megan said, "The way I feel today, I don't give a shit what they know. I need some ox. I'm sick."

"It's nice to hear you say something," Jonas said, "even if it's bitching at me. Usually I talk in an echo chamber."

She didn't respond and he said, "See that house on the left, the one two houses from the corner? See the security camera on the roof? I could just climb up on that garage and throw a bag over it. But first I'd have to know if the house belongs to a careless celebrity. We gotta stop at the library or the computer café and get on the Internet and find out who lives there. It's a promising target."

Jonas drove aimlessly until they were on one of the top streets, looking down at a midsize residential property on a corner lot, where an elderly woman in a bathrobe and sun hat was sitting on a chaise longue beside a swimming pool. She was drinking what looked like a glass of iced tea and watching a small TV that sat on a table next to her.

Jonas parked, continuing to look down at her, and said, "If we

happened to be really desperate I could go to the door of that house and say I'm looking for the Lohan residence or something. And you could open the pool gate and go in there and grab that TV. We could easy trade it for at least an ox or two down at Pablo's Taco Shop."

"I'm really feeling awful, Jonas," Megan said.

"You down for it?"

She paused and said, "I guess so."

"You really down?" he asked. "Don't wuss out on me."

"I'm almost desperate enough to do Wilbur for a couple of OCs," Megan said, tears in her eyes. "That's what I've come to."

He looked at her closely. She really was all smoked out. She was jonesing way worse than he thought. He couldn't believe she'd even think about fucking that disease-ridden drug dealer. If she ever did something like that, he was dumping her ass for sure.

Jonas said, "Okay, we're gonna do this thing just for you. Just to score you an emergency bean or two."

He didn't want Megan to know how nervous he was when he stopped the car two houses from the corner and said, "Walk to the swimming pool gate. When you hear her go into the house, open the gate, run in and jack the TV, and meet me right here. If she's home alone, we're cool. If she's got a maid or if somebody else answers the door, we pass. Okay?"

Her chin quivered when she said, "Okay."

He drove down the hill and stopped thirty yards past the pool gate. The plaster-white wall around the pool was six feet high, and the pool gate was on the side street for the pool cleaner's easy access. He figured it might be locked but Megan could climb the wall with no trouble.

Jonas grinned at Megan with feigned insouciance when she got out and closed the car door. He drove around to the front of the house and parked at the curb by the driveway, where his license plates were not facing the residence.

It was one of the ubiquitous "Spanish-style" homes with red-tile roofs that dot the upscale hillsides all over Southern California, the kind that wouldn't look too crazy within five hundred miles of the Mediterranean Sea. He walked boldly to the front door of the house and was about to use the black metal knocker when he saw the doorbell and pressed it. He was expecting an intercom voice and he had a story ready about a neighbor he was looking for.

There was a wait of over a minute, which was a good sign, and then the door opened and the elderly woman in the sun hat, her face tanned and creased like old leather, said in annoyance, "Are you from Manny the Plumber? I've been waiting all morning for you."

Jonas said, "Uh, no, Manny couldn't make it but he wanted me to come and set up another appointment if that's okay."

"Can't you even fix a clogged toilet?" the woman asked, doubly annoyed now. And she opened the door as though thinking that any fool from a plumbing company could unclog a toilet if he'd just come in and look at it.

"No, ma'am," Jonas said. "I just work in the office and—"

He didn't get to finish it. An eighty-five-pound golden retriever barking deliriously leaped past the woman and slammed Jonas in the chest with both front paws and all his weight behind it.

"Sigmund!" the woman yelled. "Down! Down, Sigmund!"

Jonas was knocked flat on his back, and the dog began wagging and squirming, and for a moment Jonas thought his spine was broken. He felt a spasm when he tried to get up, but the dog was sitting on Jonas's head and drooling on his crotch.

The woman grabbed the beast by his collar and tried to pull him away, saying, "Bad boy! Bad Sigmund!"

But Sigmund didn't give a shit what she said, and he gave Jonas a big lick on the mouth before he decided to surrender to his mistress.

Jonas struggled to his feet in agony, his right hand pressing his lower back, and said, "I could sue you for this, lady!"

"Oh, please!" the woman said. "Sigmund didn't mean to hurt you. He loves people too much."

"He's a menace," Jonas said, moaning as she managed to get Sigmund inside and close the door.

"Let me take down your name and address," the woman said. "I'll call my insurance company immediately. Please believe me, he's an adorable dog. I'm so sorry."

When she opened the door and went inside to get a pen and paper, Jonas carefully descended the two steps, each one causing pain to shoot down his leg. He limped to his car, started it up, and made a U-turn just as the woman opened the door again, notepad in hand.

Jonas made a quick left and drove halfway down the block, where Megan came running to his car with the TV set.

"I did it," she said, opening the Volkswagen's door and putting the TV on the rear seat.

"You drive," he said. "Drop me at home and then go trade for the ox. A mad dog just attacked me. Oooooooh, my fucking back!"

Raleigh Dibble liked his job of overseeing the Brueger estate so much that he could go almost an entire day without thinking about Nigel Wickland. The art dealer was spending a great deal of time at the custom photo lab of his associate, learning enough photographic tricks to be able to do what he had to do. He phoned Raleigh every day on Raleigh's cell to report his progress. And every time that Raleigh considered Nigel's plan, he vowed to call it off. He'd lie beside the Brueger pool on hot afternoons and think of the dozen ways that this could go sideways.

And then Raleigh would wonder when Nigel was going to call and tell him that this was the day. He wished that Nigel wasn't a homo. In prison the more flamboyant butt pirates were always snitching on the straight guys to make points with the COs. Of course, that didn't mean that Nigel would go all fluttery if something did go

wrong, and drop a dime on him. Nigel might turn out to be a stand-up guy. Maybe.

And then he'd remember how awful the federal prison had been, and he'd imagine how much more horrible state prison would be. He wouldn't be serving time with tax cheats and white-collar criminals and organized-crime guys, as he had at Club Fed. No, this time he'd be in with the vilest of psychopaths: rapists and serial killers and thugs and cutthroats of every stripe. His life would be in danger when he was just walking across the yard. He could be murdered by gang members just for talking to the wrong guy, or even to the right guy at the wrong time.

His fear would make Raleigh appreciate how this Brueger job was the sweetest setup he'd ever had. In some ways it was even better than when he'd had his own catering business, when he had always had to worry about finding decent meat and fish and produce for a price. And hiring people who actually gave a shit. And paying taxes. All that made him think of $500,000, tax-free. Tax-free! He'd get a safe-deposit box, and that's where it would stay until he could see what was what. He'd go to the bank from time to time just to visit his money. He'd take it out and run his fingers over it.

Or if the recession got worse and property values went in the toilet, maybe he'd use the money to buy the little condo he'd always dreamed of owning. Cash would be king if real estate really tanked. And he'd have cash, more than he'd ever had in his life. A condo that was worth a million nowadays could probably be had for half a mill when California eventually went bankrupt and Arnold Schwarzenegger went back to making dumb movies.

Raleigh grabbed his cell impulsively and dialed the Wickland Gallery, and when Ruth Langley transferred him to Nigel, he said, "Do you have a minute?"

"Only a minute," Nigel said.

"Is it okay to talk on your office phone, or do you want to call me back?"

"Ruth's with a customer," Nigel said. "Go ahead."

"When are you coming?"

"Are you getting eager?"

Nigel's tone was annoying, and Raleigh said, "No, I'm not that eager. But I want this thing to move along at a faster pace."

"I'm just about ready," Nigel said. "I've practiced at my friend's place of business, and after a couple of unsatisfactory attempts, I was successful the last time. Very successful. The work was perfect. You'd be amazed."

"So when're you coming?"

"Try to contain your emotions, dear boy," Nigel said. "It will happen at the right time, and that time is nearly at hand. Be prepared for a call this week. All right?"

When Raleigh closed his cell, he thought that's what he'd hated most about working in London, having to deal with supercilious condescending snobs. Just the sound of their flutey voices could be unbearable, especially the patronizing bitchier teabags like Nigel Wickland.

★ ELEVEN ★

BY THE END of the week, the surfer cops were unlucky enough to be on duty when there was a Hollywood moon, that is, a full moon over Hollywood, when anything could happen. Sergeant Murillo conducted the midwatch roll call, and after warning everyone that there would be a Hollywood moon in the sky that night, the last thing he did was search his Darwin list for something that might be a morale booster for the troops.

"And now it's time for the Darwin list," he said, turning to a recent bulletin. "That means people we're better off without. Last night in West L.A. a burglar who'd entered a commercial building through an A/C duct with a flashlight in his mouth fell twenty feet onto his face and the flashlight jammed in his throat and suffocated him. It looks like a clear case of death by Ever Ready."

The troops all cheered and whistled, and then he said, "Tonight we have a full moon. A Hollywood moon, and as you know, that makes citizens do all kinds of strange things. For you new people, that also means that I buy a large pizza with the works for the team that brings in the weirdest story at end-of-watch. Okay, let's hit the bricks."

Everyone gathered their gear and each cop touched the Oracle's picture for luck before heading for the kit room and then the parking lot.

*   *   *

The sizzle of the Santa Anas on the boulevards generated rays of heat rising from the blacktop and left people scratching their bone-dry skin and dabbing moisturizer on their lips. After the feverish glow of twilight, and well before the Hollywood moon rose in the sky, a call came into Communications Division from east Hollywood that set a tone for the evening. Despite the immigrant mix in the area that made the school district a Tower of Babel, there were not many African American households within the geographic boundaries of Hollywood Division. The "shots fired" radio call took them to the cottage of a black family who were not African Americans but recent immigrants from the Dominican Republic.

When 6-X-32 pulled up in front of the cottage of the person reporting, Jetsam unlocked the shotgun and took it with him to the door. He was followed by Flotsam, who was driving that evening.

The call had come from a Dominican neighbor of a Salvadoran family from whose house the gunshot had emanated. The person reporting was a Dominican woman who worked as a waitress at a Mexican restaurant on Western Avenue, and she was waiting for them. She was middle-aged and looked to the surfer cops like she ate too many of her restaurant's gorditas. Although she was only five feet tall, she easily outweighed Flotsam, who towered over her.

"I hear somebody fire a gun," she said. "Een there!" And she pointed to the ramshackle residence next door.

By then, 6-X-66 had squealed to a stop, and Hollywood Nate and Snuffy Salcedo jumped out to back up the surfer cops.

Snuffy spoke briefly to the woman in Spanish and was told that she did not know the Salvadoran family, who were recent arrivals to the neighborhood. She thought there was a mother, and a man who might or might not be the father, and at least six children, maybe more. They all lived in the two-bedroom rented bungalow, which was owned by the same slumlord who owned the house of the Dominicans. And then she added that there was also a very old *abuelita* living there.

"A grandma?" Hollywood Nate asked, and Snuffy nodded.

"There's a big houseful of people in that little crib," Snuffy said.

Before the surfer cops got to the front porch of the Salvadorans, a team from Watch 3 arrived to cover the back door. Just then, a detective car pulled up in front, and the night-watch detective, Compassionate Charlie Gilford, got out, wearing a food-stained tan cotton blazer and sucking his teeth, as usual. He was wanting an entry for his log in order to prove that he did leave the station from time to time to assist the bluesuits, and not just to grab a free meal at places where a plate of greasy fare was a full pop to coppers on the beat and half price to anyone else with a badge.

Nate always thought that one of the great mysteries of Hollywood was how the lazy detective—who took the night-watch assignment only to avoid the real work of handling a daytime caseload—could always manage to find a new necktie that was even uglier than the last one he wore. The base color of this one was uncertain because of the swirl and patterns of garish clashing colors snaking over the entire tie, but it was a cinch to hide salsa stains. Nate figured that Charlie showed up only because he had heard the hotshot call, being a few blocks away leeching freebie tostadas by badging the boss at the local taco shop.

When Compassionate Charlie was halfway between the car and the house, he saw that he'd arrived too soon. The uniformed coppers hadn't made entry and secured the situation yet, so he stayed where he was instead of walking into a potentially dangerous incident.

Jetsam angled off at one side of the screen door and tapped on it with the muzzle of the Remington 870 shotgun. Flotsam held his Glock down by his right leg.

"Police!" Jetsam yelled. "Anybody inside, step out now with your hands on your head!"

The inside door opened slowly and seven Salvadoran children,

most of them in T-shirts and shorts, emerged onto the porch with their hands on their heads. They ranged in age from about four to thirteen. Three of the youngest were crying and the older ones were plenty scared. The one who looked about thirteen had his hair buzzed down to the scalp and was already wearing wannabe gang rags: a plaid flannel shirt and a baggy pair of denim shorts that extended well below the knees and were hanging halfway off his butt. He was apparently trying to connect as a junior with one of the gangs in the area, possibly the Salvadoran's Mara Salvatrucha, aka MS-13, the largest gang in the world.

"What happened in there?" Flotsam asked him.

"My big brother got shot," said the boy in good English.

"Who shot him?" Jetsam asked, his shotgun held at a ready angle across his chest.

"I don't wanna say," the boy said.

"Where is he?" Flotsam asked.

"He ain't here," the boy said. "He got in his car and went to the hospital."

"Where was he hit?" Flotsam asked, figuring it was probably a gang drive-by.

"Here," the boy said, taking a hand down and touching his left buttock.

"How old is he?" Flotsam asked.

"Eighteen," said the kid. "Can I take my hands off my head now?"

Flotsam nodded and said, "Which hospital did he go to?"

"I dunno," the kid said. "He was really mad and swearing and everything, so he didn't wanna talk to nobody."

"Is your mother home?" Flotsam asked.

"No, she's at work."

"Did one of you shoot him?" Jetsam asked.

"None of us kids," the boy said.

"Then who shot him?" Jetsam asked.

This time the kid burst into tears and shook his head. "I can't tell you," he said, looking toward the bungalow.

"Is the shooter in the house?" Flotsam asked, elevating the muzzle of his pistol, ready for anything.

"Uh-huh," the kid said, and now he really started bawling.

Hollywood Nate and Snuffy Salcedo, along with a second team from Watch 3, deployed near the front porch with their pistols drawn. Flotsam said to them, "The shooter's inside."

Then Flotsam and Jetsam quickly gestured for all of the kids to move from the porch and onto the tiny patch of grass that passed for a lawn. Flotsam nodded to his partner, who nodded back, and Jetsam entered the bungalow quickly with the stock of the shotgun tucked against his hip, followed by Flotsam.

Jetsam yelled, "Police officers! Step out of the bedroom with your hands on your head!"

No answer, but they could hear the television going.

Flotsam crouched, his pistol extended in both hands and moved out of the kill zone. He said, "Now, goddamnit! Come out now!"

Still no answer.

Jetsam advanced in a semicrouch. The gloom of twilight made it hard to see clearly into the darkened bedroom where the television was playing, but they could hear Spanish-speaking voices delivering their melodramatic lines with lots of intensity and plenty of volume. But that was all they heard.

"Come out!" Flotsam ordered again.

Jetsam, his back to the wall and still inching forward, craned his neck, and peering around the doorjamb, he found the shooter.

She was sitting where she always sat, on a lumpy Barcalounger with her legs up, intently watching an old TV that sat on top of a chest of drawers. The antenna wire ran from the TV set to the window, where presumably it led to a roof antenna.

A rusty old .32 caliber revolver was lying on a table beside her, next to a telephone.

Jetsam said, "Bro, get in here and check this out!"

Then he entered the tiny room, moving quickly to the table, and picked up the revolver, with Flotsam right behind him.

She hardly looked at them but seemed to concentrate harder on the program, where a shirtless man on a tropical beach at night was kissing a voluptuous woman who sighed and said, *"¡Carlos, Carlos, mi amor!"* He answered with, *"¡Isabel, mi vida!"*

"Dude," Flotsam said. "She's like, a hundred years old."

As it turned out, he wasn't far off. At first glance, she seemed mummified. The ancient Salvadoran woman was the color of mocha coffee with curdled cream. Her hair, what there was of it, was a patch of colorless frizz. Her milky eyes were sunken deep within their sockets, and her eyelids looked like crumpled tissue paper. Her crusty lips hung open, baring blackened gums and a few amber teeth. She wore a faded cotton dress large enough for two of her, and fuzzy Donald Duck bedroom slippers. Her bare arms and legs were brittle sticks, and her crinkling flesh was parchment-dry and looked too delicate to withstand the slightest human touch.

Jetsam said, "Bro, what we got here is the über oldster of Hollywood."

"¿Inglés?" Flotsam said to her. *"¿Habla Inglés?"*

The old woman glanced at him with her milky eyes and shook her head and went back to watching television.

"Get Snuffy in here," Jetsam yelled to the cops now milling around on the front porch.

After a moment Snuffy Salcedo entered the bedroom, looked at the woman, and said to the surfer cops, "Are you kidding me?"

Then he squatted beside the Barcalounger and talked to her. She answered softly in a surprisingly strong voice but never took her eyes off the television program while Snuffy delivered a series of questions.

After she gave a few short answers to him, Snuffy said to Flotsam

and Jetsam and Hollywood Nate, "Her name's Irma Beltrán. She's the great-grandmother of the kids, and she thinks she's either ninety-eight or ninety-nine years old, she can't remember which. But she's having a big party here on her hundredth birthday and there's gonna be *pupusas* and *curtido* and *tres leches* birthday cake. And we're all invited."

Flotsam and Jetsam looked at each other, and Jetsam said to Snuffy, "Ask her who shot the kid."

"I already did."

"Don't keep us in suspense, dude," Flotsam said.

"She shot him," Snuffy said.

"Maybe she's covering for somebody," Jetsam said hopefully. "Maybe for the kids' father?"

"She's very definite," Snuffy said. "She shot him."

"Ask her if it was an accident," Flotsam said. "I'll bet it was an accident."

Snuffy spoke to her again and listened to her answer and said, "Nope. She said she shot him on purpose." Then, enjoying the surfer cops' discomfort, Snuffy said, "Want me to read her the Miranda rights? A felony bust will look good on your recap."

Ignoring the wisecrack, Jetsam said, "Ask her why she shot him."

"I already did," said Snuffy. "She shot him because he wouldn't stop talking on the phone when she's trying to watch her favorite *novela*."

After a moment of deliberation, Flotsam said, "So what're we gonna do with her?"

"This is one shooter I ain't handcuffing," Jetsam said. "You touch her and she might crumble into pieces. Maybe into powder. You'll need a dustpan to pick her up. Maybe we better call a supervisor."

"Aw, shit!" Flotsam said. "Ask her if maybe she was just sorta trying to scare him away from her telephone and cranked one off

sorta in his general direction, and it sorta accidentally nailed him in the ass."

Snuffy Salcedo spoke to her again and listened to her answer, and then turned to the other cops and said, "She says she always hits what she aims at. And would the big policeman please move away from the television set because she thinks Carlos is very handsome and this is a really good part."

Flotsam stepped aside so Irma Beltrán could see what Carlos was going to do now that he had Isabel lying helpless on the sand in a swoon from his blazing kisses. Isabel's right breast was partially exposed now and that even got Jetsam engrossed in the program.

Then Flotsam said to his partner, "Keep your mind in the game, dude, and pay attention here. We got a Hollywood moon coming up tonight, so maybe she caught an early lunar vibe and this ain't all her fault. Think of a graceful way outta this so we don't gotta move her from that chair."

Hollywood Nate said, "Just book the gun. The kid probably went to the ER at Hollywood Pres. By now he's chill. I bet he'll sign off that the old lady capped him by accident, or maybe you can suggest that he did it himself while practicing his quick draw. And you might remind him to stop using the phone when Granny Oakley's watching her soap operas."

Just then, Compassionate Charlie Gilford sauntered into the crowded little bedroom, and said, "What's taking you guys so long?" When he saw Irma Beltrán, he froze and said, "What the fuck's Norman Bates's momma doing here?"

"She's the shooter," Flotsam said. "It was an accident, though. She thought the gun was the TV remote. It could happen to anyone."

"Put her back in the fruit cellar!" Compassionate Charlie said with a shiver of distaste.

"We think the victim's at Hollywood Pres," Flotsam said to the detective. "He's her great-grandson. Butt shot is all. No biggie."

They were interrupted when a copper from Watch 3 came into

the crowded room and said, "Breaking news. The oldest of the kids just told us his great-grandma's a hundred and three years old."

Hollywood Nate said to the detective, "This might win the Hollywood moon award, Charlie. This has got to be the longevity record for local female shooters. A hundred and three!"

Compassionate Charlie sucked his teeth for a few seconds, then shrugged and said, "So what? Something weirder will happen around here tonight." And then he added the mantra heard so frequently in that geographic police division: "This is fucking Hollywood."

The detective took a notebook from his pocket to find the number for Hollywood Presbyterian Medical Center, but when he walked to the table and reached for the telephone, both Flotsam and Jetsam scared the crap out of him when they yelled in unison, "Don't touch the phone!"

Jonas Claymore wasn't affected by the full moon over Hollywood. He was in bed with a heating pad on his lower back, bitching even when Megan Burke came in with a watson for him that she'd scored along with two OCs in trade for the stolen TV set.

"Is the pain as bad as yesterday?" she asked.

"What the fuck do you think?" Jonas grumbled. "Christ, the heat ain't helping at all. Rub me down again with that hot gel, will ya? Oh, my fucking back. I'd like to go back there and toss that mutt a hamburger loaded with rat poison."

"You should watch TV or something," Megan said, sick of his whining. "If you could just get yourself out of bed, you'd feel better."

"Easy for you to say," Jonas said. "Make me something to eat, will ya?"

"What do you want, Jonas?"

"Oh, maybe prime rib with garlic mashed potatoes. Or a filet mignon with grilled onions. Whadda you mean, for chrissake?"

Megan sighed and said, "I'll see if there's a can of tomato soup left. If there is, do you want crackers with it?"

"Surprise me with your culinary art," Jonas said.

"Maybe it was an omen," Megan said. "Being attacked by an animal on our first crime. Maybe we should stop while we can."

Jonas said, "Didn't you kinda get a rush from snatching that TV from that house? I was hoping that maybe for a little while you could get into grabbing small stuff to trade for ox. I mean, just till we get on our feet. Then I was hoping you might be ready to try going into one of those big houses up in the Hollywood Hills."

"I still think it's scary."

"I told you from the jump, we won't do anything that ain't safe."

She thought about it and said, "Okay, I guess maybe I'm in. Temporarily. Just till we're on our feet."

"I'll be good to go in a couple of days," Jonas said. "Now, how about that food?"

She was gone for fifteen minutes, and when she came back, she had a bowl of tomato soup and a few saltine crackers on a paper plate. Jonas picked up a cracker and it was so soggy it bent in his fingers.

"Is it okay?" Megan asked when he tasted a spoonful.

"Savory," Jonas said. "One of your better dinners, I'd have to say."

★ TWELVE ★

VIV DALEY AND Georgie Adams had been removed from the field after the shooting of Louis Dryden and would not be returned to field duty until a BSS shrink and the chief gave an okay, per LAPD policy. That left only two women working the midwatch on that night of the Hollywood moon. P3 Della Ravelle, a twenty-two-year cop, was the Field Training Officer for P1 Britney Small, who was born a year after her FTO had been appointed to the LAPD. They were working 6-X-46, and Della Ravelle was driving, with young Britney Small doing the report writing.

Britney Small, who was in the last phase of her probation, was one of the most reticent and shy women that Della Ravelle had ever encountered in law enforcement. But her former FTO, a highly disciplined Korean American cop named Rupert Tong, had always given her glowing evaluations, so Della figured the probationer must've been assertive enough when she needed to be. Tong had transferred to a long-awaited detective assignment at Robbery-Homicide Division, and Della Ravelle was taking over Britney Small until the end of her eighteen-month probationary period, two months hence.

Since Britney Small was so near the end of her probation and Della Ravelle was so laid-back, Della insisted that the boot not keep calling her ma'am. Britney had never stopped calling Rupert

Tong sir until their last night together, when the former Navy SEAL said to her, "Be sure and let me know if you need anything or have any questions about something you've learned from me. You've got my cell number."

It was only after Britney had said, "Thank you, sir, and good luck to you," that he'd smiled broadly and given her a farewell hug, saying, "You're a real copper already, Brit. You can call me Rupert anytime."

Britney Small was so willowy that Della Ravelle called her "my bluesuit ballerina." The creamy-faced rookie loved working with this female FTO, telling her on their first night together that it was great to work with someone even older than her mom, for the wisdom it would bring.

"Thanks for that," Della said, thinking what everyone past forty would think at such a moment—Older than her mom? Where did it all go? How the hell did this happen to me?

Della Ravelle was forty-four years old, with smart hazel eyes and a friendly grin for everyone. She had to go to a hairdresser more often than she liked these days in order to keep her hair brown. "I'll dye till I die" was her motto. She was always struggling to lose ten pounds despite frequent workouts in the Hollywood Station weight room, where Hollywood Nate pumped iron almost daily.

She was twice married and twice divorced, with two sons aged nineteen and seventeen, who lived with her in her South Pasadena house. Zach and Jonathan were students, one at Pasadena City College and the other at South Pasadena High School. Della always thought it was nothing more than sheer luck that she had married slightly better the first time, back at a time when she'd wanted children. That marriage was to an IRS auditor who was diligent with his child support payments throughout the years, even though during their marriage he was so nitpicking and clueless that he almost drove her crazy. To him, police work was something that could be

analyzed like the tax returns of the deadbeats he delighted in tormenting. He could never understand the emotional hazards of the Job, and the powerful bonds that developed among the blue brethren in Della's strange fraternity of the badge.

The second husband was a worse mistake because he, too, was a cop, an alpha male, LAPD macho copper, mustache and all. They had battled from their honeymoon on, but thankfully the marriage was brief with no children. So now, with the days and nights of hiring babysitters behind her, Della Ravelle hoped to enjoy the six years she planned to remain on the Job before retiring at age fifty to a peaceful future where the size of the moon over Hollywood did not matter a whit.

At 9 P.M. that night, she looked up while driving and said to Britney Small, "Wonder when it's gonna bring its wrath down on us."

"What?" Britney asked.

"The Hollywood moon," Della said. "We're due."

So far, their watch had been routine, but the full-moon motorists were already feeling the effects of it. There had been three traffic collisions on the boulevards, and both Della and Britney had written traffic citations for moving violations. On their third call, they caught a "415 family dispute" on their dashboard computer, indicating the penal code section for disturbance of the peace. Such routine calls often escalated, so on the way to the call, Della said to her probationer, "About these routine four-fifteen family disputes, I want you to always keep in mind that you and me don't go hands-on with people until backup arrives. Don't be shy about using your rover to call for assistance or help if you have to."

"Right," Britney said.

Della said, "A few years ago, two women officers here in Hollywood got into a knockdown street fight with a large, violent guy, and one of the women got badly hurt. A few firefighters on a lunch break were standing there watching the tussle and didn't lift a

finger to help the officers. The fire department later sent a battalion chief to all our roll calls to apologize and try to rationalize it, but every copper at Hollywood Station was extremely pissed off. A few of the mouthier ones told the battalion chief that the next time fire-fighters were being pelted with rocks or shot at by street thugs, we'd sit and watch just like they did. There were very hard feelings for a while. Moral of the story is, you can only depend on your brothers in blue to help in the rough-and-tumble altercations. Your last FTO was a very good copper, but he was a man. Don't ever forget that you're a woman. You're never gonna impress some of the old guys, no matter what you do."

"I've noticed that for sure," Britney said. "The OGs aren't very friendly with female boots."

"I repeat, Britney," Della said. "Don't ever forget out here that you're a woman."

"Roger that," Britney said. "I won't."

Della said, "We can be outstanding police officers but we can't morph into men during the hands-on stuff. And by the way, female scrappy drunks can be worse than men when it comes to down-and-dirty street fights, so be wary in those situations. But we usually have better verbal skills than men, and sometimes we can talk things down just by being reasonable and by being women, where the men can't. Sometimes our gender can de-escalate things. For these last few months of your probation I'm gonna give you a lotta cop-style girl talk that Rupert Tong couldn't give you. You okay with that?"

"Of course, ma'am—I mean Della," Britney said. "I'm really grateful to learn the woman stuff from another woman."

"I'll bet Rupert Tong never talked to you about underwear, did he?" Della said.

"Underwear? Lord, no!" Britney said.

"Well, it's an important thing for women officers to know about. Never rush off to work with your underwear inside out. And don't

wear grandma underwear, although at your age I'm sure you never do. This is in case something bad happens. Would you want a bunch of guys in the ER to see you in funny underwear that's inside out?"

"I see your point," Britney said with a giggle.

"And for the same reason, don't go to work without shaving your legs. How'd you like it if a gossipy ER nurse told some of the Watch Five coppers about your stubble? You just know they'd all start calling you 'cactus legs.'"

"No cactus legs," the rookie said. "Got it."

"And don't wear an underwire bra under your vest. I tried to take the vest off Millie Boyle after she got rear-ended in a TC at Hollywood and Vine, right before we put her into the RA. And her goddamn padded underwire bra popped off like it was spring-loaded. One of the midwatch coppers found it on the street and later taped a cell phone photo of the bra to the wall in the roll call room with a note that said, 'Will the person who lost this piece of equipment at the scene of a TC at Hollywood and Vine please claim it with Harry the kit room king.' It was all very embarrassing for Millie."

"No underwire bra. Okay, boss," Britney said cheerfully. "This is real good information to have."

"Poor Millie," Della said. "She married and divorced two lieutenants early in her career, so pretty soon every guy she worked with proposed. They'd say stuff like, 'I know you don't like me, but if I marry you I might get promoted to lieutenant, so how about it?'"

It was a two-story house on a residential street several blocks south of Paramount Studios. They heard the yelling from the street when they got out of their black-and-white. Both women grabbed their side-handle batons. The call came from next door, and a young woman in an orange leotard stood on her porch and pointed to the

walkway between the houses. There a large-screen plasma TV was shattered to pieces below an open upstairs window. Della nodded to the woman in the leotard, who went back inside and closed the door quickly.

Britney knocked at the door, and after several seconds, one of the potential combatants, a dark-eyed, olive-skinned, beefy woman older than Della, with enough hairspray to be an ozone threat, opened the door. She was dressed in the work uniform she wore at Farmers Market, where she served coffee and pastries at one of the open-air shops. Her husband was her age and even more overweight, and appropriately enough, he wore a sweat-stained wifebeater. But neither side had yet inflicted any violence. His boozy face was blooming like a rose and he was scowling at his wife.

The cops stepped inside and Britney said, "One of your neighbors called. Is there a problem here?"

The man pointed at the woman and said, "My wife thinks she can cheat on me and I'm supposed to lay down and take it!"

"May we have your names, please?" Della said, trying for some simmer time.

"I'm John Gianopoulos," the man said, "and this backstabbing adultress is my wife, I'm sorry to say."

The woman turned to the older cop for empathy and said, "This fool thinks I'm bonking my hairdresser, Jackie, who happens to be gayer than a bouquet of daisies. In fact, Jackie's shack bitch is a little guy who's way prettier than me and a hell of a lot younger. And his shack bitch even has tits thanks to hormone therapy. Why would my hairdresser wanna fuck me, for chrissake?"

Britney's look to Della said, Why would *anyone* want to?

In a quiet voice, Della Ravelle said, "Could we all keep it down? You're scaring the neighbors."

"She's killing me," her husband wailed. "Killing me!"

Then both cops took a closer look at him. There were bald patches all over his head. He had only a little patch of eyebrow over

his left eye and none over his right eye. Even his arms looked peculiar. The left forearm was thick with black hair but there were large spots of bare skin showing, just as on his head. His right arm had almost no hair left on it. When Della took a closer look, she saw that though he was obviously meant to be a very hairy man, he had no eyelashes at all.

John Gianopoulos was obviously used to having people stare at him. He said to the cops, "She did this to me. I was a healthy man before she tricked me into marriage by saying her uncle would put me in his house-painting business." He pointed to his head and said, "Look at what being with her does to me!"

Britney gaped and said, "Do you have a skin disease? Like mange or something?"

"I have trichotillomania," he said. "Thanks to her evil ways."

His wife shook her head and said, "They call it an impulse-control disorder. He pulls out his hair when he's stressed, which is most of the time. Sometimes he wears a wig, and believe me, it's no improvement."

Della said, "Have you two considered breaking up?"

"I just needed a push," Mrs. Gianopoulos said, "and maybe having you cops coming here is the push I need."

Della said, "It would be a good thing if one of you could leave for a while until the two of you cool down. I think we have a potentially volatile situation here."

"Let him leave," she said. "He can just walk down to the corner saloon and get shit-faced, which is what he usually does anyway."

"And you can leave permanently," he said. "Take everything and go home to your dago mother. Just get out!"

"When I walk outta here," she said to him, "I'll take my clothes and my plasma TV, which I paid for, by the way, and that's all I want from this sick marriage." She looked at the cops and said, "He can keep the pots and pans and the dishes he's never washed and the bills he's never paid."

"Did you just get home from work?" Della asked her.

Mrs. Gianopoulos said, "Ten minutes before you arrived. Why?"

"Did you happen to use the walkway on the west side of the house?" Della asked.

"No," she said. "I parked in the alley and came in the back door. Why?"

"Uh-oh," Britney said.

Della said quickly, "Mr. Gianopoulos, I think it would be wise and better for both of you if you would leave here for a couple of hours. Do it now, please. And we'll have a brief chat with Mrs. Gianopoulos after you're gone."

He took the hint, put on a Members Only jacket that could never close over his huge belly, and walked out the front door, slamming it behind him. After the cops broke the news to Mrs. Gianopoulos about her plasma TV, and after she finished cursing loud enough to scare the goldfish in the living room, Della strongly encouraged her to load her car and head for her mother's house, and no charge for the marriage counseling.

Della concluded with, "We don't want you to kill him in his sleep tonight. You'd be charged with first-degree murder."

"It might be worth it," Mrs. Gianopoulos said with too much sincerity.

"You'll both be way better off if you leave him," Britney Small said. "Mr. Gianopoulos might even start growing eyelashes again."

After 6-X-46 cleared from that call and was heading north on Van Ness Avenue, Della Ravelle said to her probie, "That was a pretty routine family beef, all things considered. But I can think of a dozen ways a he-said-she-said can go sideways. That one went okay because we were calm and we were businesslike and we're women. Even though that dude mighta been crazy enough to toss a two-thousand-dollar TV out an upstairs window, you noticed he was

obedient with us. Probably has mommy issues, but whatever, we use our gender to our advantage out here. Right, partner?"

"Roger that, partner," Britney said, and earnestly began logging the call on their daily field activity report.

Della Ravelle watched Britney and smiled and wondered what it would've been like to have a daughter.

Their next stop resulted in a judgment call for young Britney Small. The Hollywood moon was rising higher in the heavens, and they got a call about an illegally parked car blocking the driveway of a residence up near Lake Hollywood. By the time they got there, the car was gone, but since they were there in the Hills, Della took a drive to a lover's lane where the cops used to catch teenagers smoking pot. She figured that nowadays kids would be doing meth or ox if they still parked up there. That part of the Hollywood Hills was full of stunted trees and brush that had to be controlled to prevent wildfires. Deer, coyotes, raccoons, opossums, and skunks lived there, feeding on the leavings of nearby human inhabitants.

Della said, "One time I got a call when a baby deer got hit by a car up here. The fawn was lying on the road, and there was an old motor cop there ahead of me, standing next to his bike and looking at the animal. The motor cop was one of those dinosaurs whose partners probably have to chew his food for him. One of those old saddle-sore vets that everyone calls Boots when they don't know his name. And then another two radio cars rolled up. And when I called in what had happened and asked for animal control to come and deal with it, the RTO conferred with somebody and came back saying there were no animal control people available, and told me we were authorized to shoot the animal."

"Did you?" Britney asked. "Did you shoot the baby deer?"

"I looked at that fawn, at the terror and pain in its eyes and I wanted to put it out of its misery," Della said. "Hollywood Nate was also there, and a unit from Watch Three, and nobody could shoot the fawn, not even the old motor cop, who I figured would

just step up and show us what wusses we were. One of the coppers from Watch Three was a real shit magnet who worked gangs in Southeast, down where schoolkids don't have earthquake drills, they have drive-by drills. Anyway, he'd been in three righteous gunfights down there where he killed a couple of guys, but even he couldn't shoot the deer. Fortunately, the poor little thing went into shock and died."

"I kinda like that story, though," Britney said.

"Whadda you like about it?"

"That the LAPD gunfighters couldn't shoot a baby deer. Somehow that makes me sorta proud. Know what I mean?"

Della smiled at her young partner again and said, "Okay, we're coming up on the lover's lane here. It's a piece of land that goes out a ways. The coppers call it Point Peter Puffer."

Then they spotted a car in the darkness and Della switched off her headlights and turned down the radio and let their car drift closer. It was a white Honda Civic, and it was bouncing and rocking like the hydraulic-aided, tricked-out lowriders that parade up and down Ventura Boulevard in the Valley.

Della said, "They're not doing dope at the moment, that's for sure. But maybe they smoked some to prime the pump, and maybe we can find what's left there in Daddy's car. Wanna check them out?"

"Sure," Britney said. "I'm good to go."

Della let the black-and-white roll into the parking area as close as she could without alerting them. She parked and they got out quietly, leaving their car doors open, and approached in the darkness, Della on the driver's side and Britney on the passenger side. They looked over the roof at each other, turned on their streamlights and jerked open the doors.

Britney said, "Get outta the car!" And she shone her light onto the couple in the backseat.

Della saw the situation first and said, "She can't."

The amorous couple was not in Daddy's car. A sweating middle-aged man was on top, his pants pushed down around his ankles. The woman on her back underneath him didn't look as frightened as he did. In fact, Britney later remembered seeing what she thought was sadness in the woman's face. When the man sat straight up, the rookie saw that the woman had no legs, only scarred stumps ending six inches higher than where her knees should have been.

Della looked over the roof of the Honda at her startled partner to see how she was going to handle this one.

Britney decided fast and simply mumbled, "Sorry." And closed the car door, retreating quickly to the black-and-white with Della following.

When they drove away, Britney said, "I don't think I wanna know her story."

Della said, "I'm gonna enjoy being your FTO, kiddo. You've got what they can't teach at the academy — good old common sense."

"There was nothing else to say, was there?" Britney asked.

Della said, "No, but a lotta male coppers woulda tried. The more macho they are, the more they can fuck things up."

At that very moment a pair of seriously macho cops were hoping to assist in an attempt to serve a warrant for murder on a Mexican national from the Arellano-Félix cartel, who was supposedly living in southeast Hollywood on one of the residential streets near Beverly Boulevard. A snitch had supplied information that the fugitive, whose name was Jaime Soto Aguilar, was hiding out with a woman who owned a house in that vicinity, but as to which house, or even which street, the informant could not say. A detective had gone to roll call and requested that all units make a note of the license number and location of any very old cars in restored condition that might be parked in that neighborhood, because Aguilar was a car nut who couldn't resist restoring classic cars. The detective said

they'd follow up on any car leads as time permitted. The fugitive's description was given along with information that he had a tattoo of a rattlesnake with dripping fangs coiled around his neck.

Flotsam and Jetsam had listened with interest during roll call, especially about the car, because they had recently noticed a restored Chevrolet Malibu cruising around that area, and a guy who looked Latino was driving it. After noticing the apple-green eye-catcher, they'd discussed how cool it would be to drive a car named after their surfing beach.

When they were not answering calls on that very warm and windless late summer evening, the surfer cops covered every residential street in that vicinity on both sides of Beverly Boulevard. And when the full moon was rising high over Hollywood, they spotted the apple-green Malibu parked on a street that was jammed with other parked cars. Flotsam and Jetsam put their sun-streaked heads together and cooked up a scheme that would require some assistance. Jetsam requested that 6-X-66 meet 6-X-32 in a certain alley off Beverly Boulevard.

When Hollywood Nate and Snuffy Salcedo showed up and the two black-and-whites were parked side by side, Flotsam said, "Post up and keep an eye on that bitchin' Malibu. The owner of that cherry ride's gotta be in a house real close to it. And the owner might just be Aguilar. The license plate don't mean shit. It's registered to some chick named Johnson in Pomona."

"Where're you beach rats going in the meantime?" Nate wanted to know.

Jetsam said, "To collect some noisy junk." Then Flotsam dropped it into gear and off they went.

Snuffy Salcedo said to Hollywood Nate, "This is stupid. If they're so sure the car belongs to Aguilar, why don't they request a stakeout?"

"Because the chances are so remote that it's Aguilar's, nobody would do it," Nate said.

"Then why're we doing it?" Snuffy said. "We were told just to write down license numbers and locations if we saw a restored car."

"Based on my experience, it pays to indulge them," Nate said. "Somehow, Neptune or whoever the surfer god is bestows crazy blessings on those two. Besides, my curiosity is killing me, isn't yours? Noisy junk?"

When the surfer cops returned to the alley in twenty minutes, they had the backseat of their shop, as well as the trunk, loaded with empty cans of all sizes, along with two battered old metal trash cans.

"What the fuck?" Snuffy Salcedo said when he got a look at their cargo.

"We are stupendously grateful for Chinese restaurants," Flotsam said. "You hardly ever find metal trash cans these days."

"And food cans galore," Jetsam said cheerfully.

Flotsam said to Snuffy Salcedo, "Dude, can you drive like Jimmie Johnson?"

Snuffy looked to Nate in utter puzzlement before he turned and said to Flotsam, "What?"

"They work in mysterious ways, partner," Nate explained to Snuffy. "Let's do what they want and see where it goes."

Flotsam said to Snuffy, "Anyways, dude, try to drive like Jimmie Johnson tonight, okay? We want you to go to the top of the street and come screaming down till you're almost opposite that pristine machine, and then lock 'em up. All four wheels. We wanna hear that rubber scream like a whore for a hundred-dollar tip."

"And what will you two be doing in the meantime, pray tell?" Hollywood Nate asked.

Flotsam said, "Me and my pard, we're gonna be dumping the trash cans full of junk onto the street and, like, making more noise than Chinese fucking New Year."

"If the guy that owns that Malibu ain't boning his old lady, he's

gonna run to his ride, to see if it's in pieces all over the street," Jetsam explained.

"Even if he is boning his old lady, he's gonna pull right outta her and run to his ride," Flotsam said. "He can find a bitch anywheres, but where's he gonna find a mint Malibu like that one?"

Snuffy looked at Nate again and said, "Know what? On a night this hot, everybody in a no-A/C neighborhood's got their windows open. Maybe it's me being back in Hollywood where anything can happen, but this is so loopy I think it might work."

Ten minutes later, Snuffy Salcedo was parked at the north end of the block, revving the engine of the Crown Vic. When he received a flashlight signal from the other end of the block, he floored it, and the black-and-white roared south until he was twenty yards from where the Malibu was parked and then he stood on the brakes.

The wheels locked up and the car's rear end started sliding until Snuffy got off the brakes and sped past the Malibu and the waiting surfer cops, each of whom was holding overhead a metal trash can full of junk. Snuffy could hear the explosive crash of cans and other metal before he drove into the alley to conceal the radio car.

Flotsam, Jetsam, and Nate hid between houses and behind cars, and within a minute, people were running out of their houses to see which car had been smashed in the collision. Several car owners scurried to see if they still had fenders intact, but only one man, shirtless and barefoot, ran straight to the Malibu.

He was checking the driver's side of the car when he was lit by flashlight beams and a tall blond cop said to him, "Dude, I don't know if you speak English, but if you even fart too loud, I'm gonna blow the eye right outta that rattlesnake."

A shorter blond cop said to him, "No, go ahead and rabbit. I love the smell of gunsmoke in the evening."

Snuffy Salcedo came running back from the alley with tobacco juice dripping down his chin as the fugitive was being handcuffed.

Jetsam said, "Read him his rights in Spanish, bro."

Snuffy Salcedo told Jaime Soto Aguilar in Spanish of his Miranda rights, and when he was finished, the fugitive made one brief comment to Snuffy in Spanish.

"What'd he say?" Flotsam asked.

Snuffy replied, "He said he thinks he's gonna have a heart attack."

"Bitchin'!" Flotsam said. "Tell him we never made a cardiac arrest."

"Do they rehearse this shit?" Snuffy Salcedo asked Hollywood Nate.

"They don't have to," said Nate. "They're in lockstep. I think they were Siamese twins separated at birth and raised apart. Probably by jackals."

During the ride to Hollywood Station with the fugitive handcuffed in the backseat of their shop, Jetsam said to his partner, "Bro, do you think this is, like, unusual enough to qualify for a pizza from Sergeant Murillo? Or does it have to be more like Hollywood weird? Like, more in the freak-show mold?"

While the surfer cops were locking up first prize for the Hollywood moon award, 6-X-46 was down from the Hollywood Hills, and Della Ravelle was still lecturing her probationer in the ways of women in police work.

As she drove east on Santa Monica Boulevard, Della said, "I can talk a lot about common sense, Britney. It's a good copper's most valuable trait. Things're gonna be a whole lot better for you on this Job than they were for women like me back in the day. When I was a boot, the old guys never got tired of playing little tricks on us. Like when I worked Central, I can remember a time when a couple of OGs had me do a pat-down search on a basehead down on skid row who was wearing spandex. After I patted her down and told them she's clean, my P3 said, 'Good job. I'm gonna write a comment

card on you.' Then when I wasn't looking one of the other OGs, a former SWAT guy who thought he was Mr. Tactical and smoked cigarettes in his teeth instead of his lips, puts his hideout gun on the ground and says, 'You missed this, rookie. She had it tucked under her crotch.'"

Britney said, "What'd you do then?"

"For a few seconds I almost panicked, but then my common sense kicked in and I said, 'No, sir. She was wearing spandex and there were no bulges on her except the ones nature gave her.' The OGs had a laugh and I was a step closer to acceptance."

"I try to never forget that it's still a man's world out here," Britney said.

"Yes, but it's lots better now," Della said. "I won't even try to tell you about the sexual harassment we used to put up with. And there were always the goddamn tricks. After a woman boot would search under the seats in her shop before she hit the streets, an OG would invariably drop a bag of rocks or some other kind of dope under the backseat and say, 'What the fuck's wrong with you, baby girl? You missed this.' It got so lame after a while that even they got tired of it. But we had to live with it till they did."

"How'd you finally win the OGs over?"

"By trying to be a better cop than they were without them noticing. And by always staying a woman and making them respect that. I've seen women on this Job trying to become one of the boys, but that never works out. And women have to deal with the impostor syndrome. That's where the woman copper starts to fear that the boss is gonna find out how unqualified she truly is. She starts to believe that she's only faking competence, because every second she's being scrutinized, way more than the men are, and it starts working on her self-esteem. It's like the actor's syndrome, but it's all internal bullshit. You *are* competent and you don't have to fear anything except the people out here who can hurt you. And that's a healthy fear to have."

"You were right, Della," Britney Small said. "I never learned this kind of stuff from Rupert Tong."

Della said, "I'm sure you've already learned on your own that when you meet men away from the Job and they find out you're a cop, they all get a doofus grin and say, 'Can you handcuff me?' I hate that shit. I just tell them, 'Get outta my face, asshole.'"

"You're right!" Britney said. "That already happened to me when I went out to a club with a couple of civilian girlfriends. Lame, isn't it?"

"You're way lucky to be here in Hollywood for your probation," Della said. "I remember the first time I found a gun after transferring here. Of course, guns recovered on radio calls don't count, only observation guns. So one night on Hollywood Boulevard when the beat officers and a midwatch unit were jamming some Rolling Sixties gangsters who came up from Watts, I spotted this brother bopping along the Walk of Fame, pretending to be a tourist watching Tickle Me Elmo posing for pictures. But I saw that when he sauntered past one of the Rolling Sixties, he tried to take a little two-inch wheel gun from one of the bangers who hadn't been patted down yet. I drew down on him and yelled for him to freeze and get down on his belly, and when everything settled and they were all proned out, I recovered my first obs gun here in Hollywood Division. And the sergeant we called the Oracle showed me off around the station and told everyone how I'd caught a gangster dumping a strap, and the watch commander wrote me an attagirl, and it was pretty cool. Of course it wasn't a big burner, but size does not matter when it comes to guns."

Britney said, "I've got a couple of classmates who're doing their probation in Central Division. After hearing you describe it, I'm real glad I caught Hollywood, believe me."

Della was silent for a moment, remembering how it had been back then, remembering the smell of skid row, the fluffy acrid miasma. And then she said, "I truly hated being a boot down there.

The smell of shit and piss and rotting flesh and general decay was everywhere in those days. It got into the fabric of our uniforms. People had lots of scabies. You could grab someone and your hands would slip right off their wrists. I got scabies twice from searching skid row hookers. They were like itchy fleabites. They get on your arms, your thighs, and your stomach. Good thing I never got them on my gizmo."

"Gross!" Britney said.

"And the guys enjoyed it when I had to search the obese ones who liked to hide crack under their humungous breasts. Their tits would be sticky. The guys would say, 'Sticky boobs hide crack.' Once I was searching this monstrous woman in a muumuu who was so fat they claimed she'd flipped a bus bench. And I thought I found a stash in the rolls of fat around her middle. But when I dug it out, it turned out to be an Oreo cookie and some Doritos she was keeping there to snack on. The guys really enjoyed watching me running like mad to a faucet to clean up."

"Disgusting!" Britney said.

Still reminiscing, Della said, "That wasn't even the real bad stuff. Once we found a dead baby in a backpack. It had blue eyes."

Della stopped talking then and they rode in silence. Della broke the silence when she said, "So whadda you think we should do about code seven tonight? My dad sent me three hundred bucks for my birthday, so I'll treat. We can do sushi on Melrose or a spicy chicken salad in Thai Town or maybe some rice and lamb in Little Armenia. No noshing on manly burritos and burgers for the girls of Six-X-Forty-six. Sound good, partner?"

"Can we wait awhile?" Britney said. "For some reason, I don't seem to have an appetite right now."

A trap that had been set by the narks two weeks earlier prompted a radio call on that night of the Hollywood moon that made Britney Small the talk of the station for days to come. A tip from a citizen

had led narcotics detectives to the backyard of a vacant house that had been in foreclosure for a number of months. A local Realtor happened to be checking out the property one afternoon and he recognized a large number of cannabis plants on one neat little patch of ground in that overgrown backyard. The Realtor phoned the office of the narcotics detectives, who were housed a block from the main police station, and had a chat with a detective there.

The resourceful detectives not only confiscated the marijuana but they left a note pinned to an olive tree in that yard. The note said, "Sorry about your grow. Call if you'd care to negotiate." They left a cell number used for situations like this and were happily surprised when a call came in the very next day. The caller offered $500, no questions asked, for the return of the plants. A female undercover cop met the pot grower by the parking lot of the Hollywood Bowl, and after the grower made his offer in person, he was arrested by other narks watching the action through binoculars.

The marijuana cultivator was a two-striker who wanted to deal and was eager to give up associates and fellow dealers. He offered the narks information about a male nurse of an anesthesiologist in Venice who had a shaky medical license. The nurse resided in an apartment building in the Las Palmas neighborhood, where he provided his client list—consisting of many drag queens and transsexuals—with forged prescriptions supposedly written from a medical office in Culver City.

One of the things that the two-striker had said, resulting in a search warrant, was, "The quack's nurse writes enough scrips in there to smoke out every dragon and trannie in Hollywood." And hoping to curry favor he added, "But he's bipolar and mega-goony most of the time, so watch out. I've been told he might have a gun in there."

Two teams of narks and their D3 had intended to serve the warrant on the night of the full moon. The nurse was supposed to be at

home with his lover, a post-op transsexual called Molly Black, who had been Marvin Black in another life and whose last surgery had completed the gender transformation. At the last minute, one of the teams of narks was pulled away for the arrest of another prescription drug dealer whom they'd been trying to get for months. The three remaining detectives needed a backup team, so they put in the call for a patrol unit to meet them on Las Palmas Avenue. The call was given to 6-X-46 of the midwatch.

Britney Small was excited about this one and wondered if the full moon was going to produce something weird enough for them to win the pizza prize. Also, she'd never been on a forced-entry raid of any kind, and she was stoked when the detectives asked her and Della to accompany them to the third-floor apartment. Their D3 decided to watch the outside window in case evidence came flying out. The entry team wanted women officers with them because of the post-op tranny in there. She was now officially a woman and would have to be searched by a woman.

After they were quickly briefed near Las Palmas Avenue under the white glow of the full moon, they were ready. The two narks who were making entry wore LAPD raid jackets, and the younger one carried a metal ram, the first one that Britney had ever seen.

The older nark said, "No more kicking doors for me. I kicked clear through a plywood panel last year and tore my Achilles tendon."

The younger of the narks, who Britney thought was pretty cute, kept smiling at her, and Della whispered, "Watch out for him. He's got a rep. A real vampire, and he likes fresh, young blood."

After they entered the building and ran up the staircase, Britney was pleased to see that she was not as winded as the narks, and certainly not as winded as Della Ravelle, who was toting the shotgun just in case the rumor was true about the nurse being strapped. They hurried along the darkened corridor to the apartment, and the two narks stood in front of the door with the ram at the ready.

Della angled on the left side of the door and Britney on the right. On the preplanned signal, which was a simple nod to Britney, she was to bang on the door with her baton and give the command. She was surprised how hard her heart was pounding.

Della shone her light onto the door so that the younger nark could accurately slam the ram right next to the dead-bolt lock. Della held the shotgun muzzle up, and Britney had her pistol drawn and muzzle down against her right thigh, with her adrenaline peaking.

The older detective on the left of the ram nodded to Britney, who yelled, "Police! Open the door!"

They heard what sounded like a feminine scream from inside and high-pitched voices yelling to each other and footsteps scurrying. The detective didn't hesitate and slammed the ram once against the heavy door, but it didn't budge. And then the moment occurred that made both detectives actually burst out in roars of laughter before the young one rammed the door a second time.

The door crashed open and the nurse and his tranny lover were caught throwing bags of prescription drugs out the window, where the D3 ran around catching them like a Dodgers center fielder. Lots more detective snickering continued all during the arrest, and even Della Ravelle tried in vain to control her own giggles. It had all been triggered by a moment that won for Britney Small a consolation-prize burrito from Sergeant Murillo for an unforgettable moment on the night of the Hollywood moon. All of Hollywood Station talked about it for days.

When Della Ravelle saw that the battering ram hit six inches higher than the dead-bolt lock on the first attempt at forced entry, she had shouted to the detective, "Lower! Lower!"

But it was Britney Small, in a fever of high-pitched excitement, who had instantly obeyed that command from her FTO. She dropped her voice a few octaves, gamely trying for baritone, and repeated, "Police! Open the door!"

★ THIRTEEN ★

THE CALL FROM Nigel Wickland came at 8 A.M. on Monday. Raleigh had just finished cleaning up the dishes after taking a tray of Cream of Wheat and stewed prunes to Marty Brueger. The old coot was watching something on E! that he'd recorded the night before. Raleigh thought how interesting it was that the young bubbleheads and the old bubbleheads enjoyed the same shows. He figured there must be some demographic dynamic at work here that he didn't understand.

The caller ID showed "Wickland Gallery" on the display. He picked up the phone and said, "Yes, Nigel?"

"We should practice not mentioning each other's names when we speak," Nigel said with that superior tone of his.

Raleigh suppressed his annoyance and said, "Okay, double-oh-sixty-nine, what's on your mind this morning?"

A silence while Nigel suppressed his own annoyance. Then he said, "This is it. I'm coming today."

That got Raleigh's attention. He felt a cold rush of fear in his belly, and he said, "What time today?"

"What time do you prepare lunch for..." Nigel paused, trying to keep from mentioning Marty Brueger's name.

"The geezer," Raleigh said. "About twelve thirty. Then it's nap time from about one until three."

"I'll see you at one," Nigel said. "Precisely."

Raleigh scowled at the receiver when he put it back on the cradle. "Precisely." That was so like the boarding school assholes who frequented the London bistro and left him nothing but their pitiful Brit gratuities. They'd tipped on average less than car-wash employees in Los Angeles might tip for food and service. Well, he'd be ready *precisely* at 1 P.M., and then he'd see if that teabag was the mastermind he purported to be. Raleigh tried to concentrate on his daily chores, making sure that he had the household schedule and Leona Brueger's instructions carefully notated.

The swimming pool cleaner came on Tuesday mornings unless Raleigh called to change the time. Ditto for the gardening crew, who came on Thursdays at about noon. Leona Brueger had offered to hire Raleigh a housekeeper for a biweekly visit or give him an extra $1,200 a month and let him hire his own help. He opted for the money, figuring he could find some Mexican housekeeper in the neighborhood who would drop in once a week to dust, vacuum, and clean his bathroom, and do whatever needed doing in Marty Brueger's cottage. That would cost him less than $400 a month and he could pocket the rest. So far, he'd been doing the light housekeeping himself and hadn't needed to hire anybody.

He decided to drive to the supermarket and pick up the week's groceries just to have something to occupy his mind for the next few hours. Marty Brueger would need more of that pricey Irish whiskey he liked, and Raleigh could pick up a bottle of Jack Daniel's for himself. Working in the catering business had taught him that bars on the west side of Los Angeles could get by if the only booze left on earth was Jack Daniel's and just about any premium vodka. But of course the codger in the cottage insisted on whiskey that required an extra stop at a liquor store on Hollywood Boulevard.

Raleigh went to his bedroom for his wallet and car keys and studied himself in the mirror. He imagined what he would look like with a little bit of help, like maybe that chin tuck he'd been thinking

about. And a slight eye lift would help, as well as a hair transplant. He knew he'd need serious liposuction to unload the depressing blubber that encased his torso like a truck tire. Well, now he'd be able to afford all of that and more. Lots more. It certainly was not too late to meet an older woman of means, maybe one who lived in the Hollywood Hills, maybe in a house like Casa Brueger.

Raleigh tried to affect a confident self-assured smile at the mirror, but he thought he saw fear in the pale, watery eyes looking back at him.

Jonas Claymore woke up first, as usual. He extended his legs over the side of the bed gingerly but was surprised not to feel the stab of back pain this morning. Then he put his hands on his bony knees, leaned forward, and pushed himself upright. There was a twinge but nothing he couldn't handle.

He gave Megan a smack with his open hand on the bottom of her foot, and she sat up saying, "Huh?"

"I'm feeling okay today," he said. "It's time to go to work."

She began coughing almost at once and was feeling her own burning pain in her shoulder joints and knees. She hoped there were some perks left or even some zannies lying around.

"I'm glad you feel okay," she said. "Because I don't feel okay."

"A chick your age should be able to bounce back," he said. "You oughtta take better care of yourself. Do some workouts once in a while. We gotta get some cash to tide us over. When was the last time you called your mom?"

"Maybe a month," she said.

"Go take a shower," he said. "Clear your head. Think about asking your mom to give us another loan. Tell her you'll pay her back with a high rate of interest."

Megan got painfully out of bed, walked to the little bathroom, and said, "Sure. My mom's gonna believe I'll pay her back. Like she believes in honest lawyers and leprechauns."

"We're gonna cruise today," Jonas said. "Nothing serious yet. Just cruising and casing. We ain't making the same mistakes the Bling Ring made. We'll make sure we know what's what before we ever set foot on anybody's property, unless we spot some easy pickings like we did the last time. Then we go for it."

Megan sat down on the toilet and said, "How easy was it last time, Jonas? You've been flat on your back for days." And she slammed the bathroom door before he could whine about hearing her pee.

At 12:30 P.M., Raleigh Dibble was sitting in the kitchen of the Brueger home, waiting and clock-watching. He'd done every chore he could think of. He tried to consider every way that Nigel Wickland's plan could go wrong, but whenever he did, he thought of what it would be like to stroll into a bank and put half a million into a safe-deposit box and some mad money into his checking account. But why did it have to be only half a million? Nigel had told him that his European auctioneer claimed that a million was the *least* they would get in today's market for the two Impressionist works. Maybe they'd get 1.2 million. Maybe 1.5 million! Or maybe it was crazy to aim for the stars at his age. But since this was all about art, why not dip the brush of imagination into the colors of fantasy and boldly paint a portrait of a future life? Then again, isn't that what people who end up looking at the stars through steel bars and chain-link did? Right before somebody pisses all over their palette?

When the phone gave two brief rings, indicating someone was at the gate, Raleigh jumped from the kitchen chair. He looked at his watch and saw it was 12:50. Not *precisely* 1 P.M., but he was glad Nigel was early. His hands were shaking when he picked up the receiver and said, "Yes?"

"It's me," Nigel said.

Raleigh pressed the key to open the electric gate and went to the

door. Nigel pulled into the faux-cobblestone driveway in his Chevrolet cargo van and made the circle, parking by the entrance door. Raleigh stepped out and walked to the driveway as Nigel got out. They were both too nervous to even think about shaking hands. Nigel opened the side door of the cargo van.

Raleigh looked at "Wickland Gallery" on the side of the van and said, "I'm surprised you brought your own wheels, Nigel. A man as careful as you."

"I had no bloody choice," he said. "I told Ruth that our van needs a tune-up and I asked her to bring her brother's truck to work today. She said she would, but then she called in sick. Believe me, I don't want some nosy neighbor asking Leona what the Wickland Gallery was doing at her house while she was gone. But I didn't think your frayed nerves would withstand a postponement, so here we are. Now that I look around more carefully at this place, there's no need to be worrying about nosy neighbors."

Just like him, Raleigh thought. He fucks up and covers by blaming it on my nerves.

Of all the things that Raleigh did have to worry about, he figured the Wickland Gallery van was the least of it. The Bruegers' mini-estate was secluded by many olive, lemon, and orange trees, and especially by the wall of junipers planted both inside and outside the encircling five-foot wall. He doubted if anyone would notice or even see the van when it entered.

"Help me unload the equipment, will you?" Nigel said.

For the next few minutes, they carried into the house a tripod, two floodlights on lightweight stands, and two umbrella reflectors. Nigel carried the Canon 350 digital camera that he believed was simple enough for him to handle.

The moment they were inside, Raleigh began worrying about Marty Brueger. He ran to the French doors and looked out at the cottage to make sure the old man was inside and not strolling in the garden.

Nigel was trying to take careful measurements of both canvases and he said, "For god's sake, Raleigh, can't you relax a bit and help me?"

Suddenly Raleigh's nerves began to crack, and he said, "How much practice did you do, Nigel?"

"I've been practicing nearly every day for two weeks," Nigel said. "My friend at the lab and I both made different mistakes, but eventually we learned from those mistakes. The last few times I photographed a painting of similar size, it turned out perfectly."

"Did you use the same camera?" Raleigh wanted to know.

"Yes, and the same goddamn tripod and the same lights. Now please close the drapes and stop fretting. You're making me nervous."

It was the first time that Raleigh had ever closed the heavy drapes in that part of the house and he was surprised how dark the great room and corridor became. Then he realized that the drapes were lined with blackout material because the Bruegers used to show movies in that room. There was a screen that lowered from the ceiling at the touch of a button.

Nigel pulled two pairs of latex gloves from his pocket and said, "Put these on. I don't want our fingerprints on these pieces."

"Why do we need to worry?" Raleigh asked. "According to you, they're not even going to notice anything for months. And the moving guys will be handling the pictures, won't they? Their prints will be all over them."

"Just do it, Raleigh," Nigel said. "Why do we have to debate everything?"

Raleigh pulled on the latex gloves and said, "I thought there was no risk here."

"All the so-called art lovers in this town hang their pictures too high," Nigel complained as he set up his umbrella lights. "These baroque gilded frames are just what I'd have expected from Sammy Brueger and his ilk."

Raleigh thought the frames looked okay. And who gave a shit

about the frames anyway? He couldn't stop himself from checking his watch obsessively.

It took Nigel Wickland nearly an hour to carefully remove both canvases from their frames and rehang them from little wires that he carefully stapled to the stretcher bars.

Then Nigel said, "Get me something steady to stand on. A small stepladder, perhaps."

Raleigh ran to the laundry room and came back with a six-foot ladder, opened it, and placed it behind Nigel. And trying to be helpful, Raleigh turned on the lights over both paintings.

"No, no!" Nigel said petulantly. "We must have the painting lights off."

After he sulked for a moment, Raleigh said, " I don't know anything about photography. Will these be developed as slides or what?"

"Digital photos, just as I told you before," Nigel said. "The lab will download them onto a computer and blow them up to any size we want. And thanks to my trial-and-error rehearsals during the last two weeks, I know precisely how large I want them."

There he goes again, Raleigh thought. *Precisely.*

Nigel put the ladder where he wanted it and placed the umbrella lights at each side of the largest painting, *The Woman by the Water,* which looked to Raleigh to be almost four feet tall and nearly five feet wide.

Nigel stood on the first step of the ladder and said, "Move that light a bit to the left. They must be level with the painting."

Raleigh did as he was told and Nigel said, "That's too much. Come back half an inch. There. That's good. Now do the same with the other one. I've got to make sure to line it up so that there's no perspective."

"Okay, just get it done!" Raleigh said.

Still looking through the viewfinder, Nigel said, "And I must get the piece as big as I can get it within the frame."

Raleigh was sweating and thinking, It's only the lights that're making me sweat. I'm not really that scared. Then he blurted, "What if Marty Brueger comes here to the main house and starts banging on the door?"

"Bloody hell!" Nigel said. "I'm trying to compose this shot!"

Raleigh's courage was leaking out like the sweat that was running from every pore, and he said, "What if somebody comes by for some other reason and catches us? What would we say?"

Nigel sighed and stepped off the ladder. He took the inhaler from his pocket and had a puff. He waited a moment and said, "Well, then, we would simply tell them that as Mrs. Brueger's art adviser, I decided to photograph the paintings to have the pictures put onto greeting cards as a surprise for my dear client."

"And then what would we do?"

Nigel took a deep breath, blew it out, and said in sheer exasperation, "And then of course we would abandon this little project and I would go back to being a gallery owner on the verge of bankruptcy. And you would continue as a domestic servant who will spend his old age living off welfare and Social Security. Now, will you please act like a man so we can proceed and get this job done?"

Raleigh glared at him for a long moment, feeling the anger swell his throat. This flouncing Nancy boy was telling him to act like a man? But all he said to Nigel was "Okay, let's proceed."

Nigel got back on the ladder and aimed the camera again. Before he shot his first picture he calmed himself by talking, and he said, "I chose these Impressionist pieces precisely because Impressionist art is blurry. It is, after all, the artist's impression, is it not? The Impressionist artist is not interested in photographic clarity. They're perfect for our needs."

Raleigh gave up counting the shots that Nigel took. Finally Nigel said, "Voilà! It's done. Now to *Flowers on the Hillside*."

"Damn!" Raleigh said. "That took too long. The second one

won't take as long, will it? Marty Brueger will be waking up pretty soon."

"Not a problem," Nigel said. "The second one will go fast."

For the very first time, Raleigh took a look at the other painting. It was a blur of colors that suggested a field of flowers on a hillside with something that looked like a windmill in the distance. "This one's worth almost as much, huh?" Raleigh asked. "It's a lot smaller."

"You have no idea," Nigel said, moving the light stands and the tripod. "*Flowers on the Hillside* could possibly fetch even more than *The Woman by the Water*. Now, let's position everything exactly as we did before."

At that moment, Raleigh had a head-slapping thought: What if these paintings did bring in way more than a million as he'd fantasized? What if they brought in 2 million? How would he ever know? What if Nigel told him that the recession is bad in all the cities he'd mentioned? What if he claimed that he could get only $300,000 for both pictures? How would he ever know if Nigel was lying? He quelled his suspicions by reminding himself that this was only the first phase of the scheme.

Raleigh decided that he needed to work out some details with his prissy partner before Nigel came back to do the switch. But how would he do that? He knew nothing about the European auctioneer and what the art could reasonably fetch. Was he completely at the mercy of Nigel's true intentions? The more he came to dislike Nigel Wickland, the more worrisome the scheme became.

Ten minutes later the phone buzzed from the cottage and Raleigh uttered a choked-off cry. Then he said, "It's Marty Brueger!"

Nigel lowered the camera and said, "Go tend to him, then. Christ, he's virtually senile. You can handle it." And he went back to composing his shot.

Raleigh hurried out the side door and ran to the cottage. When

he entered, Marty Brueger was in his pajamas, looking as though he'd forgotten why he rang.

"Yes, Mr. Brueger," Raleigh said. "Do you need something?"

"My teeth," Marty Brueger said. "Where's my teeth?"

"Aren't they in the glass where they usually are?"

"Don't you think I looked there?" the old man said.

"We'll find them, Mr. Brueger," Raleigh said. "Why don't you just sit in your chair and relax and watch *The Girls Next Door*? That Hugh Hefner's really a card, isn't he?"

"It's not on now, Raleigh, and I can't find the most recent videotape."

"You don't need videotape anymore, Mr. Brueger," Raleigh said. "All of your favorite shows have been recorded for you, remember?"

"I always forget how to do that TIVO shit," Marty Brueger said.

"I'll go over it again with you," Raleigh said. "Everything's there for you anytime you want to watch. You just go to your stored programs and select whatever you wish."

"Even *Showbiz Tonight*?" Marty Brueger asked.

"Every single episode," Raleigh assured him. "You've got them there waiting for you."

"I still need my teeth," the old man said.

"I'll do a thorough search for them," Raleigh said.

"If you find them, I'd like to go to one of those new trendy places for dinner," Marty Brueger said. "Like Mr. Chow's."

"Mr. Chow's has been around a long time," Raleigh said. "It's not new but it's still very popular with movie people."

"Spago isn't new anymore either, is it?" Marty Brueger asked.

"No, sir," Raleigh said. "I think it's older than Mr. Chow's. And you might see some celebrities there as well."

"It's funny how time plays tricks on your memory," Marty Brueger said. "Do famous people still go to the Polo Lounge for lunch? People in the business who're my age?"

Raleigh thought, There's nobody in the business your age, but he said, "I think so. I'll find out for sure."

"Talking about restaurants has made me hungry," Marty Brueger said. "Maybe I'll stroll up to the house and look for something in the fridge that I can eat without teeth."

"No, no, Mr. Brueger!" Raleigh cried. "Just sit down and relax. I'll fix you something tasty for a snack, but first you need something to chew with, don't you?"

"I'll tell you, Raleigh," Marty Brueger said. "It's a sad time in a man's life when his dick's gone missing and he can't even find his fucking teeth."

While Raleigh Dibble searched for Marty Brueger's teeth, Jonas Claymore and Megan Burke were driving toward Woodrow Wilson Drive, eyeing many potential targets, as well as checking their maps and addresses for any homes belonging to stars or celebutants.

"I think Outpost has some juicy targets," Jonas said to Megan, who had downed two perks and was zoning as he drove. "But I like it way up here, too."

"I think we're going to die like Bonnie and Clyde," Megan said bleakly.

"Who?"

"The old movie? You know, about the bank robbers? A guy and a chick rob banks and it's all a trip until they get shot to pieces. I think that's how we'll end up."

"Who wants to get old?" Jonas said.

"Yeah, but it might be nice to get old enough to walk in a bar and buy a drink without showing a phony ID. Is that asking too much?"

"You got no imagination," Jonas said.

"Yes, I do," she said. "I can imagine us checking out like Bonnie and Clyde now that we've decided to really go bad."

Ignoring her, Jonas said, "I musta seen a hundred houses that look good to me. Like that one there."

He pointed out one of the many Spanish Colonial Revivals, usually done in the mission- or hacienda-style with a red-tile roof and white-plastered walls. This one was large, with a detached guesthouse and a solid barrier of junipers that almost hid the main house from view except from the road above. Jonas pulled to the side and stopped.

"Get out for a minute," he said.

"What for? I'm tired!"

"You're always tired," he said. "Get out."

Megan opened the door, mumbling, got out, and shuffled along behind him. He strolled over to the junipers and pulled two of them apart, peeking in at the property.

"See," he said. "This place has more land than the others. Do you know what land costs up here?"

Megan just shook her head, and Jonas said, "Plenty, that's how much. I bet there's a tennis court down behind there. This is the kinda place we should go for. But not now. Look, there's a van down there by the garage. It says something on the side but it's parked at an angle, so I can't read it. Probably a delivery guy or a plumber or something."

"Can we go home now?" Megan said.

He said, "What we gotta do is come back here sometime when there's no car in the driveway and no gardeners around and ring the bell."

"There's a big gate," Megan said.

"We ring the bell at the gate," Jonas said. "There must be one. And if there's no answer we go over the wall and check it out and see what we can see."

"And what if there's another dog like last time?" Megan said. "Maybe a vicious guard dog?"

That stopped him. His back was still sending him messages

from time to time. He said, "Okay, we'll come by a couple more times on other days before we try out a house like this. Meanwhile, we can go for more conventional places where we can see the yards and figure out if there's a guard dog or not."

"Let's go home and I'll call my mom," Megan said.

"For what?"

"I'll beg her for a loan of two hundred. I'll say that I'm staying with a friend and we're being evicted on Saturday unless we can come up with the money. She always says she'll never give up on me. I'm her firstborn and I don't think she'll let me down. Not that I'm proud of it." She paused and said, "I just need a taste of ox."

Jonas pressed hard on the small of his back, groaned, and said, "I wonder why God is letting me get knocked on my ass so much lately?"

Raleigh Dibble found Marty Brueger's missing dentures in the trash can by the toilet, but how they got there was anybody's guess. He figured it was the result of too much Irish whiskey. If the old man had any cash to speak of, that probably would've ended up shit-canned as well. But only Raleigh had access to the modest checking account at the local bank that Leona Brueger had left for groceries and other items in order to keep the house running smoothly while she was gone. She had opened the account with $4,000 and told him to phone her in Tuscany if any sort of emergency came up requiring more funds.

"Mr. Brueger," Raleigh said, "why don't you sit in your chair and watch *Oprah* or something? I'm going up to the house now to make you a nice snack. How about one of my special omelets?"

Marty Brueger nodded and said, "Got any more whiskey in the butler's pantry up there?"

"No, but I'll run out and get some later," Raleigh said.

"Why don't I go up there with you and look?" Marty Brueger said.

"No, Mr. Brueger!" Raleigh said. "Just rest. There might be another bottle. I'll be right back."

"I'll have all the rest I need pretty soon," the old man muttered.

Raleigh was a wreck by the time he got back to the house. But he was overjoyed to see that the floodlights had been turned off in the great room, and the tripod was lying on the floor. Nigel Wickland had finished.

Raleigh said to him, "Did you get it done the way you wanted?"

"It's a wrap, as they say in Hollywood," Nigel Wickland said with a satisfied grin. "The next trip here will be far briefer. These are all conventional frames, even if the paintings are not of a common size. It'll be easy enough to make the poster board fit nicely. I think Sammy Brueger had them reframed with those ghastly ornate monstrosities in the past dozen years or so."

Raleigh was so relieved, he felt like sitting down. Now he had a headache, and he was a man who seldom got one. "When're you coming back?"

"It depends on how it goes at the lab," Nigel said. "I'll apply as much pressure as I can to my friend and I'll offer him a bonus of several hundred dollars if he can speed up the process. But it can't be done overnight, you know."

"Will you call me as soon as it's done?"

"Of course," Nigel said. "But be careful never to use your name if you ever ring my office again. And don't use my name when I ring you here. We must proceed precisely as planned."

We're going to come to a new understanding before we're through, Raleigh thought. But all he said was, "Yes, precisely."

★ FOURTEEN ★

VIV DALEY AND Georgie Adams were "off the beach" and cleared for street duty while Force Investigation Division worked on building a twelve-inch-high stack of reports that would be presented to a Use-of-Force Board within nine months of the officer-involved shooting of Louis Dryden. Viv was not as jocular as she had been before that night, and nor was Georgie. Neither would ever speak of Cindy Kroll or her murdered baby again, at least not to each other.

They both had been ordered down to Chinatown, where Behavioral Science Services had their offices, and each one spoke with a BSS psychologist about the event in Little Armenia. Georgie had given brief answers to every question that the shrink asked regarding the taking of a human life. He said that he'd killed a few insurgents in Iraq and that this had felt no different to him afterward. He simply shook his head when he was asked if he had gone upstairs and seen the strangled baby. Both officers had the typical cop's distrust of shrinks from having seen and heard all that the profession had done with their "expert" opinions as witnesses for and against the prosecution in criminal cases.

Viv said that as far as she was concerned, they had killed a boogeyman and she felt not a shred of doubt or remorse about

his death. She was less forthcoming when asked by her questioner to talk about what she'd seen in Cindy Kroll's apartment. The psychologist was a generation older than Viv and had gentle eyes and a motherly manner. At the very beginning of their session, she had come from behind her desk to sit next to Viv in one of the two client chairs. She asked Viv to call her Jane, but Viv never used the woman's given name at any time during that meeting.

When pressed repeatedly about her feelings concerning that horrific event, Viv reluctantly admitted to the psychologist that she'd grappled with impulses to contact the Department of Children and Family Services about the surviving child of Cindy Kroll. Viv said she'd thought about inquiring into the possibility of fostering the toddler, who she'd learned was named Carly, at least until a responsible relative could be found or until the child could be placed for adoption.

But Viv then added, "Of course, that was a silly thought. It made no sense at all. Here I am, a single woman with a job that requires me to work half the night, and then of course I have to sleep half the morning. Why would they ever give an infant to someone like me to foster?"

"I agree with you that they certainly would not," the psychologist said. "Still, you say you had impulses about being a foster parent, even if it was impossible given your lifestyle. Why was that, do you think?"

"I don't know," Viv said. "Pity, I guess. It was all so...pitiful."

Viv refused to do more than shake her head when asked if she felt any residue of guilt or responsibility for what had happened to Cindy Kroll and her baby that night, and Viv bristled when the psychiatrist pressed her on it.

"Why should I?" she said.

"You shouldn't," the shrink replied. "But sometimes our unconscious mind doesn't understand words like *should* and *shouldn't*."

"Well, I don't," Viv said. "Just because I had a random thought about how that apartment could be attacked doesn't mean I had a premonition or something. I'm not a mentalist, you know."

"No," the psychologist said. "You're not. You were less cynical than the two detectives and your partner."

"What do you mean?" Viv asked suspiciously.

The psychologist said, "Police officers become prematurely cynical from seeing the worst of people and ordinary people at their worst. They don mental and emotional armor in self-defense. They tend to scoff at anything extraordinary. Your suggestion regarding the ladder and the roof was rebuffed as far-fetched, but it wasn't. You were not cynical. You were trying to be a good police officer by imagining a very unlikely scenario that ultimately came true."

Viv didn't say anything and the psychologist said, "Had you ever seen something very horrific before? Something involving helpless children?"

Viv hesitated and then said, "I remember one case when an Eighteenth Streeter who called himself the Tax Collector pistol-whipped a street vendor for not paying protection money. He decided he needed to teach all the vendors a lesson and he shot the man's baby right there in his stroller."

The psychologist shook her head slowly and said, "I can only imagine how you felt when you got there."

Viv said, "And there was the time we got a call that taught me why detectives who work child abuse are the only coppers who're never asked about their work by their civilian friends. The call came right after we cleared from roll call. This tot had been burned real bad in the bathtub and his mother said it was an accident. Except that his flesh was burned off from his elbows, straight down from that demarcation line. That meant that the child had been held by the wrists and put down into the scalding water. It turned out that the mother's boyfriend did it when he got frustrated during a potty training session. When the man was arrested, he said he

didn't know the water was that hot. I was told later that they had to put the skin from dead people on the third-degree burns. It happened on the child's second birthday. His name was Stevie."

The psychologist said, "You know that you can come back and see me anytime, Vivien. You don't have to wait until you're ordered to come here."

Viv gave the shrink a lopsided smile and said, "Don't you know that cops consider it wussy to run down here and talk to you people?"

The psychologist smiled and said, "Oh, yes, how well I know. We have a lonely job around here because of the rampant machismo and super-self-reliance of your colleagues in blue. Believe me, I know all about that."

"Well, then, you get it," Viv said and fell silent.

The psychologist was quiet for a moment watching Viv gaze through the window as though she'd like to escape. Then she said, "Had you ever felt a strong impulse to foster a child before the incident in Little Armenia?"

"No, I hadn't," Viv said, and looked at the shrink again with a hint of defiance. And again she said, "Why should I?"

"You shouldn't," the psychiatrist said. "But this case was different, wasn't it? This had to do with Carly's mother and her baby brother, and feelings of great...discomfort that you were experiencing because of what happened to them. Isn't that true?"

"Maybe," Viv conceded. "Are you trying to tell me that you think I do feel somehow responsible?"

"That man Louis Dryden was responsible," the psychologist said. "Cindy Kroll bore some responsibility also. She refused to go to a shelter where she and her children would've been safe until your detectives could have contacted Louis Dryden and warned him to stay away. You are obviously an extremely responsible person, Vivien, but none of this should become your burden. Given all that was known, the actions of you and your colleagues were reasonable and understandable. This event was an anomaly."

"Have we been talking about some sort of...hidden guilt feelings here?" Viv asked. "Is that what we're talking about?"

"If we are, I hope we can dispel it," the shrink said. "The event itself was exceptionally horrific. You saw things that night that nobody should ever see."

"I suppose so," Viv said. Then she said, "That incident in Little Armenia...it would rattle anybody, wouldn't it?"

"It certainly would," the shrink said.

"And on top of that..."

The psychologist was quiet until she finally said, "And on top of that? What, Vivien?"

"Carly was so traumatized and confused that she kept...she kept calling me...Mommy."

Both women were silent and Viv was startled to taste tears in her mouth. And then she broke down and wept in her hands. The psychiatrist moved a box of tissues from her desktop closer to Viv Daley's chair and waited for her tears to stop.

At midwatch roll call that evening the word was passed from cop to cop that one of the Department's highest-ranking brass had been caught on a dark street in south L.A. with a hooker in his car. And she was not some special Beyoncé look-alike but just a grungy old streetwalker who probably had every known STD and some new ones that weren't yet cataloged. When he badged the patrol unit that caught him, he offered the lame excuse that he was "interrogating" the hooker, who quickly got out of his car and continued on her way.

The two cops assured him that this contact would remain confidential, but by the end of watch they had each texted more than a dozen coppers, who each texted a dozen more, in a chain that didn't end until everybody in the LAPD and beyond knew about it. It was a perfect example of how well things remain confidential in police work, and why cops howl in laughter when cop-hating commenta-

tors on TV refer to "the blue wall of silence" or "closing ranks" in controversial cases involving allegations of excessive force and other misconduct, usually involving ethnic minorities.

On that subject, Sergeant Murillo said at roll call, "I could offer to buy a brand-new car to any copper around here who could keep something on the down-low for even one day, and I'd never have to worry about ever touching my life savings. Which I think amounts to about four hundred dollars last time I checked."

After they cleared for calls that evening, Flotsam and Jetsam were not on the street five minutes before a late-model Mustang cruising slowly in the curb lane blew a stoplight on east Sunset Boulevard and caused several drivers to jump on their brakes and yell curses.

"You're up," Jetsam said and did a U-ee, pulling behind the Mustang with his lights flashing. He honked the horn to get the driver to notice.

The driver was so busy talking on his cell phone and driving so erratically that they thought he was DUI. When he finally saw them in his rearview mirror, he pulled to the curb. He was fumbling around so much that they thought he might be trying to hide some contraband or even a weapon, so both cops jumped out quickly and ran up to the Mustang, Flotsam on the driver's side with his hand on his Glock.

Jetsam approached on the passenger side, and since it was still light, they could both see well, and what they saw was a white-collar guy with his shirttail hanging out his fly.

Flotsam said, "License and registration, please."

The tall cop looked across the Mustang roof and grimaced at his partner. Since this was sometimes a whore track after dark, it figured that the motorist was looking to pick up a hooker on the way home from work. It was reasonable to assume that maybe he was doing some phone sex at the same time and it all got to be a libido overload.

Flotsam wrote the ticket on the hood of their shop, and Jetsam said, "Bro, whatever you do, don't shake hands with him."

Flotsam got back to the car and handed the man the citation book and his ballpoint pen. While the driver signed the ticket, Flotsam looked at the damp spot on the man's shirt where he'd wiped his fingers, and said, "You can keep the pen, sir. Compliments of the city of Los Angeles."

Hollywood Nate and Snuffy Salcedo got a message on their dashboard computer regarding "a female 5150 at Hollywood and Highland" on the Walk of Fame. Snuffy punched the en route button, and Nate glanced at the message and said, "A female mental case on the Walk of Fame. How remarkable. That description could apply to *anybody* on Hollywood Boulevard, since gender around here is always questionable anyway."

"I wonder which wack job it is," Snuffy said.

"Just pick anyone that's off the hook and making more noise than the others," Nate said.

When they got to the famous intersection and started cruising westbound very slowly, it didn't take long to spot her among the tourist throngs. She was a black woman about forty years of age who weighed upward of two hundred and fifty pounds. Her hair was dyed the color of a traffic cone, and her costume consisted of a man's olive-green battle jacket, World War II vintage, complete with combat ribbons. From her ample waist south, she wore Day-Glo pink tights and cowboy boots. She was banging two trash can lids together like cymbals and chanting gibberish. Of course, tourists and Street Characters scattered when she got near them, but there was one who did not move fast enough.

The cops saw her suddenly bang Wonder Woman on the head with a trash can lid, and that was enough for 6-X-66. She was an apparent danger to herself and others.

Hollywood Nate pulled to the curb and said, "This one will do, but she's probably not the looniest on the boulevard by any means."

"Loony but not lonely," Snuffy said. "There's always someone inside their heads to talk to."

The woman was cheerful and smiling when both cops approached her on foot, and Nate said, "Could I please see your cymbals?"

She proudly handed him the trash can lids, saying, "Okey-dokey."

"I'll bet you have lots of cymbals," Nate said. "How would you like to come with us and play for some nice folks?"

"Okey-dokey," she said.

"What's your name?" Snuffy asked.

She pondered until some cognition kicked in, and she said, "Pearl."

"I'm Snuffy and he's Nate."

"Whoopdedoo!" Pearl said, happy to meet new friends.

Pearl was so affable and even cute that Nate said, "I don't have the heart to hook her up, partner. Let's try her out in the backseat without the cuffs. If she kills you with a hidden hat pin, it's all my fault."

Nate opened the rear door and Pearl got in, fastening her seat belt without being told to do it.

"She's done this before," Nate said.

Snuffy looked at her through the cage and said, "You really shouldn't whack people on the bean, Pearl. It's very naughty."

"Very naughty, very naughty!" Pearl agreed.

Snuffy said quietly to Nate. "A good sign. Utter remorse."

As they drove east on Sunset Boulevard at twilight, they began to realize that Pearl had a peculiar tic where she not only repeated fragments of what she'd just heard but seemed to take particular delight in it if she was told to stop.

At one point Snuffy looked at a silver Porsche cruising past and said to Nate, "Don't you love that too-cool nine-eleven?"

Pearl said, "Too-cool!"

Nate turned to look at the Porsche and said, "Yeah, it's sweet."

"It's sweet!" Pearl said.

Testing her, Snuffy said, "Don't say it's sweet, Pearl."

"It's sweet, it's sweet!" Pearl said with more enthusiasm.

They rode in silence for a while, heading for Parker Center, to the Mental Evaluation Unit for a commitment approval. After that, they would transport her the few miles to the USC Medical Center on the grounds of the old county hospital. These were the last weeks for the venerable LAPD main headquarters building before it would be abandoned and torn down to the ground. Everything was in the process of being moved to the new Police Administration Building, literally in the shadow of City Hall.

The new PAB was across the street from the Department of Water & Power, whose building the cops said looked like the Death Star in the *Star Wars* movies. There was extremely inadequate parking in the immediate area of the new PAB, and the Department of Transportation was only too eager to write tickets to any radio cars that they found temporarily parked in white and yellow zones. Of course, that produced noisy internecine bitterness.

Outside the new building were large, expensive, and controversial metal sculptures that were meant to give the impression of six bears and two monkeys. The cops figured that soon enough they'd be arresting sex offenders for humping them. The building was designed in such a way that the glass windows facing north caught the reflection of City Hall, which was directly across First Street. The coppers said that the dominant City Hall reflection seen from the new building was a chillingly sinister omen of what the future had in store for them.

As they were nearing their destination, Nate said to Snuffy, "Do you get all nostalgic going back to Parker Center, where you spent all those years driving for those sixth-floor power freaks?"

"Power freaks!" Pearl said.

Snuffy said sotto to Nate in order to keep Pearl quiet, "Mister is the one I'll always remember. One of his favorite movies is *North by Northwest*. You know, the Hitchcock movie where Cary Grant and his chick get chased over the presidents' faces on Mount Rushmore?"

Ever the movies buff, Nate whispered back at him, "Of course. That chick was Eva Marie Saint."

Snuffy forgot to whisper and said, "Yeah, well, I think the reason Mister loves that movie is because he always saw *his* face up there. He imagined they were running across *his* eyebrows and jumping on *his* upper lip."

"His upper lip!" Pearl said.

"I wish she'd stop that," Nate said. "It's getting on my nerves."

Snuffy said to Nate, "Lower her window halfway. I wanna try something."

When the window beside Pearl came partly down, they were stopped at an intersection on east Sunset Boulevard in the Silverlake district, where there was urban renewal going on, with younger people moving into apartments and lofts. Waiting to cross the street was an attractive woman talking to a guy in a Joseph Abboud suit who had that self-important, young professional look, water bottle and all.

Snuffy said, "Pearl, do *not* call that man a yuppie dipshit."

Pearl looked at the man, and when the light turned green and they were moving, she startled the couple by yelling, "Yuppie dipshit!"

Snuffy whispered, "She'll say exactly what we tell her not to say. There's gotta be something we can do with this."

As it turned out, there was. When they got to Parker Center and parked underneath, Snuffy felt a chill of remembrance. Here he was, back in the place where he'd worked for so many years. The criminal element referred to it as the Glass House because of the walls of windows on the north and south exposures. The faces

of the various chiefs he had driven for and protected swam before his eyes. For a moment he struggled to remember something good about those recent years. His reverie was shattered and he could hardly believe it when the door leading from the building to the parking lot opened. Snuffy saw one of his old friends and fellow security aides. And who emerged behind the aide but the Man himself!

As Nate pulled into a parking space, Snuffy said quietly, "It's Mister! Jesus, Mary, and Joseph, it's Mister!"

The chief and his aide were both wearing uniforms on this day, and the security aide paused when the chief said something and looked at his watch.

Snuffy whispered to Nate, "He's probably trying to remember how many stoplights there are between here and where they're going, and he's gonna decide exactly how long it should take them to get there."

The chief and his aide had to pass right by the space where Nate had parked their shop, and Snuffy scooted down in his seat, concealing his face with his hand, pretending to write in his log.

He whispered to Nate, "Partner, this is destiny." Then he turned toward the cage and said, "Pearl, pay attention to this. Do *not* call that man an egomaniac."

When Mister and his aide were passing the car, Pearl stuck her face out and yelled, "Igloo maniac! Igloo maniac!"

The chief of police flinched and glanced sharply to his right. He saw Pearl smiling beatifically through the open car window. He ignored her and kept on walking toward the SUV with the ominous tinted windows. His security aide opened the door for the chief and he got in.

Hollywood Nate said sotto, "So that's your idea of get-back? Snuffy's revenge has come down to calling the chief of police a crazy Eskimo?"

Snuffy Salcedo whispered back, "When you get right down to

it, she mighta got it right. He's been giving the L.A. media and City Hall a major snow job for the past seven and a half years."

When they got out of the car and entered the building, Snuffy said, "Anyways, Pearl did her best. On our way to the funny place, let's stop and buy her some ice cream."

"Ice cream! Whoopdedoo!" Pearl cried, and yodeled merrily as she frolicked along the corridor and into the depressing basement office of the Mental Evaluation Unit, inside the doomed old building that for more than half a century lawbreakers had called the Glass House.

FIFTEEN

MARTY BRUEGER SAID to Raleigh Dibble, "It's Thursday and I'm sick of sitting around here. If I'm gonna stroke out and die, I want it to be in Chasen's eating a big bowl of chili."

Raleigh said, "Mr. Brueger, Chasen's has been closed for a very long time, don't you remember?"

"Oh, shit, that's right," Marty Brueger said. "Oh, my mind."

Raleigh was removing the breakfast tray from the table in the cottage and trying to keep his game face on, even though the old coot was starting to smell ripe. It took an effort for Raleigh not to turn away when he needed to take a breath. He also wanted to trim the tufts of hair sprouting from the geezer's ears.

"Elizabeth Taylor loved Chasen's chili. I saw her there many times," Marty Brueger said.

"Yes, I know," Raleigh said.

"She was usually with her husband, Rex Harrison."

"Richard Burton," Raleigh said.

"What's he got to do with it?" Marty Brueger said.

"She was married to him. Not to Rex Harrison."

"Oh, shit!" Marty Brueger said. "Don't ever get as old as me, Raleigh. Take the gas pipe before you do. An old man's life is for shit!"

"There, there, Mr. Brueger," Raleigh said. "Why don't you take a nice bath? It'll make you feel better."

"All right. Then I wanna talk about going someplace. I'm sick of this fucking place."

"Do you need help getting into the bath?" Raleigh asked.

"Raleigh, the day I can't go into a walk-in shower and sit on a bench and turn on the water, that's the day I'll ask you to go out and buy me a gun."

"Okay, Mr. Brueger," Raleigh said. "I'll give you an hour and then I'll come back and we'll talk about an outing. Maybe we could drive to the beach and look at the pretty girls. You said you used to like to do that. Or maybe we could go to the movies in Westwood. Or maybe—"

Marty Brueger interrupted Raleigh with plaintive eyes that looked somehow touching through those Coke-bottle glasses. He said, "I can't even remember the last time I was able to get an erection. I should have had it carbon-dated."

This time it was Megan Burke dragging Jonas Claymore out of bed. Jonas had done way too much Vicodin before going to sleep and he'd washed it all down with screw-top wine. He opened his eyes in utter disorientation when she shook him and said, "Jonas, wake up! You gotta get up right away."

"What?" he said. "What?"

She said, "Mr. Casper's on his way."

Jonas raised himself on his elbows and said, "Who?"

"Your landlord, that's who," Megan said. "He just phoned your cell and he wants his rent money. Twelve hundred dollars."

Jonas yawned, sat up, and said, "It ain't no thing. Give it to him. You got it from your old lady, didn't you?"

"Jonas, focus! I got two hundred from my mom, remember? And we spent half of it last night. Do you remember saying you wanted vike and vino?"

"Oh, Christ," he said, vaguely remembering. "Is that all this fucking world's about? Greedy rich people keeping people like us as serfs and slaves?"

"You have to talk to him," she said. "He says he'll shut off your water and have you evicted."

"Like hell he will," Jonas said. "That little slumlord kike can't push us around."

"Get dressed," Megan said, "and think of something."

"Okay, that does it," Jonas said. "We're going up to the Hollywood Hills in earnest today. No more casing. This is the real thing. Where does Paris Hilton live these days? Anybody can walk into *her* crib and she won't even know it."

While Jonas was trying to swallow a bite of scrambled egg with stale toast, Megan tried to tidy up the little apartment. She stacked the pizza boxes and paper plates on top of the fridge and piled the other debris in the kitchen sink, since the trash can was full of soft-drink cans and candy wrappers.

Then she hurried into their tiny bedroom, and Jonas said to her, "Where you going?"

"To make the bed. In case he goes in there to check things out."

"Get the fuck back here," Jonas said. "You think I'm gonna let that little hebe cocksucker walk into our bedroom? He's gonna talk to us from outside the door."

"No, Jonas!" Megan said. "We have to invite him in. You need another rent extension, so you have to be nice to the man. You get more flies with honey, right?"

"We got more than enough flies in this fucking place," Jonas said. "We don't need no more."

He was making a halfhearted attempt at brushing his teeth in the bathroom when the knock came at the door. He heard Megan say, "Good morning, sir. Come in, please. I'm a friend of Jonas and I'm visiting for a couple of days."

Jonas was shirtless and shoeless when he entered the living room

in his last pair of jeans that still had the knees intact. He gave the landlord a sulky nod and said, "Good morning."

Contrary to Jonas Claymore's description, Mickey Casper was not little. He was several inches shorter than his lanky young tenant, but he had impressive arms, a chest that stretched his cotton shirt, and veined hands that belonged on a larger man.

He spoke with a very slight Israeli accent and said, "Jonas, I told you last time that I don't need this aggravation month after month. I'm going to have to ask you to leave."

Jonas said, "I got laid off from my job, Mr. Casper. Times are tough right now. We need you to be patient till I get another job."

"This has been going on too long," the landlord said. "I'm giving you notice."

"Now, wait a minute," Jonas said. "I got an interview today with the manager of a Starbucks. I'll be going to work on Monday if he likes me. And I know he'll like me. He said I'm just what he's looking for."

"Which Starbucks?" the landlord asked.

"The one at Sunset and Cahuenga," Jonas said.

"There is no Starbucks at Sunset and Cahuenga. I know that area very well," the landlord said.

Jonas stared at the man, trying to think of what to say, but the fucking headache was killing him. He couldn't think.

Megan said, "Could you please just give him a couple of weeks, Mr. Casper?"

"I'm sorry," the landlord said. "This has been going on too long. I've giving you notice, Jonas."

At that moment Jonas's headache peaked and he exploded with, "Okay, you little kike bastard, but for now this is my residence. Get out."

The landlord went pale around the mouth and started to speak but then changed his mind. He walked toward the door, but it wasn't fast enough for Jonas Claymore. As the landlord stopped

and was about to say something, Jonas gave him a little shove and said, "Get the fuck out now!"

The landlord reacted with a blow to Jonas's solar plexus. It was a punch that only moved eight or ten inches but it was delivered with power and in exactly the spot where he was taught to hit when he'd done some boxing as a young man. Jonas sucked in a breath, started coughing, and went down on one knee and then flopped onto his back.

The landlord directed his fervent apology to Megan, saying, "I'm sorry, miss. I didn't mean to respond like that, but you saw that he pushed me. It was instinct on my part. I'm sorry."

"I didn't see him touch you at all, Mr. Casper," Megan said. "I hope you didn't crack his ribs or something."

Then she knelt beside Jonas, who was mooing like a cow, and said, "Jonas, are you okay? Can you talk?"

Jonas just shook his head slowly and Megan said to the landlord, "I think you'd better leave, Mr. Casper. I'll have to take him to Cedars ER. It could be very serious."

"He shoved me! You must have seen it," the landlord said. Then he added, "Look, Jonas, I'll...I'll give you another two weeks, okay? If you come up with the money then, we can see what's what."

"All right, Mr. Casper," Megan said. "And now, if you'll please go, I'll get him to the ER to see if there's been any damage done."

After the landlord was gone, Jonas rolled over and said, "Fuck! I don't know which hurts more now, my back or my gut."

"That was impressive, Jonas," Megan said.

"What impressive? What the fuck you talking about?"

"The way you goaded him," she said. "The way you made him hit you."

"Are you just stupid or what?" Jonas said, struggling to stand. "He sucker-punched me. That was no act. We're gonna sue that

fucking Jew and take everything he's got. My guts're destroyed. Help me up."

"It'll take a long time to sue him," Megan said, "since you don't even know a lawyer. And I don't think this is the kind of case that lawyers are going to rush to handle. But meanwhile it bought us some time. If we're ever to do what you've said we have to do, it's now or never. We've got no ox, no perks, and no norcos. We're screwed, Jonas. Life is just one long screwing for losers like us."

His headache was thumping now. His brain felt swollen. He went into the bathroom and splashed cold water on his face and looked in the mirror. It took him a moment to count how many times he had been knocked on his ass in this terrible month. Then it hit him: That stupid bitch just said we're losers!

Marty Brueger had opted for a nostalgic visit to the Griffith Park Observatory that day, but when they got there, he didn't care to go inside. He wanted to sit in the car and gaze at the building, with Raleigh wondering what was going on in the old coot's head. Was he remembering some girl he took there ages ago? Was he thinking about those long-dead actors James Dean and Natalie Wood and Sal Mineo in *Rebel Without a Cause,* where this building was featured? Raleigh Dibble didn't have the interest or energy to inquire. He kept thinking of what he could do with half a million dollars to change his situation in this world.

Then, just as impulsively as he had asked to be driven there, Marty Brueger said, "Okay, Raleigh, let's go home. I need a nap."

"Would you like to have lunch somewhere?" Raleigh asked.

"No, just stop at the liquor store and get me some more of that special Irish whiskey. Three bottles this time."

After they had bought the whiskey and got back to the house, Raleigh made sure that the old man was tucked in with a tumbler of whiskey next to his dentures, and he said, "Have a nice sleep, Mr. Brueger. What would you like for supper?"

"Cyanide," Marty Brueger said before closing his eyes. "Just pour it in the whiskey and don't bother me till it's over."

That was the first time that Raleigh Dibble felt truly sorry for the old geezer. When he got back into the main house, his cell rang, and he looked at the number of the Wickland Gallery.

He felt a tightness in his throat when he said to Nigel Wickland, "Okay, what's going on?"

"Progress has been fantastic," Nigel said. "We're going to do it tomorrow."

Raleigh's bowels began to rumble. Tomorrow! They were really going to do it. He'd been longing for this call, but now it terrified him. "What time?"

"When the old man's napping. How about one o'clock?"

"Well...okay."

"Why do you hesitate?"

Raleigh knew it was just nerves on his part, and he said, "No, it's fine. But stay on your cell in case there's a change for any reason."

"Why would there be a change?"

"How the hell would I know?" Raleigh said. "Shit happens, Nigel. Just keep your cell handy, okay?"

"I told you *not* to use names, damn it," Nigel Wickland said.

When Raleigh closed his cell, he muttered, "Arrogant fucking fairy."

Then his bowels rumbled again and he ran to the bathroom.

Megan was even more exhausted and pain-racked than Jonas by the time they finished their work. It had been a day of endless cruising past celebrities' addresses that they found online by using the rented computer at the cybercafé, a commercial enterprise where a hundred computers were operating 24/7. The cybercafé was a favorite haunt of identity thieves, hookers, drug dealers, and scam artists of all kinds. Jonas had insisted on spending a lot of time

there these days, seeking out the addresses that he was convinced would bring them the fortune that the Bling Ring had had in their grasp but lost because of careless planning.

When they finally got back to their apartment, Megan said, "Jonas, I'm hurting bad. My elbows, my knees, everywhere." And then she started that incessant coughing that was getting on his nerves.

"I'm the one that got suckered by that kike asshole," Jonas retorted. "What're you complaining about for chrissake?"

"I'm telling you, I'm in pain. I think I've got arthritis," she said.

"Yeah, arthritis at twenty," he said. "Sure."

"I need something for the pain!"

"You're jonesing," he said. "I told you it'll go away as soon as we can make some money to buy enough ox. As soon as we get it together, I'm sending you for a quick trip to rehab for a spin-dry."

"Sending me to rehab?" she said. "We can't afford rehab. Anyway, I never smoke as much as you do. Why don't you go to rehab?"

"I don't wanna talk about this every time you get sick," Jonas said. "Just go fix supper, will ya? I gotta look at our star maps. I think tomorrow we're gonna shoot for our first real target. We're gonna get serious at last. I got four celebrity cribs picked out and we're gonna get inside one of them. We need sleep so we can keep our heads clear."

Speaking of his head made him realize that his headache was almost gone, so he thought he could maybe use a sleep inducer.

"We got any wine and watsons left?" he asked. "That should fix me up till tomorrow. Like my mom used to say, I'll be right as rain then."

"We had real rain in Oregon," Meg said despondently. "This goddamn place is just a glitzy desert."

SIXTEEN

SERGEANT MURILLO LIKED to send the troops out on the streets in good spirits, so he invited humorous comments as soon as he finished reading the crimes and other roll call material. He said, "Has anything noteworthy happened lately that you would like to share?"

Flotsam said, "Yeah, Sarge, the other night we got a call from a drunk hooker on the Sunset track who made an ADW report against some dude that kicked her in the giz when she refused to boink him for twenty bucks. When we got her to the ER, the doctor examined her and said there was something weird about her labia. She thought he said Libya, and she goes, 'I ain't no terrorist. I'm an American.'"

That one got a few hoots and some thumbs-down from skeptics who didn't believe it happened. And then Snuffy Salcedo said, "We pulled over a guy on Cahuenga last night for busting a light, and when I said he had a mutilated driver's license, he said, 'My license don't mutilate for another year.'"

That one got more hoots and a few thumbs-up.

Before he dismissed them, Sergeant Murillo made an announcement that concerned Britney Small and Della Ravelle.

"Six-X-Forty-six," he said, "I'd like you to stop by the library on Ivar and talk to the librarian about the Wedgie Bandit. He's at it again."

The veteran midwatch cops groaned at the news, and Sergeant

Murillo said, "For you new people, the Wedgie Bandit is a white male, about thirty years old, five ten, one forty, brown and blue. He usually wears long-sleeved jerseys or sweatshirts, jeans, and tennis shoes. And he is an unparalleled menace to the safety and security of Hollywood's citizens. It's imperative that we get this villain off the street."

Snuffy Salcedo said, "Wedgie Bandit? Why do they call him that?"

Sergeant Murillo said, deadpan, "He assaults any unsuspecting person he encounters with very forceful wedgies."

"With wedgies?" Snuffy said.

"Do you know what a wedgie is, Officer Salcedo?" Sergeant Murillo asked. "It's very unpleasant. How would you like someone to give you one?"

"I know they're unpleasant, boss," Snuffy said, "but why does he do it to strangers?"

Sergeant Murillo said, "That is the question that the watch commander wants answered, and the station captain, and the division captain, and the bureau commander. I wouldn't be surprised if the chief of police wants to know his motive. When he's caught, we'll find out why he does it, but we can't catch him. Six-X-Thirty-two almost caught him one time, I believe. I'm not sure what happened."

Flotsam said, "Yeah, my little pard here chased him through Griffith Park, but the Wedgie Bandit left him panting on the grass with his tongue hanging out like one of them Frisbee-chasing border collies that scoot around there all day."

"He runs like a cheetah," Jetsam said defensively.

Sergeant Murillo said, "You all should be aware of how serial wedgies are committed. This fiend just walks up behind victims of either gender, even senior citizens, and grabs a handful of underwear from the back and pulls up as hard as he can. Then he beats feet and vanishes."

Jetsam said, "I almost had that little booger eater till he ran right through a bunch of bird-watchers that're always out there looking for the Painted Redstart, whatever the hell that is. One of the old babes was, like, taking a bunch of pictures with a telephoto lens and another one was chirping with a birdcall. And pretty soon both were sitting on the grass after he bowled them over. I'm only surprised he didn't stop long enough to give one of them a wedgie."

Flotsam said, "Sarge, remember the time the vice unit helped us out and put an undercover guy out there, and the bandit snuck up behind him and gave the UC cop a wedgie? And got away again!"

"Yes, he's been imaginative and resourceful," Sergeant Murillo said, still deadpan. "If a unit from Watch Five can jam him tonight, I will buy *two* large pizzas with the works for that team. Of course, with the price of two pizzas, I hope you'll wait until about, oh, two thirty for me to buy them, when they're older and cheaper, at an hour when only coppers will eat them."

Hollywood Nate said to Britney Small of 6-X-46, "Be super-careful at the library, Britney. Make sure Della's got your back at all times. It'd be a real feather in his cap to give a uniformed female copper a wedgie."

Britney blushed and the troops hooted and whistled and were all ready to go out and do police work.

When Watch 5 cleared and was on the streets, there was a cyclist causing a disturbance on Santa Monica Boulevard. But this wasn't any ordinary cyclist. He was unique even for this attention-getters Mecca. This cyclist kept cruising on the sidewalk past a beauty shop, honking a horn attached to his handlebars. He wasn't satisfied until he got several women to go to the windows with their hair rolled in goop and tinfoil, with strands protruding in all directions. Then he'd ride no hands and wave at them.

The cyclist was reptile-thin, of indeterminate age, with his hair done in purple spikes, and as far as face metal went, there was

nothing left to pierce. He had rings or studs through his nose, ears, eyebrows, lips, and tongue. He was inked on most of his upper body and had only a bit of bare flesh untatted from his knees down.

He wore flip-flops and violet short shorts decorated with sparkles. The proprietor of the beauty shop, a no-nonsense Cambodian woman, went outside several times and yelled, "You stop this! You go way! I call police!"

But that only made him emit a lunatic laugh and honk his horn and make another pass in front of the beauty shop window.

Finally one of the customers said, "I'm sick of this shit!"

She went outside, still wearing her black wraparound smock, and when the cyclist cruised by again, she shouted, "Hey, freako! Get outta here!"

All she got was the cry of a loon, and he sped right past her no hands as she yelled, " You asshole!"

Which turned out to be the apt epithet. She got a good look at him from the back, and when she ran inside to call the police, she said to the other women, "There's no seat on the bike!"

Six-X-Seventy-six got the call about a "415 cyclist" at the beauty shop, and Viv Daley said to Georgie Adams, "The message doesn't say how he's disturbing the peace."

"In Hollywood it could mean anything," Georgie said. "Probably DUI and doing wheelies to impress the ladies while they're getting their hair bleached. I'm glad you don't go in for that highlights stuff, sis. It's so lame and boring. I think half the people in Hollywood do it these days, even Flotsam and Jetsam."

"Those surfer boys swear their golden streaks are from the sun and surf," Viv said as she turned eastbound through the Sunset Boulevard early evening traffic.

"Yeah, right," Georgie said.

"Where the hell does all this traffic come from?" Viv said.

"It can't be explained," Georgie said. "I think it's immaculate congestion."

When they arrived at the beauty shop, the outraged proprietress met them at the curb and pointed to the cyclist, who pedaled off in the opposite direction very fast upon seeing the black-and-white.

The Cambodian beautician tried to explain to them in broken English about the cyclist causing a disturbance, but "Look at ass!" was the best they could get from her.

Not knowing what that meant, 6-X-76 made a dodgy U-turn through the traffic and caught up with the cyclist. Viv beeped her horn and gestured for him to stop, and when he did, she pulled the Crown Vic to the curb beside him.

"What the hell was that woman trying to tell us?" Georgie said. "I don't get it."

They got out and approached the cyclist, who was still astride his bike with one foot on the sidewalk. Since he was wearing only the sparkled short shorts, there was no need for a pat down.

Georgie said to Viv, "The dude's got enough face metal to trade at a junkyard for a 'sixty-eight Torino."

"First of all," Viv said to the cyclist, "you're riding a bike on the sidewalk. Secondly, you were beeping your horn and causing an unnecessary disturbance." Then she took a closer look at him and said, "Get off the bike, sir."

Obediently he swung his leg over the saddle, except there was no saddle. Georgie looked at the steel seat post and said, "What the hell?"

Viv said to the cyclist, "Turn around sir and face away from me."

He smiled amiably and complied, and she got a rear view of him and said, "Don't look, Gypsy. You're too squeamish for this."

But Georgie looked anyway and saw the opening in the shorts. After that he refused to look at either the man's shorts or the metal seat post.

"You talk to him," he said to Viv Daley. "I'm getting nauseous."

"Sir," Viv said to the cyclist, "where's the seat that goes on this bike?"

"Wore it out," he said.

"Why don't you buy another one?"

"I got used to this," he said. "It's more comfortable. And I think it gives me greater control of the bike. Why? Is there any law against it?"

"You're exposing yourself indecently," she said.

"No, Officer," he said. "I'm all covered, if you'll notice. The hole in my shorts is only an inch and one eighth in diameter to fit snugly over the metal post. So you see, I'm not indecent at all."

Viv said patiently, "If I don't write you a ticket for riding on the sidewalk, will you promise me to go home and get yourself a bike seat and never ride like this again, even if it gives you greater control of your bike?"

His mouth turned down at the corners. No mean feat with all the lip rings and studs, and he sighed and said, "If you say so, Officer. I want to always obey the law."

"Okay," Viv said. "Walk your bike home, sew up your shorts, and buy a bike seat ASAP."

When they got back in the car, Georgie Adams said, "We should get a pay bump for dealing with Hollywood weirdness."

Viv said, "The next time you go for a bike ride..."

"Please don't clown me, sis," Georgie said. "I'm feeling queasy. There's stuff out here that you people with X chromosomes can handle but us Ys can't. This is definitely one of them."

That evening started out on an annoying note. There was a disturbance at a house just off Franklin near Bronson Avenue where there had been any number of disturbances in recent years. A Goth family who played their role to the hilt occupied an old two-story house. Every family member, including children under the age of ten, was always clothed in black. And their parents, a pair of scarecrows in their late forties, usually wore theatrical makeup with their hair dyed black, parted in the middle, and combed down to

their shoulders. It was said that the wife had a trust account that provided the money for the spooky games they played, as well as for their toys and exhibits. The cops referred to them as Mr. Goth and Mrs. Goth.

In their large living room were three coffins and an antique embalming table. In two of the coffins there were mannequins that popped up and scared the hell out of anyone who had never been to the house before. The Goths had drug parties in that living room, which detectives had tried unsuccessfully to infiltrate. The couple would probably be chosen as the area's most despised householders by the cops at Hollywood Station because they were Addams Family wannabes. And in their efforts to be "authentic Goths," they sometimes invited what they considered to be interesting party guests to their home, who often ended up being more than troublesome to their hosts.

Six-X-Sixty-six was called to the Goth residence just after midnight, and Mrs. Goth was waiting on the sidewalk in front. She was in her Morticia costume: a straight, black, floor-length, form-fitting gown with a neckline plunging almost to her naval. Her lashes were an inch long and her eye shadow was so black and heavy, it looked like patches of corduroy.

Hollywood Nate and Snuffy Salcedo followed her into the residence, and Snuffy paused to gape at the coffins with mannequins lying in repose. The candelabras, which contained not wax candles but electric fixtures, were lit, and baskets of plastic flowers surrounded the coffins. The antique embalming table was in a spotlight and made to look like a medical surgery in Victorian times, and the sound of an organ playing a funereal dirge was coming from stereo speakers in the walls.

Mrs. Goth said to them, "One of our guests won't leave and go home. We don't really know him very well. He's a friend of a friend, and, well, he's a bit frightening."

Hollywood Nate, who had twice been called to the Goth house

for similar disturbances and thought they were about the lamest of Hollywood's present crop of attention getters, said, "Upstaging you, is he? When you're supposed to be the weird and scary ones."

Mrs. Goth was trying to decide how to respond to that impertinence when Snuffy Salcedo said, "Did you tell him to go home?"

"A dozen times," she said. "He's a very difficult and very strange man."

They could hear a television going, and Snuffy said, "What's he doing in there?"

"Watching porn," she said.

Hollywood Nate asked, "Where'd he get it?"

"My husband gave it to him," she said. "A mistake. My husband sometimes gets enthusiastic when he's with barbarians, and he tends to indulge them."

"Where's your husband?" Snuffy asked.

"With our children."

"In the house?"

"No, he took them for a hamburger until it's over. He always leaves me to deal with the party detritus."

"Until what's over?" Snuffy Salcedo asked.

"Whatever happens between you and him," she said. "He claims his name is Rolf Thunder. That's all I know."

"Let's have a look at your barbarian," Snuffy said.

Mrs. Goth just gestured down a darkened hallway.

Snuffy Salcedo led the way to a lighted sitting room and quietly pushed the door open a few inches to take a peek inside. Rolf Thunder sat in a La-Z-Boy recliner in the lamp-lit room eating potato chips and watching porn. They could hear the heavy breathing and orgasmic moans coming from the video. One hand was holding an object on his lap.

Snuffy Salcedo came back into the corridor and said to Mrs. Goth, "What's that on his lap?"

"A penis pump," she said.

189

"Where did he get it?" Nate asked.

"My husband lent it to him," she said. "We didn't know he'd fall in love with it and decide to spend the night playing with it."

Snuffy Salcedo turned to Nate, who had not yet had a look at Rolf Thunder, and said, "Let's get some backup here."

"Any particular reason I should know about?" Nate said.

"About two hundred eighty of them," Snuffy said. "That's about how many pounds he weighs. And I'd guess it's spread over about six and a half feet of very large and heavy bones. And on his shoulder he's got some White Power jailhouse tatts, so I'm pretty sure he doesn't like Mexicans. And he won't like Jews either, so hide your nameplate."

Nate said, "Are you sure we'll need backup? He's only one guy."

Snuffy said, "Partner, I got a real bad feeling about this one. He's only slightly smaller than a bulldozer and he's ready to tear things down. Take my word for it. I'm older and wiser than you."

Hollywood Nate walked back to the living room with Snuffy to make the backup request on his rover. Like all male cops with sufficient machismo, Hollywood Nate was reluctant to request code 2 assistance, and only once or twice in his entire career had he resorted to a code 3 "officers need help" request. He just spoke into the rover and subtly requested "a unit to assist" at the Goth family address.

He got two units: 6-X-46, with Della Ravelle and Britney Small, and 6-X-32, with Flotsam and Jetsam. Mrs. Goth walked to the street to meet the arriving radio cars, and she looked decidedly uncomfortable to see Flotsam and Jetsam get out of their black-and-white. They had been called to the Goth house on other occasions.

"Dude, I truly hate these Goth show-offs," Flotsam said to Jetsam. "They are mega-phony."

When the surfer cops entered the living room of the house, Snuffy said to them, "I got a bad vibe going here. An acquaintance

of this lady and her husband does not want to leave their premises and I think he ain't gonna listen to reason."

"Have you talked to him yet?" Flotsam asked.

"Not yet," Snuffy Salcedo said.

"Why not?" Jetsam asked.

"He's busy pumping his penis," Snuffy Salcedo said. "I figured it's best to wait till he's finished."

"What?" said Flotsam.

Just then Della Ravelle and Britney Small entered the house to join the other cops, and Snuffy said to them, "I'm glad to see you have your regular batons with you and not those cheesey expandable ones. I would prefer we had Louisville sluggers for this gig. I suggest you be ready with Tasers and pepper spray. And an M-sixteen if you got one."

"Who're we evicting this time?" Della asked. "King Kong?"

"Pretty close," Snuffy Salcedo said. "If King Kong was a skinhead with jailhouse swastikas on his twenty-two-inch neck and a pentagram inked on the side of his shaved melon. And if King Kong liked penis pumps."

"What?" Britney Small said.

"Do you want us to try talking to him first?" Della asked. "The woman's touch?"

"It's our call to handle," Hollywood Nate said. "We wanted backup just in case."

Snuffy Salcedo led the way to the sitting room, followed by Hollywood Nate, with the other four midwatch cops standing outside in the corridor near the living room.

Snuffy pushed open the door and saw that nothing had changed. Rolf Thunder was still watching porn and still wearing the penis pump. He looked to be in his late forties, about the same age as Snuffy Salcedo.

He didn't look up until Snuffy said, "Mr. Thunder, we need to talk."

Only then did the man glance at Snuffy with unfocused brown eyes, and Snuffy could plainly see that the guy was fried, probably on crystal or some other lowlife drug. Rolf Thunder didn't say anything to Snuffy but just went back to watching the porn video.

Hollywood Nate stepped in behind Snuffy and said, "Dude, you're gonna have to get up and leave here, so you might as well understand that. You got any ID?"

Finally, Rolf Thunder spoke without looking at Nate, saying, "Yeah, do you?"

"I'm wearing mine," Nate said.

Rolf Thunder then looked at both cops and smirked. "Are you bad cop?" he said to Nate. "And what's little homeboy, good cop? Do you two make tamales after work and sleep together or what?"

When he grinned, they saw at least three teeth missing from his upper grille. The man had a simian brow and flaring nostrils exposing what looked like a nose full of steel wool. His jaw was massive and square with a bulldog underbite, and he looked like he could chew through handcuff links. Flotsam and Jetsam stood in the doorway so the giant could clearly see how badly he was outnumbered.

Rolf Thunder looked at the surfer cops and said, "Oh, so you brought a couple of the other girls along. I like blond candy. We woulda had fun with them up at Corcoran."

"Yeah, we get it that you're a badass ex-con," Snuffy said, "so don't even go there."

"Our posse's got lots of pain tools and we jump ugly," Nate said. "So chill and think it over."

Rolf Thunder's massive jaw muscles flexed and he looked at Hollywood Nate and said, "Up at Corcoran the screws called me 'Bio-hazard' because everyone I choked out shit his pants."

Jetsam said sotto to Flotsam, "Bro, there's some very bad juju here."

Flotsam said sotto, "This dude's more dangerous than a Toyota floor mat."

"Get your savage on, bro," Jetsam said.

Della Ravelle whispered to Britney Small, "If this turns into a melee, don't try to be a man. Stand back with your Taser and your baton and pick your shots. And don't be shy about calling for help if we need it."

Britney's blue eyes were wide when she nodded at her partner and waited, pepper spray in one hand, baton in the other.

Back in the sitting room, Snuffy Salcedo said, "How about you just get outta that chair now."

"Sure, homie," Rolf Thunder said, standing up so fast that both cops took a step backward. He was still wearing the penis pump on his drooping member.

And he was even bigger than Snuffy Salcedo had thought. He was tall enough to look down at Flotsam, and Snuffy's estimate of 280 pounds was way off. They all figured he weighed three bills if he weighed an ounce.

"Take that thing off," Snuffy Salcedo said, pointing to the penis pump.

"You take it off, sweetie," he said to Snuffy with a wolfish grin. "But then you'll have to marry me."

Hollywood Nate said, "Turn around and put your hands behind your back."

The behemoth drilled Nate with death-ray eyes and said, "Why don't I put them behind *your* back, cupcake?" Without another word he lunged forward, roaring, and grabbed Hollywood Nate in a bear hug and began crushing him.

Flotsam, Jetsam, and Snuffy Salcedo swarmed Rolf Thunder. Jetsam tried pepper spray and got the side of Rolf Thunder's face as well as his partner's. Flotsam bellowed from the burn but the giant didn't flinch, and he released Hollywood Nate, only to start throwing wild punches that mostly missed their target. But even blows that hit them on the chest or back were stunningly painful and knocked the wind out of them. He managed to break free and

run into the hallway, crashing into Britney Small and sending her sprawling. When he reached the living room, he made his stand.

Mrs. Goth let out the most chilling scream that had ever emanated from a house that featured recorded screams and other spooky special effects. She ran outside, where neighbors had begun to gather. And all the time the recorded organ played a funeral dirge.

Britney Small leaped to her feet and ran into the living room after Rolf Thunder, but Della Ravelle grabbed her by the back of her Sam Browne belt and said, "Don't jump into that. Stand back and pick your shots!"

And since female officers did not have to struggle with machismo, Della felt no compunction about putting out a code 3 call on her rover, which she knew would bring units from everywhere, and fast.

The four male cops charged into the great room in a bunch and hit Rolf Thunder high and low. Flotsam received a punch on the side of the head and it knocked him off his feet and set his ears to ringing. Jetsam dug two baton thrusts into the big man's belly, but it didn't faze him. Hollywood Nate smacked him on the elbow with his baton, but the giant only backed up a couple of steps and waited, hands hanging low at his sides and grinning.

Snuffy Salcedo drew his Taser and said, "Back away from him!"

When the other cops backed off, Snuffy Salcedo fired the Taser into the big man's chest from five feet away. The blue thread of light snapped and Rolf Thunder stood straight up and grimaced from the 50,000 volts.

But then to the horror of all present, he pulled the dart out and said, "You jist opened yourself a can of whup-ass, homie."

He charged Snuffy Salcedo and Hollywood Nate both, taking one of them in each arm and driving them into the wall, and that stopped the organ music. Flotsam jumped onto the back of the

giant and tried to get a choke hold, which vocal police critics considered to be de facto excessive force in almost all cases. But Rolf Thunder was stronger than Flotsam and pried his grip loose and swung a roundhouse that caught Snuffy Salcedo between the eyes, shattering the bridge of his nose.

Rolf Thunder scrambled to keep his feet before he was driven into the nearest coffin by Jetsam, who hit him low with his shoulder. When the giant went down, Della Ravelle whacked him across the knees with her baton and Britney Small shot him with another Taser dart but with the same effect. He stiffened, grimaced, and pulled out the dart.

When Snuffy Salcedo stood up with blood pouring into his mouth, he hit the giant across the forehead with his baton, knocking him backward against the second coffin, which dumped the mannequin onto the floor, where its mechanism was triggered. It kept popping up in a sitting position over and over like a lunatic cheerleader enjoying the macabre violence.

Rolf Thunder got up and ran at Flotsam, and the two tall men crashed into the antique embalming table, spilling all of the paraphernalia onto the floor. Then Jetsam was on Rolf Thunder's back, trying for another choke hold, but he was spun around and hurled into another coffin, where a second mannequin was ejected. It fell across Flotsam and they lay together like lovers for an instant until the surfer cop pushed it off and scrambled to his feet.

At that point, Hollywood Nate kicked Rolf Thunder in the groin, and that doubled him over for a moment, giving Jetsam and Snuffy Salcedo time to begin whacking him anywhere and everywhere with their batons, including a few head strikes that sounded like rifle shots. Britney Small stepped in close and gave him a good dose of pepper spray, which missed the other cops this time and entered the mouth of the giant.

The pepper spray got him coughing but he still got to his feet somehow. That gave Jetsam the chance to drive the end of his baton

into the big man's groin, the only place where he seemed vulnerable, and Rolf Thunder dropped to his knees, clutching at his throat and at his groin. And when he was in that position, Snuffy Salcedo, his face a blood mask, played catch-up and smashed Rolf Thunder across the face with his aluminum baton, doing more damage to the giant's nose than his own had suffered.

At last, Rolf Thunder tumbled to the floor on his back, concussed but still not completely unconscious. He writhed and struggled to breathe and pulled his legs up to protect his groin. Both surfer cops jumped on him and with the help of Snuffy Salcedo got his hands twisted behind him. They feared for a moment that the handcuffs would not fit around those enormous wrists, but after a struggle they managed to get the first few ratchets to grip and hold.

Breathing hard, Flotsam said to him, "They'll stretch with wear, dude."

Della Ravelle made another call on her rover to request two rescue ambulances, one for their prisoner and one for Snuffy Salcedo, who was sitting on an overturned coffin, trying to stanch the blood from his nose. The creepy mannequin kept popping up and looking at Snuffy until he hauled off and smacked it with his baton, knocking its head clear off.

Everyone else was sitting or standing, wheezing and chuffing and panting, and Rolf Thunder lay still for a moment and then croaked out some words. He said, "Wasn't that fun?"

Snuffy wiped his bloody face on his uniform sleeve and said breathlessly, "Yeah, you masochist freak, that was tons of fun. I only wish I could put a few forty-caliber rounds in your belly to show you a real good time."

"Yo, homie," Rolf Thunder said, his own face a mask of blood from shattered bone and dislodged teeth, "can't you handle a little sound and fury?"

"Go outside and wait for the RA, Snuffy," Hollywood Nate

said. "We'll deal with Sasquatch. When he gets to County USC, he's gonna need a needle and lotsa thread."

His partner nodded, got up painfully, and shuffled to the open door, where he could hear the sirens on their way. Black-and-whites responding to Della's help call were screeching to a stop on the street in front, and a wall of bluesuits came running toward Goth House.

Inside the living room, Hollywood Nate pointed to the penis pump, held in place by a constriction band, and said, "We should get that thing off him."

"Not me, dude," Flotsam said. "That's way beyond my pay grade."

"Ditto," said Jetsam.

Flotsam said to Della Ravelle, "Would you mind taking that thing off him, Della?"

"Do it yourself," she said.

"I never touched another guy's junk before," Flotsam said.

"You've touched your own often enough," she said.

"That's different," Flotsam said. "Mine belongs to me. I even got a pet name for it."

"Don't look at me," Jetsam said. "I ain't touching it. Come on, Della, you probably touched lots of them in your time."

"Go screw yourself, surf rat!" Della said.

"No, wait," Jetsam said. "I'm just saying, like, a woman of your... maturity, like, probably in her lifetime..."

"Aw, shit," Della said, and went over to Rolf Thunder, who was lying handcuffed in a fetal pose and going in and out of consciousness now. She knelt and loosened the constricting band and removed the penis pump and tossed it at Jetsam, saying, "Here, would you like to book this as evidence?"

The surfer cop leaped aside like the thing was radioactive as the penis pump flew past him.

Snuffy Salcedo was taken by ambulance to Cedars-Sinai

Medical Center, where an ER doctor said that his nose would probably be "almost like new after surgery." He was told he'd be kept overnight for observation and surgery in the morning.

When 6-X-46 was alone in the women's locker room at Hollywood Station, Della Ravelle helped Britney Small apply an ice pack to her right eye where she'd been slammed by Rolf Thunder's elbow as he'd bolted into the coffin room to make his stand.

"Keep the ice on it till the second-guessers get here," Della said. "You've got a mouse growing already and it's turning purple."

"I'm in better shape than any of the guys," Britney said, touching the swelling gingerly.

"This has been a learning experience for you, girlfriend," Della said. "You see how male coppers are? They pride themselves on never putting out an officers-need-help call. Their machismo prevents even an assistance call. There's just a whole lot of cowboy in them. If I'd been running that show, I would've backed off in the beginning and at least put out the code-two call the second Mr. Frankenstein made it clear he was gonna go the hard way. But with six of us there, no guy gunslinger would ever humble himself to do that. Well, girl, now you've seen some real whup-ass. And now you see that all the grappling holds and everything else you learned at the academy are worth shit out here in the real world when you come up against a walking reign of terror. I know you're brave, but what good would bantamweight Britney Small have done in the midst of half a ton of raging beef crashing around that room? If you ever face something like that by yourself, just remember that you carry a forty-caliber Glock, and if your back's to the wall, do not hesitate to pull and kill the bastard before he kills you. Don't think about whether you're justified by policy or by law. Remember the old copper saying: It's a whole lot better to be judged by twelve than carried by six."

Because of the kind of violence inflicted, which could have included choke holds, baton strikes, and kicks, Force Investigation

Division had been immediately called out to determine if all action was in policy. The five ambulatory cops spent the rest of the night being interviewed at Hollywood Station, where they tediously had to deconstruct the battle and justify each move they made.

What they all *wanted* to say to FID was "When it comes to subduing a monster with no pain receptors, the Marquis of Queensberry's just some tranny on Santa Monica Boulevard. So stop fucking with me!"

Rolf Thunder, whose true name was Filmore McClain, was transported to the jail ward on the thirteenth floor at USCMC, the old county hospital, and later told investigators that it had all been worth it and he had no complaints. The institutionalized man said that he'd enjoyed his vacation in the free world for a while but that it had gotten too stressful. He said he had been trying to find a fun way to violate his parole and go back to prison, which was the only place he'd ever been really happy. It was where he could be taken care of and kick back and never have to make decisions and experience life the way he'd always known it since he was fifteen years old. Prison was security. Prison was home.

The only positive note that the male cops took from the event at Goth House was that after the battle they all got a good look at the penis of the giant when he was strapped onto the gurney by paramedics.

Della Ravelle noticed their satisfaction and later said to Britney Small, "Did you see the smug little smiles on the surfer cops and Hollywood Nate when Jumbo was on the gurney? What they'll remember most about the war at Goth House is that their little willies are just as big as Goliath's. They might even stop using male-enhancement products."

★ SEVENTEEN ★

RALEIGH'S SLEEP WAS fitful and fraught with strange dreams that he could not interpret. He awakened every hour or so until he gave up and rose at 5:30 A.M. He watched TV with his breakfast but couldn't eat much. Then he took Marty Brueger's breakfast on a tray to the cottage, but he found the old man still sleeping. He left the tray and walked back to the main house and tried to read the *L.A. Times,* but he could not concentrate.

His thoughts kept returning to the months he'd spent in federal prison, where he'd met several inmates who had served very hard time in state penitentiaries. One of them told Raleigh that comparing Club Fed to state prison was like comparing hemorrhoids to colon cancer, and the inmate was a man who had suffered both.

There was still time, Raleigh thought. He could pick up the phone and call Nigel Wickland, using both his given name and surname just to piss him off, and cancel the whole thing. After all, his life in the Brueger house was pretty good, and he'd never been a greedy man. Why should he risk arrest and trial and a sentence at one of the nightmare factories run by the state of California, where each hour of each terrible day his life would be put at risk? This was madness, this fantasy that had been sold to him by one of those "toffee-nosed poofs," as his fellow workers in the London bistro used to call the upper-crust homos.

He went to the butler's pantry and got a notepad and pen and began making a list of all the ways in which this thing could go sideways. When he got to number six, he tore it to bits and then set fire to the paper scraps in the sink. He sat down again. Then the phone buzzed, and he picked it up, knowing it was the cottage line.

"Yes, Mr. Brueger?" he said.

Marty Brueger's morning voice said, "I'm sick of this fucking place, Raleigh. With Lorena away, I feel like a prisoner in solitary confinement."

"I'm sorry, Mr. Brueger," Raleigh said. "Maybe we can take a drive later this morning? Is there somewhere you'd like to go? We can take any one of Mrs. Brueger's cars. How about the big Mercedes? You could sit in back with a flask of whiskey and take in the sights and I'll be your chauffeur."

"I was thinking about a longer drive," Marty Brueger said. "I was thinking maybe you could take me to Palm Springs and I could look at all the old places I used to know when Sammy and me were young bucks."

And there it was! One of the ways things could go sideways, and it wasn't even on his list. Palm Springs was three hours away. He couldn't take the geezer to Palm Springs and be back by 1 P.M.

"Mr. Brueger," he said. "It's still too hot in Palm Springs. In a couple of months it'll be nice there and we can go and get a hotel for an overnighter. You could gamble in the Indian casinos. Maybe catch a show. But you don't want to go to Palm Springs now."

"I'm lonesome," Marty Brueger said. "Come on over and let's talk about it. Or I can come up to the house."

"I'll come to you, Mr. Brueger," Raleigh said.

He hung up and thought about this. Was it fate, destiny, or divine providence? Today of all days, something had made that old man decide he wanted to go to Palm Springs. Something or somebody was trying to help Raleigh out of the incredible scheme

concocted by Nigel Wickland. All he had to do was call the man and tell him that Marty Brueger wanted to go to Palm Springs today, which was the truth. After that, he could tell an untruth and say that Marty Brueger had decided to move into the main house because he was lonely. And with Marty Brueger in the main house, it would effectively end Nigel Wickland's plot to make a million dollars. Raleigh could save face with that pompous limey, as if he needed to, and the bad dreams would be over.

Suddenly he felt like a free man. He felt wonderful. He sauntered down the walk to Marty's cottage and literally stopped to smell the roses. He knocked twice, as he always did. He entered and found Marty Brueger on the floor in the bathroom, wearing only urine-soaked underpants.

"Mr. Brueger!" Raleigh ran to the old man, stripped off his underwear and carried him to his bed.

Marty Brueger looked at him and said, "Wa-wa-wa..."

"Are you trying to say my name, Mr. Brueger?" Raleigh said in panic. Then he muttered, "My god, it's a stroke!"

Raleigh Dibble picked up the phone and dialed 9-1-1.

Megan Burke was shocked to be awakened by the smell of actual food. She opened her eyes and found Jonas sitting on the bed, fully dressed, with a glass of orange juice in a Styrofoam cup and an Egg McMuffin on a plate.

He said, "I got up early. This is the first day of our new life as successful people. I went out and had breakfast and brought yours home. We gotta be healthy and strong today. Eat, baby, eat."

Megan rolled out of bed with her feet on the floor, stood up painfully, and lurched into the bathroom. Jonas went to the kitchen, and she could hear water running. When she finished in the bathroom, she saw the plate of Egg McMuffin on the kitchen table with the orange juice. And he was actually making the coffee, another first.

"We ain't doing drugs today, Megan," he said. "We're working and we ain't coming home till we hit a target. We're aiming for nothing but bull's-eyes today. We're finding a likely crib and we're going in. Nothing can stop us."

Megan sat and sipped some orange juice and nibbled at the Egg McMuffin without interest. She thought, Right, I don't get to do any drugs today, but look at him! She figured he'd had a taste of something, the way he was amped. It made her surly and resentful. She always got the short end because he was the man, or so he thought.

"Come on, sweetie, take bigger bites," he said. "And chew, chew, chew."

She had a momentary fantasy of picking up a kitchen knife and cutting his throat.

Raleigh's panic had subsided before the ambulance arrived, and after they'd loaded Marty Brueger in and taken him to Cedars-Sinai, he went into the main house and took a shower. He had the old man's piss on his clothes and he wanted to stand under hot water for a long time. The paramedics had verified that it looked like a stroke, and they had wasted no time in getting their patient out of there, so now Raleigh was alone for the first time in Casa Brueger. He needed to think, but first he needed the shower.

When he finally was out and had toweled off, Raleigh stood before the mirror and thought about all the things he had planned to do with his fifty thousand tax-free dollars. He was going to be physically transformed, easily losing ten years from his appearance, thanks to the cosmetic magicians on the west side of Los Angeles. He had also planned to purchase a modest condo, his own home at long last. And there was the dream of hooking up with an older wealthy woman, like the kind he'd met through his catering business. And why not? He could cook and he knew food and wine. He could manage a house and he could drive. And he was, if he did say

so himself, a presentable companion who could converse with anyone. But what was going to happen now that Marty Brueger had suffered a stroke? Was this yet another act of providence, or fate, or destiny? If so, what did it mean?

Then again, if he did go forward with Nigel Wickland, it would make it all far easier and less stressful with Marty Brueger off the property and in the hospital, wouldn't it? Things would be simpler and safer in many ways. But he didn't dare keep the fact of Marty Brueger's hospitalization from Marty's sister-in-law, Leona Brueger. He had to phone Tuscany. That much was certain. But what would she say and do?

Ten minutes later Raleigh made a call, but he did not phone Leona Brueger in Tuscany. He phoned Nigel Wickland's cell phone.

When Nigel answered, Raleigh said, "The old guy's had a stroke. He's at Cedars."

Nigel Wickland did not speak for several seconds and then said, "All right, that doesn't change anything."

Raleigh said, "Doesn't change anything? What if she decides to come home? He's an old man in poor health. He might die at any time."

"She doesn't care about him any more than she cared about his brother," Nigel said. "Tell her it's a stroke but downplay it. Let her know that you think he'll be fine and that they should continue with their long holiday and you'll let them know if something untoward happens."

Untoward, Raleigh thought. The supercilious asshole always had to use his boarding school vocabulary. "What if they still decide to come home right away?"

"They won't, I promise you," Nigel said. "She'll be happy if the old bastard dies. So calm yourself."

"I'll talk to you later," Raleigh said.

"You'll see me later," Nigel said. "Nothing has changed."

When Raleigh finished the call, his bowels began rumbling again and he ran to the bathroom.

An hour later, after more dithering, Raleigh called Tuscany and got Leona's voice mail. He said, "Mrs. Brueger, it's Raleigh Dibble. Please call me as soon as you get this message."

At 12:30 P.M., thirty minutes before Nigel Wickland was due to arrive at the Brueger house, Raleigh was stunned to hear a vehicle in the driveway. He ran to the main door, opened it, and saw the gardener's truck parked on the faux-cobblestone driveway. The electric gate was wide open as was always the case when the crew was there tending to all greenery on the outside as well as the inside of the garden walls.

Raleigh ran out and said to the first worker he saw, "What're you doing here today?"

The Mexican shrugged and said, "No Eeng-lish."

In utter frustration, Raleigh dashed around the property, looking for the boss, a burro of a man named Angel.

When he found him he said, "Angel, what're you doing here today?"

"Mee-sus say to come today to reseed all the grass," the gardener said. He took a pocket calendar from his back pocket and showed Raleigh that the date had been circled.

"Oh, shit!" Raleigh said. "Can't you do it some other day?"

The gardener looked at his crew of five men, who were already pruning and trimming as well as scalping the lawn, and he said, "No, sir. Sorry. Thees ees the day I can be here."

Raleigh said, "Okay, please try to hurry."

He went out to the street, looking at his watch. He didn't see the van from Wickland Gallery yet, so he hurried back to the house, picked up his cell phone, and dialed Nigel's cell number.

He got voice mail and felt like throwing the goddamn phone through the window. He ran back out to the street and trotted fifty yards down the winding road until he had to stop to catch his

breath. He was standing there panting when he saw the cargo van make the turn in the road and climb the street toward him.

Raleigh stepped into the middle of the road and waved his arms. The van came to a sudden stop and Nigel Wickland said, "What the hell are you doing?"

"The gardeners are here!" Raleigh said. "There're Mexicans all over the place. I couldn't stop them."

"You said the gardeners came on another day. Not today," Nigel said.

"I know, but this is something special that Mrs. Brueger set up. She didn't tell me about it. It's not my fault."

"Not his fault," Nigel said, looking away.

Raleigh said, "First Mr. Brueger has a stroke, and now this. Maybe fate's trying to tell us something."

"Don't you lose your nerve!" Nigel said. "I've planned this and spent a lot of money, and worked on this without proper sleep or rest. I've got two perfect pictures in this van that are identical to the originals. And we're going through with it, Raleigh."

"With the gardeners here?"

"How long will they be here?"

"I don't know. Usually only a few hours, but this is a special job."

"Shit!" Nigel said. "Did you phone Leona about her brother-in-law's stroke?"

"Yes, but I only got her voice mail. I left a message for her to call me."

"Christ!" Nigel said. "Call me the minute you find out when the gardeners are leaving."

"I will," Raleigh said. "If you'll turn on your cell phone."

Nigel reached into his pocket and took out his cell phone, looked at it, and said, "Right."

Then he pulled into a neighbor's driveway, turned around, and drove back down toward the flatland.

Raleigh was surprised at how much satisfaction he'd gotten in

demonstrating to Nigel Wickland that his cell had been turned off and he wasn't so fucking perfect. He hurried back to the house, but the way the lawns were being scalped, it didn't look like this would be a quick job. When he got inside the house, he checked the answering machine. He distinctly remembered giving Leona Brueger his cell number as well. He wondered if she'd lost it. He turned on the TV just for the noise it made.

That lovely day in early autumn was the longest day in the life of Raleigh Dibble. Leona Brueger never called. At 4:50 P.M., the gardeners finished their work and Raleigh notified Nigel Wickland that they were gone. Then he went into the bathroom and threw up.

Nigel Wickland rang the gate bell at 5:30 P.M., and Raleigh buzzed him into the Brueger compound. Raleigh walked outside and watched Nigel turn his cargo van all the way around and park it facing the gate.

When Nigel got out of the van, Raleigh said to him, "What's the three-sixty for? A quick getaway?"

Nigel ignored that and said, "Help me with the material."

He was wearing white coveralls with "Wickland Gallery" embroidered over a breast pocket. He opened the side door and put his ring of keys on the van roof temporarily, in order to free up both hands. He picked up his toolbox and handed it to Raleigh. Then he removed the two photographs on poster board, each individually wrapped in a furniture mover's blanket. He leaned them carefully against the garage door and went back to the van for a floodlight and a light stand.

"What's that for?" Raleigh asked.

"I want good lighting in that dark corridor when I do the switch," Niegel said. Then he handed the floodlight and light stand to Raleigh and said, "Take all of this inside. I'll carry the pictures."

While Raleigh was walking into the house, Nigel closed the door of the van and picked up the photo reproductions.

After they carried everything across the Mexican-tile floor in the foyer, Nigel rested the blanket-covered pictures against a wall and said, "I could use a cold drink. Get me a Perrier, will you?"

With an edge to his voice, Raleigh said, "You'll settle for another brand if I can't find Perrier, won't you?"

"Yes, yes," Nigel said with a dismissive toss of his head. "Any mineral water will do."

"Does it have to be carbonated?"

"For heaven's sake, Raleigh, no! It need not be carbonated."

Raleigh left Nigel to his work and walked into the butler's pantry, muttering. He scooped a few little cubes from the ice maker into a tumbler and filled it with water from the faucet.

When he came back, Nigel was adjusting the floodlight, and he took the glass, drank half of it, and said, "Thanks. I was thirsty."

Raleigh said, "That's Vichy Catalan mineral water. I hope it's okay."

"Yes, perfect," Nigel said. "Put these on." He removed a pair of latex gloves from the back pocket of his coveralls and gave them to Raleigh. Pulling a second pair onto his own graceful hands, he said, "Now, carefully remove a blanket from one of my pictures and spread the blanket on the tile floor. Be very careful in handling them."

Raleigh obeyed while Nigel got the floodlight shining down onto the mover's blanket that Raleigh had spread. Then Nigel carefully removed *The Woman by the Water* from its place on the wall and, carrying the painting to the blanket, placed it facedown.

"Bring me my toolbox," he said to Raleigh.

Raleigh did as he was told and was putting the toolbox on the floor next to Nigel just as the house phone rang.

"Is that the gate?" Nigel asked.

"No, the gate has a special ring," Raleigh said, and he ran to the kitchen to answer it.

When he picked it up, he heard the grating voice of Rudy Ressler, who said, "Raleigh? This is Mr. Ressler. We got back last night from

a couple of days in Rome and were so tired we crashed. I just got up to go to the bathroom and noticed your voice mail. What's up?"

Raleigh said, "Mr. Ressler, I'm sorry to say that Mr. Brueger has had a minor stroke. At least I think it's minor. He's in Cedars-Sinai. I wanted Mrs. Brueger to know right away."

The line was quiet for a moment and then the director said, "Leona's dead to the world. It's three o'clock in the morning here. I'll tell her when we get up. I gotta go back to bed now. This whole scene over here is supposed to be restful, but don't believe it. Every fucking thing that could go wrong with this villa has gone wrong. I'll call you when we get outta bed."

"Okay, Mr. Ressler," Raleigh said. "When you tell Mrs. Brueger about it, please say that there's no cause for alarm. I'm sure he'll be fine. He's a tough old man."

"Yeah, okay, Raleigh," the director said. "I'll call you in a few hours."

Raleigh hung up and returned to the foyer, where Nigel Wickland had *The Woman by the Water* removed from the frame and leaning against the wall under the light stand.

"That was Rudy Ressler," Raleigh said. "They've been away from the villa for a couple of days. I told him about Mr. Brueger."

Nigel stopped working. "And?"

"He said he'd talk to Mrs. Brueger when they get up in the morning and then get back to me."

"Did you tell him it wasn't serious?" Nigel asked petulantly.

"Yes, I told him," Raleigh said, thinking he'd give a sizable piece of his share of the money just to never see this bastard again or hear his flutey voice.

Next, Nigel took down *Flowers on the Hillside* and carefully placed the framed painting on the mover's blanket. He began painstakingly removing the fasteners from the stretcher bars while Raleigh looked at his watch. That exercise took nearly fifteen minutes. This wasn't supposed to be such a lengthy ordeal.

When Nigel was finished, he gingerly lifted the smaller painting from the frame, brushed some dust and wood residue from the edges of the canvas, and leaned it against the wall by the larger painting.

"That's a million dollars resting against the wall, Raleigh," Nigel said.

Raleigh looked at him, at his narrow patrician nose looking as though it wanted to sniff the paintings like a dog. The man was actually leering. His greed had completely overcome any normal fear factor. And that made Raleigh Dibble even more frightened of this entire goddamn scheme.

Megan Burke was feeling better now that the watsons had kicked in. At least the pain in her knees and other joints had diminished. They had almost attempted entry at five separate houses, but each time something had happened. At one of them, the Hispanic house-keeper answered the door after they were positive that nobody was at home, just as Jonas was ready to attempt entry through a window. At another one, a newspaper in the driveway convinced Jonas that the residents were at work, but then a yappy dog ran out, and Jonas dashed back to their car and said, "Fucking dogs! I wish all the goddamn bucket heads in this town would eat them like they do in their fucked-up countries. You don't see dogs running all over the yards in China, I bet."

Something happened to frustrate Jonas at every residence that looked likely. Megan was afraid the pain would return and she was thirsty and tired. She'd always liked the sky over Hollywood at twilight, and there was a beautiful sky up there now, with red and gold and violet splashing across the heavens as the sun was sinking into the Pacific Ocean. Back when she felt healthy and hopeful, she'd had a fantasy of trying to paint the twilight sky over Hollywood. That seemed like a lifetime ago, back when she felt healthy and hopeful.

Jonas parked for a moment off Woodrow Wilson Drive near Mulholland and said, "Let's cruise a little ways down and have a look at that big place again."

"What big place?" Megan asked.

"The Spanish-style place with the wall around it and the big house with a guesthouse? That one. Remember we peeked through the trees at it?"

"We've looked at so many, I don't remember," Megan said.

"All you gotta do is trust me," Jonas said. "I got a memory like a rhinoceros."

"A rhinoceros," she muttered. "Oh, god!"

EIGHTEEN

THE MIDWATCH ROLL call was a bit subdued at first. It was always that way after an officer had been hurt. Although Snuffy Salcedo had not been seriously injured, he had gone through surgery that morning at the hands of a plastic surgeon who came recommended by the specialists at Cedars-Sinai Medical Center. Hollywood Nate Weiss, who had not gotten much sleep after the incident at Goth House and the interrogation by Force Investigation Division, talked to Snuffy on the phone before coming to work. Snuffy had taken full responsibility for the "unintentional" baton blow to the face of the colossus as well as all other "unintentional" head strikes. And because baton head strikes generated nearly as much paperwork as officer-involved shootings in the closely monitored LAPD, he was officially removed from the field until FID was satisfied and a shrink from BSS as well as the bureau chief gave the okay for his return. And that was just fine with Snuffy, who needed time off to recuperate. He told Nate that his injuries made him look like a raccoon that got mauled by a grizzly.

It had always been a matter of pride in a warrior culture to quickly return to duty after a battle, but Jetsam had to take a few sick days. He had been stricken with a muscle spasm in his neck that began when he was being questioned by FID and got worse after he went home to his apartment and tumbled into bed. When

he woke up at 2 P.M. the next afternoon, he could not turn his head without great pain and had to see a doctor.

The remaining combatants sitting at roll call, Hollywood Nate and Flotsam, had suffered hematomas, contusions, abrasions, with even a couple of lacerations—the whole ball of bash—and their movements were slow and painful, but each cop was serviceable. Oddly enough, the only one with a genuine black eye was Britney Small, who sat next to Della Ravelle at roll call wearing a black eye patch for laughs, but she took it off when all the cops begged to see her shiner and wanted cell phone photos.

Sergeant Murillo had to change the lineup and team Hollywood Nate with Flotsam in 6-X-32, since they were both missing a partner, and before dismissing roll call, he said to them, "If any citizens ask why you both have bumps and bruises, explain that they came from fighting a bad guy. We have enough of a PR problem around here without people thinking we're lumping up each other nowadays."

As all the troops touched the photo of the Oracle before leaving the roll call room, Hollywood Nate Weiss wondered if maybe Snuffy Salcedo had failed to touch the picture yesterday. He couldn't remember seeing him do it.

Twenty-five minutes after roll call ended and the midwatch was on the streets, Jonas Claymore, accompanied by Megan Burke, made a rolling stop on his way to a last pass up into the Hollywood Hills before darkness. So far, it had been another fruitless search for a residence to burgle. Jonas heard the toot of a horn behind him and looked in the mirror to see a black-and-white with lights oscillating.

Georgie Adams was driving, with Viv Daley riding shotgun in 6-X-76, and they had just responded to a call far from their beat. They were up north in 6-A-15's area and complaining about it when they spotted the VW bug roll through the stop sign. They pulled over the old Volkswagen on Mulholland Drive.

"You're up," Georgie said, and Viv grabbed her citation book.

Jonas said to Megan, "Can anything more happen to me this fucking month?"

Megan was trying to massage her knees and said, "Jonas, I'm in pain. We've got to at least get some norcos or perks."

Viv approached on the driver's side and said, "Your license and registration, sir."

Jonas took the registration from the glove box and handed it to Viv along with his driver's license, saying, "Look, Officer, I'm outta work and we're hurrying to a job opportunity in the Hills. Some rich people need a handyman around the house. See, we got a sick five-month-old baby at home and this job is important. Can't you give us a break?"

"Is this lady your wife?" Viv asked.

"Yeah, my wife," Jonas said, but amended it. "Well, we're not officially married, but now that our baby's here, we're gonna take care of that."

Jonas Claymore could not have known that he had exactly the right officer from Hollywood Station at this time to be telling about an infant in need, and Viv Daley said to Megan, "Who's taking care of your sick baby?"

Megan Burke's pain threshold had been reached, and she turned her welling eyes to the cop and said, "My...my mom!" And the tears spilled down her face.

"Okay," Viv said, handing Jonas Claymore's license and registration back to him. "Make complete stops. You don't want your baby growing up an orphan."

"God bless you, Officer," Jonas said.

When Viv and Georgie got back in the car, he said, "They looked like tweakers."

"Gypsy, you're a cynic," Viv said.

"Didn't they look like dopers to you?"

"They certainly did," she said.

"So why'd you kick them?"

"I thought maybe they were telling the truth about a sick baby at home."

Georgie Adams didn't say any more about it. They didn't talk about infants in need.

After Jonas started driving again, he said, "That was fucking fantastic the way you turned on the water! You even had me believing it."

"I wasn't acting, Jonas," Megan said. "I'm hurting."

"You gotta man-up," Jonas said. "We got work to do."

"I can't," Megan said. "I feel like I'm dying."

He looked at her closely then and pulled to the side of the road. He said, "As soon as we get a stake, you're going to rehab. Here, get your watsons on." And he reached in the pocket of his jeans and took out two Vicodins that he'd been keeping for an emergency. She snatched them from his hand, popped them in her mouth, and chewed them up.

Nigel had the poster-board photograph of *The Woman by the Water* nailed snugly in place, and it fit even more perfectly than he had hoped. He lifted the baroque frame under the floodlight and said, "I am a genius!"

"I'll try to always remember that," Raleigh said.

Nigel carefully hung the frame with the poster-board impostor in it, stood back, adjusted it on its hanger, stood back again, and said, "Could you tell the difference between this and the original under normal lighting? That is, if you were someone who seldom studied this piece or any of the other art that you own? Simply put, if you were silly Leona Brueger or her idiot boyfriend?"

"I have to say, you did a great job," Raleigh said grudgingly.

"Okay, now we do the second one and we're finished," Nigel said. "Could you get me another glass of that refreshing Vichy water?"

Nigel carefully covered *The Woman by the Water* canvas with the mover's blanket and tore off strips of masking tape to secure the corners of the folds while Raleigh refilled Nigel's glass with tap water and a few ice cubes.

When Raleigh brought the water back, he didn't see that Nigel had moved one of the paintings. *Flowers on the Hillside* was leaning against the opposite wall, and when Raleigh stepped around the light stand, he accidentally kicked it and it fell over.

"Goddamnit!" Nigel screamed. "You clumsy fool!"

"I'm sorry," Raleigh said. "I didn't see it. You moved it."

"Bugger all!" Nigel said, as he ran to the painting and picked it up, examining it under the floodlight.

"It fell on the back of the canvas," Raleigh said. "I didn't hurt it."

Nigel took deep breaths to calm himself and said, "All right." Then he took the water tumbler from Raleigh and drank.

When he put the tumbler down, he said, "We're bundling this piece now before you destroy it. Help me."

Raleigh spread the mover's blankets on the tile floor, and each painting was wrapped separately in a blanket and secured with duct tape.

When they were finished, Raleigh said, "I'm getting these paintings into your van before something else happens to make you have a fucking stroke like Marty Brueger."

Nigel saw that Raleigh's waning diffidence had morphed into mounting anger, and he was about to say, "No, I'll do it," but instead he said, "Okay, I'm sorry I blew up. Yes, take them to my van, but be as careful as you have ever been in your life. Lay them down on the floor of the van, near the rear door. I'll secure them in place when we finish here."

Raleigh picked up the blanketed bundles and started for the door, when Nigel said, "Wait a minute. You'll need the keys." He felt his pocket and said, "I must've left them in the van." Then he

began to fit the poster-board photograph of *Flowers on the Hill-side* into the smaller gilded frame, having to make more adjustments before getting it shimmed snugly into place.

When Raleigh got outside, carrying a bundle under each arm, there was not much left of twilight. Darkness was falling fast on the Hollywood Hills. He had to lean both bundles against the front fender of the van in order to open the door. After he got it open, he picked up each bundle separately and crawled into the van twice, placing each painting on the floor, neither bundle touching the other.

When he was finished, he closed the van door and heard the phone ring. He thought, Mrs. Brueger!

Raleigh ran into the house, raced across the foyer to the wall phone, picked it up, and said "Hello?"

A voice said, "Hi. My name is Amber. May I please speak to the lady of the house?"

Raleigh said, "She's on the floor right now," and hung up. He looked at his watch and saw that it would be almost dawn in Tuscany. His nerves. His goddamn nerves were shredded.

There wasn't enough daylight left for Jonas Claymore to see clearly from his vantage point, peeking over the wall between two junipers. Jonas whispered to Megan, "What's up with that? Did you check out how careful he put that stuff in the van?"

Megan could make out the lettering on the side of the van and whispered, "Wickland Gallery. It's gotta be art or something."

Jonas said, "Whatever it is, it's gonna belong to us in about two minutes."

"You're going down there?" she said.

"Yeah, go start the engine. When I come over the wall be ready to move."

"They looked like pretty big things he was carrying," she said. "Whatever it was might not fit in the VW."

"We'll make it fit," he said, and in a few seconds he had squeezed between the junipers and pulled himself up and over the wall.

Jonas scrambled down the little hill that was planted with ivy to hold the soil. In a moment he was creeping along the cobbled driveway. When he got to the side of the cargo van, he grabbed the handle, opening the door as quietly as he could. He peered inside, and even in the darkening shadows he could see that Megan was right. The two bundles were too large to fit in the VW. He crawled inside and lifted one and saw that it was not heavy. He guessed that they were paintings. He thought that in a house like this they must be valuable. Maybe worth five grand, maybe even more. But they were too big to transport in the VW bug.

He was feeling frustration overload and crawled out of the van quietly, ready to scurry back to safety. But while standing outside the van, the tall young man saw that just above eye level on the roof of the van was a ring of keys, where Nigel had put them. He closed the van door quietly and grabbed them, easily locating the ignition key.

Inside the Brueger house Nigel Wickland was so overjoyed, he was actually whistling softly, and he just about had the smaller Impressionist painting shimmed into place inside the gilded frame.

Nigel said, "Raleigh, hand me that small screwdriver from my toolbox. The one under the—"

"Shut up!" Raleigh said. "What's that?"

"What's what?" Nigel asked.

"It's a car engine," Raleigh said. "It's your van!"

Raleigh bolted for the front door and switched on the driveway lights in time to see the cargo van stopped momentarily at the security gate until the electronic beam caused the gate to swing open wide.

"Hey!" Raleigh screamed. "Hey!" And he began running after the van, which sped through the gate and headed down the hill, followed by an old Volkswagen bug.

"Hey," Raleigh said weakly as the gate closed with him inside.

Raleigh stood there staring at the left taillight of the VW bug, the right one having burned out. The little car chugged down toward the flatland, growing smaller, its one eye winking at Raleigh Dibble as it descended in the darkness.

Megan Burke had an epiphany as she followed her partner down from the Hollywood Hills after his shocking theft of the van. She thought of how she had told Jonas, "There are some things I won't do." But she was doing them. First the old woman's TV and now this van. And she thought, I am a thief. I have become a common thief. My life is in ruins. Hollywood is killing me.

Nigel Wickland was standing in the foyer, looking forlorn and helpless, when Raleigh jogged back into the house.

Raleigh said to him, "Why did you leave the fucking keys in the van? Goddamn you, why didn't you put them in your pocket?"

Nigel's voice was a rasp when he said, "I told you I had left them in the van, you blockhead. Why didn't you bring them in?"

"The keys were your responsibility, not mine, you fop," Raleigh said. "Now what do we do? Now what?"

Nigel turned his back on Raleigh and walked back to the unfinished job. He stood under the floodlight, tall and gaunt, his white hair sparkling beneath the glow. Nigel Wickland had a dizzying moment when he felt like a doomed protagonist in a Shakespearean tragedy. And like Lear he screamed.

Raleigh's shock and terror were pushing him into a kind of somnambulate state, but Nigel Wickland's primal scream jolted him out of it. Raleigh froze in place, standing in the foyer watching Nigel Wickland collapse into himself and drop onto the floor on his knees. Then the gallery owner started to weep, and he reached for his inhaler and took two puffs, inhaling deeply and holding his breath until he had to exhale and weep some more.

Raleigh tiptoed past him to the butler's pantry for a fresh

tumbler. He threw in some ice cubes and filled it under the tap. When he returned to the foyer, he put it down beside his crime partner and said, "More Vichy water?"

Nigel wiped his eyes on the sleeve of his coveralls and said, "We're finished, Raleigh. I think I shall shoot myself before going to the penitentiary. I'm too old for prison."

For the first time the roles were reversed and Raleigh Dibble felt that it was up to him to salvage something from this catastrophe. But what?

He said, "Shouldn't we call the police? The cops may get lucky and catch them before they get too far away."

Nigel stopped weeping entirely and let out a scary laugh, shook his head, and said, "You are really the most benighted human being I have ever met."

"It's not too late," Raleigh said. "The cops might get them."

"It's too late," Nigel croaked. "Too fucking late."

"Nigel!" Raleigh said desperately. "Even if they get the paintings they'll probably just dump the van down on one of the boulevards and the police might get fingerprints or DNA or something, and locate them. And they might get the paintings back. I'm calling the police."

Nigel got to his feet then and said, "If you touch that phone, I swear I will kill you."

"But why not call them, goddamnit?"

"Because, you fucking fool," Nigel said, "the *last* thing we want is for the police to arrest the miserable scum who stole my van!"

Raleigh's mind was racing now as his panic grew. "But they might catch them before they dispose of the pictures and we could get them back and everything could be okay before Mrs. Brueger gets back from Tuscany and—"

Nigel interrupted, saying, "What do you suppose the police would do if they arrested the thieves and recovered the paintings?"

"They'd find out from the crooks where they stole them, and they'd come here and give them back."

"Think," Nigel said, "if that's possible. They would *not* bring them here. They would impound the paintings as evidence. They would need the owner of the paintings to testify in court that they were taken from her home. And the owner of the stolen van, who happens to be your partner, would also have to testify how and where the vehicle was stolen." His voice rose when he said, "So you see, Raleigh, it would all unravel like a filthy fucking ball of yarn that a terrier has dragged through a kennel full of dog shit!"

"You can still report the van as stolen," Raleigh said, his mouth dusty dry, "if you say it was stolen from your gallery or someplace other than here."

Nigel looked toward the garish floodlight, then at the poster-board counterfeit hanging on the wall, and then closed his eyes and said, "I've partnered with a madman. He is insane." Nigel opened his eyes and said, "For the reason just explained in the Queen's English, I cannot risk that the police might get lucky and arrest somebody. Because as soon as they make the vile cretin confess, it would all come right here to this house, where Leona Brueger would ask the police how it was that my van was stolen from her driveway on this lovely night. And then the cock-up would be plain even to the stupidest policeman. Even to Leona herself."

"What will you say if the van turns up somewhere? Maybe it'll be parked in a red zone and get impounded."

"Then I shall be notified and will pay the impound fee and pick it up, saying that I lent it to my wayward nephew and look what he did with it. The best thing that could happen now is if the thieves get in a fiery crash and kill themselves and burn the goddamn paintings to ashes." That made Nigel's eyes well, and Raleigh thought he might start bawling again.

"And what's going to happen to us if the thieves take the

paintings to an art dealer here in town? Maybe to an auction house and try to sell them?"

"I believe that their provenance would be discovered soon enough," Nigel said, looking like a man on a gallows. "And the police would be called in without hesitation, and whether or not they caught the thieves, they would end up here at this house, and through Leona Brueger the police would quickly discover the switch. In which case I might decide to test the aging ammunition in my pistol. I'm too old for prison."

Raleigh sat trancelike while Nigel completed mounting the poster board into the frame belonging to *Flowers on the Hillside*. After that, he placed the framed poster board on the original hanger and said, "The work is finished and perhaps so are we."

"I'm getting sick," Raleigh said, and ran to the powder room off the foyer. When he returned, he was pale and beads of sweat had popped out on his upper lip and forehead. He wiped his mouth with a hand towel bearing the Brueger monogram.

He said, "Nigel, I'm desperate. I have one last idea. Please hear me out."

Nigel was putting his tools away and folding the light stand and didn't stop working when he said, "Go ahead. Impress me with your acuity."

Raleigh said, "What if we take the framed poster-board pictures and get rid of them? Burn them up somewhere or break them into pieces and drop them in a Dumpster. And I drive you home and come back here and call the police and say that home-invading robbers got in through an unlocked side door and put a gun on me and stole the pictures."

"Oh, that is brilliant!" Nigel said. "I'm sure they would believe a fucking domestic servant who has only been employed here for a matter of weeks. And who happens to have a prison record. Oh, yes, and I wonder what you would say when they asked you to submit to a lie detector? And in the hopefully unlikely event that they

catch the thieves, it would make it ever so much easier to figure out what was going on here, especially after they were able to place my van at the crime scene. Oh, there would be such a jolly time at the station house when they brought you in handcuffed. Do you know what the joke would be for weeks to come?"

Raleigh sat down on a carved antique chair with a needlepoint cushion, his chin hanging almost to his chest, and said, "Tell me the joke. I'm dying to laugh."

Nigel said, "The joke would be, the butler really did it."

Raleigh's head was still spinning when he drove Nigel in the Brueger Mercedes to his Beverly Hills gallery, where his car was parked. Neither spoke for the first twenty minutes. Then Raleigh said, "If the paintings never surface, things can proceed as originally planned, right? You'll help Mrs. Brueger pack and ship all the art to her storage facility just as you said?"

After a moment Nigel said, "Yes. Just as I planned. Except that I've spent a few thousand at the photo lab and I've lost a van, at least for now. And I believe that I've lost several years from my life as a result of this disaster. But if that should happen, I would be so happy that I'd throw a party and invite everyone I know. Except you."

Raleigh continued his train of thought and said, "So a long time from now, if the switch is discovered when the art is taken from the storage facility, it'll be blamed on one of the transporters or a storage yard employee, right?"

Nigel sighed and said, "From your lips to God's ear."

"A part of me would feel okay if that happened," Raleigh admitted. "Maybe we dodged a bullet. I could just go back to being what I am and you can go back to being—"

"Bankrupt," Nigel said.

"Whatever," Raleigh said. "At least we won't be in prison if those crooks never get caught."

"Raleigh," Nigel said suddenly, and this time his tone had

softened. He sounded almost conciliatory. "If anything untoward should happen..."

There it was again, Raleigh thought. *Untoward.*

"Yes?"

If something did go wrong sometime down the road...that is, if something came back on you, would you really bring me into it? I mean, haven't I suffered enough?"

Raleigh turned to gape at Nigel and almost rear-ended the car in front of him at the stoplight. He said, "Haven't *you* suffered enough?"

"Raleigh, there'd be nothing to gain by informing on me," Nigel said. "What could you really profit from saying that you had a crime partner? I could take a second mortgage on my condominium and sell my business if I had to do it. I could put half of everything I realize from the sale into a trust account for you. I'd do it, gladly."

"You really are a piece of work, Nigel," Raleigh said. "Please forgive my clichés, but you are a piece of fucking work."

"So you'd bargain with my freedom just to curry favor with a prosecutor and have maybe a year or two lopped from your sentence, is that it?"

Raleigh said, "I'd trade your ass to have two months cut from my sentence. Or two weeks. I'd do it for no sentence reduction at all, just to see how you handle your inferiors in the prison yard, you pompous flouncing popinjay!"

There was no more said until Raleigh parked behind Nigel's gallery, where they unloaded the light stand, floodlight, and toolbox.

Nigel Wickland said, "I don't suppose we shall need to see each other after tonight."

"Not in this life," Raleigh Dibble replied, and headed for the Hollywood Hills.

※　　　※　　　※

There was just enough room to park the Volkswagen on Jonas and Megan's street, so Jonas had to double-park the van beside the car of a tenant who seldom went anywhere at night. They were excited when they got the bundles inside and removed the tape and the mover's blankets.

Jonas picked up the largest canvas and placed it on the back of the sofa, leaning it against the wall, and then he stepped back to appraise it.

"It's what you call an Expressionist picture," he finally said to Megan.

"Oh, really?"

"Yeah, it's a picture where the expression on the person's face tells you what the artist had in mind."

Megan said, "You can hardly see the woman's expression if that's what you're looking for."

"That's the way Expressionists paint," Jonas said. "You have to look through the fuzzy brushwork and guess what she's thinking."

"Do you think it's really worth five thousand?" she asked doubtfully.

"Just look where it came from. The crib up there in the Holly-wood Hills is worth gazillions."

"Where will we sell it?"

"I don't know. Not at a swap meet, that's for sure. We gotta do some research."

"How about the other one?"

"Not as much," Jonas said. "It's smaller, and flowers are over-done these days. All the swap meets have lotsa framed pictures of flowers. But we might get a few Franklins for it."

"Do you think you'd better get rid of the van? The cops proba-bly have a report on it by now."

"Yeah," Jonas said. "I'm gonna dump it over on Normandie after I wipe off all my fingerprints. Gimme a dish towel, will ya?"

When they got out to the street, Jonas was barely seated in the

van when 6-X-32 pulled up behind him with red and blue lights on and gave a short toot on the horn. Megan, who was about to get into the VW bug, saw them and headed back to the apartment, having to force herself to walk slowly.

Hollywood Nate approached on the driver's side of the van and Flotsam on the passenger side, shining his streamlight in on Jonas's hands. Nate said, "License and registration, please."

"Sure, Officer," Jonas said, his chin quivering. "What did I do wrong?"

"Do I have to tell you it's illegal to double-park like this?" Nate said.

Jonas was so relieved, he felt like crying, and said, "I'm sorry, Officer. I had to make a delivery for my boss. I been working all day and this is the last stop. I'm sorry. Please don't write me a ticket."

Jonas tried hard to keep his hand from trembling when he offered the driver's license to Hollywood Nate, hoping that the registration was in the glove box. Nate didn't even bother to take the license from him. He looked at the side of the van and said, "Wickland Gallery. This doesn't look like a gallery neighborhood."

"We sell good art and crappy art, Officer," Jonas said. "Real affordable stuff. You and the missus should stop by sometime if you're thinking about —"

"Crappy art," Nate said. "I'll keep that in mind if I ever have another missus and need anything crappier than I've got now."

With that, Nate turned and walked back to the radio car. When they were cruising again, Flotsam said, "Why didn't you write that one? Double-parker, dude. One for the recap."

Nate said, "This recession's been tough on working stiffs like that kid. Besides, all my bones hurt. I just wanna sit in our shop tonight and think of ways I can burn the fucking Goth House to the ground."

"That reminds me," Flotsam said, taking out his cell phone to check on Jetsam for the second time.

When the black-and-white pulled away, Megan ran to the Volkswagen and headed toward Normandie Avenue. She drove south for a few blocks until she saw the Wickland Gallery van just past Melrose in front of a liquor store. Jonas was already out and walking northbound when she picked him up.

"I was so scared, Jonas!" she said. "I thought they had a report on the van and you were busted."

"I'm starting to think I can talk my way outta anything," he said. "He didn't even look at my license, so I can't be connected to the van even if they pick it up. Two cops in one day have tried to hack me and I'm still here. This might be, like, kiss-met."

"What?"

"It means that destiny is calling. Something big is in my future. You're lucky you hooked your wagon to a star!"

"I only hope I didn't hook my wagon to a wagon," Megan said. "A beat-up old Volkswagen that might end up driving us both straight to jail."

★ NINETEEN ★

RALEIGH MANAGED TO get to sleep as the rising sun was providing the citizens of Hollywood, California, with new hope on the cusp of autumn. Just as he was beginning to dream, the phone rang. He sat up when he heard Rudy Ressler say, "Raleigh, it's Mr. Ressler. How's Marty?"

During all the turmoil at the Brueger estate, Raleigh had hardly thought about the old man, and hadn't even phoned Cedars-Sinai since Marty Brueger was admitted.

"He's fine, Mr. Ressler," Raleigh said. "You and Mrs. Brueger have nothing to worry about. I'll let you know if there's any bad news at all."

"You won't have to," Ressler said. "I've booked a flight. We're coming home."

This time the blast of fear sent blood surging through Raleigh's skull. He jumped out of bed and stood naked and tense. "But Mr. Ressler," he said. "You have several weeks left on your vacation rental. Mr. Brueger is fine. Stay and enjoy yourself."

"To tell you the truth, it's not all that enjoyable," Ressler said. "The villa isn't what it was cracked up to be. The toilets work half the time and the water's never hot enough. This guy Silva who's supposed to be our translator is a greedy little wop who's always in

our pockets for something or other. I'm not enjoying it at all and neither is Mrs. Brueger. We're leaving here."

Raleigh caught his breath, swallowed hard, and said, "I see. Do you know when you'll be arriving at LAX?"

"Not yet," the director said. "I'll let you know. We'll expect you to pick us up."

"Of course," Raleigh said. "I'll be in the big Mercedes."

After he hung up, Raleigh Dibble experienced the terror of being utterly out of control. The boiling heat in his head topped a roiling stomach that sent him to the bathroom again.

He phoned Nigel Wickland's cell phone ten minutes later and was not surprised to find his partner awake.

"It's me," Raleigh said.

Nigel said. "Please don't tell me there's something wrong with the replicas."

"No," Raleigh said. "The Bruegers are leaving Italy and coming home."

Silence on the line and then, "My work will be tested a lot sooner than we thought. All right, what of it? Just don't lose your head. The replicas look perfect. Just behave as you always do and it will be fine."

"You haven't heard anything about your van yet, have you?"

"Of course not."

"If you do hear anything... let me know ASAP."

"Why?" Nigel said. "Are you going to reimburse me if the thieves strip it?"

"I'll feel a lot better when you get the van back, that's all," Raleigh said. "So just let me know if it gets impounded for any reason."

Nigel clicked off without responding.

Raleigh wondered if Nigel Wickland was serious when he talked about shooting himself if the thieves got caught. If that happened, suicide didn't seem to Raleigh like such a bad idea.

*　　*　　*

Jonas Claymore and Megan Burke had decided to spend every last dollar she'd wheedled from her mother and buy enough ox to chase the dragon all weekend. This because they would have a windfall as soon as they figured out the best way to approach art dealers with the paintings. It was when he felt euphoric that Jonas got his latest idea.

He tried to roust Megan out of her stupor and was only half successful. He said, "Baby, I got it."

"Got what?" she mumbled.

"It's too fucking risky to be messing with art dealers or auction houses. What I think we should do is make them pay us ransom!"

"Ransom?" she said drowsily.

"Yeah," he said. "We call the Wickland Gallery on Monday morning and we talk to the boss there and we say we know how they fucked up the other night and got their paintings swiped, but we'd like to help get them back. Shit, I could even tell him where to pick up his van as an act of good faith. You on this?"

"Uh-huh," she muttered.

"Then get your head in it. All we gotta do is negotiate the price and tell them if they go to the police, we slash the paintings to pieces. Then we set up a money drop. I seen this done a million times in the movies, so I know all the tricks."

"Tricks?" she said.

"What's the use?" he said. "You're all spun out. I could get more companionship from a hamster."

Jetsam's neck spasm was not responding to muscle-relaxing drugs and he was advised by his doctor to take a few days off and rest at home. When he phoned Flotsam and told him about it, his partner said, "Do what the croakers tell you, dude. There's some good surfing coming down and you don't wanna miss it. So take it easy and rest up."

When Jetsam found out that Flotsam was partnered with Nate, he said, "Bro, I'm glad you got teamed with Hollywood Nate. He is like, so hormonally ingenious and cinematically dialed-in, he might put you onto some scintillating starlets from his movie ventures."

"He ain't done it yet, dude," Flotsam said. "But if he does, I'll save them for when my li'l pard comes back. I won't use them all up without you."

Hollywood Nate was glad that Snufffy Salcedo was still recuperating, because roll call that night would have driven him mad. The watch commander was conducting it instead of Sergeant Murillo, and he was droning on about the chief's pet program, the thing he brought with him to the LAPD from the East Coast.

The lieutenant said, "You should pay particular attention to reporting districts six-forty-three and six-forty-four. CompStat indicates unusual four-five-nine activity there. I'd like some explanations as to why these crimes are happening."

Everyone glanced at one another and eyes rolled, and Sergeant Murillo arrived in the nick of time, entering the room and saying, "Lieutenant O'Reilly, call for you from the captain. About the inspection next week."

"Oh, yes," the watch commander said, and went downstairs to take the call.

Sergeant Murillo sat and said, "Let's see, what were we talking about?"

The whole attitude of the troops changed with Sergeant Murillo in charge, and Flotsam said with a smirk, "The super chief's baby, of course. CompStat. You know, like, let's explain why this crime happened, where it happened, how it happened, et cetera. What I'd like to say is, it happened because some dude's been shooting up too much dope and needs money and he kicked down a door to find some. Period. End of story."

"We can't say things like that," Georgie Adams griped. "With

CompStat, nothing is allowed to be random crime. *Random* is not in the CompStat lexicon. Yet, these're just jump-on crimes, Sarge. They happen."

"But we gotta come up with some goofy answer," Hollywood Nate said, echoing what he'd heard so many times from Snuffy Salcedo. "Because Mister brought it from back East, and the mayor thinks it's some kind of special juju, and the media has bought into it, and it's bullshit."

"It's all about putting the cops on the dots," Viv Daley said. "You put a pin map on a PowerPoint and it's supposed to do some kind of magic numbers-crunching."

Della Ravelle said, "It's nothing but pin maps that've been around a hundred years but without the computers back then. CompStat is supposed to figure out trends, but what if, like Georgie says, most of street crime is random? We're expected to invent trends to justify a theory. Mister is a master at stroking City Hall and conning the media."

Viv Daley said, "Back East where Mister comes from, not everybody has a car, so crimes can come in clusters in a small area, and cops can maybe look for trends there. But L.A. is a city on wheels. Everybody has at least one car. Everybody's in motion. One bad guy can scatter his offenses like cold germs all over the map. Where's the trend?"

Hollywood Nate said, "I'm gonna create a two-sentence book called *CompStat for Dummies*. The book will say, 'It's a computerized pin map, stupid. Now just go in there and do your Kabuki dance for the chief.' Think it'll sell down at PAB?"

It all stopped when Lieutenant O'Reilly came back into the roll call room and said to Sergeant Murillo, "Did you discuss CompStat and its importance?"

"Absolutely," Sergeant Murillo said. "And everybody here is onboard a hundred percent. It's the best thing that's happened to the LAPD since Kevlar vests and semiautomatics."

Lieutenant O'Reilly looked for irony in his sergeant's expression but nodded and said, "Fine. Let's go to work."

The moment 6-X-32 drove out of the parking lot and cleared, Hollywood Nate got a cell call. He didn't recognize the number but answered, and Leona Brueger said, "Hi, gorgeous."

"Mrs. Brueger!" Nate said. "Are you home?"

"Leona, remember?" she said. "And no, I'm not. It's the middle of the night here and I couldn't sleep and started thinking of you."

"That's . . . that's flattering," Nate said.

"I had too much champagne at dinner," Leona Brueger said. "It always wrecks my sleep. How about talking sexy to me until I get drowsy?"

Nate said, "I'm, uh, just leaving Hollywood Station with my partner beside me, preparing to crush crime and terrify lawbreakers. I don't see how I can do that."

"Bad timing," she said. "The story of my life."

"Maybe you'll invite me to a dinner party when you get back," Nate said. "With some of the industry people?"

"You actors," she said. "One-track minds. Okay, I'll let you guardians of law and order do your thing, but how about checking on my house? Rudy told me that our butler sounded a bit stressed the last time he called. Just make sure everything's okay."

"Absolutely," Nate said. "I'll stop by this evening. See you when you get back."

"You'll be seeing me sooner than you think," she said. "Bye-bye, gorgeous."

Nate closed his cell and said to Flotsam, "I need to make a quick stop up in the Hills."

That piqued Flotsam's interest. "Yeah?" he said with a leer. "You got some smokin' hot Hills honey up there? Maybe a stupendous starlet from one of your SAG jobs? How about an introduction? My li'l pard and me, we'll take your leftovers."

"Not exactly that," Nate said. "I met a director who's asked me to check on the house of his girlfriend. They're off in Italy for a couple of months. I've been meaning to stop but I haven't had time."

"What's the girlfriend look like?"

"Old enough to be your mother and mine," Nate said. "But she's still pretty hot."

"The miracles of modern medicine," Flotsam said. "My partner met a chick a year or so ago that was rebuilt from spare parts. T and A, all of it. She looked great, but he said he was scared to touch her for fear something would fall off."

"We'll just take a minute to ring the bell and ask the butler if everything's okay," Nate said. "And I'll leave my card to prove I've been there."

"Is he, like, gonna put you in a movie?"

"That's the idea," Nate said. "I'm thirty-eight years old. My time's running out."

"I'm thirty-five, dude," Flotsam said. "That's the good thing about the surfing life. You can do it till your libido expires and way beyond. There's no sell-by date as long as your knees keep working."

As Nate drove up toward Woodrow Wilson Drive, he said, "Magic hour. This is the best time to shoot movies. The light ... it's magic up here."

"Dude, when you get to be a star and buy a crib up in the Hills, I'd like to be your part-time houseboy. I know you're gonna have them starstruck Susies all over you, and my partner and me, we could take turns working for table scraps and whatever Bettys you leave still breathing when you're done with your monkey sex."

"I'll try to leave them breathing," Nate said.

"I hear that the homicide teams ain't too fond of the people that live up in the Hills," Flotsam said. "They're, like, way too busy arranging their toothbrushes according to feng shui to talk to coppers. The detectives are, like, 'Well, please give us a call after the

kid's yoga, soccer, and lacrosse. It's only serial murder we're looking into.' Me, I prefer the people in east Hollywood, who have their
kids the old-fashioned way. The brats up here go around saying,
'We're in vitro twins,' or, 'I'm a reversal,' referring to daddy's vasec-
tomy turnaround. It's all too weirded for me. But I wouldn't mind
one of them trophy bride Hills-honeys who like to get their religion on."

"What's that supposed to mean?"

Flotsam said, "You know, they go, 'Oh my god, oh my god!'
when they finally get nailed by someone from their own generation
after sleeping so long with semi-erect sugar daddies."

"I'll try to remember all that," Nate said. "When I get to be a
star."

Hollywood Nate found the address written on Rudy Ressler's
card, stopped at the drive-in gate, and pushed the call button.

Raleigh Dibble's voice said, "Yes? Who is it?"

"Police officers," Hollywood Nate said. "Could you let us in,
please?"

Raleigh stood petrified in the billiards room, where he'd been
shooting pool to kill time as the hands of the clock on the wall
seemed locked in place. And now he was paralyzed by the telephone voice. The voice said again, "Hello? Police officers. We need
to come in, please."

Raleigh pushed the appropriate phone key, put down the pool
cue, and walked into the foyer. He vaguely thought about getting
something warm to wear because he knew from experience that a
jail cell was a chilling experience, even during an arid day like this,
when the Santa Anas were baking the Hollywood Hills.

The black-and-white had already parked in front of the entry
arch, and the uniformed officers were getting out by the time
Raleigh opened the door, hoping that the handcuffs would not be
cinched so tightly this time. He remembered how they'd bruised
his wrists when he'd been transported from courtroom to jail.

He thought that it would be detectives who brought him in this time, but then he remembered that detectives might not be working on the weekend, and he would no doubt see them on Monday morning. He decided to tell these uniformed cops that he had no wish to speak to them without a lawyer present, but on Monday he would make a deal with the detectives and spill his guts. The first thing he'd talk about would be the mastermind, Nigel Wickland.

The tall, suntanned cop was looking around at the grounds as though he were a potential buyer. The good-looking one was smiling, and he presented a business card to Raleigh, saying, "I'm Officer Nate Weiss from Hollywood Division. Mr. Ressler asked me to stop by and check on the property. And you are?"

He needed to swallow twice before saying, "Raleigh Dibble. I'm the butler and caretaker here. Mrs. Brueger is away."

"Yes, that's what I was told by Mr. Ressler," Nate said. "I just wanted to introduce myself and tell you that we're keeping an eye on things, and if you need anything from us, call me personally. My cell number is on the back."

Raleigh said with much emotion, "Thank you! Thank you, Officer!"

"Do you know what date they'll be returning?" Nate asked.

"Tomorrow," Raleigh said. "They're coming back tomorrow, I think."

"Really?" Nate said, wondering why Leona Brueger had not mentioned that. The woman was full of secrets and surprises.

Raleigh displayed a lopsided toothy smile that seemed inappropriate to Nate, especially when the butler said, "Mrs. Brueger's brother-in-law had a stroke and they're coming home to take care of him."

"I'm sorry to hear that," Nate said. "Please tell Mrs. Brueger and Mr. Ressler that I stopped by and that we've been keeping an eye on the place since they've been gone. Will you be sure to tell them that?"

"I'll be glad to, Officer," Raleigh said.

When the cops were driving out the gate, Flotsam said, "I was hoping he'd invite us inside. I wanted to take a tour of that crib to see what it's gonna be like when I'm your houseboy."

"He's a peculiar guy," Nate said. "He looked like he just got bad news from an oncologist when we arrived, but at odd moments his smile got beamier than Oprah's ass."

"Who cares? I'll bet the swimming pool's big enough to surf on," Flotsam mused.

"Something's not normal with that guy," Nate went on.

"Dude, you were expecting normal?" Flotsam said. "This is fucking Hollywood."

A short time later they spotted a young man running south on Orange Drive from Hollywood Boulevard, dodging pedestrians, holding something under his shirt. They felt sure he'd snatched a purse from one of the tourists on the Walk of Fame and they closed in on him and caught him two blocks south. They ordered him to put his hands on his head.

He did, and the hidden object fell to the pavement. It was a box containing a pepperoni pizza that he was trying to keep warm until he got back home with his girlfriend to watch *American Idol*.

"See what I mean, dude?" Flotsam said to Hollywood Nate. "It's this geography."

★ TWENTY ★

ON MONDAY MORNING, Jonas was awake early, feeling electric at the prospect of making real money for the first time ever. He felt the old vibration mode as though he'd been doing crystal meth again, which he had not. He believed that his tweaking days were over now that he'd learned the joys of ox. Jonas's hands were shaking noticeably while he was trying to get some orange juice into himself to wash down one of the peanut butter sandwiches that Megan had made for their breakfast.

She swept the little kitchen and made a halfhearted attempt to wipe down the stovetop. But when she opened the refrigerator to give it a wipe, she gave up. There was so much spilled juice and milk and jelly and ice cream on the shelves that she'd have needed a garden hose to clean it.

Megan had even washed a load in the coin-operated washer in the community laundry room that they shared with five other apartments, and she had the clothes in the dryer by the time Jonas finished his sandwich. She was hoping for a word of appreciation.

"Try to dress a little nice for once" was all he said, sneering at her cutoffs and coffee-stained T-shirt.

Even when she was feeling halfway decent he managed to ruin it for her, so she said, "Why? Are we doing lunch at the Bel Air Hotel?"

"Meg," he said, as soberly as possible. "This is gonna be the biggest day of your life. This is way big. You and me gotta look and act...professional. In case."

She leaned against the drainboard, one hand on her hip, and said, "In case of what, Jonas?"

"That's the thing!" he said. "I don't know. I'd like to call that house up there if I had the number, but I don't. So we're gonna call the Wickland Gallery and jist—"

"Wing it."

"Right."

Megan said, "Don't think for one minute that I'm going to talk for you on this one. Like when you had me talk to the maid after you got the phone number of that no-name actress whose house we were supposed to burgle. She told me to go fuck myself in Spanish and English both."

Jonas said, "Don't start bitching at me, Megan. Put on something clean and we'll go to the public phones at the cybercafé and make the call. I gotta think of the best way to show the owner that we're serious people he can deal with."

Ruth had opened the Wickland Gallery that morning, which was a bit unusual. Normally, by the time she arrived Nigel Wickland would already have coffee brewing and croissants set out. She was as meticulously groomed as ever and had removed her teal jacket, hanging it in the little closet in Nigel's office.

When he did arrive at 10 A.M., he looked terrible. His eye pouches sagged and his orbs were red-rimmed and watery. His beautiful mane of white hair had been hastily combed, and he was wearing exactly the same shirt, jacket, necktie, and trousers that he'd worn on Friday. That had never happened before in the years she'd worked at Wickland Gallery.

She said, "Good morning, Nigel. Is everything all right? You look a bit...tired."

He had a distant look on his face when he said, "I'm knackered, Ruth. I may have to lie down in my office for a bit. I couldn't sleep last night."

"Is anything wrong? Are you sick?"

"Not now, I'm not," he said. "I think the sea bass I ate for dinner had turned. It smelled fishy, and as they say, if it smells like fish don't eat it."

"Where's the van? It's not in the carport."

"Oh, I . . . I lent it to my nephew, Reginald. Have I ever told you about him?"

"Not that I recall."

"He's a bit one-off, that lad. My sister's boy. Said he needed to move some things from his girlfriend's house, and he promised he'd bring it back by tomorrow."

"I hope we don't need it today," she said.

"The way business has been, that's unlikely," said Nigel Wickland. "Very unlikely."

"I'll bring you some coffee," she said.

Ruth had the coffee poured and had spooned in his sugar and cream when the phone rang. She went to her desk and picked it up.

Jonas had actually come close to paying Megan a compliment when he said, "I ain't seen you in a dress since I met you, Meg. You don't look so bad."

She was wearing a candy-striped baby-doll shirtdress that she'd worn to a dance in high school. Now high school seemed to Megan like half a lifetime ago. Sometimes she felt like checking her driver's license to be sure that she was only twenty years old. The dress came to midthigh and she thought it would look better if she wore heels, but her ankles and knees were hurting too much, so she wore her only pair of flats, on which the soles were worn through. The lip gloss and eyeliner made her feel feminine for a change, and that gave her a bit of a lift.

Jonas was wearing the only sport coat he owned, a green-checked cotton blend. He wore it over a clean black T-shirt with faded jeans and tennis shoes. He seldom shaved his wispy facial hair, hoping in vain to grow it into a real five-day stubble like all the rich young dickheads whose cars he parked, but so far he couldn't produce a manly growth.

When Jonas and Megan arrived at the shopping mall that housed the cybercafé, Jonas said to Megan, "Don't interrupt me when I'm talking to the guy. Just stand there and listen. Remember, this is my game plan and I'm the quarterback."

They chose the public phone that was farthest from the cubicles full of people who rented the computers at all hours seven days a week. Business was brisk on a Monday morning, and the downstairs customer closest to Megan and Jonas was a black man in a tracksuit and very pricey tennis shoes. He was sitting beside a curvaceous blonde with sultry eye shadow, wearing shorts, ankle strap platforms, and an apricot top that came down far enough to just cover her silicone rack but was high enough to display her gleaming navel ring.

Jonas mouthed the words "pimp and whore" to Megan, as if she didn't know. He was so nervous, he dropped one of his quarters and she had to pick it up for him.

When Ruth answered and Jonas asked to speak to the gallery owner, she said, "May I ask the reason for your call? I might be able to help you."

"I gotta speak to the owner of the Wickland Gallery," Jonas said. "It's important."

"I'm sure I can assist you," Ruth said, "if you'll just tell me what it's about."

Jonas said, "My aunt died and I'm inheriting some very valuable paintings. I wanna sell them through your gallery. But I gotta speak to the owner or I won't do business with you."

"Just a moment, please," Ruth said.

Jonas winked at Megan, put his hand over the phone, and said, "Official bitch."

"Officious," she said.

"What?"

"Officious," Megan said.

"What?"

"Never mind."

A mellifluous but weary voice came on the line and said, "This is Nigel Wickland. How may I serve you?"

Jonas said, "I was thinking about how I can serve *you*. I think I may have some property that belongs to you."

The line was quiet and then Jonas heard the sound of a door closing. The gallery owner got back on the line and said urgently, "Who are you?"

Jonas said, "I'm the guy that wants to help you out. Are you missing a van?"

Nigel's heart raced and he said, "Yes, how did you know?"

"Was it stolen?"

"I haven't reported it stolen," Nigel said.

"Bullshit. Don't talk to me like I'm an idiot."

"Yes, it was stolen," Nigel said, changing tack quickly. "And yes, I reported it. Where is it?"

"First we gotta negotiate," Jonas said. "See, I saw the van parked on the street early this morning with some black teenagers inside. I figured they stole it for joyriding. I watched them open the door and start to take out a big wrapped object. I yelled, 'Hey, get outta that truck.' And they ran away. So I looked inside and saw two wrapped objects. And I took them out and I got them at home. I saw the name on the van and called information and here we are."

Nigel massaged his left temple and said, "I see. You're a Samaritan."

"A what?"

"Never mind. I would like to know the location of the van and I would like to get my property back."

"Is there a reward?"

"Yes, I think we can arrange for a reward."

"There's a problem here," Jonas said.

"Yes, I thought there might be," Nigel said, his stomach aflame.

"Who do the items in the van belong to?" Jonas asked.

"Why do you ask?"

"I'm trying to help you, dude," Jonas said. "I'll ask the questions."

"They belong to me," Nigel said.

"Are you sure?" Jonas said. "Because if they belong to somebody else, like one of your customers, then I gotta negotiate a reward with them and not with you, right?"

"Did you unwrap the...objects?"

"Yeah, and they look like very expensive art."

"Are they damaged in any way?"

"No. I rescued them from the little niggers jist in time."

Nigel said, "They do not belong to my client. They belong to me personally. I was at a client's home trying to persuade the client to buy the paintings when the van got stolen." Then he added, "No doubt by the black youths that you chased away. So there's no reason for you to deal with anyone but me."

"What did your client say when your van got snatched?" Jonas asked.

"He was as shocked as I was."

"Did you call the cops from your customer's house?"

Nigel paused again and said, "Yes, from there."

"How much were you trying to sell the paintings for?"

Another long hesitation, and Nigel said, "Look, sir, business is rotten during this recession. People do not go out and buy art when they have to tighten their belts. I'm looking at bankruptcy, but if you'll be reasonable, I could offer you a handsome reward for saving my property from the thieves and returning them to me."

Jonas liked being called "sir" but he said, "I'm getting impatient. How much were you trying to sell them for?"

"Eight thousand dollars," Nigel said.

Jonas gave Megan a thumbs-up and said, "And the van must be worth fifteen grand, even though it ain't new. I saved you twenty-four grand."

Nigel was overjoyed now but knew he had to negotiate to keep from arousing the scum's suspicion, so he said, "The eight thousand included my profit. The two paintings are only worth four thousand total."

"You make a hundred percent on your goods?"

"Yes."

"Damn," Jonas said. "I'm in the wrong business. So how about the van?"

"I have it insured, of course. But I should think I couldn't sell it on today's terrible market for more than ten thousand."

"Four thousand and ten thousand," Jonas said. "So a decent reward would be fourteen thousand bucks, right?"

Nigel thought he must not accept quickly, so he said, "Sir, I have a wife and four children. My business is in ruins. And it's your duty as an honest man to return goods that you know are stolen, but I agree that you deserve a reward. For the van and the pictures I would like to offer you a reward of eight thousand dollars."

Jonas said, "Well, I think I should get a reward of twelve thousand."

"Done," Nigel said.

"Done?"

"Yes, I accept," Nigel said. "Now, please, where is my property and where is my van? I'll need the van in order to transport the paintings."

"Is the big one worth more than the smaller one?" Jonas wanted to know.

"A little more."

"I thought so," Jonas said. "It's got better brushwork and the Expressionist artist had a better sense of color and light. So he got her expression jist right."

"You are a connoisseur, sir," Nigel said. "I'm so glad to be dealing with a man of taste and decency."

"One more thing," Jonas said. "I don't want the police to know anything about me and my reward. They might think I was in on this theft."

"I understand."

"Even if they don't think that, they'll say it's my duty as a citizen to return your property and tell you where to find your van. And they might try to screw me outta my reward."

"I wouldn't let that happen," Nigel said. "I'm so very grateful to you."

"Yeah, but the cops might not be," Jonas said. "So I wanna give you your paintings and get my reward in a really private and confidential way."

"I understand."

"That means I'll call you later about where and when we meet. I'll take the money then and tell you where your paintings are."

"I'll have to trust you, is that it?"

"Yeah," Jonas said, "but to show my good faith, I'm gonna tell you where your van is so you'll have a way to transport your art."

"Thank you."

"You got an extra key for it?"

"Yes."

"It's right in front of the Lucky Star liquor store on Normandie, south of Melrose. I'd suggest you pick it up quick because the store owner might call and get it impounded if it sits too long. In fact, there's a parking meter, so you'll probably have a ticket on it."

Nigel gripped the receiver so tightly, his knuckles went white, and he was close to weeping when he said, "I'll go and collect it now, sir. Thank you very much."

"What's your name?" Jonas asked, feeling bold, feeling in control, feeling wonderful!

"Nigel Wickland."

"One thing more, Nigel—" Jonas said.

The call was interrupted by an automated voice, and Jonas had to drop more coins into the coin slot. Then he said, "One more thing. Why did you first try to tell me that you didn't report the stolen van to the cops?"

"Sir," Nigel said. "At first I thought that I was getting a . . . ransom call from the person who took my van. It was cynical of me and I'm sorry. I'm only too happy to be dealing with someone like yourself."

"Okay, go get your van. You'll hear from me."

"I shall go now," Nigel said.

"My head's spinning," Jonas said to Megan after he had hung up. "Let's go home and figure things out. Any ox left?"

"A quarter," she said. "Why didn't you ask him for his cell or home number?" Megan said. "Then you wouldn't have to go through a store employee."

Jonas hesitated and then said, "Because my fucking head ain't clear. Let's go smoke that quarter so I can think better."

Nigel opened his office door and said, "Ruth, I need you to give me a ride to east Hollywood. My stupid nephew left my van there all night and I have to pick it up."

Ruth looked up from the inventory list she was checking at her desk and said, "Why in the world would he leave it there?"

"He's a fool," Nigel said. "Thirty-five years old going on fifteen. He's off to Las Vegas with some friends and said he didn't have time to bring it back to me."

Ruth got into her jacket, grabbed her purse, and said, "I hope that's the last time he ever drives it."

"You can depend on that," Nigel said.

Ruth went to fetch her car, and Nigel got the extra van key from his desk. On the drive, he hardly heard Ruth nattering on about the irresponsibility of relatives. When they got to Normandie and Melrose, he thought that the miserable thief had duped him. But then he saw the van half a block south parked in front of a liquor store.

Ruth dropped him off at the van, and Nigel got in and started the engine. He rolled down the window and waved to Ruth. Everything was just as the thief had said it would be. And even though the van was parked in a metered zone, he didn't even have a ticket on it.

Nigel looked at his watch and realized that Leona Brueger probably had not arrived back in L.A. yet, so he drove straight to the Hollywood Hills. He had a few random thoughts about the possibility of pulling this off by himself, but he realized it would be impossible. There were two thieves at least, the one who drove the van and the one who drove the Volkswagen. Nigel needed his moronic crime partner, Raleigh Dibble, and he wanted a conversation face-to-face.

It was astounding to hear Nigel Wickland on the gate phone. Raleigh, still in his pajamas, bathrobe, and slippers, truly thought that he'd seen the last of Nigel. It was infinitely more astounding to look out and see Nigel parking the Wickland Gallery van on the faux-cobblestone driveway.

Raleigh jerked open the door and said, "They caught them?"

Nigel walked right past him into the house and said, "No, they didn't catch them."

"Then how . . . what . . . ?"

"I'm afraid it's come down to a life-or-death situation, Raleigh. It's us or them."

Raleigh and Nigel sat at the kitchen table, and Raleigh listened slack-jawed to the incredible turn of events that resulted in Nigel recovering his cargo van. And when Nigel was finished, he said,

"They've got our paintings. They're blackmailers as well as thieves. Of course, they could testify that I was here in the van, and that you and I had stolen the Brueger paintings before they stole the van. They could put you and me in prison if they wish to. Or I can pay them twelve thousand dollars and hope that the blackmail does not continue for the rest of my days."

Raleigh said, "The important thing is to keep them from being arrested, is that it?"

"Precisely," Nigel said.

"Stop saying that," Raleigh said.

"What?"

"Never mind. Do you have twelve thousand dollars?"

"Just," Nigel said. "As soon as I leave you, I'm going to the bank. It will clean out my reserve account and I'll have trouble explaining it to Ruth, especially since I'm about to lay her off." He paused then, shook his head wearily, and said, "It's the hardworking people like me who are hurt the most by this fucking recession."

"Nigel," Raleigh said after some thought, "if this isn't some kind of police setup and you're able to buy the paintings back, we could still come out of this thing."

"I'm positive it's not a police setup," Nigel said. "With all the things he said to me, it would be considered entrapment. I've watched enough television to know that much. No, he's our louche little thief and he's not in police custody."

"Well, then, if we wait and we do the deal, we're not much worse off, other than you losing twelve grand. Which you can take out of my half million."

"Oh, that is magnanimous of you, Raleigh," Nigel said. "Magnanimous and fucking obtuse."

"One of these days you're going to call me one name too many," Raleigh said, "you arrogant pansy."

Ignoring that, Nigel said, "There is one thing of great concern here. The thieves will spend their twelve thousand on women or

drugs or whatever they fancy, and then they might have a bit of a think. They might try to find out about the provenance of the paintings. It's not hard to do since you may have noticed that Sammy Brueger's name, address, and phone number were on a card stapled to the stretcher bar on both pieces. Every art dealer and auction house on the west side of Los Angeles knew about Sammy Brueger and his collection. The thieves could learn the approximate value of the pieces and feel they'd been cheated. Yes, the fucking thieves would then feel that *we* stole from *them*. That would let the cat out and they'd know something is amiss and come after me for everything I've got."

"What could they do? Go to the police and say they stole the van?"

"No, but the worm I was talking to might have a smarter crime partner who could contact Leona Brueger either by letter or phone and ask some pertinent questions about *The Woman by the Water* and *Flowers on the Hillside*. And perhaps offer Leona some information for a price, information that concerns Nigel Wickland and his van. Leona is a fool in many ways, but she can be shrewd and ruthless when she wants to be. She'd put her finger on it. And she'd call the police, and our whole scheme would unravel."

With that, Nigel walked to the larger replica on poster board and said, "Come here, Raleigh. Touch this."

Raleigh complied, and then Nigel said, "Walk down the corridor and touch a few of the legitimate pieces."

"Yes," Raleigh said. "If she literally puts her finger on it, she'll know. They feel completely different from the real paintings."

"Precisely," Nigel said.

"Well, what're you suggesting here, Nigel?"

"I think you know," Nigel said. "Were you able to see anything other than silhouettes when they drove out of here?"

"No, I saw one person in the van and one person in the VW bug."

"Both were men, I presume?"

"I don't know. I suppose so."

"They're thieves," Nigel said. "And blackmailers. They're scum who don't deserve to live."

Raleigh Dibble said, "I'm not killing anyone, Nigel. Not for a million and not for ten million."

"Not even to keep from going to state prison?"

"You'd bring me into it, wouldn't you? You'd tell them everything."

"Turnabout is fair play," Nigel reminded him. "I'd make the best deal I could with the prosecutors. I learned that from you."

"You're a miserable shit," Raleigh said.

Nigel said, "Can you make me a goddamn vodka martini, please? It might make it easier if I should decide to go home and shoot myself."

Raleigh felt like weeping the entire time he was making martinis for both of them. When he was finished, he said, "I gave you a twist instead of an olive. You don't look like an olive person."

"Thank you," Nigel said quietly. "I take that as a compliment."

"Okay, we won't be safe until we get the paintings back," Raleigh said. "That much I can see. So what if we get them and put them back in the frames where they belong?"

"And forget the million dollars?"

"Yes, and just be grateful not to be going to prison."

Nigel thought for a moment and said, "And if the thieves demand more extortion money not to tell Leona Brueger how her paintings got to be temporarily stolen, then what?"

"You just deny everything. You were never here, which I would verify. The person who contacted her with the ridiculous story about her paintings being stolen is just some Hollywood madman. The town is full of lunatics."

"When're they arriving?" Nigel asked.

"I still don't know. I've been expecting a call all morning."

"All right," Nigel said. "Then it depends on when the thieves call me and when we can deliver the money and get the paintings. We would have to get the paintings back here and into the frames before Leona Brueger enters this house again. But we still would not be safe from future danger. Is this what you really want?"

"Stay in close touch with me today, Nigel," Raleigh said.

"Don't worry, I shall."

Raleigh said, "When you threatened to shoot yourself, I was wondering, do you really have a gun?"

"Yes, at the gallery for protection. Why? Could it be that you are possibly coming around to the conclusion that if we are ultimately faced with losing the million dollars *and* going to prison, then we would have no option but to try our very best to remove the thieves from our lives?"

Raleigh drained his martini, shaking his head slowly back and forth. But as he thought about it longer, he nodded slowly and said, "Precisely."

TWENTY-ONE

For THE VERY first time since they began smoking OxyContin together, Megan Burke did not join Jonas Claymore in the chasing of the dragon. She swallowed a perk instead, and although it helped ease her nausea and joint pain, she still longed for the euphoria that she got from the ox. Before he zoned, she tried to talk to Jonas about what they were doing.

She squeezed his cheek between her finger and thumb and said, "Jonas, don't get all smoked out on me. We've got to talk."

His voice was thick when he said, "I know. That's why I needed the ox. So I could work on my plan and we could talk."

"I've been thinking," she said. "That guy was very quick to cut a deal with you. Even though he might not believe a thing you said, because to tell the truth, it wasn't too convincing. He might be talking to cops right now, getting ready to set a trap for when he hands over the money. Maybe we should try to find out something about these paintings and simply sell them. Maybe we should stay away from the guy we stole them from."

"Okay," Jonas said. "Later. Man, that was good smoke. I'm toasted."

He was zoning hard and Megan Burke longed to join him, but she summoned all the self-control she had left in her increasingly frail body and mind. She took both paintings from behind the sofa

and looked at them closely. She went to the bedroom and got her cell phone and photographed both paintings in case she decided to make inquiries about them. Then she turned them over and saw the framer's cards stapled to the stretcher bars.

She read the name of the customer, Sammy Brueger, along with an address and phone number. It took her a minute to realize that the address was the house where they had stolen the van!

"Snap out of it, Jonas!" she said, slapping his face lightly.

"What?" he said. "What the fuck's wrong with you?"

"The pictures," she said. "They don't belong to the gallery guy! They belong to the guy who lives at the big house. His name's Sammy Brueger. So the gallery guy doesn't really care about making a deal with you for the pictures. He just wanted to get his van back, and now he's gonna work with the cops and maybe set a trap for us when we go meet him for the money!"

"Later," Jonas mumbled, not understanding a single word she said. "I gotta push the off button for a while."

"Fuck you!" Megan said.

She went to the bathroom and touched up her makeup, shocked to see how pale she looked. A touch of blush on her cheeks brought a bit of life to her face, and she tried to separate her eyelashes with a safety pin, but her hands were so shaky she feared she'd poke her eyeball. When she figured she looked as good as she could, she grabbed her purse and Jonas's car keys and left.

This was by far the most dangerous idea she'd ever had, but she was going to act on it. If it worked and if real money somehow came from the paintings, she was going to get away from Jonas Claymore for good. For her freedom, for her sanity, for her life.

When she'd phoned home for that last $200 loan, her mother had said to her, "Megan, your life has gone from bad to worse since you went to Hollywood. You've got no chance until you leave that terrible place and come home to people who love you."

Megan had never told her mother about moving into the

apartment of Jonas Claymore, and she certainly had never told her mother that they were both straight-up drug addicts by now. She hated thinking about all the money she'd begged and borrowed from her mother, who still had Terry, Megan's sixteen-year-old brother, to support. And it hadn't been easy for her mother, with what she made doing a man's work in the department store warehouse. Bitter experience had taught Megan that the more she thought about her mother, and the more guilt that brought on, the more she'd long for the honeycombed tranquillity of an OC high. She was desperate for money now, more desperate than she'd ever been. And it was that desperation that overcame her fear and propelled her back up into the Hollywood Hills in the little VW bug.

During the drive, Megan ran through in her mind several approaches to get access to that house. She wasn't sure what she'd find there, but she wanted to see the man, Sammy Brueger, to get a sense of whether they could work with him now that she knew for certain that Nigel Wickland had lied about being the owner of the paintings. In order to bolster her courage, she kept telling herself that this was just an exploratory visit to test the real ransom target, Sammy Brueger.

She parked the VW bug fifty yards south of the Brueger estate, facing the flatland in case she needed a fast getaway. Then she walked to the gate phone and pressed the button.

"Yes?" Raleigh Dibble said. "Who is it?"

"My name's Valerie Turner," Megan said. "I'm your neighbor from down the road."

"What is it?" Raleigh asked.

"It's my dog, Cuddles," she said. "He's on your property."

"There's no dog here," Raleigh said. "This place is completely fenced."

"He's a Chihuahua," Megan said. "He slipped through the gaps in your metal entry gate. I saw him and I have to get him or I'll get in big trouble with my mom."

Raleigh said nothing, but he pushed the phone key, and the electric gate swung open slowly and Megan walked in. The mini-estate looked bigger from the inside. She was glad she wasn't wearing heels when she walked over the uneven driveway, and she could feel the rough stones through the holes in her shoes.

A pie-faced, chubby, balding man who looked pretty old to Megan opened the door and said, "Have you tried calling him?"

"For the last half hour," Megan said. "I'm glad to meet you, Mr. Brueger."

"I'm Mr. Dibble," Raleigh said. "I look after things here. Mr. Brueger is in Cedars-Sinai. He had a stroke."

"Oh, that's too bad!" Megan said. "I'll tell my mom. I think she knows him."

"You can walk the property and call your dog," Raleigh said. "Let me know when you want to leave and I'll open the gate for you."

"Thank you, sir," Megan said.

She walked around the garage toward the pool that was designed like a lazy lagoon with a six-foot waterfall. "Cuddles!" she called. "Here, Cuddles!"

She thought five minutes was enough. She rang the bell and Raleigh came to the door again.

"Did you find your dog? he asked.

"No, the brat," she said. "I know he's hiding here. He does this when he doesn't want to be found."

"If you'll leave your phone number, I'll call you if I find him," Raleigh said.

"Do you have something I can write on?"

"Come in," Raleigh said, and she entered the foyer while he went to fetch a notepad and pen.

Megan walked into the great room and marveled. She'd never been in a house like this, and the thing that impressed her most was the art. There were paintings everywhere. The corridor along the

foyer was lined with paintings, all of them with lights attached to the top of the frames.

And then she saw *The Woman by the Water* and drew in her breath. And next to it was *Flowers on the Hillside*. They were identical to the paintings that she and Jonas had in their apartment! What did it mean?

Raleigh returned with a notepad, and she scribbled a fictitious number.

"I majored in art in community college," she said. "And I'm very interested in art. Do you know a lot about the paintings here?"

Raleigh thought she was a very pretty girl in a waiflike way. She looked so touchingly anemic and vulnerable, and she didn't do that Valspeak where they made every damn sentence sound like a question. He said, "I know a bit."

She strolled along the wall of paintings and said, "This one?" pointing at a small British watercolor that Raleigh knew nothing about, and he said, "I think that's by a German Impressionist. Can't recall his name. An interesting piece."

"Wow!" Megan said, and pointed at an oil painting of red-coated hunters riding to hounds. "This must be British, right? It looks like the scenes you see on public television."

"Yes, I believe it is British," Raleigh said, feeling a sensation in his loins that he had not felt for ages. He couldn't think of the last time he'd slept with a woman. And this tulip of a girl with alabaster skin was flirting with him. He was almost sure of it.

"This is interesting," Megan said, pointing to the replica of *The Woman by the Water*. It had looked identical to the one in their apartment until she got very close. Then it was somehow different, but she couldn't say exactly how. She wondered if this was the original and hers was a copy. Or was it the other way around? And why would Sammy Brueger want a copy anyway?

Megan was thoroughly confused when she said, "My mom has

always said that Mr. Sammy Brueger is a big art collector, but I had no idea."

Raleigh said, "Sammy Brueger is dead. His brother, Marty, lives here. He's the one who had a stroke."

"Oh," Megan said. "I've always heard her mention the name Sammy Brueger. I never met any of the family. How many Bruegers are there?"

"Mr. Sammy's widow, Leona, lives here. Your mother's probably met her."

"I guess," Megan said. Then, "Would you mind if I had a glass of water? I'm pretty hot from roaming around the property looking for Cuddles."

"Sure," Raleigh said. "Come into the kitchen with me. It's a gourmet setup. You might be interested."

Megan followed Raleigh, who took more than one glance at Megan's calves and thought, The girl has natural curves, but she's so thin. She looks so childlike in that candy-striped dress. And then the peril he was facing with Nigel Wickland entered his mind and he lost some of the nostalgic itch in his loins. He hadn't realized how lonely he'd become.

"Would you like a soft drink?" he asked. "Or maybe you're old enough for a cocktail?"

"I'll have a white wine if you'll join me," Megan said.

He saw that look in her violet eyes again. Her smile was playful and provocative, and now he was sure of it. She was flirting with him! "I'd be pleased to join you," he said. "I have a lovely Chardonnay in the wine cellar that I've been saving. Why don't you have a seat in the great room?"

Raleigh went to the wine cellar, which wasn't a cellar but a very large closet lined in redwood and located just off the butler's pantry. He found a good California Chardonnay that still had the sticker label of $180. He put it in a silver bucket, surrounded it with

tiny cubes from the ice maker, folded a white linen napkin over the bucket, and brought it along with two crystal wineglasses to the great room.

He placed the bucket on the table between two side-by-side overstuffed chairs, poured the wine into the glasses, and, handing one to her, said, "Mademoiselle."

"Merci," she said, and there it was again. That look.

Raleigh raised his glass and said, "Here's to Cuddles for bringing a new friend to this lonely house."

Megan giggled and said, "To Cuddles."

"I hope it's not too tannic," Raleigh said. "It didn't get a chance to breathe."

"It's great, Mr. Dibble," Megan said, smiling at him over the rim of her glass.

"Raleigh. Call me Raleigh," he said.

"Okay, Raleigh," she said, taking another sip and licking her lower lip.

She was so young! He felt a shiver in his stomach that went clear to his toes. "I'm an excellent chef," he said. "You should let me prepare a meal for you sometime. And your parents, of course."

"That would be nice," she said. Then Megan added, "You said it's a lonely house. Who lives here with you besides Mrs. Brueger and Mr. Marty?"

"That's all. But Mrs. Brueger's getting married soon, and the house will be put up for sale. I'll miss it."

"That's too bad," Megan said. "What will happen to all the beautiful art?"

"It'll go into storage," Raleigh said. "And eventually it'll be moved to their vineyard in Napa. She thinks she wants to live there and make fine wine. That was a common fantasy in pre-recession days. She may change her mind. I can tell you, it's not easy to produce a fine wine."

"This one's sure good," Megan said.

"It's amusing," Raleigh said.

"Oh, that reminds me," Megan said. "A few nights ago...I don't remember when it was...my mom was out walking with Cuddles just after dark, and she said an art truck sped out of your driveway like mad and flew down the hill."

"An...art truck?" Raleigh said.

"She said it had an art gallery name on it or something like that. I didn't get the whole story."

"Nope," Raleigh said, taking more than a sip this time to quell the starburst of fear. "Not here. She's mistaken."

"That's funny," Megan said. "She said the truck came from the Brueger driveway. It scared her because it almost ran over Cuddles."

"No, I've been here every night since Mr. Brueger has been in the hospital. There was no one here in a truck or a car."

"She must've been wrong," Megan said. "She gets a little rattle-brained these days. But speaking of art, what would some of these paintings be worth?"

She looked so innocent, so like the child she really was, that Raleigh longed to impress her. He said, "Valerie, you might not believe it, but there are paintings in this house that're worth half a million dollars."

"Really?" she said. "For one painting?"

"For one painting," he said.

"Wow!" she said, and it made him chuckle with pleasure. Her eyes popped wide like the little purple umbrellas he used to put in mai tais when he was catering parties. Then she said, "I like so many of them. I'd love to have an inexpensive copy of a few of them. I forget what you call copies of paintings."

"Lithographs?"

"Yes, lithographs. Are there any places where I can buy a lithograph of some of these?"

"No, I've been told that each painting you see is an original and there's not another like it on the planet."

"Wow!" she said again.

He loved hearing her say that. "If there was an inexpensive lithograph available for some of these pieces, I'd buy them myself," Raleigh said. Then he looked over the edge of his glass at those violet eyes and said, "I'd present one to you as a gift if I could."

"You're very sweet, Raleigh," Megan said, finishing the wine.

"More, Valerie?" he asked quickly.

"I think I'd better take another look around for Cuddles and then walk home," she said.

Raleigh was about to offer her a few calendar dates to choose from for the home-cooked dinner, when the house phone rang. He hurried to the kitchen phone for privacy, and when he picked up, he heard the now-familiar voice of Rudy Ressler.

"Raleigh," the voice said. "It's Rudy Ressler."

"Yes, Mr. Ressler," Raleigh said. "I've been waiting for your call."

"We're in New York," he said. "It's been hell getting flights on short notice. Unless plans change, we'll be arriving at LAX late tonight, and we are totally drained. You can pick us up and drop me at my house. Then be prepared to do a light supper for Mrs. Brueger before she hits the hay. She'll sleep for twelve hours, at least."

Raleigh felt cold again and his limbs went weak. He had to ask Rudy Ressler to repeat the airline and the flight number. Meanwhile, Megan Burke was standing in the corridor, running her fingers over the poster-board replica of *The Woman by the Water*.

Raleigh hung up the kitchen phone and returned to Megan, now in the foyer by the door. She smiled and said, "Thanks for a wonderful time, Raleigh."

"Yes, it was lovely, Valerie," he said, looking agitated now. "I hope you find your little dog."

"I will," she said. "I'm just going to call him a few more times. He'll come home when he's tired. He always does. Will you open the gate for me?"

"Certainly," Raleigh said.

"One thing, Raleigh," she said. "Could I maybe call you some-time? I really enjoyed talking to you. Maybe we could go somewhere and have another glass of wine. I know a good little bistro."

Stunned, he said, "Yes, of course. Call my cell." And he ran to get the notepad and wrote down his number for her.

She kissed him on the cheek and said, "You're a doll."

That kiss from this delightful young woman would have made him happier than he'd been in months, except for the dread he felt over Leona Brueger's homecoming.

He opened the door and watched her striding up the driveway, calling, "Cuddles! Here, Cuddles!"

Raleigh pressed the button on the wall panel inside the door, and the gate swung open. When she was out, he dialed Nigel Wickland. After the third ring came the voice that he had come to hate.

"Yes?" Nigel said.

"They'll probably be home tonight."

"Tonight?"

"Yes, tonight," Raleigh said. "Has that goddamn thief called you yet?"

"Not a word since the first time," Nigel said. "This is somewhat worrisome."

"This is disastrous," Raleigh said.

"Don't lose your head."

"Stop saying shit like that!" Raleigh said. "I have a right to lose my head. For listening to you and your crazy scheme in the first place."

"If you hadn't left the keys in the van . . ."

"Okay, let's not go over all that again. Now what?"

"Now we sweat it out, Raleigh. The ball is in the court of my mentally challenged tormentor. Now, either we stay out of prison and make a million dollars or—"

"Don't tell me about the *or* again."

"All right, dear boy," Nigel said. "As long as you are clear that despite your obvious aversion to gays, we two are in bed together for the foreseeable future."

Megan was so excited and her mind was working so furiously, she feared she'd have an accident on the dangerous winding road as the VW descended from the Hollywood Hills toward the roaring traffic below. She only hoped that Jonas had recovered enough to understand the significance of her amazing discovery. Their scheme had changed completely. Before she arrived in east Hollywood, she had decided on a whole new game plan, and Jonas Claymore was no longer the quarterback.

He was standing in the shower when she got to the apartment. She dropped her purse on the kitchen table and entered the bathroom, but Jonas didn't even see her. He was still coming down from the euphoria and never saw her hand reach inside the shower curtain and turn off the hot water. A blast of cold water made him squeal.

"What the fuck you doing?" he said, shutting off the water.

"Here, dry off," she said, handing him a towel that was reasonably clean.

"Where you been?"

"Out," she said.

"Yeah, I figgered that. But where?"

"I was trying to score some ox at Pablo's, but there was nobody there that I knew or even recognized."

"What were you gonna use for money?"

"I was going to try to talk somebody out of a quarter."

"Goddamnit, girl," Jonas said. "How many times I gotta tell you that nobody in Hollywood sells ox on the fucking installment plan. This ain't Bend fucking Oregon. Christ, Megan, is your brain totally wacked, or what?"

"I'm just not as smart as you," Megan said, going to the kitchen for some milk and cereal. Anything to settle her stomach.

When he was dressed in the same jacket, shirt, and pants he'd worn to the cybercafé, he joined her in the kitchen, running a comb through his hair. It looked to Megan like a sopping mound of straw. Like they'd mucked out of the stable back in Bend, where she'd taken riding lessons that her mother couldn't really afford, a lifetime ago.

It was growing harder for Megan to believe that she'd ever been attracted to Jonas. But at times like this, when some inner defense mechanism allowed her to think and remember her past life, she could realize and admit that it had never been Jonas, it had been the ox. They had both mounted the ox and had ridden it into the arena that was Hollywood, and after that wild ride, her world had changed.

She said to him, "I know you're running the game, but I think we should go right to that man Nigel Wickland and collect our money and make arrangements for him to pick up the paintings."

He stared at her and said, "You do?"

"Yes."

"And if he's told the cops about us and they're all staked out there, or maybe have the place wired, then we're busted, right?"

"I don't think we have to worry about that," she said.

"Oh, you don't?"

"No, in fact, I'll do it."

That made Jonas push the calico cat off the kitchen chair and sit. He couldn't believe this new boldness he was hearing. He said, "Yeah, you must be smoked out."

"Yes, you always say that," Megan said. "Maybe I am, and of course you aren't, because you can handle it. Well, what do you have to lose? I'll go in and get the money and tell him where to find the paintings."

"And if it's a setup and the cops move in and bust you, what am I supposed to do, fly to Rio? They'll put you in a room and you'll spill your guts and we'll both be sleeping in jail tonight."

"I give you my word that if it's a police setup, I will not involve you. I'll go to jail and say nothing. My mother's address is on my driver's license, not your address. And she doesn't know your last name or anything about where we live. You'll be safe."

"Megan," he said, "what makes you so positive that the guy didn't tell the cops that I phoned him? Jist tell me that."

"I think he doesn't want to lose his paintings. I think they might be worth a few thousand more than he told you. I think he wants them back, no questions asked."

"How much do you think they're really worth?"

"More than he says."

"And you're willing to risk getting arrested by walking in there and collecting our twelve large?"

"Yes."

Megan could almost see his thoughts whirling. She got some cat food from the cupboard and fed Cuddles, then refilled her water dish. She gave the calico cat a bonus saucer of skimmed milk and stroked her until Jonas finished thinking.

Finally Jonas said, "Here's what I'll do. I'll drop you a block from the gallery. Go in there and talk private with him and tell him if he wants his goods, he has to give you half the money right now to show good faith."

"Six thousand?"

"You got it. And tell him the next meeting will be for the balance and we'll have his property with us. Tell him he'll get instructions by phone. Get his cell number. I ain't going through that official . . . officious bitch again."

"You'll be close by?"

"Right. I'll be parked somewhere and watching. And if this is a

setup, I'm leaving you there. And I'm trusting that you'll take the heat and you won't rat me out. I'm trusting you, Megan."

"Okay, you can trust me," she said.

"I never been in jail except once for DUI," he said.

"I've never been in jail for anything, but I'll take a chance," she said. "I think I can do this."

"If he don't have the twelve grand after the talk we had today, then there's something wrong, and you better leave and walk west on Wilshire. Keep walking till I pick you up."

"Let's get going before the gallery closes," Megan said. "I'm getting burbly thinking about it."

TWENTY-TWO

RUTH WAS GETTING ready to lock up when Megan walked into the Wickland Gallery.

"We're about to close," Ruth said. "May I help you?"

"Yes," Megan said. "I'd like to see Mr. Wickland."

"I can help you," Ruth said.

"I'd really like to talk to him personally," Megan said. "Please tell him that I've been sent by the gentleman he spoke to on the phone this morning."

Ruth said nothing but turned and walked through a door behind the showroom to the gallery owner's office and said, "Nigel, there's a young woman to see you. She claims she was sent by someone you spoke to this morning."

He started to jump to his feet but caught himself and said, "Send her in, Ruth. And you may go home. I'll lock up."

"Is this something I should know about?" Ruth asked.

"A man has inherited some art that may or may not be valuable," Nigel said. "There are other parties involved in the family's will and they want a secret appraisal. Mum's the word, and all that."

Ruth said, "Oh, one of those hush-hush appraisals. Okay, see you tomorrow."

When Megan entered the office, Nigel didn't get up. He said, "Close the door, please."

Megan sat in a client chair in front of Nigel's desk and he studied her. "You're not what I expected," he said.

He was pretty much what she had expected: a tall, elegant older man with a mane of snowy hair. She thought that his hands, with long, tapered fingers and manicured nails, were the most beautiful hands she had ever seen on a man.

She did her best to project sophistication and confidence, but her legs were trembling. She smoothed her dress down, trying to cover her knees, but the shirtdress was so short it was hopeless. Her lips were parched and felt stuck to her teeth when she said, "I've come for the reward money."

"Where is my property?"

"Did you get your van back?"

"Yes, but where is my property?"

Megan said, "I believe my partner told you to have the reward money today."

"Yes, you'll get it," Nigel said, looking at this . . . this child who was brazenly extorting him in his own office!

"I'll have to have it now, Mr. Wickland," she said. "Those are my instructions."

"Does your partner really think I'm going to hand over twelve thousand dollars and let you walk out of here with it?"

"I think you will, Mr. Wickland," she said. "And I think you'd be better off talking only to me and not to my partner."

Nigel didn't speak for a moment. Then he smiled sardonically and said, "Young woman, you interest me. I cannot imagine what you could be thinking, but I do find you interesting. What are you trying to tell me?"

Megan said, "I'm trying to tell you that I'm willing to deliver your paintings, but it will cost you the twelve thousand that you had better have with you today. As well as a bonus."

"I might have known," Nigel said with a sneer. "I told your partner that this gallery is on the verge of bankruptcy, and that's the truth."

"Yes, I know what you told him," she said. "The recession has been hard on everyone. But I'm still going to require a bonus."

His fury was mounting, and he gripped the edge of his desk so hard, his knuckles went white, alarming Megan Burke. "And how much of a fucking bonus do you require?" he said, feeling a tremor in his voice. He knew then that he was capable of killing both of them, given half a chance. He kept thinking of the 9-millimeter pistol in his middle drawer.

She said, "One hundred thousand dollars."

He didn't know whether he should laugh in her face or play it differently. He sat back and said, "What could you possibly be thinking?"

Megan said, "I'm thinking that one hundred thousand dollars is a small price to pay for staying out of jail and completing the theft of the two paintings you stole from the home of Leona Brueger."

She watched the blood drain from his face. When he went pale he looked older, and his mane of white hair almost seemed to fade to the gray of his flesh. She was aware that her own heart was hammering in her chest. She was suddenly very frightened of this man, and she said, "My partner is watching this gallery right now, and if I don't walk out of here with the money, you'll be in jail before the night's over."

When he could find words he said, "You little bitch. You fucking little bitch. What're you talking about?"

"The Bruegers have paintings that're worth a lot of money," she said quickly, her teeth clicking together. "They have a very valuable collection."

He thought he understood now. She'd seen the identification tickets that the framers had stapled to the stretcher bars. Perhaps she'd taken the paintings or photos of the paintings to someone who knew or thought he knew their provenance.

"Whoever you've consulted has grossly inflated the value of those paintings," he said. "You can try to sell them, but you'll get arrested when the art dealer calls the police."

"We agree with the second part," Megan said. "That's why we're selling them back to you."

"Young woman," he said. "You are being absurd. I truly don't understand what you think you know about these paintings."

Megan took a breath and said, "I think I know about the pictures in Leona Brueger's house that are identical to the paintings that my partner has safely put away." Then she said, "Well, not identical but almost. They don't feel the same when you touch them, but you did a good job of reproducing them, however you did it."

Nigel Wickland felt that he might faint. All he had to do was open the desk drawer and take out the gun. But there was the other thief, the fucking idiot partner.

She was terrified by the look on his face now. Her voice rose when she said, "Believe me, my partner is watching this gallery, and if I don't return safely to his car, you're finished, Mr. Wickland."

He wished he had a glass of water. He loosened his necktie and unbuttoned his collar. He took the inhaler from his pocket and took a puff, holding it in his lungs for a moment, and then said, "Who *are* you?"

"I'm the partner of the man who has your paintings," Megan said. "And you need them. And you need to keep your plans a secret. That's okay with me. I don't need to know anything about your plans. I don't care how much you sell the paintings for. That's your business. I agree that we'd get arrested if we tried to sell them to a gallery owner like you. So the best thing to do is sell them back to you. I'm not being greedy in charging you one hundred thousand."

"You have been in the Brueger house?" He couldn't believe it, but he said it again. "You have actually been inside Leona Brueger's house?"

"Yes," she said. "And her brother-in-law is in the hospital with a stroke. I believe his name is Marty. Would you like me to describe the house and where the fake paintings are hung?"

Nigel said, "And has your partner been in the house, too?"

"No," she said. "And it'd be better not to talk to him about it if he calls you again. Just do all business through me."

"Yes, I see," Nigel said with a hiss. "You are the one with the brains. He is obviously a cretin. Yes, I shall deal with you."

Megan almost jumped up and bolted when he opened his desk drawer. But he removed a fat envelope and tossed it across the desk. "A hundred and twenty hundred-dollar bills," he said. "Just as your half-wit partner demanded." Nigel added, "Before his ambitious little partner devised a way to increase the reward considerably."

Megan picked up the envelope and put it into her purse, saying, "Thank you. Let me have your cell number, please, and wait for a call from me. If you get a call from my partner on your business phone, just disregard whatever he says and wait for a call from me."

"I think I understand," Nigel said. "Would you happen to know a man named Raleigh?"

"Mr. Dibble's very nice," Megan said. "I met him today."

"Yes, I thought as much," Nigel said. "And how may I reach you?"

"You can't. Just wait for my call."

"And your name?"

"Valerie," she said.

"Does your partner know about your meeting with Raleigh?"

"No, I did it on my own," Megan said.

"Well, Valerie," Nigel said. "Since you and I both seem to be partnered with imbeciles, it does appear that you and I should exclude our partners from all future dealings. I take it that you will never see or speak to Raleigh again?"

"Of course not."

"Then if Raleigh thinks that the paintings have been kept by the thieves and lost forever, nobody would ever tell him any different?"

"Not me," she said.

"And not your partner?"

"He's not part of my bonus plan," Megan said. "He'll be very happy to settle for the twelve thousand that you promised him. He believes the paintings belong to you and he knows nothing about the Bruegers."

"And if I am able to get a mortgage on my home and manage to scrape together one hundred thousand dollars, that bit of business will remain between you and me, correct?"

"Correct. So whatever you get when you sell the paintings will not have to be shared with Raleigh," Megan said. "But that's your business."

"It will take a couple of days, I'm sure," Nigel said.

"Okay," Megan said. "I would like the cash in one-hundred-dollar bills, no later than forty-eight hours from now, just before you close for the day."

"I'll know tomorrow if I can do it," Nigel said.

"You'd better do it, sir," Megan said. "I'll call you tomorrow to see about your progress."

"All right. Always use my mobile number," Nigel said. He wrote his number on a notepad, tore off the sheet, and handed it to her.

Megan said, "And remember, someone will deliver me here and wait for me when I come for the money. My companion will be a hired driver, and he will not know anything about our arrangement. But if I don't walk out of here in fifteen minutes, he will make a nine-one-one call and present the arriving police with a letter that I've written. You will be in way more trouble than you are in now if something bad happens to me when I come to this place of business."

Nigel emitted a bark of a laugh for the first time and said, "You are truly a very bright girl, Valerie. Believe me, nothing is going to happen to you."

"I used to be a bright girl," she said. "And I'm trying to be a bright girl again. That's why I'm here."

Nigel took a hard look again at her undernourished body,

nervous hand movements, and agitated watery eyes, and he said, "Drugs?"

She nodded and said, "You're a smart person, too, Mr. Wickland."

"Not half as smart as you, Valerie," Nigel said. "I should hope that I won't see you some time in the future when your drug money runs out. It would be a big mistake on your part to come at me again."

"Believe it or not, Mr. Wickland," she said, "I'll be using a big chunk of the money to get out of this state and go to a rehab and get clean. And learn how to stay clean."

"And the rest of the money?"

"I'm giving it to my mother."

Nigel laughed heartily and said, "Good lord! You're so convincing that I can almost believe that, too, Valerie."

"Good-bye for now, Mr. Wickland," Megan said. She stood and opened the office door, walking briskly to the street door and out onto Wilshire Boulevard.

After Megan left the Wickland Gallery, Nigel dialed the cell phone of Alec Townsend, the manager of his bank, a personal friend who also frequented the gay bars of west Hollywood.

When he reached the bank manager, he said, "Alec, Nigel Wickland here. Listen carefully. I need to loot my savings account and my commercial account. I must have one hundred thousand dollars as soon as possible. I have a chance to purchase a painting of immense value, but it's a bit dodgy because its provenance is unknown to the seller. Someone else will get it if I don't grab it at once. This investment will produce a windfall profit."

He listened to the bank manager's warnings and protests and said, "Alec, I am not being scammed and I am not being extorted. This is a chance of a lifetime. I want the money in hundred-dollar bills by tomorrow."

After a moment of listening, he said in frustration, "I don't care about your currency transaction reports or your goddamn deposit-

demand account. It's my money. And I stand to reap a return of one thousand percent in a few months. Can your fucking bank do that for me?"

He listened again and said, "I'm sorry. I didn't mean to get angry. But Alec, it is my money to risk as I see fit. Can you pull strings and have it for me by the day after tomorrow at the latest? In hundred-dollar bills. I'll owe you, my friend. Please help me."

When Megan Burke left the Wickland Gallery with the envelope in her purse, she had to walk two blocks until a very cautious and supremely nervous Jonas Claymore had the courage to pull the VW bug to the curb beside her.

She jumped in and said, "Go, Jonas."

He almost sideswiped a gleaming Rolls-Royce parked on Wilshire Boulevard and she said, "Watch where you're driving."

"Did you get it?"

"Yes, I got it."

"Let's see it."

"When we get home."

"Now, bitch!" he said.

She looked at him but said nothing. Then she turned the rearview mirror and looked at herself.

"What're you doing?"

"I'm trying to see who I am," she said.

"What the fuck you talking about?"

"I should say that I'm trying to see who I've become. Sitting here with a loser like you who can't utter a complete sentence without using words like *bitch*. In fact, someone who can't utter a complete sentence period."

"Me, a loser?" he said. "I jist got you six fucking grand. Me, a loser? Gimme that money!"

"It's in my purse and you'll have it when we get to the apartment," she said firmly. "Now drive me home."

"It ain't your home, it's my home," he reminded her. "And first I'm stopping at Pablo's Taco Shop and you're gonna give me some of that bank and I'm gonna buy some OCs. And then I'm going home and I'm chasing the dragon, and if you don't like it, move the fuck out. But first gimme what you got in your purse."

Jonas was driving as fast as the rush-hour traffic allowed, and he kept glaring at her, but Megan was past anger, past all intense feelings. She had never been so tired in her life. She reached into her purse, withdrew the envelope, opened it, and handed him five hundred-dollar bills.

"Go ahead, stop at Pablo's," she said. "Get yourself busted. Get me arrested, too. That'd be about what I'd expect from you."

"What you can expect from me is a bunch of good ideas, and this is only the start of it. When we get home, the first thing we do is get rid of those paintings."

Megan looked at him and said, "What do you mean, get rid of them?"

"We got paid for our work, so why do we need to take any more chances with them? I'll give them to Wilbur for some ox. He can unload them at a swap meet."

"No!" Megan said. "I gave the man my word."

Jonas looked at her and said, "Your word? What's this, something you picked up in Sunday school? Your word?"

"It's a bargain," Megan said. "We made a bargain with the man and we took his money."

"So now you're running the show, huh? Well, news flash, girlfriend. That ain't gonna fly. I'm the man. I'm the quarterback and I'll call the signals. You reading me?"

She was silent. Then she sighed and said, "Yes, you're easy to read. You're a comic book. You're what I deserve for riding the ox."

Feeling gravely insulted, Jonas said, "When we get back to the apartment, maybe I'll give you what you got coming and let you take your fucking cat and your clothes and get the fuck out."

"And what do I have coming?"

"I'll have to think about that."

"Think hard," she said. "I faced the man and got the money. I deserve a fifty-fifty split."

She heard him cackle like a movie witch, and he said, "I been saying you're all smoked out. Your brain's more shriveled than your puny tits."

"What split do you have in mind, Jonas?" she demanded. "I walked in there and got the money."

"Okay, I'll be big about it," he said. "An eighty-twenty split. The eighty is for the brains."

"I see" was all Megan said.

They spoke no more until they arrived in Hollywood at Pablo's Taco Shop on Santa Monica Boulevard, where he drove into the parking lot at twilight.

"Please take me home, Jonas," Megan begged. "We can't afford to get busted now. There might be some narks watching this place. Everybody knows it's a hangout for dealers. Please take me home first."

He parked at the far end of the little strip mall and said, "I ain't scared of five-oh. I can smooth-talk any of them. Anyways, I ain't got time to drop you. I want those green beans now, and you do, too."

"I'm not smoking ox with you anymore, Jonas," she said. "Or anything else."

"Hah!" he said. "Let's see what you do when that beautiful snowbird starts to cook."

"All right, get me some perks or norcos," she said. "Anything to get me past the joneses. But I'm not smoking ox with you."

"We'll see," he said with a smirk, and left her sitting in the car. He walked ten yards, stopped, and came back. He reached through the open window and took the keys from the ignition, saying with a wicked little grin, "Can't leave you here with my keys *and* my bank. The temptation might be too much for you."

He got out but left his cell phone in the ashtray, where he always kept it while driving.

He was gone only for a moment when she saw the black-and-white wheeling into the parking lot.

Six-X-Seventy-six had just cleared from roll call, and Viv Daley and Georgie Adams thought it was time for a cruise through the strip mall on a routine check for tweakers and other drug users who did business at the taco shop.

Megan Burke grabbed Jonas's cell phone, opened the door of the VW bug, got out, and walked east on Santa Monica Boulevard as fast as she could. When she was a safe distance away, she stopped and watched the parking lot to see what was going to happen.

Jonas Claymore had to use his hand to shield his eyes from the late rays of the sun. The dying fireball was giving Hollywood a last blast of its power before settling into the Pacific. Jonas peered into an old Mazda and found a dude he'd done business with on a few occasions. What was his name? Earl, that was it.

He was a scrawny little rat-faced tweaker with what everyone said looked like terminal acne. His face was a flaming pus ball, and it was sickening to score from him, but he had pharmacy connections and was usually good for norcos and perks and sometimes OCs.

The Mazda's windows were open and Earl was eating one of Pablo's lard-fried tacos filled with what Jonas thought was probably horsemeat.

"Earl, whazzup?" Jonas said.

Earl looked at Jonas, recognized him, and said, "I'm living the dream, dude."

"I need ox," Jonas said. "I'll take four if you got 'em. And I need a few norcos or perks for my bitch. I'll give you two Franklins."

"Bite it," Earl said, ferociously chewing the taco, grease the color of dishwater running down his chin and dripping onto his cutoff sweatshirt.

"Okay, dawg, I ain't got time to fuck around," Jonas said. "I'll

give you three Franklins for the four OCs and maybe a dozen nor-cos or perks."

Earl held up four fingers and took another bite from the taco.

"Aw, fuck it!" Jonas said, tossing four hundred-dollar bills onto the Mazda seat, which Earl snatched up so fast, Jonas hardly saw his little hand move.

"Go get a Coke," Earl said. "I'll see you inside."

Jonas did as he was told, wondering vaguely where Earl's drugs were stashed. They could be concealed inside the car's headliner, or taped under the dash, or hidden under the spare tire, or even up Earl's ass. He hated to think about that, but he was so desperate, he pushed all questions from his mind and ordered a soda at the counter.

He sat at a table near a Mexican family with a bawling baby and waited. Earl entered after a few minutes and went to the counter, where he removed several paper napkins from the dispenser. He wiped his greasy face with the napkins and when he got to his mouth he spit a tied-off condom into the napkins, dropping the crumpled mess onto Jonas's table before exiting.

Jonas stuffed the wad of napkins into his pocket, put the soda cup in the trash container, and sauntered out, trying to walk casually to his car.

Georgie Adams was driving the black-and-white, and he said to Viv, "Hey, sis, isn't that the guy we stopped a few days ago? The one who said he was heading for a job in the Hills with his crying wife?"

Viv Daley looked at him and said, "Yeah, the one with the sick baby."

"Told you they looked like tweakers," Georgie said.

"Let's jam him," Viv said.

Jonas had reached his VW bug and was looking around, wondering where the hell Megan went, when the black-and-white stopped, blocking his exit, and he saw two cops get out. He recognized the

tall woman cop as the one he'd talked out of a ticket, and he said to himself, Do not panic. You did it before and you can do it again. But he didn't like the dark, sinister look of the shorter cop with her.

Viv said to Georgie, "There it is. The over-the-shoulder look."

"Hi, Officer!" Jonas said to Viv. "I remember you from the other day."

"And I remember you," Viv said. "How's your sick baby?"

"Getting better every day," Jonas said. "Thanks for asking."

"Where's your wife?" Georgie asked.

"I was just looking for her. She musta went across the street to buy a doughnut. I'll tell her I saw you."

He started to step to his car, but Viv said, "What's that bulge in your pocket?"

"Bulge?" he said. "Nothing."

"It could be a weapon. It could be drugs," Georgie said. "Did you know tweakers hang out here and do deals?"

"No, I didn't know," Jonas said, aware that his jaw was trembling but unable to stop it. Then he said, "Oh. I almost forgot. It's a bunch of napkins in my pocket. I ate a taco in there."

"How much did the taco cost you?" Viv said.

"I didn't pay much attention," Jonas said.

Georgie said to Viv, "This dude's like a dog. Eye contact makes him jumpy."

"Why didn't you throw your napkins in the trash can?" Viv asked.

Jonas said, "I . . . I brought them to wipe off the windshield. I got a big bug splatter on the glass."

"Go ahead," Viv said. "Wipe your windshield."

"Later," Jonas said. "I don't wanna waste your time."

"No problem," Georgie said. "Wipe your windshield. You gotta have good visibility when you drive on these busy Hollywood streets."

"Maybe I'll wipe it later," Jonas said. "It's my windshield, ain't it?"

Georgie looked at Viv and said, "More contempt of cop from the baseball-cap-turned-backward set."

Jonas said, "All I meant is, what's wrong with a couple dead bugs on the glass?"

Georgie said, "Don't make me use my uppercase voice, dude. You're wasting my minutes."

Jonas reached into his pocket and both cops looked like they might shoot him if he moved too fast. In fact, he heard the male cop say, "Take your napkins out real slow. We're the nervous type."

Jonas removed the big wad of greasy paper napkins with the condom in the middle of it and started rubbing the crumpled napkins across his windshield.

"Wouldn't it work better if you unfolded that wad?" Viv said.

Jonas turned to answer her and the greasy condom fell out of the wad of napkins and landed on the hood of the VW bug, then slid down onto the asphalt by the zip-up black boot of Georgie Adams, who said, "Uh-oh. What *are* they serving in their tacos these days?"

Viv said, "Turn around." And when Jonas did, she handcuffed his hands behind his back.

"You searched me without my permission," he said.

"We didn't search you at all," Viv said.

"This ain't fair!" Jonas wailed.

Viv said, "Dude, your GPS is off. A fair is where you eat candy apples and get your pocket picked. This is a different place."

"Can't you just warn me again?" Jonas whined.

"Yeah," Georgie said. "I'm warning you that those OCs will turn your brain to meat loaf. Now shut the fuck up while I read you your rights."

After seeing Jonas Claymore being handcuffed, Megan Burke

entered a 7-Eleven store and bought cat food and vegetable juice in order to break one of the hundred-dollar bills. The Pakistani proprietor asked if she had a smaller denomination and she apologized but said that she did not. Instead of using Jonas's cell to call a taxi, she asked the Pakistani to do it and tipped him $5 for his trouble. It was the first time in months that she'd had enough money to tip anyone and it was a good feeling.

An Eritrean taxi driver drove her to Jonas's apartment in Thai Town and she tipped him another $5, and used the key that Jonas kept hidden behind the exterior wall sconce to open the door. The calico cat ran to her, and Megan put her groceries down and picked her up, hugging the purring feline to her face.

"You're going to Oregon, Cuddles," Megan said. "I think you'll like it there."

Then she called the only dependable drug dealer she knew, even though he often came on to her when Jonas wasn't with her. He was a revolting street creature who always reeked of body odor and onions, but she needed him badly now.

Megan called on Jonas's cell and he answered as always on the second ring. She said, "Wilbur, it's Megan. We need norcos and perks. Twenty of each. As fast as you can get here. We'll pay twenty-five bucks extra for home delivery."

Wilbur said, "No OCs?"

It took all the willpower she had to say, "Not this time."

"What's wrong?" he said. "Ain't Jonas with you no more?"

She said quickly, "Yeah, he's sick in bed."

"Why don't you drive over to my place?" Wilbur said. "Save the twenty-five. I got some beautiful leaf you might like. Makes you feel gooooood."

"I can't leave Jonas," Megan said with a shudder of disgust. "Could you hurry, please?"

When she closed the cell, she vowed that the business would be

conducted outside the apartment, no matter how much Wilbur liked privacy. She would not let him slither inside, where he'd discover that Jonas was not at home.

She bent down to pet the cat again and said, "Cuddles, we just have to survive the next two days somehow. And then we're going home at last."

She called the airline that had brought her to Los Angeles from Oregon, and while she was inquiring as to ticket prices, Cuddles leaped onto the kitchen table, putting her face against Megan's and purring in her ear. Megan thought that Cuddles was trying to tell her that she wasn't in this thing all alone.

When 6-X-76 brought Jonas Claymore into the station and was putting him in the holding tank, Hollywood Nate passed them on his way to the report room. He glanced at Jonas through the heavy viewing window of the holding tank and stopped.

"Hey, Gypsy," he said to Georgie Adams, pointing at Jonas, who was sitting on the bench in the little room. "What'd he do?"

"Bunch of pills," Georgie said. "Ox, perks, that kinda shit. Do you know the dude?"

"He was double-parked in a van the other night and I warned him to move on," Nate said.

"Yeah? He seems to get a lotta warnings," Georgie said. "We also gave him one a few days ago."

"Was he driving a cargo van at the time?"

Georgie shook his head and said, "A VW bug."

"He works for an art gallery," Nate said with a grin. "He'll sell you crappy paintings on the cheap."

"Not him," Georgie said. "He's unemployed."

"Bullshit," Hollywood Nate said. "Open the tank for a minute."

Georgie opened the door, and Nate said, "Hey, man, remember me?"

Jonas gave Nate a glum look and said, "No."

"You were double-parked in Thai Town delivering crappy art. Remember?" Nate said.

"You got the wrong guy," Jonas said, alert now and worried.

"Dude," Nate said. "You were driving a fucking van. It had the name of an art gallery on it. Wicker. Something like that."

"Not me, Officer," Jonas said. "I'm outta work. This officer and his partner stopped me last week when I was on my way to a job interview up in the Hollywood Hills." He turned to Georgie Adams and said, "Ain't that right, Officer?"

"Wickland," Nate said. "It was the Wickland Gallery. You were doing a delivery for them."

Jonas managed his most sincere smile and said, "I look like a bunch of people, Officer. This always happens. People confuse me with somebody else. No, it wasn't me. I'm unemployed."

Hollywood Nate looked at Georgie Adams and said, "I even remember his voice. It's him. What the hell's going on here?"

Before Nate and Flotsam went back into the field, Nate decided to call the Wickland Gallery, but he got a recorded message giving the gallery's daytime store hours. Then Nate called the Beverly Hills Police Department and tried to find out if there had been a van reported stolen by the owner of the Wickland Gallery on Wilshire Boulevard. Viv Daley was on the computer, doing what she could without having a license number to work with. All responses were negative.

"Better leave a note for the detectives or call them in the morning," Viv suggested to Hollywood Nate.

"He was double-parked in front of an apartment building," Nate said. "I wish I'd seen which apartment he came out of."

Georgie said, "If that van wasn't hot, then Jonas Claymore does work for the Wickland Gallery and he was doing something

extracurricular over there in Thai Town that night. It could mean anything."

Flotsam said to Hollywood Nate, "Dude, maybe he lives there and went home to check his voice mail. Or, like, maybe his girlfriend lives there and he went by for a quickie and he don't want the boss to know about it."

Georgie said, "The art gallery oughtta clear it up for you one way or the other."

"Yeah, it's probably nothing much," Hollywood Nate agreed. "I'll call the gallery tomorrow before I send the detectives on a wild goose chase."

Raleigh Dibble had been trying all evening to reach Nigel Wickland on his cell phone, but all he got was voice mail. He was certain that Nigel was avoiding him. At 7:30 P.M. Raleigh became convinced that fate had provided a gift of unfathomable worth. Rudy Ressler phoned and said that they weren't coming home yet. They'd decided to stay over in New York to visit old friends of Leona's because she was exhausted from the long journey.

"I don't mind telling you I can't wait to get back to L.A.," Ressler said to Raleigh. "This doesn't make me happy. By the way, how's Marty?"

"Serious but not critical," Raleigh said. "He's in and out of consciousness. I call every day." They had bought him time!

"I'll call when we're sure of our flight, but right now it looks like Wednesday," Rudy Ressler said. "I think we'll be at the Waldorf for old times' sake. That's where Leona and Sammy went on their honeymoon."

"Enjoy yourself in New York," Raleigh said. "Why don't you take in a Broadway show? Stay as long as you like. Everything here is out of control."

" 'Out of control'?" Rudy Resssler said.

"No, I said *under* control," Raleigh said quickly.

When Raleigh hung up, he tried again to reach Nigel Wickland, who at last answered.

"Where the hell've you been?" Raleigh said.

"I've had a very busy day. What's happened?"

"You tell me. Did they make contact today? What've you heard?"

"Nothing," Nigel said. "There was nothing to report since his first call to me, so I didn't phone you."

"Well, I phoned you. Half a dozen times."

"My mobile went dead. I forgot to charge it. I'm sorry."

"Next time I'm calling your gallery phone whether you like it or not," Raleigh said.

"Don't do that," Nigel said. "Ruth is already getting suspicious."

A pause and then, "Suspicious about what? Is something going on?"

"No, I just meant that she's observing my anxious behavior and asking me if there's anything wrong. She's not used to having people wanting to speak to me personally. She's not stupid, Raleigh."

"Okay, keep your cell phone charged and in your goddamn pocket. I have some good news to report. Mrs. Brueger won't be coming home until the day after tomorrow at the earliest. We have time, Nigel!"

"Time?"

"Time to return the paintings to this house and get ourselves out of this nightmare. And if those thieves ever come at you again with demands, you just lie and deny and nobody can prove anything."

"Yes," Nigel said, "but restoring you to your former blissful existence depends on the thieves phoning me, doesn't it? I have the twelve thousand they want, but I can't do a thing until they make contact, so calm yourself until then."

"Calm myself?" Raleigh said. "I'm having erratic heartbeats.

Any day now I could stroke out and end up in the hospital bed next to Marty Brueger."

"Raleigh," Nigel Wickland said. "If our thieves perform as planned, I'll pay them off and we'll return the paintings to their vulgar frames in the home of your parvenu mistress. But I should've thought it would be better to risk being in a hospital bed next to a Marty Brueger than to spend the rest of your life as a domestic servant, wiping his ass or the ass of someone like him. But I guess you've already made your career choice, haven't you?"

When Raleigh hung up, he thought, What an offensive, elitist, supercilious fucking faggot! He hated Nigel Wickland more than he'd ever hated anyone. His face was aflame and his hands were shaking when he went to the butler's pantry and poured a stiff shot of Jack Daniel's. Then he felt his pulse again. It was beating more erratically than ever.

He went into the great room and sat, trying to get some comfort from the wealth surrounding him. Something was nagging and it didn't come to him until after he'd finished the Jack. Then he realized, the thief surely should have called Nigel today but Nigel didn't seem at all upset about it. What had Nigel said about his employee? he tried to recall. Something about Ruth being already suspicious *enough?* Could there be something going on at the Wickland Gallery that would arouse real suspicion from her?

Raleigh had always doubted that Nigel Wickland would give him an honest fifty-fifty split when the paintings were sold in Europe, and he had intended to deal with that when the time came. He decided to visit the gallery tomorrow whether Nigel Wickland liked it or not.

TWENTY-THREE

Jonas Claymore did not like the bunk, the food, or his cell-mate in the Hollywood Station jail, where he spent the night. The cellmate was a Latino with a vicious-looking scar that ran from the bridge of his nose across his jaw to his throat. He was fully inked out with gang tatts, and he snored so noisily that Jonas couldn't have slept even if he hadn't been jonesing.

Jonas had tried to reach Megan on the phone an hour after he was booked, but she did not answer his cell. He wasn't sure if they'd impounded his car or left it locked in the strip-mall parking lot as he had begged them to do, but either way the cell might still be in the car. The disloyal bitch had probably bailed the second she'd seen the cops pull into the lot. She could've run into Pablo's and warned him, but no, all she'd thought of was herself. She didn't care that he was in a place where a guy looked up his ass like a plumber inspecting a drainpipe. Jonas decided then to just give her a few Franklins when he saw her next and kick her out of his apartment along with her fucking cat.

The next morning Jonas learned that he'd be taken by sheriff's deputies to arraignment at Division 30 of the Criminal Courts Building downtown on Temple Street, but he would have to spend another night in the Hollywood jail while the paperwork was being done. He was outraged.

* * *

Megan Burke's night had been slightly better than Jonas Claymore's. The perks she'd bought from Wilbur had helped her get a few hours' sleep all curled up with Cuddles, who seemed overjoyed to be sleeping on the bed with his mistress in the place that Jonas previously claimed. In the morning the calico cat crawled up on the pillow and purred happily while Megan stroked her, and they stayed like that until Megan decided that Cuddles needed her breakfast.

She knew there'd be hell to pay when Jonas got out of jail, so she made several calls and was told that his bail would be set later, or he might be given an OR release before day's end. She was told to call back in the afternoon for further information. Instead, she began calling motels with ads that said pets were welcome.

Megan packed what clothes were worth packing along with enough cat food for a few days, and by 1 P.M., a Sikh taxi driver was helping her carry her suitcase, a carrier containing Cuddles, and two large objects wrapped in mover's blankets. Those he had to strap to the luggage rack. She took the Sikh's cell phone number and promised him a $100 tip if he would pick her up whenever she called him and take her and her possessions to a destination in Beverly Hills and then to LAX. She said to be sure to bring the same taxi with the luggage rack for the bundles.

Before Megan left Jonas Claymore's apartment for the last time, she wrote a note and left it on the kitchen table. It said, "You told me there would be an 80–20 split and that the 80% was for the brains. I agree. Here is your 20%, less the $500 that I gave you last night." She left $1,900 on the kitchen table beside the note, along with her apartment key and his cell phone.

Hollywood Nate woke earlier than usual that day, probably because he had the Wickland Gallery on his mind. He phoned and Ruth answered.

He said, "This is Officer Weiss at Hollywood Division, LAPD. I had occasion to question someone in a Wickland Gallery cargo van the night before last, and we need to know if your van was stolen."

Ruth said, "Oh, that must've been Mr. Wickland's nephew. He borrowed it and left it in east Hollywood. We had to pick it up yesterday morning."

"That explains it," Nate said. "Is his name Jonas Claymore?"

"Reginald something," Ruth said. "He's a bit of a black sheep, according to Mr. Wickland. Is he in trouble?"

"He was arrested for possession of a controlled substance," Nate said. "For some reason he's denying ever being in the van. We're not sure why. It's possible that he was using it to do drug deals or for some other illegal activity."

"I'm not surprised," Ruth said. "That may explain why he just abandoned the van on the street the way he did. Mr. Wickland's gone to the bank. I'll tell him when he gets back, but I don't think he's going to drive over there and bail him out."

"Okay, thanks," Nate said. "At least I know now that he didn't steal the van from you."

When Nate got to work, he told all of the midwatch officers who knew about the Wickland Gallery van what he'd learned.

"I figured it was nothing," Georgie Adams said. "Just some little ass-wipe taking advantage of his uncle."

Nigel had to endure an in-person meeting to convince the bank manager that neither a bunco artist nor an extortionist was victimizing him, and that he had a good and legitmate reason for needing such a large amount of cash. He was told that he could pick up the $100,000 the next afternoon after 1 P.M. That withdrawal had wiped out Nigel's savings account and put his commercial account in grave jeopardy. He planned to call his European art auctioneer to find out if he could get a wire transfer of some advance money as soon as the paintings were received over there.

When he got back, Ruth said, "The LAPD called. Your nephew got himself arrested for drug possession. You can call Officer Weiss at Hollywood Station if you're interested."

"What?"

"Yes, it appears that he was stopped in our van on the evening you loaned it to him and now they have him on a drug charge."

"Did they give his name?"

Ruth smiled quizzically and said, "Don't you know your own nephew's name?"

Nigel said, "He might have used an alias."

"You said that his name is Reginald, but they have him under the name of Jonas Claymore."

"That's him," Nigel said. "He's using his father's name. Always in trouble, that boy." He entered his office and closed the door behind him.

Forty minutes later his cell phone rang.

"It's Valerie," Megan said. She was in her motel room, lying on the bed with Cuddles, who seemed excited by their new surroundings.

"I'll have it tomorrow, sometime after two P.M.," Nigel said.

"Why not today?"

"You can't walk into a bank and draw out that kind of money unless you're superrich. That money is all I have. I'm penniless now."

"You'll be okay when you sell the paintings," Megan said. "They're very valuable, according to Mr. Dibble."

"Yes, dear Mr. Dibble." Then he said, "Is your partner still in the dark about our bonus arrangement?"

"He's very much in the dark," Megan said. "He believes the paintings are yours and he doesn't even know the name Sammy Brueger. He's a brain-dead addict, to tell you the truth."

"Will he be accompanying you here tomorrow when you bring the paintings?"

"Of course not."

"Just wondering," Nigel said, trying to decide how he could use the information he'd just learned from Ruth. Her crime partner was in jail. Would she be alone? Was violence still an option? Could he possibly eliminate both of the thieves?

"But I *will* have protection," Megan said as though telepathic. "There *will* be someone delivering me and the paintings and waiting for me outside. You'll be able to see him."

"My dear girl," Nigel said. "I am not a dangerous man. You have nothing to fear."

"I'm going to be with a gentleman in a turban," Megan said, "who looks like he could easily cut the throat of anyone who tried to hurt me. But first he would call the police immediately if I didn't walk out of your gallery wearing a happy face."

Raleigh Dibble couldn't bear it any longer. He pulled the Brueger Mercedes out of the garage and drove to Beverly Hills late that afternoon. Another day was almost over, and still no call from Nigel Wickland. His suspicion that Nigel was secretly dealing with the thieves was overwhelming now, and his nerves were in tatters. He dressed in his best sport coat over somewhat threadbare gabardine trousers with a white dress shirt and necktie. He arrived at the Wickland Gallery thirty minutes before closing and was met by Ruth, who was turning out the painting lights over some of the more valuable consignment pieces.

"May I help you?" she said.

"I need to see Mr. Wickland," he said. "My name is Raleigh Dibble."

Ruth smiled and said, "Oh, yes, Mr. Dibble, I remember you. Sorry, but Mr. Wickland left early today."

"Really?" Raleigh said. "I talked to him today and he didn't say he was leaving."

Ruth looked at Raleigh and said, "I don't recall taking a call from you today for Mr. Wickland."

"I called him on his cell," Raleigh said, trying a convivial smile. "I'm a personal friend."

Ruth looked doubtful until Raleigh rattled off Nigel's cell phone number. Then she said, "Sorry. It's just that so many people seem to want to talk personally to Mr. Wickland these days."

"I know how it is," Raleigh said. "We're working together on an estate sale for my aunt, and I'm dealing with some of the same people." Then he took a wild shot and said, "I guess the fellow came in yesterday that I've been working with? Or was it today? Anyway, I told the gentleman to come and speak with Nigel personally and bring a couple of the estate's paintings. Did he arrive?"

"Nobody brought any paintings in yesterday or today," Ruth said.

"Oh," Raleigh said, feeling that maybe he had it wrong after all. "Didn't someone come and ask to see Nigel privately?"

"Not a gentleman," Ruth said. "Only a young lady yesterday. I don't know if she was from the estate or not."

"I see," Raleigh said, and now he was sure it was hopeless. Nigel would be furious when he found out that he was pumping this employee for information. He made a last feeble attempt and said apologetically, "I guess it wasn't my client, unless the young lady happened to bring some paintings here with her."

Ruth laughed and said, "Dear me, no. The poor little thing was lucky she could carry her purse let alone any paintings. She was so frail."

Raleigh looked away quickly and felt that sensation again, the blood rushing to his head and ice cubes in the gut. He said, "Was she a very young woman with dark hair?"

"Yes, she was so adorable in her little candy-striped dress," Ruth said. "I guess she's also working with you on this estate sale?"

After a long pause Raleigh said, "Yes, she's the granddaughter of my aunt. Everybody's trying to get in on the money from the family art collection."

"I know what you mean," Ruth said.

"I'll give Nigel a call after I get home," Raleigh said. "Thanks."

Raleigh genuinely feared he might go the way of Marty Brueger as he drove up into the Hollywood Hills. He was almost hyperventilating as he neared home and had to practice normal breathing and tell himself to stay calm. At last he understood all of it. The theft of the van was not a random act at all! It was part of the carefully planned scheme of Nigel Wickland. Valerie, or whatever her name was, and her companion thief were part of Nigel's conspiracy from the beginning. Nigel had induced Raleigh to allow the theft and reproduction of the million-dollar paintings. But for all Raleigh knew, they might be worth $2 million. Or $3 million! And then Nigel had hired a pair of young criminals to help him remove Raleigh from the conspiracy.

Nigel would eventually tell Raleigh that it's a terrible tragedy but the thieves apparently did not intend to ever call him again. It was such a simple but brilliant scheme, and he, Raleigh Dibble, was the dupe. The fall guy. The patsy. The fool. The thing that made it so diabolical was the trick with the van keys. Nigel had banked on Raleigh not looking for the keys, which Nigel said he left in the van. Nigel knew that Raleigh would not search for the keys, not inside a gate-guarded estate. And it had worked beautifully by allowing Nigel to shift the fault for the van theft to Raleigh.

What would Nigel have done if Raleigh had found the keys and brought them into the house? Well, that, too, was explainable. In that eventuality, Nigel's young crime partners probably had a spare key, and Nigel would have covered their escape by claiming that they must've hot-wired the van. But that wouldn't have been quite as neat. That might have thrown up a red flag for Raleigh. No, it had all worked perfectly, just the way Nigel had planned it.

Raleigh wondered where Nigel had found frail little Valerie. So vulnerable, so delicate, so young, so ruthless! Raleigh remembered how she'd kissed his cheek before she'd departed and asked if he'd

like to meet at a bistro, and how that gesture had touched his heart. When Raleigh pulled into the Bruegers' five-car garage, tears were streaming down his cheeks.

Raleigh let himself into the foyer, turned off the burglar alarm, and recalled that Leona Brueger had informed him that because of the burglaries in the Hollywood Hills, she now kept a handgun in her bedroom. He was going to find that gun. He was going to visit Nigel Wickland tomorrow, and the backstabbing sissy was going to bring those paintings back. Those paintings were returning home where they belonged, one way or the other.

Raleigh searched the master bedroom for more than an hour before he found the gun in a hatbox in the closet. It was a nickel-plated, snub-nosed .38 caliber revolver, and it was loaded.

Nigel returned to the Wickland Gallery at closing time, and Ruth said, "Oh, Nigel, you're back. I thought you had left for the day. There was a Mr. Dibble here insisting to see you. When I tried to find out what it was all about, he was vague and said something about an estate sale you're working on."

Nigel scratched his chin, trying to stay composed, and said, "Dibble? Would it be Raleigh Dibble?"

"Yes, that's him," Ruth said.

"He's a fool," Nigel said. "He completely overestimates the value of everything. Did he say if he was coming back?"

"No," Ruth said, "but he seemed eager to know if anyone had come here in the last few days with some paintings for you. Of course I told him no."

So that was it! Raleigh suspected that the thief had brought the paintings and been paid, and that he was being double-crossed! Nigel said casually to Ruth, "Yes, the estate sale. I didn't mention it to you because it's all part of his inflated personal appraisal of art that he knows nothing about. He's not worth a moment of my time."

"He claimed he was a personal friend," Ruth said. "He knew your cell number."

This was getting uncomfortable and Nigel wanted to end it. "He asked for my mobile number when we spoke, and in a weak moment I gave it to him. A personal friend? Never."

With that, Nigel entered his office and debated whether or not to phone and chastise Raleigh for coming and grilling Ruth because of his own uncontrollable paranoia. But he decided to let it be. Raleigh would eventually have to accept that the thieves must have disposed of the paintings themselves. What else could he think?

Because her employer had ended the discussion abruptly, Ruth hadn't bothered to mention all of her conversation with Raleigh Dibble. She thought about telling him of Raleigh Dibble's peculiar interest when she'd casually mentioned the only visitor who *had* insisted on seeing Nigel yesterday — the girl in the candy-striped dress. She decided to forget about it. After all, Nigel said the man and his estate sale was of no interest to him.

It was not a night of a Hollywood moon, but if it had been, the pizza might have gone to 6-X-46. During the first hour of their watch, Della Ravelle and Britney Small got a call to a popular bar and grill on north Vermont Avenue, where a drunk was causing a disturbance.

It was one of the older chop houses with the red imitation leather and walnut paneling that previous generations loved so much. A sixty-something hostess with a retro bouffant hairdo, wearing an inappropriate sheath dress with spaghetti straps, was standing at a tall table in the foyer taking reservations.

She put her hand over the mouthpiece of the phone when the cops entered, and said, "In the bar."

Britney started in until Della grabbed her arm and said, "Wait a minute. Let's first find out what we're walking into."

When the hostess finished taking the dinner reservation, Della said, "What's the disturbance all about?"

The hostess said, "There's a crazy man in there, buying two drinks at a time and pouring every other one into a vase."

"That's it?" Della said. "That's the disturbance?"

"He's frightening customers," the hostess said. "Several people left the bar because of him. And he's disturbing the bartender."

"Is he ranting and raving and talking gibberish or something like that?" Della asked.

"No," the hostess said. "But he seems to be talking to himself."

"Quietly?" Della asked. "There's no law against that."

"Maybe not, but it's scary," the hostess said.

"Okay," Della said. "Let's have a look, partner." When they were walking to the bar, Della whispered to Britney, "Remember, we don't hassle loony tunes if they're peaceful. This is fucking Hollywood."

Their eyes had to adjust when they got inside the barroom. It was one of those very dark, formerly elegant barrooms, where after a martini or two, the aging patrons could appear to each other the way they used to be and not the way they currently were. They saw that the hostess was right. He'd scared everyone away. He was seated on a stool at the far end of an old mahogany bar complete with a dented but shiny brass rail several inches from the floor.

The bartender looked at the cops and moved his eyes toward the lone customer, who had two bucket glasses in front of him. He was not old, but he was older than Della. She figured him for about fifty. He was losing his hair but it was mostly dark with only sprinkles of gray. He was getting a soft roll around his middle that his yellow golf shirt didn't hide, but Della thought he wasn't a bad-looking guy. In fact, he reminded her in some ways of her second husband, even to the arching heavy eyebrows. He looked to be talking softly to himself and he appeared boozy enough that he should not drive home.

Della said sotto to Britney. "You're contact, I'm cover. Go for it."

Britney walked up behind the man and said, "Evening, sir."

He didn't turn around, but said, "Evening."

"What're you doing, sir?" Britney asked.

"Having a drink," he said.

It was so dark in the bar that she couldn't clearly see the object on his lap, so she said, "Why don't you put that vase up on the bar. It makes police officers nervous when people have strange items in their hands. You can understand that, can't you?"

He picked it up carefully with both hands and put it on the bar, saying, "It isn't a vase. It's an urn."

"An urn?"

"Yes," he said, and for the first time turned on the stool and looked at Britney.

"Have you been pouring drinks into it?" she asked.

"Yes, a few. I don't think it's against the law, is it?"

Britney turned to look at Della and said, "Not that I know of, sir, but it's scaring the customers because it's so . . . unusual. Would you please tell me why you're pouring drinks into the urn and talking to yourself?"

"I'm not talking to myself," he said. "I'm talking to my dad. He's in there."

"I see," Britney said. "That urn contains your dad's ashes?"

"Yes," he said. "Digby G. Randolph was a great father and a wonderful man. This was just about his favorite restaurant. He asked me to come here from time to time and have a drink for him."

"But you had the idea to give a drink *to* him, is that what you're saying?"

"Exactly. I'm buying a few drinks for my dad."

"And when you're talking, you're not talking to yourself?"

"I'm talking to my dad. I know he can hear me."

Britney turned toward Della and then back to the son of Digby G. Randolph and said, "Are you driving tonight?"

"No," he said, "I came by taxi. I live in a condo at Sunset and Genesee."

"Okay, Mr. Randolph," Britney said. "I think you've had enough to drink tonight. The bartender thinks so, too. I'm going to ask the hostess to call you a cab, and then you and your dad can finish that last drink and go home, okay? And the next time you come here, I'd like you and your dad to take the dark corner table. Just put him on the chair beside you and whisper softly, and I don't think anyone will bother you. Do not belly-up to the bar with your dad anymore, okay?"

"I'll do what you say, Officer," the son of Digby G. Randolph said, "but Dad so liked to stand at the bar with his foot on the rail."

"I understand that, sir," Britney said. "But he had feet then. I'd like you to do it my way from now on."

"I will accede to your request, Officer," said the son of Digby G. Randolph, opening the lid of the urn and giving the last of the Jack Daniel's to his dad.

There was a reunion that night in unit 6-X-66. Hollywood Nate got Snuffy Salcedo back, complete with a bandage across his nose and a plastic noseguard. It made him look to Nate the movie buff like Lee Marvin with his false nose in *Cat Ballou*.

"Glad to be back?" Nate asked.

Snuffy said, "Yeah, my mother gets to kicking my ass after I been laying around the house too long, wounded warrior or not. She thinks idleness invites the devil."

Hollywood Nate was being extra solicitous and was doing the driving. "Let's not do anything heroic tonight," Snuffy said. "I'd like to just sit back and be the scribe. I don't wanna bump the beak before it's healed."

"Is it gonna look better when the bandage comes off?" Nate asked.

"It can't look worse than it's looked all my life," Snuffy said.

*   *   *

"Dude, I didn't think you were ever coming back," Flotsam said to Jetsam, on duty together in unit 6-X-32 for the first time since the battle at Goth House.

"Bro, I learned a few things about neck injuries," Jetsam said. "I learned you don't wanna have one. They hurt."

Flotsam had insisted on driving so that Jetsam didn't have to do too much craning at intersections. In fact, he was so solicitous that Jetsam finally said, "Bro, I ain't an invalid."

"I missed my li'l pard," Flotsam said. "Of course, Hollywood Nate's a cool dude, but he don't know shit about the beach and briny. After a while I couldn't think of what to talk about."

The surfer cops had taken a crime report just after dark from a Gallup, New Mexico, tourist who had had her purse picked while she was taking photos of the marble-and-brass stars on the Hollywood Boulevard Walk of Fame. They drove to the station to get a DR number on the report as required, and to have it signed by a supervisor, but they didn't find Sergeant Murillo in the sergeant's room. The troops, especially the surfer cops, always tried to avoid the nitpicking watch commander.

Jetsam said to Flotsam, "I hate taking our report to the kinda guy that would wear a ring on his index finger and make us call him 'His Excellency' if he had his way."

Flotsam said, "If he's in there, let's hold the report till later and get Murillo to sign it."

But at that moment Lieutenant O'Reilly wasn't in his office and Sergeant Murillo was, so Flotsam and Jetsam thought it was safe to enter.

"What's the air like?" Sergeant Murillo asked, meaning the airwaves.

"Quiet," Jetsam said. "A few calls going out to south-end units, and a prowler call in the Hollywood Hills that turned out to be a raccoon."

Much to the surfer cops' consternation, the watch commander

swept into the room just then, but not with his usual look of intensity and purpose. He was actually smiling. In fact, he was unable to contain his excitement.

He said to Sergeant Murillo, "The captain's finished with the citizens meeting at the Community Relations Office and he wants me to join him for code seven at El Cholo."

"I'm surprised he still has an appetite," Sergeant Murillo said, trying to concentrate on the report that the surfer cops had handed to him.

"Yeah," Flotsam agreed. "There ain't been a rational citizen walk into the Hollywood Crows Office since Hitler was still hanging wallpaper."

Ignoring both surfer cops, Lieutenant O'Reilly said to Sergeant Murillo, "The captain said he loves the green corn tamales at El Cholo. Tell me, are green tamales different from regular tamales?"

Sergeant Murillo looked up from the report and said, deadpan, "How would I know, Lieutenant?"

The young watch commander, who was nothing if not politically correct, was disconcerted by the sergeant's unexpected reply and said, "I just...well, I assumed..."

"That I'm Mexican?" Sergeant Murillo said.

"Well, your name and you...you look Hispanic, sort of, and I thought you would know Hispanic food."

"What's a Hispanic look like? And what in the world is Hispanic food?" Sergeant Murillo said, and now the surfer cops were grinning like hyenas, watching the lieutenant squirm and sputter.

"Damn, Murillo, you know what I mean," the watch commander said, genuinely angry that his sergeant was showing him up like this in front of two officers, especially these two.

Jetsam only made things worse when he said artlessly to the watch commander, "The sarge is just hacking on you, sir. He does that to us all the time. One time he pretended he was giving us serious roll call training and he goes, 'Listen up. Orders from the bureau

commander. Officers are forbidden to wear any off-duty clothing that reveals body ink portraying one of our female senators doing fellatio on the president of the United States.'" Jetsam chuckled and said, "He keeps our morale up with funny stuff like that."

Lieutenant O'Reilly stared icily at Jetsam for a long moment and said, "Yes, I'm certain you would find something like that amusing."

Sergeant Murillo winked at the surfer cops and said to the watch commander, "Okay, Lieutenant, I confess, I'm Mexican. Or at least my grandparents are. And I can promise you that El Cholo's green tamales will make the captain as happy as a drunken mariachi on Cinco de Mayo. You can order yourself a margarita manqué, and by the end of the meal you two will be real *compadres*."

Lieutenant O'Reilly noticed that the surfer cops were smiling fondly at their smart-ass sergeant, and it made the lieutenant angrier. He redirected his pique toward Flotsam, saying, "Don't any of the sergeants around this station ever tell you people that gelled-up surfer hairstyles are unfit for police officers?"

Flotsam looked down at the watch commander, whose nose almost touched the tall cop's badge number, and he stopped smiling.

Jetsam again tried a show of goodwill and said, "Actually, sir, only the barneys wear gel or hairspray on the beach. The real kahunas go au naturel, so to speak."

That made the lieutenant turn on Jetsam and say, "I also think the so-called sun streaks in your hair look like highlighting. It's vaguely effeminate for male police officers to highlight their hair. Didn't Sergeant Murillo ever mention that to you?"

Neither surfer cop was smiling now, and both were shooting hate beams at the watch commander, when Sergeant Murillo stood up and said to them, "Okay, we're through here. You can go back to work."

Flotsam and Jetsam were grim and silent when they strode across the parking lot to their shop. After they were in the car,

Flotsam said, "Dude, I think we should drop by Yerevan Tow Service. I got an idea."

Jetsam, who was angrily alliterative, said, "I hope it's a real brain bleacher, bro, cuz I got, like, the image of that slithering snarky slime-sucker stuck in my cerebrum. Feel me?"

"I feel ya, dude," Flotsam said.

Yerevan Tow Service was known to many of the cops at Hollywood Station as a kind of outlaw one-man tow service that picked up scraps that LAPD's official tow garages left behind or couldn't handle. Sarkis, the owner, was a happy-go-lucky Armenian, always eager to impound any vehicles at the scene of traffic collisions or radio calls, which he picked up on his police scanner.

He usually had some of his wife's stuffed grape leaves in his tow truck, and on a couple of occasions he shared them with the surfer cops. And one night he was rewarded for his generosity. On that occasion, 6-X-32 had stopped Sarkis while he was in his private car, driving home from a bar in Little Armenia, absolutely hammered.

As soon as Flotsam and Jetsam saw whom they'd stopped, Flotsam said to Sarkis, "Dude, when you get your swill on, try to remember, it's not a sprint, it's a marathon."

They locked up Sarkis's five-year-old Lincoln and drove him home in their black-and-white. Sarkis tried to invite them into his house for some leftover shish kebab, but Jetsam said to him, "We gotta get back to our beat, bro, but we got your marker. Someday we may need to collect on it."

And now was the time. Sarkis was working late at his tow garage and was happy to see his LAPD friends. He was good at bodywork and had been reassembling a damaged Ford pickup with junkyard parts. After hugs and greetings, he listened intently to what Flotsam and Jetsam had to say about a major problem at Hollywood Station.

Thirty minutes before Lieutenant O'Reilly left his office to join the captain at El Cholo, 6-X-32 received a confidential cell phone

message from one of the desk officers at Hollywood Station. It concerned the approximate arrival time for the watch commander's code 7 rendezvous with the station captain.

Lieutenant O'Reilly had a marvelous time at El Cholo that evening, going well over the allotted time for his code 7 meal break. He told the captain of the many things wrong with the personnel at Hollywood Station. He was especially critical of the midwatch troops, who worked from 5:15 P.M. until 4 A.M. four days a week. He admitted that the officers liked the four-ten shift, but he had many reasons for why the watch hours were inefficient. He said that he wished they could go back to the old eight-hour-and-forty-five-minute work shift five days a week, because efficiency trumped morale. And he told the captain how he wished he had more authority when it came to overtime being granted. He had a strong belief that many officers were padding the books with phony "greenies," as they called the OT slips, and he was planning to put a stop to it. He said that he was working on ways to make supervisors—and he mentioned Sergeant Murillo by name—more responsive to orders and roll call training from the bureau level and less attuned to all of the petty gripes and special requests from the officers on his watch, especially certain officers who flouted good discipline.

All in all, he was wrecking the captain's dinner of green corn tamales, and his boss wished it were possible to get drunk on virgin margaritas so this eager beaver could pass out on the table or something.

After their meal break, Lieutenant O'Reilly thanked the captain excessively for buying him the tamales and they said their good-byes outside El Cholo's front entrance. And then Lieutenant O'Reilly walked to his car, which he'd had to park on Eleventh Street just east of Western Avenue because of the crowded restaurant parking lot. He had his keys in his hand, preparing to unlock the door, when he saw that he couldn't.

The front door on the driver's side was gone. He stopped and

stared at the inside of his car in disbelief, only to discover that the door on the passenger side was also missing. The bolts and hinges on each side had been attacked and the doors … were … gone.

Lieutenant O'Reilly put in a code 2 call for a patrol unit to assist, and the first to arrive was 6-X-32. The surfer cops bailed out and ran to their watch commander with gusto.

"Your doors ain't here, Lieutenant!" Flotsam cried. "What happened?"

"How the hell would I know what happened?" Lieutenant O'Reilly said. "I can't believe this!"

"Those car strippers stop at nothing!" Jetsam cried. "Musta been those rotten little Eighteenth Streeters."

Two other midwatch units arrived very fast, and Snuffy Salcedo got out of the car and started snapping photos of the watch commander's car with his camera phone.

"Stop that!" Lieutenant O'Reilly yelled at him. "Broadcast a code four. We've got enough people here. I don't want anyone else seeing this goddamn travesty."

While Hollywood Nate was broadcasting a code 4, indicating that there was sufficient help at the scene, Lieutenant O'Reilly began searching the street and sidewalk with his flashlight, looking for evidence of the vandals' identity. He knew that this was no ordinary crime of malicious mischief, and he suspected that slackers from Hollywood Station had done this to humilate him. The midwatch cops at the scene were fascinated, watching the way Lieutenant O'Reilly circled the wounded police vehicle like a predator wary of dangerous prey. His eyes were bulging and his face looked like a tomato about to explode.

Flotsam said sotto to Snuffy Salcedo, "Dude, I think the lieutenant's gone to dizzyland. This here outrage should not go unpunished."

Jetsam said sotto to Snuffy Salcedo, "Bro, these are perilous times we live in. Nobody's safe no more."

Snuffy Salcedo listened to the surfer cops and whispered something to Hollywood Nate, something he'd asked before. "Are you telling me these two don't rehearse this shit?"

"Maybe some of it," Nate conceded in a whisper of his own. "They're sort of the Gilbert and Sullivan of Hollywood Station. They write and sometimes star in their little asphalt operettas."

"This looks to me like somebody's idea of a prank!" Lieutenant O'Reilly said after his search for evidence turned up nothing. "I want this unit taken to the parking lot and dusted for prints. I'm going to get to the bottom of this."

"Let's glove up, partner," Flotsam said, taking latex gloves from his pocket.

"You won't need to," Lieutenant O'Reilly said to Jetsam. "I want you to drive me to the station right this minute."

"Roger that, sir," Jetsam said.

"And you drive my unit in," Lieutenant O'Reilly said to Flotsam, handing him the keys. "Book anything you find in my car that even remotely might be evidence. A matchstick, a chewing gum wrapper, anything. I want the bastards that did this, and I'm going to get them."

"I'm on it, sir," Flotsam said. "I'll do a diligent search for clues. We sure wouldn't want the doors to turn up at a swap meet or maybe in an *L.A. Times* story."

Jetsam opened the passenger door on 6-X-32's shop for the watch commander to get in, but Lieutenant O'Reilly paused and showed all present a grimace of a smile. He probably thought it showed self-confidence and was intimidating, but Hollywood Nate thought it looked like the other contenders' smiles on the night they lost the Oscar to Kate Winslet.

When Jetsam got behind the wheel, he said, "If this does happen to get in the news, don't let it embarrass you, Lieutenant. It's not your fault. This is fucking Hollywood."

Flotsam enjoyed driving a car with no front doors, and he

decided to take Hollywood Boulevard so that he could cruise past Grauman's Chinese Theatre and give the tourists a show. When he was stopped for traffic directly in front of Grauman's forecourt, a clutch of tourists with cameras ran to the curb and started snapping photos of the doorless police car.

Flotsam waved and yelled, "Tough town! Last week somebody stole my front fenders!"

TWENTY-FOUR

THIS WAS THE day of reckoning as far as Raleigh Dibble was concerned. He did everything he could to make time pass faster. He dusted and vacuumed the master suite for Leona Brueger's return and even washed her windows. That involved some precarious labor on a tall stepladder. He drove his own car to the markets where his employer had charge accounts and made sure that there was enough fresh produce, chicken, and fish to provide meals for several days in case she was too tired to dine out.

When he was finished with chores, he called Cedars-Sinai and received a report on Marty Brueger. His condition was not as serious as had been thought, and it was hoped that the old man could soon be moved to a managed-care facility. Raleigh was living in such a state of fear for his own plight that he hadn't had time to pity Marty Brueger. But now Raleigh thought that if Marty Brueger was moved to a less-structured facility, he would take the poor old geezer some of his favorite Irish whiskey. It pleased him to be concerned with someone else for a change.

When Raleigh was finished with everything he could think of to do, he found himself wondering if he would even be there to prepare a homecoming meal for her or if he would be in jail. Or would he be dead? He sat in his bedroom and stared at Leona Brueger's nickel-plated revolver. One thing he knew for sure, for the first time

he was capable of violence, at least as far as Nigel Wickland was concerned. Nobody in his life had ever harmed him so grievously. Regardless of the consequences, he was not going to let that arrogant son of a bitch get away with it. He knew exactly what he was going to do.

Raleigh planned on going to the Wickland Gallery at 4 P.M., but not to enter. He could watch the gallery entrance from the coffee shop across the street to know if Nigel left. Just before the gallery's closing time of 5 P.M., Raleigh was going to enter, demand to see Nigel, and strongly suggest to him that he send Ruth home because a private talk was essential and unavoidable. And of course Nigel would be angry that Raleigh had come, but when they were alone, the anger would turn into something else. Mr. Nigel Wickland, the master schemer and manipulator, was going to experience a bit of what Raleigh Dibble had been living with ever since he'd been insane enough to join the gallery owner's plot. Nigel Wickland was going to experience fear! Every time Raleigh looked at the nickel-plated revolver lying on his bed, it made his palms sweat.

At 1 P.M., Megan Burke made the call to Arjan, the Sikh taxi driver to whom she had promised the $100 tip. She had packed her bag, leaving space for a thousand hundred-dollar bills. She had no idea how big a package that would be, but there was plenty of room in her suitcase, since she had so few clothes left after her year of riding the ox in Hollywood.

She was surprised that she did not feel worse than she did. The joint pain from her opioid withdrawal was still severe, but the diarrhea had abated and she wasn't vomiting as much. She looked in her pill container and saw that she had enough medication to get her home to Oregon, and from there it would be a few hours of hugs and kisses with her mother and brother and then she'd go directly into rehab.

She had spent the morning talking and crying with her mother

on the phone, after which her mother phoned several Oregon rehab facilities until she found one close to home that would permit Megan to bring Cuddles with her to the ninety-day treatment program. Megan's mother told her that she would go to the bank and see if she could take out a second mortgage to cover the $25,000 cost, but Megan told her not to worry about it, because she had won a big prize in the California lottery and she was paying for her own rehab.

The last thing Megan said to her astonished mother was that there would be $75,000 left from the prize money after taxes. She insisted that her mom take it all, along with profound apologies for having been such a miserable daughter.

Before they hung up, her mother said to Megan, "Honey, you could never be anything but a wonderful, loving daughter. I can't wait to have you home. The only mistake you ever made in your life was going to Hollywood, California."

Megan went to the bathroom to dry her tears and touch up her makeup and then called Nigel Wickland on his cell number. When he answered, she said, "I'll be there at two o'clock. Are you ready for me?"

"Yes," he said. "I've given my assistant the afternoon off. I'll be here alone."

"I won't be alone," she said.

"I don't doubt that," Nigel said, ending the conversation.

When Jonas Claymore arrived in court, he looked for Megan, but she wasn't there. He was growing very concerned for his money. Thinking about it made him uncontrollably jittery. When he'd had his fill of waiting, he jumped up and told a bailiff that he demanded to speak to a public defender. He also demanded an own-recognizance release. He said he'd never been arrested before except once for DUI, so he deserved to be OR'ed as soon as possi-

ble. He said he wanted immediate access to counsel, any counsel. He said he'd even settle for one that advertises on bus benches and takes his orders from sleazy bail bondsmen.

The bailiff told Jonas if he was smart, he'd zip his lips.

Jonas Claymore was still sitting with other in-custody defendants when court convened after lunch. He had been able to speak with a harried public defender, who had verified that Jonas had only one arrest on his rap sheet, for DUI, and he agreed to represent Jonas and ask for an own-recognizance release. The judge, who was just as harried as the public defender, and who was looking at a roomful of miscreants and their friends and families, granted the OR release. Jonas was set free and his property was returned, which included a cheap wristwatch and a wallet containing the only hundred-dollar bill he had left. He used that money to call a taxi to take him to his car in the parking lot at Pablo's Taco Shop, where he paid the driver and looked around in vain for someone he knew who might have some ox.

All the way to the apartment he thought of what he was going to say to Megan Burke, who had left him rotting in that filthy jail with smelly savages who'd terrified him. She hadn't tried to post bail, she hadn't come to his arraignment, and she hadn't done shit to help him, despite all he had done for her during the year they'd been together. He had shared his life and everything he owned with that cunt! He had never laid an angry hand on her, but he thought that just might change when he got home. It would all depend on what she had to say for herself.

When he got home, he found out what she had to say for herself. It was on the note. And beside the note were his cell phone, her key, and $1,900. He read the note three times, his rage mounting. Her clothes and bag were gone and so was her cat.

He snatched the money off the table, put it in his pocket, and phoned Wilbur. He was jonesing bad and needed something to

smooth him out so he could think. So he could do what he had to do. The bitch had robbed him and he was going to find her if he had to check every motel in Hollywood. He'd get her when she went to Pablo's to score, or maybe when she called Wilbur for some ox. He'd slip Wilbur a President Grant to tip him off as to where she was staying with his fucking money.

When Jonas looked behind the sofa, he was shocked. The paintings were gone! She had even stolen his paintings. His outrage turned to fury. He felt like he might keel over in a faint. He wished she'd left her cat there so he could kill it.

There was only one thing she could have done with them. She must've kept her schoolgirl promise and returned them to the gallery owner. And now she was out there spending Jonas's money. She'd probably already spent a few grand on ox and was holed up somewhere chasing dragons with some other stupid bastard who was dumb enough to take her in. Well, somebody was going to pay for how he'd been screwed. She'd pay dearly if and when he found her. But until then he wasn't taking this like some screwed-over pussy. He was going out and getting what was coming to him.

Wilbur didn't answer, so he got in his car and drove to the cyber-café, where he saw a guy named Beatle who he used to buy crystal meth from, back before Megan, back when he was a tweaker. Beatle used to run a chop shop and would do anything for meth. He was now so strung out, he'd kill you for your liver if he could find a buyer for it. He could slam a gram and think nothing of it.

Jonas gave Beatle a pair of Jacksons, and Beatle showed teeth like jagged licorice drops, and he said, "Dude, you bought yourself a meth run on my shit pipe. Follow me to my crib."

They went to his nearby rat hole of an apartment, and Jonas smoked crystal meth once again. It was nothing like smoking ox, but it was better than nothing. He remembered how he used to love it, but now he hated it. After riding the ox, meth seemed like nothing but a lowlife drug smelling like cat piss. Nowadays he was way

better than this. Still, it beat jonesing, so he smoked a lot of it. And when he was finished, he found that it made him feel agitated. It made him feel paranoid. It made him feel wild!

When he was about to leave Beatle's apartment, the tweaker showed him eyes as empty as a haunted house and said, "Don't trip, potato chip."

It was just after 2 P.M. when Megan and her Sikh taxi driver walked from his parked taxi to the front door of the Wickland Gallery. Megan was wearing a long-sleeved red jersey, jeans, and tennis shoes, and was carrying a tattered suitcase in one hand and in the other hand an airline-approved cat carrier with Cuddles inside it. The tall, bearded Sikh wore a cobalt-blue turban, a guayabera shirt, khakis, and sandals, and carried the two blanket-wrapped paintings, one under each arm.

Megan opened the door and saw Nigel Wickland waiting at Ruth's desk in the main room of the gallery. He was as elegant as ever in a double-breasted navy pinstripe, a white button-down shirt, and a rose-colored silk necktie. He looked very tense, and there was even a tic working the corner of his left eye.

Nigel stood and said to the Sikh, "You can lean those items against the wall."

The Sikh looked at Megan, who nodded to him. Only then did the taxi driver comply. Then she handed the Sikh the cat carrier and said, "Arjan, please wait just outside the door with Cuddles. I'll be in here no more than fifteen minutes."

The Sikh nodded again and left the gallery, taking Cuddles with him. Nigel could see him through the gallery window, standing on the pavement with the pet carrier firmly in his grasp.

Nigel gave Megan a lopsided smile and said, "Yes, I see that you are well protected. But you have nothing to fear from me. Not anymore. In many ways you have done me a favor."

"By eliminating your partner?"

He didn't respond to that but said, "Let's go back to my office to complete our business."

Nigel picked up a wrapped painting in each hand, and Megan followed him to his office, and this time she did not feel frightened when he closed the door.

"Have a seat," he said, indicating a client chair in front of his desk.

She sat and put her suitcase flat on the floor and opened it. He looked at the suitcase and said, "I'm afraid I can't fill up a bag that big, but I have your entire bonus as requested. Although first I'd like to examine my merchandise."

He opened a door from his office that led to a storage room with a large sliding door leading from there to the alley. The cargo van was parked inside the storage room, and there were gallery supplies on shelves and benches. Nigel Wickland entered and turned on a light over one of the benches. He cut the duct tape and unwrapped the largest bundle. He lifted the painting and held it under the light, inspecting it closely. Megan stood in the doorway of the storage room and watched him.

"Ah, yes," he said. "*The Woman by the Water.* Isn't she lovely?" He carefully rewrapped the painting and then unwrapped the second one, holding it under the light, and nodded with a smile on his face.

"Satisfied?" Megan said.

Nigel said, "I am, indeed."

He rewrapped *Flowers on the Hillside* and opened the side door of the van, putting both bundled paintings inside on the floor. Then he closed the door of the van and said, "Now let's complete our business before your turbaned friend comes in here and dispatches me with his dagger."

They went back to Nigel's desk, where he opened a deep bottom drawer and removed a shipping carton without a lid. He placed it on his desk and said, "Go ahead and count it. I already have."

Megan picked up a packet of hundred-dollar bills, her heart beating in her ears, and counted. When she got to fifty, she stopped and fanned through the rest of the packet. Then she fanned through each of the other packets without counting. It was too staggering an amount of money. She said, "It looks okay. I trust you, Mr. Wickland."

Nigel emitted a burst of nervous laughter at that, and even Megan had to giggle. Then she put each packet into her large suitcase among a jumble of underwear, jeans, two books, T-shirts, and tank tops. When she was finished, she closed and locked the suitcase with a small luggage key.

"Yes, that should get through an airport baggage scanner with no problem," Nigel said. "I'll bet you'll be waiting anxiously for it to come down the carousel when you reach your destination, wherever that is."

Megan smiled without comment. Then she simply picked up the suitcase, opened the door of his office, and walked across the display room of the gallery to the Wilshire Boulevard door.

Before she opened it, Nigel called to her, saying, "Have a good life, Valerie. Your ambition has been for me a blessing in disguise."

She didn't respond but wiggled her fingers at him in a final farewell. When she got outside, the Sikh took her suitcase, and she carried the pet carrier to the taxi for the ride to LAX. Megan Burke was so overjoyed that she decided to increase Arjan's tip to $200.

And on that ride to the airport, with her hand inside the pet carrier stroking her cat, Megan Burke tried to take with her something positive from her two years away from home. But the addiction that had resulted in her physical, emotional, and moral decline had obliterated all positives. And then she thought, no, there was one gift that Hollywood, California, had given her. It came when she had walked into the animal rescue facility fourteen months ago. Hollywood had given her Cuddles the calico cat.

TWENTY-FIVE

RALEIGH DIBBLE HAD taken the longest shower of his life. He never wanted to leave the hot water. When he did, he went to the bathroom sink and shaved with a new blade and did as good a job as he could in combing his thinning hair. He laid out his best sport shirt and newest chinos. He even brushed the lint from his best blazer and ran a cloth over his old loafers. He'd seen movies of men who were facing momentous events in their lives who took such care, sometimes before putting a gun to their heads and pulling the trigger.

By 4 P.M., he was across the street from the Wickland Gallery, having first ascertained that the lights were on inside and the gallery was open for business.

Jonas Claymore was on a meth ride that he hadn't been on in more than a year. He was driving in frenzy from east Hollywood to Beverly Hills through rush-hour traffic. His central nervous system had come unwired and his hands were out of control. He kept touching the instruments in the VW bug. He'd make sure the headlights were not on and the emergency brake was not on and the radio controls were working and the heater switch was off. Every time he finished he'd do it all over again. His hands didn't belong to him anymore. They just kept fiddling and fretting in perpetual motion.

He knew how much he needed some ox to get himself under

control, but there was no time to waste. He fantasized that Megan Burke might be there when he arrived. He would deal with her if he found her there. Oh yes, he would. They were laughing at him, Megan and that gallery guy who had *his* paintings. She'd stolen them from him. They'd been his to dispose of as he chose, but she'd clowned him. Now they were both laughing at him.

He had to remind himself to slow down and obey the traffic laws. He couldn't afford to get stopped by the cops again. It was bizarre, but everyone he saw on the streets looked like an undercover cop, and they all seemed to be watching him. But they couldn't stop him from doing what he had to do. Nobody could.

Jonas only wished he'd had time to talk to Wilbur to see if he could sell him a burner. He'd never had one before, but he was sure he'd handle one okay. Maybe a pistol like all the cops carried on *CSI*. But he hadn't had time to strap up. All he had was the large carving knife that was riding inside his waistband, the handle of it digging into his sunken belly. It would be enough because he was starting to feel invincible.

Five minutes before its scheduled closing, Raleigh Dibble crossed Wilshire Boulevard and entered the Wickland Gallery. He didn't see the woman at her desk, so he walked back to Nigel's office just as Nigel was coming out of the little restroom.

"Surprise," Raleigh said, and sat in the client chair, trying to stay cool.

Nigel frowned and said, "I didn't hear you come in. What're you doing here? You should know better than to come here again."

"Oh, your assistant told you I was here the other day?"

"Yes."

"Why didn't you call me to complain about that, Nigel?"

Nigel sat on the corner of his desk and said, "What good would that have done? I've tried everything in my power to persuade you to be patient until the thieves contact us. What more can I do?"

"I've forgotten your employee's name," Raleigh said.

"Ruth is her name. You look tense, Raleigh. Can I get you a cup of coffee? Tea, perhaps?"

Raleigh said, "Did Ruth tell you what we talked about when I came looking for you yesterday?"

"Yes, she said you inquired whether a man came here asking to talk to me personally."

"Did you understand why I asked that?"

"Of course," Nigel said. "You think that I'm doing business with the man who phoned me and that I'm concealing it from you."

"Yes, that's right," Raleigh said, thinking, Calm. Stay calm.

"Well, it's silly, Raleigh," Nigel said. "We may never hear from them at all, and if that's the case, I'm the only one who's out any expenses."

"There's nothing to worry about, then?" Raleigh said.

"Nothing," Nigel said. "Leona will never notice what we did, and I will proceed with assisting her to crate and store the replicated pictures when the time comes."

"I see," Raleigh said. "Then it was just a big swing and a miss, our whole caper?"

"In your baseball terms? Yes, that's what it was. I'm sorry for you and I'm sorry for me. I spent money on this plan, if you'll remember."

"Yes, I certainly do remember," Raleigh said. "More money than I knew about."

"What's that supposed to mean?"

Raleigh's demeanor changed and he said, "I'm referring to the money you paid your accomplices to screw me after you used me up."

"The pressure's become too much for you," Nigel said, standing up from his perch on the corner of his desk and walking around to his desk chair.

"I don't think so," Raleigh said. "I know that you hired two

316

people from the get-go to pull that bogus theft of your van so that you could cut me right out of the picture. After I helped you switch the paintings, I was taken right out of it, as neat as you please."

"Jesus wept!" Nigel said incredulously, looking at the door to the storage room, which was ajar. "Is that what you really think? That I hired a couple of blokes to pretend to steal my van so that I could cut you out of the arrangement?"

"That's what I think," Raleigh said.

"On my word as a gentleman," Nigel said, "my van was stolen by unknown persons. Full stop. End of story."

"You're no gentleman, you son of a bitch," Raleigh said, smoldering now.

"Get out, Raleigh," Nigel said. "You're making a fool of yourself."

Raleigh watched Nigel's face very closely when he said, "And how about the girl in the candy-striped dress?"

"The what?" Nigel said instantly.

He was good, Raleigh thought. He didn't flinch. But the tic at the corner of his eye began working overtime. "Valerie, if that's her name."

Nigel felt truly gob-smacked. How did Raleigh know that Valerie had come here? He said, "Please explain yourself, Raleigh. You're not making sense."

"You're a conniving bastard, aren't you?" Raleigh said. "Me, I'm just a dumb old ex-con who's a servant for rich people and makes their meals and wipes their asses, just like you said. But now I realize that I was actually pretty content with my lot in life until I met you. Now that I see what you are."

"This is going nowhere," Nigel said. "Whatever I tell you won't matter. You're simply overwhelmed by paranoid thoughts. Believe me, I wish as much as you do that we'd never met, but if wishes were fishes, as they say."

"Tell me about the girl in the candy-striped dress," Raleigh said.

"Tell me about darling, adorable little Valerie. Why did she come to see me? That's the only thing that puzzles me. What was that all about? Was she doing a little work on her own as a private agent? Maybe she wanted to see what other art was in the house so she and her thieving partner could steal more from Leona Brueger? I can't figure out that part of it. Why did she come to the Brueger house? Tell me that much, if you know."

Nigel Wickland was more exhausted than he'd been when they'd done the switch and watched it all implode with the stealing of the van. He was more exhausted than he'd been anytime in the past several days when he'd worried that the police would come to his gallery to say that they'd caught a man with his van and some blanket-wrapped paintings that he would need to explain. He was drained. Raleigh Dibble had most of it wrong but enough of it right. He had let himself be trapped by a fool.

Then it came to him. "Ruth," Nigel said. "Ruth mentioned the girl in the candy-striped dress to you, didn't she?"

"You kept her a secret from me," Raleigh said.

"Bloody hell," Nigel said. "Yes, I have kept some things from you, but for good reason, trust me."

"I'm all ears," Raleigh said, "like a cornfield in summer. Enlighten me, Nigel."

"They truly stole the van," Nigel said. "A man I've never seen and the girl we both know as Valerie. Will you at least believe that much?"

"Go on," Raleigh said.

"She's a smart girl, infinitely smarter than her crime partner, whom I've never met. She saw the Brueger name and address on the framer's tag that's stapled to the stretcher bars, and she figured out that something was wrong with my claim that the paintings belong to me. She went to you on her own to try to work it out, and I guess she charmed you into inviting her into the house, where you generously showed her around. And she saw *The Woman by the Water*

and *Flowers on the Hillside*. All because you showed the goddamn paintings to her, Raleigh. You caused all this. It's all your fault, not mine!"

"I've never stopped wondering about the generosity of the thieves," Raleigh said. "You, know, the way they gave back your van as a show of good faith?"

"They're not master criminals, those two," Nigel said. "They're addled drug addicts who got extremely lucky. You saw Valerie. Couldn't you see that she's physically unwell?"

"And they took your twelve thousand and gave you back the paintings as promised, right along with your van, didn't they?"

"Good lord!" Nigel said. "No, I haven't paid them anything yet because I haven't heard any more from them since Valerie came here and blackmailed me. All because you invited her into the fucking house."

"And did she tell you how much more money she wanted not to break it all down for the police or for Mrs. Brueger?"

"No!" Nigel said. "I've been waiting to hear from them. I decided that your nerves were so frazzled you couldn't take another shock like this, so that's why I wasn't going to tell you until I received their demand. Don't you understand?"

"You were protecting me. That's kind of you," Raleigh said.

"I was protecting both of us. Believe me, this has become so convoluted I don't know where I am half the time. I knew that you couldn't possibly deal with more stress. Of that much I was certain."

"So all we can do is wait to receive the new instructions from Valerie or her partner, is that it, Nigel?"

"That's about it," Nigel said. "We must wait."

"That's not about it," Raleigh said. "I have another plan in mind."

The buzzer sounded in the office, indicating that someone had entered the gallery door on Wilshire Boulevard.

"Oh, Christ!" Nigel said. "I should've locked up. Will you excuse me for a moment?"

Nigel got up and left the office, and when he entered the display room, he turned and said, "Raleigh, if you want coffee, it's on the table by the restroom door. Help yourself."

Jonas Claymore, who was standing in the middle of the display room, heard what Nigel said and realized that the gallery owner was not alone.

It was hard for Nigel to repress a sneer of disgust when he saw the gangling, disheveled young man in a hooded gray sweatshirt looking at him with a crazed expression. Nigel thought that the Beverly Hills police should do a better job in keeping panhandlers from harassing the business owners along Wilshire Boulevard.

"I'm afraid we're closed," Nigel said to Jonas. "I'll be locking the door as soon as my last customer leaves."

Without a word, Jonas scowled, turned, and slouched across the display room to the door with Nigel following after him. When Jonas stepped out onto Wilshire Boulevard, the gallery owner locked the door behind him, pulled a blind over the glass door, and placed a "Closed" sign in the display window.

Okay, you prissy asshole, Jonas thought. We'll play, but it's my move. He walked around to the alley and saw that the gallery had a large sliding door big enough to accommodate a van. There were two parking spaces in the alley, one of them containing a red BMW roadster. Yeah, that's his, Jonas thought. A fag car.

He hurried to his VW bug, moved it to the end of the alley, and sat there watching the rear door of the gallery, thinking he'd trade three Franklins for just half an ox at this moment. An elderly woman left the door of the jewelry store behind him to empty a trash container in a Dumpster. Jonas eyed her in his rearview mirror and she looked to him like an undercover cop.

When Nigel Wickland had finished locking up and turning out

the lights, he returned to his office and found himself looking at the muzzle of a gun.

Raleigh was standing by the door to the storage room, and he said, "Let's you and me have a look in here, Nigel. If the paintings aren't here, we'll take a ride to your condo and look for them there."

And at last Raleigh Dibble saw something that he had longed to see ever since the entire misadventure had begun. He saw something that he knew too well from his own experience. He saw real fear in the face of Nigel Wickland.

"What're you playing at?" Nigel said, and Raleigh was pleased to see that the tic at the corner of Nigel's eye had intensified.

"I'm not playing," Raleigh said. "Not anymore."

"Please, Raleigh!" Nigel said.

"You're looking at a desperate, angry man," Raleigh said. "I believe that I'll spend many years in prison if I don't put this thing right, and that's what I'm going to do tonight, one way or the other."

"You won't use that," Nigel said. "You can't!"

"I will certainly kill you, Nigel," Raleigh said, "if you don't walk into that storage room right now. And then I might kill myself. Don't test me."

Nigel didn't just walk, he skated. He seemed to glide along the floor with his hands held in front of him palms up, as though to ward off any bullet that Raleigh might fire. When he stepped into the storage room, he switched on the light.

"You see," he said, "there's nothing here but store supplies..."

"How about your van," Raleigh said.

"Go ahead and search," Nigel said. "This is ridiculous."

Raleigh said, "Get me a flashlight. It's too dark in here."

"On the workbench," Nigel said. "But I'd like you to put the gun away."

Raleigh saw the toolbox, the one that Nigel had had the day

they removed the paintings from their frames and installed the replicas in their places. The small flashlight was in the top tray. Raleigh took it out and said, "Turn around, Nigel, with your hands held high."

"What're you going to do?" Nigel said, sounding like he might weep. Sounding the way he did on the night that the thieves stole the van.

"Just be very still," Raleigh said, shining the beam into darkened crannies and inside cabinets and even up to the exposed beams.

"Satisfied?" Nigel said. "Can we stop this charade now?"

"Not yet," Raleigh said.

When Nigel heard the door to the van open, he said, "For god's sake, Raleigh!"

"Do not move a hair," Raleigh said. Then he shined his beam inside the van and saw the familiar blanketed bundles.

"Raleigh...," Nigel said, unable to immediately come up with more than that. "Raleigh, Raleigh..."

"Do I need to have you take these out and open them?"

Nigel turned his face and spoke over his shoulder, saying, "I swear to you that I didn't know anything until the girl Valerie marched in here today with the paintings. I gave her the twelve thousand and she marched out again."

"And you were going to tell me about it when you got around to it, weren't you?"

"Can I put my hands down?"

"No, but you can turn around and face me."

Nigel turned, hands still held high, and said, "I couldn't tell you! All you've been talking about lately is how much you've regretted what we've done. You wanted to return the paintings to the house. I was afraid you would do it. I wasn't going to tell you about this until I shipped them to Europe and made the deal. Then I was going to surprise you with your share of a million dollars. I swear it's the truth, Raleigh!"

"You're amazing," Raleigh said. "You're an utterly amazing liar and four-flusher."

Nigel then began wheezing and reached frantically for his inhaler, but Raleigh said, "Move those Joan Crawford hands very slowly, Nigel."

Nigel said, "I...I...can't...can't catch my breath!"

"Slowly," Raleigh said, and Nigel complied, taking two puffs from the canister and inhaling deeply.

When his breathing improved, he said, "We can still make this work, Raleigh. There's no real harm done. You can't turn back now. Let me do what I was going to do. Half a million, Raleigh. Tax-free!"

"Very carefully, toss me the van keys," Raleigh said.

Nigel took his key ring from his pocket and tossed it ten feet across the storage room to the floor. Raleigh picked it up, returned the flashlight to the toolbox, carried the toolbox to the van, and put it behind the passenger seat.

"Get in the van behind the wheel," Raleigh said.

"This is madness," Nigel said. "Madness!"

"Get in!"

Nigel scurried to the van and got in the driver's seat.

"How do you open the sliding door?" Raleigh asked.

Nigel's voice was nearly inaudible when he said, "I have a remote here in the van."

Raleigh sat in the passenger seat and said, "Open the door."

Nigel pressed a remote clipped to the visor, and the door slid open.

"Drive," Raleigh said. "I think you know where."

"Madness!" Nigel Wickland said.

Jonas Claymore started his engine the minute the storage room door slid open. He saw the cargo van drive out and the door slide shut again. Darkness was arriving sooner now that Los Angeles was experiencing its version of autumn weather. It was too dark for

Jonas to see if the gallery owner was alone in the van. The other man in the office could have gone out the front door, for all he knew. Alone or not, the gallery owner would be coming back for his little red car, but Jonas opted to tail him rather than just to sit there. There might even be a better place to confront the sissy and make him give Jonas what was coming to him. And anyway, the crystal had made Jonas feel too supercharged to wait.

Jonas had to control himself as he drove in the early nighttime traffic. He didn't figure that the gallery owner would be looking for a tail, so he could get close, but in the heavy traffic he couldn't get close enough to see if the man was alone in the van.

He almost lost the van on Sunset Boulevard when it turned north on Fairfax. He picked it up again going east on Hollywood Boulevard but lost it for a moment when it made a left turn on Sierra Bonita. He picked it up again when it was eastbound on Franklin, and he lost the van completely when he was stopped by a traffic light on Outpost Drive. Jonas sat meth-crazed in his VW bug, and he banged on the steering wheel and kept his other hand on the horn, screaming out the window at the cars, at the traffic light, and at life in general.

A man next to him in a new Lexus lowered the window and said, "What's wrong with you, buddy?"

Jonas pulled the kitchen knife from his waistband, waved it, and said, "Nothing if I could cut your fucking eyes out, you rich cocksucker!"

The Lexus sped away and Jonas turned onto Outpost Drive, moving northbound aimlessly until a thought occurred to him. If he kept on going to Mulholland and veered left, he'd be climbing high into the Hollywood Hills on his way toward Woodrow Wilson Drive. Could the van be going back there? Back to the big house where all this had started in the first place? Where his betrayal had begun?

*　　*　　*

Raleigh Dibble made Nigel Wickland remove the bundles from the van at gunpoint while he carried the toolbox into Casa Brueger. Once inside, Raleigh turned on the foyer and corridor lights, and he sat on the carved antique chair with the needlepoint seat cushion, and said, "Go to work, genius."

Nigel sighed, removed his suit coat, opened his collar, loosened his tie, and took down the framed replica of *The Woman by the Water*. He unwrapped the original painting and worked silently, trying not to think about the fact that he'd given away $112,000 of his own money to be right back where he'd started days ago. He was a ruined man now. He saw no way to save his business, not with both his savings and commercial accounts looted. The only silver lining was that there was no more fear of going to prison. But to Nigel Wickland at this moment, prison didn't seem as terrifying as facing old age penniless.

When he removed the replica, he tossed it onto the mover's blanket and replaced the original painting in its frame. Then he removed the framed replica of *Flowers on the Hillside* and did the same. It was slow and tedious because he loved and respected the Impressionist pieces too much to do anything less than his best for them. He felt a sudden sentimental wish that someone who appreciated them as much as he did might possess them someday.

When Nigel was nearly finished, he said, "Could you at least get me another of those Vichy waters?"

Raleigh said, "It was tap water, you supercilious snob. You can have all you want when you're done."

Jonas Claymore had let out a howl of triumph the moment he'd seen the van in the Brueger driveway. He couldn't imagine why the man had come back to the house unless he was making another attempt at selling them the two paintings now that Megan had returned them for 12K. *His* 12K. Gone!

Jonas was getting itchy now. The meth was producing all sorts

of side effects that he hadn't felt before, at least not to this extent. His whole body was twitching. He felt like his teeth were twitching. It was all he could do to stand there peeking through the junipers again and not run down and kick in the door and put the knife at the throat of that art dealer who'd double-crossed him with Megan. He could only hope the fucker knew where Megan was holed up. He would make him talk, oh, yes.

Jonas took a piss on the junipers and then passed the time fantasizing about climbing into the window of wherever Megan was staying and cutting her tits off. But they were so small it would be no big loss to her.

"Can you please put the gun away now?" Nigel said when he had both worthless replicas loosely wrapped in the mover's blankets.

Raleigh tucked the gun in his pocket and picked up the toolbox, saying, "You carry the replicas. Maybe you can get a few bucks for them somewhere. They're almost as beautiful as the originals. You might try craigslist."

"I couldn't get enough to pay for the lab work we did," Nigel said. "I'll just use them as remembrances of things past. When I'm residing on skid row."

"You'll be all right, Nigel," Raleigh said. "An English gentleman of your quality can easily get a job doing what I do. I can see you as a domestic servant for a rich old man who needs someone cultured to wipe his ass."

Raleigh Dibble walked outside with Nigel Wickland, who tossed the blanketed replicas onto the floor of the van. "I won't ask you for a ride back to my car, Nigel," Raleigh said. "I'll taxi down and pick it up tomorrow. I think we've seen enough of each other."

Nigel said, "Perhaps I'll have to see you again if Leona still plans to use me to supervise the storage of her artwork. But I certainly hope not."

Raleigh said, "Good-bye, Nigel. Sorry how things have turned

out for you. I guess you'll just have to face old age as irrelevant as the rest of us."

Nothing else was said. Raleigh watched the van drive away over the fake cobblestone driveway for the last time. He turned and entered the house, not seeing the one taillight of the little VW bug following the van, and winking at him just as before.

When Raleigh Dibble fell into bed, he knew he'd be able to sleep soundly at last. He didn't have great prospects for a successful future, but he thought that perhaps he'd get a good reference from Leona Brueger before she sold the house and moved away. He thought it would be wonderful if the new buyers of this house needed a butler chef with his skills. He wanted to stay in this house. He liked it here with or without all the artwork.

He was lying in bed with the window open watching moonbeams fluttering across the wall of his bedroom, and he was content. Before drifting off to sleep, he thought of the fragile, charming tulip of a girl with alabaster skin who had kissed his cheek. She was so wistful, so delightfully young. Raleigh Dibble would always remember her as the girl in the candy-striped dress.

TWENTY-SIX

HE DIDN'T NEED to take the trouble to stay behind the cargo van. Jonas knew where it was going and he wanted to be there before the van arrived. He drove so fast that he didn't make the yellow and blew through a red light on Sunset Boulevard. He looked around frantically for a black-and-white but saw none. When he reached Beverly Hills, he pulled onto the side street next to the Wickland Gallery and ran into the alley, relieved to see that he had not been wrong about the red BMW Roadster. It belonged to the fairy art dealer, he was sure of it. The man would be back.

He squeezed his bony body behind the Dumpster in the alley, but since the container was full of trash, he couldn't budge it, and he had trouble folding his tall frame so that his head was not protruding. It was miserable there, and he was still flashing on paranoid thoughts. His discomfort made him ever more furious at what this sissy and Megan had conspired to do to him. He was bent over in an angular squat, listening to all the nighttime traffic on Wilshire Boulevard, when he heard the van enter through the alley. Jonas took the knife from under his sweatshirt, pulled up his hoodie, and got ready to attack.

Nigel thought he'd need to sleep around the clock to recover from this horror. He touched the remote-control button and the door slid open. He drove the van into the storage room, turned off

the headlights, and pushed the button to close the door. When he stepped out of the van, the interior van lights stayed on briefly, and he used the light to open the side door and remove the blanketed replicas. He tossed them contemptuously onto the workbench. And then he felt the knife at his throat.

Jonas Claymore, who was even taller than Nigel, grabbed him from behind by the collar of his suit coat and pressed his cheek to Nigel's, saying, "Don't fucking twitch."

"Oh, my god!" Nigel said. "Oh, my lord!"

"Right now I'm your lord," Jonas said. "And you better do what your lord says."

"Anything!" Nigel said, his hands in the air just as before. "Anything!"

"Turn on the lights in here."

"The switch is by the door to my office," Nigel said.

"Move over there real slow," Jonas said.

Nigel could smell the hooded man's body odor. It was foul. He moved awkwardly to the light switch, like a dog whose master had him by the collar, and he switched on the lights.

"Where's my paintings?" Jonas said.

The voice! Yes, it was the thief who'd called him with his demand for a reward. Nigel said, "Sir, please release me and take away the knife so we can talk."

Jonas tightened his grip on Nigel's collar and stayed behind him, saying, "We're gonna talk, but first, where's my paintings?"

"Sir," Nigel said. "I truly don't know what you're talking about."

Jonas said, "I'm talking about cutting your head off like a fucking Eye-raqi dune coon, that's what I'm talking about."

It was too much. Too much terror for one night. It was so unbelievable, he felt like screaming himself awake. But he didn't scream. He peed. Jonas saw it running from under the cuff of Nigel's trousers onto the concrete floor of the storage room.

"You fucking dick-drip," Jonas said. "You pissed your pants."

Nigel Wickland hadn't heard him. The sweat poured from him and he was sobbing, his body heaving so hard against the knife that the blade broke the skin and his throat burned. He managed to say, "Don't hurt me. I'll do anything. I'll give you anything!"

Jonas moved Nigel sideways until they were standing beside the workbench. And he said, "Pull the cloth off those paintings."

Nigel reached over and gave a yank on the mover's blankets, and Jonas stood looking at *The Woman by the Water.* "My paintings!" he bellowed.

"Oh, no!" Nigel said. "Dear god, this can't be happening!"

"Get in there and turn on the light," Jonas said, shoving Nigel forward from the storage room into the office.

"May I sit at my desk?" Nigel said, and he concentrated on one thing: the pistol in his middle drawer. But the drawer was locked!

Jonas said, "Sit!"

Nigel recognized the hooded young man now. He was the panhandler who had come into the gallery just before he and Raleigh left in the van for the Brueger house.

Jonas was feeling omnipotent. He was in total control. He was powerful. He kept moving the blade of the knife twelve inches from Nigel's face, and he enjoyed the naked terror he saw there.

Nigel reached up and ran his fingers across the burn on his throat. He saw the bright blood on his fingers and said, "Sir, I'm hurt."

"You ain't hurt," Jonas said. "Yet."

Nigel's wheezing sounded like radio static, and he said, "Sir, I'm asthmatic. Please let me use my inhaler. I can't breathe."

"Go ahead, but take care," Jonas said.

Nigel drew the inhaler from his pocket, took two puffs, and held his breath.

Jonas looked at him and said, "Hurry the fuck up or it'll be your last breath."

When he could breathe again, Nigel said, "I paid the young

woman the twelve-thousand-dollar reward you wanted. I did everything you asked me to do. Why are you here now? Why am I being treated like this?"

"You and that cunt scammed me," Jonas said. "You made a special deal that I didn't know about. She gave you the paintings behind my back. Did she give you a blow job, too?" Then Jonas said, "On second thought, you wouldn't want one from a girl, would you?"

"Sir," Nigel said. "She did not give me my . . . I mean *your* paintings. Those pictures in the storage room are replicas. They're not the originals."

"Listen, butt-lust," Jonas said. "Don't talk to me like I'm straight-up stupid. I got eyes. Those're my paintings on the workbench. And if you wanna keep *your* eyes, talk to me like I got some brains in my head."

Nigel was weeping now and he cried out, "Dear god! Why won't anyone believe me?"

"Stop your bitch-bawling and talk to me while you still can," Jonas said.

Now Nigel didn't know what to say. How could he be logical with an obviously doped-out maniac? Everything he said would be rejected as a lie. He decided to say what the thief wanted him to say.

"Here's what happened," Nigel said. "Your friend Valerie came here—"

"Megan."

"Right, Megan," Nigel said. "She came here a second time. She said you sent her to give me back my . . . *your* paintings to complete our deal. How was I to know she didn't tell you about it? I assumed you were waiting for her in the car or something. Sir, I did everything you wanted."

"How do I know you didn't give her more money the second time?" Jonas said. "I know those paintings're worth way more than you said."

"They're not, sir," Nigel said. "I haven't been able to sell them."

"Have you tried lately?" Jonas said, eyes narrowing.

"No, I just keep them in my van in case a client seems like a prospect."

"You lie!" Jonas said. "You took them back to that same house tonight. I tailed you, you fucking rump ranger. You got something going with that house and these paintings. They're worth a whole lot, ain't they?"

The sweat had soaked clear through Nigel's shirt. He could only stare at the knife blade floating in front of his face. This gaunt, hooded specter with the menacing eyes would surely begin slashing him if he didn't say the right thing. He said, "Sir, that client wanted to see them again, but he said the same thing as last time, that they're not good enough. But I have an idea. May I share it with you?"

"Go ahead," Jonas said.

"Why don't you just take them with you? I'd be pleased if you would. If perhaps you could sell them and make a few dollars, more power to you. Would you do that, please? Just take the paintings and go. My heart can't withstand this kind of tension. I'm not a well man. I have asthma and a heart murmur."

Jonas said, "You got no shame in your game. So, okay, maybe I'll call your bluff. Maybe I will take my paintings back. But you're still gonna come up with something for all you and that bitch put me through. Now where's Megan at?"

It took Nigel a moment, but he could think of nothing to say except the truth: "I don't know. She didn't say where she was going."

"I think she did," Jonas said. "Your twitchy eye tells me you're lying. And I think she got more money outta you. But me? I got shit for all I went through. You and that cunt thought you could jist hoop my flow and kick me to the curb, didn't ya?"

Nigel opened the expansion band on his wristwatch, tossed it on the desk, and said, "Here, this is a Rolex. Take it. And I've got about a hundred dollars in my wallet. May I get it for you?"

"Yeah, get it," Jonas said.

Nigel reached into his pocket and removed his wallet, tossing it onto the desk next to the Rolex.

Jonas put the wallet and the watch in the pocket of his jeans and said, "The paintings're worth a lotta money, ain't they?"

Nigel sighed and paused and finally said, "Yes."

"I knew you didn't wanna give them back to me. How much're they worth?"

"Thirty thousand, maybe more," Nigel said. "You can get that much from any art dealer in L.A. Take them with you and go. Please go."

"Now we're finally getting at the truth," Jonas said. "So let's have all of it, you fucking pole climber. Where did Megan say she was going to?"

And that did it. Nigel Wickland decided that he was at the end of this night's terrible journey. There was nowhere else to verbally run and hide. He concluded that drug-crazed paranoia trumps logic and lie and everything in between. So he summoned courage born of despair and said, "I've got about three hundred dollars in the petty cash drawer. You can have that, too. May I get it?"

"Get it," Jonas said.

"The drawer's locked," Nigel said.

"Get the key," Jonas said.

Nigel opened a papier-mâché box on his desk, removed a desk key, and unlocked the middle drawer with hands so sweaty he almost dropped the key. Then he opened the drawer and said, "Here it is."

Jonas didn't see the Smith & Wesson 9-millimeter pistol until it was halfway out of the drawer. Then he took a wild swing with the knife and cut Nigel across the mouth, opening up a grotesque smile from the corner of his mouth to his ear. Then a flash and explosion blinded and deafened Jonas for a moment. Nigel had fired a round

next to Jonas's face that missed by inches. Jonas dropped the knife and fell onto Nigel's lap, grappling for the gun.

The desk chair overturned and both bodies hit the floor, Nigel screaming and Jonas screaming, as each had hold of the pistol. Then Nigel closed his bloody mouth over his assailant's ear and bit down, grinding the gristle, and Jonas screamed louder than ever. Then it was a test of strength as four hands tried to wrest the pistol free.

Drugs had reduced Jonas's strength by half, but he was much younger, so the struggle was even. They moaned and grunted and growled and occasionally sobbed as they lay face-to-face on the floor. Then, for a brief second when the gun muzzle was pointed up toward the face of Nigel Wickland, Jonas Claymore got a finger through the trigger guard.

The explosion inches from his head made Jonas's ears ring, and the blowback from the muzzle blast hit him in the face. The smell of cordite penetrated his brain, and the 9-millimeter slug penetrated the brain of Nigel Wickland after first passing through his twitching left eye, and that ended the struggle.

Jonas looked at the art dealer in horror, at the macabre bloody smile and the mangled, oozing orbit that would never twitch again, and at the skull fragment lying on the floor beside Nigel's head. He got to his feet, so weak he almost collapsed. Then he turned and ran to the storage room in panic, looking for a button to open the siding door so he could escape. He couldn't find it and then realized that, since the door had opened when the van pulled up to it, there must be a remote control inside the vehicle.

He opened the van door and saw the remote button and was about to push it and run to his car, when a single thought knifed through the panic. The paintings in the blankets, his paintings, were worth $30,000 anywhere! Nigel Wickland had said so. But he couldn't carry them in his VW, so he ran to the body, keeping his eyes averted as he rummaged through the dead man's pockets until

he found the key ring. He picked up the bloody knife and the pistol, both of which bore his fingerprints, and he ran back to the storeroom, opening the passenger door of the van and throwing the weapons onto the passenger seat.

Then he covered the pictures in the mover's blankets and placed both of them on the floor in the cargo section. He closed the door and, getting behind the wheel, pressed the button on the remote device attached to the visor. He felt a burst of elation when the storage room door slid open.

"I'm gonna make it!" Jonas said aloud, and he drove out of the storage room into the alley and headed toward the safety of his apartment in Thai Town.

TWENTY-SEVEN

Six-X-THIRTY-TWO was cruising westbound on Sunset Boulevard when Jetsam said, "While I was off, I got thinking about the Wedgie Bandit. You know the apartments by Ivar and Franklin? The white building with all the palm trees in front?"

"Yeah, I think I know which one you're talking about."

"I got thinking that the Wedgie Bandit lives in that building. That's why he strikes more in the vicinity of the library. He don't have to run so far to get home. I worked out a plan."

"What's that?"

"The next time we hear any kind of call about a four-fifteen man anywhere near the library, we haul ass straight for that apartment building. If anything jumps off, we're ready. I'm about the only copper at Hollywood Station who can ID him."

"You can ID the back of him," Flotsam reminded his partner. "He left you in the dust when he shifted to his fourth gear."

"The doofus can run," Jetsam had to admit. "But next time I'm gonna catch him. Losing that guy feels like a stain on my career. I gotta make it right."

"Okay, dude," Flotsam said. Six-X-Thirty-two is gonna be the unit to catch the Wedgie Bandit. If we do, you think the sarge will buy us a pizza?"

*   *   *

Viv Daley said to Georgie Adams, who was the driver in 6-X-76, "Don't rock the boat, Gypsy. I ate the world's hottest curry last night and my stomach's still reeling from the abuse. That's the last time I date a Thai guy in Thai Town."

Georgie Adams said, "Most Thai guys are no taller than me, sis. Didn't you two look funny together?"

"No, I got to enjoy the top of his head after looking at it all night. He had bad hair plugs, and pretty soon I started counting the hairs in each plug when I didn't know what he was talking about. He has a really strong accent, but he's rich and it was a lot nicer than my last date, with a class-action lawyer who pops up on Channel Five every other day with an offer to make you rich. But no more dinners in the Thai guy's 'hood."

"Why would you date a trial lawyer that advertises on TV?"

"We all kiss a frog at least once in our lives."

"Frogs, yes, cobras, no," Georgie said.

She turned the rearview mirror to check her lipstick and Georgie said, "Why do you always have to do that when I'm driving in heavy traffic?"

"You're getting very territorial for a Gypsy boy, aren't you?" Viv said.

Georgie was silent for a moment and then said, "Well, if you're dating short people with bad hair plugs, not to mention slithery trial lawyers, maybe you oughtta do something semiworthwhile for a change and go with me to the track next week. I got a few hundred bucks burning a hole in my checking account."

Viv turned to Georgie with a hint of a smile and finally said, "Okay, it's a date, if you promise to look in your crystal ball like a good Gypsy and pick a couple of winners for us."

A horny businessman on his way home to West L.A. from downtown almost sideswiped 6-X-46. His problem was that he was

ogling the streetwalkers who emerged after dark on the east Sunset Boulevard track. Two of the hookers were black and one was white, and they were dressed for duty in tank tops, short skirts or shorts, and leggings or nosebleed stilettos.

"This one's for momma at home with the kiddies," Della Ravelle said to Britney Small when she turned on the red-and-blues and honked him to the curb.

To explain his erratic driving he said to Della, "I'm sorry, Officer. Something blew in my eye."

After she'd written the citation and he was gone, Della said to Britney, "It's another kind of blowing he's interested in. We mighta saved him from a flaming STD, which would be hard to explain to the little missus."

Britney said, "Have you noticed how quiet things have been all week? Hardly any code-three calls."

"That's okay for an old lady like me," Della said. "But I know what follows quiet times. Remember where you work, kiddo."

Britney giggled and said, "Right, I almost forgot. This is fucking Hollywood."

Jonas Claymore was coming down fast from the methamphetamine frenzy, but there was still plenty of residue paranoia. He was in the number-one eastbound lane on Hollywood Boulevard, passing Grauman's Chinese Theatre, and he looked over at Barney the Dinosaur, who was talking to the Incredible Hulk, and both street characters seemed to be looking at him.

Narks! he thought. They're undercover cops. Then he saw Spider-Man say something to Darth Vader, and he was sure they were pointing at him. They were all fucking narks. He suddenly got so terrified he began panting. They wanted him for murder! They wanted to execute him! There were two cars in front of him stopped by heavy traffic at Hollywood and Highland, even though the traffic light was green.

Jonas looked toward Grauman's again. Now Batman was looking at him. Then a second Batman walked to the curb, and he was looking also. And pointing. They were all narks! Jonas Claymore pulled the van out into the westbound lane right at the oncoming traffic and sideswiped the rear fender of a Prius that had swerved just in time to avoid a head-on crash. Jonas kept driving eastbound and just failed to make the yellow light, and when the Wickland Gallery van roared into the busy intersecion, all north and southbound traffic had to screech to a stop, causing two whiplashing rear-enders and lots of horns blowing and a huge traffic snarl. But Jonas Claymore was past the famous intersection, and the stream of traffic had thinned, and there were no more narks dressed as Street Characters staring and pointing at him. He was heading home. He had escaped them all.

Six-X-Thirty-two was waiting to turn right onto Hollywood Boulevard from Vine Street when the Wickland Gallery van drove past, heading eastbound.

"Whoa!" Flotsam said. "That's the van that Nate and me checked out the first night you were off."

Jetsam said, "What was wrong with it?"

"Turns out nothing," Flotsam said. "The guy driving was a nephew of the owner, but the way I got it from Nate, he shouldn't be driving it anymore. Wanna check it out, dude?"

"Go for it, bro," Jetsam said. "Nothing else to do."

Flotsam sped around the traffic until he was behind the van and then turned on his red-and-blue wigwags and beeped his horn. The van kept going. Then he flicked the switch and hit the siren.

Jonas Claymore had been seeing so many hallucinatory cops everywhere he looked that he almost didn't recognize real ones. Then he heard the yowl of the siren and he looked in his sideview mirror. Now he was sure of it. They were onto him. They were

stalking him. They were going to kill him! He jammed the pedal to the floor and pulled out into the number-one westbound lane, causing all oncoming traffic to swerve right.

Jetsam keyed the hand mike and said, "Six-X-ray-Thirty-two requesting a clear frequency! We're in pursuit!"

After that, he gave the make, model, and color of the van, including the California license plate number. And then, over the din from the wind rushing through their open windows and the yelps of the siren and the RTO's squawking radio voice repeating the streets and direction of travel that Jetsam was yelling into the mike, Flotsam hollered to his partner: "Tell them it's got Wickland Gallery on the side of the van! I want Nate and Viv and Georgie to know who it is!"

The black-and-white Crown Vic suddenly skidded at Hollywood and Bronson after braking for the driver of a Toyota who they figured had to be deaf. And after the radio car got straightened out, Jetsam yelled into the mike, "Cargo van has Wickland Gallery printed on the side panels!"

When the RTO at Communications Division repeated that information, Hollywood Nate, who was already racing toward the pursuit, said to Snuffy Salcedo, "Hey! That's the van I checked out when you were off getting the nose job. Man, there's something going on with that guy."

Six-X-Seventy-six was one of the many units coming from several directions, all hoping to intercept the pursuit vehicle. The driver, Georgie Adams, said to his partner, Viv Daley, "Yo, sis! I think that's the van our boy Jonas Claymore was driving when Nate and Flotsam jammed him, wasn't it?"

Viv Daley cinched her seatbelt a bit tighter and said, "If it's him, I can't wait to hear his explanation this time. Hit it, Gypsy!"

Six-X-Forty-six, the only midwatch unit that was too far away to be racing toward the pursuit, was driven by Della Ravelle, who said to her rookie partner, "Damn, Britney, we had to get that call

way up in thirty-one's district. Those lazy bastards're probably screwing off as usual. I wanted you to get in on your first pursuit. And this sounds like a good one. Damn."

"My luck," Britney Small said with a little sigh of resignation.

Jonas Claymore decided that getting anywhere close to his apartment in Thai Town was hopeless. He looked in his rearview mirror and saw at least three cars with red-and-blue lights flashing. There were too many headlights and too many cops and too much traffic. He couldn't go fast enough to shake them. The yelping siren made it hard to think.

Then he thought of where there wouldn't be so much traffic at this time of evening. An area where he could abandon the van and escape into the brush and hide in the darkness where cops couldn't find him. And lately it was an area that he had come to know. He made a hard, sliding, screeching turn northbound on Gramercy Place and then turned westbound on Franklin Avenue. He was heading for the Hollywood Hills.

Della Ravelle said, "Hey, they're coming our way. Maybe we're not completely out of it after all."

"They'll probably double back and head east again," Britney Small said glumly. "With my luck."

The lead chase car, containing the surfer cops, careened up over the sidewalk on the north side of Franklin Avenue to avoid a bicyclist with no lights who'd darted across the wide street at midblock. When the black-and-white came crashing back down onto the street, the Crown Vic was lurching and nosediving. The tires screamed when Flotsam jumped on the brakes, but then he jammed down on the gas pedal again, and silhouettes rocketed past on both sides and horns blared.

Jetsam groaned and said, "Our shop's shaking like a shuttle entering orbit. I think I just got me another muscle spasm."

"Sorry, dude!" Flotsam said, cranking the wheel hard to the right when the car fishtailed again.

"I'm gonna try to parallel them on Yucca," Hollywood Nate said to Snuffy Salcedo, who once again cinched up his seat belt and replied, "Is this any way to treat an old man with a new nose?"

Georgie Adams was doing his best to stay close to 6-X-32 by riding in their siren draft, but he drifted back a few car lengths when they hit heavy traffic at Cahuenga and even worse traffic at Highland.

Jonas Claymore was beyond reckless now and he simply blew across Highland Avenue heading west with complete disregard for the red light and the traffic moving north and south. He caused three fender benders before he miraculously crossed the busy thoroughfare and kept going west. That slowed Flotsam and Jetsam, who had to weave around the traffic collisions, siren still blaring, and it allowed Georgie Adams and Viv Daley time to catch up.

By then, Lieutenant O'Reilly and Sergeant Murillo were monitoring the chase in the office. The lieutenant was almost apoplectic because of the dangers posed to motorists by this wild pursuit.

"Get on tac! Get on tac!" he yelled to Sergeant Murillo. "There're too many units involved. Tell them to drop off!"

But of course in a pursuit like this, with adrenaline erupting and endorphins exploding, the risen Christ couldn't have made them drop off, and Sergeant Murillo knew it. Still, he issued the order on the tactical frequency, knowing that none of his coppers would listen to a drop-off order at this moment. And they didn't.

When Jonas Claymore made the northbound turn onto Outpost Drive, he felt like cheering. This seemed familiar. This seemed possible. This was the area he'd been casing with that bitch that deserted him. This was Bling Ring country. This was the Hollywood Hills!

Della Ravelle and Britney Small were still driving east on Woodrow Wilson Drive approaching Mulholland Drive when they heard Jetsam yelling into the open mike that the pursuit had turned north on Outpost.

"No shit!" Della Ravelle said, making a hard right turn onto Mulholland.

The Wickland Gallery van careened north on Outpost Drive with three midwatch units behind it. And when 6-X-46 heard Jetsam yelling into the mike that the van was now turning west on Mulholland, Della Ravelle said to her young partner, "They're coming right at us! Unlock the shotgun!"

She turned on her red-and-blues and her high beams to get the Mulholland traffic out of the way of the pursuit that was coming right at them. Jonas Claymore saw those lights in the distance just after he passed the big house where he'd first stolen this van. He was hyperventilating and had trouble filling his lungs, and now with cops behind him and cops ahead of him he considered bailing out, but then thought, No, not here. He was going to bail by the big house where it had all started. Where he had first set eyes on this vehicle that was taking him to his destiny.

He made a sliding, squealing U-ee and was heading back down only a hundred yards away from the cars coming up. And then he lost it. He veered too far right and hit a large steel mailbox in front of a view home and the van went skidding left on a collision course with the first chase car.

Flotsam yelled, "Hang on, partner!" And tried to crank it left to swing around the fishtailing van coming right at them, but their Crown Vic was T-boned and got spun into a 360, crashing into a eucalyptus tree before coming to a steaming stop.

The van had almost rolled, but another eucalyptus saved it from turning over, and Jonas felt the hardest jolt he'd ever felt in his life when the driver's side of the van slammed into that tree, the hubcaps cartwheeling across the asphalt. And then he had to get out. He had only seconds. He crawled across the passenger seat. He could look out and hear yelling. He could see cops running with flashlights. His left hand was on the floor and it found the pistol. He wasn't going down easy, not for murder.

He took the pistol with him and bailed out the door and limped toward the brush, where he thought he'd be safe. Where they'd

never find him. Where he'd have time to wait them out and then go home. He had money. If he could just get away from this place. If he could get to a taxi, he could still make it!

But Jonas didn't make it to the thick brush on the hillside. He almost limped right into a small figure with a flashlight. He heard a woman's voice behind the beam of light yelling, "Drop it! Drop it!"

He didn't drop it. He raised the pistol toward the flashlight, toward the voice, and Britney Small fired her Glock from ten feet away.

Jonas Claymore saw the first fireball and that was all. Two of the .40 caliber rounds missed him completely but three slammed into his bony chest and sunken belly. He went down on his back, eyes open, and they never closed again.

There was pandemonium then, with Della Ravelle running to Britney, her shotgun pointed at the supine body of Jonas Claymore. And Viv Daley came running with her shotgun, and Georgie Adams pointed his pistol at the unmoving body.

Hollywood Nate and Snuffy Salcedo helped pry open Flotsam's door. He had blood on his face and on one hand, but he wouldn't get out of the car. He was yelling at them, "Get an RA! Now, god-damnit!" Then he turned to Jetsam, who was moaning in agony, his right foot trapped by mangled metal, and Flotsam said, "Easy, bro! Easy, partner! We'll get you outta here!"

It took both Hollywood Nate and Snuffy to pull and pry at the passenger door of 6-X-32's Crown Vic before they got it open, and when Nate shined his light onto Jetsam's right foot, he yelled to Viv Daley, "Get me a tourniquet or a belt or anything!"

By the time the rescue ambulance arrived, Jetsam was lying on the roadside and was going gray. Kneeling beside him, Flotsam waved away Della, who'd torn open a first-aid kit and wanted to tend to the bleeding contusion at Flotsam's hairline.

He kept saying to his partner, "Easy, bro. Stay with me. Don't

go nowhere, bro. Stay here with me. I ain't gonna leave you, so don't you leave me!"

The tall surfer cop insisted on riding in the back of the ambulance when they loaded Jetsam aboard, and he talked to him all the way to Cedars-Sinai, even when the paramedic said that the officer was showing signs of shock and wouldn't understand him. Flotsam remained outside the ER until Hollywood Nate and Snuffy Salcedo came to get him and transport him to Hollywood Station.

Before they were separated and before Force Investigation Division arrived at the station, Della Ravelle took her rookie partner to the women's locker room and said to the shaken young woman, "You have nothing to fear from FID or anybody else, Britney. It was an in-policy shooting, a good shooting."

"Funny thing," the young cop said. "It doesn't seem right to call killing somebody a good shooting. It doesn't feel good. I don't feel good."

"He's dead and you're alive," Della said. "That's good. Very good."

"He was my age," Britney said.

"And you would never have gotten a day older if you hadn't done what you did," Della said. "Now listen to me. After you get interrogated and after they say you can return to duty, you're gonna be treated different. The male cops, particularly the macho OGs, will pat you on the back and praise you and show you some deference. You won't get treated like a rookie anymore."

"Because I killed somebody?" Britney said.

"Because you've proven yourself to them," Della said. "Just go with it and smile politely and you'll find that your job will go better in this man's world we live in. From now on, you won't b female boot they make fun of. They'll respect yo you. Like it or not, girl, you're now an gunfighter."

*   *   *

By daybreak, both Hollywood Division and Beverly Hills homicide detectives had worked out what had transpired at Wickland Gallery on Wilshire Boulevard. Their reports said that Jonas Claymore, who had recently been arrested for felony possession of controlled substances, had probably been in a drug-induced state when he'd entered the gallery and caught Nigel Wickland by surprise in a blitz attack, cutting his face with a knife that was found in the wrecked van. There were signs of a life-and-death struggle in which Nigel Wickland apparently managed to get his hands on a Smith & Wesson 9-millimeter pistol registered to him. However, he was overcome in the struggle and was shot dead by the assailant, who then stole the gallery owner's wallet and wristwatch, which were found in Jonas Claymore's pocket after he was shot and killed.

Because an art gallery wasn't the kind of business that would be a normal target for this kind of attack, the detectives made a note that the gallery owner was openly homosexual. They surmised that because Jonas Claymore was a handsome young man, he may have had a past intimate relationship with the victim, a relationship that had soured and turned violent. The fact of the van having been in Jonas Claymore's possession on at least one other occasion when officers of Hollywood Division had questioned him tended to validate the theory of an intimate relationship between victim and assailant.

By the next afternoon, Ruth Langley, the only employee of the Wickland Gallery, told detectives through copious tears that she was led to believe that the young man who had borrowed her employer's van on the prior occasion was his nephew. Nigel Wickland had described him as a kind of black sheep. But the deceased killer's mother, who lived in Encino, denied that they were related to Nigel Wickland. She could offer no explanation for her son's bizarre behavior other than that he had been using drugs heavily and had lately been living with a young woman whose name she not know. Jonas Claymore's mother suggested that the young

woman had no doubt enticed her son into the drug use that led to his death.

Ruth Langley of Wickland Gallery could not account for the poster-board photographs of two Impressionist paintings that were found in the wrecked van. She told detectives that they must have been something that Nigel Wickland had picked up from one of the many art dealers he knew, perhaps to frame and hang in his condominium. She told the detectives that the pictures had no value other than as decorative art and that she would like to have them as mementos of her years working at the Wickland Gallery.

Two days after the murder of Nigel Wickland, Hollywood Nate Weiss went to Cedars-Sinai before reporting for duty at Hollywood Station. The floor nurse told him that the patient's mother and two sisters had just been there, and the patient's father had visited separately. She added that the police partner of the patient was in his room now and that the patient should only have visitors for brief periods of time.

She asked Nate if he was aware that the patient's foot could not be saved, and Nate said that everyone at Hollywood Station knew about it. She said that if he wished, he could join the officer and the patient's partner for a little while but added that the patient would soon need to rest.

Hollywood Nate walked down the corridor and was surprised that his palms were moist. He didn't know what he'd say to Jetsam other than something trite: "You're looking great. Are they treating you okay? Everyone sends their best. Is there anything you need? Anything at all?"

Nate stopped at the door to Jetsam's room to try to think of something better to say and he heard the voices from inside. He decided to listen to them for cues on how he should handle this. Flotsam's voice sounded somber even though his words were meant to be uplifting. Jetsam just sounded feeble.

Flotsam said, "Dude, I talked to the captain, and you don't have to worry about only working the desk when you come back. You'll be working in the field with me just like always."

"With one foot? They might as well retire me," Jetsam said.

"I been talking to people," Flotsam said. "LAPD once had a cop with one hand. He got it blown off by a bomb. He got a cool prosthesis. The gangsters started calling him Captain Hook. He was, like, kinda famous after that. And we had some coppers that got an eye shot out. They stayed on the Job and did good work."

"A cop's gotta be able to walk, bro. A cop's gotta be able to run."

"You'll walk. You'll run. I been talking to people about the kind of prosthetic foot they can give you. It's gonna be better than your old foot, dude. You'll be good to go. You'll see."

"My foot, it hurts bad sometimes, but it ain't there. They call it phantom pain."

"I know," Flotsam said.

"I wouldn't mind so much but . . . but I'm a surfer."

"You're a *great* surfer," Flotsam said. "You're way better than me, dude. You're way better than I ever could be. Why, I seen you do chocka backsides that nobody at Malibu could do. You're a crusher. Nothing can stop you."

"I don't wanna lay on the beach like a stranded seal and just watch," Jetsam said. "I wouldn't wanna do that."

"That ain't gonna happen," Flotsam said. "Sure, maybe at first we gotta take it easy. I'm gonna take you to Malibu every day if you wanna go, and we'll let the ocean heal you. The ocean is a great healer. And soon as you're ready, we're gonna get you that new foot. They can make you a prothesis that'll grip that board like Elmer's Glue."

"What'll I do at the beach till it heals, bro?"

"We'll bodysurf or boogie board."

"I ain't no booger, bro. Can you see me, like, sponging-in on a real kahuna and getting in his way like some snarky squid?"

"Dude, the boogie board would be temporary till we heal," Flotsam said. "Till we get our new foot."

"I guess the Wedgie Bandit's safe now, bro," Jetsam said.

Flotsam said, "Trust me. Real soon it's gonna be us two kahunas ripping like always. And we'll get that Wedgie Bandit, you and me. Don't cry, dude."

"You'e the one that's crying, bro," Jetsam said. "In case you didn't notice."

Hollywood Nate turned then and walked back down the corridor past the nurse's station, heading for the exit.

The floor nurse said, "Aren't you going in?"

"Not today," said Hollywood Nate. "Not today."

TWENTY-EIGHT

THE SECOND YEAR of the Obama presidency saw big changes at the Los Angeles Police Department. The Eastern chief had resigned and moved back to New York to take a top job with the private security firm that had been overseeing the federal consent decree under which the LAPD had suffered for so many years. Some said that his connection to that security firm had been a conflict of interests, but the fact was, he was gone for good.

The new chief was not an outsider, far from it. He was second-generation LAPD. His father had been a deputy chief. His son and daughter were both LAPD officers, and his wife was retired from the L.A. Sheriff's Department. Even his sister was a retired cop. They didn't come more insider than this one. He inherited the tough job of being chief in the great recession that had just about bankrupted the state of California, and the city of Los Angeles right along with it. There had to be lots of maneuvering of personnel, including sending a large number of officers from the elite Metropolitan Division back to patrol.

But there was at least one officer going from patrol back to Metro. One quiet evening on patrol, Snuffy Salcedo said to Hollywood Nate, "I went downtown and talked to a few people and I'm gonna be taken back as a security aide to the new chief."

"Is it my deodorant?" Nate said. "What brought this about?"

"Don't get me wrong, partner," Snuffy said. "I've really enjoyed working here at Hollywood Station, and it hasn't been too awful having you as a partner."

"I'll put that in my diary," Nate said.

Snuffy said, "But I think for the next few years, till I pull the pin and say adios, I should take it easy. And the new chief ain't nothing like Mister. So I see myself driving for him for three more years and then I'll retire and spend the rest of my life cutting grass and trimming trees like a typical Mexican gardener, except it'll be my grass and my trees."

"Was it stuff like the rumble at Goth House that made you wanna leave Hollywood?" Nate asked.

"Naw," Snuffy said. "It was fun tuning up Rolf Thunder, sort of. I even got a new and better nose out of it. It's just that patrol needs people who have real thick skin. Young people. So they can look at stuff like that baby in Little Armenia and go home and say, That's not my tragedy. That's somebody else's tragedy. That has nothing to do with me. When you get old like me, the skin thins out and bleeds."

"Who's gonna bring me homemade enchiladas then?" Nate said. "Tell me that."

"You'll find some other Mexican whose mother can cook," Snuffy said.

Nate said, "On this sad occasion I'd like to devote a few minutes to my own future. Would you mind if I stop by a house in the Hollywood Hills? I gotta see a director about making me a star."

"Anything you wanna do," Snuffy Salcedo said. "I'm just a short-timer along for the ride."

Nate drove up Mulholland Drive to the vicinity of the crash that had cost Jetsam his foot and Jonas Claymore his life. He stopped at the gate of a particularly large estate and pressed the button.

A man's voice answered and Nate said, "This is Officer Nate Weiss. I'd like to see Mr. Ressler if he's there."

The male voice spoke to someone and came back, saying, "Come in."

Nate and Snuffy Salcedo entered the gate, driving over the faux-cobblestone driveway, then circled around the fountain and parked next to the front door.

"Just be a minute," Nate said and got out.

"Take your time," Snuffy said. "I'll have a siesta."

Raleigh Dibble opened the door and said, "Good to see you again, Officer Weiss. Mrs. Brueger is in the great room."

Nate found her in silk pajamas and a matching peignoir, sitting on a lounge with a glass of wine beside her and a copy of *Cosmopolitan* in her lap. The music coming from surrounding speakers was Duke Ellington's "In a Sentimental Mood," one of Nate's favorite background melodies for any movie that promised glamour and sophistication.

"My, my, Nathan," she said. "You're even more handsome in uniform."

"Evening, Mrs. Brueger," Nate said.

She said, "It's Leona, remember? Can Raleigh get you anything to drink? Coffee, maybe?"

"No, thanks," Nate said. "My partner's waiting."

"Bring him in," Leona Brueger said. "Or her."

"Can't stay but a minute," Nate said. "The reason I'm here is that I've called Mr. Ressler half a dozen times in the last few months and only hooked up with him once. He said he'd be starting to prep his movie in February, but here it is March and I haven't heard anything. He hasn't returned my calls lately. You said you might be able to help me get this job and, well, here I am. Hopes and dreams, remember?"

Leona took another sip of wine and said, "Oh, Nathan, I'm so glad I'm not an actor. The truth of it is, after we got back from Europe, things went from bad to worse for poor Rudy. His investors pulled the plug on him and the project died, but he doesn't

want to admit it to anyone. That's probably why he's dodging your calls. He's scratching and clawing and trying to stay afloat, but the fact of the matter is, his career is circling the drain. He's drifting into irrelevancy, and in Hollywood that's Hell's last circle. A living death. I'm sure you know that the irrelevant are Hollywood's zombies."

Nate was silent for a moment and said, "I see."

"Aren't you used to it yet, Nathan?" Leona Brueger asked. "The rejection?"

"I should be," Nate said.

The phone buzzed and Nate heard Raleigh Dibble answer it in the butler's pantry, and then Raleigh entered the great room.

He said, "Mr. Brueger needs his heating pad and perhaps a back rub. I'll be in the cottage, Mrs. Brueger."

"Fine, Raleigh," Leona said.

After Raleigh was gone, she said to Nate, "My brother-in-law had a stroke last year but he's doing pretty well for a codger his age. I think he'd be dead without Raleigh. I can't imagine a more dedicated caregiver, not to mention that he's a fine butler and a divine chef. I'm so lucky to have him. I'll never let him go."

"Give my regards to Mr. Ressler, please," Nate said and turned to leave.

"Oh, he's gone the way of all second-raters," Leona said boozily. "He was only going to marry me for my money, which was okay with me until his limited charm ran out in Tuscany. I've decided not to move to Napa. I'll just drink wine and forget about making it. I think this house in the Hollywood Hills is a good place to grow old in. What do you think, Nathan?"

"It's a beautiful home," Nate said.

"Money is an answer," she said. "How soothing money is when we can't attain our real dreams. Thousands of failed actors will never know that because they'll never see enough of it."

"That sounds like me you're talking about," Nate said. "If I was

a method actor, I'd think of a grapefruit or something else I hate and start crying now."

"Why don't you visit me from time to time, Nathan?" she said. "Who knows? I might meet another director. Maybe even a first-rate director who could actually promote you. Maybe I can help you keep your dream alive. Would you like that?"

He was silent for a moment and remembered what this fire-proof aging woman had said to him when they'd first met: that in Hollywood everything is for sale if you know how to shop. Then Nate said, "Somehow I don't think I'm ever gonna see my name on the curb at one of the studios. Thank you anyway, . . . Mrs. Brueger. I gotta get back to my beat now."

Leona Brueger gave him a long look, and then with a sigh of resignation and sadness she said, "Bye-bye, gorgeous."

Snuffy Salcedo was gone from Hollywood Station on the next transfer. And Hollywood Nate found himself teamed with Flotsam again during the new deployment period.

On their first night together in early March, Nate said, "How's your partner?"

Flotsam said, "Dude, my li'l pard's not only ready to come back to the Job, he's ready to try out his new foot at Malibu. I am totally amped. We been going to the beach for months and I think he's ready to go for it. I know for sure he's ready to do police work, but surfing, that's another story. But if anybody can do it, he can."

At 8 P.M., a call was given to 6-X-46 to see the woman at a souvenir shop on Hollywood Boulevard. It seemed that the Wedgie Bandit was back. He'd slipped into the store with a clutch of customers, and when an attractive young woman was bent over a shelf examining some Hollywood memorabilia, he sidled up behind her, grabbed her underwear, and gave her a world-class wedgie.

Nate said to Flotsam, "Hey, I've had some thoughts about the Wedgie Bandit and where he lives in relation to the library. You

know that apartment building on Franklin near Ivar? The white one? Let's just post up over there and see who we find running home in a hurry."

Hollywood Nate was heading for Franklin Avenue when Flotsam said, "Dude, the Wedgie Bandit's a series offender. He likes to do a few jobs at one time. Maybe we should check the subway station. There's lotsa potential victims down there."

"I like my idea," Nate said. "Let's first check out the apartment building on Franklin."

Flotsam said, "Maybe he headed for Grauman's. All those tourists looking at Batman and Spider-Man? They'd never notice that little freakazoid sneaking up behind them."

The urgency in the surfer cop's voice puzzled Nate for a moment, but then he remembered the hospital conversation and he got it. Nate said, "Maybe you're right. My idea is dumb. Let's cruise on over to Grauman's Chinese Theatre. The Wedgie Bandit's probably there right now going after big game. Maybe the Green Lantern or even Darth Vader if he can get under Darth's cape."

Flotsam grinned in relief when Nate turned away from the apartment building on Franklin Avenue and headed west. He said gratefully, "Dude, until my li'l pard gets back, I gotta teach you some vocabulary so we can, like, communicate as equals, okay? Now to start with, a fibro is a surfboard."

"Fibro," Nate said. "Got it."

"Getting tubed is when you're inside the wave, right? So it might apply to certain things in life."

"Roger that," Nate said. "Getting tubed."

"A goat-boater is one of those donks that kayaks into our surf. So that's a pushy dude."

Nate said, "Never goat-boat the kahunas. How am I doing?"

"You're boglius, dude," Flotsam said. "That means you are one coolaphonic copper and it is rad to be sharing your shop for a while."

Nate said wistfully, "And I guess being a coolaphonic copper is even better than being a movie star the way you see things."

"That is rightous, dude. So, are you, like, finally coming around to that conclusion in your own life? Has the old acting bug been sorta swatted?"

"No way," said Nate. "It's just been on hiatus. I'm still determined to grow old and die in the Motion Picture and Television Country House. You can come see me when I'm there and feed me Jell-O shots. Just check my diaper if you bring fastidious people with you, and pour some premium vodka in my sippy cup when the nurses aren't looking."

"Whatever happened to your movie connection up in the Hollywood Hills? Where we dropped the business card on the butler that time?"

"Didn't work out," Hollywood Nate said. "I've seen *Sunset Boulevard* too many times."

"What's that supposed to mean?"

"Joe Gillis always ends up facedown in the swimming pool."

"He shoulda went to the beach," Flotsam said, "where they got lifeguards."

"Speaking of old movies," Nate said, "we'd better head for Grauman's Chinese Theatre right this minute before we're too late."

"Go for it," Flotsam said. "It'd be way wack and totally bleak if little kids witnessed the dude giving a humungous wedgie to Batman."

"And can you even imagine the shock and awe on the Walk of Fame," Hollywood Nate added, "if that fiend had the gall to give a wedgie to, let's say, Marilyn Monroe? Oh, the horror! Would it be scenery chewing to drive there code three?"

ABOUT THE AUTHOR

JOSEPH WAMBAUGH, a former LAPD detective sergeant, is the bestselling author of nineteen prior works of fiction and nonfiction, including *The Choirboys* and *The Onion Field*. In 2004, he was named Grand Master by the Mystery Writers of America. He lives in Southern California.

Contents

CONTENTS

Part III THE LONG VOYAGE HOME

Part IV VICTORY

APPENDIXES

List of Photographs

List of Maps

[xi]

Author's Acknowledgments

Yet again I must first of all thank my wife Ruth for accurately typing a fair copy of a much edited and added-to working script, for pointing out lapses in clarity or style, and for so ably fulfilling the roles of one-woman general staff and commissariat.

Secondly I wish to express my deep gratitude to Admiral of the Fleet The Lord Lewin, KG, GCB, LVO, DSC, for reading the entire typescript and making numerous criticisms and suggestions, and thereby saving me from many errors of fact or interpretation. I wish similarly to thank Commander Michael Wilson, RN, and Mr Dan Van Der Vat for their painstaking scrutiny of the typescript and their comments and suggestions; Brigadier Shelford Bidwell, OBE, for his kindness in commenting on the draft chapter on the Italian campaign; and Commander Sir Godfrey Style, CBE, DSC, RN, for his advice and help. The errors of fact or historical judgment that remain are entirely the responsibility of the author.

I wish to express my gratitude to my publishers, Mr Ion Trewin and Mr John Bright-Holmes, for all their support and good counsel; to Mrs Stephanie Darnill for her meticulous editing and compilation of the index; to Mr Alec Spark for drawing the charts and maps; and to Miss Katherine Bright-Holmes for finding the pictures, mainly from the Imperial War Museum (Mr Paul Kemp) and the Hulton Picture Library. To my present and past colleagues in the Churchill Archives Centre (Miss Elizabeth Bennett, Mr Victor Brown, Miss Lesley James, Mrs Sheila Clare, Mrs Marilyn Collins, Mrs Caroline Gill and Mrs Margaret Williams), I give my special thanks for all their help in various ways during my research in the naval collections held in the Centre. For access to these collections, I wish to thank the Master, Fellows and Scholars of Churchill College in the University of Cambridge.

I would like to express my indebtedness to the Deputy Keeper of Public Records, Mr Duncan Chalmers, and his Search Room staff at the Public Record Office, Kew, for their unfailing helpfulness and courtesy; to Commander David Brown, RN and his staff at the Naval Historical Branch; and to Air Commodore Henry Probert, MBE, Group-Captain T. C. Flanagan, RAF, and the staff at the Air Historical Branch for their valuable and freely given assistance, as well as to Miss Mary Kendall, Librarian of Churchill College, and the staffs of the Library of the Royal United Services Institute for Defence Studies, the London Library, and the Library of the University of East Anglia. I would also like to give my thanks to Mrs Joan Revel-Walker and to Mr and Mrs Alan Eden-Green who also helped.

The author wishes to pay tribute to his late colleague Captain Stephen Roskill's monumental official history *The War at Sea*, which remains after a quarter of a century unrivalled in its closely detailed coverage of all British naval operations. The author has also enjoyed the good fortune to be able to draw on the abundance of unpublished material in the Roskill Papers and other important naval collections in the Churchill Archives Centre. The author wishes to pay tribute likewise to the work of the late Rear-Admiral R. M. Bellairs and subsequent Heads of the Naval Historical Branch and their research teams in compiling the Naval Staff Narratives and Battle Summaries (now in the Public Record Office) from original logs, signals and reports of proceedings. These accounts have constituted an indispensable source for all later historians of the war at sea, including the present author. The author also wishes to express a particular debt to Professor Sir Harry Hinsley and his co-authors, E. E. Thomas, C. F. G. Ransom and R. C. Knight, for their magnificent study *British Intelligence in the Second World War*, which has placed every aspect of the war in a new light, and to pay tribute to the late Dr C. B. A. Behrens for her study of *Merchant Shipping and the Demands of War*, an invaluable and enlightening source in regard to the logistics of British seapower and Britain's oceanic economy.

The author is indebted to the following for permission to quote from private papers in their copyright: Mrs Philip Doyne-Ditmas for the letters of her father Commander Robert Bower, RN; Mrs Jane Smith for the letters and papers of her father Mr Hugh Clausen; the Earl of Cork and Orrery for the letters of his father Admiral of the Fleet The Earl of Cork and Orrery; Mr William Crutchley for the letters of his father Admiral Sir Victor Crutchley; Lady Cunninghame-Graham for the letters and papers of her husband Admiral Sir Angus Cunninghame-Graham; Mrs Sophie Forgan for the letters of her father Admiral Sir William Davis: the Rt Hon. The Lord Denning, PC, LLD for the unpublished memoirs of his brother Admiral Sir Norman Denning; Mr David Edwards for the letters and diaries of his father Admiral Sir Ralph Edwards; Vice-Admiral Sir John Hayes, KCB, OBE, for his own letters; Professor Richard Keynes, FRS, for his own letters and papers; Admiral of the Fleet Lord Lewin for his own wartime midshipman's log; Admiral Sir Julian Oswald, GCB, ADC for the letters and papers of his father Captain G. H. Oswald, RN; Captain George Pound for the letters of his father Admiral of the Fleet Sir Dudley Pound; Major-General Charles Ramsay, CB, for the letters, diaries and papers of his father Admiral Sir Bertram Ramsay; Mr Nicholas Roskill for the papers of his father Captain S. W. Roskill, RN; Commander John Somerville, RN, for the letters of his father Admiral of the Fleet Sir James Somerville; Commander Sir Godfrey Style, CBE, DSC, RN, for his own letters; Mrs Peter Thellusson for the letters of her father, Admiral of the Fleet Sir Philip Vian.

The author has made the most exhaustive efforts to trace all copyright owners of unpublished material quoted in this book, including taking advertisements in national newspapers, but in several cases without success. To these copyright owners he expresses his apologies, and his hopes that they will get in touch with him through his publishers, so that proper acknowledgment may be made in future editions.

The author is also indebted to the following publishers for permission to quote from copyright works in their control: B. T. Batsford Ltd for *The Battle of Matapan* by S. W. C. Pack; Book Club Associates for *Winston S. Churchill* by Martin Gilbert; Cassell plc for *The Second World War* by Winston Churchill; Faber and Faber Ltd for *The Nine Days of Dunkirk* by David Divine; HMSO for *Victory in the West* by L. F. Ellis and *Grand Strategy* by Michael Howard; Hodder and Stoughton Ltd for *The Right of the Line* by John Terraine; Hutchinson and Co. for *Sailor's Odyssey* by Admiral of the Fleet Lord Cunningham; and Lionel Leventhal Ltd for *Memoirs: Ten Years and Twenty Days* by Admiral Karl Dönitz.

Extracts from Crown Copyright material are reproduced with the permission of the Controller of Her Majesty's Stationery Office to whom I and my publishers would like to express our gratitude for being allowed to draw on the information in certain of the maps in Captain S. W. Roskill's *The War at Sea* as well as to quote from its text and reproduce certain illustrations.

Author's Preface

This book is first and foremost the story of the ships' companies of the Royal Navy in their service from the first day to the last of a six-year war. It is a study of how duty, discipline, comradeship and a quenchless sense of humour prevailed over extremes of fatigue and hardship, and triumphed over fear even among the worst of hazards. It describes how these qualities, allied to superb seamanship and a Nelsonian readiness always to engage the enemy more closely, brought the Royal Navy through the most dangerous crisis in its history and rewarded it with victory.

The heart of the narrative consists therefore in the Royal Navy's operations in all their varied nature and in waters from the Arctic to the Indian Ocean and the Pacific – fleet actions; desperate rescues of defeated expeditionary forces; unequal battles against enemy air attack; prolonged struggle with the U-boat for Britain's very survival; work of the little ships such as minesweepers; exploits of British submarines; and finally amphibious landings of ever greater scale and complexity, culminating in the invasion of Normandy on 6 June 1944. Into this account is woven that parallel struggle between British and enemy cryptographers for the priceless ability to read the other side's mind and purpose.

Operations then – the unceasing and ubiquitous demands of the sea service from the outset of the conflict – provide the keynote of the Royal Navy's war. It makes a striking contrast with the Royal Air Force's dominant theme of the gradual development of the bomber offensive against German cities, or the British Army's theme of expansion after early disasters into a mass citizen force. The contrast goes further. By 1943, when Royal Air Force Bomber Command and the British Army entered their period of largest-scale fighting and severest casualties, the Royal Navy had already fought its most desperate battles and suffered the majority of its wartime losses in ships heavier than a corvette, including all five of those capital ships and all five of those fleet aircraft carriers that were sunk.

Yet this is not a history of naval operations and their conduct in the narrow traditional sense. It ranges from the policies of Cabinets and Allied summit conferences to the design of warships, their armaments and other equipment; from portraits of political and service leaders to industrial resources; from national wealth to naval training; from grand strategy to inter-service and inter-Allied cooperation – and rivalry. It examines such questions as the dispute between the Admiralty and the Air Ministry over the use of airpower at the time when the Battle of the Atlantic was in its most crucial stage. It reassesses Britain's 'blue water' strategy in the Mediterranean and Middle East, and traces how the Americans were also drawn into it despite their own preference for a 'Continental' strategy of reopening a Western Front in France. The book also probes deeper, into the very nature of twentieth-century British seapower. For the purpose throughout is to place the war fought by the Royal Navy in the context of all those decisions (pre-war as well as wartime) and all those factors which determined where and when the ships' companies must fight, for what object, with what kind of ships and aircraft, and against what odds.

May 1990

CORRELLI BARNETT
East Carleton, Norfolk

Churchill College
Cambridge

NOTE FOR THE READER.   For the sake of clarity the narrative concentrates in due sequence on one campaign or theatre or main topic at a time, rather than advances chronologically across the board. Given, however, that the same ships fought in more than one sea area, the reader should be warned that it sometimes happens that a ship sunk in one chapter turns up afloat in a later chapter.

'Engage the Enemy More Closely'

*Nelson's last signal at the battle of Trafalgar,
flying in HMS* Victory *until shot away*

PROLOGUE 1918

'The German Ensign Will Be Hauled Down At Sunset'

At 7.30pm on 15 November 1918 – thick fog and pitch dark – an officer in the gold sleeve rings and stars and the prim wing collar of a rear-admiral of the Imperial German Navy came aboard the battleship HMS *Queen Elizabeth*, the flagship of the Grand Fleet moored in the Firth of Forth; his mission to negotiate the ending of the most recent of all the last two centuries' challenges to British mastery of the sea. As Rear-Admiral Meurer and his staff stepped out of the night on to the holystoned deck, they found brilliant electric lights glaring upon them – the first intimidating device in the deliberately dramatic stage-management of the occasion by Admiral Sir David Beatty, the Commander-in-Chief, Grand Fleet.

Two British naval officers wearing swords now conducted Meurer and his colleagues between lines of Royal Marines with fixed bayonets to the companion ladder that led down to Beatty's great dining cabin. Here Beatty himself, sitting beneath an old portrait of Viscount Nelson, Vice-Admiral of the Blue, victor of the Nile and Trafalgar, greeted Meurer with the question: 'Who are you?' Only when Meurer had identified himself and produced his credentials as plenipotentiary for the German Navy did Beatty invite him to be seated.

The scene in the great cabin was set with all the ceremony of formal surrender. Beatty – handsome, arrogant, an actor-manager's visage – flanked by his senior colleagues sat on one side of the baize-draped

[1]

table, and the tense, pallid Meurer and his staff of four on the other. Behind the German delegation, on chairs set back against the bulkhead, sat the two British escorting officers, with hands on the pommels of their sheathed swords. Beatty handed Meurer a document bearing in two columns the conditions to be imposed and the operational orders to be obeyed. Meurer asked for, and was granted, permission to consult his high command, whereupon he was conducted back through the Royal Marines and the blinding lights to embark for the twelve-mile journey back to his own ship, the *Königsberg*, through the midst of the most powerful concentration of seapower in history. Next day he returned, again in dense fog, to sign the documents proffered him, his attempted cavils brushed aside, himself visibly on the point of collapse.

On 21 November 1918, a clear day, there followed the climax of Beatty's studied drama. Early in the forenoon he took the entire Grand Fleet to sea, thirteen squadrons deployed in two great columns: 33 battleships (five of them from the United States Navy), nine battlecruisers, 27 cruisers and flotillas of destroyers. At about 8.30am the German High Seas Fleet was seen ahead, approaching in a single column headed by the cruiser HMS *Cardiff*. At the appointed rendezvous 50 miles east of May Island *Cardiff* led the enemy ships between the two columns of the Grand Fleet on the opposite course. When the two fleets were abeam Beatty made the prearranged flag signal 'ML',[1] and the Grand Fleet turned 180 degrees to take station on both sides of the High Seas Fleet; guards escorting a prisoner. As the two fleets steamed in three columns for the Firth of Forth at 12 knots, the British crews for the first time could observe at close quarters the great German vessels which had hitherto only been glimpsed as distant North Sea silhouettes or reeks of funnel smoke along misty horizons. In the van was the battleship *Friedrich der Grosse*, flying the flag of Rear-Admiral von Reuter (commanding the High Seas Fleet), followed by eight more battleships; in the centre, the battlecruisers that had fought so skilfully at Jutland, *Seydlitz*, *Derfflinger*, *von der Tann*, *Moltke*, and the newer *Hindenburg*; in the rear, seven light cruisers and 49 destroyers.

In contrast to the immaculate ships of the Grand Fleet, the German vessels made a depressing spectacle of failure and despair – gone the bright brasswork and shining grey paint of pre-war Kiel regattas, and instead tarnish and rust. On the neglected decks unkempt sailors casually leaned against the rails: the sullen face of the régime of revolutionary sailors' councils that had ruled the ships since that mutiny of the High Seas Fleet on 3 November which had precipitated the final collapse of Imperial Germany and the ending of the Great War.

At 11am Beatty made a signal to Rear-Admiral von Reuter: 'The German Flag will be hauled down at sunset today, Thursday, and will not be hoisted again without permission.'[2] That evening, with both fleets at anchor in the Firth of Forth and as British buglers sounded the call of 'Sunset' across waters reflecting the last of the wan November sun, the Imperial German ensign was obediently hauled down. Here was the perfectly contrived conclusion to the Royal Navy's day of triumph; the quiet fall of the curtain on Beatty's entire stage-management from the moment of Meurer's first visit to the *Queen Elizabeth*. But the stage-management had a purpose beyond ceremony and celebration. It was intended to proclaim the triumphant victor taking the abject surrender of a beaten enemy fleet – exactly because Beatty himself well knew that such was not the truth.

The High Seas Fleet had not surrendered to the British or even to the Allies as a whole; it was being interned as part of the general armistice which suspended hostilities on 11 November 1918. And Beatty and his Grand Fleet had been merely appointed the agent for the Allies in executing the internment, which would have taken place in neutral ports if a neutral country could have been found willing to take the German ships. Nor had the High Seas Fleet ever been beaten by the Grand Fleet. Instead it came to the Forth as a prize of the national defeat of Imperial Germany brought about by the victories of the Allied armies over the German Army on the Western Front from July 1918 onwards; victories which were in turn the fruits of the grim battles of attrition in France and Flanders in 1916–17, if partly also of the Allied naval blockade. This was no aftermath of Trafalgar, then. Neither Meurer nor von Reuter was a Villeneuve giving his sword on the quarterdeck of the *Victory*. When Beatty had learned that the High Seas Fleet had mutinied rather than go to sea again, so denying him his last chance of destroying it in battle, he wrote to his mistress: 'The Fleet, my Fleet, is brokenhearted, but are still wonderful, the most wonderful thing in Creation and although it would appear that they can never achieve their hearts' desire, they preserve a cheerfulness which is extraordinary.'[3] Fearing that 'we are not going to win in the [Allied War] Council all that our great Silent Victory entitles us to,'[4] Beatty had urged that Britain should insist on the German High Seas Fleet surrendering to him as Commander-in-Chief, Grand Fleet, the capitulation to be signed on the quarterdeck of his flagship. But in the face of opposition from Allied delegates, surrender to the Royal Navy was emasculated into internment by a neutral power, later to internment by the Allies as a whole. It was entirely appropriate therefore that Admiral of the Fleet Sir Rosslyn Wemyss, the First Sea Lord, should write to Beatty conveying his sympathy with the Grand Fleet over the 'incompleteness' of the victory.[5]

Yet this incompleteness, so successfully masked by Beatty's stage-management of the German internment, went much deeper than a failure to destroy the enemy fleet in Nelsonian style in battle. Despite all the seamanship, courage and endurance of the ships' companies, the Royal Navy's record during the Great War as a whole was tarnished by doubts about the professional abilities of its officer corps; about its staff work and doctrine; about the technology of its ships, weapons and equipment. More deeply still, the course of the war had put in question the very strategic and economic basis of the worldwide oceanic trading empire which British seapower had grown up to protect.

From 1904, when the fast expanding Imperial German Navy was first perceived by the Admiralty as the major threat Britain now had to face, British naval policy had been obsessed with outbuilding the Germans in 'Dreadnought' battleships (with all-big-gun main armaments) and battlecruisers, so that in a war Britain could bring overwhelming strength to bear in the expected decisive battle for naval mastery with the German High Seas Fleet in the North Sea. When the Great War broke out in 1914, Britain had won this building race, with the Royal Navy outnumbering its opponent by 24 modern battleships to sixteen, and with four more under construction, as compared to Germany's three; in battlecruisers it outnumbered the Imperial German Navy by nine ships to five.[6] Not surprisingly, therefore, the High Seas Fleet showed no eagerness to encounter such odds in open battle, preferring diversionary sorties in the hope of catching and destroying a detached portion of the Grand Fleet. Although after the outbreak of war British seapower quickly swept the world's seas clear of German shipping, and in a matter of months caught and sank Admiral Graf von Spee's squadron of cruisers in the southern oceans, the Grand Fleet itself had remained an impotent spectator during the decisive land campaigns of 1914 on the Western and Eastern Fronts that shaped the future anatomy of the conflict. It was proof of the limitations of seapower in a struggle against a great continental state.

Not until 31 May 1916 had the Royal Navy been offered the chance of realising its dream of a steam-driven Trafalgar in which British seamanship and British broadsides would annihilate the upstart High Seas Fleet. For the plan of the German Commander-in-Chief, Admiral Reinhard Scheer, to entice part of the Grand Fleet into a trap went wrong and instead Admiral Sir John Jellicoe, the British C-in-C, brought him to battle at Jutland with 28 battleships to sixteen and nine battlecruisers to five. Yet the results of the encounter proved so discreditable to the Royal Navy that dispute over who or what was responsible for the failure to destroy Scheer was to smoulder on for decades. The Battle of Jutland put the entire British naval system to proof and failed it.

In the first place the tally of losses told heavily in German favour. The High Seas Fleet sank 111,980 tons of British warships and inflicted casualties of 6,945. The Grand Fleet sank only 62,233 tons of German ships (including a badly damaged battlecruiser later sunk by the Germans themselves) and inflicted casualties of 2,921.[7] In the preliminary action between Admiral Beatty's Battle Cruiser Fleet of six battlecruisers and four fast and powerful Queen Elizabeth class battleships and the five battlecruisers of Admiral Hipper's Scouting Group One, Beatty had lost two battlecruisers blown up; Hipper none. Whereas Hipper's ships scored 52 hits, Beatty's scored only 32.[8] In the main encounter of the fleets later that day, another British battlecruiser (*Invincible*) was also blown up and sank instantly. Although the German battlecruisers took the most appalling cumulative punishment in the course of the battlecruiser action and then in the fleet battle (*Lützow* sustained 22 heavy shell hits), none sank in action. No wonder Beatty observed to his flag captain as he saw the *Queen Mary* explode and vanish under a pall of smoke: 'Chatfield, there seems to be something wrong with our bloody ships today.'[9]

The blatantly adverse balance of material and human loss at Jutland led to exhaustive investigations and discussions by the Admiralty, and has been the subject of detailed researches by distinguished naval historians ever since.[10] The cumulative results of these investigations show that in every particular British naval technology was inferior to German.

Because of the mistaken belief that speed and gunpower were more important than protection, British battlecruisers were much more lightly armoured than the Germans': *Queen Mary*, for example, displaced 27,000 tons as against the 24,000 of *Seydlitz*, yet carried only 3,900 tons of armour compared to the German ship's 5,200 tons. A 6- to 9-inch armoured belt amidships on British battlecruisers (depending on the 'vintage') compared with a 9¾- to 13-inch belt on

German.[11] The British battlecruisers were particularly vulnerable to plunging fire striking the upper side of the hull or the deck, and it is believed that all three sunk at Jutland succumbed to closely grouped salvoes of this kind; the effect probably being made the more instantly catastrophic in at least one instance by a flash down into a magazine from a cordite fire in a turret. Firing tests after the war against the armour plate of the German battleship *Baden* suggested that German plate was in any case superior in resistant quality to British.[12]

Such German superiority in quality of armour only served to accentuate the consequences of another British technological short-coming – in the armour-piercing shell and its burster. British steel (made by the ordinary open-hearth process) was inferior to German (made in electric crucibles) and tended to break up on first striking armour plate. Moreover, the British burster, amatol, was more un-stable than TNT, the German burster, and tended to explode prema-turely on impact. British guns and shells, taken together, possessed poorer ballistic qualities than the German, because the steel from which British guns were manufactured and the method of fabrication were both inferior to German. Even before the war it had been Admiral Jellicoe's opinion, as Controller of the Navy, that German guns, though lighter and smaller in calibre than their British equiva-lents, performed better in all respects.[13]

Yet British inferiority in armour, guns and ammunition does not supply the whole explanation of why the balance sheet of losses so favoured the High Seas Fleet. The High Seas Fleet had shot more accurately too, partly because of its own superb stereoscopic range-finders, but mostly because the British Admiralty before the war had refused to adopt a revolutionary fire control system designed by Arthur Pollen, a brilliant young inventor. His 'Argo Clock' produced constantly updated ranges and bearings of the enemy, and automati-cally corrected them for the changes in both its own and the target ships' courses and speeds during the flight of the shell; in other words, it was a mechanical analogue computer.[14] It had been eventually rejected by the Admiralty in 1908 without a final trial, in favour of a more elementary system designed by a naval officer in imitation of Pollen's invention; an example of the 'Not Invented Here' syndrome which says much about the closed institutional mind of the Navy 'Establishment' in this era.[15] Had all British capital ships been equipped with Pollen's 'Argo Clock' at Jutland, so ensuring swift target acquisition and accurate ranging throughout all the alterations of course made by the two fleets, the outcome of the intermittent salvoes amid the mists might after all have been that destruction of the High Seas Fleet by sheer weight of numbers for which the Royal Navy pined.

Yet defective technology, reflecting the scientific and technical backwardness of British industry, was not the only ingredient in the British failure to annihilate at Jutland. During Britain's post-Trafalgar mastery of the oceans in the tranquil decades of the Victorian peace, the Royal Navy's whole system of command and control, its doctrines and its style of leadership, had become the reverse of Nelsonian. Efficiency came to mean precisely executed but unrealistic evolutions – the naval equivalent of parade-ground drill: it came to mean ships as bright as a Life Guard's breastplate, even if gunnery practice, so dirtying to the decks, had thereby to suffer. The ten years of breakneck modernisation and reorganisation begun after 1904 by the ruthless Admiral Sir John Fisher as First Sea Lord did much to jerk the Royal Navy from a kind of exclusive yacht club into a modern fighting service: manoeuvres became more realistic; the range at which gunnery was practical lengthened from 2,000 yards in the 1890s to 14,000 yards just before the Great War.

Yet the reforms were too short-lived to be more than superficial. In 1914 the Royal Navy still remained wedded to a discipline more rigid and authoritarian than that of the Prussian army; its concept of command and leadership was still based on the principle of blind obedience to orders and unquestioned deference to the wisdom of superiors. As a result, initiative was extinguished in favour of all-pervasive centralisation of decision. This reached its apogee in the Grand Fleet at Jutland, when Jellicoe tried to control the whole fleet from the flagship *Iron Duke*; and momentary opportunities to engage the High Seas Fleet as it sought an escape route home were missed because those British ships or squadrons which actually sighted the enemy shrank from acting without orders. Such extreme centralisation naturally entailed a dense traffic of signals from a flagship: in the case of Jellicoe's *Iron Duke* at Jutland, one flag signal every 1.7 minutes during the daylight action; in the case of Beatty's *Lion* one every 2.4 minutes.[16]

The same authoritarian belief that all thinking and all decision should be vested in one man at the top had also led to the Royal Navy's stubborn opposition to the creation of a general staff (that Prussian innovation for the collective management of modern war which every European army had adopted long before the Great War) and to the accompanying neglect of proper staff training and higher professional education. Not until 1912 had the Naval War Staff been set up (and even then with less power and responsibility than its military equivalent, the Imperial General Staff), together with an embryo Staff College. The Navy still remained essentially true to the tradition of the God-given authority of 'salt-horse' admirals who had learned their trade by successively driving ships, squadrons and fleets – self-educated 'practical' men. The Admiralty therefore entered the Great War without any comprehensive and pondered strategy for waging it, relying instead on such obvious expedients as blockading Germany (in the event damaging to the German war economy) or seeking to bring the High Seas Fleet to battle, or such wild notions as landing an expeditionary force on Germany's Baltic coast.

The want of a well-run-in staff system at the Admiralty, and the trained and experienced staff minds to work it properly, was tragically displayed during the Jutland battle, when the Operations Division, in its contempt for the work of the Intelligence staff of 'Room 40', either passed on to Jellicoe misleadingly incomplete versions of signals intelligence obtained by Room 40's decrypting of German radio traffic or failed to pass vital decrypted signals on at all. In particular this denied Jellicoe exact information about the High Seas Fleet's escape course for home on the night after the battle.[17] The lack of fruitful cooperation between the Operations Division and Room 40 was the more lamentable in that Room 40's performance under Admiral 'Blinker' Hall in intercepting and deciphering German radio traffic rendered it one of the outstandingly brilliant facets of the wartime Royal Navy.[18]

Because the Admiralty had no corporate brain capable of thorough intellectual analysis of strategic and operational problems, Britain very nearly lost the war altogether in the first half of 1917. Germany's sink-at-sight U-boat campaign against Allied and also neutral shipping (in designated war zones) caused such colossal and rising losses of merchant ships as to threaten Britain with imminent starvation and the stoppage of her war industries. In the event it was not the High Seas Fleet and its great battleships, on which the Royal Navy's anxious eyes had been so long focused, that proved to be the mortal danger to Britain, but some 100 frail submersible craft manned by only 5,000 German sailors. By April 1917, a month when nearly 900,000 tons of merchant shipping were lost, this tiny fraction of the German war effort had brought the world's greatest seapower within sight of total national catastrophe, for the Admiralty had absolutely no idea how to defeat the U-boat, since its own cherished expedient of patrolled sea lanes for merchant ships was so evidently a failure. Jellicoe, now First Sea Lord, warned the War Cabinet: 'It is impossible for us to go on with the war if losses like this continue.'[19] In the amateurism of its staff work, the Admiralty even made the elementary howler of wildly exaggerating the number of ships arriving and leaving British ports each week by counting in small coastal craft and cross-Channel ferries as well as ocean-going trade,[20] so proving to its own satisfaction that it would be impossible to convoy such a volume of traffic.

Only after prolonged argument, pressure from Cabinet ministers, and urging by Beatty (now C-in-C, Grand Fleet) did the Admiralty reluctantly and belatedly adopt the convoy system in May 1917.[21] This marked a return to the well-proven expedient of the age of sail against French (and in 1812–14, American) surface raiders. By July sinkings had dropped back to 500,000 tons; by September to 350,000 tons – figures which spelt failure for Germany. In defeating the U-boat the Royal Navy made its greatest contribution to the Allied victory in the Great War, for by so doing it enabled Britain herself to survive as an arsenal, a base and a source of armies; it made the Atlantic safe for the passage to France of hundreds of thousands of American troops month by month in 1918.

Thanks to the convoy system the U-boat's targets were no longer scattered abundantly along the sea lanes, but gathered into relatively few groups of up to fifty ships. As a result the U-boat found the horizons emptied of shipping; she might cruise for days without sighting a victim. When she did encounter a convoy, her limited underwater speed only enabled her to attack one or two vessels before the convoy drew out of range. And to launch an attack on a convoy invited immediate and deadly counter-attack by the convoy escorts. For in 1917–18 the Royal Navy quickly became the world's leader in anti-submarine warfare tactics and equipment, thanks to close cooperation with university scientists mobilised into the war effort and to new technologies developed in British industry; all a happy contrast to the record of the Grand Fleet. While lurking submerged the U-boat faced detection by hydrophone listening gear and destruction by depth-charges lobbed from the sterns of warships in convoy escorts or hunting groups.

Yet there was a revolutionary new dimension to this twentieth-century version of the old struggle between convoys and raiders – airpower. Flying boats and non-rigid 'dirigibles' or airships (really powered sausage balloons) ranged over the North Sea from bases as far spread as the Shetlands and Dunkirk, searching for U-boats as they cruised on the surface to and from their hunting zones.[22]

The Royal Navy had already taken to the air before the outbreak of war, when powered heavier-than-air flight was still less than a decade old. In December 1911 Lieutenant Sampson successfully flew off the forecastle of HMS *Africa*, the first of several such experiments. In May 1912 the Naval Wing of the Royal Flying Corps was formed; in 1914 it became the Royal Naval Air Service. From a strength of 93 aircraft and 727 personnel on 4 August 1914, the Navy's air component was to grow to nearly 3,000 aircraft and 55,000 personnel by April 1918.[23] The Great War was a time of groping towards the true future of maritime airpower; it witnessed prolonged debate over the proper roles and the most suitable kinds of flying machines; tension between a sceptical and obstructive old guard at the top of the Navy and a youthful generation of flying enthusiasts backed by a few far-sighted admirals, among whom Sir David Beatty was the most eminent and influential.[24]

At first it was believed that the rigid airship, as spectacularly developed by Count Zeppelin for the German Navy, would provide the ideal instrument of air cooperation with the fleet; a steady platform with long endurance for distant reconnaissance. By 1917–18, however, the emphasis had shifted to shipborne heavier-than-air aircraft, partly because of British technical backwardness in airship construction; partly because of the rapid progress made in fixed-wing aviation at sea during three years of war. In 1914 the Admiralty had converted three cross-Channel steamers into seaplane carriers, the seaplanes taking off by means of discardable wheeled trolleys and, on return, landing on the sea by means of their floats next to the carrier for recovery by crane. On Christmas Day, 1914, occurred the first sea-borne airstrike in history, when seven aircraft from these carriers attempted unsuccessfully to bomb Zeppelin sheds at Cuxhaven.[25]

However, by the end of 1916 the Admiralty had become convinced that aircraft with wheeled undercarriages, as used on land, were superior to seaplanes for fleet work: faster, easier to handle on shipboard. On 2 August 1917 Squadron-Commander E. H. Dunning made history by being the first man to land an aircraft on a ship under way when he put his Sopwith 'Pup' down on HMS *Furious* in Scapa Flow. *Furious* herself marked an intermediate stage in the development of the true aircraft carrier. Originally a battlecruiser, her forward main turret had been replaced by a flying-off deck. In 1918 the after turret was replaced in turn by a landing deck, but her two flight decks still remained separated by the conventional placing of masts, bridge and funnel amidships on the centre line. Although the first true aircraft carrier with a full-length flight deck, HMS *Argus*, was launched in December 1917, she was still undergoing flying trials when the war ended.[26]

Nevertheless, the Grand Fleet by this time was carrying over

100 aircraft in its conventional warships for reconnaissance and interception, flying them off turntable launch platforms mounted on gun turrets, as recommended in February 1917 by the Grand Fleet Aircraft Committee (one of Beatty's initiatives). These aircraft eclipsed Germany's earlier air superiority over the North Sea with the Zeppelin, now demonstrated to be slow, unwieldy and very vulnerable.

As early as 1912 pioneering minds had looked to torpedo-carrying aircraft as a means of sinking warships at far longer ranges than even the biggest gun. There followed in July 1914, at Calshot, a naval air station on Southampton Water, the first successful attempt to drop a torpedo into the sea from an aircraft. The cause was vigorously promoted by Captain Murray Sueter, Director of the Air Department of the Admiralty in 1914–15 and Superintendent of Aircraft Construction in 1915–16, an outstanding personality among the band of young, radically-minded naval officers who gravitated to the exciting new field of aviation. In spring of 1915 he won Admiralty permission for an experimental strike against Turkish shipping in the Dardanelles, and on 14 and 17 August that year three seaplanes from the seaplane carrier *Ben-My-Chree* succeeded in torpedoing and sinking three Turkish steamers at anchor. As the commander of the *Ben-My-Chree*, C. L'E. Malone, reported to Sueter, the operation had to be regarded as 'the forerunner of a line of development which will tend to revolutionize warfare'.[27] And in 1917 Sir David Beatty, as C-in-C, Grand Fleet, urged that a major attack on the High Seas Fleet in harbour by 121 aircraft from eight carriers (to be improvised from merchant ships) should be put in preparation.[28] Unfortunately various problems, most notably immense delays in delivery of the aircraft by the manufacturers, meant that the intended air strike could not be launched before the war ended.

In contrast, then, to the sclerotic conservatism prevailing in the traditional 'big-gun' Navy, the Royal Naval Air Service was alive with new ideas and creative enthusiasm, placing the Royal Navy ahead of all others in development of airpower at sea. Yet even before the Great War came to an end this British leadership in naval aviation had been touched with blight; its future already placed in doubt.

For on 1 April 1918 a third armed service had been inaugurated in Britain, in the shape of the Royal Air Force. This radical innovation had been recommended by a Cabinet Committee on Air Organisation and Home Defence against Air Raids (chaired by Field-Marshal Smuts) which had been set up in 1917 as a consequence of the light damage but vast alarm caused in the London area by raids in June and July of that year by German Gotha heavy bombers. Against all the other operational evidence of the war that airpower was simply an extra dimension to land and sea warfare respectively, the Smuts Committee fatefully argued that

> an air fleet can conduct extensive operations far from, and independently of, both army and navy ... the day may not be far off when aerial operations with their devastation of enemy lands and destruction of industrial and populous centres on a vast scale may become the principal operations of war, to which the older forms of military and naval operations may become secondary and subordinate.[29]

Thus out of panic reaction to a few small German air raids on London was born that fallacious concept of the independent nature of airpower and of its future capability to win wars on its own which was to exert the most profound consequences on British grand strategy and defence policy in the 1920s and 1930s and later during the Second World War.

It followed from this new belief in the independence and unity of airpower that, as the Smuts Committee recommended, and the Cabinet approved, an Air Ministry should be created 'to control and administer all matters in connection with aerial warfare of all kinds whatsoever . . .'[30]

And so, on All Fools' Day, 1918, the Royal Naval Air Service (along with the Royal Flying Corps) disappeared, its assets and personnel being vested in the new Royal Air Force. Henceforth the future of Britain's maritime airpower lay primarily in the hands of a service and a ministry holding the doctrinaire belief that an air force's main task lay in the strategic bombing of enemy cities, and that all else was secondary, if not actually wasteful diversion. Before two months had elapsed the First Lord of the Admiralty, Sir Eric Geddes, was already complaining that 'our fears as to the desirability of the transfer are being confirmed as time goes on. The use of aircraft with the Navy is not developing as it should . . . we do not feel that our particular and rather specialised side of the problem is receiving the attention that it should.'[31] Yet the new organisation was not merely causing short-term difficulties; it was also setting in train grievous long-term consequences in regard to the Royal Navy's own appreciation of the potential of maritime airpower. For almost all the Navy's bright air-minded officers opted to transfer from general naval service to the new Royal Air Force; men such as Arthur Longmore, Frederick Bowhill, Christopher Courtney, who would make outstanding air marshals before and during the Second World War. This loss impoverished the Navy of talent of which it would one day stand in dire need;

it served also immeasurably to weaken the voice of aviation within the Navy between the world wars, so allowing the 'big-gun and battleship' school to dominate the Navy's doctrine and development.

The Royal Navy therefore emerged from the Great War with an ambiguous, even contradictory, record. In the kind of sea warfare for which it had almost exclusively prepared – the clash of battlefleets – it had disappointed itself and the nation. At unforeseen and novel forms of sea warfare – against the U-boat and in the air – it had shown remarkable powers of innovation and operational effectiveness, even though this could hardly be said of the Admiralty Board itself. In any case the Royal Navy in 1918 was confirmed and strengthened in its historic position as the world's greatest instrument of seapower, with 61 battleships (including old pre-Dreadnought types) to defeated Germany's 40, France's 40, the United States' 39, and Japan's 13; 120 cruisers to Germany's 35, the US's 35, France's 29 and Japan's 26; 443 destroyers to Germany's 200, the US's 131, France's 91 and Japan's 67.[32]

And yet, and yet, even this colossal naval preponderance had not been enough by itself to guarantee the security of the British Empire, that global scatter under the Union Flag of colonies and dominions, of protectorates and bases, of islands and continents and portions of continents. To meet the German challenge after 1904 Admiral of the Fleet Sir John Fisher, as First Sea Lord, had thinned out Britain's distant fleets and squadrons – in the Far East and Pacific, even the Mediterranean – in order to concentrate in home waters. During the Great War it was the French Navy which had been largely responsible for securing the Mediterranean, that key to the imperial route to India via the Suez Canal, while the Imperial Japanese Navy (thanks to the Anglo-Japanese Alliance of 1902) had been responsible for the Far East and Pacific, even escorting Australian and New Zealand troop convoys to the European theatre.

The various countries of the British Empire themselves were quite incapable of their own defence. The white dominions – Canada, South Africa, Australia and New Zealand – possessed only small citizen armies with which to protect vast territories; and only tiny navies, the largest, the Royal Australian Navy, numbered one battle-cruiser, four light cruisers and three destroyers. India had no navy to defend her long coastlines; and even during the war had swallowed a garrison of 15,000 British soldiers. Far from being the massive buttress of British power the British people believed it to be, the Empire was in reality appallingly vulnerable and dependent on Britain.

This was a truth obscured by the particular pattern of the Great

War. It was a European war; the Mother Country, not the dominions or India or the colonies, had lain under attack. The Empire had therefore been free to send its forces overseas to Britain's succour in her fight with Germany. But if, through a future shift in the world strategic balance, this lucky pattern of the Great War was not repeated, and the Empire and its vital sea routes – in the Far East and Pacific; in the Mediterranean – came under direct threat at the same time as Britain, then the Empire (and especially Australia and New Zealand, 10,000 miles away from the Mother Country) would represent not a limited source of strength to Britain, but an immense source of weakness and, above all, an insoluble strategic problem for the Admiralty. As the Australian Prime Minister, Billy Hughes, was to tell the 1921 Imperial Conference:

> Look at the map and ask yourselves what would have happened to that great splash of red down from India through Australia to New Zealand, but for the Anglo-Japanese Treaty. How much of these great rich territories and portions of our Empire would have escaped had Japan been neutral? How much if she had been our enemy? It is certain the naval power of the Empire could not have saved India and Australia and still been strong enough to hold Germany bottled up in the narrow seas . . .[33]

If the Great War, with all its pride and propaganda about the Empire's contribution to victory, had concealed from the British that the Empire was a potential drain on British strength, a cause of strategic overstretch, it had all too brutally demonstrated the United Kingdom's own vulnerability as an island and commercial power dependent for survival on ships steaming to and from the ports of the globe; a vulnerability especially as compared with continental economies with safe internal land communications such as the United States and Germany. After all, even with only a single major naval foe to cope with, and powerful allies at sea, the Royal Navy had only narrowly averted national starvation and the collapse of British war industry at the hands of the U-boat. In the high Victorian era of Free Trade and unchallenged British naval mastery, the pattern of island Britain at the centre of an oceanic world economy had seemed the very secret of Britain's industrial and commercial success. Now in a different world it rendered Britain's existence more precarious than that of any other great power.

Yet in the aftermath of victory and the beginning of a new era (as men hoped and believed) of peace and prosperity, such gloomy analyses were far from British minds. On 21 June 1919 even the physical relics of the German naval challenge vanished when the High

Seas Fleet was defiantly scuttled by its own crews in its last place of internment in Scapa Flow. A week later the hapless German delegation to the Paris Peace Conference signed the Treaty of Versailles in the Hall of Mirrors in the Palace of Versailles; a treaty which limited the future German Navy to six obsolete small battleships, six light cruisers and twelve destroyers; limited new armoured ships built as replacements for the old battleships to 10,000 tons displacement; forbade submarines and naval aircraft altogether; provided for the demolition of all naval installations and defences within fifty miles of the German coast and for the destruction of the fortifications of the island of Heligoland, outer barbican of the German North Sea bases. Here, then, was the total elimination of the latest challenge to British naval mastery. The Royal Navy, overwhelmingly the greatest in the world, now cruised on seas shared only with the fleets of friendly powers; and Britain and her Empire had never seemed more safe.

Yet only two decades later this naval mastery had vanished, and instead the Royal Navy was facing the prospect of the hardest fight of its history. In June 1939, exactly twenty years to the month after the signing of the Versailles Treaty, the Chiefs of Staff spelt out the predicament in which the Navy had come to be placed:

> We are now faced with the situation in which we may be involved in a war against Japan . . . and with the probability that Germany and Italy will also be ranged against us. The question, therefore, at issue is whether, in existing circumstances, our defence forces are strong enough to safeguard our territory, trade and vital interests against these three Powers simultaneously . . .[34]

The Royal Navy, wrote the Chiefs of Staff, had only eleven capital ships ready for sea. Yet a fleet sufficient to meet the Imperial Japanese Navy alone would have to number eight capital ships: 'i.e., one less than the Japanese'. But in order to secure the European theatre, including the United Kingdom and its sea communications – 'the decisive theatre', in the judgment of the Chiefs of Staff – 'we must therefore retain at least six capital ships in Home Waters and the Atlantic. In addition, three capital ships are required to retain control of the Eastern Mediterranean . . .' The conclusion was plain: 'Having regard to the strengths of the German and Italian Fleets, it is clear that the despatch of eight capital ships would endanger our position in Europe to an extent which . . . would be quite unjustifiable.' Therefore only two capital ships could be sent to the Far East in the event of a Japanese attack – six short of the minimum needed.[35]

Here, then, were the mathematics of potential catastrophe; the outcome of a prolonged double process of reduction in the fighting power of the Royal Navy and of multiplication of Britain's likely enemies, old and new. And indeed the root causes of all the Navy's coming tribulations and enduring strategic dilemmas during the Second World War, of its worst disasters and most tragic losses, are to be found in the twenty years of national illusion, neglect and belated awakening that had gone before.

PART
I

BRITANNIA LETS THE TRIDENT SLIP

1

Dreams of Peace and the Shrinking Navy, 1918–1931

Even by the time the Versailles Treaty was signed on 28 June 1919 new anxieties, new dilemmas, had begun to confront the Admiralty and the British Cabinet; and at the root of them all lay the enduring conundrum of how a small island nation could find the resources to protect an Empire scattered across the face of the oceans and incapable of defending itself.

In 1914 the British national debt had stood at £650 millions; by 1919 it had swollen to £7,435 millions. Here was one obvious measure of the lasting drain on the nation's wealth caused by the Great War. In addition, Great Britain had accumulated debts to the United States of £1,365 millions.[1] With the urgent need to restore the economy to its pre-war prosperity, and to recover export markets lost while British industry was mobilised to produce munitions, it was little surprise that Lloyd George's coalition government looked in 1919 for huge cuts in government expenditure, and especially in the service estimates. At Treasury behest, the service departments were told to plan future expenditure on the basis that Britain would not be engaged in a major war for ten years; the beginnings of what became known as 'the ten-year rule'. Whereas expenditure on the Navy in 1918–19 had been £344 millions, in 1919–20 it fell to £154 millions, and by 1920–21 to £76 millions.[2] Worse was to come. In 1921 the post-war economic boom collapsed, and the heavy industries which had formed the foundation of British pre-eminence as 'the Workshop of the

[19]

World' – steel, shipbuilding, cotton, coal – lay in deep slump, their export markets lost to new competitors often with more modern plant and more up-to-date methods.

Nor was this to be merely a temporary recession, as was hoped at the time; it was to persist right through the 1920s when the rest of the industrialised world was enjoying unexampled prosperity. Moreover, the war and the new political and economic world patterns that were its consequences destroyed Britain's old position as the centre (especially the financial centre) of a global web of trade and payments; and in particular New York and the dollar began to rival London and the pound sterling. In the eighteenth and nineteenth centuries, British seapower and Britain as a trading nation had risen together to world supremacy: the Royal Navy had protected the trade and helped in the conquest of markets, while in turn the trade and the markets paid for the Navy. Now the opposite, downward spiral had begun.

In the wake of the 1921 slump the government appointed a Committee on National Expenditure under Sir Eric Geddes, which recommended ruthless cuts in government spending ('the Geddes Axe'), including the armed forces. It wanted the Navy estimates for 1922 to be reduced by a quarter, from £81 millions to £60 millions; a reduction to be bitterly fought by the Admiralty, but with only partial success.[3]

Yet at this very same period of straitened national resources and sharpening financial stringency the Admiralty was having to face the prospect of a new naval building challenge on a vast scale, this time from the United States, for Anglophobes on the US Navy Board were determined to destroy British naval supremacy. In autumn 1919 the Admiralty warned the Cabinet that if Great Britain failed to build new heavy ships and America completed her 1916 building programme (six battleships and six battlecruisers), then by 1923 'we shall have passed to the position of being the second naval power'.[4] Even the Japanese would by then have four new battleships and four new battlecruisers, all more powerful than Britain's latest ship, the battle-cruiser *Hood*, completed in 1920. But how could war-weakened Britain hope to outbuild the richest and most powerful industrial country in the world?

This was not the only dilemma, however, to impale the Cabinet and the Admiralty at this period. The Anglo-Japanese Treaty was due to expire in 1922. Should it be renewed or not? To renew it would alienate the United States, already antagonistic towards Japanese expansionist ambitions in China and the Far East; and this would hardly help Britain to reach an accommodation with the American government on naval limitation that would spare her the choice between a ruinous naval race and accepting that the Royal Navy must now take second place to the United States Navy. But not to renew the treaty would offend the Japanese, on whose goodwill and naval cooperation the security of the British Empire east of Suez had depended during the Great War; and whose potential (let alone actual) hostility would immensely add to Britain's intractable problems of imperial defence.

The British government was in the event rescued from both dilemmas by an American invitation to participate in an international conference in Washington in 1922 to settle outstanding problems in the Far East and Pacific, and to reach agreement on limitation of naval armaments. But the result of the Washington Conference was to weaken British naval strength while increasing the potential dangers to the British Empire. For the hapless British delegation accepted American proposals for a 5:5:3 ratio in capital ships as between the United States Navy, the Royal Navy and the Imperial Japanese Navy, with a total tonnage of 500,000 each for America and Britain and 300,000 for Japan. Even Beatty, the First Sea Lord, had by now accepted that Britain's historic naval supremacy was finished, and that parity with the United States was the best that could be hoped for. The Washington Treaty also limited the size of battleships to 35,000 tons as compared with the 48,000-ton battlecruisers then on the Admiralty's drawing-board. The two new battleships permitted to Britain under the Treaty, designed in 1922 and completed in 1927, HMSs *Nelson* and *Rodney*, proved ugly and cumbersome beasts, handling badly and unable to fire their 16-inch guns (all forward of the tower) abaft the beam because of the blast effects on the control tower.

Moreover, the United States proposed a 'ten-year holiday' in naval building (that is, with few exceptions no new building of capital ships whatsoever). Beatty fiercely resisted this, arguing (rightly, as was to be proved in the event) that such a total cessation of new construction would lead to the decay and disappearance of the specialised dockyard and technological resources needed to build battleships and their heavy armaments. He strove – in vain – for a slow but steady replacement programme instead; and warned that as British ships were already older than American, the end of the 'ten-year holiday' would find the Royal Navy inferior in fighting power to the United States Navy. He was overridden by the politicians leading the British delegation – Balfour, the Foreign Secretary, and Lord Lee of Fareham (an Americanophile), the First Lord of the Admiralty – in their eagerness for a settlement that would avert the costs of a naval building race.

Henceforward, therefore, British naval policy was to be governed not by changing strategic need, but by the 5:5:3 ratio. And the 5:5:3 ratio was purely arbitrary, taking no account of the fact that while America was a continental state with few overseas possessions and relatively little dependence on foreign trade, and Japan was a regional Pacific power, Great Britain had a global Empire and an enormous and vital seaborne trade to protect. So it was that only four years after the German High Seas Fleet steamed into internment under British guns, and as a result of a diplomatic defeat in the face of a far stronger American bargaining position, Britain had had to yield up her maritime supremacy and also accept a future navy of a size totally unrelated to her strategic commitments.

All this was potentially the more dangerous because of another treaty signed in Washington, a vague and woolly Four-Power Pacific Treaty between Britain, the United States, France and Japan which replaced the old Japanese alliance. From this time on, Japan was to figure in all British strategic discussions as the principal naval menace Britain had to meet. As Beatty told the 1926 Imperial Conference, whereas before 1914 the strategic centre of gravity had been in Europe, now it had shifted to the Far East.[5]

Nevertheless the Washington Conference was acclaimed at the time as a major first step towards the goal of universal disarmament. Such disarmament, along with the new League of Nations (founded in 1919) and its machinery for peacefully settling disputes between nations and curbing aggressors, would ensure that there would be no more war – or so believed the romantic internationalists, such as Lord Robert Cecil, Clifford Allen and Gilbert Murray, who now dominated British opinion. All three political parties in Britain during the 1920s were committed to faith in disarmament and in the League of Nations as the keys to the security of the British Empire.[6] This faith all too conveniently justified the cuts in defence expenditure pursued by both Conservative and Labour governments in the 1920s in order to limit the burden of taxation on Britain's lagging economy. Back in 1918, when the concept of a league of nations was originally under study in Whitehall, the Admiralty had warned that a covenant obliging Britain to take action other than for self-protection actually *increased* British strategic responsibilities, and might require a *larger* navy.[7] Such a commonsensical view was far remote from the minds of politicians and public opinion in the decade of peace propaganda that culminated in the Kellogg Pact of 1928, by which the signatory nations renounced war as an instrument of policy.

Indeed, British Cabinets even chose to neglect the naval defence of the British Empire itself against the one evident potential threat – that of Japan. As the Conservative Chancellor of the Exchequer, Winston Churchill (the pre-war battleship-building First Lord of the Admiralty, but now a Gladstonian economiser who successfully urged that the 'ten-year rule' be made permanent), told his Prime Minister, Stanley Baldwin, in 1926, there was not 'the slightest chance' of war with Japan in their lifetime.[8] The barometer of British naval policy in the 1920s with regard to Japan was provided by the rate of progress on the Singapore naval base, because without a fully equipped and defended base in the Far East Britain would be unable to dispatch her battlefleet from home waters and the Mediterranean, and would therefore be powerless to protect her interests and territories, or even exert any decisive political leverage in Far Eastern affairs. In 1922 Beatty, as First Sea Lord, had wanted the base to be fully operational by 1925, but Baldwin's incoming Conservative government decided on the grounds of financial stringency to proceed only slowly with the construction work. In 1924 Ramsay MacDonald's minority Labour government cancelled work on the base, putting its faith instead in the League, disarmament and a new international spirit of conciliation. In November 1924 Baldwin's returning government decided to restart work on the base in principle but not in fact, instead appointing a sub-committee of the Committee of Imperial Defence (CID) to report on the whole question. This sub-committee recommended postponing work on the main defences until 1926. In that year further modest instalments of construction were authorised. In 1928 the Chiefs of Staff, after further study, recommended more delays in the construction of the defences, partly because of shortage of money, partly because of unresolved technical and tactical uncertainties. Even the first stages of the defensive shore batteries were not now to be completed until 1933. In December 1928 the Conservative Cabinet agreed to a Committee of Imperial Defence recommendation that no work on shore batteries at Singapore should be carried out in 1929–30, during which time the technical and tactical questions relating to the base's defence were to be studied yet again. The base was now not to be fully completed until 1935 at the earliest – ten years later than Beatty had wanted. In 1929 the new Labour government stopped all further work yet again, in defiance of a warning by the naval staff that without Singapore the British Empire in the East and Pacific was defenceless. It did so partly because the Treasury wanted to save money, partly because a new naval disarmament conference was pending, and as the Cabinet Fighting Services Committee recorded, '. . . we consider that to continue the entire Singapore scheme in complete disregard of the possibilities of the Conference would be indefensible . . .'[9]

This naval conference, held in London in 1930, completed the demolition work on British seapower begun at Washington in 1922 and continued piecemeal by Conservative and Labour Chancellors of the Exchequer thereafter. By the London Naval Treaty the Labour government agreed to cut the number of cruisers from 70 to 50, even though in 1929 the then First Sea Lord, Admiral of the Fleet Sir Charles Madden, had warned that 50 was 'a starvation number' when measured against the needs of an oceanic Empire and a homeland utterly dependent on seaborne supplies.[10] In any event, Britain's actual cruiser strength had by this time dropped to 54, with only four under construction, as against the 114 at the outbreak of the Great War, a total which had proved operationally insufficient in the event. Of the fifteen capital ships permitted under the Washington Treaty, seven were unmodernised veterans of the Great War, five had been sent to the dockyards between 1924 and the 1930s for superficial modernisation (new anti-torpedo bulges; modified funnel and bridge structures), one (*Hood*) dated from 1920 and was already obsolescent (especially with regard to armour protection), and only two vessels (the battleships *Nelson* and *Rodney*) could be said to be truly up-to-date, even if of a flawed compromise design, both being completed in 1927.[11]

Thus the opening of the 1930s found the Royal Navy technologically obsolescent as well as truncated by treaty – no longer a war-hardened fighting service, but once again a kind of fashionable yacht club more apt for elegant displays of ship-handling and royal tours of the Empire than for battle; its old Victorian vices of social and technical snobbery, stiff hierarchy and spit-and-polish once more in the ascendant. The Royal Naval Colleges at Osborne and Dartmouth continued to instil unthinking obedience to superiors, while the élite gunnery school, HMS *Excellent*, avoided all painful analysis of the lessons of the Great War in favour of uncritical loyalty to tradition and a belief in parade-ground smartness.[12]

Worse, the Royal Navy now lagged behind where in 1918 it led the world – in carrier-borne airpower. This was not a question of the numbers of carriers themselves, for in 1932 Britain possessed six (including *Courageous* and *Glorious*, 22,000 tons, completed in 1928 and 1930, and based on the hulls and machinery of light battlecruisers completed in 1917) to Japan's three and America's three. The British inferiority lay in aircraft, with a total of only 150 obsolete aircraft of limited performance (and mostly gunnery spotters)[13] to the US Navy's over 400 aircraft, including 90 embarked in each of its big new 33,000-ton carriers *Lexington* and *Saratoga*. Moreover, both the American and Japanese Navies had developed far more advanced carrier-borne aircraft (torpedo-carriers and dive-bombers), together with heavy armour-piercing bombs.[14] Though all major navies still continued to rate the battleship as the arbiter of seapower and the core of the fleet, the US and Japanese Navies had by now developed a semi-independent role for the carriers as a long-distance strike force, whereas in the Royal Navy the carriers were still seen very much as an adjunct to the battlefleet, with their primary roles reconnaissance, air defence (though the strike role was not excluded), and spotting the fall of shot for ships' guns (the last especially the role of aircraft embarked in battleships and cruisers). In sum, naval aviation enjoyed nothing like the relative importance within the Navy in Britain that it did in Japan and America.

Part of the problem lay with the uncertainty as to whether the aircraft of the period really could sink free-moving battleships in war, as opposed to peacetime trials such as the famous occasion in 1921 when US Army Air Corps bombers under the redoubtable General 'Billy' Mitchell sank the interned German battleship *Ostfriesland*, a defenceless hulk at anchor. In all the major navies the proponents of airpower and the believers in the battleship fiercely debated the question right through the 1920s. In Britain it was studied by two heavyweight Whitehall committees, the Post War Questions Committee (set up in 1919; reporting in 1920)[15] and the Bonar Law Committee (set up in 1921 to consider the whole question of future battleship construction).[16] The evidence to both committees consisted more of emotional assertions by 'big-gun' admirals and airpower fanatics like Air Chief Marshal Sir Hugh ('Boom') Trenchard, the Chief of the Air Staff, than of numerate operational analysis. Although these committees pronounced in favour of a continued future for the battleship, the argument, feeding on further inconclusive trial bombings, smouldered on into the 1930s without being resolved – as indeed it did in the American and Japanese Navies too. But in Britain the debate was complicated and embittered by the circumstance that the protagonists were two rival departments of state, the Admiralty and the Air Ministry. What should have been purely technical and tactical questions became rallying cries in a fierce Whitehall power battle as to which department and which armed service should control carrier-borne aviation.

For the decision in 1918 to transfer the naval air service to the new Royal Air Force did not go unchallenged. Throughout the 1920s the Admiralty and the Air Ministry pulled and tugged at each other over the key question of how the responsibilities for the Fleet Air Arm should be shared between them. The matter was pondered at length by yet more high-powered government committees.[17] In the end it took an intervention by the Prime Minister himself, Stanley Baldwin, in 1926 to impose the final fuzzy compromise settlement that was to endure until 1937, though this by no means put a stop to the skirmishing between Admiralty and Air Ministry. Baldwin ruled that the RAF was to continue to be responsible for 'raising, training and maintaining' the Fleet Air Arm (as it was called after 1924), while the Admiralty was to exercise operational and disciplinary control over it at sea. The Fleet Air Arm's pilots were to be drawn from the Navy and Air Force in the ratio of 70:30.[18]

Thus the entire development of carrier aviation in Britain – ships, aircraft, weaponry, strategic role and tactics – came to depend on collaboration between two mutually suspicious departments of state, each jealously pursuing its own group interest and each with very different priorities, in contrast to the US and Japan, where carrier aviation was the exclusive responsibility of the Navy. To make matters worse, the Admiralty had abolished the wartime Air Division of the naval staff under a flag officer, and relegated air questions to a minor section under a captain. Not even within the Navy itself, therefore, did carrier aviation enjoy strong advocacy from an officer of authority, such as the US Navy enjoyed in Rear Admiral William A. Moffett, Chief of the Navy Department's Bureau of Aeronautics from 1921 to 1933.

Yet if the Royal Navy was technologically backward, its paint was fresh and its brasswork bright. When the pale grey vessels of the Mediterranean Fleet were joined by the dark grey of the Atlantic Fleet in some anchorage in the sun such as Gibraltar or Pollensa (Majorca) or Grand Harbour, Malta, for the annual fleet manoeuvres, the spectacle was magnificent enough for British seapower at its Victorian apogee. And this very reversion from the wartime Grand Fleet to the two main fleets of the Victorian era in itself lends emphasis to the neo-Victorian character of the Navy in the late 1920s and early 1930s, a character manifested by the routine and pleasures of peacetime naval life; the 'Upstairs-Downstairs' social divide between upper-middle-class deck officers and the rest, be they engineer officers, petty officers or lower deck, which showed little change from the 1880s. A letter from Admiral Sir William Fisher, C-in-C, Mediterranean Fleet, written on board his flagship HMS *Queen Elizabeth* in the Greek port of Navarino in 1932 catches the atmosphere perfectly:

> Nevil and I had a very memorable early morning partridge shoot in Cyprus – starting at dark and catching the dawn – chill – and then hot sun . . . Athens was a scream. Ciss and Ros going great guns and having arrived in *Briony* three days before I got there in *Queen Elizabeth*, they were in the big Athens society whirl when we met. Dinners, dances, night clubs, etc. Athens is thoroughly demoralised anyhow when the Fleet is there . . .[19]

On the China Station, it would be tennis and duck shooting and the fleet regatta; sundowners and supper on the veranda of the club; and even the lower deck would have their Chinese servants.[20] The Navy's ports of call as it 'showed the flag' round the world might have been chosen from a luxury travel brochure – Villefranche on the Côte d'Azur, Hawaii, Samoa, Bermuda – all of them calling for cocktail parties under broad awnings spread above white decks as the Royal Marine band played the latest popular hits; and for return visits ashore for balls and picnics. The duties of His Majesty's ships in this era of an apparently Victorian peace restored and of imperial power apparently perpetuated could include such heavy tasks as transporting colonial governors in full dress and befeathered cocked hats from island to island in the West Indies, with salutes of fifteen or seventeen guns being ceremonially discharged at every landfall.[21]

The actual fitness of the Royal Navy for the sterner purposes of defending British dominions and colonies, British trade and British interests, and providing essential leverage behind British foreign policy (let alone fulfilling Britain's limitless obligations under the Covenant of the League of Nations) was bleakly described in April 1931 by the then First Sea Lord, Admiral of the Fleet Sir Frederick Field, in a memorandum to the government committee preparing for the forthcoming League of Nations disarmament conference. While other countries had increased their naval spending in recent years, wrote Field, the British Commonwealth 'has accepted a naval strength which, in certain circumstances, is definitely below that required to keep our sea communications open in the event of our being drawn into a war. In defensive material, in the modernisation of ships . . . we are below the standard of the other powers . . .'[22] Field went on to spell out British weaknesses item by item, the worst of them being printed in his report in heavy black type:

The number of our capital ships is now so reduced that should the protection of our interests render it necessary to move our fleet to the East, insufficient vessels of this type would be left in Home Waters to ensure the security of our trade and territory in the event of any dispute arising with a European power.[23]

Field once again stated the naval staff's conviction that 50 cruisers was 'definitely insufficient'. In destroyers too the Navy was dangerously weak. In 1918 Britain had possessed 433, all of which had been needed in the Great War. The permitted figure under the 1930s London Naval Treaty was some 120. Moreover, Field pointed out, 55 of these would be obsolete by 1936. The Fleet Air Arm numbered only 159 shipborne and land-based aircraft, as compared with Japan's 115 shipborne and 296 land-based. Under current plans the Fleet Air Arm would still only number 225 aircraft by 1937. There were no adequately defended ports in the entire Commonwealth.

Field capped his dismal survey by making clear that the Royal Navy had not only declined in its *relative* strength, but 'owing to the operation of the "Ten-year decision" and the clamant need for economy, our *absolute strength* also has . . . been so diminished as to render the fleet incapable, in the event of war, of efficiently affording protection to our trade.'[24]

Barely twelve years had passed since that day when Beatty and the Grand Fleet had escorted the German High Seas Fleet into internment, and British seapower had stood at its apogee. And it was to be only four months after Admiral Field wrote his anatomy of British naval weakness that, on 18 September 1931, the Japanese Army began to occupy the Chinese province of Manchuria, in clear breach of the League of Nations Covenant and in brutal challenge to the faith of idealistic internationalists and disarmers that the League of Nations could ensure the peace of the world. The Japanese action marked the opening of a new era in world affairs wherein the harsh realities of aggression and military force would dispel the illusion of the 1920s that great powers like Britain could find security on the cheap by disarming and putting their faith in the League. But the damage to the Royal Navy had already been done. To repair it would not be so simple. It would take time and money – if there proved to be enough of either.

2

The Triple Threat and Belated Rearmament, 1932–1939

As the Chiefs of Staff remarked in their 1931 Annual Review of imperial defence, the Manchurian crisis had come 'out of a clear sky'.[1] Since under the League of Nations Covenant Britain was obliged in the last resort to join in military action to curb aggression and restore the status quo, she was suddenly confronted with the possibility of armed conflict with Japan – ten years earlier than allowed for under the current 'ten-year rule'. In January 1932 the possibility came nearer when Japanese and Chinese forces clashed round the International Settlement of Shanghai, so directly menacing British investments and trading interests in China. The Chiefs of Staff therefore made 'prompt enquiry as to our own readiness to face sudden aggression by Japan', and concluded that the position was 'as bad as it could be':[2]

In a word, we possess only light naval forces in the Far East; the fuel supplies required for the passage of the Main Fleet to the East and for its mobility on arrival are in jeopardy; and the bases at Singapore and Hong Kong, essential to the maintenance of a fleet of capital ships on arrival in the Far East, are not in a defensible condition. The whole of our territory in the Far East, as well as the coastline of India and the Dominions and our vast trade and shipping, lies open to attack.[3]

Given this state of disarmament, it is hardly surprising that in the end Britain limited her actions over the Japanese occupation of

[29]

Manchuria to voting in support of a toothless League of Nations statement in February 1933 calling for the restoration of Chinese sovereignty in the province. But when Japan simply walked out of the League, so dealing a shattering blow to its mystique, Britain began to pay the long-term price for having sided diplomatically against Japan. Henceforward she had to treat Japan as a live and ever-present menace to the British Empire in the East and Pacific rather than as a sleeping one. That was strategic problem enough – especially for the Royal Navy. But on 30 January 1933 Adolf Hitler became Chancellor of the German Reich, with a stated political programme of destroying the 1919 Versailles peace settlement, especially its restrictions on the strength of the German armed forces. In October 1933 the Foreign Office warned the British government that Germany 'was once more manifestly a public menace; the spirit of that country is worse than at any time since 1914'.[4]

The consequence was, as the Chiefs of Staff pointed out in their Annual Review for 1933, that Britain now had to face threats at both ends of the British imperial 'dumb-bell': 'The Far East . . . remains a potential danger zone, and its importance from the point of view of Imperial Defence has in no way diminished. But, during the last year . . . a second danger zone has appeared in Europe itself.'[5] The Chiefs therefore again confronted the reluctant politicians with stern realities: '. . . we should like to put on record our opinion that Germany is not only starting to rearm, but that she will continue this process until within a few years hence she will have to be reckoned as a formidable military power.'[6]

However, the Chiefs of Staff could at least take comfort from the good relations existing with France and Italy, powers whose fleets and air forces in the Mediterranean lay athwart the principal line of communication between the United Kingdom and the other end of the imperial 'dumb-bell', in India, the Far East and Pacific; and especially since, in the Chiefs of Staff's words, 'our defensive arrangements in the Mediterranean are in many respects obsolete'.[7]

By the spring of 1935, when Hitler openly reintroduced conscription and announced the existence of the Luftwaffe (both major breaches of the Versailles Treaty, soon to be followed by another, the rebuilding of the U-boat arm) the twin threat to the opposite ends of the British Empire had become brutally plain; the dilemma for British strategy – above all, naval strategy – deeply disquieting. For in May 1935 Hitler generously announced that he would accept a limit for the German Navy of 35 per cent of the Royal Navy. At the resulting Anglo-German negotiations in London in June the German delegation revealed what this limit meant – six new battleships, 44,000 tons of aircraft carriers, eighteen cruisers, 37,500 tons of destroyers and 17,500 tons of submarines to be built by 1942.[8] But such was the Admiralty's anxiety in the face of the Japanese menace that it reckoned any limitation on the future German Navy to be better than none; and it advised the Cabinet to close with the German *diktat* without delay, lest it should be increased. In the face of German rush tactics and blackmail Britain therefore threw away the provisions of the Versailles Treaty which prohibited the rebirth of the German naval challenge[9] – accepted that in the future the Royal Navy might again have to face German heavy ships in the North Sea and Atlantic, and the lurking U-boat, but this time on top of the Japanese naval threat in eastern waters.

As the Defence Requirements Committee (set up by the Cabinet in 1933 to consider all aspects of imperial defence and rearmament) wrote in its third report in November 1935:

> We cannot over-emphasise the difficulties of conducting naval warfare against highly efficient enemies in two theatres so widely separated . . . it would be suicidal folly to blind our eyes to the possibility of a simultaneous or practically simultaneous threat on both fronts; and if we do not possess forces sufficient to provide a deterrent this double emergency is the more likely to occur. If there is a danger from Japan at all, it reaches its maximum from the point of view of probability and extent when we are preoccupied in Europe. Unless we can provide a sufficient defence for that emergency, Australia, New Zealand, India, Burma, the rich colonies East of Suez and a vast trade will be at their mercy, and the Eastern half of the British Empire might well be doomed.[10]

No wonder the Chiefs of Staff in their Annual Review in April that same year had anxiously reminded the Foreign Office: 'That should we be called upon to fight Germany and Japan simultaneously without allies is a state of affairs to the prevention of which our diplomacy would naturally be directed.'[11]

But instead British diplomacy now proceeded to raise up a *third* potential enemy, and, moreover, an enemy exactly endangering that main imperial line of maritime communication through the Mediterranean. The enemy was Fascist Italy, which, in the course of 1935, first threatened to invade Abyssinia and then, in October, finally did so. Although Britain herself had no imperial interest at stake at all in this quarrel, she chose to align herself against Italy in the League of Nations in accordance with the League Covenant and in the cause of 'collective security', largely because of the pressure of British public opinion as influenced by vociferous idealists such as the League of

Nations Union. The strategic consequences of Britain's quixotry were aptly summed up by the First Sea Lord, Admiral of the Fleet Sir Ernle Chatfield:

> It is a disaster that our statesmen have got us into this quarrel with Italy who ought to be our best friend because her position in the Mediterranean is a dominant one ... the miserable business of collective security has run away with all our traditional interests and policies, with the result that we now have to be prepared to fight any nation in the world at any time.[12]

As the Abyssinian crisis worsened, the British Cabinet found itself caught in the scissors between the demands of British public opinion that Britain should lead the League of Nations in 'stopping' Italian aggression, and the strategic reality of British naval and military weakness. It was indeed a grim irony that the very peace propagandists who in the 1920s had successfully urged unilateral disarmament on British governments were now in 1935 no less fervently urging that Britain take strong action (such as oil sanctions) against Italy, even at the risk of war. Yet the Chiefs of Staff had warned the Cabinet in the early days of the crisis that a naval war with Italy was bound to lead to losses of British ships, so that 'the British fleet, already weak, will be still further reduced. There is bound to be a danger, therefore, that the results of a war with Italy would be to leave the British fleet temporarily weakened to such an extent as to be unable to fulfil its world-wide responsibilities.'[13]

Even the prolongation of the Abyssinian crisis without war proved enough to swallow up Britain's available striking power at sea. In February 1936 the First Lord of the Admiralty warned the Cabinet that 'the position of the Fleet in the Mediterranean was becoming intolerable. Seven months ago we brought it up to war strength without mobilisation. The result was that the leave of large numbers of personnel was long overdue and many ships ought to be recommissioned.' He added: 'If a capital ship were withdrawn and paid off it would mean we should have only seven capital ships in commission ... we could not afford to overlook Japan.'[14] By May that year the Navy was indeed left with only seven capital ships in service out of a paper total of fifteen, which, as the First Sea Lord remarked to a Cabinet Committee studying the problem, 'was quite inadequate for any other purpose than the present contingency'.[15]

The flight of the Emperor of Abyssinia to London on 2 May 1936 and the complete occupation of his country by the Italians mercifully put an end to the British Cabinet's immediate dilemmas over the

Mediterranean. Nevertheless, Britain's half-hearted chivalry on behalf of Abyssinia at the League of Nations left behind another grim long-term strategic legacy; and again above all for the Royal Navy. For, as the Chiefs of Staff pointed out in their Annual Review for 1937, 'we must face the fact that, whether Italy is friendly or the reverse, the days are past when we could count automatically on a friendly and submissive Italy. For henceforward we will have to look to a rival . . .'[16]

Thus it had come to pass that Britain had raised up a *third* potential threat on top of those from Germany and Japan; and from a naval power lying astride the main British imperial lifeline through the Mediterranean. Could British diplomacy remove any of these menaces and so find escape from an otherwise insoluble strategic dilemma? Although Neville Chamberlain, as Chancellor of the Exchequer in the National Government in 1934, had urged on his colleagues the importance of making a deal with Japan at China's expense in order to restore the old Anglo-Japanese entente, the Cabinet would not stomach the idea, partly because of its own scruples, partly because it feared the scruples of public and parliamentary opinion. Chamberlain's later attempts as Prime Minister in 1937–39 to rid Britain of the German menace by offering Hitler a free hand in Central and Eastern Europe in return for a new European 'peace' settlement proved a humiliating catastrophe. His equally naïve efforts to ingratiate himself with the Italian dictator Mussolini were mercilessly snubbed.

As a result, therefore, in 1939 the British Empire in its worldwide spread still had to face the triple threat. Moreover, Britain had been unable to make a countervailing alliance against Japan with America which could have enlisted the United States Navy in the defence of Australia and New Zealand. Tentative exchanges with Washington in 1937, when Japan had embarked on a full-scale invasion of China proper (and had actually sunk an American gunboat on the Yangtse by air attack), and low-level naval staff conversations early in 1938 had failed to produce any firm Anglo-American commitment for naval cooperation in the Far East and Pacific. In 1939 the United States still remained sunk in deep isolationism; no comfort for the beleaguered British Empire there.[17] In the case of France, the British Cabinet (supported by the Chiefs of Staff, who were only too conscious of the weakness of the British Army and the obsolescence of its equipment) had dourly refused until the spring of 1939 to contemplate a formal alliance for fear of being drawn into a ground war on the continent of Europe. Chamberlain and his colleagues only recanted in January–February 1939 because a rumour that Germany was about to invade the Netherlands panicked them into at least recognising the somewhat obvious fact that the Low Countries and France were vital to Britain's own security, and more so than ever in the age of the bomber.

The gruesome plight into which British illusions and diplomatic folly had delivered Britain and her unfortunate armed forces by 1939 was eloquently summed up by the Chiefs of Staff in a memorandum that April:

> We are considering a situation in which we, allied to France, would be engaged in war with Germany and Italy simultaneously and when Japan would also be a potential enemy ... The British Empire and France would thus be threatened at home, in the Mediterranean and in the Far East at the same time, and it would be hard to choose a worse geographical combination of enemies.[18]

The strategic problem thus presented to Britain was the more desperately intractable because the various parts of the British Empire made such small contributions to their own defence and to the common imperial defence. In 1935 the New Zealand squadron of the Royal Navy possessed only two cruisers, while the Royal Australian Navy numbered an active fleet of no more than three cruisers, three destroyers, two sloops and a survey ship. The Royal Canadian Navy, designed for coast defence, comprised four destroyers in 1935 and six in 1939.[19] Even by 1939 no common imperial strategic plans existed; no common commands, staffs or headquarters. The truth was that as a peacetime naval and military alliance the British Empire did not exist, except for representative dominion ships and military contingents taking part in the Spithead Reviews and the London processions held to celebrate George V's Silver Jubilee in 1935 and George VI's Coronation in 1937.

From the Imperial Conference of 1921 to that of 1937 British governments under the urging of service departments (especially the Admiralty) had sought to evolve a collective imperial defence policy with agreed contingency plans and joint staff structures, so that dominion forces could be slotted into place under British leadership in time of war. In particular, the British government sought some formula by which the dominion navies could become pieces in an imperial naval mosaic arranged by the Admiralty. The British attempts utterly failed, even at the 1937 Imperial Conference, held in the shadow of the now evident triple threat; torpedoed again and again by the Afrikaner-dominated government of South Africa and by Canada under the premiership of Mackenzie King, a man jealous of Canadian independence and resentful of Britain's traditional domi-

nance. In every imperial conference South Africa and Canada successfully blocked any proposal, any form of words, which suggested
that the British Empire constituted or should constitute a collective
strategic entity.[20] Even a conference of Britain and the 'loyal' dominions of Australia and New Zealand on defence in the Pacific, held
in Wellington at the invitation of New Zealand in April 1939, resulted
in no joint regional command or staff structure, no common strategy,
although New Zealand agreed to man a third cruiser in the New
Zealand squadron and Australia to increase her cruisers from three
to five, while both dominions agreed to closer cooperation with the
Royal Navy.[21]

The minuscule size of these dominion navies, even when thus
expanded, underlines how overwhelmingly the responsibility for defending the Empire in its global sprawl continued to rest on Britain,
a European offshore island state now directly menaced by the German
prong of the triple threat. The Admiralty in particular stood committed
by the oft-repeated but increasingly hollow promise to Australia and
New Zealand to despatch the British main fleet to Singapore in the
event of Japanese aggression – 'this heavy commitment', as Admiral
of the Fleet Lord Chatfield (now Minister for the Coordination of
Defence) described it in spring 1939.[22] Thus the security of the
United Kingdom and the Empire alike came to depend on the
timeliness, speed and scale of Britain's own rearmament.

Already in 1932, with the crisis following the Japanese occupation of
Manchuria and with German democracy all too evidently dying under
the impact of the world slump and political extremism, had come the
deepening swell and falling glass that warned of approaching storm
after the international sunshine of the 1920s. Nevertheless, and despite
the urgent warnings of the Chiefs of Staff, the National Government
under MacDonald and Baldwin had refused to sanction any rearmament, but instead merely abolished the 'ten-year rule'. In November
1933, with Japan and Nazi Germany (as it had now become) both out
of the League of Nations and Germany out of the world disarmament
conference (and known to be secretly rearming), the Cabinet appointed the Defence Requirements Sub-Committee of the Committee
of Imperial Defence to study the whole field of grand strategy and
defence policy. It reported in March 1934, taking Nazi Germany as
the paramount threat and estimating that Britain had five years in
which to make good her defences.

In July that year the Cabinet sanctioned a modest five-year programme of remedying the accumulated deficiencies in the *peacetime*

strengths of the armed forces, including major refits and modernising of some of the Navy's now obsolete capital ships, *Malaya*, *Warspite* and *Renown*. In 1935, in the face of the worsening international turbulence and the stiffening winds of crisis – Abyssinia; the German announcement of conscription and the existence of the Luftwaffe – the Cabinet approved an enlarged programme for the RAF, but nothing extra for the Navy or the Army. Not until February 1936 and after many more months of deliberation and report did the Cabinet finally heed the storm warnings and opt for large-scale rearmament – true expansion of the armed forces, including, at long last, a major warship building programme. It was just one month before the first squall blew of the tempest to come: the German Army's reoccupation of the demilitarised zone of the Rhineland in defiant breach of the Versailles Treaty.

Thus the British Cabinet had only decided to make a start at restoring the combat power of the Royal Navy *four years* after the Chiefs of Staff and the Admiralty had given their measured warnings in the shadow of the Manchurian crisis. Now, under the new programme, ships were to be laid down in 1936–37 for commissioning in 1940–41. The time lost was thus irrecoverable. What then accounted for this dangerous delay in beginning to repair British seapower? There was a cluster of inter-related reasons. In 1932–34 the National Government under Ramsay MacDonald and Stanley Baldwin was reluctant to load the slump-hit British economy with a costly rearmament programme, especially since the government continued to delude itself with naïve hopes that something might yet be salvaged from the now moribund World Disarmament Conference. Moreover the Cabinet was all too conscious of the prevailing pacifistic tenor of public opinion, which, fearful of another war combining the horrors of the 1914–18 Western Front with the terrors of the destruction of British cities by the bomber, still reposed its faith in disarmament and the League of Nations. Inside and outside Parliament the Labour and Liberal opposition parties bitterly denounced even the modest programmes for making good deficiencies in peacetime defences announced by the government in 1934–35.

Not until November 1935 did the government feel able to go to the country in a general election with defence (allegedly in support of the League and 'collective security') as a major theme in its manifesto – and only after its crushing victory in that election did it feel able to embark on the large-scale rearmament programme announced in February 1936. Even then the programme was denounced as 'war-mongering' and 'the road to war' by the Labour and Liberal parties.[23]

In the case of the Royal Navy, moreover, there was an added reason for the delay – the building 'holiday' for capital ships under the Washington Treaty, as extended by the London Naval Treaty of 1930, did not expire until the end of 1936.

It was one thing to decide on the rearmament programme, including new ships for the shrunken and obsolescent Navy; quite another to carry it out by the general target date of 1940. Britain's sagging economy and increasingly fragile balance-of-payments set financial limits on how much could be done and how quickly, while material bounds were set by what the Defence Policy and Requirements Committee called 'the limited output of our existing industrial resources'.[24] This combination of financial and technological weakness impelled the Cabinet more than once between 1935 and 1938 to reject proposals for a 'New Standard Navy' big enough to secure European waters and the Atlantic while at the same time deterring or fending off a Japanese attack in the Far East – twenty battleships, fifteen aircraft carriers, 100 cruisers, 198 destroyers, 82 submarines.[25] Instead the rearmament programme aimed at a Navy of fifteen capital ships, eight aircraft carriers, 70 cruisers, 144 destroyers and 55 submarines by 1940 – in fact, a fleet not greatly larger than that of 1936 except in cruisers, but composed of new or modernised ships rather than the worn-out and obsolete.[26]

For the government had had to accept that Britain's economic resources were simply not big enough to meet the naval demands imposed on her by the existence of the British Empire and by the triple threat to it; certainly not on top of the cost of the RAF's expansion, to which the Cabinet in its fear of the bomber gave overriding priority. The resulting strategic conundrum had to be left to the Admiralty to solve as best it could.

Even the agreed building programme, calling for five new battleships and four carriers to be laid down in 1937–39, plus five cruisers every year, ran into severe enough production difficulties. Just as Beatty had unavailingly warned at the Washington Conference in 1922, the battleship building 'holiday' had in the event caused the decay of the specialised plant needed to manufacture heavy guns and their mountings. The firm of Beardmores, before 1914 one of the two main British suppliers, presented in 1937 the problem, according to Lord Weir (the government's Chief Industrial Adviser), of 'raising what might be termed a scrap-heap to an efficient unit'.[27] The British steel industry could not supply enough armour plate for the new cruisers and carriers, and so orders for 15,000 tons had to be placed in Czechoslovakia.[28] In spring 1938 the decision had to be taken to buy

40mm anti-aircraft guns from the Swedish firm of Bofors, because the equivalent Vickers design had proved useless. It was not even possible to produce the Bofors gun under licence in Britain because, in Lord Weir's words, of the 'limited and inexperienced capacity' in the United Kingdom for manufacturing automatic guns and their mountings.[29] Indeed, wherever precision engineering was required, the Admiralty encountered especially grim production problems. For instance, British contractors found it difficult to manufacture intricate fuze mechanisms to the fine accuracy needed for reliable operation.[30] Delivery of radio and Asdic* equipment became worryingly late. But the Admiralty's special anxiety lay in the field of gunnery fire control systems, without which a warship's ability to acquire and destroy targets is crippled. In late 1937 the Admiralty was reporting in tones of despair that the country 'has been scoured to find firms willing to undertake the task, but without success'.[31] As a result, wrote the Admiralty, new cruisers would be delivered in 1937 without their high-angle fire control systems, which were essential against aircraft (see below, p. 47).[32]

The design, development and delivery of new and battle-worthy carrier aircraft were likewise bottlenecked by the backwardness and incompetence of the manufacturers. The Royal Air Force too suffered from this same problem in the late 1930s: the Spitfire, for instance, was over a year late in reaching the squadrons.[33] But the two principal aircraft firms allotted to supplying the Fleet Air Arm, Blackburns and Faireys, were inefficient even by the standards then generally prevailing in the industry. As late as November 1937 Blackburns could not promise that deliveries of the new Skua fighter/dive-bomber (specification issued 1934) would reach sixteen per month before December 1938, and even so the Air Ministry reported that the Director of Aircraft Production 'has no confidence in this programme, and is unable to forecast deliveries at present'.[34] In 1938 further production hold-ups and technical problems with the Skua confronted the Navy with the prospect of sending its carrier pilots to war in Nimrods and Ospreys, slow and obsolete biplanes. A stop-gap ordered off the drawing board from Faireys, the Fulmar, proved an equal disaster in production and performance.[35] By the time both were in service in the first half of 1940, they were already obsolescent by Japanese or American standards.[36] And Faireys made no less of a muddle of the design, development and production of the Fleet Air Arm's designated replacement for its sturdy but out-of-date biplane

---

* Today called 'sonar': the term generally employed in this book.

torpedo/reconnaissance aircraft, the Swordfish. The new Albacore was ordered in May 1937, but did not enter carrier service until 1941, when it too was already obsolescent.[37]

Yet these problems over new carrier aircraft partly derived from the pernicious transfer in 1918 (confirmed in 1926) of responsibility for aircraft procurement for the Fleet Air Arm from the Admiralty to the Air Ministry. In the closed mind of the Air Ministry and Air Staff in the 1930s the strategic bomber came first and foremost in order of priority, with the land fighter (for United Kingdom air defence) a grudging second, and maritime aviation (whether carrier or shore-based) relegated to the leftovers in terms of administrative drive and industrial resources.[38]

In 1936, with a major expansion of the Fleet Air Arm at last in the offing, the Admiralty therefore called for a fresh government examination of the 1918 compromise dividing responsibility for the Fleet Air Arm between the Navy and the Air Force. There ensued another bitter Whitehall battle, this time between the current Chief of the Air Staff, Air Chief Marshal Sir Edward Ellington (an immovable Trenchardite in his conviction that the heavy bomber supplied the answer to every problem of modern war), and the First Sea Lord, Admiral of the Fleet Sir Ernle Chatfield, together with their 'front men', the Secretary of State for Air (Lord Swinton) and the First Lord of the Admiralty (Sir Bolton Eyres-Monsell). A parallel campaign was fought out in the letter columns of *The Times* by such veterans as Admiral of the Fleet Sir Roger Keyes, Trenchard himself, Marshal of the Royal Air Force Sir John Salmond and Admiral Richmond, the naval historian and commentator.

The battle ran on into 1937, with two major enquiries and reports by the new Minister for the Coordination of Defence, Sir Thomas Inskip.[39] In his second report, in July 1937, Inskip pronounced that 'when so much that concerns the air units depends upon the Naval element in the ship and the Fleet, the Admiralty should be responsible for selecting and training the personnel, and generally for the organisation of the Fleet Air Arm'.[40] Nevertheless, Inskip disallowed the Admiralty's demand for a return of all shore-based maritime airpower (such as flying boats) as well, which remained under Royal Air Force control, and subject to persistent neglect, with unfortunate consequences during the Second World War. The Cabinet approved Inskip's recommendations on 29 July 1937. So after nearly twenty years of fumbling and neglect the Navy was at least handed back responsibility for its own carrier aviation. The Admiralty forthwith proceeded to restore the Great War post of 'Fifth Sea Lord and Chief of the Naval Air Services' and the Air Division of the Naval Staff in order to discharge that responsibility; and appointed Admiral the Hon. Alexander Ramsay, a former Rear-Admiral, Aircraft Carriers, as the new Fifth Sea Lord.

Nonetheless, the reorganisation brought in its train many detailed problems concerning transfers of personnel from the RAF, recruitment, a shortage of technical and middle-rank officers, and the transfer of necessary Fleet Air Arm shore bases,[41] just at the time of an all-too-belated attempt vastly to expand naval aviation. Here was yet another factor in the backwardness of the Royal Navy's carrier arm and its concept of carrier warfare in the late 1930s compared with the American and Japanese Navies.

Those navies, while also still regarding the battleship as the key to command of the sea, had long been practising long-range air strikes by fast carrier task groups. In an exercise in 1929 by the United States Navy over 260 aircraft took part in a 'battle' between two fleets for control of the Panama Canal. Manoeuvres in the Pacific in 1932 with three fast carriers demonstrated that airpower would in the future dominate the attack and defence of convoys, and that the first phase of a clash of fleets would take the form of an attempt by the rival carrier forces to destroy each other – exactly as was to happen in the battles of the Coral Sea and Midway in 1942.[42] In the Imperial Japanese Navy, Admiral Isoruku Yamamoto, who in 1935 was appointed Chief of the Navy's Air Division and who in earlier posts had done much to build up the Japanese carrier arm, himself ardently believed that the future at sea belonged to the carriers and their torpedo and dive-bombers; and in 1941, as C-in-C of the Combined Japanese Fleet, he was to plan the strike on Pearl Harbor.[43]

The design of American and Japanese aircraft carriers reflected this positive belief in airpower. Lightly armoured – the American ships had unarmoured decks – and with the flight deck and hangar deck built as a superstructure above the hull, they were indeed aircraft *carriers*, their overriding purpose to carry and fly the maximum number of aircraft. The USS *Lexington* and *Saratoga* embarked 90 aircraft each on their 30,000 tons; the three-ship Yorktown class (commissioned 1938–39) up to 80 aircraft on 19,000 tons displacement. The Japanese *Kaga* and *Akagi* (completed 1928) embarked 60 aircraft each on displacements of 30,000 tons; the *Soryu* and *Hiryu* (completed 1938) 63 each on 16,000 and 18,500 tons displacement. It was the American and Japanese philosophy that preservation of the carriers themselves from air attack was the job of their fighter aircraft, although the Americans had also developed advanced techniques of damage control, such as contra-flooding after a torpedo hit to maintain the ship on even keel.

The Royal Navy, however, despite occasional air strike exercises, continued to see the principal roles of the carrier as air defence of the fleet and distant reconnaissance. It placed much more emphasis on the carrier as a *ship* able to preserve itself from attack by means of a well armoured hull and flight deck. In the new Illustrious class (23,000 tons displacement; four ships laid down from 1936 onwards) as in the *Ark Royal* (23,000 tons; laid down 1935; commissioned 1938), the hull was carried up to the flight deck, making an integral boxlike structure of immense strength. The side armour was 4½ inches thick; the deck armour 3 inches thick. It was indeed British doctrine in the 1930s that the carrier's defence under close air attack should be to stow all aircraft below and turn the ship into a shut-up armoured shelter. Yet a severe penalty in striking power had to be paid for the weight of the armour – the Illustrious class had only a single hangar and could embark only 36 aircraft, less than half the complement of the equivalent American Yorktowns, and significantly fewer than the 63 aircraft in the smaller Japanese *Hiryu* and *Soryu*, or the 72 in the *Ark Royal*.[44]

The design of Britain's new battleships presented a much more important problem (as it seemed to the Admiralty) and at the same time a more complicated one. So many factors had to be balanced one against another in order to produce an optimum fighting 'package'. In the first place, the 35,000-ton displacement limit under the Washington Treaty was not due to expire until the end of 1936; and in the meantime there seemed at least a chance that it would be prolonged afterwards by voluntary option on the part of the principal naval powers, according to the terms of the second London Naval Treaty, signed in March 1936, along with a limit of main armaments to 14-inch calibre. Government concern for economy also impelled the Admiralty towards a choice of the 35,000-ton battleship as the smallest and therefore the cheapest practicable size. Moreover, given the new need for powerful but weight-consuming anti-aircraft armaments, the Admiralty decided that the 14-inch gun was technically the heaviest main armament that could be comfortably installed on 35,000 tons.

In April–May 1936 the resulting design for the future King George V class was finally agreed – twelve 14-inch guns in three novel quadruple turrets (later modified to ten guns in two quadruple turrets and one twin), a dual-purpose (surface and anti-aircraft) secondary armament of sixteen 5.25-inch guns, plus some 80 assorted rapid-fire light anti-aircraft guns; a speed of 27½ knots. In particular – the lessons of Jutland here – the new ships were given immensely strong armour protection, the weight being concentrated over vital areas: up to 15 inches on the sides and 6 inches on the deck. The 'KGVs' were in fact better armoured than either their German or American contemporaries in design, even though these well exceeded the 35,000-ton limit. The stolid rectangular lines of the British ships belied their fighting effectiveness, just as the beautiful shapes of the *Bismarck* and the American Iowas with their clipper bows gave an impression of immense power that was belied by their thinner armour and, in the case of *Bismarck*, an outdated concept of distributing armour protection. Moreover, the 'KGVs' represented a far better investment than the two Japanese 64,000-ton 18-inch gun monsters, *Yamato* and *Mushashi*, which for all their unexampled weight of armour, proved, like British, German and American battleships, to be all too sinkable by air attack.[45]

The first ship of the new class, *King George V* herself, was laid down in January 1937, but not commissioned until October 1940, and the second, *Prince of Wales*, laid down at the same time as the *KGV*, was not completed until March 1941.[46] While they were under construction, the Royal Navy therefore had to look to the modernising of Great War veterans to provide it with capital ships sufficiently up-to-date in armaments, fire-control, armour and machinery to be fit for war in the age of the bomb and torpedo. In 1936 the battleship *Malaya* emerged from a three-year refit; next year *Warspite* completed a four-year reconstruction that included new engines and boilers as well as extra armour, a new bridge structure, new anti-aircraft armament and a modification to her 15-inch guns to give a maximum elevation of 30 degrees and a range of 32,000 yards. Nevertheless she still retained her obsolete 6-inch guns in battery, not turrets. In 1937 similar programmes of reconstruction were put in hand with the *Queen Elizabeth* and *Valiant*, both of whom had their 6-inch batteries replaced by twenty 4.5-inch dual-purpose guns in twin turrets. In the event these reconstructions were not completed before war broke out in September 1939. In 1936–39 the battlecruiser *Renown* too was virtually rebuilt from the hull upwards, but not her sister ship the *Repulse*, nor the *Hood*, at 41,200 tons displacement Britain's largest warship. *Hood*'s reconstruction, planned to start in 1939, was abandoned because of the outbreak of war:[47] as a consequence her impressive size and beauty of line served to disguise the reality of an obsolete and vulnerable ship.

With cruisers and destroyers too the legacy of international naval limitation – even though it had never amounted to a building 'holiday' as with capital ships – added grievously to the Royal Navy's problems in designing and building new vessels in the mid-1930s. By the 1930 London Naval Treaty the Labour government had accepted the 'starvation number' of 50 cruisers within an overall tonnage limit of 328,200 tons. Because of the unique scale and vulnerability of Britain's seaborne trade, the Admiralty had elected in the early 1930s to plan for the maximum number of new cruisers possible within the total permitted tons displacement even though this had meant going for 6-inch gun ships of only 7,250 tons displacement (the Leander class, launched 1931–34), or even 5,220 tons (the Arethusa class, launched 1934–36), as against the proportionately fewer 8-inch or 6-inch gun 10,000-ton cruisers being built by Japan and the United States or later by Germany. When in 1935 the Admiralty came to select cruiser designs for the new rearmament programme, it again had to strike a difficult balance within restricted funds and shipyard resources between ships powerful enough to meet enemy heavy cruisers in battle and yet numerous enough to protect British trade and also work with the main fleets. It found its compromise solution in the design of the Towns class of 6-inch gun heavy cruisers (9,100 tons displacement; later ships 9,400 tons; and of which HMS *Belfast*, commissioned in August 1939 and now moored as a museum ship in the Pool of London, is the last survivor). The first 'Town', HMS *Southampton*, was completed in 1937. There followed in the 1938 estimates the Colonies class design of heavy cruiser (8,000 tons and twelve 6-inch guns), a development of the 'Towns' design. All were still building when war broke out. Though all lighter than their foreign equivalents, these new cruiser designs were to prove stout fighting ships alike in the freezing gales of the Arctic, the huge seaways of the Atlantic and the blue, brilliant, bomber infested Mediterranean. The rearmament period light cruiser design, the Dido class (5,450 tons; later ships 5,770 tons), was supposed to carry ten 5.25-inch guns in twin turrets, but because of the demands of the new battleships and aircraft carriers for these turrets, two 'Didos' had to make do with eight 4.5-inch guns.[48]

With the design of destroyers the Admiralty faced a similar hard choice between sheer numbers and the fighting power of the individual vessel, for here too the 1930 London Naval Treaty had imposed a limit: of 150,000 tons overall. In the early 1930s the Admiralty had – as with cruisers – opted for the maximum number possible, even though this meant vessels of around 1,500 tons displacement compared with the destroyers of 2,500 tons – virtually light cruisers – favoured by the French and German navies. But in the case of destroyers the Admiralty added to its own problem by conceiving the primary role of this type of vessel in Jutland terms as 'massed attacks [on enemy fleets] by day and attacks against screened fleets by night', coupled with defence of British fleets against submarines by providing a sonar screen.[49] Up to 1936, therefore, a British destroyer's main armament lay in torpedo tubes rather than guns. However, by this time the Japanese Fubuki class destroyers were carrying six 5-inch guns in twin turrets, while Germany was about to build destroyers with five 5.9-inch guns – almost the calibre of the main batteries in cruisers. Between 1934 and 1936 the Admiralty therefore evolved a new generation of bigger destroyer which mounted eight 4.7-inch guns in twin turrets, as well as a short-range anti-aircraft armament, on a 1,850 tons displacement (the London Treaty limit) at the price of reducing the number of torpedo tubes.[50]

The first ships of the new generation, the Tribal class, were launched from June 1937 onwards, but problems with the delivery of gun mountings meant that in 1938 completed vessels had to be sent on sea trials while still devoid of guns.[51] Unfortunately the Admiralty's continued fixation with future Jutlands led it to give overriding priority in the new designs (within the limits of space and weight) to low-angle fire against surface targets (such as enemy destroyers) over high-angle fire against aircraft, especially dive-bombers; and the Tribals' 4.7-inch guns had a maximum elevation of only 40 degrees. This mistaken choice in otherwise admirably sturdy ships was to be tragically punished by the Luftwaffe off Greece and Crete in 1941.

But Jutland – that is, a future Jutland fought against the Japanese fleet in Far Eastern waters – befogged the Royal Navy's thinking over the entire horizon of maritime warfare in the years before the Second World War, and not just with regard to the design of destroyers or the relative importance of battleships and carriers. The role of the British submarine service, for its part, was seen merely as ancillary to the operations of the battlefleet: reconnaissance, attacks on enemy warships; defence of fleet bases such as Singapore against approaching hostile squadrons. Construction of new submarines therefore took a low priority in the Navy's rearmament programme after 1936, and the number of orders up to 1939 (eighteen to 1937, fourteen in 1938–39) only equalled boats either already over age or due to be over age by 1939.[52] But far more dangerous was the Admiralty's parallel neglect of the potential threat to Britain's own survival posed by *enemy* submarines. The neglect – or rather, minimising – of this was truly remarkable in view of the dreadful experience of 1917, when the U-boat had brought the United Kingdom within a few weeks of famine and industrial standstill. Despite that grimly effective demonstration of the true role of the submarine, the Admiralty in the 1920s and 1930s chose to believe that technical progress in the performance of sonar (echo-sounding gear for detecting submerged U-boats) would 'greatly lessen the effectiveness of the submarine as a weapon against shipping'.[53] Since Germany was in any case forbidden U-boats under the Versailles Treaty (a restriction only formally lifted in 1935 by the Anglo-German Naval Agreement) the Admiralty was convinced in the early 1930s that British commerce had much more to fear from German surface raiders such as the Deutschland class of 10,000-ton 11-inch gun 'pocket battleships'.

The Admiralty's faith in improved sonar, coupled with the priority given anyway to types of ship for service with the battlefleet, also misled it into neglecting the construction of anti-submarine escort vessels. In 1934 it reckoned that some 100 such ships would be needed for all purposes, whereas in 1918 the Navy had been deploying 300 in protection of convoys alone.[54] Only in 1937, with the rearmament programme now gathering momentum and all Britain's great departments of state urgently studying solutions to the practical problems of future war, did the question of securing Britain's essential imports (guesstimated to amount in wartime to 47 million tons a year)[55] come to be seriously examined afresh. A Shipping Defence Advisory Committee was set up under the Committee of Imperial Defence (CID) in February 1937, composed of representatives of the Admiralty, the Board of Trade, Lloyds and the Shipping Federation, to produce recommendations across the whole field of trade defence. It soon accepted that once again Britain would have to resort to the convoy system. But the Admiralty – and despite its belief that improved sonar had greatly lessened the menace posed by the U-boat – had to admit that in the opening stages of a war 'the naval forces are hardly adequate to provide fully effective numbers for escorting our convoys'.[56] In an attempt to remedy this want, the Shipping Defence Advisory Committee sponsored such emergency measures in 1937–39 as putting 6-inch guns into strengthened fast liners (later commissioned under the White Ensign as 'Armed Merchant Cruisers'). It mooted the idea of equipping as many merchant vessels as possible with rapid-fire light anti-aircraft guns (foreign again: this time the Swiss 20mm Oerlikon; a British design again proving unsatisfactory).[57] The idea was not to be realised in full until the middle years of the war.

It must therefore be accounted the Admiralty's most serious failure of judgment in the years between the world wars that, with eyes focused on the battlefleet, it ducked until too late the enormous operational and quantitative problems of once again having to set up a complete convoy system and defend this against the U-boat. Indeed, as late as 1939 some admirals still hankered after the 'offensive' tactic, discredited in 1917, of the 'hunting group' roaming the seas after U-boats.

Yet at the root of this failure, as of other misreadings of the true naval lessons of the Great War – to say nothing of want of vision with regard to the potential of carrier striking power – lay a single common factor: the want of organised, scientifically conducted operational research. No such department was set up by the Admiralty until 1942. In the case of the long-running argument about the warship's future chances against air attack, for example, it was not until 1935 that an anti-aircraft department was created at HMS *Excellent*, the Navy's gunnery school; not until 1938–39 that numerical calculation and objective analysis took the place of dogmatic assertion by rival enthusiasts, thanks to the reports of the ABE Committee ('Assessors on Bomb versus Battleship Experiments' Committee; renamed in March 1938 the 'Sub-Committee on Bombing and A-A Gunfire Experiments'). The second interim report of the committee in 1938 specifically indicted the lack of facilities for research and development in the field of anti-aircraft fire control.[58] Its third report in January 1939 estimated that two hits would be scored by aircraft on every carrier and one on every cruiser for each bomber shot down by the ships' gunfire, and that destroyers were 'virtually defenceless against air attack':[59] hardly welcome mathematics to the admirals (see below, pp. 47–8).

This was not the only example of the uneven coverage and quality of Admiralty research between the wars. Despite the founding of the Admiralty Research Laboratory in 1920, 'salt-horse' sailors continued to be suspicious of intruders such as scientists into their traditional craft 'mystery'. There was, for instance, no research department concerned with the structure and design of ships, including a structures laboratory, despite repeated urging by successive Directors of Naval Construction since 1918. Not until June 1943 was the Naval Construction Research Establishment created.[60]

Broadly it could be said that while those technical shortcomings revealed by battle experience during the Great War had been cured by 1939, the problems arising out of new developments, especially air power, had not. The modernised capital ships and the new ones under construction by 1939 certainly enjoyed much better armour protection, better underwater subdivision and much reduced vulnerability of magazines to flash cordite fires than ships at Jutland. Thanks to prolonged study leading to the adoption of new detonators and bursters, British heavy shells no longer suffered from a tendency to break up on impact or detonate prematurely; instead it was to be German shell technology that would be found wanting in the Second World War. With regard to fire control of main armaments against surface targets, most of the Royal Navy's ships had been equipped by 1939 with calculators virtually identical to Pollen's 'Argo Clock'.[61] But it was another story with the fire control of anti-aircraft guns, where the Navy committed just the same kind of blunder before 1939 as it had before 1914 in regard to fire control against ships: it opted for an inferior system, and in this case founded on fallacious principles.

In the words of Captain Stephen Roskill, the distinguished naval historian, gunnery specialist and in 1939 a member of the naval staff,

> The truth was that as long ago as the late 1920s the Admiralty had gone for the wrong sort of control system – one in which the enemy aircraft movements were in effect guessed instead of being actually *measured* and the measured results used to provide the required control data. This latter, called a 'tachymetric system', was the proper answer . . .[62]

In Roskill's judgment the culprits were the Naval Ordnance Department and its specialist officers 'not properly trained in scientific design and armament engineering', and unwilling to seek outside expert advice. The Admiralty's decision may also have been influenced by pressure from British engineering firms, which were incapable of designing and manufacturing such sophisticated precision equipment as the tachymetric system, and could hardly cope with the cruder equipment finally adopted (see above, p. 38).[63] In 1937 the inefficiency of the chosen system (HACS = High Angle Control System), now very belatedly getting into quantity production, was alarmingly displayed in a trial during which a Queen Bee radio-controlled target aircraft circled the Home Fleet for two and a half hours unscathed by the fleet's fire.[64] By this time it was too late to switch to a true tachymetric system – not least because Britain could not make it. In 1938 the Admiralty's Director of Scientific Research, C.S. Wright, described HACS as 'a menace to the service'.[65] Unlike the German and United States Navies, which had adopted tachymetric anti-aircraft fire control systems, the Royal Navy was to enter the Second World War firing at enemy aircraft with the hopeful wildness of aim of a tyro shot trying to bring down fast flying grouse. The Mediterranean Fleet in particular was to be cruelly handicapped in its prolonged battles in 1940–42 with the Regia Aeronautica and the Luftwaffe by the shortcomings of

HACS – colossal expenditure of ammunition without commensurate protection of the fleet or destruction of enemy aircraft. HMSs *Prince of Wales* and *Repulse* were similarly to suffer under Japanese air attack off Malaya in December 1941.

It was no compensation that in 1939 experimental air-warning radar had been fitted to two ships (the battleship *Rodney* and the cruiser *Sheffield*) and that in August that year the anti-aircraft cruiser *Curlew* was fitted with the prototype of all the wartime Royal Navy's air-warning sets. By this time, in any case, the German Navy was beginning to equip with the Seetakt gunnery-ranging radar, and the United States Navy with the XAF air-warning and gunnery radar.[66] These pioneer developments in three navies marked the beginning of the radar revolution that was to transform every aspect of sea warfare during the wartime years.

As serious – perhaps more serious – was the Admiralty's neglect between the wars of Intelligence, in both its operational and technical aspects. The superb radio intercept and cypher breaking organisation built up by 'Blinker' Hall in Room 40 which had read the vital German signals during the Jutland action was quickly run down after the Great War, and in 1922 responsibility for cypher Intelligence was transferred from the Admiralty to civilian control. Even in the 1930s, and despite urging by Captain Lord Louis Mountbatten, little technical research was conducted into cryptoanalytical technology. Although the Admiralty conducted trials with encyphering machines (the prototypes of the wartime German 'Enigma' and the RAF 'Typex'), the work was dropped. As a result of such neglect, the Admiralty even by the outbreak of the Second World War could not read either the German or Japanese naval cyphers. On the other hand B-Dienst of the German Navy's Intelligence Division had penetrated the Royal Navy's own cyphers, and during the Abyssinian crisis in 1935–36 had been able to monitor all the movements of the Mediterranean Fleet.[67] Operational Intelligence too grew sleepy between the wars: there was no accurate evaluation of the future U-boat threat; no recognition of the potential danger of U-boat surface attacks at night (a tactic already practised before the end of the Great War), and against which the Royal Navy's vaunted sonar would be useless.

Not until the mid-1930s did the Naval Intelligence Division of the Naval Staff experience a revival and swift expansion under Vice-Admiral Sir William James's encouragement as Deputy Chief of Naval Staff. In 1936 – the year when in Intelligence, as in so many things, Britain finally resolved to prepare itself for war – the Joint Intelligence Committee was founded, through which the three services and the

Foreign Office pooled resources and results in order to provide the Chiefs of Staff Committee with the Intelligence necessary as a basis for strategic policy making and decision. In June 1937 Lieutenant-Commander Norman Denning was tasked with designing a wartime Operational Intelligence Centre (OIC), and in November that year the Centre was formally set up and staffed with signals experts. From this beginning was to grow the collective brain and nerve centre of the whole war at sea. Under Rear-Admiral J. A. G. Troup, the Director of Naval Intelligence from 1936 to 1939, High Frequency Direction Finding (HF/DF) stations were constructed in the north of the British Isles in order to monitor German Navy signals traffic and ship movements; and a teleprinter net was installed to link the OIC to naval headquarters and stations, coastal watchers and RAF Coastal Command.[68]

Coastal Command was itself yet another product of the year of 1936, the UK-based Royal Air Force then being reorganised into the three great Commands – Coastal, Fighter and Bomber – with which it was to wage the Second World War. Between that year and the outbreak of the conflict in 1939 Coastal Command, under its first three Air Officers Commanding-in-Chief, Air Marshal Sir Arthur Longmore (in 1936: naval flyer in the Great War), Air Marshal Sir Philip Joubert de la Ferté (1936–37) and Air Marshal Sir Frederick Bowhill (1937–41: another former naval flyer), began to reforge the links between the shore-based component of maritime air power and the Navy which had rusted away since 1918. Nevertheless, for all the good will displayed by its chiefs towards the Navy, their keenness for close cooperation, Coastal Command from its birth was to be the poor relation within an air force entranced by a dream of strategic bombing; and it was to remain in 1939 weak in numbers, obsolescent in aircraft and with its principal role the passive one of reconnaissance.[69] In particular, the question of air cover for convoys (and air attack on U-boats) was little considered – not least because the Admiralty, in its sublimely complacent playing down of airpower, remained persuaded that the anti-aircraft fire of the escorts would by itself ensure the protection of convoys from enemy aircraft, and that the improved sonar would enable the Navy to hunt down U-boats without much need for help from the RAF.

Taken all in all, therefore, the Royal Navy's responses to the technical and operational puzzles involved in refurbishing British seapower in the late 1930s suggest a narrow professionalism of outlook too much influenced by loyalty to tradition and too little blessed with innovative imagination. And indeed the Navy's topmost leadership on the eve of the Second World War failed to measure up to the standards of Nelson or Barham or Beatty in broad strategic wisdom, sharpness of intellect or sheer personality. The shortcoming did not lie in the fleet commands. Admiral Sir Andrew Cunningham, appointed C-in-C, Mediterranean Fleet, in June 1939 – salty, vigorous, blunt-speaking – was the embodiment of the Royal Navy's best tradition of fighting sailors that extended back through Hawke, the victor of Quiberon Bay in 1759, to Blake, the Commonwealth's formidable 'general at sea' and the scourge of the Dutch. Admiral Sir Charles Forbes, the C-in-C, Home Fleet, shared Cunningham's characteristic of unshakability. A subordinate judged him to have had 'a fine brain and a tremendously powerful character'.[70] Nevertheless, and unlike Cunningham, he lacked, according to the same witness, 'that panache of which one would have liked to see more in a great commander-in-chief. I had, for example, at the request of many captains, to *force* him to visit ships and their people. When he got there and spoke – shortly and to the point – to ships' companies, he impressed as a rock of ages type of character.'[71]

The problem lay with the Navy's chief himself, the First Sea Lord after June 1939, Admiral of the Fleet Sir Dudley Pound. Pound was only appointed at that time because sickness, premature death and early retirements had thinned the field of choice. In 1935, Rear-Admiral B.H. Ramsay, an exceptionally able officer, resigned as Chief of Staff of the Home Fleet because the Commander-in-Chief, Admiral Sir Roger Backhouse, set aside the modern staff system in favour of tightly personal command by himself, down to dealing in detail with all incoming fleet signals and business. Ramsay was later to return to active service, and command the Dunkirk evacuation in 1940 and the Allied naval forces in the D-Day Landings in 1944. In 1936 the then second-in-command of the Mediterranean Fleet and a potential First Sea Lord, Admiral Sir Geoffrey Blake, suffered an accident and had to be invalided. In 1937 Admiral Sir William Fisher, a sailor of imposing presence who had brought the Mediterranean Fleet to a high state of efficiency during the Abyssinian crisis, and another among potential First Sea Lords, died suddenly at the age of 62 – 'a very great blow', as Admiral of the Fleet Sir Ernle Chatfield put it.[72] Chatfield himself, whose professional stature, experience and sagacity were unrivalled, became Minister for the Coordination of Defence in January 1939, and so was lost to the Navy. His successor as First Sea Lord was Backhouse, the arch centraliser; a man who as well as hating a staff system avoided larger questions of naval strategy and policy in favour of close interest in technical detail. One colleague judged him 'too weak; too fearful of accepting responsibility'.[73] But Backhouse in any case resigned in June 1939 because of ill health, and died of a cerebral tumour in July. From a now scant field Admiral Sir Dudley Pound, the C-in-C, Mediterranean Fleet, was duly appointed Backhouse's successor.

Pound was to hold the key post of First Sea Lord until his own death in 1943. The Royal Navy was therefore to be directed for the first three years of the Second World War by a stop-gap appointee who had never been earmarked for promotion to so exalted a strategic role. Chatfield had in fact once specifically told Pound that he was *not* going to be First Sea Lord.[74] In 1936 Admiral Sir John Kelly, the C-in-C, Portsmouth, had told Chatfield in a letter that 'D.P. would not be a success in my opinion. In the first place, he suffers from being not quite a gentleman: a disastrous lacuna in a First Sea Lord. He is too pig-headed; too unwilling to recognise that there may be another side of the question.'[75] For Pound was a hard-working plodder of limited intellectual range and interests; another arch centraliser in the Victorian/Edwardian naval mould; a 'good plain cook' devoid of personal charisma. His Flag Captain when he was C-in-C, Mediterranean Fleet, judged him many years later as 'certainly not a genius and I question whether he was even a great man. He had a slow but good brain and got to the top by sheer hard work . . .'[76] Another witness who was at that same period on the staff of the Navy's Tactical School wrote of Pound:

We used to get all his exercise papers and I remember that the Orders for an exercise contained detailed plans for practically every unit during [the] whole exercise, this of course meant that the enemy were told what to do! 'Initiative' was obviously considered a dirty word.[77]

Did Pound immerse himself in detailed executive driving of his fleet because he felt himself out of his depth and inferior in larger questions of naval strategy? Another former subordinate, Admiral Sir Gerald Dickens, records of him as Commander of the Second Battle Cruiser Squadron in 1929–31:

When I joined *Repulse*, fresh from the I.D.C. [Imperial Defence College], he said 'How do I study strategy?' I laughed – thinking he was getting at me – and said, 'Too late now, Sir.' He looked rather surprised, but showed no sign of annoyance. The fact was that – at least that was my impression – he had never given much time to reading and the teachings of history, which explains much about his composition . . .[78]

Pound's lack of wide strategic grasp and his habit of directing in detail were the more a potential handicap in war because the Admiralty, unlike the War Office or Air Ministry, was an operational head-quarters; it exercised supreme command over the Royal Navy in all seas and oceans. Whereas the Chiefs of the Imperial General Staff and the Air Staff could only issue broad strategic directives to Command or theatre commanders-in-chief, the First Sea Lord (and Chief of Naval Staff) could, if he so wished, personally control the day-to-day dispositions of fleets, task forces, squadrons and convoys, even individual ships. And Pound was by no means a fit man in 1939, being disabled by an arthritic hip which gave him great pain and denied him sleep. 'When I saw him just after the war started,' writes an eyewitness, 'he hobbled into the ops-room at Coastal Command, & I noticed with horror that he had become a worn-out old man. His hair was snow-white and wispy, his face seamed and ashen, & there was a noticeable distortion of one eye . . .'[79]

At the beginning of 1936 it had been planned to complete the British rearmament programme in the course of 1940. That was the year when the first of the Royal Navy's new battleships and aircraft carriers would, it was hoped, be commissioned. But in September 1938 the Munich crisis put Britain's rearmament and Britain's armed forces to the test of imminent danger of war, and, unsurprisingly, found them wanting. The aftermath of the crisis therefore witnessed searching inquests in Whitehall into the state of progress in rearmament; the drafting of urgent measures to speed up the re-equipment of the services – and especially expand production of fighter aircraft for the defence of British cities against the dreaded bomber. There was anguished consideration of how the cost of such accelerated rearmament (and particularly the RAF programme) could be squared with Britain's rapidly worsening balance-of-payments problem.[80]

The Admiralty, for its part, reported in October 1938 to the new Cabinet Committee on Defence Programmes and Acceleration that there were not enough escorts for all duties, and that it therefore wished to order a new type of vessel costing half as much as a destroyer. These vessels, later called 'corvettes', were to become the indispensable workhorses of the Battle of the Atlantic. The Admiralty also reported that there existed 'extremely serious deficiencies' in the Fleet Air Arm; that there was a shortage of skilled ratings; and that more armour plate would have to be ordered from Europe.[81] Britain's limited technological resources were still acting as a powerful brake on rearmament. The Minister for the Coordination of Defence reminded the Defence Programmes and Acceleration Committee that 'the real bottlenecks consist of certain highly specialised products, e.g., fire control gear, gun-mountings, predictors and the like . . .'[82]

As 1938 turned to 1939 the sense of urgency, of time running out, sharpened. It was now known in London that Hitler had conceived a total contempt for his dupe at Munich, Neville Chamberlain; a contempt all too likely to dissolve any remaining diplomatic caution. Moreover, France, deprived of her militarily strong Czechoslovakian ally by the Munich surrender and now alone face to face with the German Army, was bringing heavy pressure on Britain to promise to fight alongside France if she were attacked, and in particular commit a British Expeditionary Force to the French Army's support. Such a policy of 'continental commitment' had always been anathema to Chamberlain. It took the panic rumour in January 1939 that Hitler was about to invade the Netherlands to induce Chamberlain and his Cabinet to reverse this strategic isolationism, and undertake to send an expeditionary force to France in the event of war. But this belated switch in grand strategy meant that the Royal Navy would now have the extra task of protecting the British Expeditionary Force's line of communication across the Channel; it meant that Britain became more deeply committed to resisting the German prong of the triple threat; even more strategically stretched and divided in purpose. For while the Navy still thought primarily in terms of fleet battles (and that could only mean the Japanese), the British Army now looked to a renewed Western Front, and the Royal Air Force to the air defence of the United Kingdom against the German bombers and its own bomber offensive against German cities.

Henceforward through the passing months of 1939 the sense of the imminent approach of war grew ever keener – the background and the spur to the Admiralty's own last-minute efforts to bring Britain's available naval strength up to combat readiness. On 15 March German troops occupied the rump of Czechoslovakia, so finally shattering Chamberlain's policy of appeasement. Panicked by rumours of a further German coup, this time against Romania, Chamberlain now issued 'guarantees' to Romania and Poland. In the Polish case Chamberlain committed Britain to going to war if ever Poland believed her independence to be threatened, so forfeiting Britain's freedom of military decision in regard to Germany. In April Fascist Italy invaded and occupied Albania, an alarming reminder of the Italian prong of the triple threat.

That same month Britain and France held high-level staff meetings in London in order to concert their operational war plans and evolve a common grand strategy. In May Italy and Germany signed the 'Pact of Steel', a formal military alliance. In June Japanese troops violated the British concession area at Tientsin in China, subjecting British citizens to brutal indignities; a sudden flare-up in the Japanese menace at the worst possible time, which evoked anxious recognition by the Admiralty and the Cabinet that Britain could not hope to find a fleet for the Far East as well as guard against the German and Italian Navies in the European threatre. And in August Hitler began fomenting a new crisis, this time over the League of Nations Free City of Danzig (today Gdansk) and the so-called Polish Corridor between West and East Prussia (taken from Germany by the 1919 peace settlement), certain that Chamberlain would give way again, just as he had at Munich.

Meanwhile the Admiralty had been month by month hastening on its final preparation for war. Early in 1939 it sought to overcome a shortage of junior executive officers by forming a list of some 3,000 supplementary reserves with nautical experience (such as amateur yachtsmen). These, together with the peacetime Volunteer Reserves and later the 'Hostilities Only' officers formed 'the Wavy Navy' (so called from the undulating gold rings on their sleeves), who were to serve with such professionalism during the Second World War, even rising to command their own ships or submarines. The regular long-service establishment of the Navy was enlarged from 119,000 to 178,000.[83] In the spring the Admiralty brought the Operational Intelligence Centre (OIC), with its interlinked Surface Ship Plot and Submarine Tracking Room, to a state of war readiness.[84] An operational handbook for 'Defensively Equipped Merchant Ships', together with instructions on signalling, was issued to the Merchant Navy. Measures were finalised for introducing war-risks insurance (as in the Great War) and for placing the entire British merchant fleet under Admiralty control. That March new *Fleet Tactical Instructions* and *Fighting Instructions* were also issued, both documents still laying emphasis on the manoeuvring of battlefleets of up to a dozen capital ships.[85] The *Fighting Instructions* struck a note of true Jutland-style rigidity: 'Prior to deployment, the Admiral will control the movements of the battle fleet as a whole. He will dispose the guides of divisions on a line of bearing at right angles to the bearing of the enemy battle fleet . . .'

But no equivalent instructions had been drafted for convoy operations; a notable omission. On 26 May 15,000 reservists were called up in order to bring the Reserve Fleet (composed of older warships) to a state of readiness by 15 June.[86] In June a special section of the Trade Division of the naval staff was created to carry out the task of installing defensive armaments in all the 5,500 vessels (3,000 of them ocean-going) of the Merchant Navy.[87] That same month a commander from the Plans Division was sent to Washington for talks with Admiral Leahy, the American Chief of Naval Operations, and his Director of Plans about possible cooperation in the Far East and Pacific. As was the case with the earlier talks in 1938, no firm commitments resulted. Nevertheless the meetings marked a further modest step from the Anglo-American naval rivalry of the 1920s towards the close and cordial alliance of the 1940s.

In August, as the crisis over Danzig and the Polish Corridor erupted, the Admiralty set in motion the last detailed arrangements for bringing the Navy to full war readiness. Between 15 and 21 August joint Navy and RAF exercises were held to test Coastal Command's operational plans, and when they ended most of the RAF squadrons moved to their war stations. Almost immediately Coastal Command began flying reconnaissance patrols to monitor German warship, submarine and merchant ship movements. On 26 August the Admiralty assumed control of all British merchant shipping. On the last day of August, with the Polish crisis now at exploding point and the German Army massed and poised along the Polish frontier, all the ships of the Home Fleet reached their war stations.

That same day Admiral Sir Charles Forbes, flying his flag in HMS *Nelson*, sailed from Scapa Flow with the Home Fleet (four capital ships, one carrier, two cruisers and ten destroyers: a small fraction of the fleet Sir John Jellicoe had commanded in 1914) in order to patrol the waters between the Shetland Isles and Norway – Germany's only maritime access to the world. On 1 September 1939, as the panzer divisions squealed and clattered their way into Poland and the howling Stukas dive-bombed all who moved on Polish roads, be they soldiers or old women or young children, the Admiralty sent warning telegrams to the Navy naming Germany and Italy as potential enemies, and ordered the general mobilisation of naval reserves.

At 1117 on 3 September, seventeen minutes after the British ultimatum to Germany to withdraw her troops from Poland had expired without reply from the German government, the Admiralty despatched a 'Special Telegram' marked MOST IMMEDIATE to all His Majesty's ships:

'TOTAL GERMANY repetition TOTAL GERMANY.'[88]

The Royal Navy was once more at war – in such fighting strength and against such potential odds as had been bequeathed by the policies of successive British governments over the previous twenty years.

3

'Winston Is Back'

At 1800 hours in the evening of England's first day of the Second World War, Winston Churchill entered the red-brick Georgian Admiralty building in Whitehall to take up once again the post of First Lord of the Admiralty which he had occupied with such dynamic impact from 1911 to 1915. In anticipation of Churchill's early arrival, the Admiralty had already signalled the Navy: 'Winston is back.' The Prime Minister, Neville Chamberlain, had offered Churchill his old post and invited him to join the War Cabinet only a few hours after Chamberlain's own toneless radio announcement to the British people that Britain was at war with Germany. Now, with the ultimate failure of his stubborn effort to avert war by placating Hitler, Chamberlain sought to lend a semblance of fighting spirit to his Cabinet by asking the arch critic of his policy of appeasement to accept office under him.

For Churchill himself his return held a curious Rip-van-Winkle-like quality:

> So it was that I came again to the room I had quitted in pain and sorrow almost exactly a quarter of a century before, when Lord Fisher's resignation [as First Sea Lord] had led to my removal from my post as First Lord and ruined irretrievably, as it proved, the important conception of forcing the Dardanelles. A few feet behind me, as I sat in my old chair, was the wooden map-case I had had fixed in 1911, and inside it still remained the chart of the North Sea on which each day, in order to focus attention on the supreme objective, I made the Naval Intelligence Branch record the movements and disposition of the German High Seas Fleet. Since 1911 more than a quarter of a century had passed, and still mortal peril threatened us at the hands of the same nation . . .[1]

Later that evening he presided over his first meeting of the Admiralty Board, sitting in the familiar high-backed dark leather and mahogany First Lord's chair at the head of the broad table, a portrait of Nelson watching him from the opposite wall of the floridly carved eighteenth-century room. Here in this same room, his predecessor Lord Barham and his colleagues, bewigged beneath the coffered ceiling, had plotted the strategy that defeated the landlubber Bonaparte's naval combinations in 1804–5 and led to the annihilating victory of Trafalgar and that long British naval mastery which, since 1918, the internationalists, disarmers and economisers (including Churchill himself when Chancellor of the Exchequer) had whittled away. For Churchill, with his sense of history as a continuing drama, to sit again in that chair in that room marked a deeply emotional moment – as was evident to the admirals looking along the table at their new chief. The then Third Sea Lord wrote later:

> To a few words of welcome from the First Sea Lord he replied by saying what a privilege and honour it was to be again in that chair, that there were many difficulties ahead but together we would overcome them. He surveyed critically each one of us in turn and then, adding that he would see us all personally later on, he adjourned the meeting. 'Gentlemen,' he said, 'to your tasks and duties.'[2]

Presently the First Sea Lord, Admiral of the Fleet Sir Dudley Pound, came to see Churchill in his room. At this first meeting each eyed the other, according to Churchill, 'amicably if doubtfully'.[3] And wary might Pound well be, for Churchill's previous tenure of the Admiralty had bequeathed a memory of a restlessly interfering First Lord who liked to order in detail the deployment of fleets and the manoeuvres of ships and squadrons; who was prone to urge irresistibly on his colleagues grand but unsound strategic visions, such as the calamitous attempt in 1914 to hold Antwerp against the German Army by means of a hastily thrown together Royal Navy landing force, or the later and even more calamitous attempt in 1915 to force the Dardanelles Straits and reach Constantinople, capital of Germany's ally Turkey, firstly by means of sending battleships up the narrow and mine-infested channel between hills bristling with shore batteries, and then by means of an improvised expeditionary force lacking proper landing ships and craft. But on Churchill's part there was also reason for wariness at this first official encounter with Pound, for his previous First Sea Lord in 1914–15, Admiral of the Fleet Lord Fisher, had fought him over the conduct of the Dardanelles campaign with a cumulative violence and bitterness that passed the bounds of the pathological. The quarrel had culminated in Fisher's furiously abrupt resignation in May 1915, which precipitated the fall of Asquith's Liberal government, and Churchill's own traumatic loss of office.

However, the admiral who now limped in on a stick to see him was no Fisher, no near genius blazing with energy and self-will and driven by visions of a technological revolution in sea warfare. Pound's big-nosed features were homely, rugged, undistinguished; those of a countryman in from the plough or the forge – or a sailor from a windjammer home from the sea. The voice was deep, enhancing the impression of ruggedness; the manner slow and steady. And appearance did not mislead, for this was a man whom his contemporaries judged a plodding second-rater, with a mind untroubled by large strategic visions. A simple man and solidly middle-class, he did not belong to that brilliant, even flashy, political-cum-social world which was Churchill's milieu – as it had also been Fisher's and Beatty's. One colleague, for example, noted Pound's 'simplicity of soul and desire for affection'[4]; another that while Pound enjoyed 'an orderly and logical mind' he was 'not perhaps a man of great imagination or insight',[5] while a third was to recollect: 'Old Pound, splendid chap as he was, did not engender confidence. We felt rightly or wrongly he never had any very abiding convictions as to the proper and correct strategical deployment and use of naval forces.'[6]

Nevertheless, he was, according to the same colleague, 'the personification of loyalty';[7] and loyalty to the extent of dog-like devotion was what from that day forth Dudley Pound, the plain and simple sailor, gave to Winston Churchill the heroic leader. Here then was exactly the naval instrument for which Churchill would have wished: a Berthier to his Napoleon. For straight away Churchill laid his own grasp on the tiller of British seapower – no mere political head presiding over a service department, but a supreme naval commander running the entire complex of strategy and operations through Pound as his executive Chief of Staff or even sometimes directly. That first night of war Churchill, elated at his release from the impotence of his 'wilderness years' as a mere back-bencher, worked on into the small hours; next morning he issued the first of a never-ending torrent of urgent enquiries and instructions, each of them embodying his restless will to action. These missives were to be nicknamed 'the first lord's prayers', because so many began with the formula 'Pray inform me . . .' or 'Pray why has . . . not been done?' He had indeed much the same sharpening effect on the Admiralty, the naval staff and the Navy at large as a new and ruthlessly exacting captain on a ship's company.

'From the very first day,' remembered the then Deputy Director of the Trade Division of the naval staff, 'even I in my subordinate situation became aware of this presence and I amongst others began to receive little notes signed W.S.C. from the private office demanding weekly reports of progress direct to him . . . It was like a stone thrown into a pond, the ripples got out in all directions, galvanising people at all levels to "press on" – and they did.'[8]

Mercifully the worst strategic horrors imagined in pre-war Admiralty and Chiefs of Staff appreciations had so far failed to come about. Japan remained neutral, her army not only deeply embroiled in the war with China but also having suffered a stinging defeat in Mongolia in June 1939 at the hands of a Soviet army under General Georgi Zhukov. A war of conquest against the European empires in the Pacific and South-East Asia was at present far from the Japanese government's mind. To the British naval staff the Imperial Japanese Navy therefore remained a potential menace rather than an immediate threat likely at any moment to demand the deployment of the British main fleet in the Far East. Italy, the central prong of the triple threat, likewise remained neutral, Mussolini's 'Pact of Steel' with Hitler turning out for the time being to resemble a pact of well boiled spaghetti. For Italy was once again waiting to rush to the aid of the victor, as a French diplomat had put it in 1915 when Italy belatedly entered the Great War on the side of the Allies. But if Italy ever went to war the British and French fleets in the Mediterranean together should have no difficulty in dealing with her navy. The Italian Navy was at present outnumbered by two battleships to three British and five French, and seven 8-inch gun cruisers to three British and six French. Only in 6-inch gun cruisers and destroyers did the Italians enjoy a modest superiority in surface ships, of eleven cruisers to three British and four French, and 61 destroyers to a combined Allied total of 57. In submarines the Italians' superiority was greater – 105 to 65.[9]

And the German Navy, the one active enemy at sea, remained in 1939 far short of the formidable threat it had constituted in 1914, or *would* have constituted if the war had begun in 1944, the date to which, at Hitler's behest, the German naval construction programme had been geared. Admiral Erich Raeder, Commander-in-Chief of the German Navy, had been aiming in his 'Z Plan' eventually to create a fleet of thirteen fast battleships, 33 cruisers, four aircraft carriers, some 250 U-boats and a swarm of big destroyers – all of them modern ships to the best specifications German technology could contrive.

Raeder intended that the surface ships should not operate as a single body like the Imperial High Seas Fleet, the strategic failure of which in the Great War was now plain, but in the form of task forces ranging the Atlantic to destroy the shipping that alone made it possible for Britain to wage war. A Royal Navy so much smaller in all classes of vessels than in 1914 and with a relatively small proportion of new or modernised battleships (even when current building plans had been completed) would have been hard put indeed to cope with such an offensive even if Italy and Japan had remained neutral.

Fortunately Hitler's diplomatic miscalculations over Poland plunged the German Navy into a war for which it was relatively even less ready at the time than the Royal Navy. Its heavy ships numbered only the two fast battleships *Scharnhorst* and *Gneisenau* (31,800 tons displacement; nine 11-inch guns; 32 knots); the three 'pocket' battleships (*Panzerschiff*): *Deutschland* (renamed *Lützow* in November 1939), *Admiral Graf Spee* and *Admiral Scheer* (all 12,100 tons displacement; six 11-inch guns; 26 knots); and two ancient battleships, the *Schlesien* and *Schleswig-Holstein*, obsolete even before the Great War. Otherwise it consisted of five cruisers (including the 8-inch gun heavy cruiser *Admiral Hipper*), seventeen destroyers and 56 U-boats, of which but 35 were immediately operational, and only 21 suitable for service in the Atlantic.[10] Captain Karl Dönitz, in 1939 the *Führer der U-boote*, bitterly condemned the neglect of U-boat construction in 1937–39 in favour of surface ships. 'Seldom indeed,' he was to write in his *Memoirs*, 'has any branch of the armed forces of a country gone to war so poorly equipped. It could, in fact, do no more than subject the enemy to a few odd pin-pricks. And pin-pricks are no means with which to try and force a great empire and one of the foremost maritime powers in the world to sue for peace.'[11] And yet even in that first autumn of the war the Royal Navy was to discover how deep and painful a local wound could be inflicted by such a 'pin-prick'.

German maritime aviation in September 1939 was in little better state than the U-boat arm. No aircraft carrier having yet been completed, all aircraft except for a few reconnaissance aircraft catapulted from battleships were land-based: 120 of them at North Sea bases and 108 at Baltic ones. The majority were the slow Heinkel 115 twin-engined general purpose/torpedo-bomber floatplane (186 mph; range 1,740 miles). In addition the Luftwaffe had earmarked six *Gruppen* of Heinkel He111 bombers for mine-laying and attacks on shipping.[12] The German Navy therefore offered no such formidable and concentrated air threat to surface warships as did the Imperial Japanese Navy's superbly practised and equipped carrier arm.

On a mere count of ships and aircraft, therefore, the Royal Navy at the outbreak of war appeared to enjoy an overwhelming superiority over its single current enemy, and this was so even after allowing for such imperial diversions as deploying a fleet of three battleships, a carrier and six cruisers in the Mediterranean to watch the Italians, and a carrier (the old *Eagle*) and four cruisers on the China Station. The Home Fleet at Scapa Flow in the Orkneys alone comprised five battleships (*Nelson, Rodney, Royal Oak, Royal Sovereign* and *Ramillies*); two battlecruisers (*Hood* and *Repulse*); two carriers (*Ark Royal* and *Furious*); fifteen cruisers and an anti-aircraft cruiser; seven destroyers; and twenty-one submarines. The Humber Force numbered two cruisers and nine destroyers; the Channel Force two battleships (*Resolution* and *Revenge*), two carriers (*Courageous* and *Hermes*), two cruisers and an anti-aircraft cruiser and five destroyers. In addition there were eighteen destroyers based on Plymouth, ten on Portsmouth, nine on Dover, six on Portland and eight on Rosyth and Milford Haven. All this amounted to an apparently formidable total with which to hold the ring in the North Sea, block the exits to the Atlantic, and defend home waters. Moreover North Atlantic Command and South Atlantic Command added another ten cruisers (eight of them in the South Atlantic) and thirteen destroyers to the forces available to defend the trade routes.[13] Further distant still were stationed four cruisers (including His Majesty's Australian Ship *Perth*) on the American and West Indies Station, and three more cruisers on the East Indies Station. And the dominions also made their modest contribution to the Empire's global naval strength: four cruisers in the Royal Australian Navy (apart from *Perth*) and five destroyers; two cruisers in the New Zealand Division of the Royal Navy; six destroyers in the Royal Canadian Navy.[14] The French Navy too, even though its main effort lay in the Mediterranean, contributed powerful extra support in the North Atlantic in the shape of its '*Force de Raid*' of two modern fast battleships (*Dunkerque* and the *Strasbourg*), a carrier, three cruisers and ten destroyers (one of them a 2,500 tonner).[15]

Yet when the comparative modernity of British and German ships is taken into consideration, and with it comparative speeds and fighting strength, the British margin of superiority becomes much more slender. Of Admiral Sir Charles Forbes's heavy ships in the Home Fleet (the very core of British seapower), only two, *Hood* and *Renown*, were both fast enough and powerful enough to catch and fight the *Scharnhorst* and the *Gneisenau*, or even the three 'pocket battleships'. *Nelson* and *Rodney* with their 16-inch guns (though dating from 1927, the Royal Navy's most modern capital ships) could not steam faster

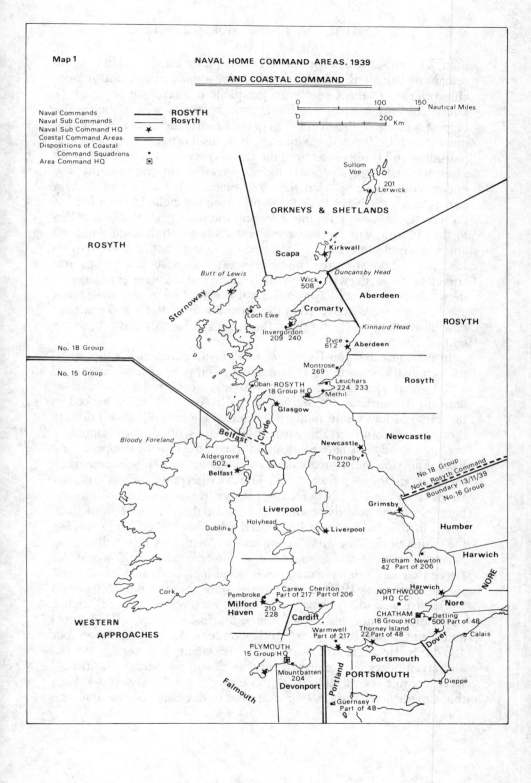

Map 1

NAVAL HOME COMMAND AREAS, 1939

AND COASTAL COMMAND

Naval Commands ——— **ROSYTH**
Naval Sub Commands ——— Rosyth
Naval Sub Command HQ ★
Coastal Command Areas ═══
Dispositions of Coastal
   Command Squadrons •
Area Command HQ ⊡

0   100   150 Nautical Miles
0   200 Km

Sullom Voe
201 Lerwick

ORKNEYS & SHETLANDS

Scapa
Kirkwall

Butt of Lewis
Wick 508
Duncansby Head

ROSYTH

Aberdeen

Stornoway
Loch Ewe
Cromarty
Kinnaird Head
Invergordon 209 240
Dyce 612
Aberdeen

ROSYTH

Montrose 269
Oban ROSYTH
18 Group HQ
Leuchars 224 233
Methil

Rosyth

No. 18 Group
No. 15 Group

Glasgow
Belfast Clyde

Bloody Foreland
Aldergrove 502
Belfast

Newcastle
Thornaby 220

Newcastle

No. 18 Group
Nore, Rosyth Command
Boundary 13/11/39
No. 16 Group

Grimsby

Liverpool

Dublin ○
Holyhead
Liverpool

Humber

Bircham Newton
42 Part of 206

Harwich

Cork ○

Pembroke
**Milford
Haven** 210 228

Carew Cheriton
Part of 217 Part of 206
Cardiff

NORTHWOOD
HQ CC

Harwich
Nore

NORE

**WESTERN
APPROACHES**

Warmwell
Part of 217
Thorney Island
22 Part of 48

CHATHAM
16 Group HQ
Detling
500 Part of 48

Dover

Calais

PLYMOUTH
15 Group HQ
Mountbatten 204
Devonport

Portland

PORTSMOUTH

Portsmouth

Dieppe

Falmouth

Guernsey
Part of 48

than 23 knots, as against the German battleships' 32 knots. The remaining British 'R' class battleships were unmodernised and vulnerable veterans of the Great War, incapable of making more than 21 knots. And, of course, the *Hood*, though fast as well as being the biggest warship in the world, was herself a virtually unaltered floating museum of 1920 naval technology. In cruisers, those workhorses of patrolling and trade protection, the Royal Navy was desperately weak, given the vast sweeps of water to be covered – and given too that the enemy could pick his own time and place to launch a sortie. As a consequence the Navy was soon to find itself compelled to supplement the cruisers on its patrol line covering the exits from the North Sea to the Atlantic with 'armed merchant cruisers', bulky, unarmoured and vulnerable liners newly equipped with 6-inch guns. Destroyers for fleet and convoy work, humble escort vessels such as sloops and corvettes, were likewise desperately scarce, minesweepers too; and these shortages would continue until the first of twenty new Hunt class escorts were delivered in the second half of 1940, and fourteen new minesweepers (ten of them the improved Bangor class) from the end of 1940 onwards.[16]

In maritime aviation Britain was still ill-prepared either to defend its own battle squadrons and merchant shipping against enemy air and U-boat attack, or to counter-attack the German Navy on or beneath the surface. Of the 60 Fleet Air Arm aircraft embarked in the Home Fleet's sole modern carrier *Ark Royal*, 42 were obsolete though rugged and versatile Swordfish biplanes, fifteen the disappointing and already obsolete Skua, and three of the equally disappointing Roc. The Channel Force carriers *Courageous* and *Hermes* embarked together another 45 Swordfish. The Mediterranean Fleet's carrier *Glorious* was in little better case, with twelve Sea Gladiator biplane fighters (a type already obsolete as a land fighter) and 24 Swordfish, plus a further twelve Swordfish based ashore at Dekeila in Egypt. On the China Station the *Eagle*'s complement, at eighteen Swordfish, was a mere gesture towards maritime airpower.[17] Nor could Royal Air Force Coastal Command make up for the Fleet Air Arm's deficiencies, for in September 1939 its aircraft too were few and out-of-date. Its workhorse was still the Avro Anson, with a range of only 510 miles, endurance of four and a half hours, a cruising speed of 114 knots and a tiny bomb load of two 100-pounders. As early as November 1937 the Air Staff had wanted a replacement but here again the aircraft industry let the armed services down, for neither the Bristol Beaufort nor the Blackburn Botha torpedo-bombers were to reach the squadrons before 1940; and the Botha was to prove in the event another complete operational failure.[18] Because of these production delays, 250 Lockheed B14s (named by the RAF the 'Hudson') had therefore to be ordered from America, but by the outbreak of war only one squadron had been equipped with them. The Hudson enjoyed almost double the Anson's range, five times the bombload, and could fly faster and for longer. In the meantime two Coastal Command squadrons were still flying the 1928 Vickers Vildebeest! The position with regard to flying boats for long-distance sea surveillance was even worse: the new Saro Lerwick had proved another of the British aircraft industry's fiascoes, and only two squadrons had so far been equipped with the Short Sunderland, one of its successes.[19] Here Britain had again to resort to American technology, and order the Consolidated PBY-5 flying boat (to be known to the RAF as the 'Catalina'), in service with the United States Navy since 1936; however deliveries to Britain were not expected until 1941.[20]

It was therefore an ironic enough comment on these weaknesses in maritime aviation and on the related obsession of the RAF with the idea of a bomber offensive against enemy cities that the very first British air operations in the Second World War took the form of Bomber Command attacks on the German naval bases at Wilhelmshaven and Brunsbüttel. Fifteen Blenheims set out for Wilhelmshaven on 4 September; ten of them found the target through thick cloud, but only one hit an enemy vessel, the pocket battleship *Admiral Scheer*, the bombs bouncing harmlessly off the armoured deck into the water. The only actual damage to the enemy was caused by a Blenheim crashing on to the fo'c'sle of the training cruiser *Emden*. Of fourteen Wellingtons despatched to Brunsbüttel the majority turned back or failed to locate their objectives due to bad weather, the only damage inflicted here being to the sides of the dock.[21] A squadron of British warships in the North Sea at the last moment averted an attack on them by a section of three Wellingtons by belatedly making the Royal Navy's recognition signal for the day. The operations of 4 September cost the RAF seven out of 29 aircraft.[22] All in all, as John Terraine points out in *The Right of the Line*, it proved a sharp first lesson for the RAF in the harsh school of war in terms of all-weather navigation and target acquisition.[23]

Yet for the Royal Navy too the opening phase of the conflict – in fact, the whole period of Churchill's tenure of the Admiralty – was to prove a time of painful learning; but in the Navy's case, often of relearning old lessons forgotten or disdained since the Great War. For Churchill himself it was to be a time also for reinventing old strategic follies in new guises, but with no happier results than in 1914–15.

The first of the lessons had not been slow in coming. At 2100 on 3 September 1939 the outward-bound liner *Athenia*, 13,581 tons, was torpedoed and sunk some 250 miles north-west of Ireland by the U-30, with the loss of 112 lives, including 28 American. It was this event that next day prompted Churchill's first 'prayer' in office, demanding from the Director of Naval Intelligence 'a statement of the German U-boat forces, actual and prospective, for the next few months . . .'[24] The news of the sinking evoked in the public memory the torpedoing of the Cunard liner *Lusitania* by a U-boat in 1915, also with the loss of American lives; and the British press treated the incident as a timely reminder of unchanged German frightfulness. In fact, the commander of the U-30, Lieutenant F. J. Lemp, had breached Hitler's strict orders to wage submarine warfare according to the Hague Convention in order not to embitter Britain and France against the peace moves he meant to make once Poland was crushed. Only by stages did Hitler relax restrictions on U-boat operations until by mid-November 1939 all ships, including liners, could be attacked without warning if 'clearly identified as hostile', while neutral shipping was warned not to enter a designated war zone eastwards of Longitude 20° West, that of Iceland.[25]

By this time, however, the reintroduction of the convoy system had robbed the U-boat of such prey as the *Athenia*, ships sailing singly out of peacetime into war. The very first convoy, of eight ships, actually left Gibraltar for Cape Town on the day before Britain declared war. From 6 September shipping along the East Coast between the Thames and the Firth of Forth was organised into convoy. Next day outward bound ocean convoys began, sailing on alternate days from Southend and Liverpool. They were escorted only as far as Longitude 12° West, just west of Ireland, and two days after losing their escort the convoys dispersed into individual sailings. Southward bound ships from both these alternate convoys were re-formed off the Scilly Islands into new convoys for Gibraltar, escorts from which picked them up west of the Straits of Gibraltar. The first homeward-bound convoy sailed from Freetown, Sierra Leone, on 14 September; next day there followed the first from Kingston, Jamaica. On 16 September convoy HXF1 steamed away from Halifax, Nova Scotia; the first of all the long procession of Halifax convoys that were to sustain the British war effort in the next five and a half years with North American weapons, aircraft, machine tools and food despite all the hazards of tempest,

U-boat, surface raider and marauding German aircraft. Convoys between Bergen in Norway and Methil in the Firth of Forth began to operate in the first week of November 1939, a week or so before the U-boats were finally freed to sink at sight.[26]

The routines of the escorts' war established themselves. At Defence (Cruising) Stations men could go below to eat and sleep in closed-up mess decks crammed with bodies, kit and hammocks; the bulkheads running with condensation, the air thick with human exhalations. At Action Stations at guns and depth-charge launchers on decks often swept with spray or during long watches on equally open bridges, cold and tiredness were kept at bay with snatched meals ('Action Messing') of the ubiquitous Navy pea soup and corned beef 'wedgies' (or 'sarnies': sandwiches), or mugs of 'kye' (or 'ky' or 'ki'), the thick cocoa drink made from crumbled slabs of unsweetened chocolate mixed with condensed milk – the high spot of a night watch. Down below, engine-room and boiler-room staffs sweated in their deafening, oil-stinking ovens; sonar operators sat in their cubby-holes, earphones clamped to head, intent to catch the echo rebounding from the hull of a U-boat submerged in ambush.

Yet the operational lesson apparently taught by the opening phase of the struggle with the U-boat was misleading, for it seemed to confirm the complacent pre-war Admiralty appreciation that the convoy system plus improved sonar had neutralised the menace, even though it was known that the enemy at present had only a few boats at sea. In September, a month when many ships were still sailing independently, the Allies lost 41 ships (153,879 tons). In October the total fell to 27 ships (134,807 tons); in November 21 ships (51,589 tons); in December it rose modestly to 25 ships (80,881 tons). These were totals far short of the horrific 881,000 tons lost in April 1917 alone; and in any case only twelve of the 114 ships lost had been sunk in convoy.[27] And meanwhile German shipping had been once again swept from the seas by British seapower. Of the individual vessels which tried to sneak home to Germany after the outbreak of war no fewer than seventeen were intercepted by the Royal Navy between 7 September 1939 and 4 January 1940.[28] This renewed ring of blockade was completed by the establishment of contraband control over neutral shipping. The Navy's Northern Patrol, watching the seas between south of the Faeroes to Iceland, intercepted and sent into port for search (mostly Kirkwall, the main contraband control base) over 300 neutral ships in the first four months of the war.[29]

Blockade rated as a major factor in the Allied grand strategy for eventually bringing down Nazi Germany, for economic warfare experts in Whitehall believed that the German economy was already stretched to the limit, and therefore vulnerable either to shortages of key raw materials or to strategic bombing of vital industrial plants. Yet the economists miscalculated; Germany was still operating an almost peacetime economy, with immense potential for industrial mobilisation. Moreover, the Russo-German Pact of August 1939 gave Germany general access to Soviet oil, coal and wheat; and Hitler's pre-war development of 'Autarky' (economic self-sufficiency) had successfully put German technological genius to work on inventing substitutes for such imported raw materials as rubber. In the Second World War Germany was not to be the economic prisoner shut up by blockade in Central Europe and progressively starved which she had been during much of the Great War. In fact, contrary to the prevailing assumption among Whitehall planners in 1939, Germany was far better placed economically to last out a long war than Britain herself, despite Britain's vaunted access by sea to the resources of the world. For by the outbreak of the war Britain was, as the Treasury warned, already within a year or so of running out of foreign exchange with which to buy those resources.[30]

Whatever might be the hopes for the eventual slow strangulation of Germany by blockade, it was all too immediately apparent that British seapower could do nothing to succour Poland in her brief, lone and desperate fight against the German armies converging deep and fast into her heartland. From the first day of the war Admiral Sir Charles Forbes took the Home Fleet on repeated offensive 'sweeps' across the North Sea, but netted nothing; vain gestures with silent guns in the mists and rain. Here to be learned afresh was an old lesson that dated back through the Great War and the conflict with Bonaparte to the struggle against Philip II's Spain under Elizabeth I – that seapower alone is impotent in relation to the outcome of a decisive land campaign on the continent of Europe.

It was exactly this galling impotence – together with the apparently only passive defence against the U-boat offered by escorted convoys – which stirred Churchill's restlessly aggressive mind to look for means by which the Royal Navy could directly strike at Germany and her armed forces. Only two days after his return to the Admiralty, he was urging the formation of 'Units of Search', consisting of one cruiser and one aircraft carrier, to seek and find surface raiders such as pocket battleships. He also favoured hunting groups to range the seas after U-boats, his views here chiming with a strong school in the Admiralty itself which included Pound. But during the very next week following Churchill's memorandum to the First Sea Lord advocating 'Units of

Search', the enemy wrote his own lethal comments on this 'offensive' concept. The Admiralty had temporarily detached the Home Fleet carrier *Ark Royal* and the Channel Force carrier *Courageous* with small destroyer escorts as two hunting groups against U-boats in the Western Approaches. On 14 September the *Ark Royal* was attacked by the U-39 west of the Hebrides, but fortunately the torpedoes exploded prematurely – at this period German magnetic pistols for detonating torpedoes were unreliable; a failure in German technology – and the *Ark*'s escorting destroyers promptly sank the U-boat. Although the encounter thus ended well, the Royal Navy came very close to losing its single modern carrier.

But only three days later the U-29 (Lieutenant-Commander Schuhart) sighted the *Courageous* (Captain W. T. Mackaig-Jones) in the Bristol Channel escorted by only two destroyers, two others having been sent to the aid of an attacked merchant ship. Thanks to 'Horchdienst' ('listening service') intercepts of British radio traffic and B-Dienst's ability to read the Admiralty cypher, the U-boat command was well aware that *Courageous* was cruising in this sea area. At 1950 (British time) Schuhart fired three torpedoes at the huge bulk of the 22,500-ton carrier at a range of less than 3,000 yards. Two of them struck home, and within fifteen minutes *Courageous* sank with the loss of 518 lives, including her captain. In that single brief encounter and in the course of a relatively minor mission Britain had lost one-sixth of her strength in large carriers; a grievous and needless waste of assets.[31] This marked the abrupt end of the Navy's employment of fleet carriers as submarine hunters. The sinking reminded Churchill himself, with his ever-present memories of the previous war, of the day almost exactly 25 years ago when the U-9 sank three old British cruisers in quick succession off the Dutch coast, and demonstrated for the first time the submarine's true potential as a free-ranging predator.[32]

On 26 September *Ark Royal* again came perilously near destruction – this time at the hands of the Luftwaffe; a new lesson for the Royal Navy to learn, if it were willing to do so. The *Ark Royal* was at the time serving as part of a task force including capital ships, sent to the Heligoland Bight to cover the escape on the surface of a damaged British submarine, *Spearfish*. It was a bright morning, beginning with a sunrise like, wrote an eyewitness, 'a luxurious fan spread from horizon to horizon'.[33] Since *Ark Royal* had no radar, warning of imminent air attack depended on lookouts with binoculars. At 1100 shadowing aircraft were seen low on the horizon. By this time *Ark Royal*'s Swordfish aircraft were already on distant patrol. Skua fighters were flown, and one shot down a Dornier flying boat; so far, so good. But then began the first air attack in history on a fleet at sea, striking suddenly out of high clouds. As the *Ark Royal*'s anti-aircraft guns opened fire, and the great ship heeled as she steamed at full speed under full starboard helm, a Heinkel He111 bomber dived on her from 5,000 feet, releasing a 1,000-kilo bomb at 1,500 feet. The bomb exploded in the water only twenty feet from the port bow.

'It was so close,' wrote the *Ark Royal*'s gunnery officer, Lieutenant-Commander T. V. Briggs, 'that the whole ship reared up and heeled several degrees to starboard. We thought we had been hit.'[34] So did the German pilot; and German propaganda broadcasts, claiming that the *Ark* had been sunk, mockingly asked the Admiralty: 'Where is the *Ark Royal*?' Wrote Briggs later, 'This was a superb and bravely executed attack against fierce A.A. fire.' It was followed by low level attacks against the fleet, although only HMS *Hood* received any damage at all: '. . . one could see through binoculars that a great flake of armour had been knocked off her side plating, where a bomb had hit it and it glanced off into the sea'.[35] But the Admiralty only drew from this novel experience the lulling lesson that the danger of air attack on a fleet had been much exaggerated.[36]

Only a month after the U-29 torpedoed the *Courageous*, another of Dönitz's U-boats gave a fresh and even more sensational demonstration of the Royal Navy's continued vulnerability to underwater attack, sonar notwithstanding, and also taught again another of the old lessons unlearned by government and Navy after the Great War: in this case, the importance of secure fleet bases. In the small hours of 14 October 1939 – a clear but moonless night sky brightly flared by the northern lights – the U-47 (Lieutenant-Commander Prien) slid on the surface into the Home Fleet main base of Scapa Flow via Kirk Sound, the eastern gap between the Orkneys mainland and the island of Lamb Holm. Riding the top of high water, Prien successfully crept through the very narrow channel between the sunken blockships across the Sound and the mainland; an operation to prickle the neck, not least when the U-boat's hull scraped the bottom and ran her bows into the cable of a blockship. Once through into the wide waters of the Flow Prien sighted (as he thought) two battleships alongside the north shore: in fact, the battleship *Royal Oak* (27,500 tons) and the old seaplane carrier *Pegasus*. At 0058 on 15 October he fired three torpedoes at the *Royal Oak*; only one hit home and that was so far up in the bows as to cause little damage. On board *Royal Oak* the Captain (Captain W. G. Benn, RN) and some of his officers who went forward to investigate concluded that it must have been some minor internal explosion.

Meanwhile Prien, with exemplary coolness of nerve, turned away to reload, then attacked again at 0116. This time all three torpedoes struck, and the *Royal Oak*, one of Britain's only eleven operational capital ships, capsized thirteen minutes later with the loss of 833 members of her company including Rear-Admiral H. E. C. Blagrove (commanding Second Battle Squadron). While British vessels frantically depth-charged the Flow behind him, Prien took U-47 out of the narrow passage past the blockships against a 10-knot current. The whole operation had been carefully planned by Dönitz, the *Führer der U-boote*, on the basis of a complete set of aerial photographs of the British base taken by the Luftwaffe, which had revealed the gap past the blockships exploited by Prien.[37]

When Churchill was brought the news of the sinking, recalled an eyewitness, 'tears sprang to his eyes and he muttered, "Poor fellows, trapped in those black depths."'[38] Yet he had other reasons for strong emotion over the loss of the *Royal Oak*. For only a month earlier, and within a fortnight of taking office, he had travelled to Scapa Flow to visit the Home Fleet and confer with Admiral Forbes. Here he had learned at first hand that, just as at the beginning of the Great War in 1914, Scapa Flow (Britain's main fleet base in conflicts with Germany) was so deficient in defences as to render it unsafe for the fleet to use it as a haven; truly an old lesson now to be painfully relearned. All the elaborate boom and net defences against submarines, all the shore defences and batteries erected during the Great War had been demolished in the years of 'peace' and economy that followed; and never restored. The anti-submarine defences at the outbreak of the Second World War consisted only of a single line of nets across the main entrance of Hoxa, Switha and Hoy, while the eastern entrances (including the one used by U-47) were only partially blocked by what remained of the 1914–18 blockships and a few extra recently placed hulks. Of three more blockships despatched since the war began to close these eastern channels, two had been sunk en route, and a third arrived the day after the *Royal Oak* was lost.

Nor was Scapa better defended against the new threat of bomber attack, for it was equipped with one temporary radar station, only eight obsolete 4.5-inch anti-aircraft guns, and altogether lacked short-range anti-aircraft batteries. A letter from Forbes to the Admiralty on 5 September had explained just why Scapa was so ill-prepared. In the first place – and this was, of course, Chamberlain and the final gasps of appeasement – the government had instructed even in 1939 that nothing must be done which would indicate to the British public and press or Germany that the Royal Navy was preparing for war against Germany. Secondly, there was a lack of local labour to carry out various works, while outside labour could not easily be brought in because of shortage of accommodation. And finally there were the hiatuses caused by deaths of the Controller of the Navy (Vice-Admiral Sir R. G. H. Henderson), in May 1939 and the then First Sea Lord (Backhouse) in July.[39] As a result of Scapa's vulnerability Admiral Forbes was compelled to rotate his fleet between Loch Ewe, the Clyde and Rosyth when not at sea hunting German warships (as he in fact was when the U-47 sank the *Royal Oak*).

Three days after the *Royal Oak* went down it was the Luftwaffe's turn with two squadrons of Junkers 88 twin-engined bombers to test the defences of the Home Fleet's main base, but they found the Flow empty now except for the Great War veteran battleship *Iron Duke* (once Jellicoe's flagship), now used as a base ship and floating coastal defence battery. The German bombers damaged her so badly below the water line with a near miss as to compel beaching her in shallow water. One Junkers was shot down by anti-aircraft fire. The base's fighter defence, obsolete Fleet Air Arm aircraft, was too slow to intercept the 280 mph Ju 88s. This raid came the day after attacks in similar strength on warships in the Firth of Forth, slightly damaging the cruiser *Southampton* (mercifully a bomb passed through her without exploding) and a destroyer. The Forth lay within the air cover provided by the modern aircraft of Fighter Command, which shot down two of the Junkers. The Luftwaffe's raids on British naval bases had therefore so far proved hardly more successful than Bomber Command's on German.

Nonetheless, as Churchill now wrote to Pound, the Home Fleet had been 'driven out of Scapa through pre-war neglect of its defences against air and U-boat attack'.[40] So began fresh and urgent discussions to resolve the problem of this outcast fleet. On 31 October Churchill, Pound and the Deputy Chief of the Air Staff (Air Vice-Marshal R. E. C. Peirse) visited Forbes in his flagship, then moored in the Clyde. All agreed that Loch Ewe, being even more undefended than Scapa though some 130 miles more distant from German bases, exposed the Fleet to great danger. The Admiralty opinion favoured basing the Fleet in the Clyde but Forbes strongly urged that this was too remote (200 miles south of Loch Ewe) to enable him to intercept German sorties into the Atlantic via the Iceland–Faeroes gap. Rosyth was ruled out because the narrow single channel through the Firth of Forth would facilitate enemy air or U-boat attack. Forbes finally convinced Churchill that Scapa Flow was still strategically the right place for the Fleet's base, and that its defences should therefore be put in order as an utmost priority. The conference thereupon agreed to do the work that ought to have been done in peacetime: extra booms, nets and blockships for the eastern channel into the Flow, minefields, electric indicator loops on the seabed to detect the passage of hostile vessels, more patrol craft, coastal defence batteries to cover every approach, 88 heavy and 40 light anti-aircraft guns, searchlights, balloon barrages, an extra radar station. Two squadrons of modern monoplane fighters would be stationed in the North of Scotland to provide air cover, with a further four squadrons available to meet heavy attack. But all the new base installations would take four to five months to complete. In the meantime the Home Fleet would have to continue resorting to its temporary and hazardous anchorages on the west coast of Scotland, hundreds of miles further distant than Scapa from the key strategic areas of the Norwegian and North Seas.[41]

Now a further tragic instalment in sailors' lives was about to be paid for pre-war political folly and neglect – in this case, the Labour government's insistence in 1930 on accepting the 'starvation number' of 50 cruisers in the London Naval Treaty negotiations, despite the pleas of the then First Sea Lord, Admiral of the Fleet Sir Frederick Field; a number only increased to 58 (including eight dominion ships) by the outbreak of war. At 1551 on 23 November 1939 – rain showers but otherwise good visibility; wind north-north-west, Force 5, sea rising – the armed merchant cruiser *Rawalpindi* (16,700 tons; Captain E. C. Kennedy, RN) on the Northern Patrol between the Faeroes and Iceland sighted a German fast battleship (classed by the Royal Navy as a 'battlecruiser') four miles to westwards; and reported the sighting to Admiral Forbes, C-in-C, Home Fleet, in the Clyde. Shortly afterwards Kennedy signalled that the enemy ship was actually a pocket battleship, the *Deutschland*. In fact his first identification had been the correct one: for he had seen the *Scharnhorst*, which was steaming on a course 300° in company with her sister ship *Gneisenau* on their first joint sortie of the war.

Kennedy, with four elderly 6-inch guns mounted in his high-sided, unarmoured and highly vulnerable vessel, was therefore confronting a combined broadside of eighteen radar-directed 11-inch guns. Even the odds which Kennedy believed he was facing were heavy enough – six 11-inch and eight 5.9-inch guns mounted in a well armoured warship. It was now to fall to Kennedy to be the first commander of a King's ship in the Second World War to demonstrate instinctive

[73]

obedience to the spirit of Nelson's final flag signal at Trafalgar: 'Engage the enemy more closely!'

Gneisenau and *Scharnhorst* had sailed from Wilhelmshaven on 21 November, Vice-Admiral Wilhelm Marschall (Flag Officer in Command) flying his flag in the *Gneisenau*. His operation order laid down the purpose of the sortie:

> In accordance with the directive of the C-in-C Navy on the threatening of the N. Atlantic shipping routes and the consequent diversion and concentration of the enemy forces attainable by it, I intend to break through into the area Iceland–Faeroes. From this position to advance towards the suspected enemy patrol lines, to feint a break-through with the battleships into the N. Atlantic by steering a westerly course, and finally by sheering off to the North and by use of the long nights, to make home waters again at high speed.[42]

Neither German ship glimpsed any British aircraft during their run northwards to the Norwegian coast and then north-westwards into the Iceland–Faeroes gap on 21–23 November; an indication of Coastal Command's poverty of resources for long-range sea surveillance. It was the *Scharnhorst*, on *Gneisenau*'s starboard beam, which at 1507 (British time) on 23 November spotted the *Rawalpindi* to starboard, reporting accordingly to the flagship. After an exchange of VHF radio signals between the two German ships, the *Scharnhorst*, on Vice-Admiral Marschall's command, changed course from 300° to 000° and increased speed from 18 to 24 knots in order to investigate the strange merchant ship; 'a large ship,' according to *Scharnhorst*'s radio report, 'two masts, one funnel.' At 1532, at a range of 21,000 yards, 'after ascertaining from the foretop that this was a vessel of considerable size and considering it possible from her constant alteration of course that she was an auxiliary cruiser', recorded Captain Kurt Hoffman later in *Scharnhorst*'s log, 'I ordered "Action Stations!"' A minute later, as his ship's company tumbled to Action Stations to the blare of klaxons, Hoffman signalled Marschall: 'Large merchant vessel. Course approximately 180°. Vessel turning away. I am closing her.' At 1535, course 060°, position 63°48'N, 11°40'W, *Scharnhorst* signalled *Rawalpindi*: 'To British merchant cruiser – Heave to. Do not use radio. Where from and where bound?' Then in English: 'What ship? Do not use your wireless.' The *Rawalpindi* replied that she had understood, but instead of compliantly heaving to, she altered course further to the south-east and increased speed. At 1539 *Scharnhorst*'s main batteries reported ready for action. *Rawalpindi* now bore 055°, range about 17,000 yards and shortening. By 1555, with the November dusk already beginning to dim the light, the range was down to under 9,000 yards. Seven minutes later, as *Rawalpindi*'s crew began dumping smoke floats overboard, Captain Hoffman ordered a warning shot to be fired across her bows. One minute later, as more smoke floats were dropped, and it being 'now beyond a doubt that the vessel was a merchant cruiser', he immediately gave orders to open fire.

At 1604 *Scharnhorst*'s radar-directed guns fired their first salvo at a range of about 8,250 yards, the 11-inch shells soon smashing through the *Rawalpindi*'s thin plating and setting her ablaze. At 1607 the British ship returned the fire, probably inflicting at this time the one hit suffered by *Scharnhorst*, a 6-inch shell on the quarter deck which failed to penetrate the armour. While *Scharnhorst*'s guns pounded the *Rawalpindi*'s unarmoured bulk, the British ship's salvoes were falling some 100 yards astern of her enemy. At 1610 Kennedy and his crew enjoyed a brief respite because the *Rawalpindi* was momentarily screened by smoke, mist and shell splashes, but next minute the *Gneisenau* joined in too. By now the *Rawalpindi* was burning fiercely amidships. Yet her guns were still in action, their fall of shot now some 400 yards on *Scharnhorst*'s port side. At 1614 hours *Scharnhorst* turned away to starboard because of false reports of approaching torpedo tracks. At 1617 the German ships ceased fire. The action had lasted barely ten minutes.

The November afternoon had now thickened into deep dusk under a bright moon, so that the flames from the doomed *Rawalpindi* were the more luridly visible from the German ships. At 1630 there was an explosion on board. Fifteen minutes later the German ships began looking for and picking up survivors in boats. Between 1715 and 1735, as the *Rawalpindi* was riven by further explosions, came her repeated last signal: 'Please send boats.' She remained afloat until 1920, when after two more explosions the flames that had marked her position were engulfed by darkness. Kennedy and 270 members of his ship's company perished; 38 survived, 27 of those being picked up by their adversaries.

In the meantime there had occurred a further encounter in the dusk and rain squalls. At 1814 hours, *Gneisenau* sighted a strange vessel some six and a half miles distant, and Vice-Admiral Marschall ordered his ships to cease picking up survivors and steer to the eastward at high speed. Very soon *Scharnhorst*'s after range-finder and her foretop also reported what appeared to be a large warship astern showing no lights. The ship was in fact HMS *Newcastle*, which had almost simultaneously sighted the German ships. The *Newcastle*, nearest cruiser to the *Rawalpindi* in the Northern Patrol line, had steamed at utmost speed to her support as soon as she heard her initial signals that she was in the presence of the enemy. At 1815, according to her log, HMS *Newcastle* (9,500 tons; Captain J. Figgins) 'sighted darkened ship Brg [bearing] 070° 13000^x [yards]'.[43] Two minutes later she 'sighted 2nd darkened ship to Starbd of first'. Henceforward Admiral Forbes and the Admiralty knew that they had to deal with two German battleships. At 1822, with the enemy apparently closing, Captain Figgins turned the *Newcastle* away and reduced to 15 knots. At 1824 when visibility had dropped to two cables (about 400 yards) in rain squalls, the *Newcastle*, lacking radar like most British ships at this time, lost touch with the enemy. At 1833 Figgins adopted a course and speed 'as requisite to regain contact'. Twenty minutes later the *Rawalpindi* was sighted bearing 140° 'heavily on fire'. At 1859 the *Newcastle*'s log noted: 'Light reported brg 290° ... increased speed to 25 to investigate ...' But the light was not confirmed, and at 1917 the *Newcastle* altered back towards the *Rawalpindi* – just about the time the merchant cruiser finally sank. The German battleships, for their part, did not seek to attack and sink the unidentified British warship, being dissuaded – too easily? – by the poor visibility and the need to put about in order to engage. They slipped away at high speed behind a smoke screen and trailing curtains of rain. The German tactical retreat proved the prelude to strategic retirement. Vice-Admiral Marschall, knowing from Horch-dienst radio intercepts that his presence had been reported by the *Rawalpindi* and that all available British forces would be hunting for him, now abandoned his plan of feinting into the North Atlantic, and instead began to follow a tortuous route home – no question here of 'Engage the enemy more closely', nor of the bold enterprise of such earlier corsairs against the Royal Navy as the Frenchman the Bailli de Suffren or the American John Paul Jones.

Nonetheless, Marschall had by now achieved one of the major objectives of his sortie, namely, 'the consequent diversion and concentration of the enemy forces'. For British seapower was like a tightly stretched web: pressure at one point pulled it and weakened it elsewhere. On receipt of *Rawalpindi*'s report of a pocket battleship in the Iceland–Faeroes gap Admiral Forbes ordered the Home Fleet, then in the Clyde, to raise steam as quickly as possible, while the Admiralty began to redeploy all Britain's naval strength in the North Atlantic and home waters in order to hunt down what was suspected to be the *Deutschland*. But these very counter-measures in turn show up item by item how scanty the Royal Navy's available resources, how inadequate its preparedness for war, were in relation to its

(Above) 'All the ceremony of formal surrender.'
Admiral Sir David Beatty, Commander-in-Chief of
the Grand Fleet, receives a German delegation in his
flagship HMS *Queen Elizabeth,* to negotiate the
internment of the Imperial German High Seas Fleet, 15
November 1918. Painting by Sir John Lavery. (IWM)

(Below) 'Her impressive size and beauty of line served
to disguise the reality of an obsolete and vulnerable ship'
– the battlecruiser HMS *Hood* (41,200 tons displacement),
which was sunk by the *Bismarck* on 24 May 1941. (IWM)

(Above) British battleships in line ahead in peacetime – 'Before the Second World War . . . a future Jutland against the Japanese fleet in Far Eastern waters befogged the Royal Navy's thinking.' (IWM) (Below, left) Admiral Sir Charles Forbes – 'a sea officer of faultless manners and a deep sense of loyalty' – Commander-in-Chief, Home Fleet, 1938–40. (IWM) (Below, right) Admiral of the Fleet Sir Dudley Pound, First Sea Lord and Chief of Naval Staff, 1939–43. 'He ran the Navy as if he were the executive officer of a ship, endlessly prying into and arranging matters of detail.' (IWM)

'No fewer than eight powerful hunting groups were formed to deal with two German ships. . . .' The Pocket Battleship *Admiral Graf Spee (right)*, six 11-inch guns, raided, with her sister ship *Deutschland,* Allied shipping in September–December 1939. The *Graf Spee* was scuttled off Montevideo on 17 December 1939 after being attacked by the cruisers *Exeter, Ajax,* and *Achilles.* (Hulton) *(Below)* 'Churchill laid his own grasp on the tiller of British seapower' as First Lord of the Admiralty, 1939–40, Prime Minister and Minister of Defence, 1940–45. Here he is being cheered by the ship's company of HMS *Exeter* in February 1940 when they returned to Plymouth from the *Graf Spee* battle. (Hulton)

(Left) 'Nothing could have been more Nelsonian.' The German-occupied Norwegian port of Narvik after the attack, on 10 April 1940, by British destroyers under Captain Warburton-Lee, RN, later awarded the Victoria Cross. (IWM) (Below) The harbour at Dunkirk – 'that horrific landfall' – showing the moles from which the majority of the 338,000 Allied soldiers rescued during 'Operation Dynamo' were lifted. (IWM)

commitments, even in the face of so limited a threat as the existing German Navy; and, in the present case, so limited an apparent threat as Marschall's sortie.

It was because of the defenceless state of Scapa that Forbes was temporarily based in the Clyde, which in turn meant that he required an extra 24 hours' steaming to reach the sea area for intercepting an enemy retirement. In any case, his own strength had been reduced by detachments and the loss of the *Royal Oak* to two battleships (*Nelson* and *Rodney*), the cruiser *Devonshire* and seven destroyers. He had no carrier with him, for the battleship *Warspite* was away escorting a Halifax-bound convoy, while the battlecruiser *Repulse* and the carrier *Furious* were already at Halifax, Nova Scotia, ready to cover a homeward-bound convoy; the *Hood* was in Plymouth. This dispersal of striking power to cover the Atlantic routes in the face of another threat (see below, pp. 78–80) had been inevitable in view of the Royal Navy's overall shortage of capital ships, carriers and cruisers.

Now the Admiralty sought in haste to reconcentrate its scattered strength in order to meet the German sortie (known from *Newcastle*'s reports to consist of two heavy ships). The *Warspite*, *Repulse* and *Furious*, together with cruisers at present spread out on patrol or escort duties, were all ordered to converge on a blocking position in the Denmark Strait, gateway to the Atlantic, while the *Hood* and the French battleship *Dunkerque* were also ordered to the same area from the south. But all this was exactly what Vice-Admiral Marschall and his C-in-C, Admiral Raeder, had hoped for; and what they now knew from Horchdienst intercepts and B-Dienst decrypts of Admiralty encyphered signals that they had successfully brought about.

Admiral Forbes's own hopes of getting between the supposed *Deutschland* and the other unidentified German warship sighted by *Newcastle* and their home base were to be spoilt by further British deficiencies. The Naval Intelligence Division, not having broken the German naval cyphers, could offer no such guidance to Forbes about Marschall's movements as German Intelligence was providing to Marschall about Forbes's. Having no carrier with him, Forbes could not carry out his own air search, while Coastal Command failed to locate the enemy amid the North Sea mists and cloud. On the contrary, it was German flying boats which reported the position of some of Forbes's ships, so helping Marschall to choose the best timing and courses for his evasive manoeuvres on the successful run home. Even the original departure of the *Scharnhorst* and *Gneisenau* from Wilhelmshaven without detection had been made the easier because Coastal Command lacked the appropriate aircraft and equipment to carry out regular reconnaissance or aerial photography of the German fleet bases.[44]

As it was, Forbes could only sweep the sea from a midway position between the Faeroes and Norway like a blind man waving a stick, while Marschall danced round him, making adroit use of the cover provided by bad weather and poor visibility to slip through the British cruiser screen and back to Wilhelmshaven, reached on 27 November.

But this was not the sum of Forbes's woes. Firstly, the *Rodney* had developed serious rudder defects and had to be sent back to port. Then, on 4 December, when Forbes, returning from his fruitless hunt for Marschall, took his fleet into Loch Ewe on a brief visit in order to refuel his destroyers, the hull of his flagship *Nelson* was severely damaged by a magnetic mine laid in the Loch by a U-boat. The *Nelson* was thus another important casualty of the Navy's lack of a secure base; and another triumph for the German Horchdienst or 'Y' Intelligence and cryptoanalysis, which had revealed the Home Fleet's supposedly top secret occasional use of Loch Ewe. *Nelson* was not to return to active service until August 1940. The total of fifteen capital ships allowed Britain under the Washington Treaty had now shrunk to nine actually available for sea: here was taught again the old lesson about the inevitability in war of attrition of numbers by enemy action, mechanical wear and tear, and the need for major refits. Moreover, the *Hood*, herself badly overdue for a refit, could only steam 25 knots – not fast enough to catch a German pocket battleship (26 knots) let alone a German battleship (32 knots). Not until the end of the year was Admiral Forbes (by then flying his flag in the *Warspite*) again to command a balanced fleet, *Rodney*, *Repulse* and the carrier *Furious* all having rejoined him.

Even as Forbes was returning to port at the beginning of December after his failure to intercept the *Scharnhorst* and *Gneisenau*, another hunt was already up for a German raider – this time far off in the South Atlantic.

On 21 and 23 August 1939, during the final diplomatic crisis over Danzig that led to the outbreak of war, the pocket battleships *Admiral Graf Spee* and *Deutschland* had sailed from Germany for their intended zones of operation – the *Graf Spee* in the South Atlantic and the *Deutschland* in the North Atlantic. Their simple strategic purpose was to strain British seapower to the uttermost by offering a constant but elusive threat to merchant shipping routes, as the German Naval Staff operation order of 4 August 1939 spelt out:

Enemy naval forces, even if inferior in strength, are only to be attacked if this should be necessary to achieve the main objective. Frequent changes in the operational area will provoke uncertainty and delays in the sailing of enemy shipping, even if no material success is achieved. The temporary appearance of German warships in remote areas will add to the enemy's confusion.[45]

The two pocket battleships were only permitted by Hitler to commence operations on 26 September, after the failure of his 'peace' initiative in the wake of the crushing of Poland. On 1 October the Admiralty's suspicions that at least one raider was at large were confirmed when the crew of the merchant ship SS *Clement*, sunk by the *Graf Spee* off Pernambuco on 30 September (and her first victim), reached South America after being picked up by another vessel. Then on 21 October 1939 the crew of a sunk Norwegian ship, landing in the Orkneys after being rescued from their boats, reported that their ship had been destroyed by the *Deutschland* on 14 October some 400 miles to the east of Newfoundland. This alerted the Admiralty that two powerful raiders were at large in the Atlantic.

Its response to the sinking of the *Clement* was prompt and on the largest scale possible within straitened overall resources – just as the German naval staff had intended. From 5 October onwards and in collaboration with the French Navy no fewer than eight powerful hunting groups (in all comprising three aircraft carriers, three battleships and fifteen cruisers) were formed to deal with two German ships. Force F (the cruisers *Berwick* and *York*) covered the North American and the West Indies Station; Force G (the cruisers *Exeter* and *Cumberland*; joined later by the *Ajax* and *Achilles*) the eastern coast of South America; Force H (the cruisers *Sussex* and *Shropshire*) the Cape of Good Hope; Force I (the cruisers *Cornwall* and *Dorsetshire*, and the carrier *Eagle*) off Ceylon; Force K (*Ark Royal* and *Renown*) the area Pernambuco–Freetown; Force L (the battleship *Dunkerque*, the carrier *Béarn* and three 6-inch gun French cruisers) was based on Brest; Force M (two 8-inch gun French cruisers) on Dakar in French West Africa; and Force N (the battleship *Strasbourg* and the British carrier *Hermes*) the West Indies. As soon as the *Deutschland*'s presence at sea became known on 21 October, the cruisers of Force F were reallotted to escort work with Halifax convoys. To form these hunting groups ships had to be drained away from the Home Fleet (*Ark Royal* and *Renown*; hence Forbes's weakness a month later when chasing *Scharnhorst* and *Gneisenau*); the Channel (*Hermes*); the Mediterranean (*Sussex* and *Shropshire*); and China (*Cornwall*, *Dorsetshire* and *Eagle*).[46]

On top of all this, the Admiralty allotted three extra battleships (*Warspite*, *Resolution* and *Revenge*) and two extra cruisers (*Emerald* and *Enterprise*) to the escort of North Atlantic convoys; and moved the battleship *Malaya* and the carrier *Glorious* through the Suez Canal to the Indian Ocean.

It was a mark of Admiral of the Fleet Sir Dudley Pound's limited powers of strategic comprehension that he should have been puzzled as to the German objective in bringing about this dispersal of Allied naval strength; surely, he asked, the enemy should have desired to induce its concentration in the home waters where it would be exposed to attack by his powerful air force?[47] Churchill rather agreed: how, he asked in a memorandum to the First Sea Lord, Deputy Chief of Naval Staff and the Controller on 23 October 1939, could the enemy have 'foreseen the extent to which we should react on the rumour of the *Scheer* [in fact, the *Graf Spee*] in South Atlantic? It all seems quite purposeless; yet the Germans are not the people to do things without reason . . .'[48]

The scale of the Allied counter-measures against the two pocket battleships also offered a tribute to the innovative technical skill of the ships' designers. Although the ships were much more heavily armoured than a large cruiser, their main battery of six 11-inch guns in two triple turrets, together with a secondary armament of eight 5.9-inch guns, outgunned even big 8-inch gun cruisers, let alone Britain's light 6-inch gun cruisers. Their 54,000 brake horsepower diesel engines gave them full power at instant readiness, unlike orthodox steam-turbine ships, which required many hours to raise steam from cold, and even took time to work up from cruising speed to maximum speed. Diesel propulsion also gave the pocket battleship a radius of action of 10,000 miles at cruising speed, even without refuelling from their attendant supply ships – more than twice that of a steam-turbine-propelled heavy ship. A catapult seaplane and search radar enabled the pocket battleship to scan the seas for victims or enemy warships. On the basis of comparative specifications, therefore, Allied cruisers, though they could outsteam the pocket battleships' 26 knots, were too weak in main armament to fight them, while Britain's old battleships, at speeds of 21 to 23 knots, were too slow to catch them. Only the battlecruisers *Renown* and *Repulse* (*Hood* being in need of a refit) and the modern French battleships *Dunkerque* and *Strasbourg* (specifically built to deal with the German vessels) were both fast enough and sufficiently heavily gunned and armoured.

The *Deutschland* (Captain Paul Wenneker) in the North Atlantic strictly obeyed the German naval staff's order during the course of her two and a half month's cruise, sinking only two merchant ships and capturing (but later releasing at a Norwegian port) another, the American SS *City of Flint* – just enough to advertise her presence, keep the Admiralty sweating for the safety of its convoys, impose maximum strain on the Royal Navy in those waters, and especially weaken the Home Fleet. In the middle of November the *Deutschland* (soon to be renamed the *Lützow*, because it would hardly do if 'Germany' were ever to be sunk) slipped back home via the Denmark Straits between Greenland and Iceland. The *Admiral Graf Spee* (Captain Hans Langsdorff), however, continued to pose an ubiquitous threat to British merchant shipping, true to the tradition established in 1914 in the same southern oceans by the admiral after whom she was named. Once again Churchill, with his memories as First Lord in the Great War, was struck by the sense of history and a strategic dilemma repeating themselves:

> The disproportion between the strength of the enemy and the counter-measures forced upon us was vexatious. It recalled to me the anxious weeks before the action at Coronel and later at the Falklands in December 1914, when we had to be prepared at seven or eight different points, in the Pacific and South Atlantic, for the arrival of Admiral von Spee with the earlier edition of the *Scharnhorst* and *Gneisenau*. A quarter of a century had passed, but the puzzle remained the same.[49]

The puzzle was that of locating a tiny sliver of metal on a vast surface of water; a sliver always in secret, unpredictable motion. Sea-borne or land-based air search could do little to help, given Britain's exiguous air resources and mostly obsolete and short-ranged aircraft. Instead Forces G, H and K, under the operational command of the Commander-in-Chief, South Atlantic (Admiral G. H. d'Oyly Lyon), lurched blindly about the ocean, guided only by such radio reports as some of *Graf Spee*'s victims were able to transmit before being silenced. Captain Langsdorff, for his part, struck at points as unexpectedly far apart as he could contrive. After sinking the *Clement* off Pernambuco (Brazil) on 30 September, he steered eastwards for the still mostly unconvoyed shipping route off Africa between the Cape of Good Hope and Europe, sinking four ships between 5 and 10 October; then doubled back into the central wastes of the South Atlantic to destroy another merchant ship, the SS *Trevannion*, on 22 October, before ceasing operations and lying quiet for a period in order further to confuse the Royal Navy. Luck had, however, been with him, for the cruiser *Cumberland* had failed to pass on to Admiral Lyon a radio report from the *Graf Spee*'s victim of 5 October, the SS

Newton Beech, relayed on by another merchant ship, that she had been stopped by a pocket battleship. The *Cumberland*, observing radio silence, had wrongly assumed that the report would anyway have been passed to the British naval base at Freetown, Sierra Leone, which in fact it had not. Then again, on 9 October aircraft from the *Ark Royal* (on passage to Freetown) sighted a stopped merchant ship near the Cape Verde Islands – in fact, the *Altmark*, the *Graf Spee*'s supply ship. However, the *Altmark* successfully bluffed that she was the American SS *Delmar*. Vice-Admiral Wells (Vice-Admiral, Aircraft Carriers) in the *Ark Royal*, having no destroyers with him (another result of the Navy's shortage of ships), decided not to close with the alleged 'SS *Delmar*' in order to verify her identity.

After sinking the SS *Trevannion* on 22 October, Langsdorff had taken the *Graf Spee* eastwards round the Cape of Good Hope into the Indian Ocean, turning up off Mozambique on 15 November to sink a small tanker and next day stop a Dutch ship. He thereupon doubled back westwards into the central wastes of the South Atlantic; then eastwards again to attack the Cape-to-Europe shipping route once more, sinking the SS *Doric Star* on 2 December and the SS *Tairoa* the day after. Now he doubled back yet again, this time due west, sinking another ship in mid-Atlantic on 7 December. All this time Lyon's hunting groups had been clutching for Langsdorff and missing – Forces H and K south of the Cape of Good Hope, Forces M and N patrolling from Dakar; Force G spread between the Falklands, the River Plate and Rio de Janeiro.

Then at long last had come hard and relatively up-to-date intelligence, when a distress signal was received from the *Doric Star* in the middle of the South Atlantic on 2 December. Admiral Lyon immediately redeployed his hunting groups: Force H to protect the Cape shipping route in the area of St Helena; Force K to sweep north-westwards to 28° South, 15° West before steering for Freetown. But these sweeps, too, missed the *Graf Spee*, by now steaming clear to the westward. For all the technology of twentieth-century war, the Admiralty and British admirals at sea were just as much groping and guessing with regard to the *Graf Spee* as their predecessors of the age of sail in 1804–5 seeking Admiral Villeneuve's fleet after its escape from Toulon, when even Nelson guessed wrong and searched the eastern Mediterranean while Villeneuve was in fact heading for the West Indies.[50]

And it was successful guesswork, or professional intuition, of the traditional kind which now enabled Commodore Henry Harwood, commanding Force G (flying his broad pendant in HMS *Ajax*; Captain C. H. L. Woodhouse), at last to solve the puzzle. Although the *Doric Star* had been sunk some 3,000 miles to the east of Harwood's present position off the estuary of the River Plate, Harwood reckoned that the enemy might now choose to attack the abundant merchant shipping clustering round the Plate and Rio de Janeiro – as Harwood had always believed he would do sooner or later. Harwood, calculating that the *Graf Spee* could reach Rio by 12 December and the area of the River Plate a day later, concentrated Force G accordingly. He ordered HMS *Exeter* (8,390 tons; six 8-inch guns; Captain F. S. Bell) up from Port Stanley in the Falklands, whence she had gone for repairs, to join *Ajax* (7,030 tons; eight 6-inch guns) and her sister ship the New Zealand manned *Achilles* (Captain W. E. Parry) at a rendezvous some 150 miles off the entrance to the River Plate by 0700 on 12 December.

With his squadron united, Harwood then steamed towards the position 32°S, 47°W, 'chosen from my Shipping Plot', wrote Harwood in his despatch, 'as being at that time the most congested part of the diverted shipping routes, i.e., the point where I estimated that a raider could do most damage to British shipping'.[51] Harwood – a well-jowled face beneath the uniform cap; tropical white jacket tight on a big-framed body verging on the portly – might have stepped from a Reynolds portrait of an eighteenth-century British sea officer; he certainly exemplified the fighting and tactical instincts of the best of them. At 1200 on 12 December 1939 he signalled his captains as to how he meant to fight the *Graf Spee* if and when they encountered her: 'My policy with three cruisers in company versus one pocket battleship, Attack at once by day or night. By day act as two units, 1st Division (AJAX and ACHILLES) and EXETER diverged to permit flank marking. First Division will concentrate gunfire. By night ships will normally remain in company in open order.'[52]

By thus attacking the *Graf Spee* from two sides Harwood hoped to divide the German fire, so giving his lighter ships the best chance of overcoming the longer range and heavier broadside of the *Graf Spee*'s six 11-inch guns.

At 0614 next day, 13 December 1939, with the squadron steering 14 knots on a course 060°, position 34° 34'S, 49° 17'W, the *Ajax* spotted a hazy line of smoke to the north-west, and Harwood ordered the *Exeter* to close and investigate. At 1616 the *Exeter* reported by signal lamp: 'I think it is a pocket battleship'; and almost simultaneously made the flag signal: 'Enemy in sight.'[53] Even as the alarm rattlers and bugles were sounding in the British ships for Action Stations, with many sailors tumbling straight out of their hammocks, the *Admiral Graf Spee* fired her first salvo.

Captain Langsdorff had chosen to head for the abundant prey off the River Plate even though on 4 December the German naval staff had given him – thanks again to 'Y' intercepts and decrypts of British signals – a broadly accurate picture of British dispositions in the South Atlantic, including information that *Ajax*, *Achilles*, *Exeter* and *Cumberland* (the latter in fact at the Falklands for repairs) were covering the South American coast. When *Graf Spee*'s search radar revealed the presence of ships to the south-west at about 0500 on 13 December, Langsdorff had altered course to investigate them – and so unwittingly helped Harwood to spring the trap tight shut. The *Graf Spee*'s reconnaissance aircraft being unserviceable, it was her lookouts which sighted the masts of the British squadron in the brilliance of a southern sunrise, at first reporting that it consisted of the *Exeter* and two destroyers. This information tempted Langsdorff to close on them in order to destroy so weak a force. Too late he realised that he was committed to battle with three cruisers. Now, using the immediate acceleration of his diesels, he steered for his enemy at 24 knots, hoping to engage before the steam-driven British ships could work up from cruising speed to full power.

It was a fine, clear sunny day, with a moderate south-easterly breeze and a slight sea. As the action opened, *Graf Spee* – a squatly piled silhouette dominated by the tall control tower typical of German naval architecture – was steering south-east, with the *Ajax* and *Achilles* steaming north-east to cross her bows and work round to her port beam, and the *Exeter* breaking away from her consorts north-westwards to engage the enemy to starboard; the British cruisers, in contrast to the *Graf Spee*, almost yacht-like in their low, racy lines. From the *Exeter*'s fore- and main-mastheads, yardarm and gaff streamed four Battle Ensigns, while the *Achilles* proudly flew the New Zealand flag from her mainmast. It was still to be flying after her White Ensign had been shot away.

From her very first salvo at a range of 19,000 yards, which threw up gouts of water round the *Exeter*, the *Graf Spee*'s gunnery (its ranging aided by the ship's radar) lived up to the exemplary standards of quick and sustained accuracy set by Hipper's battlecruisers at Jutland in 1916 and Vice-Admiral Graf Spee's own ships in the South Atlantic in 1914. With both her triple 11-inch turrets concentrating on the *Exeter*, her third salvo straddled the British ship, scoring one hit which wrecked the *Exeter*'s Walrus aircraft just when it was about to be catapulted as a gunnery spotter. At 0624, after the *Exeter* had fired eight 8-inch gun salvoes in return, the *Graf Spee* landed a direct hit on the *Exeter*'s 'B' turret, putting it out of action, a hail of shell splinters sweeping the bridge and wrecking the wheelhouse communications. Captain Bell had thereafter to con the ship from the after steering position, and even then for a time only by a chain of messengers passing instructions. Nevertheless still steering to engage the enemy more closely, *Exeter* twice fired torpedoes but without success. Although the *Exeter* had been hitting the *Graf Spee* again and again, her 8-inch shells had neither disabled the German ship nor her main turrets. The *Ajax* and *Achilles*, closing the range from 19,000 yards to 13,000 and steaming at 28 knots to get across the *Graf Spee*'s bows, were also firing fast and accurately, but their 6-inch guns were even less able to inflict immediately critical damage. They themselves were coming under heavy fire from the German ship's secondary armament of 5.9-inch guns.

At about 0636, with the *Ajax* and *Achilles* now almost ahead of the *Graf Spee*, Langsdorff hauled round from an easterly course to the north-west and laid smoke. Now on a roughly parallel course to the *Exeter* instead of opposite, the *Graf Spee* continued to smash at Harwood's most powerful ship with relentless accuracy, until by 0650 the British cruiser was taking water forward, listing heavily to starboard, and reduced to only one of her three turrets. Telephone and radio communications alike were knocked out; fires were burning fiercely below decks; and yet still the *Exeter* steamed at full speed, still her remaining turret kept firing. Forty minutes later, however, water thrown up by a near miss by an 11-inch shell came flooding through a shell hole in the side and short-circuited the electricity supply to her remaining turret. Captain Bell was forced to break off the action and turn away to the south, his main anxiety now to keep his ship afloat.

This was Langsdorff's opportunity to follow and finish off the helpless *Exeter*. Instead he allowed himself to be distracted by the combined fire of the *Ajax* and *Achilles*, ordered by Harwood at 0710 'to close the range as rapidly as possible' in order to take the pressure off the *Exeter*.[54] At 0720 both ships 'turned to starboard to bring all guns to bear. Our shooting appeared to be very effective, and a fire was observed amidships in GRAF SPEE.'[55] Langsdorff, himself a torpedo specialist, took his heavy ship westwards with rapidly jinking alterations of course and smoke screens in order to avoid British torpedo attacks and throw off the British gun-layers. At 0725 the *Graf Spee* put the *Ajax*'s two after turrets out of action with a direct 11-inch shell hit, while at the same time her secondary armament of 5.9-inch guns scored two hits on the *Ajax*'s bridge. All this time the British cruisers were firing fast and accurately, although their 6-inch shells still could only inflict superficial damage to the *Graf Spee*'s structure and equipment. By 0738, with the range down to 8,000 yards, Langsdorff was on the verge of finally crushing his remaining opponents; and Harwood was having to accept that his bid to defeat a pocket battleship with three cruisers had for the moment failed. As he wrote in his despatch:

> At this time I received a report that AJAX had only 20 per cent of ammunition left and had only three guns in action, as one of the hoists had failed in 'B' turret and 'X' and 'Y' turrets were both out of action.
>
> GRAF SPEE's shooting was still very accurate and she did not appear to have suffered much damage.
>
> I therefore decided to break off the day action and try and close in again after dark. Accordingly at 0740 AJAX and ACHILLES turned away to the east under cover of smoke.[56]

One of the *Graf Spee*'s last salvoes brought down the *Ajax*'s main topmast: it fell, said an eyewitness, in true Trafalgar-like style.

This was again a time for Langsdorff to 'engage the enemy more closely', with every chance of destroying Harwood's two light cruisers. But, just as earlier when the *Exeter* had seemed at his mercy, he failed to do so, continuing to steer away westwards, instead of going about in order to attack. Even when Harwood turned his ships again to follow the *Graf Spee* at a range of 19,000 yards, *Achilles* on her starboard quarter, and *Ajax* on her port, Langsdorff kept to his course westwards, content to fire the occasional salvo to warn his British shadowers to keep their distance. To fail successively in this way to finish off the crippled *Exeter* and now two heavily outgunned light cruisers, one of them damaged, displays a fatal want of judgment on Langsdorff's part, or perhaps of professional nerve, although his personal courage is not in doubt. More inglorious still, he had decided – without consultation with his senior officers – to seek refuge in the neutral Uruguayan port of Montevideo on the north side of the estuary of the River Plate, slipping in without a pilot in the dark towards midnight.

Why did Langsdorff take these un-Nelsonian decisions, so much in contrast with Harwood's resolute attack with inferior forces? According to his own battle report to Berlin signalled from Montevideo on 15 December:

After EXETER has moved off, light cruisers move off to a great distance and remain to the NE and SE. To break out to open sea and shake off these two cruisers is obviously impossible.

Inspection of direct damage reveals that all galleys except for the Admiral's galley have been badly damaged. Water entering flour store endangers bread supply while a direct hit on the forecastle makes ship unseaworthy for North Atlantic in winter. One shell pierced armour belt while the armoured deck is torn in one place. Damage in after part of the ship . . . As ship cannot be made seaworthy for breakthrough to the homeland with means on board, decided to go into the River Plate at risk of being shut in there.[57]

It was a tribute to the shooting of the lighter British ships that they had succeeded in inflicting this amount of damage – damage sufficient to destroy Langsdorff's will to fight, if not immediately to disable his ship. However a more personal factor may have contributed to Langsdorff's loss of will, according to later testimony by several of his officers. Already over-strained by more than two months of lone operations under constant threat of detection and destruction by the Royal Navy, Langsdorff had suffered two flesh wounds and had also been knocked temporarily unconscious during the action with Harwood. Did he abandon an encounter more than half won and make for Montevideo because his powers of decision and judgment had been enfeebled by shock?[58] What is certainly true is that Harwood had embarked on the action having expected it and having decided how he meant to fight it, whereas Langsdorff stumbled into it, and thereafter played it by ear: decisions made in haste amid the racket of battle, the fall of shot, the temporary obscuring of the bright day by his own and enemy smoke screens; amid the need to order frequent changes of course to dodge British shell fire and torpedoes. Yet it is hard not to think that Langsdorff's and Harwood's contrasting fighting decisions were instinctively guided by their national maritime heritages. Behind Harwood stood four centuries of victory in close quarters attack; behind Langsdorff a naval tradition barely forty years old, and, with brief and rare exceptions, one of raiding and evading and ultimately of defeat.

Far off in London the First Lord of the Admiralty had excitedly watched every move in the hunt for the *Graf Spee* from his map room in the red-brick Admiralty building overlooking the gravel sweep of Horse Guards parade; a spectator on a distant touchline eager to tell his team how to win. On the basis of radio reports via America at six hours' delay, wrote an eyewitness:

. . . Winston was most anxious to send telegrams to Harwood about the dispositions of the three cruisers off the River Plate, and various other instructions. Pound insisted that Harwood should be allowed to deploy his ships as the situation demanded, and that information from the Admiralty should be confined to the reinforcements being sent, oil tankers, repair facilities, etc . . .[59]

Now it was time for the crews of the *Graf Spee* in the Plate and for Harwood's ships still at sea to tackle the grim aftermath of battle: to try to patch up men and metal alike torn and ripped or scorched by fire; to wrap the dead in canvas for burial. It was time too for the opposing commanders to decide on the future courses of action. Harwood, for his part, knew that for the next twenty-four hours he would have to meet a sortie by the *Graf Spee* with only *Achilles* and the damaged *Ajax*. The crippled *Exeter* was limping away to the Falklands for emergency repairs; her replacement, the *Cumberland* (ordered up from Port Stanley by Harwood at 0946 on 13 December) would not arrive before the evening of the 14th. The Admiralty had signalled the *Ark Royal*, *Renown* and the cruiser *Neptune* to fuel at Rio and then to steam at once for the Plate. Yet this overwhelming strength could not be in place until noon on 19 December. The conclusion was plain. 'I requested His Britannic Majesty's Minister, Montevideo,' wrote Harwood in his despatch, 'to use every possible means of delaying GRAF SPEE's sailing, in order to gain time for reinforcements to reach me . . .'[60]

For Langsdorff, suddenly removed from the anonymity of the ocean spaces and placed under the glare of world publicity, his damaged ship offshore the object of the curiosity of the crowds of Montevideo citizens, the dilemma was very different. No powerful warships were ever coming to his rescue; safe return of the *Graf Spee* depended on himself and his ship's company, and the seaworthiness and battleworthiness of his ship. Partly on the advice of his engineers, partly in order to give time for U-boats at least to reach the area, Langsdorff asked the German ambassador to obtain permission from Uruguay for the *Graf Spee* to remain in Montevideo for fourteen days – later 30 days – in order to effect essential repairs. Thus both the British and German commanders and their countries' ambassadors were seeking the same objective – to delay the *Graf Spee*'s sailing. In the event the Uruguayan government gave Langsdorff 72 hours only.

In order to dissuade Langsdorff from making an early sortie, the British government now released false information that the *Ark Royal* and *Renown* had already left Rio and were approaching the Plate. This 'disinformation' was apparently confirmed when two officers in the *Graf Spee* separately reported that they had 'seen' a carrier and a battlecruiser in the estuary. Writhing mentally in the trap of his own making, Langsdorff decided that to seek battle would lead to the certain loss of his ship and the pointless sacrifice of his crew. In Berlin Grand Admiral Raeder, the C-in-C of the German Navy, and Hitler both agreed that it was out of the question to accept internment of the *Graf Spee* by Uruguay. An attempt to seek sanctuary in the Argentinian capital and port of Buenos Aires was ruled out. This left only one alternative, discussed by Langsdorff with his officers: to scuttle the ship outside Uruguayan territorial waters. Raeder and Hitler left the final decision to Langsdorff.[61]

At 1815 on 17 December 1939, the *Graf Spee*, with a skeleton crew, weighed anchor and moved slowly away into the estuary. At 1936 her white, black and red swastika ensign was hauled down. Twenty minutes later the *Graf Spee*'s structure was shattered by a series of carefully placed explosions, and, reeking flame and smoke, she settled on a sandbank. HMSs *Ark Royal* and *Renown* were still 1,000 miles distant. Three days later Langsdorff, wrapping himself in the Imperial German ensign, shot himself in the temple, because, as he wrote in a final letter, 'I alone bear the responsibility for scuttling the Panzerschiff ADMIRAL GRAF SPEE. I am happy to pay with my life to prevent any possible reflection on the honour of the flag.'[62] In the fate of the ship and her captain there was, therefore, more than a hint of Germanic *Götterdämmerung*; an echo of the hauling down of the Imperial ensign in the High Seas Fleet in November 1918 and the scuttling of that fleet in 1919; an echo too of the final destruction of Admiral Graf Spee himself and his ships at the Battle of the Falklands in 1914.

In the Admiralty there was justified jubilation. After two and a half months of fruitless steaming and the loss of two great ships, the Royal Navy had been rewarded with a triumph in traditional style; to be celebrated in due time by march pasts and civic receptions when Harwood's ships returned to England and New Zealand early in the New Year. The task forces mobilised from the Navy's already stretched resources to deal with *Graf Spee* and *Lützow* could be redeployed now that the first major threat to British sea communications of the war had been overcome.

But already German technology had been posing a fresh threat – the magnetic mine – and compelling the Royal Navy to relearn another forgotten lesson.

After the outbreak of war both the Royal and the German Navies began to lay barrages of orthodox contact mines as in the Great War. The principal German minefield ran some 80 miles north from the Friesian Islands to the latitude of Jutland in order to protect the North Sea naval bases from a direct British approach, while the Admiralty attempted to protect Britain's east coast shipping by declaring a mined area between the Tyne and Humber, later extended to the whole east coast between the Pentland Firth and Essex. But in fact no mines were laid until 1940. The old Dover barrage of 1914–18, barring the Straits of Dover to U-boats attempting the direct passage from their bases to the Atlantic, was re-created during the first month of war – two successive barriers of shallow and deep-laid mines, comprising nearly 7,000 in all, with a double system of electric indicator loops on the seabed between them to reveal the passage of U-boats. After three U-boats were destroyed in the new Dover barrage in October, Dönitz abandoned the attempt to use this direct route, and his captains now had to make the long passage round the north of Scotland to their hunting areas, so drastically reducing their operational range.

From the first week of the war, however, Germany embarked on a campaign of offensive minelaying – ambushes beneath the sea off Britain's own ports, coasts and naval bases. Most of these were of orthodox contact mines, of which the German Navy had over 20,000 in stock. One such minelaying operation, off the Tyne, by five destroyers covered by the cruisers *Leipzig*, *Nürnberg* and *Köln*, on 12–13 December gave the British submarine service the opportunity for its biggest success so far in the war. The *Salmon* (Lieutenant-Commander E. O. B. Bickford), which had already sunk the U-36 with torpedoes, attacked the German squadron on its homeward voyage in the Heligoland Bight at dawn on the 14th, damaging *Nürnberg* and *Leipzig* so severely that they were out of action until May and December 1940 respectively – a serious reduction in Germany's slender strength in cruisers during what was to be a decisive campaigning year at sea. Nonetheless, the German minelaying campaign in British waters, quite apart from causing vast disruption to coastal traffic, was to lead to the loss of 79 merchant ships, totalling 262,697 tons, in the first four months of the war.

As early as 16 September the damaging of the SS *City of Paris* by an underwater explosion confirmed Admiralty fears that the enemy was also using magnetic mines – that is, mines laid on the seabed and exploded by the influence of a ship's magnetic field on the mine's electro-magnetic detonating mechanism. In the shallow waters of the Continental Shelf round the British Isles, such seabed explosions could seriously damage or sink a ship. It was such a mine laid five weeks earlier by a U-boat which on 4 December had put the battleship HMS *Nelson* out of action for nearly a year. On 21 November the back of the new 10,000-ton cruiser *Belfast* was broken in the Firth of Forth by another one, compelling her virtual reconstruction later in the dockyard. In December Captain Lord Louis Mountbatten's ship, the destroyer *Kelly*, had her stern blown off.

By now the Luftwaffe had joined in, dropping magnetic mines by night into such vital and constricted sea areas as the Thames Estuary. For the Admiralty the problem lay not in the quantity of magnetic mines to be swept – in fact only 470 were laid in the first three months of the war, while Germany's total stock on the outbreak of war came to more than 1,500 – but in that at present no technical means existed either to neutralise ships' magnetic fields, or to sweep magnetic mines. The disruption to British shipping was therefore out of all proportion to the number of mines. In November only two out of three deep-water channels in and out of the Port of London through the Thames Estuary remained open, and it was feared for a time that Britain's largest port might be closed altogether. In November the problem came before the War Cabinet itself, which considered it so serious as perhaps to constitute Hitler's vaunted 'secret weapon'.[63]

Yet the magnetic mine was no novelty. The Royal Navy itself had laid an early type off Zeebrugge and the mouth of the River Scheldt in 1918; and had its own design ready for production in 1939, a pilot order being given in July. As the First Sea Lord wrote on 24 October 1939 to Admiral Sir Andrew Cunningham, the C-in-C, Mediterranean Fleet: 'It is really the limit that after knowing about magnetic mines since the last war, no practical method of dealing with them had been evolved.'[64] Meanwhile the Germans themselves had conducted trials with a magnetic sweeping device as early as summer 1938, although it was not fitted operationally until October 1939.[65] In fact the Admiralty had carried out some research in the 1930s, but it had yielded no practicable results: another consequence of the rivalries and overlaps between the various research establishments.[66] Now emergency development of counter-measures was confided to the Electro-Magnetic Group at the Admiralty Research Laboratory. Its work was vitally assisted when on 25 November a complete unexploded magnetic mine was recovered intact from the mudflats off Shoeburyness and taken apart by Lieutenant-Commander J. G. D. Ouvry with exemplary skill and courage, so revealing its precise electro-magnetic principles.

The Admiralty Research Laboratory found the eventual answer to the magnetic mine in installing 'de-gaussing' coils (named after the nineteenth-century German mathematician, K. F. Gauss, an out-standing scientist in the field of electro-magnetism) round the hulls of ships in order to render them magnetically neutral. But the conversion of more than 3,000 vessels in the Royal Navy and the Merchant Marine imposed colossal demands on the cable manufacturers and the shipyards, and the work could only proceed slowly. For the moment, as the German naval staff gleefully recognised at the end of October 1939, the Royal Navy was unable to sweep these mines. By January 1940, the Germans embarked with high hopes on mass production of mines, with a target of 48,000 contact mines and 21,500 magnetic by March 1942[67] – by which time the British would have completed their de-gaussing programme.

The truth was that with regard to the magnetic mine the German naval staff had committed the classic military blunder of prematurely introducing a potentially decisive weapon at a time when only small quantities were as yet available. As 1939 turned to 1940 it was not British counter-measures that led to the waning of the threat, therefore, but exhaustion of the small German stocks of this kind of mine.[68]

The first three months of the war at sea had thus resembled the initial circling of two wrestlers – their tentative attempts to get a hold – before they close in a grapple for victory with all powers stretched to the limit. The German Navy, however, had succeeded in causing disruption to British seaborne trade and stretching the Royal Navy's resources out of all proportion to the relatively few submarines, surface warships and mines which it had so far employed. Understandably Churchill chafed at this opening phase of the war at sea, and especially at the almost wholly defensive nature of the Royal Navy's operations as it reacted to the enemy's various 'pin-pricks'. He itched to use British seapower as a grand strategic instrument that would pluck the initiative in the war at sea as a whole out of Hitler's hands. As he wrote to Pound on 5 December 1939:

> An absolute defensive is for weaker forces. If we go on indefinitely like this we shall simply be worried & worn down, while making huge demands upon the national resources ... I cd never be responsible for a naval strategy wh excluded the offensive principle, & relegated us to keeping open the lines of communication. Presently, you will see the U-boats in the outer seas. What then?[69]

It had been only three days after his return to office that he first mentioned to the First Sea Lord a visionary concept for a seaborne offensive against Germany. On 12 September he had embodied the concept in a five-page memorandum for the benefit of his naval advisers. Soon he was to dub his scheme 'Operation Catherine' – not because it represented the First Lord's own brain spinning on its axis throwing out sparks, but after Catherine the Great, Empress of Russia.

Churchill's plan envisaged a self-supporting task force of two or three old 'R' class battleships, a carrier, five cruisers, two destroyer flotillas, some submarines, supported by supply ships and 'turtle-backed blistered tankers' (against both air and submarine attack) carrying three months' supply of oil. The battleships would also each be rendered invulnerable to air and submarine attack by means of 2,000 tons of extra armour plate and anti-torpedo blistering, at the sacrifice of two out of four of their 15-inch gun turrets. A dozen specially converted vessels would serve as 'mine-bumpers' to precede the task force as it steamed at some 15 knots (the maximum speed of the old battleships after conversion) through the Skagerrak, Kattegat and the narrow 'Sound' between Denmark and Sweden into the Baltic. Having established British command of the Baltic, the task force would cut Germany off from her vital Swedish iron-ore supplies and other imports. Even more important, it would, in Churchill's reckoning, very likely induce the neutral Scandinavian states to enter the war on the Allied side, so providing the task force with a Swedish base. It could even persuade Soviet Russia, now linked to Nazi Germany by the 1939 Treaty of Friendship, to fight in the Allied cause. All in all, Churchill believed 'Operation Catherine' to be 'the supreme naval offensive open to the Royal Navy'.[70]

'Operation Catherine' belongs not to the world of real war but rather to that of imaginative war fiction, taking as it did little heed of tedious nuts-and-bolts, whether strategic or matériel, such as (for example) the difficulty of obtaining the necessary armour plate out of the restricted capacity of the British steel industry at a time when Britain was proposing to embark on mass tank production for the Army on top of the existing programme of warship construction. It came into the same category of Churchillian cigar-butt strategy as his 1915 brainwave of capturing the Friesian island of Borkum, or even the Dardanelles expedition itself: glibly attractive when arrowed broadly on a map of Europe, but a nonsense in terms of the technical means and military forces available, of the enemy's potential reaction, and of all the wider political and strategic probabilities.

In particular, it meant robbing Admiral Sir Charles Forbes, C-in-C, Home Fleet, of three of his precious battleships, so it was no wonder that he was largely kept in the dark about 'Catherine'. When the First

Sea Lord, Sir Dudley Pound, wrote to Forbes in his own hand on 15 September he only mentioned that

> the First Lord may say something to you about the scheme which is called by a name beginning with the letter 'C'. For this scheme has the idea of fitting some of the 'R' class with deck protection and extra bulges. I think there is a very good deal to be said for the scheme when the situation is sufficiently cleared for us to be able to put two or three of the 'R' class into dockyard hands for something like nine months . . .[71]

Here then was the first occasion when Pound, as professional head of the Navy, had to deal with one of Churchill's grandiose strategic inventions; and he now adopted what was to be in his invariable policy in the coming years of not openly challenging Churchill's views but, instead, under cover of an apparent willingness, patiently bringing up all the nuts-and-bolts problems in the course of a deliberately protracted study. As he confided to Forbes in this same letter:

> . . . until we are quite certain that neither Italy or [sic] Japan will join Germany, I feel it would be quite wrong to reduce the strength of our battlefleet by that number. Please do not raise this question, but if the First Lord mentions it it would be helpful if you took this line. I am just as keen on what is termed the 'Naval Offensive' as he is, but I do not feel that we are justified in risking our whole sea supremacy on what must, after all, be something of a gamble.[72]

And on 20 January 1940, after 'Catherine' had been finally put in abeyance, he explained his tactics more openly to Forbes: 'My feelings also were largely influenced against throwing cold water on any offensive operation so long as it appeared feasible. Hard facts and the attitude of Russia have brought the powers that be round to my way of thinking . . .'[73]

In pursuance of this policy of attrition Pound had therefore written encouragingly to Churchill on 19 September 1939 that there can be 'little doubt that if we could maintain control of the Baltic for a considerable period it would greatly enhance our prestige'.[74] But then came the cavils aimed at starting the rivets of Churchill's project and inducing it eventually to founder. It could only succeed if Russia did not join Germany's side, and if Britain was sure of 'the *active* co-operation of Sweden for the supply of oil and the use of a base and her repair facilities'. Moreover, the Baltic task force '*must* be such that we can with our Allies at that time win the war without it, in spite of any probable combination against us'[75] – in other words, even if the Royal and French Navies had to fight Italy and Japan as well as Germany. In laying down these preconditions Pound – or the Plans Division of the naval staff – had exposed the fundamental unrealism of 'Catherine'. For none of those preconditions could be met. In the first place, it is hard to comprehend how Churchill could hope that Sweden would abandon her profitable neutrality because of the entry of a British task force into the Baltic, or that Russia would wish to invite a German attack. The task force itself would lock up a considerable portion of British seapower, which, as the events of the next two months were to demonstrate, was hard pressed enough to deal with four German battleships, a handful of U-boats, and some 1,000 magnetic mines; let alone find a 'main fleet' to fight Japan as well if need be. The task force's line of communication through the Sound, Skagerrak and Kattegat and thence back across the North Sea would lie on the immediate flank of the German Navy based at Kiel and Wilhelmshaven, to say nothing of the Luftwaffe operating at relatively short range, while a pounce by the German Army through virtually unarmed Denmark and the establishment of heavy shore batteries on the Sound would effectively cut the task force off in the Baltic.

Nonetheless, although Churchill acknowledged in reply to Pound's first note on the topic that at present his decision 'is only for exploration; & no question of *action* arises,' he added: 'But the search for a naval offensive must be incessant.'[76] So studies for 'Catherine' were to go on, involving more and more staff time and resources. Indeed, Churchill secured the appointment of Admiral of the Fleet the Earl of Cork and Orrery, a fiery 65-year-old veteran on the half-pay list, to head a planning staff. Cork's first appreciation on 26 September proposed assembling the task force in the second week of January 1940, giving it a month of training and rehearsal, and then steaming off for the Baltic on 15 February – absurdly optimistic timings in view of the industrial and dockyard work needed for converting the ships into armoured turtles. In any event, Cork upped Churchill's original estimate of numbers by two carriers and nine cruisers.[77] Come November and the 'R' class battleships had had to be diverted to protecting North Atlantic convoys against the German surface raiders; and on the 22nd of the month Churchill postponed the operation until 30 April 1940. Perhaps most potentially serious of all Churchill's euphoric miscalculations related to the question of air attack on the task force by the Luftwaffe, for he believed as strongly as any 'gun and battleship' sailor that the fleet's own anti-aircraft fire would be enough to protect it against aircraft; the false lesson learned from the Luftwaffe's near-miss of the *Ark Royal*. As he wrote to President

Roosevelt on 16 October: 'We have not been at all impressed with the accuracy of the German air bombing of our warships. They seem to have no effective bomb sights.'[78]

With the cunning of an old badger (which he so closely resembled), Sir Dudley Pound gradually wore Churchill down over the months by his strategy of apparent willingness coupled with the protracted identification of operational difficulties. By the end of the year Pound felt able to voice open opposition to 'Catherine'. On 31 December he wrote to Churchill: ' "Catherine" is a great gamble, even if there were adequate fighter protection for the Fleet, and if Russia were on our side and we had the use of Russian bases. As neither of these conditions will be present, I consider that the sending of a Fleet of surface ships into the Baltic is courting disaster.'[79] On 10 January 1940 Pound submitted a further memorandum which relentlessly listed all the hazards, foreseeing that the fleet would be 'battered and mauled' by air attack, mines and U-boats on its way into the Baltic, where, having no secure base of its own, it would have to resort to an ill-protected Swedish anchorage where it would be exposed to further air and U-boat attack. Then there were the far-reaching strategic risks: 'The loss of such a large proportion of our Fleet would be the surest inducement to either Italy or Japan to come in against us.' Pound therefore urged 'most strongly' that all special preparations for 'Catherine' should be dropped.

Right up to this point Churchill had been arguing back tenaciously in defence of 'Catherine'; now, partly because Lord Cork reported that small progress had been made in the necessary ship conversion work so far, he 'reluctantly' agreed that 'Catherine' was off for 1940, although a small staff should continue to study it. The single casualty of 'Catherine' was Captain V. H. Danckwerts, Naval Staff Director of Plans, sacked almost certainly because of his trenchant criticisms of the scheme (reflected in Pound's memoranda); the first, but by no means the last, officer in all three services to be hounded out of his post during the war for opposing Churchill's will.[80]

Thus Pound's devious strategy of wearing Churchill down by protracted indirect resistance had proved ultimately successful – but at what cost in waste of time and staff resources? In any event, Churchill had had another naval stratagem in view since September, and one no less guaranteed in his estimation than such earlier dead certs as the forcing of the Dardanelles and the capture of Borkum (to say nothing of 'Operation Catherine') to cripple a great continental power.

4

'A Very Hazardous Affair': Norway, 1939–1940

Mined round Gällivare in northern Sweden, the iron ore upon which depended Germany's great steel industry, the basic sinew of her power, was shipped for most of the year from the port of Luleå down through the Baltic. However during the winter months when Luleå was closed by ice the ore was railed westwards to the ice-free Norwegian port of Narvik, and thence taken by ship down the length of the Norwegian coast. During the Great War this winter traffic had sought refuge from the Royal Navy by making use of the Innereled or 'Inner Leads' – the narrow stretch of Norwegian territorial water lying between Norway's outer string of islands and the mainland – until in 1918 Allied pressure induced the Norwegians to lay mines therein.

On 19 September 1939, having already discussed the matter (along with 'Operation Catherine'), with his naval advisers, the First Lord of the Admiralty proposed to the Cabinet that detailed plans should be put in hand for the Royal Navy to mine Norwegian territorial waters if Norway should prove unwilling to do it again herself; and on the 23rd he followed up with a powerful written broadside: 'It must be understood', he wrote, 'that an adequate supply of Swedish iron ore is vital to Germany and the interception or prevention of these Narvik supplies during the winter months, i.e., from October to the end of April, will greatly reduce her power of resistance.'[1] One of the aims of 'Operation Catherine' was of course to block the shipment of the ore direct from Sweden to Germany from May to September via the Baltic.

Henceforward, till the beginning of April 1940, Churchill was tirelessly to urge 'by every means and on all occasions'[2] his case for naval action to close Norwegian waters to German iron-ore supplies and German warships. Chamberlain and his Cabinet, however, proved deeply reluctant to contemplate violating Norway's neutrality, both out of moral scruple and out of fear of the political consequences in terms of world opinion. On 14 December, armed with fresh evidence of shipments of ore via the 'Leads' and also of recent violations of the neutrality of Norwegian waters by German warships, Churchill proposed that four or five destroyers shall be sent forthwith into 'the more lonely parts' of Norwegian waters 'for the purpose of arresting all ships carrying ore to Germany'.[3]

He followed this up two days later with another of his broadside memoranda, in which he argued to his Cabinet colleagues that the stopping of this traffic would rank 'as a major operation of war', and that no other expedient 'for many months to come' would give so good a chance of 'abridging the waste and destruction of the conflict, or perhaps preventing the vast slaughters which will attend the grapple of the main armies'.[4] He further claimed that if Germany's supplies of ore could be cut off from all sources until the end of 1940, 'a blow will have been struck at her war-making capacity equal to a first-class victory in the field or from the air, and without any serious sacrifice of life'; it could even prove 'immediately decisive'. He was not at all bothered at the thought that the Germans might respond by intervening with 'brute force' in Norway and Sweden, because in his judgment there was no reason why, with Britain's command of the seas, British and French troops should not 'meet the German invaders' on Scandinavian soil. 'At any rate,' he proclaimed with his usual assurance, 'we can take and hold whatever islands or suitable points on the Norwegian coast we choose. Our northern blockade of Germany would then become absolute.'[5]

By this time, however, Churchill's purely naval scheme had been overshadowed by a far more grandiose project – nothing less than the commitment of an Anglo-French expeditionary force to northern Scandinavia.

On 30 November Soviet Russia had invaded Finland. Soon her lumbering armies were halted or routed in the winter snows by a brave and brilliantly conducted Finnish defence. In the democracies sympathy and admiration welled up for the gallant Finns, another small nation defending its independence against tyranny; volunteers sprang forward to go and fight with the Finnish Army; the despatch of (all too scarce) arms and equipment was set in hand. In such a climate of opinion larger possibilities seemed to open up. Churchill himself expressed them to the War Cabinet on 11 December: 'It would be to our advantage if the trend of events in Scandinavia brought it about that Norway and Sweden were forced into war with Russia. We would then be able to gain a foothold in Scandinavia with the object of helping them, but without having to go to the extent of ourselves declaring war on Russia.'[6] This foothold would permit Britain to use Norwegian ports in the North Sea and Swedish ports in the Baltic against Germany.

On 19 December while the British War Cabinet was still chewing over how best to play the Finland card, the Allied Supreme War Council in Paris recommended that an expeditionary force of 3,000–4,000 men land at Narvik and proceed to seize the Swedish orefields round Gällivare. Norway's and Sweden's consent to this invasion was to be obtained – naïve hope – on the score that the Allies were joining them in support of Finland and in their own defence against Soviet attack.[7] Next day at the British Cabinet's Military Coordination Committee Churchill enthusiastically supported this ambitious proposal[8] – as he was to continue to do at all the anxious Cabinet discussions on it during the rest of December and on into the New Year.

On 31 December the Chiefs of Staff (COS) submitted a 22-page blessing: the opportunity 'is a great one, and we see no prospect of an equal chance being afforded us elsewhere'.[9] The possibility of obtaining decisive results, wrote the COS, rendered the operational risks acceptable. If the Germans sought to forestall the Allied intervention, then a scratch force would have to be put ashore at Narvik with the task of picketing the railway to the Swedish orefields and destroying the port facilities at Luleå; this force to be later strengthened by 'an adequately equipped and properly prepared expedition'.

In another report of 5 January 1940, the COS pondered the consequences of the Germans establishing themselves in southern Norway, and drew the conclusions that the Allies could not stop the enemy landing at Oslo and Kristiansand by surprise, nor reaching Stavanger if he employed airborne troops rather than seaborne, but that they could hope themselves to occupy Bergen and Trondheim before him since a German seaborne attack on these ports was 'extremely improbable' and an airborne landing 'scarcely less so'.[10] Narvik was not mentioned at all, being quite out of the question as a German objective. The COS recommended that from the moment the Allies finally decided to stop the iron-ore traffic a contingency force of troops and transports should be held ready 'for instant despatch' to seize Stavanger, Bergen and Trondheim. They warned that in any case the Allies could not be ready to land at Narvik to protect the railway to Gällivare until the end of March. Thus the proposal to mine the 'Leads' and the larger project of an expeditionary force to Norway and Sweden alike assumed that German action would be tightly constrained by British command of the sea. Indeed at this time neither Churchill nor Chamberlain believed that a German invasion of Norway was likely.[11]

When the War Cabinet debated Scandinavian strategy on 2 and 3 January 1940, the Chief of the Imperial General Staff (CIGS) warned them that an expedition against the inhabitants' wishes would be a 'very hazardous affair', and he noted that 'we had no ski-troops immediately available' – a point of some importance in regard to terrain snowbound until summer.[12] Prompted by his military advisers, the Secretary of State for War, Oliver Stanley, pronounced against landing troops at Stavanger, Bergen and Trondheim: 'History pro-vided many examples of campaigns which had begun by the despatch of minor detachments, and which had ended by swallowing up large armies.' But the First Lord of the Admiralty insisted that the Allies should be ready to send battalions 'at any rate' to Stavanger and Bergen. 'There was no reason,' he went on, 'why this small diversion should develop into a large commitment, unless we wished it to.'

Now began three months of havering on the part of the War Cabinet as to what to do and when to do it. Fierce opposition by Norway and Sweden to diplomatic soundings about a possible Allied intervention induced the Cabinet on 12 January to postpone both the First Lord's minelaying plan and the larger land project, while asking the COS to report on the operational problems of capturing the Gällivare orefields in the face of Norwegian and Swedish opposition.[13] In their report on 28 January[14] the COS proposed landing five Allied divisions at Trondheim and Namsos in central Norway, and two brigades at Narvik with the job of marching up the railway to Gällivare. It would also be necessary to deny the Germans Bergen and Stavanger. Up to 40 destroyers (about a quarter of Britain's total operational strength) would be needed for close escort work, as well as a mass of merchant shipping, while it would become the Home Fleet's principal task to protect the convoys. The COS calculated the necessary air cover as one fighter squadron for Narvik; two fighter, two bomber squadrons and one army cooperation squadron operating over southern Sweden, plus an advanced base for four heavy bomber squadrons operating from the United Kingdom – around 160–180 aircraft in all.

The tally of naval, air and land forces required ought to have damned the whole idea of intervention in Scandinavia for good, given the Allies' overall scarcity of well-equipped troops and modern aircraft. But all three Chiefs of Staff – even the Chief of Air Staff, Air Chief Marshal Sir Cyril Newall – dangerously underestimated the decisive nature of the threat posed by the Luftwaffe, although in an earlier section of their report of 28 January, they did acknowledge that the air forces which the Allies could make available 'would be unlikely to satisfy' the Norwegian and Swedish governments (as an inducement to abandon their neutrality) in the face of the 'overwhelming scale of air attack' which the Germans could apply.[15] Moreover the COS grossly underestimated the possible speed and northward reach of the German moves into Norway. Then again, they failed to point out to the politicians, as they ought to have done, the military and naval realities underlying the whole project of a major campaign in Scandinavia: the strain on the Royal Navy and British merchant shipping of sustaining indefinitely an 800-mile-long supply route across the North Sea; the fact that the available land forces mostly consisted of ill-trained and grossly under-equipped Territorial divisions quite unfit to meet the Wehrmacht in battle; and the strategic danger of diverting large Allied resources to Scandinavia when a massive German invasion of France and the Low Countries was expected any month.[16] Churchill may therefore be forgiven for his own consistent neglect of the realities of comparative combat strength and efficiency in his enthusiasm for a 'supreme strategy to carry the war into a theatre where we can bring superior forces to bear, and where a decision can be obtained which rules all other theatres . . .'[17]

Racked by debate and torn by doubt, Chamberlain's Cabinet alternately tottered towards, and then away from, a final decision; with Churchill urging that his project for mining the 'Leads' should go ahead without delay, rather than wait until it was eventually decided to land expeditionary forces in Norway. On 7 February the Cabinet instructed the COS to begin tri-service preparations for such expeditionary forces. On 17 February there came by way of an interlude to the Whitehall discussions a *Boy's Own Paper* adventure when, on Churchill's instructions, the destroyer HMS *Cossack* (Captain P. L. Vian, RN) sent a boarding party with revolvers and drawn cutlasses aboard the *Graf Spee*'s old supply ship *Altmark* as she lay in Jössingfjord in Norwegian territorial waters. The *Altmark* was on her way home with captured British merchant seamen locked below decks, undetected by the Norwegians who 'searched' the vessel at Bergen. With the boarding party's shout of 'The Navy's here!' resounding in the ears of a delighted British public, Churchill tried to persuade the Cabinet that here was the perfect excuse and timing for launching his minelaying operation. But the Cabinet would only authorise him to 'make all preparations', so that if it were subsequently decided to lay a minefield in Norwegian territorial waters, 'there would be no delay in carrying out the operation'.[18]

Now it was March; and on the 12th the War Cabinet finally reached a decision to land a force at Narvik first of all, with follow-up landings later at Trondheim as soon as Narvik was taken, and possibly also Stavanger and Bergen.[19] They also appointed Major-General P. J. Mackesy to command the Narvik land force and Admiral Sir Edward ('Teddy') Evans, a sixty-year-old Great War destroyer hero, to command the naval side. On the very next day the Finns, having been at last overwhelmed by Russian weight of numbers, made peace with the Soviet Union, so destroying the Allies' essential pretext for military intervention in Scandinavia. What now to do? Churchill, true to his pugnacious instincts, urged that the Narvik landing should still go ahead. But on 14 March the Cabinet decided to cancel the operation, and stand down and 'disperse the expeditionary forces prepared for the Scandinavian expedition'.[20] So ended dismally the months of argument for and against Churchill's minelaying proposal and that grander project of maritime strategy of opening up a major theatre of war in Norway and Sweden.

Within a fortnight the enemy began to make his own impact on this scene of procrastination and futility. For from 26 March onwards came hardening evidence that Germany might herself be about to mount some kind of Scandinavian operation. But what?

As early as 10 October 1939 Grand Admiral Raeder had proposed to Hitler that it would be advantageous to secure U-boat bases along the Norwegian coast. When he raised the question again in December, a pro-Nazi Norwegian politician, Vidkun Quisling, was also proposing to Hitler that a coup d'état should be carried out with German help which would bring Norway within Germany's strategic perimeter. Hitler expressed the view that, while he would prefer the Scandinavian states to remain neutral, he could not allow them to be used by the Allies as a means of strangling Germany. He therefore ordered planning to begin for two alternatives: one, a coup d'état by Quisling assisted by minor German forces; and two, a full-scale invasion and occupation. Detailed planning by a special working group of the OKW (Oberkommando der Wehrmacht) began on 27 January. The British boarding of the *Altmark* on 17 February 1940 clinched growing

German suspicions based on Sigint ('signals intelligence') that the Allies might be intending to land in Scandinavia on the pretext of aiding the Finns. On 21 February Hitler placed General von Falkenhorst in command of the project, reporting directly to himself. The strategic aim was to give cover to the right wing of the German Army on the continent of Europe, to provide wider scope to the German Navy, and to secure the iron-ore route.

Falkenhorst was allotted six divisions – all that could be spared in view of the pending great offensive on the Western Front; and, except for one mountain division, troops recently recruited and, by German standards, not highly trained. Falkenhorst had at his disposal an inter-service planning staff. On 1 March Hitler issued the directive for 'Fall Weserübung' ('Operation Weser Exercise'); three days later, with mounting apprehension lest the British soon intervene, Falkenhorst issued orders that preparations should be so advanced by 10 March that 'Weserübung' could be launched at four days' notice. On 26 March Raeder was arguing that despite the Finnish surrender Britain was bound sooner or later to seek to control Norwegian coastal traffic, perhaps even invade Norway. He therefore urged that Germany should strike before the nights grew too short, that was, before 15 April; whereupon Hitler fixed the date for 'Weserübung' for 7 April, about the time of the new moon. On 2 April he postponed the operation to the 9th because of continuing winter ice in the Baltic.

Except for a few training vessels and for ships in the dockyard, the entire German Navy was committed to ferrying, and covering, no fewer than six separate groups of landing forces which were to seize Norwegian ports from the capital, Oslo, in the south all the way to Narvik in the far north – and in the face of British seapower. Artillery, equipment and supplies for the landing force were to be embarked separately in transports disguised as merchant ships, which (being slower than the warships) would sail earlier in order to arrive on time. The Luftwaffe was to provide 500 Junkers transport aircraft for the rapid forward deployment of troops (including parachute troops), 290 bombers, 40 divebombers, 100 fighters, 40 long-range reconnaissance aircraft, and 30 coastal patrol aircraft. For the Luftwaffe, as well as the German Navy and Army, 'Weserübung' required meticulous planning for the forward movement of essential ordnance, airfield equipment and installations. All in all, this complex combined air, land and sea operation over distances of up to 1,000 miles and improvised in less than two months, displays German staff work and inter-service cooperation in their brief springtime of high professional achievement.[21] Success depended on speed, single-minded boldness of execution and, above all, surprise. As Raeder reported to Hitler on 9 March:

> The operation is in itself contrary to all principles in the theory of naval warfare. According to this theory, it could be carried out by us only if we had naval supremacy. We do not have this; on the contrary, we are carrying out the operation in the face of a vastly superior British Fleet. In spite of this, the C-in-C Navy believes that, provided surprise is complete, our troops can and will successfully be transported to Norway. On many occasions in the history of war those very operations have been successful which went against all the principles of warfare, provided they were carried out by surprise.[22]

On 3 April the tankers and merchant ships of the supply echelons slipped out of North German ports towards their Norwegian destinations. At 0300 on 7 April – a new moon; a dark night – the task forces with the furthest distances to go – Groups 1 and 2 destined for Narvik and Trondheim, with their troops crammed into fourteen destroyers – were led out of Schillig Roads by the battleship *Gneisenau* (wearing the flag of Vice-Admiral Günther Lütjens) in company with the *Scharnhorst* and the heavy cruiser *Admiral Hipper*. Lütjens was aware that in the course of his more than 800-mile voyage he would be exposed to the threat of an overwhelming potential concentration of Allied seapower: up to seven battleships, one or two aircraft carriers, fourteen cruisers, six destroyer flotillas. He could only put his trust in secrecy and surprise, and in the cover provided by the bad weather and poor visibility predicted by the meteorologists. The bad weather soon materialised – by the evening of 7 April Lütjens's squadron was pitching and rolling in a Force 7, and still rising, south-westerly gale, with green seas sweeping the destroyers from stem to stern so that it was difficult to keep them on course at the designated squadron speed of 26 knots; and with the miserable soldiers who were packed into their narrow spaces being violently seasick.[23] Nonetheless, 35 aircraft of Bomber Command found Lütjens's task force and bombed it, hitting nothing. Next day, 8 April, the remaining task forces put to sea for the nearer destinations of Bergen, Egersund, Kristiansand and Oslo. Except for troops for the overland invasion of Denmark, the parachute units for the seizing of Norwegian airfields and the Luftwaffe's aircraft, the 'Weserübung' forces were now irrevocably committed to the gamble.

As early as December 1939 the first whispers hinting at a possible German move against Scandinavia had been picked up by the British

Secret Intelligence Service (SIS) – reports of the assembly of expeditionary forces, of combined operations exercises in the Baltic and of the conversion of merchant ships to carry warlike stores.[24] Similar reports in January 1940 were confirmed in February when the British military attaché in Stockholm passed back to Whitehall a warning by his Romanian colleague that Germany was preparing to occupy southern Norway and the Swedish orefields. On 11 March the Foreign Office was told by a secret German source that an operation was being planned against Denmark and Norway. From 26 March to 6 April came a series of circumstantial reports via the British embassy in Stockholm pointing at imminent German action – concentration and loading of ships in Baltic and North Sea ports and the massing of troops and aircraft; reports from the Swedish general staff and the American ambassador in Copenhagen pointing at a German attack on Norway (including Narvik) and Denmark on 8 April. On the night of 6–7 April Bomber Command aircraft sighted much activity in certain German ports, while a photo-reconnaissance of Kiel by Coastal Command revealed similar sinister bustle. A heavy increase was noted in German radio traffic. On 7 April took place the unsuccessful attack by Bomber Command on Lütjens's task force, reported by the aircrews as consisting of one battleship, two cruisers and a destroyer escort.

Yet Whitehall failed to collate all this cumulative but disparate data into a clear picture of German intentions – a failure in Intelligence akin to that of the Americans before the Japanese strike on Pearl Harbor in December 1941, although the British in 1940 lacked the clinching evidence of intercepted enemy cypher traffic.[25] Here lay a crucial factor in the disastrous course of the coming campaign in Norway. It occurred firstly because the Intelligence services had not yet recovered from pre-war neglect and disorganisation. Each branch tended to work in its own compartment without an effective agency to coordinate their efforts and results. The Admiralty's own Intelligence services were particularly fragmented. While NID 1, as the geographical branch of the Naval Intelligence Department covering Germany, processed the various SIS and embassy reports about German plans, the Operational Intelligence Centre (OIC) did not receive the same comprehensive spread of material. To make matters worse, NID 1 and OIC were anyway in a state of mutual distrust so often characteristic of departments in a bureaucracy, while NID 17, the Director of Naval Intelligence's executive branch which was supposed to coordinate their work, failed to do so. In these lapses in liaison can be heard an echo of similar Admiralty failures during the Battle of Jutland.

There was a second reason why Whitehall failed to read German intentions. It fell into the classic error of believing or disbelieving Intelligence reports according to whether or not they fitted in with its own *idées fixes*. Thus Military Intelligence, identifying six German divisions in North-West Germany, could not believe that a major campaign was in train because it reckoned that 20 or 30 divisions would be needed for an invasion of Scandinavia. When the NID received the report via the American ambassador in Copenhagen that the Germans were going to seize Narvik on 8 April, it simply refused to credit it, at first thinking that 'Narvik' must be a misprint for 'Larvik', a port in southern Norway. Foreign Office officials for their part thought such reports amounted to no more than 'the usual [German] threats'.[26] Even when on 7 April Bomber Command found the powerful German task force steering north-west towards Norway, the DNI (Director of Naval Intelligence) himself in passing the information on to Forbes at Scapa added: '. . . all these reports are of doubtful value and may well only be a further move in the war of nerves.'[27] As late as 8 April a Military Intelligence appreciation, although acknowledging that Germany could carry out 'limited operations' against the Norwegian coast, saw such action to be 'by no means likely' and of not much advantage to the Germans; it saw no profit at all for Germany in occupying Denmark. In the words of Professor Sir Harry Hinsley, the official historian of British Intelligence in the Second World War:

> It was a conclusion which reflected the outlook of the whole of Whitehall at this time when, in the absence of the incontestable intelligence from Sigint and from regular photographic reconnaissance, there was also no adequate machinery, within the departments or between them, for confronting prevailing opinions and lazy assumptions with rigorous and authoritative assessments of the massive but miscellaneous information about the enemy that was nevertheless available.[28]

In this needless fog of uncertainty the Allies took the final decisions over their own action in Norway. On 28 March the Supreme War Council finally agreed to mine Norwegian waters ('Operation Wilfred') on 5 April.[29] What with the rumours of impending German moves of some kind and the likelihood of a German reaction to the mining, the question now arose again of possible Allied military action in Norway. This caused the Secretary of State for War, Oliver Stanley, to remind the Cabinet on 29 March that as a result of its decision a fortnight earlier to disband the expeditionary force, it was now 'out of the question' to send the two divisions originally intended, while only a brigade remained available to go to Narvik and another small force to Stavanger.[30] The Chiefs of Staff therefore began to ponder afresh the contingency of landing Allied troops at Bergen and Trondheim 'in sufficient force to secure them as bridgeheads for possible extended operations' – which meant of course 'at least the possibility that it might be necessary' to reassemble the troops and transports dispersed since 14 March.[31] There were now only four days left before the 'Weserübung' supply echelons were due to sail; eight days before the German task groups for Narvik and Bergen would steam out of Schillig Roads; only eleven days before all the 'Weserübung' forces would strike home with ruthless energy.

On 3 April occurred an unconnected event which would nevertheless exercise its own fateful influence over the campaign in Norway. Winston Churchill succeeded Admiral of the Fleet Lord Chatfield as the regular Chairman of the Cabinet's Military Coordination Committee – its executive organ for deciding strategy and overseeing operations. (Chatfield had resigned as Minister for the Coordination of Defence, and was not replaced.) On the eve of 'Weserübung', therefore, Churchill added to his existing authority over maritime operations as First Lord the chairmanship of the committee which would (subject to ultimate Cabinet approval) run the Norwegian campaign.

On 5 April the Cabinet postponed the execution of 'Wilfred' to the 8th, but the minelaying task force sailed nevertheless on 5 April. 'Wilfred' consisted of three separate minelaying operations: Force WB (two destroyers) was to simulate the laying of mines off Bud (62° 54' North, 6° 55' East); Force WS, consisting of the minelayer HMS *Teviot Bank* (5,087 tons) and four destroyers was to lay mines off Stadlandet (62° North, 5° East); and Force WAV, with four minelaying destroyers and four escort destroyers, was to mine off Hovden in Vestfjord in the approaches to Narvik (67° 24' North, 14° 36' East).[32] On hearing a report that all four Norwegian coastal defence ships were in the Narvik area, Admiral Forbes ordered Vice-Admiral W.J. Whitworth (Flag Officer, Battle Cruiser Squadron) to sea with HMS *Renown* and screening destroyers *Greyhound*, *Glowworm*, *Hyperion* and *Hero* in order to protect the minelayers from Norwegian interference.

No landing forces were despatched at this time, but a contingency plan had finally been drawn up whereby Stavanger, Bergen, Trondheim and Narvik were all to be seized as soon as it became clear that the Germans were taking the offensive in retaliation for the British minelaying. The troops (amounting to eight battalions in all) were ready to move by 7 April: those for Stavanger and Bergen in the cruisers *Devonshire*, *Berwick*, *York* and *Glasgow* at Rosyth, and those for Trondheim and Narvik in transports in the Clyde, under the escort of the cruiser *Aurora* (flying the flag of Admiral Sir Edward Evans) and six destroyers. Since none of these forces was to sail until clear evidence had been received of a German attack, the initiative and the advantage of time, those priceless and usually irrecoverable assets in war, were thus tamely handed to the enemy. Moreover, Churchill and Pound omitted to order Forbes and the main body of the Home Fleet out of Scapa to a covering position in the central North Sea ready to intervene in whatever events might be provoked by 'Wilfred'.[33]

On 6 April, in the face of the mounting evidence that the Germans were going to launch a major operation on the 8th, the Deputy Director of Operations (Home) on the Naval Staff, Captain Ralph Edwards, sought to persuade Pound and Churchill to delay 'Wilfred' for twenty-four hours – but in vain. Next day, a Sunday, when the First Sea Lord was away fishing at Romsey, Edwards renewed his urgings in favour of postponement, this time to Churchill and the Deputy Chief of Naval Staff, Rear-Admiral T. S. V. Phillips. Neither would agree; and Churchill, for his part, could not bear to see yet another postponement of 'Wilfred' at this last moment after so many earlier setbacks. As Edwards noted at the time: 'I am sure we ought to cancel Operation Wilfred. Winston however is obsessed with the idea of forcing enemy ships out of the fjords into the open waters and I fear we shall be compelled to continue.'[34]

But there was another reason why Churchill, Pound and Phillips all discounted the likelihood of an imminent large-scale German invasion of Norway. They interpreted the air sighting of Lütjens's task force by Bomber Command as revealing a fresh attempt by the German battlecruisers to break out into the Atlantic via the Iceland–Faeroes gap and attack British shipping routes.[35] When Pound returned to the Admiralty about 2000 on 7 April, he 'went' for Edwards, in Edwards's own words, 'for – as he put it – trying to lead the naval staff away from the main objective which was the defence of the Atlantic convoy routes. He would not listen to my arguments that all the evidence tended to suggest that Norway was to be the victim.'[36]

In any case, the sailing of the Home Fleet from Scapa was delayed some four hours that day because of an inexcusable Admiralty failure promptly to pass on to Forbes, the C-in-C, the report from the Bomber Command force that at 1325 it had attacked Lütjens's squadron steering north-west off the entrance to the Skagerrak. Not until 1727 did Forbes order his Fleet to raise steam, and not until 2015 had the whole Fleet cleared the Flow.[37]

Now followed two further errors of judgment. In the first place,

Forbes left his one available carrier, *Furious*, in the Clyde because of apprehension lest she suffer the fate of *Courageous*, even instructing her to release some 120 seamen to the destroyers to serve as possible boarding parties. It was not until 1630 on 8 April that the Admiralty intervened to order the *Furious* to join the Fleet; not until 0400 on 9 April that she embarked aircraft, though no fighters. Once at sea she steamed at 28 knots in order to catch up.[38]

Admiral Sir Charles Forbes himself was the human equivalent of the eighteenth-century 74-gun ship-of-the-line – a solid, reliable, and rugged performer in all situations and all weathers; a sea officer of faultless manners and a deep sense of loyalty both to superiors and subordinates. His Flag Lieutenant, Godfrey Style, was to recall how Forbes, physically of small stature, 'stood on his own bridge, always calm, always the same and ALWAYS correctly dressed, without mufflers or other fancy gear . . . never more than his British Warm [a short, close-fitting navy-blue overcoat] . . .'[39] Now this 'foursquare'[40] sailor, flying his flag in HMS *Rodney*, was leading the Home Fleet into the first, and one of the most important, of the maritime campaigns of the Second World War. However, foursquare traditionalist that he was, and in common with most admirals of his generation, Forbes did not yet appreciate the crucial importance of seaborne airpower; hence his decision to leave the *Furious* behind. Now came his second error of judgment. He led the Home Fleet at high speed on a north-easterly course which would take it well outside the tracks of the German task forces heading towards central and southern Norway. This error also sprang from traditionalism of outlook – for Forbes too shared the preoccupation with the majestic clash of heavy ships. His mind, like Churchill's and Pound's, was focused on the German battleships and their supposed sortie towards the Atlantic via the Iceland–Faeroes gap, and on the importance of intercepting them and bringing them to action: this it was that determined his choice of a north-easterly course. But the German naval command was in fact successfully selling its opponent a dummy, for at around 2000 hours on 8 April Lütjens, having left Group 2 west of Trondheim and escorted Group 1 to the vicinity of Narvik, sheered off with *Gneisenau* and *Scharnhorst* to the north, intending later to turn west, so simulating an attempt to break out into the Atlantic.

All that therefore stood in the direct track of the German invasion forces were submarines, the destroyers of 'Wilfred's' minelaying groups and Vice-Admiral Whitworth with HMS *Renown* and her escorting destroyers. These now proceeded to redeem as best they might the strategic misjudgments of the C-in-C and the Admiralty.

[109]

At 0815 on 8 April the destroyer *Glowworm* (which had become detached from Whitworth's screen during the night when searching for a man overboard) encountered the German destroyers of Group 2 (the Trondheim group) in a Force 8 gale, and despite the heavy odds immediately steered to engage. At 0950 the heavy cruiser *Admiral Hipper*, sent back by Lütjens, found *Glowworm* in close action with the German destroyer *Bernd von Arnim*. At 0957 *Hipper* opened fire with her 8-inch guns at 9,000 yards, hitting *Glowworm*'s bridge with her first salvo. The *Glowworm* replied with torpedoes and a smoke screen. As *Hipper* in pursuit emerged from the smoke, she saw *Glowworm* at close range on the starboard bow, and *Hipper*'s captain (Captain Heye) decided to ram the smaller British vessel. However, the *Hipper* answered her helm so slowly that the *Glowworm* succeeded in ramming the German cruiser first, ripping off some 150 feet of *Hipper*'s side plating before passing astern with her own bow broken off, a heavy list, and sinking. At 1000 *Glowworm* blew up and disappeared. The *Hipper* rescued one officer and 37 of her ship's company, although her captain, Lieutenant-Commander G. B. Roope, was lost when he fell back into the gale-swept sea while being hoisted aboard. For his unhesitating engagement of more powerful warships in superior numbers even to the point of ramming, Roope was to be posthumously awarded the Victoria Cross.[41]

On intercepting the *Glowworm*'s 'enemy' reports, Forbes redeployed his forces: the battlecruiser *Repulse*, the cruiser *Penelope* and four destroyers were detached to *Glowworm*'s aid while Whitworth in *Renown* was ordered to cut off the enemy if heading for Vestfjord. At this point the Admiralty (really Churchill and Pound, as inseparable in naval command as Rodgers and Hammerstein in music) made the first of its disastrous direct interventions in the campaign, by ordering all the destroyers of Force WAV (the Vestfjord minelaying group) to join Whitworth, which thus left Vestfjord and the approach to Narvik without direct cover.

By now even the Admiralty had accepted that yesterday's Intelligence about a German invasion of Norway might be true. Confirmation had come when the Polish submarine *Orzel* sank the enemy troopship *Rio de Janeiro* off Kristiansand early on 8 April. Although the Admiralty informed Forbes that an invasion operation was taking place, the Commander-in-Chief continued to steer north-east rather than east to intercept it. At 1430 on the 8th a flying boat flown off by Forbes to search ahead of him reported a battleship, two cruisers and two destroyers in 64° 12′ North, 6° 25′ East steering west – in fact, *Hipper* and four destroyers marking time (hence the meaningless westerly course) before attacking Trondheim according to schedule on the morrow. Forbes therefore altered course by stages to north-west in order to intercept what he believed might be the enemy's main body.[42] By this time Forbes too had run into the same rising gale which had been tossing Lütjens's ships about, and it compelled him to reduce speed for the sake of his destroyers. The C-in-C now appreciated that there could be one enemy battleship north of him en route for Narvik, and other strong forces down south in the Skagerrak or Kattegat. He therefore ordered the battlecruiser *Repulse*, the cruiser *Penelope* and some destroyers to reinforce Whitworth to the northwards while he himself turned south with the battleships *Rodney* and *Valiant*, the cruiser *Sheffield* and a destroyer screen.

In the event it was Whitworth with the *Renown* who encountered the *Gneisenau* and *Scharnhorst* and their destroyer escort at 0337 on 9 April (D-Day of 'Weserübung') some 50 miles off Vestfjord as the German ships were steering north on their diversionary course. It was now blowing a full gale, with mountainous seas and sudden curtains of snow or rain. At 0405 the *Renown* opened fire with her 15-inch guns at a range of about 15,000 yards. Twelve minutes later she knocked out the *Gneisenau*'s main gunnery control system, which persuaded the enemy to run for it. In the stern chase now ensuing, Whitworth hit the *Gneisenau* twice again at 0434 and knocked out a forward turret. However the weather itself was on the side of the German ships as Whitworth was later to recall:

> The chief feature of this running action was a heavy head sea, which forced *Renown* to slow down in order to fight her fore turrets. The Germans on the other hand could disregard the damaging effects of heavy water coming over their forecastles and continue to fight their after turrets whilst steaming at high speed.
>
> It is noteworthy that the Germans always jinked when they saw our salvoes fired, thus throwing us out for line.[43]

Although at times Whitworth drove *Renown* up to 29 knots, the two German ships had disappeared from view amid the squalls by 0660. Nevertheless, a British force had once again asserted the moral supremacy born of centuries in attacking without hesitation a more powerful enemy force. Yet the fact that Whitworth had been compelled to fight with one lightly armoured and elderly battlecruiser against two modern battleships was a mark of the Admiralty's failure (and, initially, Forbes's too) to read German strategic intentions correctly and concentrate Britain's naval resources in the key sea area.

Now followed the calamitous penalty for all the failures of

Intelligence and the resulting mistaken deployment of the Fleet. On 9 April, while Whitworth was fighting the *Gneisenau* and *Scharnhorst*, all the 'Weserübung' task groups enjoyed a clear run to their objectives except for valiant resistance by Norwegian coastal defence vessels and shore batteries. Despite losing the new heavy cruiser *Blücher* to the guns and torpedoes of Norwegian forts in Oslofjord, Group 5 successfully landed an infantry division round Oslo while parachute and airlanding troops seized the airfield. Group 4, led by the cruiser *Karlsruhe* and helped by heavy bombing by the Luftwaffe, were in possession of Kristiansand and Arendal by mid-afternoon. Group 3, with part of 69th Infantry Division embarked in the cruisers *Köln* and *Königsberg*, took Bergen despite damage to the *Königsberg* by shore batteries – to the vast relief of the Group Commander, Vice-Admiral Schmundt, who had considered that his force was the most likely of all to be intercepted by the British fleet. Stavanger, the other objective of Group 3, succumbed to air assault. After heavy preliminary bombing, parachute troops took the nearby airfield, so permitting two infantry battalions to land in Ju 52 transports. The infantry then took the city, some eight miles away, from the landward side.

At Trondheim, Group 2 began creeping in through the tortuous fjord at 0300 led by the *Hipper*. Unscathed by the fire of shore batteries (later captured by landing parties) the *Hipper* and a destroyer anchored off the city, whereupon two companies of the 138th Mountain Regiment landed at the quay from motor boats and marched up the street to take surrender of the local Norwegian commander at his headquarters. Furthest north of all, at Narvik, Group 1, its soldiers embarked in nine destroyers, seasick, cold and tired after the gales, crept into Ofotfjord in the dawn amid snow showers. Two destroyers were detached to land troops on both sides of the narrowest neck of the fjord to seize shore batteries; a third landed troops on Baroy Island, which commanded the southern seaward entrance to the fjord. The remaining six destroyers moved up the fjord, sinking the feeble Norwegian coast defence vessels *Eidsvoll* and *Norge* on the way. By 0800 Narvik and its surroundings were in German hands; the operation was complete which Churchill and the naval staff had always taken to be utterly out of the question.

Meanwhile German army units moving overland, coupled with seaborne landing forces, had occupied the whole of Denmark, a virtually unarmed country, by the time many of its inhabitants awoke that Sunday morning – an event which hardly confirmed the argument of the pre-war British disarmament movement that defencelessness would ensure immunity from aggression.

'Weserübung' had thus far proved an audacious gamble brilliantly executed; a success thanks to the crystal-clear overall aim and the resolute, energetic tactical offensives by Groups 1 to 6. In Norway the Germans had won the priceless advantage of possession of the ground – certainly possession of the essential keys to the ground, such as major ports and airfields. It remained for them to pour in the remainder of their six divisions and advance inland up the valleys against weak Norwegian forces to complete their occupation. The German success also meant that from this moment onwards the Allies could only react belatedly and piecemeal, whether by sea, land or air – like a boxer already sent staggering by his opponent's first sudden punch. To this disarray were now to be added confusions and contradictions in the directing of Allied counter-measures; and most of all in the Admiralty itself.

After news had come in of the German attacks on Norwegian ports, Admiral Forbes (now reinforced by nine more British and French cruisers and thirteen destroyers but still critically lacking a carrier) proposed to attack the German task force at Bergen. The Admiralty, however, wanted him to attack Trondheim and watch Narvik as well. At 1130 Forbes therefore detached Admiral Layton with four cruisers (*Manchester*, *Southampton*, *Glasgow* and *Sheffield*) and seven destroyers to destroy the one German cruiser believed to lie at Bergen. However, Layton had some 80 miles to go. In such circumstances cruisers were a poor substitute for a strike by carrier aircraft. In the early afternoon and before he could arrive, RAF reconnaissance aircraft reported that there were in fact two enemy cruisers in Bergen (the *Köln* and *Königsberg*) plus the old training cruiser *Bremse*. Nevertheless, Forbes still wished Layton to press home his attack. But now came another of the Admiralty's interferences – an order cancelling the operation, apparently in the mistaken belief that the shore batteries were now operational in German hands. Here was the first great muffed opportunity in a scramble of a campaign, for Layton would have caught not only the three German cruisers but also the rest of Group 3's ships, and at a time when in fact German army units had not yet restored Bergen's batteries to readiness.[44] Instead Layton and his cruisers, together with those of Admiral Edward-Collins, swept the Norwegian coast as far south as Utsire in order to interrupt supplies and reinforcements for the German garrisons at Stavanger and Bergen. They met nothing.

Meanwhile Forbes with the main body of the Home Fleet, now including the carrier HMS *Furious*, having steamed south as far as

59° 44′ North, 2° 57′ East (off the Norwegian coast roughly midway between Bergen and Stavanger), turned again to the north. In the afternoon of 9 April, under a cleared sky, he encountered for the first time what was to prove the decisive factor in the Norwegian campaign whether at sea or on land, when Luftwaffe bombers swung down to attack his fleet. Although only the destroyer *Gurkha* was sunk and minor damage inflicted to other ships (including the flagship) the fleet's anti-aircraft fire had failed to prevent the enemy pressing home his attacks – even despite some ships expending up to 40 per cent of their stocks of ammunition. The C-in-C quickly drew the appropriate lesson: henceforward even with a carrier present the Home Fleet would not operate within the zone controlled by German land-based air power; that was, the whole sea area from Bergen (inclusive) southwards.[45]

At Narvik more British confusions of orders and intentions on 9–10 April were to result in an episode of heart-stirring but needless courage and sacrifice. In conformity with instructions received directly from the Admiralty in the late forenoon of 9 April Captain Warburton-Lee (commanding the 2nd Destroyer Flotilla in Whitworth's squadron) led five destroyers – *Hardy*, his own ship; *Hotspur* (Commander H. F. H. Layman); *Havoc* (Lieutenant-Commander R. E. Courage); *Hunter* (Lieutenant-Commander L. de Villiers); *Hostile* (Commander J. P. Wright) – up Ofotfjord in order to sink or capture enemy ships and transport in Narvik, and, at his discretion, put a landing party ashore to recapture the town. Enquiry of a Norwegian pilot station at the entrance to the fjord revealed to him that he faced six big German destroyers (in fact it was ten). When Warburton-Lee reported this to Whitworth and Forbes, adding the words 'Intend attacking at dawn high water', Whitworth (who had now been joined by a second battlecruiser, *Repulse*) considered reinforcing him with the battlecruiser *Renown*, even though it would mean some delay. He decided not to, partly because the Admiralty had bypassed him to deal directly with Warburton-Lee. As Whitworth wrote later: 'I have always regretted that I did not intervene, and order Warburton-Lee to postpone his attack until *Renown* could join him. Now that I know that the Admiralty had no special intelligence not available to myself, this regret is all the more poignant.'[46]

The Admiralty (this meant Churchill in a high state of executive excitement in the map room, as an eyewitness noted)[47] signalled Warburton-Lee at 2200 on 9 April (over the signature of the First Sea Lord, although the language is unmistakably Churchillian): 'You alone [author's note: what about Forbes or Whitworth?] can judge

[114]

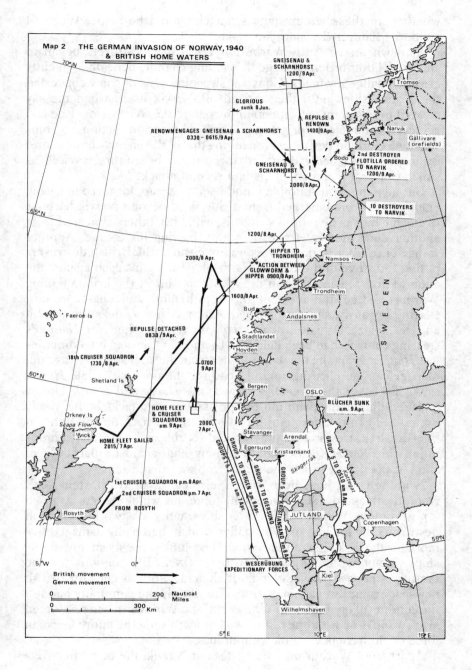

Map 2 THE GERMAN INVASION OF NORWAY, 1940
& BRITISH HOME WATERS

70°N

GNEISENAU &
SCHARNHORST
1200/9 Apr.

Tromso

GLORIOUS
sunk 8 Jun.

REPULSE &
RENOWN
1400/9 Apr.

Narvik

RENOWN ENGAGES GNEISENAU & SCHARNHORST
0330 - 0615/9 Apr.

Gällivare
(orefields)

GNEISENAU &
SCHARNHORST

Bodo

2nd DESTROYER
FLOTILLA ORDERED
TO NARVIK
1200/9 Apr.

2000/8 Apr.

10 DESTROYERS
TO NARVIK

65°N

1200/8 Apr.

HIPPER TO
TRONDHEIM

2000/8 Apr.

Namsos

ACTION BETWEEN
GLOWWORM &
HIPPER 0900/8 Apr.

1600/8 Apr.

Trondheim

S W E D E N

Faeroe Is

Bud

Andalsnes

REPULSE DETACHED
0830/9 Apr.

Stadtlandet

Hovden

18th CRUISER SQUADRON
1730/8 Apr.

0700
9 Apr

N O R W A Y

60°N

Shetland Is

Bergen

OSLO

BLÜCHER SUNK
a.m. 9 Apr.

Orkney Is
Scapa Flow

HOME FLEET
& CRUISER
SQUADRONS
a.m. 9 Apr.

2000/
7 Apr.

Stavanger

Wick

Arendal

Egersund

Kristiansand

HOME FLEET SAILED
2015/7 Apr.

Skagerrak

1st CRUISER SQUADRON p.m. 8 Apr.

2nd CRUISER SQUADRON p.m. 7 Apr.

FROM ROSYTH

JUTLAND

Copenhagen

Rosyth

55°N

5°W

0°

British movement
German movement

0   200   Nautical
                            Miles
0   300   Km

WESERÜBUNG
EXPEDITIONARY FORCES

Kiel

Wilhelmshaven

5°E

10°E

15°E

GROUPS 1 & 2 TO BERGEN a.m. 7 Apr.

GROUP 3 TO BERGEN a.m. 8 Apr.

GROUP 6 TO EGERSUND

GROUP 4 TO KRISTIANSAND a.m. 8 Apr.

GROUP 5 TO OSLO a.m. 8 Apr.

whether, in these circumstances, attack should be made. We shall support whatever decision you make.'[48]

At dawn on 10 April Warburton-Lee's five destroyers began to steam up Ofotfjord in its jaggedly winding channel beneath high cliffs crowned with snowfields. Constant sweeping veils of snow concealed the British ships until they arrived off Narvik itself, when the sky cleared to reveal the new moon in the paling sky. Warburton-Lee had achieved complete surprise: in a short and ferocious action his ships sank two German destroyers (including that of the enemy commodore) by torpedo and badly damaged three more by gunfire, as well as sinking several merchant ships in a second attack.[49]

But now the British flotilla found itself in a trap, for three more big enemy destroyers emerged from a side fjord beyond Narvik harbour to engage him as he retired seawards, while two others appeared from another concealed inlet ahead of him, barring his escape. Another savage encounter in the narrow waters ensued, the British destroyers pitting four (five in the case of *Hardy*) 4.7-inch guns each against the enemy's five 5.9-inch. Soon the *Hardy* was hit in the bridge (killing Warburton-Lee and most of those with him) and engine rooms. Blazing furiously, she was beached. Astern of her, *Hunter* was also hit and set ablaze. As she lost way *Hotspur* ran into her, for *Hotspur*'s steering controls had been damaged by another German hit. Nonetheless *Hotspur*'s captain, now conning her from the after steering position, managed to get clear again and head for the open sea while *Hunter* sank. To cover the *Hotspur*'s escape, the *Havoc* and *Hostile* closely engaged the enemy, who did not press his own attacks home, partly because of acute shortage of fuel. On their way back down Ofotfjord the British destroyers encountered and set ablaze the German ammunition ship *Rauenfels*, the flames leaping high against a backdrop of snow-capped rock. Soon the *Rauenfels* blew up and sank.

Nothing could have been more Nelsonian than Warburton-Lee's resolute attack on a superior enemy force, for which he was awarded a posthumous Victoria Cross. His ships had sunk two big German destroyers for the loss of two smaller British; had badly damaged five more for the disabling of the *Hotspur*; had sunk some six enemy supply ships, including the *Rauenfels* with its essential munitions for the German troops ashore at Narvik. It all made glorious copy for British newspapers and weekly magazines. But if only the Admiralty had left the conduct of operations to Whitworth, and Whitworth had reinforced Warburton-Lee with one of his two battlecruisers, the entire German force could have been sunk without loss.

Apart from Warburton-Lee's attack at Narvik, the only effectively destructive response by the Royal Navy to 'Weserübung' during the first hectic two days when the German operation was at its most precarious and vulnerable took the form of attacks by the Fleet Air Arm and the submarine service, those junior branches of a 'big-gun' navy. Early on 10 April fifteen Skua fighter/dive-bombers from 600 and 603 squadrons from Hatston in the Orkneys – led by Captain R. T. Partridge, RM, and Lieutenant-Commander W. P. Lucy, RN, and flying at the limits of their range – bombed and sank the cruiser *Königsberg* in Bergen harbour; the first time in the history of war that a major warship had been sunk by air attack. This success contrasted with the failure of twelve Wellingtons and twelve Hampdens of Bomber Command to inflict any significant damage during an attack on Bergen the previous evening. Meanwhile British submarines in the Skagerrak were exploiting the movement of major German warships back to home ports immediately after the landings in Norway in order to evade attack by the Home Fleet. On the night of 9 April the submarine *Truant* torpedoed the cruiser *Karlsruhe* and damaged her so severely that the Germans themselves had to sink her three hours afterwards. Twenty-four hours later the submarine *Spearfish* torpedoed the pocket battleship *Lützow*, blowing off her propellers and badly damaging her stern. Towed into Kiel, she was not to be recommissioned until 1941. Other submarines, including the Polish *Orzel*, sank several merchant ships and tankers too during the early days of the campaign.[50]

Back in Whitehall, in tranquil panelled rooms far removed from heaving seas, driving snow and screaming dive-bombers – the contrast was to supply a leit-motif of the coming campaign – Britain's collective leadership strove to keep up with the rush of events. At Cabinet in the early forenoon on 9 April after the first sensational news of 'Weserübung' had come in (but not yet of the unimagined German capture of Narvik) the CIGS, General Sir Edmund Ironside, and Churchill strongly advocated that Narvik should be occupied by a British force, together with combined operations to prevent the Germans from consolidating their positions at Trondheim and Bergen.[51] There was just one snag. The very day before Churchill and Pound had ordered the disembarkation of the troops being held on board cruisers at Rosyth in the Clyde to meet the contingency of a German intervention in Norway in response to 'Wilfred'; and had despatched the cruisers without the troops to join the Home Fleet. At the same time the cruiser escort for the troopships in the Clyde was also ordered to sea, thus stranding the troopships. Britain therefore now had no ready expeditionary force whatsoever with which to intervene immediately in Norway against the German invaders. Churchill's and Pound's disastrous decision stemmed from their stubborn belief on 7 April that the reported movements of major units of the German Navy presaged an enemy attempt to break out into the Atlantic and attack British convoys; a belief which had blinded them to all the cumulative Intelligence pointing towards an invasion of Norway.

Now, in the forenoon of 9 April, the War Cabinet could only lamely instruct the Chiefs of Staff to 'set on foot preparations for military expeditions to recapture Trondheim and Bergen and to occupy Narvik';[52] just a little late. Indeed, by the time the Cabinet met again at noon that day the news had come in that the Germans had already seized Narvik anyway. From this moment forward, therefore, the Norwegian campaign was a lost cause, for the initial errors and consequent loss of time, fatal in themselves, were inevitably to lead to half-cock operations hastily mounted with scratch forces.

5

A Churchillian Disaster: Norway, 1940

On 12 April Admiral Whitworth took the battleship *Warspite* (allotted to him by the C-in-C, Home Fleet) and nine destroyers up the Ofotfjord to Narvik, while aircraft from the *Furious* bombed the harbour ahead of him; and proceeded relentlessly to hunt down and sink the remaining German destroyers in the remotest recesses of the fjords. It was the operation that he would have carried out two days earlier with *Renown* but for the Admiralty's interference vis-à-vis Warburton-Lee. Whitworth now considered the possibility of putting ashore a landing party to retake Narvik, but decided that such a party would not be strong enough to turn out a garrison of 2,000 German soldiers.

At this point Churchill in his impatience would not wait until a military force could be reassembled for this task, but wanted the Navy to do the job on its own – the same mistake he had made over forcing the Dardanelles in 1915. As Whitworth was steaming back down Ofotfjord towards the sea he received an Admiralty signal urging him to occupy Narvik forthwith 'in order to secure an unopposed landing later'.[1] Whitworth replied that this should be the function of a military force from the United Kingdom, which he judged could take Narvik 'by direct assault without fear of meeting serious opposition on landing'.[2] He was right – the garrison had lost its ammunition supply in the *Rauenfels* and its motor transport in another sunk vessel, and Hitler even thought of ordering it to withdraw. Yet Whitworth could actually have had a military force with him at that moment, if only Churchill and Pound had not stranded it in the United Kingdom by their instructions on 7 April, in which case Narvik would have quickly fallen. As it was, it did not succumb until 28 May.

On the day of Whitworth's attack, a hastily reconstituted military force under the command of Major-General Mackesy sailed from the Clyde for the Narvik area under a strong naval escort commanded by Admiral of the Fleet the Earl of Cork and Orrery (replacing Evans). Lord Cork was a fiery old Great War veteran on the retired list, and typical of Churchill's penchant for illustrious reputations won long ago. Mackesy's command consisted of the 24th Guards Brigade, which had been piled into merchant ships without artillery, engineers or transport,[3] unequipped for and incapable of either making an assault landing or advancing inland. Mackesy was instructed by the CIGS to secure a foothold near Narvik whence could be launched a major operation to eject the Germans from the town once he had been reinforced. The operation, codenamed 'Rupert' (a Churchillian invention from Prince Rupert of the Rhine), was ambitiously intended, according to the Military Coordination Committee, to secure Narvik as a base 'from which to reach out to the Gällivare orefields'.[4]

Already half-cocked as a very conception, 'Rupert' was now further compromised by command arrangements which repeated, and even improved on, all the confusions of British joint maritime operations from that of Lord Howard of Effingham and the Earl of Essex against Cadiz in 1596 to the Dardanelles itself. No supreme commander was appointed; Mackesy and Cork were supposed jointly to frame operations. True to a hallowed tradition, they quarrelled instead. Mackesy received instructions from the CIGS; Cork from the First Sea Lord and (more and more as time went on) the First Lord. Cork's command was quite separate from that of Forbes, the C-in-C, Home Fleet, who had to support him and protect his 800-mile-long lines of communication. Moreover, although Forbes's was the senior post, old Lord Cork as an Admiral of the Fleet was senior to Forbes. Thus their relations too were not always to be smooth.

To confusion of command was now added confusion over campaign priorities, which altered almost day by day, not least because the mind of the First Lord of the Admiralty and Chairman of the Military Coordination Committee was puffed this way and that by the shifting breezes of opportunity. Although on 10 April the Cabinet at Churchill's urging had chosen Narvik as the Allied objective, it authorised the COS the very next day to study a possible second operation (dubbed 'Maurice' by Churchill after the seventeenth-century Prince

of Nassau) against Trondheim too, Churchill being then all in favour.
But at a War Cabinet on 12 April he opted instead for concentrating
all resources on Narvik – as the CIGS himself urged.[5] Optimistic as
ever, Churchill claimed that plans for this 'were well advanced', and
'the landing could be made within a few days ... We could be
reasonably sure of success at this point, and a success would show
that we should be able ultimately to clear the Germans out of all the
ports in which they obtained a foothold.'[6] On 13 April, despite his
renewed plea that nothing 'must be allowed to deflect us from making
the capture of this place [Narvik] as certain as possible', the Cabinet
decided that Trondheim too should be recaptured. Next day however
Churchill, intoxicated by the news of Whitworth's devastation of the
German destroyers at Narvik, changed his mind again. He now
believed that an Allied occupation of the town 'would not be seriously
opposed', and he told the Cabinet that the naval staff thought that 'it
might be possible' to land directly at Trondheim as well. He further
reported that small scratch forces of seamen and marines were going
to be landed at Namsos (a port north of Trondheim) and Alesund
later that same day and next morning[7] – the very kind of 'ineffectual
operations along the Norwegian coast' against which he had just been
warning the Cabinet only the day before.[8] He now reckoned that a
landing to retake Trondheim 'did not appear to involve unjustifiable
risks'.[9]

That afternoon the Military Coordination Committee under his
leadership decided to divert the 146th (Territorial) Infantry Brigade
from 'Rupert' to 'Maurice', even though the Committee noted that
its training 'was not yet advanced', so tending 'to increase the risk of
the operation'.[10] Worse, the Brigade's stores and ordnance were not
'tactically loaded' in the ships for immediate use on landing, a fact
neglected by Churchill and his luckless committee as they framed
strategy off the map.[11] By this time Churchill had come to consider
Trondheim 'an even greater prize than Narvik'.[12] He had in fact now
stumbled on a strategic truth, for, as the German command itself well
recognised, the Trondheim area, the gateway to Norway's long narrow
waist, was the key to control of the whole country to the northwards,
including Narvik.

So it was that when the Allies finally became committed to major
land operations in Norway a week after 'Weserübung', they split their
hastily improvised and ill-equipped forces between two strategic
objectives 400 miles apart instead of concentrating them on one chosen
aim. For the Royal Navy the task of putting ashore, and thereafter
protecting and sustaining, these two far separate expeditionary forces

was to strain its resources in ships and the endurance of the ships' companies to the uttermost.

Norway in 1940 serves as the precursor for such later maritime campaigns as the Allied landings in French North Africa in November 1942 ('Operation Torch'), the D-Day invasion of Normandy in 1944, and the entire United States offensive against Japan in the Pacific from 1942 to 1945, for here for the first time were seen fleet carriers, battleships, cruiser forces and destroyer escorts working together to cover and support major expeditionary forces ashore. But those later maritime operations were to be thoroughly planned and prepared beforehand. Their combined task forces were to be organised and rehearsed for their roles in good time. They were to enjoy unified command chains and specially equipped combined headquarters ships. They were to include fleet trains of oilers and supply ships to maintain the fleet on station without the need to rotate warships back to a distant shore base whenever fuel or ammunition ran low. None of these favourable factors existed in 1940. Instead, Admiral Forbes and the Home Fleet had been launched precipitately into a campaign for which they (and the British Army too) were in no sense prepared, and in which they were to be called upon to cope at short notice with the vagaries of Whitehall map warfare.

But the central operational problem for Forbes lay in the Luftwaffe operating at short range from Norwegian airfields. At its peak strength in early May the Luftwaffe numbered 710 aircraft, of which 360 were bombers, 50 dive-bombers, 50 modern single-engined monoplane fighters and some 60 long-range reconnaissance types.[13] On 13 April the Air Ministry withdrew the only two bomber squadrons serving with RAF Coastal Command back to Bomber Command, so leaving Coastal Command with virtually no striking force.[14] Bomber Command itself regarded air attack on German forces in Norway as a deviation from the pure Trenchardite doctrine of the strategic air offensive against enemy industries and cities. Although this offensive had yet to begin, lest it should unleash a much more powerful Luftwaffe attack on Britain, Bomber Command was jealously conserving its strength for the great day. Between 7 April and 10 May the Command flew fewer than 800 individual sorties against targets in Norway, compared with over 600 sorties in a fortnight flown by just two squadrons of Fighter Command from forward airstrips near Narvik.[15]

Apart from these Fighter Command squadrons, which in any case did not operate until the second half of May in time for the final offensive against Narvik, and a short-lived attempt to base a few RAF Gladiator biplane fighters on a frozen lake at Lesjaskog in central Norway late in April (an experiment abruptly ended when German bombers broke up the ice), the task of air defence of the Allied expeditionary forces and their bases as well as of the Fleet itself fell entirely on the aircraft and the anti-aircraft guns of the Royal Navy. However, even when the Home Fleet's only carrier *Furious* had been reinforced by the *Glorious* and the recently commissioned *Ark Royal* from the Mediterranean Fleet (making half of the Navy's strength in fleet carriers), their 120 assorted Skuas and Swordfish could be no match for the Luftwaffe either in performance or numbers.

It may be guessed, therefore, what were Forbes's sentiments on 17 April when, as the two allied expeditionary forces were beginning their separate campaigns, he received Churchill's assurance that all that had happened 'makes me sure that Hitler has made a grave strategic blunder in giving us the right, as we have always had the power, to take what we like on the Norwegian coast'.[16] Forbes can hardly have shared Churchill's evident relish in the same letter at the prospect of 'an increasingly vigorous campaign being fought along the Norwegian coast during the summer, and I trust we shall be able to beat them out of all their lodgements and establish ourselves in their place right down to Bergen'.[17] For Churchill in the Admiralty map room, playing at moving ships and soldiers around like an absorbed Victorian child on the nursery floor, had not even begun to learn the new lesson so sharply taught to Forbes by the Luftwaffe off the Norwegian coast on 9 April – any more than he had learned the old lesson of the Dardanelles about the dangers of improvising large-scale combined operations.

On 15 April, nearly a week after the launch of 'Weserübung', the Allied attempt to eject the Germans from Norway began when Convoy NP1 – three liners carrying the 24th Guards Brigade, and escorted by the battleship *Valiant* and nine destroyers – disembarked 'Rupert-force' at the little port of Harstad in Andfjord, the northern approach to Narvik. This cluster of brightly painted wooden houses at the edge of icy water was the designated base for operations against the German garrison holding Narvik and its environs. For the first time Admiral Lord Cork, the naval commander, and Major-General Mackesy, the land force commander, met each other (having sailed in separate ships). Cork wanted to attack Narvik without delay. Mackesy did not, because snow to a depth of four feet covered the entire region; because the Guards Brigade had no field or anti-aircraft artillery whatsoever (and of course no skis, snowshoes or Arctic warfare training); and because a direct assault would involve landing from open boats *à la* Gallipoli on beaches swept by German fire. Mackesy's caution displeased Churchill, who thereupon persuaded in turn the Chiefs of Staff, the Military Coordination Committee and the Cabinet to send Mackesy a prodding signal which he had drafted. It began:

> Your proposals involve damaging deadlock at Narvik and the neutralisation of one of our best brigades [sic]. We cannot send you the Chasseurs Alpins. HMS WARSPITE will be needed elsewhere in two or three days. Full consideration should therefore be given by you to an assault upon Narvik by WARSPITE and the destroyers. The capture of the port and town would be an important success. Send us your appreciation and act at once if you consider right. Matter most urgent.[18]

Churchill also sent a 'Personal and Private' signal to Cork, so thus bypassing the First Sea Lord, the naval staff and the C-in-C, Home Fleet inviting him to sneak on his military colleague Mackesy, and so poaching on the War Office's responsibilities: 'Should you consider that situation is being mishandled, it is your duty to report either to me personally or to the Admiralty about it, and what you would do yourself.'[19] But Cork reported that he felt bound to yield to the unanimous opinion of his military colleagues that an immediate assault was not a feasible operation of war.

On 20 April, Churchill persuaded the Cabinet to appoint Cork over Mackesy as commander of all the Narvik forces. It was the first concrete manifestation in the present war of his impatience with military realism. 'It seems to me,' he told Cork in another direct personal signal just after midnight on 21 April, 'that you can feel your way and yet strike hard. Please keep us informed as much as possible. Ask for what you want. Remember Luleå [the Swedish Baltic port] is open in about a month. Count on unflinching support of your friends at the Admiralty.'[20] For Churchill was still dreaming of a swift overland march from Narvik into neutral Sweden and the Gällivare orefields, Narvik having again for him taken over from Trondheim the role of 'greater prize'.[21] But his chosen fire-eater, Lord Cork, proved no better able than Mackesy to walk over waist-high snow. On 24 April Cork took the *Warspite*, three cruisers and eight destroyers up Ofotfjord with the aim of bombarding the German garrison into surrender. After blasting away in vain for three hours against targets invisible under heavy fresh snow cover, Cork retired disconsolate. No quick success then – instead a protracted siege, during which the Allied forces in the Narvik environs were to be eventually built up to

30,000 men, including a Polish brigade, the French *Chasseurs Alpins* and a demi-brigade of the Foreign Legion, together with some artillery and tanks.

Each fresh landing or further overland advance to close the ring on the German garrison was to depend on the close support of the guns and carrier aircraft of the Royal Navy. But it was also to fall to those guns and aircraft to protect the Allied forces and their bases from the Luftwaffe, especially the main base at Harstad. The carrier *Furious* (whose aircraft had bombed ahead of Whitworth's squadron at Narvik on 12 April) remained under Cork's command as his only source of air power until 26 April when, with her speed reduced to 20 knots by two near misses by German bombs that jarred her turbines and with only six serviceable aircraft left, she returned to the Clyde for repairs. Cork was then reduced to a squadron of slow Walrus biplane amphibians until the carrier *Ark Royal* arrived on 6 May after service off central Norway. In the judgment of Admiral Forbes, the C-in-C, Home Fleet, at this time: 'The main threat to the whole area is the enemy air power, and this is so real that it is scarcely an exaggeration to say that the Allied forces are maintaining their position by bluff.'[22] He went on to list over a dozen warships or merchant ships sunk, beached or damaged by German air attack. He noted that 'HARSTAD is the main base in the Narvik area for personnel and stores, the town is built of wood and every house is crammed to the roof. The A/A protection ashore consists of four 3.7″ guns, and the fire fighting appliances are nil.' Then there was the U-boat threat as well: 'Harstad, which is the main anchorage for transports, etc, is entirely open to submarine attack . . .' It was indeed beyond Forbes's resources in escort vessels, especially destroyers (yet another enfeebling legacy of the disarmament years), to provide screens for Allied shipping in the Narvik region from both bombers and U-boats, not least because of, in Forbes's own words, 'the vast extent of water to be covered'.[23]

Yet it was the two Allied expeditions to central Norway – while they lasted – that stretched and strained Forbes's fleet even more severely still, for here the Luftwaffe was operating in much more formidable strength, while the Allied ground operations themselves proved even more catastrophically half-cocked than those round Narvik – and even more prone to interference by the eager scanner of maps and charts back in Whitehall.

On 15 April small landing parties of seamen and marines went ashore at Namsos and Andalsnes, to the north and south of Trondheim – ordered there by Churchill and his colleagues with the purpose of distracting German attention from the proposed direct Allied seaborne assault on Trondheim ('Operation Hammer'). The party at Namsos reported next day that the little port possessed no unloading facilities and that its hinterland lay under deep snow. The decision was nevertheless taken in Whitehall to land 'Mauriceforce' (146th Infantry Brigade) in order both to strengthen the hoped-for diversion from the Trondheim attack, and also to support Norwegian units inland. Under cover of darkness on 16 and 17 April Mauriceforce disembarked at Namsos amid dire confusion stemming from the fact that the ships' crews and the troops lacked the equipment and the training for such a disembarkation, especially at night in a port without unloading facilities. Next day, lacking artillery, motor transport, tanks and air cover, and having left many stores in the ships, the unfortunate Territorials of 146th Brigade were taken by train to join Norwegian troops nearer towards Trondheim.[24]

The troops for Andalsnes, 'Sickleforce', 148th Infantry Brigade (also Territorials) had to transfer at sea from their transport, the liner *Orion*, to the cruisers *Galatea* and *Arethusa* and the anti-aircraft cruisers *Carlisle* and *Curacoa* for the landing because of the danger of air attack. The original loading of supplies into the *Orion* had been muddled enough; now their further transfer to the cruisers, together with the disembarkation and unloading at Namsos, again by totally inexperienced soldiers and sailors, led cumulatively to chaos. An eyewitness wrote of the conditions of stores in the *Orion* when the time came to offload:

> At the bottom of the hold was a vast pyramid of stores of every description, with men of a number of units climbing over it like flies looking for anything with their own unit's markings. The impression was that as any load came to the cranes, it was lifted, lowered and released over the pyramid.[25]

Hardly had these unfortunate forces got ashore at Namsos and Andalsnes when their roles were abruptly changed in Whitehall from the secondary one of diversion to the primary one of capturing Trondheim. For the proposal for a direct seaborne assault on the port ('Hammer') had been reluctantly abandoned by Churchill and his Cabinet colleagues in the face of professional opposition.

When the proposal (which was to be carried out by the main body of the Home Fleet) had been first put to Admiral Forbes on 14 April, he had replied that enemy bombing 'would start almost immediately' and that 'to carry out an opposed landing . . . under continuous air attack was not feasible'.[26] But Churchill, failing to comprehend the danger posed by the Luftwaffe, sought to argue Forbes down in a signal sent at 0121 on the 15th which ended: 'Pray consider this important project further.'[27] As a sweetener, Churchill promised that the attack 'could not take place for seven days devoted to careful preparation'.[28] On the following day he also told the Military Co-ordination Committee that 'Time was necessary to plan what was a hazardous and, if successful, would be a brilliant operation'.[29] Yet only two days later, when he sent an emissary (Rear-Admiral L. E. Holland) to see Forbes in his flagship in Scapa with details of the plan and a personal letter urging its merits, the date for 'Hammer' was named as 22 April; four days' notice for an operation not yet even finally decided on.[30]

Forbes had in fact earlier consented to carry out 'Hammer' provided the troops were transported in cruisers rather than vulnerable liners. But now he was aghast at the prospect of mounting a complex combined tri-service operation against a formidable enemy with hardly more notice than would be suitable for arranging a family trip round the bay. However, fortunately for him and his fleet, the Chiefs of Staff (COS) unanimously decided on 19 April that to take an armada into the confined waters of Trondheimfjord (an almost landlocked salt-water lake) would incur too great a risk from German air attack, both to the ships and to the landing forces during their run-in.[31] It is also possible that they drew a lesson from the experience the day before of the cruiser HMS *Suffolk*, which had been given the task of closing Stavanger airfield by bombardment as a preliminary to 'Hammer' (which the bombardment in fact failed to do). In the course of her withdrawal, the *Suffolk* had to endure seven hours of continuous Luftwaffe attack before Fleet Air Arm Skuas from Hatston arrived to protect her; and finally arrived back in Scapa so badly damaged that her quarter deck was awash.

The COS having put down 'Hammer', the First Sea Lord, Admiral Pound, had then played the cunning badger again by suggesting that Trondheim should instead be taken by Mauriceforce and Sickleforce in a pincer movement overland from north and south, whereupon Churchill gave way, accepted this proposal and sold it to the Cabinet. Pound's plan was, however, a military nonsense, because such hope-lessly raw formations as 146th and 148th Brigades (initially lacking such basics as artillery) even when reinforced by regular British and French units, were to prove quite incapable of holding their own advanced positions against the German Army and the Luftwaffe, let alone push on towards Trondheim. Did Pound really believe his plan

[127]

could succeed – or did he urge it as a device to get his own service out of 'Hammer'?

In the event only a week elapsed before the Trondheim 'pincers' had both been outfought in the field and thrown into retreat. Meanwhile the Royal Navy and the ships of the French Navy had been ferrying supplies and reinforcements to these doomed enterprises through the hazards of bomber and U-boat. On 18 April Admiral Edward-Collins with the cruisers *Galatea* and *Arethusa*, the anti-aircraft cruisers *Carlisle* and *Curacoa*, and two destroyers brought in 1,000 soldiers to Andalsnes and the port of Molde, further down Ramsdalfjord towards the sea. When Edward-Collins sailed for home in the small hours of the 19th he left the two anti-aircraft cruisers behind to serve as the only protection of Mauriceforce's bases against the Luftwaffe, no land-based anti-aircraft guns being available owing to the belated rearmament of the British Army. Next day the Luftwaffe began to launch continual daylight raids on Andalsnes, which restricted port operations to the brief and shrinking hours of the northern spring nights. On 24 April, by which time the two anti-aircraft cruisers – themselves prime German targets – had fired off most of their ammunition, *Curacoa* was hit and badly damaged. For the crews of *Curacoa* and *Carlisle*, as for the crews of other anti-aircraft ships which rotated to Norwegian ports that month, the daylight hours tested professional concentration and steadiness of nerve to the limit, as bombs constantly punched up pillars of white water from the fjords, and the 4-inch anti-aircraft guns and 2-pounder pom-poms crashed and drum-rolled, and the ships heeled under helm in violent evasive manoeuvres. Here for the first time was experienced that ordeal by prolonged air attack which would later become commonplace for Allied sailors in the Mediterranean and the Pacific.

The Navy's run of supplies and troops to Sickleforce and Mauriceforce went on. On 22 April the cruiser *Arethusa* brought into Andalsnes a few light anti-aircraft guns and the RAF advance party which was to organise the air-strip on the frozen lake at Lesjaskog. Next day Admiral Edward-Collins was back with another 2,000 soldiers for Sickleforce, carried in the cruisers *Galatea*, *Sheffield* and *Glasgow* and six destroyers. Two days later it was the turn of Vice-Admiral Sir Geoffrey Layton with the cruisers *Birmingham*, *Manchester* and *York*, together with three destroyers, to deliver the last reinforcements for the unfortunate Sickleforce – 1,600 soldiers and 300 tons of stores. On each occasion the task force unloaded and sailed again as quickly as possible in order to minimise the period of exposure to air attack while helplessly secured alongside.

North of Trondheim, at Namsos, the Navy's operations in support of Mauriceforce proved shorter lived. On 19 April the anti-aircraft cruiser *Cairo* led in four French transports carrying the *Chasseurs Alpins* and escorted by the cruiser *Emile Bertin* and French destroyers. The Luftwaffe found them; the bombing began and the *Emile Bertin* was damaged by a bomb. On 22 April more French reinforcements arrived at Namsos, but by now the port was suffering such continual heavy bombing that, although the troops themselves were disembarked, their storeships could not be unloaded. Henceforth further French reinforcements were to be diverted to the Narvik area, even though some stores and guns were still landed at Namsos on 27–28 April.

Just as at Narvik, the Royal Navy's carriers did what they could to provide air cover to the expeditionary forces and their bases in the face of the huge numerical and qualitative superiority of the enemy's land-based air force. HMS *Glorious* and *Ark Royal* joined the Home Fleet from the Mediterranean Fleet on 23 April, and sailed for central Norway next day under the command of Vice-Admiral L. V. Wells (Flag Officer, Aircraft Carriers), with eighteen RAF Gladiator fighters intended to operate from the frozen surface of Lake Lesjaskog. They were escorted by the cruiser *Berwick*, the anti-aircraft cruiser *Curlew* and six destroyers. Late that day the Gladiators were successfully flown off to their frozen lake, where in three brief days of action they made another contribution to the Norwegian campaign's catalogue of courage and hapless improvisation, shooting down six German aircraft for no loss of their own in the air, but having ten of their aircraft destroyed on the ground while being rearmed and refuelled. This process proved calamitously slow because the scratch groundcrew lacked adequate refuelling and starter-battery recharging equipment and because there was only one armourer for the squadron's 72 Browning machine-guns. On 27 April fuel for the surviving Gladiators (now based on another airstrip) ran out, whereupon the aircraft were destroyed and the personnel re-embarked.[32] Henceforward the task of providing air cover for the central Norway forces reverted entirely to the Fleet Air Arm. It had already been doing its best: from 24 to 26 April a few Skua fighters were maintained over Namsos and Andalsnes, while on 25 April 34 Skuas from *Glorious* and *Ark Royal* bombed Trondheim, followed by a second strike on the 28th by eighteen Skuas from *Ark Royal*. Neither attack caused serious damage. On the previous day Vice-Admiral Wells had had to detach *Glorious* to return to the United Kingdom in order to refuel; she did not rejoin him until 1 May – another demonstration of the operational cost to the Navy of depending for resupply on United Kingdom bases.[33]

After the decisive repulse of the pincer movements on Trondheim, the prospect of evacuation from Central Norway was gloomily debated in Whitehall from 23 April onwards. Churchill at first peddled the idea of reviving 'Hammer', only to have it knocked on the head on 26 April by the COS as a 'somewhat hazardous operation'; the COS also pointed out that Britain could not find the anti-aircraft guns to protect Trondheim even if it could be captured. Thereafter Churchill veered between supporting evacuation in order to concentrate on Narvik (his first choice), and wishing to delay evacuation as long as possible. Finally he suggested that Mauriceforce and Sickleforce should be dispersed into small parties to carry on a guerrilla campaign. This idea, fanciful even for him, was overridden by Chamberlain on the advice of the CIGS; and so on the evening of 27 April, in the wake of an Allied Supreme War Council meeting, the Military Coordination Committee came to the decision that the evacuations from central Norway should begin in three days' time.[34]

Now began the Royal Navy's worst ordeals in the Norwegian campaign. For the first time in the present war it would fall to its ships to rescue a defeated expeditionary force from a foreign shore and then bring it sadly home in the teeth of ferocious air attack.

In a prelude to the main evacuations the cruiser *Glasgow* went into the little port of Molde on 29 April under cover of darkness to pick up King Haakon VII of Norway, Crown Prince Olaf, and the Norwegian gold reserve. It was a scene of lurid drama: the town blazing furiously, the British cruiser going alongside the quay with her hoses pumping water on the fires; the King and his suite welcomed aboard from a tug (they could not reach the quay because of the fires) to the squeal of the bosun's pipe; dark, flame-flickering water opening between the ship's side and King Haakon's homeland as the *Glasgow* made for the open sea.[35]

Next night, 30 April, the cruisers *Galatea*, *Arethusa*, *Sheffield* and *Southampton* with a transport and six destroyers picked up 2,200 Allied soldiers from Molde and Andalsnes; on 1 May it was the *Manchester* and *Birmingham*, the anti-aircraft cruisers *Calcutta* and *Curlew*, together with five destroyers that brought off another 1,500 men from Andalsnes. It fell to HMS *Calcutta* and the sloop HMS *Auckland* to wait behind for the rearguard of Sickleforce. This was expected to number some 200 men, but in fact more than 700 soldiers assembled on the quayside. With calm professionalism the Navy got them all aboard within a quarter of an hour; battle-weary and bomb-shaken men thankful to be relatively safe and sheltered at last. Although the

Luftwaffe had bombed Andalsnes during the daylight hours each day of the evacuation and on 30 April and 1 May even at night, it had failed to prevent the Royal Navy from completing its mission of rescue, or to sink or damage a single ship.

Responsibility for the evacuation of the survivors of Mauriceforce from Namsos fell to Admiral J. D. H. Cunningham, who had left Scapa on 29 April with the cruisers *Devonshire* and *York*, the French cruiser *Montcalm*, five destroyers and three French transports, later to be strengthened by four more destroyers which had sailed in advance. On the night of 1 May (intended to be the first of two nights for the evacuation) the masts of Cunningham's force stood clear above what should have been a concealing bank of fog – perfect aiming marks for the Luftwaffe – while Namsos itself lay in clear moonlight and already rocking to German bombs. Cunningham therefore decided to postpone the evacuation for 24 hours and complete it in a single night, judging that 'to attempt to spread evacuation over two would be courting disaster'.[36] The Commander of Mauriceforce, Major-General Sir Adrian Carton de Wiart, VC, believed that to take off some 5,700 men in one brief night was impossible. But, as he was to acknowledge, he 'learned in a few hours that the Navy do not know the word'.[37] While Cunningham with the *Devonshire*, *Montcalm* and four destroyers remained in support outside the fjord, Captain P. L. Vian in the destroyer *Afridi* led in the remaining warships and the three French transports. Two of these latter went alongside the quay directly to embark troops, while the third and the cruiser *York* took on troops ferried out by destroyers and small craft. HMS *Afridi*, with Mauriceforce's rearguard on board, was the last ship to leave, her melancholy final task to destroy by gunfire the rearguard's belatedly provided motor transport on the quayside.

But the Luftwaffe did not let go so easily. At 0845 that forenoon, when offshore fog had lifted, it began a relentless onslaught on Cunningham's ships that lasted until 1530 and the task force was 200 miles out to sea. According to Admiral (then Captain) Vian writing in 1960:

When the air attacks began, it was soon evident that the Junkers 88, which we knew by now so well, had been reinforced that morning by the Stuka dive-bomber, which we knew not at all. Up to that time they appear to have been used almost exclusively against troop formations ashore, or against guardships stationed at the ports. Almost at once a Stuka scored a hit on the *Bison*.[38]

As the *Afridi* went to pick up survivors from the *Bison* (a French destroyer) she too was hit and sunk.[39] Nevertheless the Stukas and the Junkers 88s failed to destroy any of the cruisers and transports laden with soldiers; and on 5 and 6 May Cunningham's task force steamed safely into Scapa Flow.

So in bravery and futility ended the ill-considered, ill-founded and absurdly optimistic Allied expedition to central Norway. It now remained to resolve the situation at Narvik.

The evacuations from central Norway at least brought immense relief to the Home Fleet, hitherto stretched between supporting three Allied bridgeheads hundreds of miles apart, as well as continuing its normal role of guarding against a breakout into the Atlantic by German heavy ships. In particular Admiral Forbes was now able to move his carriers north to cover in rotation the successive Allied local landings nearer and nearer to Narvik and also to protect Allied bridgeheads and bases. *Ark Royal*, which joined Admiral Lord Cork on 6 May, remained until 20 May, when HMS *Furious* ferried in some RAF Gladiators to operate from airstrips painfully constructed at Bardufoss and Bodo, and returned again to the Clyde. On 28 May the carrier *Glorious* reached Narvik waters with a squadron of RAF Hurricane 8-gun fighters, which, flying from Bardufoss, provided invaluable air cover for the final Allied offensive. Both these latter precious ships made the voyage from the United Kingdom without destroyer escort, so weak now was Forbes in this essential class of ship.[40] The siege of Narvik alone therefore sucked in, by rotation, three out of the Navy's six fleet carriers, as well as the anti-aircraft cruisers *Cairo* and *Curlew* (the latter sunk on 26 May), those substitutes for the land-based anti-aircraft batteries of which the Allied expeditionary force was so short.

It fell to the sturdy workhorses of the campaign, the cruisers and destroyers, to provide close fire support to each Allied landing or advance during the closing of the ring round the German garrison. On 7 May, in the eerie half-light of a northern summer midnight, the cruisers *Effingham* and *Aurora* and five destroyers led by the battleship *Resolution* covered a successful landing at the head of Herjangsfjord, north of Narvik, by French troops in four infantry assault craft and the single motor landing craft available. On the night of 27 May, the eve of the final successful assault on Narvik, the broadsides of cruisers *Cairo*, *Coventry* and *Southampton*, together with five destroyers, opened the way for another landing south of the town by French and Norwegian troops.[41]

However, just at this period when Admiral Forbes was enabled to concentrate his scarce resources on Narvik waters, new distractions from outside the Norwegian theatre of war served to drain ships from his command. For in the wake of the weakening of the Mediterranean Fleet in April by the transfer of the battleship *Warspite* and the carriers *Glorious* and *Ark Royal* to the Home Fleet, the long dormant Italian factor in the triple strategic threat to the British Empire had shown disquieting signs of reawakening. There were fears of Italian aggression in the Balkans; worse, that Mussolini might now choose to enter the war on Germany's side. So back to the Mediterranean went *Warspite* on 24 April, followed in the middle of May by the anti-aircraft cruiser *Carlisle*, seventeen destroyers and two sloops.[42] Nearer home there was continued apprehension that the expected grand German offensive against France and the Low Countries might soon be launched; and on 7 May the Admiralty transferred *Galatea* and *Arethusa* from the Home Fleet to Sheerness in the Thames Estuary, and eight destroyers to Harwich, on the Essex coast opposite Holland.

On 10 May apprehension became fact when 137 German divisions began to roll across the western frontiers of the *Reich*. Within five days Holland had capitulated and the French front on the Meuse had been smashed. Each further day brought the panzer divisions closer and closer to the Channel coast; the danger swiftly grew that the Allied Northern Army Group (including the British Expeditionary Force) might be cut off from the main body of the French Army and forced back to the North Sea coast of Flanders. This looming crisis drained away still more of Forbes's strength – three destroyers to the Humber on 18 May, the cruisers *Manchester* and *Sheffield* to the same destination on 26 May.[43] As a result Forbes was left with no available escorts for his precious carriers or other heavy ships: hence the appallingly risky lone voyages of *Glorious* and *Furious* to Narvik on 20 and 28 May.

By this time the German offensive in the West had brutally thrust home the strategic truth which ought to have been obvious to Churchill and his colleagues from the very birth of the idea of an Allied intervention in Scandinavia back in the winter – that, given Allied (especially British) military weakness and shortage of equipment, any forces sent to Scandinavia must be an enfeebling diversion from the crucial theatre of France and the Low Countries. Churchill was now no longer First Lord of the Admiralty but Prime Minister and Minister of Defence – by a neat coincidence of history appointed in Chamberlain's place on the first day of the German offensive, 10 May; and by an equally neat historical irony, as a result of a political crisis in which Chamberlain had been blamed for the fiascoes in Norway. In

Churchill's place as First Lord of the Admiralty was appointed the Labour and Co-operative Member of Parliament, A. V. Alexander, a Somerset countryman and a sound administrator, who, unlike his predecessor, was to enflame neither the Cabinet, nor the Admirals. So on 20 May, as the German spearheads approached Arras and the awful prospect loomed of having to evacuate the BEF from France, Churchill is found signalling Lord Cork to complain about the continued stagnation around Narvik and point out that the Narvik expedition 'is eating up large quantities of shipping and other essential supplies. More destroyers will be needed in the South very soon . . .'[44] By the 23rd he had concluded that the Narvik forces must be withdrawn; Britain was going to need them for her own defence.[45] In the meantime Cork had planned the final assault on Narvik for 28 May. It was now decided in London that its capture and the final defeat of the German garrison should merely serve the purpose of covering the evacuation of the Allied forces. This was to be completed by 8 June.

On 31 May there began therefore the dismal and hazardous process of winding up the campaign which Churchill had hoped would last all summer and culminate in the occupation of the Gällivare orefields. Under cover of darkness the advanced base of Bodo, with its airstrip, was evacuated. The town itself had now been reduced by the Luftwaffe to smouldering embers. The first convoy carrying stores, guns and tanks had already left the main Allied base area at Harstad. A second convoy carrying equipment sailed on 7 June. For Admiral Lord Cork, however, the greater problem lay in safely getting away the 24,500 Allied soldiers in and around Narvik in the face of German air power, even though the carriers *Ark Royal* and *Glorious* joined him on 2 June, their aircraft supplementing the RAF Hurricanes and Gladiators of 46 and 263 Squadrons, which operated with formidable effect from the airstrip at Bardufoss until the last moment.

In order to minimise the danger to his convoys from bombers, Cork established a rendezvous for the fifteen troopships (two of which were not needed in the event) some 180 miles off shore, and brought in the ships two at a time to Harstad, where they were loaded with soldiers and stores ferried from Narvik by destroyers. In the small hours of 7 June the first homeward convoy of 15,000 soldiers in six liners and the veteran (partly disarmed) cruiser *Vindictive* left the assembly area at sea for home. In the early forenoon of 9 June followed the second troop convoy (four liners, three small merchant vessels; 10,000 men). This convoy was later joined by the cruiser *Southampton*, which at 0900 the previous day had embarked Admiral Lord Cork, Lieutenant-General Sir Claude Auchinleck (who had replaced the luckless Mackesy as commander of the land forces), the French General Béthouart, and the rearguard.[46]

Yet all unknown to Cork his complex and protracted evacuation and his ill-protected troopships on the high seas were exposed to appalling danger. For the *Scharnhorst* and *Gneisenau*, escorted by the heavy cruiser *Hipper* and three destroyers, were off the Norwegian coast looking for just such an opportunity. Vice-Admiral Marschall, flying his flag in the *Gneisenau*, had left Kiel on 4 June with orders to attack the Allied base at Harstad. Three days later he refuelled his ships at sea 500 miles west of Tromso in northern Norway, and then turned to a course just west of south. By now he knew from the customary invaluable decrypts of British cypher radio traffic that the Allies were evacuating Narvik, and that their convoys were in the process of steaming across the North Sea for home. In the early forenoon of 8 June he spread his ships out like the fingers of a hand grasping for a victim.

Yet it was not until more than twenty-four hours later that Admiral Forbes left Scapa for Norwegian waters with the battleship *Rodney* (flag) and the battlecruiser *Renown*. No prior concentration of the Home Fleet in the north-central North Sea to cover the evacuations and convoys had been ordered, either by the Admiralty or Forbes himself, even though Cork had asked for such cover, and even though Forbes had requested to be informed of convoy movements. This initial failure to concentrate powerful forces at sea apparently stemmed from complacency induced by the failure of German warships or U-boats to interrupt Allied lines of communication during the campaign itself.[47] However, it also stemmed from yet another failure in the Admiralty's gathering of Intelligence, its evaluation and operational application. The relatively new techniques of Wireless Traffic Analysis (that is, monitoring the pattern and density of enemy radio traffic, and drawing inferences therefrom) had suggested for the previous fortnight that some kind of German naval offensive in the North Sea was pending. On 29 May and again on 7 June the Naval Section of the Government Code and Cypher School (GC and CS) at Bletchley Park repeated these indications to the Admiralty Operational Intelligence Centre (OIC). But OIC, in its scepticism about the value of such untested techniques, failed to pass the warnings on to the Home Fleet. Moreover, in a very proper concern for secrecy about the Allied evacuation movements, only a few senior staff in OIC, and no one at GC and CS at Bletchley, were informed that they were to take place; not even Coastal Command was informed, which accounts for its failure to carry out air searches of the sea areas through which the convoys had to pass.[48]

There now ensued an error of judgment curiously similar to that which had originally given the 'Weserübung' forces a clear run to their destinations on 7–8 April, and springing from the same British obsession with a German breakout on to the Atlantic convoy routes. On receipt on 5 June of a false sighting north-east of the Faeroes by a British 'Q' ship (a reconnaissance vessel disguised as a merchantman) of German heavy ships heading towards Iceland, Forbes ordered Admiral Whitworth to sea with the *Rodney* and *Renown*, two cruisers and five destroyers with the task of intercepting these supposed raiders. To meet and defend Cork's homeward-bound convoys, Forbes only despatched the battleship *Valiant*.[49] In these faulty dispositions of the Home Fleet lies one reason why Marschall with the *Scharnhorst* and *Gneisenau* now came to inflict the last and most grievous single wound of the Norway campaign on the Royal Navy.

In the small hours of 8 June eight Hurricane and ten Gladiator fighters of 46 and 263 Squadrons, RAF, from Bardufoss successfully landed on HMS *Glorious* – the first time such modern land-based aircraft and their pilots had ever carried out such a delicate evolution, and of course without benefit of arrester hooks to engage the carrier's arrester wires. *Glorious* then set a lone course for home, escorted only by the destroyers *Acasta* and *Ardent*. It has never been established for certain why Lord Cork permitted this risky procedure rather than keep her in company with the rest of his task force. What *is* known is that the captain of the *Glorious*, Guy D'Oyly Hughes, was a throwback to the worst kind of arrogant, authoritarian and choleric Edwardian naval officer. In the words of one former Fleet Air Arm subordinate, '. . . D-H was a very vain man and would not admit his ignorance on air matters and tried to enforce his views by bullying and bluster . . .'[50] D'Oyly Hughes was a submarine specialist with only ten months' prior experience in a carrier. His dangerously unrealistic orders for air operations earlier in the Norway campaign had brought him into violent collision with his Naval Commander (Air), Captain J. B. Heath, RN. When Heath protested against these orders Hughes gave way to ungovernable rage, later putting Heath ashore at Scapa to await a court martial on the charge of cowardice in the face of the enemy. It is therefore possible that Hughes, in an unbalanced desire to pursue the charge against Heath, persuaded Lord Cork to let him take *Glorious* on ahead.[51]

In the afternoon of 9 June *Glorious* was steaming homewards at a modest 17 knots with steam in only twelve of her eighteen boilers.

Not one of her aircraft was armed and at instant readiness on the flight deck, and no air search or air cover was being flown, although some aircraft in the hangar deck (congested with the Gladiators and Hurricanes) were at ten minutes' notice. It was a clear day, with maximum visibility, but nevertheless no lookout had been posted in the crow's nest. The wind was north-west, Force 2 to 3.[52] At 1600 (British summer time) the German battlecruisers sighted the funnel smoke of this flightless and sitting steel duck. At 1630 *Scharnhorst*'s 11-inch guns opened fire at 28,000 yards, the shells plunging down steeply with the usual Germanic accuracy on to the lightly armoured carrier. Serious damage to *Glorious*'s hangar deck was soon followed by more hits abaft the engine room which started uncontrollable fires.

Now once again, British destroyers sacrificed themselves in an attempt to save a situation in the face of great odds. The *Acasta* (Commander C. E. Glasford) and *Ardent* (Lieutenant-Commander J. F. Barker) laid a smoke screen temporarily to shield the *Glorious* from enemy range-finders and steamed at utmost speed to engage their 32,000-ton opponents with torpedoes. At about 1728 *Ardent*, having fired all her torpedoes, succumbed to the German battleships' crushing weight of fire and capsized. Some twelve minutes later *Glorious* herself, by now a blazing hulk with a heavy list to starboard, also capsized and sank. This did not deter *Acasta* from making a final run at the enemy, her 4.7-inch guns firing vainly at thickly armoured targets, a last salvo of torpedoes tracking for the German ships' more vulnerable hulls below the waterline. One torpedo struck home abreast of *Scharnhorst*'s after main turret, knocking out two of her three engine rooms and reducing her speed to 20 knots. But at 1808 *Acasta*, riven by huge internal explosions and with flames and smoke pouring from most of her length, was also reduced to a sinking condition. Only 45 men out of the 1,474 in the ships' companies of the *Glorious*, *Acasta* and *Ardent* were later rescued. All the gallant RAF pilots of 46 and 263 Squadrons went down with the carrier; a tragic loss and a needless waste of men of high skill, too few of which did Britain possess.[53] Thus had the Royal Navy lost one-sixth of its global strength in fleet carriers – and just as needlessly as HMS *Courageous* in September 1939. But at least Vice-Admiral Marschall and his battleships had missed the greater prize of Lord Cork's convoys packed with troops. When, after taking the damaged *Scharnhorst* into Trondheim, Marschall made a fresh sortie with *Gneisenau* and *Hipper* on 10 June, he was far too late to intercept them.

Neither Admiral Forbes in Scapa Flow nor the Admiralty had received *Glorious*'s 'enemy' report (in any case cut short by German fire), while *Acasta* and *Ardent*, in the thick of a desperate encounter, had sent none. Forbes was first alerted in the forenoon of the next day, 8 June, that the German battleships were in the area of the British convoy routes home by a report from HMS *Valiant*, which had just been informed by the hospital ship *Atlantis* that she had been stopped the day before by *Gneisenau* and *Scharnhorst* (when the troopship *Orama*, in company with her, was sunk by the *Hipper*). *Valiant*'s report was confirmed in the afternoon of 9 June in dismaying fashion by the German radio announcement of the *Glorious*'s sinking. Only now, therefore, did Forbes put to sea in the *Rodney* and with *Renown* (which had returned from the vain sortie towards Iceland), ordering the *Repulse* (still off Iceland) to join him as quickly as possible.

There then followed the last blunder of the campaign. On 11 June air search from the *Ark Royal* (which had now joined Forbes) revealed that the two German battleships and the *Hipper* lay in Trondheim harbour. It was therefore decided to launch an air strike – but with Skua dive-bombers rather than Swordfish torpedo-carriers. However, the 500-pound bomb carried by the Skua, though effective against the deck armour of a cruiser like the *Königsberg* (sunk at Bergen on 10 April), could not penetrate a battleship's deck armour. To sink or seriously damage such a ship required a torpedo. But Pound, Forbes and Rear-Admiral Phillips (Deputy Chief of Naval Staff), all traditionalists with no first-hand aviation experience, failed to understand this; and Pound in particular entertained a prejudice against the Swordfish, a much more versatile and effective weapons platform than its antique appearance suggested. Throughout the campaign there had been repeated mishandlings of naval aviation, partly owing to a refusal to seek or heed the specialist advice of the airmen in the Naval Staff's Naval Air Division – these officers having too few gold rings on their sleeves to warrant their being consulted by admirals.[54] Before the raid on Trondheim, however, the airmen on the naval staff at least were able to persuade their superiors to give Forbes latitude to use Swordfish aircraft if he wished. Forbes did not so wish. On 12 June 1940 fifteen Skuas attacked the German ships in Trondheim; one bomb hit the *Scharnhorst*'s deck but failed even to explode; eight Skuas failed to return to the *Ark Royal*.[55]

The Norwegian campaign cost the Royal Navy an aircraft carrier, two cruisers, seven destroyers, one sloop and four submarines. The German Navy suffered absolutely and relatively far worse: three cruisers, ten destroyers and six U-boats sunk; three battleships, two cruisers and several smaller vessels damaged (including two of the battleships badly damaged).[56] But this favourable balance could not disguise the fact that Britain, a great naval power, had suffered a strategic defeat in a major maritime campaign at the hands of a continental land power with a small navy – in considerable part because of flaws in the British command and control system and the errors of judgment and the vacillating purpose of the Navy's political and professional leadership. The campaign demonstrates how many old operational and strategic lessons had still to be learned afresh; how many new lessons had yet to be digested. In particular it reveals how under-equipped and backward in thinking were the Royal Navy and Royal Air Force Coastal Command in regard to the air dimension, and how poor was the apparatus for gathering and disseminating operational Intelligence compared with the enemy's. On 15 June 1940 Admiral Sir Charles Forbes (who of course could not know that the enemy was able to read much of the Royal Navy's encyphered radio traffic) reported to the Admiralty that the loss of *Glorious* owing to

> the quite unexpected appearance of enemy forces . . . shows that it is absolutely essential that our scheme of air reconnaissance should be overhauled . . . The enemy reconnoitres Scapa daily if they consider it necessary. Our reconnaissances of the enemy's main bases are few and far between . . . It is most galling that the enemy should know just where our ships . . . always are, whereas we generally learn where his major forces are when they sink one or more of our ships.[57]

But by the time Forbes wrote this report the disasters in Norway had been eclipsed by catastrophe on the grandest scale in France and the Low Countries, the consequences of which were already transforming the shape of the war, and presenting the Royal Navy with the grimmest challenge of its history.

6

'Operation Dynamo': the Dunkirk Evacuation

Like a warship lying off a city that was being engulfed by volcanic lava, British seapower could be no more than the impotent spectator of the catastrophe which overwhelmed the Allied armies in the West after 10 May 1940. While Dutch resistance was being crushed in just five days by savage Luftwaffe attack, by German airborne forces landing deep behind the inundations of 'Fortress Holland' and by a panzer division thrusting overland by means of key bridges seized by surprise, the Royal Navy could only lay a minefield off the Dutch coast, and despatch a cruiser squadron (the 2nd: Admiral Edward-Collins) and some destroyers to protect the minelayers, bring away the Dutch gold reserve, rescue Queen Wilhelmina and the Dutch Crown Princess, and attempt to demolish the port installations at Ijmuiden, The Hook and Flushing (so far as the local authorities would consent). To the south, while the German Army Group 'A' drove across the Belgian plain towards Brussels and Antwerp, frontally attacking the Allied Northern Army Group including the British Expeditionary Force (BEF), the Royal Navy's contribution consisted of sending demolition parties into the port of Antwerp, and successfully bringing back to England 26 merchant ships, 50 tugs and some 600 barges and dredgers.[1] And while the seven panzer divisions of Army Group 'B' smashed the French front on the Meuse and scythed westwards to the Channel coast, reaching it on 22 May and completely cutting off the Allied Northern Army Group from the main body of the French Army, the Admiralty could do no more than make arrangements for switching the BEF's supply route from Le Havre to Boulogne, Calais and Dunkirk. It was all a fresh demonstration of the impotence of maritime supremacy to affect the issue of a decisive campaign on land, and of the slow and uncertain effect of blockade on the ability of a continental state like Germany to wage war on the grand scale.

Even after the German panzer thrust reached the sea west of Abbeville and swung northwards in the direction of the Channel ports, so threatening to cut the Allied Northern Army Group off from the coast, Churchill and the French high command alike had continued to cherish the fantasy that a combined Allied counter-stroke from north and south of the panzer corridor could yet save the battle. But Field-Marshal Lord Gort, the C-in-C, BEF, a practical, severely realistic fighting soldier who had already measured at first hand the chaos and demoralisation of the French command system and the exhaustion of offensive power in the Northern Army Group, finally decided in the evening of 25 May that the BEF must fall back immediately on the Channel ports. Four hours later Churchill came independently to the same conclusion.

At 1900 on 26 May, therefore, the Admiralty made a signal to Vice-Admiral B. H. Ramsay (Flag Officer Commanding Dover) that 'Operation Dynamo' was to commence 'with the greatest vigour'.[2] The Admiralty hoped that this operation might at best succeed in rescuing a total of 45,000 Allied soldiers (a small fraction only of the Northern Army Group) over two days, after which evacuation would probably be ended by enemy action.

The headquarters of the Vice-Admiral, Dover, were located deep down in the chalk behind the famous 'white cliffs', in galleries and little chambers excavated by French prisoners during the Napoleonic Wars – the last time that England had faced a formidable enemy across the narrow seas. The main gallery ended in a windowed embrasure in the cliff face overlooking the harbour and the Channel; where a cannon had once pointed towards the French, Ramsay had his own office. The narrow iron balcony beyond served Ramsay as the stern walk of a ship-of-the-line; a place of momentary refuge in sun and breeze, yet in plain hearing of the unceasing guns and bombs across the Channel. Deepest inside the chalk was a large conference chamber which, during the Great War, had housed an electrical power plant and was therefore known as the 'Dynamo Room'. Since the daunting task of rescuing as many men as possible from the stricken

Northern Army Group had been assigned to the Vice-Admiral, Dover, and his headquarters, and since the Dynamo Room was to serve as the nerve centre of the operation, 'Dynamo' seemed a natural choice for the operation's codename. But in retrospect it sums up perfectly the whole character and spirit of the enterprise.

The Vice-Admiral, Dover, himself, Bertram Ramsay, as a former member of the directing staffs of the Naval Staff College and the Imperial Defence College, exemplified the younger generation of highly professional sailor. Ramsay, son of an ancient Highland family long resident in the Lowlands, combined austere personal integrity, high professionalism and a personal warmth which won the enthusiastic loyalty of his subordinates. His resignation from the Navy in 1935 as a consequence of his clash when Chief of Staff, Home Fleet, with Admiral Sir Roger Backhouse, the then C-in-C and one of the old school of 'do-it-all-yourself' admirals, had in the event caused only a temporary check in his career. While on the retired list he had been asked to report on the condition of Dover as a defended operational base. The report led to a £750,000 programme of re-equipment and to the earmarking of Ramsay himself for the command at Dover in the event of war. In September 1939 Dover Command was duly set up under him as Flag Officer, although he remained on the retired list. At first Ramsay was subordinate to the C-in-C, Nore, but soon he was reporting direct to the Admiralty. Here then was an admiral with the character to bear the weight of responsibility for a desperate and dangerous venture, and the training and mental calibre to lead what would grow in the course of 'Dynamo' into the largest staff of any admiral ashore or afloat, and tri-service at that.

The dynamo had first begun to turn a week before the Admiralty's executive signal on 26 May. A joint services conference was held at the War Office in London on 19 May to discuss the temporary (as it was then hoped) supply of the BEF through Boulogne, Calais and Dunkirk. But the meeting also considered 'the hazardous evacuation of very large Forces'; a contingency nonetheless still thought to be 'unlikely'. It was decided to delegate control of these operations to the Vice-Admiral, Dover, and to place all available shipping at his disposal. So swift was the advance of the panzer divisions and the consequent worsening of the plight of the Allied forces to the north of the German breakthrough that in the next two days, 20 and 21 May, further meetings were held, this time at Dover, to tackle the question of large-scale evacuation. It was confirmed that all sea movements would be placed under Ramsay's control, and that Army,

Ministry of Shipping and RAF liaison officers should be attached to his staff. As Ramsay confided to his wife in a letter on 21 May, '. . . things are getting even more hectic, & more & more tasks & responsibilities are being thrown on to me. The situation is really grave and I just fail to visualise what it will be in 4 or 5 days time . . .'[3]

In fact Ramsay's ships were already in the thick of the battle at Boulogne and Calais, where the French garrisons had been hastily strengthened by troops transported from England, for it was crucial to prevent for as long as possible the panzer divisions driving on up the coast to Dunkirk and so finally cutting off the BEF from rescue. The sieges of Boulogne on 22–25 May and Calais on 22–26 May set in miniature the pattern to come at Dunkirk – the Army (the Guards and Royal Artillery in Boulogne; the Queen Victoria's Rifles, the Rifle Brigade and the Royal Tank Regiment in Calais) holding fast against colossal odds until the moment came for evacuation by cross-Channel ferry steamers escorted by the Navy's destroyers; the ports themselves smashed into ruins and lying under palls of smoke; navigation in congested channels and basins amid wrecks and mines under a hail of bombs and shells demanding superb ship-handling. In the case of Calais there was to be in fact no final evacuation of the garrison, for such was the need to win maximum time for the BEF to fall back on Dunkirk that the riflemen were ordered to fight on to the end. The cost to the Royal Navy and the French Navy of these preliminary operations was high. By the time Boulogne fell Ramsay was left with only two undamaged destroyers. When on 24 May, having received fresh reinforcements, he despatched the destroyers *Grafton*, *Greyhound* and the Polish *Burza* to join the *Vimiera* and *Wessex* off Calais in bombarding German troops on shore, the Luftwaffe promptly sank the *Wessex* and damaged the *Burza* and *Vimiera*.

A letter from Ramsay to his wife on 23 May gives an insight into the strain already being imposed on him and his staff by this mere prelude to the main operation to come:

Things are so desperately serious . . . I have now been entrusted with 'What is to happen'. No bed for any of us last night and probably not for many nights. I'm so sleepy I can hardly keep my eyes open, and we are all the same . . .

We've been on the telephone to everyone from the P.M. downwards, and the situation only becomes more & more difficult from hour to hour . . .[4]

And he added, thinking of Boulogne and Calais:

It's hateful having to order ships to do things and go places where one knows they are going to get bombed to blazes and to send troops into what I know to be an inferno . . .

Yet Ramsay and his staff were also having to grapple at the same time with the much vaster problems of organising in breakneck haste the mass evacuation of the BEF and French troops from Dunkirk.

Days and nights are all one & we are dealing with a situation as complex as it is unsavoury . . . [he wrote to his wife on 25 May]. It's been my lot to operate the naval part of this & any thing more difficult and unpleasing I've never been faced with. At this very moment, we are racked with anxiety about the situation in Calais . . . We are also working in several dimensions as well at the same time and the offices are a veritable beehive of naval & military officers.[5]

By 26 May the BEF had succeeded in falling back into the Dunkirk perimeter despite the efforts of troops from two German army groups, closing in from north and south, to trap them or overwhelm them. How the BEF so succeeded belongs to the history of the land campaign: suffice to say that, while the stout defence of Boulogne and Calais helped, as did the decision by Hitler and his generals to hold back the panzer divisions for employment in the next phase of the Battle of France (against the main body of the French Army covering Paris), it was above all due to the BEF's own fighting qualities and to the imperturbable leadership and sure tactical dispositions of its C-in-C, Lord Gort.

By 29 May the remains of the French 1st Army too had poured back into the congested beach-head. Behind the protection of the devoted British and French rearguard manning the defensive perimeter some 400,000 Allied soldiers, exhausted after more than a fortnight of marching and fighting, were now spread across the wide beaches and the grassy dunes that stretched on both sides of Dunkirk, or crowded into the shattered town. The Allied army sprawled against the barrier of the sea like a great wounded beast finally cornered by the hunters; and the whole world was watching, waiting to witness its expected death throes. Yet beyond the wide sands bright under the summer holiday sunshine, between shore and horizon, the soldiers could see that the Navy was there and that they were not forsaken.

The key to 'Dynamo's' prospects of success lay in lifting capacity. But this obvious truth embraces huge problems not easy to solve under the hounding pressure of time and the enemy's air and land attack.

[144]

In the first place lifting capacity depended on the available resources of ships and craft which the Admiralty and the Ministry of Shipping could mobilise for Ramsay's use out of Britain's already tightly stretched Navy and Merchant Marine. This mobilisation began a week before 'Dynamo's' commencement; it gathered momentum during the operation as one desperate day followed another. Every strand of England's great maritime heritage came to be represented in the flotilla plying between the bomb-rocked and bullet-raked beaches, the burning port and the safety of home. The Admiralty managed to put 39 destroyers including the Polish *Blyskawica* at Ramsay's disposal – one fifth of the Navy's remaining total after the losses in Norway and off Calais and Boulogne. Given all the continuing demands of Atlantic convoy escort, the still continuing Narvik operation, the Mediterranean Fleet and the Far East, and the evident future requirements of Britain's own defence against invasion, this marked a courageous acceptance of great risk; and there was to be a moment when the Admiralty would have its second thoughts. Also under the White Ensign sailed the anti-aircraft cruiser *Calcutta*, 38 minesweepers, 61 minesweeping craft, 18 anti-submarine trawlers, a sloop, two gunboats hardly fit for the open sea, six corvettes and 76 miscellaneous small craft, including motor boats, flare-burning drifters, yachts and a pinnace.

The major contribution of the Merchant Marine lay in 36 personnel carriers – pre-war passenger ferries (four of them French) from the cross-Channel and Irish sea routes – some of the crews of which had already endured their full ration of fear and exhaustion in the hazardous crossings to Calais and Boulogne. But also under the Red Ensign served seven hospital carriers (also pre-war ferries); three stores ships; tugs and trawlers and dredgers; even a London Fire Brigade fire-boat; fishing boats (some of them still under sail); cockle boats that had never ventured beyond the shallow waters and mud banks of the Thames Estuary. And then there were the other 'little ships' that were to pass into the Dunkirk legend – the frail yachts and small craft belonging to peacetime weekenders and holidaymakers who loved 'messing about in boats'; either seagoing vessels from the little anchorages round England's southern coasts, or river craft which had never before seen the open sea. To bring together this swarm of small craft was the triumph of the Admiralty Small Boat Pool; to organise and equip it that of the Navy base organisation at Ramsgate, which issued 1,000 charts (600 of them with routes to Dunkirk already laid off) and 500 sets of routing instructions; and which carried out all the necessary mechanical and electrical repairs, in some cases on very ancient engines indeed.[6]

Yet the sea heritages of the Low Countries and France too made their important contributions. From the Netherlands came 43 'schuyts', translated in Royal Navy English as 'skoots': handy, robust motor vessels which with the Navy personnel aboard proved among the most versatile of all the vessels employed in 'Dynamo'. Belgium supplied five modern tugs, again robust all-purpose craft apt for operating in confined waters; and many trawlers as well. The French Navy deployed nineteen destroyers or torpedo boats. And all three countries furnished their own 'little ships' and the courage of their crews – launches, barges, drifters, eel boats. A total of over 900 ships and craft of all types and sizes and speeds thus passed under the control of the Vice-Admiral, Dover, and 848 of them saw service in 'Dynamo'. To organise and operate them all as a coherent whole therefore constituted an outstanding feat of staff work on the part of Ramsay and his headquarters.

The second decisive factor in determining how many soldiers could be brought home lay in the means and methods for getting them from shore to ship. The very gently shelving sandy beaches and shoaling waters of the coast on both sides of Dunkirk meant that only small craft could get in close enough to take on soldiers, and even then the soldiers would have to wade far into the sea to meet them. In Dunkirk itself the vast inner docks had been rendered totally unusable by German bombing. This left as a possible embarkation point the outer basin, embraced by two narrow latticework wooden moles of relatively light construction stretching about a mile seawards: the West Mole from the oil terminal and the East Mole from the town itself, neither designed for the berthing of ships like ferries and destroyers. With the West Mole apparently inaccessible through the burning oil terminal, and the East Mole reckoned to be unsuitable for the berthing of large vessels, it therefore seemed that 'Dynamo' could be decisively choked at the very points of embarkation.

But in any case there was a third determinant of carrying capacity – the length and duration of transit between England and Dunkirk. The shorter the route, the more voyages a vessel could make in a given timespan. Two routes were plotted at the outset of 'Dynamo': Route 'Z' direct from Dover to the French coast off Calais and then along the coastline to Dunkirk (at 39 sea miles, the shorter), and Route 'Y' round the north of the Goodwin Sands and due eastwards to a point well to the east of Dunkirk, and then abruptly south-south-west to approach the beaches and the port via the 'North Channel' (87 sea miles). However, as early as 27 May the advance of the German Army beyond Gravelines brought the final section of Route

'Z' under heavy artillery fire, so rendering it dangerous to use. Ramsay was forced to switch his effort to Route 'Y', which doubled the distance and halved the potential load capacity. Then again, this whole sea area crowded with shipping would have to be protected as best it could be against attacks by German surface ships or U-boats.

Yet another major factor determining 'Dynamo's' degree of success was supplied by the Luftwaffe. The German Navy, gutted by its losses off Norway, and the German Army were very content to leave it to the Luftwaffe to seal the fate of the Allied Northern Army Group by breaking up any attempt at evacuation. The Luftwaffe was to do its formidable best, as the losses to Ramsay's ships and the horrific experiences of his ships' companies would testify.

And still there remained the imponderable factors; above all, the weather. Even a moderately choppy sea of the kind so frequent in the Straits of Dover would bar many of the small craft, and certainly river boats, from sailing at all. Moreover, the breaking waves of such a sea would render embarkation from the beaches impossible. A full Channel gale, by no means unusual even in summer, would wreck the entire operation. But virtually throughout the course of 'Dynamo' the sea was to remain calm under a warm sun, the run of good weather marred only by occasional fog, and on 31 May by the short but unpleasant waves rolled on to the beaches by a north-easterly breeze, temporarily halting the process of picking up soldiers from the shallows. As Ramsay thankfully noted in his despatch:

> The operation was favoured by extremely good weather. It was found, however, that any northerly wind caused a surf, which greatly reduced the rate of lifting from the beaches. It must be fully realised that a wind of any strength in the northern section between South West and North East would have made evacuation impossible. At no time did this happen.[7]

If there were a true 'miracle of Dunkirk', it surely lay in this blessing of generally fine weather.

And the last of all the factors governing success, a factor again incalculable in advance: how long could the ships' companies keep going without sleep; keep on returning to the bombs, the shells, the machine-gun bullets and the vengeful scream of the diving Stukas?

No wonder that at the start of 'Dynamo' the target of the operation was limited to 45,000 men to be lifted probably only over two days, out of possibly ten times that number in the Allied armies falling back on Dunkirk. In fact on the first full day of the operation, 27 May, no more than 7,669 soldiers were brought back to England, a highly unpropitious beginning. To find solutions to an operational problem so complex and so vast in scale might have defied months of study and preparation, but Ramsay and his staff in Dover, and the Navy and Army personnel across in Dunkirk itself, could only improvise from day to day and hour to hour. If oil and coal fuelled the ships, then adrenalin fuelled those who sailed in them and those who directed them.

On that first full day of 'Dynamo' Captain W. G. Tennant, RN, sailed for Dunkirk in HMS *Wolfhound* with a beach party of twelve officers and 150 ratings to organise the embarkation arrangements on the spot as Senior Naval Officer ashore. The Luftwaffe introduced him to the operational realities by dive-bombing *Wolfhound* every half hour during the voyage out. Tennant found the situation in Dunkirk so grim that he signalled Ramsay that even a second night's evacuation was problematical. But that night, as the flames were roaring out of burning warehouses, Tennant took a desperate chance which succeeded in transforming the prospects for 'Dynamo': he signalled a ship to berth alongside the East Mole. The experiment succeeded. Henceforward the narrow planking of the East Mole and the skill of the captains who laid their ships alongside its relatively fragile latticework would provide the means of escape for thousands upon thousands of Allied soldiers. This was only the first, though the most momentous, of Tennant's contributions, for as Senior Naval Officer in Dunkirk he was tirelessly to tackle a myriad day-to-day local problems in the port and along the beaches. Then, on 29 May, the 'frontline' organisation for directing the evacuation was completed by the appointment of Rear-Admiral W. F. Wake-Walker as 'Rear-Admiral, Dover' (with two retired rear-admirals to help him) to control all movements at sea off the French and Belgian coasts.

To relieve the strain on Ramsay himself, responsible for organising and directing the entire operation and deploying all its resources, the First Sea Lord despatched Vice-Admiral Sir James Somerville as a volunteer for the role (though not the title) of second-in-command. Ramsay expressed his appreciation of this in a letter to his wife written at 0100 on 27 May: 'James Somerville is here helping me & I couldn't wish for anyone better . . .'[8] In the same letter he gave an inkling of his own state of mind as 'Dynamo' got under way:

> I have on at the moment (it's 1 a.m.) one of the most difficult and hazardous operations ever conceived and unless le bon Dieu is very kind there will be certain to be many tragedies attached to it. I hardly dare to think about it & what the day is going to bring with it . . . How I would love to cast

off the mantle of responsibility which is mine & become just peaceful & retired once again . . . Poor Morgan [Captain L. V. Morgan, his Chief of Staff] is terribly strained & badly needs a rest. Flags [Flag Lieutenant] looks like a ghost . . . All my staff are completely worn out & yet I see no prospect at all of any let up . . . As for my ships they have not a moment's rest unless they are damaged badly.

On 28 May, thanks to Tennant's successful experiment the night before with the East Mole, Ramsay shifted the balance of his resources from the slow and laborious work of lifting from the beaches towards embarkation direct from the outer harbour and its moles with larger vessels, mostly destroyers. Although crammed with machinery and weapons and not at all designed as personnel carriers, the destroyers were to pack in 900 men and more at a time during 'Dynamo'; their upper decks so covered with a bee-swarm of khaki that the guns could not be fought and the ships heeled alarmingly under helm while avoiding air attack because of the top-heaviness. That day of 28 May no fewer than 17,804 men were brought home to England – for Ramsay an encouraging result. This was also the day when the Dutch 'skoots' began an invaluable shuttle service from Ramsgate and Margate. However, on the other side of the ledger, one of the big personnel carriers, *The Queen of the Channel*, had been sunk, and several others hit.

For operations in the coming night and day Ramsay allotted seven personnel carriers, three hospital ships and two destroyers to the task of embarking from the East Mole; some twenty destroyers, nineteen minesweepers (some of them paddle-steamers), seventeen drifters, and upwards of twenty skoots and a medley of smaller craft to lifting from the beaches. This effort succeeded in bringing back 47,310 soldiers, nearly three times the previous 24 hours' total; 33,558 of them from the harbour and 13,752 from the beaches. Yet the cost to Ramsay's command had been desperately high. The destroyers *Montrose* and *Mackay* were damaged by collision and grounding, victims of the appalling navigational conditions, while the *Wakefield* and *Grafton* had been torpedoed and sunk in the night by a German E-boat and the U-62. During the day the Luftwaffe bombed and sank the destroyer *Grenade* and damaged the destroyers *Gallant*, *Greyhound*, *Intrepid* and *Saladin* and the French *Jaguar* as well as the sloop *Bideford*. Luftwaffe bombs also sank the personnel carriers *Mona's Queen*, *Normannia*, *Lorina* and *Fenella*, and damaged the *Canterbury*. The tally of Luftwaffe kills that day was completed by the merchant ship *Clan Macalister*, the boarding vessel *King Orry*, and the special service vessel

[149]

Crested Eagle, as well as many smaller craft. The *Grenade, Jaguar, Fenella, Crested Eagle* and *Canterbury* had all been caught by the same attack coming out of the late afternoon sunshine while they were alongside the East Mole embarking troops.

These losses caused Ramsay worry enough. But later that day the First Sea Lord and Chief of Naval Staff, Sir Dudley Pound, added to his anxieties by withdrawing all the big modern destroyers in an overriding concern to preserve the Navy's scarce resources in this type of ship for such tasks as escorting Atlantic convoys, on which Britain's long-term survival depended. Ramsay was left with only fifteen destroyers, some of them dating from the Great War, and capable of lifting no more than 17,000 men in 24 hours. Pound persisted in taking this decision despite Ramsay's strenuous efforts to dissuade him. It was not the only occasion during 'Dynamo' when Ramsay felt that the Admiralty did not properly support him or understand the operational realities – as for example, when it later resisted his requests that his exhausted ships' companies should be relieved by fresh ships and crews. In a letter of 7 June to his wife, when it was all over, he listed among the main sources of personal strain during the operation 'the continuous struggle with the Admiralty to make theory see the necessity of giving [way] to what is practicable'.[9]

On 30 May, Ramsay and his staff calculated that this withdrawal of destroyers would reduce his total daily lift to 43,000 soldiers, when a lift of 55,000 was needed. Early that afternoon he therefore embarked on another hard-fought action by telephone with Pound, this time successfully. In the delicate phrasing of Ramsay's despatch: 'Verbal representations being made to the C.N.S., authority was received for the return to the Dover Command of the modern destroyers released the night before.'

Ramsay had now brought a new route into operation for daylight hours, Route 'X', midway between Route 'Y' and the abandoned Route 'Z'. At 55 sea miles it meant a considerable saving over Route 'Y''s 87 sea miles; it was also better protected against surface attack by sandbanks and nearby British minefields. It took the Germans three days to discover the adoption of the new route – a welcome respite.

The day of 30 May saw 'Dynamo' bring home 53,823 soldiers. By now the shore-and-ship organisation under Rear-Admiral Wake-Walker and Captain Tennant was working as smoothly as could be hoped in such desperate circumstances. The apparent scene of sprawling confusion along the wide foreshore under the bombs and shells concealed a pattern of ordered movement by the vast regatta of

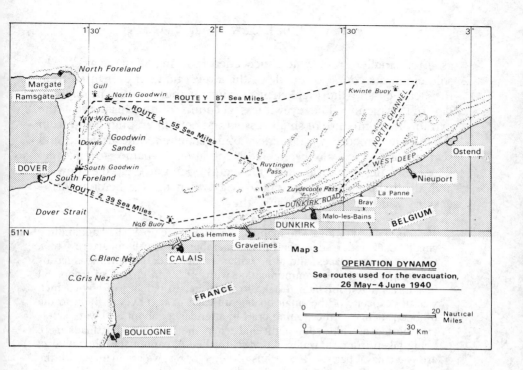

Map 3

OPERATION DYNAMO

Sea routes used for the evacuation,
26 May – 4 June 1940

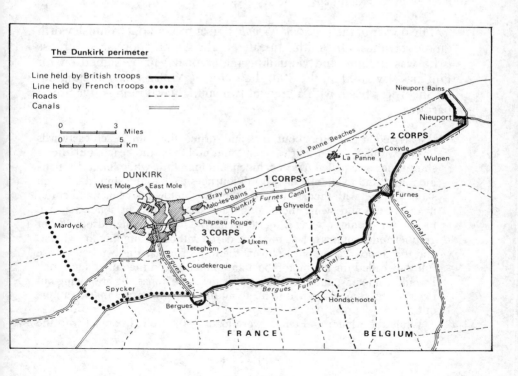

The Dunkirk perimeter

Line held by British troops ▬▬▬
Line held by French troops ●●●●●
Roads ----
Canals ══

assorted smaller craft, which succeeded in lifting as many as 29,512 soldiers in the course of the day – the largest number ever lifted from the beaches and the highest proportion of the total lift in any one day of 'Dynamo'. The eyewitness accounts of the masters of the extraordinary mixture of small vessels and craft operating to and from the beaches record with English understatement the courage and seamanship which alone enabled 'Operation Dynamo' to succeed. The coxswain of the Ramsgate lifeboat, H. Knight, describes how on arrival off the beaches late on 30 May when the freshening north-easterly wind was causing a surf, they

> . . . found naval ratings who manned wherries were not skilled at handling small boats under such conditions; members of the lifeboat crew took their boats and places, and although an intensely dark night managed by shouting to establish communication with officer in charge of troops on beach; arranged for men to take to the water in batches of eight which was the capacity of the small boats, and each boat conveyed them to the lifeboat, thence to the waiting craft in attendance; about 800 were safely transported on Thursday night and when the last three boatloads were being taken from the water, the officer called, 'I cannot see who you are; are you a naval party?' He was answered, 'No, Sir, we are members of the crew of the Ramsgate lifeboat' . . .[10]

The owner of the *Constant Nymph*, a river motor boat from Isleworth on the Thames, Dr Smith, appealed to the Commodore at Sheerness (who was fuelling and victualling motor boats) to be signed on for Dunkirk. By 1800 on the 30th the *Constant Nymph* was chugging out of Sheerness basin with a crew of two young naval ratings. Dr Smith narrates:

> We arrived at Dunkirk about dusk and turned along the beach eastwards for a few miles . . . At first we could find no life on the beach, but after a short time were hailed by Frenchmen and for a little while found French-men only, and made one or two full journeys back to the ship [the Dutch skoot *Jutland*] with them. The procedure was to tow the whaler and cutter to the beach and swing them round and cast off tow in about 3 feet 6 inches (my draught being 2 feet 6 inches). The cutter then dropped her grapnel and went in as close to as she dared without grounding the whaler, and the troops waded out to board them. As soon as the two boats were full they called for the motor-boat and pulled up on the cutter's grapnel; I would come past and take the cutter's tow rope in passing and swing out towards the ship which had to lie about three-quarters of a mile to a mile out.
>
> While the whaler and cutter were loading I patrolled parallel with the

beach . . . my job was to pick up any swimmers or waders and any odd craft which had put out from the shore.[11]

Another Thames motor boat, the *Bonny Heather*, reached Dunkirk as part of a little convoy of motor boats towing ship's lifeboats. She made seven complete round trips between Ramsgate and Dunkirk, each time crammed with 60 men and upwards – as well as working between the beaches and the ships offshore. The skipper of the smack *Seasalter* from Burnham-on-Crouch, L. W. Salmons, describes how after a day's oyster-dredging he and his crew volunteered for Dunkirk and set off in another little convoy:

It was 6 p.m. when we spotted the coast and picked up Dunkirk lighthouse right ahead. We could still hear aircraft above. Then the fog lifted altogether and the A.A. guns let loose at the planes, one of which spotted us, dived low, and machine-gunned us, but missed. He was so low I could see the crosses, the under-carriage stowed away, and the dirty oil marks.

The soldiers were coming off the beach clinging to bits of wood and wreckage and anything that would float. As we got close enough we began to pick them up and with this we went to and fro bringing off as many as it would dare hold . . . When we had got a load we would take them off to one of the ships lying off in deep water.[12]

On the following day yet another of these innumerable little convoys, this time of six cutter-rigged cockle boats from the Thames Estuary, was attacked on its way over by some 40 German bombers, but succeeded in evading the bombs by abrupt changes of course. The cockle boats then began to ferry soldiers from the outer end of the East Mole to the skoot *Tilly*. As A. J. Dench, skipper of the cockle boat *Letitia*, describes:

On going in for the third time, a shell burst between the last boat of them, and us, we turned back, to go out, but the [Navy] signaller that we had on board, and had only been 'out' for about six weeks, and never before been under fire, said, 'We've got to go in again' so we went in . . .[13]

And thus it was for the little ships day after day, the essential first link in Ramsay's chain of rescue that led from the Dunkirk perimeter across the sea to England. The tribute later paid by the captain of the destroyer HMS *Icarus* in a letter to the crew of the Margate lifeboat *Lord Southborough* may serve for them all:

On behalf of every officer and man on this ship I should like to express to you our unbounded admiration of the magnificent behaviour of the crew of the lifeboat *Lord Southborough* during the recent evacuation from Dunkirk. The manner in which, with no thought of rest, they brought off load after load of soldiers under continuous shelling, bombing and aerial machine-gun fire will be an inspiration to us all as long as we live. We are proud to be fellow countrymen of such men.[14]

Meanwhile at an inter-service conference at Ramsay's headquarters in the forenoon of 30 May, it had been agreed to continue the evacuation 'with the utmost vigour' in order to reduce the BEF to a rearguard of 4,000 men by the early hours of 1 June. This meant that Ramsay had to commit his very last reserve of small craft, known as the 'special tow'. 'The Tempo still increases,' he wrote to his wife during a brief lunch break on the 30th, 'and everyone is getting cooked to a turn. It simply can't last much longer at this pace, and what happens when we have to stop doesn't bear thinking about. It is inevitable that thousands and thousands will never be able to get off.' And he went on:

> I had quite a good sleep last night as I got to bed at 2 o'clock & got up at 7.15, the best I've had for days . . . Many fellows in my office never get to bed at all, but just lie down & doze off for an hour or so . . . There is thick fog just now which is disaster from the point of view of transport but a relief for Dunkirk and the ships at sea from bombing. But every moment is precious and I'm afraid on balance we may be badly down . . .[15]

In the forenoon of 31 May came grim tidings from Dunkirk, when Wake-Walker reported that evacuation from the beaches was being severely impeded by surf and Tennant signalled that enemy bombing and artillery fire were rendering evacuation from the moles appallingly dangerous. With ten personnel carriers and three hospital ships already despatched to Dunkirk during the night, none of which had yet returned, Ramsay decided to halt further sailings of this kind of vessel for the time being. But in the afternoon the surf abated; at dusk the 'special tow' arrived from Ramsgate in a five-mile stream of small vessels (including ruggedly beautiful Thames sailing barges); and, despite the bombing and shelling, the personnel carriers and hospital ships already at Dunkirk, along with destroyers and other ships, continued to lift from the moles. By midnight 68,014 soldiers had been embarked – 22,942 from the beaches and 45,072 from the harbour – the zenith of 'Dynamo's' daily achievement.

Next day, however, 1 June – fine, calm and sunny – marked in turn the climax of the Luftwaffe's effort to prevent the quarry from finally slipping away. The skipper of the barge *Royalty* lying off the beaches,

H. Miller, recorded the opening of this onslaught by two air fleets with a phrase that would have been familiar enough to Nelson or Hawke or Drake, and which unconsciously but very properly placed 'Dynamo' in the grand context of England's maritime past: 'We were setting our topsail . . .' he wrote, 'when a large number of German planes appeared overhead and immediately started bombing and machine-gunning us.'[16] The long bright day ahead was to prove the most devastating of all to the destroyers and the personnel carriers. The Luftwaffe first struck at 0720, when RAF fighter cover had temporarily returned to base. Until the next RAF patrol reached the scene at 0900 the German bombers had only to contend with the anti-aircraft fire of the warships – and these were now desperately short of ammunition. The Stukas howled down in relays from 10,000 feet through the shrapnel bursts at ships jinking as they best could in narrow, congested and wreck-strewn waters. The destroyer *Keith*, flying the flag of Rear-Admiral Wake-Walker, was the first casualty: seriously damaged in the first two waves of attack, she finally sank when bombs from the third wave hit her under the bridge. The master of the tug *Cervia* was an eyewitness of the first attack:

> A British destroyer outside of us began to fire at the enemy planes and bombs began to fall near her as she steamed about. At full speed with her helm hard to port nine bombs fell in a line in the water, along her starboard side, and they exploded under water, heeling the destroyer over on her beam ends, but she was righted again . . .[17]

When the *Keith* sank at last, Admiral Wake-Walker and his staff transferred to a motor torpedo boat, only to be dive-bombed yet again, though fortunately not hit. This was only the beginning: before 0900 a second destroyer, the *Basilisk*, had been lost; another, *Ivanhoe*, reduced to a wreck under tow; and four more damaged; the fleet minesweeper *Skipjack*, loaded with troops, had also been sunk. In the high sun of midday the Luftwaffe was back again in force. The French destroyer *Foudroyant*, caught in a narrow channel some four miles off the East Mole and unable to manoeuvre, was 'submerged', in the words of a French account, 'in a cloud of Stukas', and sunk.[18] HMS *Havant* was the next, but mercifully the last, to go. The day had proved as disastrous to the Royal Navy's destroyer strength as a fleet action. Yet the surviving destroyers kept at it. *Codrington*, *Sabre*, *Windsor*, *Whitshed* and *Winchelsea* brought away thousands more soldiers that day.

The big personnel carriers – the pre-war ferries which had carried holiday-makers on their way to Paris and the Côte-d'Azur, or the quieter pleasures of Ireland or the Isle of Man – also fell victim to the Luftwaffe's supreme effort to halt the evacuation. Some of these ships had been offering themselves as prime targets ever since the beginning of operations off Boulogne and Calais some ten days previously, and in Admiral Ramsay's judgment, 'the captains and crews . . . were feeling the strain when Operation Dynamo started'.[19] The unremitting nature of their task is well illustrated by the *Royal Sovereign*'s record on 30 May. At 0530 she completed embarking a full load of soldiers. At 1135 she was back in Margate disembarking. At 1300 she was steaming for Dunkirk once again. At 1820 she was at anchor taking on another load.[20] A schedule such as this is easily stated. What it meant to carry it out is vividly evoked by an account by Captain Hill, master of the hospital ship *Isle of Guernsey*, of his experiences on 30 May. The ship crept into Dunkirk harbour in the small hours to find the night sky and the whole devastated area lit up by fires. While the *Isle of Guernsey* was embarking 490 wounded men, she was 'shaken every few minutes by the explosion of bombs falling on the quay and in the water'. On the way home:

> Just outside we found the sea full of men swimming and shouting for help, presumably a transport had just been sunk. As two destroyers were standing by picking these men up, we threaded our way carefully through them and proceeded towards Dover. It would have been fatal for us to attempt to stop and try to save any of these men, as we made such a wonderful target for the aircraft hovering overhead with the flames of the burning port showing all our white paintwork up.[21]

The first personnel carrier to be sunk on the black day of 1 June was the *Prague*, which arrived at Dunkirk while the Luftwaffe was launching its opening attack. Having successfully embarked 3,000 French soldiers and set course for the English coast, the *Prague* was bombarded off Gravelines by German land-based artillery and then dive-bombed, although not directly hit on either occasion. However, the force of the explosions repercussing through the water inflicted serious structural damage and put one engine room out of action. Slowly sinking, the *Prague* made the best speed she could while the destroyer *Shikari*, the paddle minesweeper *Queen of Thanet* and the corvette *Shearwater* worked desperately to take off her load. This they largely succeeded in accomplishing before she finally beached herself.

Next to be lost was the coal-burning *Scotia*. On her way to Dunkirk she had been warned by a destroyer with gallows humour that it was 'Windy off No. 6 buoy'. So it proved: on her way home with 2,000

French soldiers the *Scotia* was attacked off No. 6 buoy by twelve German aircraft in three waves of four. Hit abaft the engine room, on the poop deck and by a bomb that went down the after funnel, the *Scotia* began to sink by the stern. The destroyer HMS *Esk* came to the rescue: her captain, Commander Couch, RN, manoeuvring his ship with consummate seamanship close up to one side and then the other of the sinking *Scotia*, succeeded in saving all but 300 of those aboard her despite continuing air attack. Nor was the *Prague* the last personnel carrier to be lost that day: in the early afternoon the paddle minesweeper *Brighton Queen*, with 700 French and Moroccan troops embarked, was hit by Stukas and sank.

And still, with very few exceptions, the remaining personnel ships sailed on between Dunkirk and England through the sunshine as if the dive-bombers could drop nothing more dangerous than could seagulls – the *Maid of Orleans* (she made six trips during 'Dynamo' and earned special praise from Ramsay), the *Royal Daffodil* (seven trips), the *Royal Sovereign* (six trips) and *King George V* (five trips: the three latter vessels also being mentioned in Ramsay's despatch), together with the minesweeper (ex-passenger ship) *Medway Queen* and the hospital ship *St Helier*. For all the Luftwaffe's day of fury on 1 June, in which it had sunk 31 vessels of various types, 64,429 Allied soldiers had been brought away from Dunkirk by midnight.

But where was the RAF during that day, and all the other days of 'Dynamo'? For the soldiers and sailors under the lash of the Luftwaffe, air cover meant the reassuring spectacle of British aircraft constantly overhead, or visibly bombing the besieging German Army. They were not afforded this spectacle; instead the sky seemed every day filled with the Luftwaffe; and their resentment grew. As Ramsay put it in his despatch:

> Rightly or wrongly, full air protection was expected, but instead, for hours on end the ships offshore were subjected to a murderous hail of bombs and machine-bullets . . .
>
> The system of co-operation between the Naval and R.A.F. Commands does not permit of direct contact with the R.A.F. operational units allocated for duty with the Naval Command. For this reason much time appears to be lost . . . Delays and lags occur, resulting often in the R.A.F. effort being brought to bear either in the wrong place or at the wrong time, or with inadequate force.[22]

There was substance in this criticism. Except for the ill-equipped Coastal Command and a handful of slow 'Army cooperation' aircraft (mostly artillery spotters), the RAF's pre-war development had concentrated on the close-range air defence of the United Kingdom and on pursuit of the Trenchardite dream of a strategic bomber offensive against the German economy. Close tactical support of the Army and Navy, at which the Luftwaffe was so proficient, had yet to come, forced on the RAF by the realities of war. Thus it was that during the nine days of Dunkirk Coastal Command flew 171 reconnaissance sorties, Bomber Command 651 (mostly at night against German rear areas), and Fighter Command 2,739.[23] The RAF shot down 132 German aircraft for the loss of 145 of its own, including 99 fighters.[24] Yet Fighter Command faced a hard problem: it dare not commit the full strength of the UK's own air defence for fear of the future; the 200 fighters of No. 11 Group actually committed were heavily outnumbered by the 300 bombers and the 550 fighters available to the Luftwaffe. To rotate continuous patrols over Dunkirk meant inferiority of numbers and defeat in detail; to despatch forces strong enough effectively to meet the Luftwaffe in combat meant gaps in cover of the kind which the Luftwaffe exploited so effectively in the early forenoon of 1 June. The dilemma was insoluble; the soldiers' and sailors' mistrust of the airmen unappeasable.

And the Luftwaffe certainly achieved one major success on 1 June. It compelled the Royal Navy to modify the scope of the evacuation, with consequent effect on lifting capacity. At 1800 Ramsay received a signal from Dunkirk: 'Things are getting very hot for ships; over 100 bombers on ships since 0530, many casualties. Have directed that no ships sail during daylight. Evacuation by transports therefore ceases at 0300. If perimeter holds will complete evacuation tomorrow, Sunday night, including most French . . .'[25] Ramsay therefore ordered all ships to withdraw before daylight on 2 June, as he signalled the Admiralty. The Admiralty itself, alarmed by the heavy losses, had in any case signalled Ramsay (the messages crossed) directing him to suspend the evacuation from 0700 on 2 June until the following night at 1730.

By this time only some 3,000 to 4,000 men of the BEF remained in the shrunken perimeter, plus an unknown number of French soldiers – perhaps 25,000, perhaps as many as 40,000. Ramsay therefore planned the coming night's operation for a lift of 25,000. From 1700 on 2 June onwards the rescue fleet began once again to set course for Dunkirk – thirteen personnel carriers, two store ships, eleven destroyers, one special service vessel, nine drifters, six skoots, two armed yachts, a gunboat, and finally the civilian motor boats crewed by volunteers and naval personnel[26] – and by midnight it had brought the 2 June total of soldiers rescued to 26,256. Half an hour before midnight, the *St Helier* had slipped her moorings and made for England with the last of the British Expeditionary Force aboard; and Captain Tennant had made the historic signal to Dover Command: 'B.E.F. evacuated'.

However, there still remained the French, including the rearguard manning the perimeter defence. It was unthinkable to abandon them, and yet Ramsay's sailors – Royal Navy and Merchant Marine alike – were reaching the point of total exhaustion where they simply would be unable to go on. In a few cases civilian masters were refusing to take their ships to sea again, some succumbing to strain sooner than others. On 28 May the master of the *Canterbury*, the large personnel carrier, had only sailed for a third trip to Dunkirk after receiving a direct order and with a naval officer and some ratings aboard 'to augment and stiffen the crew'.[27] On the 29th, and after one round trip, the captain of the *St Seiriol* had refused to sail. The ship finally put to sea after the captain had been put under open arrest and an RN party put aboard, but was hit and damaged on her way home; it proved to be her last trip.[28] In the evening of the terrible day of 1 June the *Tynwald* at Folkestone, having completed three trips in 'Dynamo', also refused to sail; and a naval guard (at which the crew shouted abuse) was posted alongside her at her berth. She sailed 24 hours later with a relief crew and a Royal Navy party, though with her chief officer serving as Master and five others of her own ship's company. She eventually completed five trips.[29]

On 2 June two other ships, the *Malines* and the *Ben-My-Chree*, also refused to sail again. On receiving a written enquiry as to whether he was willing to sail, the master of the *Ben-My-Chree* replied by letter: 'I beg to state that after our experience at Dunkirk yesterday, my answer is "NO".'[30] An armed naval guard was posted on the gangways and abreast of the ship. Then, in a distant ripple from the nerve-rasping violence of Dunkirk into this quiet English harbour, the bayonets of Royal Navy bluejackets were levelled at British merchant seamen. According to Admiral Ramsay's despatch:

> As the ship berthed the crew were demonstrating and shouting that they were going to leave the ship, and on the brow being run out, they attempted to do so with their kits. Leading Stoker Booth ordered his men to come on guard and advanced up the brow with fixed bayonets. The crew returned on board at once, where they remained until the relief crew arrived.[31]

The captain and crew then left the vessel, although here too the chief officer remained as acting skipper, as well as four other members of the crew. On sailing at 1905 on 2 June the *Ben-My-Chree* was damaged in a collision and could not complete the trip. *The Manxman*, having completed three trips out of an assignment of five, likewise refused to sail on that day, and her crew as well had to be replaced, while the *Malines*, which had refused to sail the day before, now left Dover without instructions for the quieter port of Southampton.[32]

For Ramsay the exhaustion of his ships' companies, even those of the Royal Navy, had now become the crucial factor bearing on his ability to prolong 'Dynamo' further. He wrote in his despatch with regard to 3 June:

> No assurance could be obtained that this coming night would terminate the operation and considerable anxiety was felt regarding the effect of the gradual exhaustion of the officers and men of the ships taking part in Dynamo. This exhaustion was particularly marked in the Destroyer force the remnants of which had been executing a series of round trips without intermission for several days under navigational conditions of extreme difficulty and in the face of unparalleled air attack.

And so:

> The Vice-Admiral accordingly represented to the Admiralty that the continuance of the demands made by the evacuation would subject a number of officers and men to a test which might be beyond the limits of human endurance, and requesting that fresh forces should be used if evacuation had to be continued after the coming night, with the acceptance of any consequent delay.[33]

Nonetheless Ramsay had already issued his orders for another night's operation – all his destroyers and nine out of ten personnel ships were to go, as well as the usual mixture of supporting vessels. In the evening he was informed by the British Naval Liaison Officer at the French naval HQ that some 30,000 French soldiers remained at Dunkirk, and that – welcome news this – the French Admiralty had agreed that 'evacuation should be terminated that night if possible'.[34]

And so for the last time ships under the White Ensign and vessels and craft under the Red Duster made that horrific landfall. 'We arrived off Dunkirk breakwater at 11.57 p.m.,' wrote Captain Clarke of the personnel carrier *Princess Maud*. 'We entered the pier-heads, and looked for a berth. The narrow fairway was crammed to capacity ... Wrecks dotted the harbour here and there. The only light was that of shells bursting, and the occasional glare of fires . . .'[35]

At about 0150 on 4 June the *Princess Maud*, loaded – overloaded –

with French soldiers, cast off and sailed. At 0255 the *Royal Sovereign* followed her – the last of the passenger ships to leave, and herself having completed six trips and lifted a total of 6,858 soldiers in the course of 'Dynamo', one-tenth of all those rescued by the personnel carriers.[36] There were other records set that last night – the paddle minesweeper *Medway Queen* completed her seventh trip; the old destroyer *Sabre* completed her tenth, having brought home a total of 5,000 men. Meanwhile the French Navy had been mounting its own supreme last effort to get its comrades of the Army away, with no fewer than 63 vessels of all kinds working in and around Dunkirk. Together the Allied ships succeeded in lifting a further 26,175 soldiers in the 24 hours to midnight, 4 June. But the process of evacuation had actually ceased in the small hours of that day as one by one the British and French vessels slipped their moorings and departed.

The very last ship of all to leave was HMS *Shikari*, one of the Navy's oldest destroyers (launched 1919). At 0340, in the bleak dawn light and to the rattle of German machine-guns nearby, she moved away from the East Mole with her decks packed with French soldiers, leaving astern the wrecked port and town and the pall of dark smoke that towered above it, and the French rearguard which was still staunchly holding off the German besiegers.

At 1423 on 4 June the Admiralty made a signal formally closing down 'Operation Dynamo'. Instead of the 45,000 soldiers it was originally hoped might be rescued, a total of 338,226 had been brought out – 308,888 of them in British vessels. If personnel evacuated in the week before 'Dynamo' itself are included, the grand total rises to 366,162. But the losses to the Royal Navy and the Merchant Marine were equivalent to those of a major sea battle. Of 38 destroyers, six had been sunk, fourteen damaged by bombs and twelve by collision; and at the end of 'Dynamo' the Royal Navy's total strength in destroyers not in the dockyards had dropped to only 74. Of 46 personnel carriers (including hospital carriers and stores ships) nine were sunk and eleven damaged (eight of them so badly as to force their withdrawal from service).[37]

Next day Ramsay, in a letter written to his wife – 'now all is done and the task is behind' – summed it up: 'The relief is stupendous. The results are beyond belief.' And then, expressing himself with a candour unqualified with false modesty, as a man properly may to his wife, he went on:

The success is mostly due to the first class direction and management of the show, equally with glorious courage, skill & endurance of the personnel of all the ships. The one without the other would have been ineffective. We can always count on the glorious deeds but less often on good direction and management. This may sound as self-praise but is nevertheless the plain truth. You know me well enough to know that I count little for myself & think solely of the wider aspect of the object to be gained. My staff were so well chosen & so efficient that they worked like a perfect machine . . .[38]

But perhaps the last word on 'Operation Dynamo' and what it meant to the trapped Allied army is best left to a soldier. A British officer wrote of the moment when he was hoisted from the sea off the beaches on 28 May:

From the instant I landed on my head in the lifeboat a great burden of responsibility seemed to fall from my shoulders. A curious sense of freedom took possession of me. All the accumulated strain of the last few hours, of the last day or so, vanished. I felt that my job was over. Anything else that remained to be done was the Navy's business. I was in their hands, and had nothing more to worry about . . .[39]

In reporting the final result of 'Dynamo' to the House of Commons Winston Churchill, the Prime Minister, rightly warned: 'We must be very careful not to assign to this deliverance the attributes of victory. Wars are not won by evacuations . . .'[40] Nevertheless 'Dynamo's' success may in hindsight be judged one of the deciding factors of the Second World War. Churchill himself eloquently pictured to the Commons the scale of the catastrophe that had been averted by Ramsay and his ships and sailors: 'The whole root and core and brain of the British Army, on which and around which we were to build, and are to build, the great British Armies in the later years of the war, seemed about to perish upon the field or to be led into ignominious and starving captivity.'[41] But there was more to it even than preserving the cadre of future armies; there was the question of the British nation's will to fight on alone should their French ally soon sue for an armistice (a contingency for which the British government and Chiefs of Staff were already preparing). 'Dynamo', its heroism, efficiency and success, morally drew the sting from the German triumph in the West; it gladdened and uplifted British hearts in the face of calamities about to unfold.

In the short term, however, the evacuation consummated the destruction of the Allied Northern Army Group. On 5 June the German Army attacked southwards against the remaining portion of the French Army – 140 divisions against 49 French and one British (51st Highland). Within five days the French front had been broken up and the panzer spearheads began a pursuit that was swiftly to take them to the Swiss frontier and the Atlantic coast, and induce the French government to ask for an armistice. For the Royal Navy this fresh enemy victory once again meant the hasty mounting of desperate evacuations. At St Valéry-en-Caux on 10 June fog baulked the attempt to rescue the trapped 51st Highland Division: only 2,137 British and 1,184 French soldiers were brought off the beaches beneath the tall cliffs, and next day some 6,000 men of the Highland Division surrendered. However, 11,059 soldiers were successfully lifted from Le Havre between 10 and 13 June.[42]

This proved merely the preliminary to the final evacuation from France of all British personnel (including two divisions sent to Brittany at the end of May) through the ports of Cherbourg, St Malo, Brest, La Pallice and St Nazaire from 16 to 25 June, the same day that the armistice terms between France and Germany came into effect. Here were acted out yet again the familiar scenes of hazardous navigation by vessels of all shapes and sizes under punishing air attack. At St Nazaire on 17 June the liner *Lancastria*, packed with 5,800 soldiers, was hit and set on fire, sinking within fifteen minutes with the loss of some 3,000 lives. This was the worst of the losses during these post-Dunkirk evacuations, which succeeded in bringing back to England a total of 144,171 British, 18,246 French, 24,352 Polish, 4,939 Czech and 163 Belgian troops.[43] From 19 to 22 June the Royal Navy also had to carry out the melancholy task of evacuating 22,656 people of military age, women and children from British territory soon to be abandoned to the enemy – the Channel Isles. Once seapower had protected the islands against Bonaparte; it could not preserve them against Hitler in the face of the Luftwaffe a brief flight away on French airfields.

Now in every European port from the Arctic ocean to the Spanish frontier flew the red, white and black swastika flag of Nazi Germany, and the entire grand-strategic shape of the war had been transformed.

The Western Front, that centre of gravity of the Great War where Britain had deployed an army of 56 divisions, and where the German Army had been ultimately gutted and defeated – the theatre re-created in September 1939 and where the Allies had hoped eventually to repeat their victory of 1918 – was no more. The French Army, which had borne the brunt of the fighting on the Western Front in 1914–16 while Britain was creating her mass Army, and which fielded 94 divisions in May 1940, had been struck out of the strategic balance sheet, leaving Britain with a handful of ill-equipped divisions to face a German Army with an order of battle of some 160 divisions. The Luftwaffe was no longer distant on German bases, but just across the Channel and the North Sea: an enormous enhancement in its operational effectiveness against the United Kingdom, especially in potential tonnage of bombs deliverable. The German Navy's U-boats and their covering aircraft would now enjoy direct access from occupied France via the Bay of Biscay to Britain's vital Atlantic shipping routes instead of the long circuitous route round the north of the British Isles: a vast increase in their operational effectiveness as well.

At the same time the powerful French Navy, the cooperation of which had up till now enabled the Royal Navy's global sums to come out in the black, had vanished from the war, condemned by the armistice terms to immobilisation in French ports. And to make this loss even harder to cope with, Fascist Italy had declared war on 10 June, so that the Royal Navy now confronted alone the new threat posed by the modern Italian battlefleet in the Mediterranean – four battleships (plus two nearing commission), nineteen cruisers, 52 fleet destroyers and 115 submarines[44] – to say nothing of the Italian Air Force operating over the Central Mediterranean from nearby shore bases. In the face of this threat, the main imperial lifeline and trade route through the Mediterranean had been abandoned even before the Italian declaration of war, on 16 May, so lengthening the voyage from the United Kingdom to Suez from 3,000 to 13,000 miles, and to Bombay from 6,000 to 11,000 miles.

Yet this desperate scene of strategic isolation only marked the logical denouement of – and perhaps retribution for – British foreign and defence policy from 1919 to 1939: the steadfast refusal to stand with France vis-à-vis Germany either diplomatically or militarily; the priority given in the rearmament programme to the air defence of the United Kingdom over the expansion of the Army in readiness for a Continental campaign; and indeed the refusal to accept any kind of 'Continental commitment' until as late as spring 1939, so resulting in Britain's merely minor military contribution to the great battle in the West in May and June 1940. The entire thrust of British pre-war policy had been to turn the back on the Continent of Europe, leave France to cope as best she might with the German Army, and meanwhile prepare for a quite separate struggle between Germany and Britain in the air over the United Kingdom. Now that this situation had actually come about, it no longer seemed quite such a good idea.

Moreover the irruption of Italy into the war, just at the moment when France was collapsing, marked the final pay-off for Britain's opposition at the League of Nations in 1935–36 to Italy's conquest of Abyssinia. So in June 1940 Britain without an ally found herself at war with two out of the three powers which had offered the pre-war 'triple threat' to the worldwide British Empire, while the third, Japan, could not be neglected, especially in view of the fall of France and the consequent vulnerability of French Indo-China, and indeed Britain's own evidently desperate plight. That month Japan demanded that Britain close the 'Burma Road' between her colony of Burma and Nationalist Chinese territory, over which Western supplies flowed to aid the Nationalists in their war against the Japanese invader; and Britain complied. That month too the British government had to inform Australia and New Zealand that it was now 'most improbable' that Britain could send a large enough fleet to Singapore to defend them against the Japanese, since the Royal Navy was fully committed to fighting Germany and Italy; the two dominions must therefore look to the United States for succour. Thus history was at last calling the bluff that was the British Empire.

The loss of Europe entailed other heavy consequences, particularly for British seapower. Before that loss something like twenty per cent of Britain's imports had come from near sources like Europe itself, the Western Mediterranean and North Africa; by 1941 the proportion was to drop to four per cent, while the proportion of imports from North America over the precarious 3,000-mile Atlantic sea lanes had risen from 36 per cent to 54 per cent.[45] This switch from short or medium-distance sea routes to long ones demanded a much larger commitment of shipping (and therefore of escorts too) because of the increase in 'round-voyage time' – up from an average of 99 days before the fall of France to 122 days afterwards.[46]

Deprived of a Western Front, Britain was reduced to her traditional 'blue water' strategy of using maritime power to sustain land campaigns in far-off peripheral theatres wherever she saw a chance of engaging a portion of the enemy's armies. From June 1940 onwards this meant the Italians in their African colonies of Libya, Ethiopia and Somaliland. But to maintain large modern mechanised armies and also air forces in the backward countries of the Middle East and Africa necessitated the creation of huge base facilities, virtually satellite war economies, on the spot; and especially in Egypt, the central British Middle-East base area. All the necessary equipment and supplies to establish these facilities would have to be shipped out by the 13,000-mile route round the Cape of Good Hope and the Red Sea at a further enormous expense in shipping. Similarly the build-up of the armies themselves – manpower, tanks, trucks and guns, and the continuing flow of reinforcements and replenishment – would depend on ships plying the same circuitous route. The ports too in these backward regions, in particular Alexandria, Port Said, and Suez (the main terminal points for Middle East supply and trooping), were ill-equipped and inefficient and so further wasteful of shipping resources because of slowness of turn-round. By autumn 1941 the supply and reinforcement of the British imperial military effort in the Middle East was to be swallowing up over four million tons of merchant shipping.[47]

It should not be imagined, therefore, that, because Britain was willy-nilly reduced to campaigning in the Middle East and Africa as a result of the disappearance of the Western Front, this offered (thanks to seapower) a uniquely advantageous way of making war, as some historians would have us believe. It did not: on the contrary no form of warfare could have been less cost-effective in terms of military strength in the field measured against resources invested – including, most important of all, resources of merchant shipping and also escorts, of which Britain was now so critically short. 'Blue water' strategy was to impose a terrible and sometimes near breaking strain on a Royal Navy rendered by pre-war disarmament and wartime loss too small for its global commitments.

At a deeper level still, the very foundations of Britain's world power as a maritime nation were about to collapse. That power had rested since the eighteenth century on the wealth produced by seaborne trade under the protection of the Royal Navy; wealth which had enabled Britain to wage successful war against Napoleon Bonaparte and Kaiser Wilhelm II. But by the summer of 1940 this was no longer the case. Overseas earnings (after the conversion of export industries to munitions production) were nothing like enough to support the war effort of a great power with a world empire to protect and equip; and particularly since Britain was making huge dollar purchases of machine-tools, steel, aircraft and weapons from the United States as a result of the weakness of her own industrial base. In August 1940 the Chancellor of the Exchequer, Sir John Simon, warned the Cabinet in a memorandum that the total cost of purchases from the US in the next twelve months would amount to $3,300 million, while Britain's resources in foreign exchange and dollar securities came to only £490 million. Britain would therefore exhaust her gold and dollar reserves by December 1940.[48] In a word, she would be bankrupt; incapable either of waging a war or sustaining her national life out of her own resources.

Quite apart, then, from the immediate danger of invasion, Britain after the fall of France found herself in a predicament unique in her history, largely the result of the follies and illusions of governments and people in the inter-war years – a war without an ally against two great powers and potentially three; an ill-defended and immensely vulnerable Empire; an inadequate industrial machine; insufficient national wealth; and armed forces still too weak to meet the immense strategic burdens now falling upon them. And of the three armed forces, it was upon the Royal Navy that the greatest burden and the greatest strain was to fall, for its role was all-pervasive and its service in the face of the enemy unceasing.

PART II

STORM FORCE

The Wall of England

At 0631 on 3 July 1940, with the sea calm and the Mediterranean sun climbing already warm through a haze, the ships of Force H streamed paravanes as a precaution against possible mines guarding their objective. At 0830 the hands were closed to Action Stations, but the 15-inch guns of the battlecruiser *Hood* (flying the flag of Vice-Admiral Sir James Somerville, commanding Force H) and the battleships *Resolution* and *Valiant* were kept trained fore and aft – a sign of Somerville's continuing hope that they would not have to be fired that day in the fulfilment of his task. Steaming in company with the three heavy ships were the carrier *Ark Royal*, the cruisers *Arethusa* and *Enterprise* and a screening force of eleven destroyers. At 0910 the task force arrived off its destination, the port of Oran and the nearby naval base of Mers-el-Kebir in Algeria, then constitutionally part of metropolitan France. At anchor within Mers-el-Kebir lay the most powerful single squadron of the French Navy, including the modern fast battleships *Dunkerque* and *Strasbourg* and the older battleships *Bretagne* and *Provence*.

Despite the prevailing haze, 'the upper works of the French heavy ships were clearly visible over the breakwater,' wrote Somerville in his report on the day's events, 'although only the actual tops and masts could be seen from a position northwest of the fort [guarding the entrance to the base]'.[1] These were the ships, manned by French sailors so recently the comrades in arms of the Royal Navy, which Somerville knew that he might be forced to sink within a few hours. It all depended on the outcome of negotiations about to be conducted on his behalf by his French-speaking emissary, Captain C. S. Holland, with Admiral Gensoul, flag officer commanding the French battle squadron. By prior agreement with the French authorities, Holland had already gone in ahead in the destroyer HMS *Foxhound* to rendezvous with Gensoul's flag lieutenant outside Mers-el-Kebir's defensive boom.[2] Now Somerville himself could only steam slowly up and down outside Mers-el-Kebir and Oran while he waited through an interminable furnace-hot day for Holland to signal back reports on the progress of negotiations; a time of impotence and uncertainty, that worst of combinations.

It did not relieve Somerville's anxiety or his anguished conscience in the face of the possibility of having to slaughter French sailors that he had received a signal the night before from the First Sea Lord telling him that the War Cabinet 'will be impatiently awaiting news of "Catapult". I hope therefore you will be able to send short messages at intervals such as "Emissary has made contact", "French ships in harbour", etc.'[3] This signal (the language of which strongly suggests the Prime Minister's authorship) encouragingly ended: 'You are charged with one of the most disagreeable and difficult tasks that a British Admiral has ever been faced with, but we have complete confidence in you and rely on you to carry it out relentlessly.'[4]

As early as 25–27 May, when 'Dynamo' was just getting under way, the War Cabinet (of five members, as against a peacetime Cabinet's twenty) and the Chiefs of Staff had already begun to ponder the implications of a final French collapse and capitulation. On 7 June, two days after the Germans struck at the remaining portion of the French Army on the Somme and the Aisne, Admiral of the Fleet Sir Dudley Pound held a meeting with senior colleagues in his room at the Admiralty to discuss the future of the French Fleet if France should conclude an armistice with Germany. His own view, vigorously repeated, was that: '. . . as long as the French Fleet was above water it would be impossible to stop the Germans putting pressure on the French, thus re-acting on whoever had control of the French Fleet. He was sure that the only solution was to sink the French Fleet.'[4]

When on 22 June the British leadership received news of the draft Franco-German armistice terms, it was dismayed to learn that Article 8 demanded that all French warships be collected in specified French ports, demobilised and 'disarmed under German or Italian control', while French ships at present beyond French territorial waters were to be recalled to France. However, as Pound reported to the War Cabinet that evening at Chequers, Admiral Darlan, Commander-in-Chief of the French Navy, had ordered his admirals 'not to accept orders from a foreign government' and to 'fight to the finish' if threatened.[5] It was Pound's opinion that Darlan was taking 'all possible steps' to prevent his fleet being used against Britain.

In the coming days Britain was to receive repeated assurances from the French that their fleet would be scuttled rather than be allowed to fall into Axis hands. But in view of the German record for well prepared surprise take-overs, and, more broadly, the evident hapless-ness of Marshal Pétain's new government in the face of Axis power, could Britain rely on such assurances? The Prime Minister thought not. In his words to the Cabinet on 22 June: 'In a matter so vital to the safety of the whole British Empire, we could not rely on the word of Admiral Darlan . . .'[6]

In the evening of 24 June, while the War Cabinet was again in session, news came in that the French had finally signed the armistice, which came into effect immediately. Of all the host of dangerous problems unleashed by the lapse of Britain's principal ally into uneasy neutrality, none was more urgent than this one of the French Fleet; and Churchill confronted it with the ruthless decision of a Cromwell or a Nelson, telling his colleagues that they must act 'solely in accordance with the dictates of our own safety'.[7] The Cabinet there-fore decided to despatch an ultimatum to Pétain's government de-manding that it scuttle the ships at Oran (the most formidable French squadron of all) 'within a time to be specified' or Britain would 'take action by force against them'.[8] It also discussed the operational problems of sinking the French ships, which Pound advised could only be successfully done 'in a surprise attack carried out at dawn and without any form of prior notification'. Yet even now, with Churchill and his colleagues piloting the British people through their worst storm for centuries, the Cabinet found it 'hard to make' a decision to order 'the destruction of people who only 48 hours before had been Allies . . .'[9]

Intelligence sources, including Sigint, returned no sure guidance – only the disturbing possibility that the Germans were signalling instructions to the French Navy in Darlan's name.[10]

On 27 June the news that Pétain had appointed Darlan Minister of Marine, so rendering him a willing political colleague in a collabora-tionist government instead of the professional head of the Navy, impelled the War Cabinet to make final decisions, for the active deployment of the French Navy in the service of either Britain or the Axis could sway the whole balance of the war at sea, and in particular transform the prospects for a German invasion of England.

At present, French warships were dispersed in harbours hundreds of miles, even a thousand miles, apart, so lessening the danger of a sudden complete seizure by the Axis, but equally presenting the Royal Navy with a multiple rather than a single operational problem. In British ports were the old battleships *Courbet* and *Paris*; the big destroyers *Léopard* and *Le Triomphant*, and the smaller *Mistral* and *Ouragan*; seven submarines (including the *Surcouf*, at 3,250 tons the largest submarine in the world); six torpedo boats and some minesweepers. At Mers-el-Kebir were known to lie the battleships *Dunkerque, Strasbourg, Bretagne* and *Provence*, a seaplane carrier and six large destroyers; and nearby in Oran seven more destroyers and four submarines. At Casablanca in French Morocco and Dakar in French West Africa lay respectively the new battleships (not yet completed and armed) *Jean Bart* and *Richelieu* (the latter in Pound's estimate the most powerful ship afloat). In Alexandria harbour, under the guns of the British Mediterranean Fleet, lay Admiral Godfroy's squadron of one old battleship (*Lorraine*), three 8-inch gun cruisers and one light cruiser.[11]

The War Cabinet's first overt action was to forbid French warships now in British ports and at Alexandria to put to sea – in Godfroy's case, under pain of being bombarded if he sought to do so. It also decided that the seizure or destruction of the French battle squadron at Mers-el-Kebir – 'Operation Catapult' – would take place on 3 July, the earliest date according to Pound that a superior British force could reach the scene.[12] Next day a conference attended by the Commanders-in-Chief, Western Approaches and Portsmouth, and chaired by the First Sea Lord resolved that the simultaneous seizure of French warships in British ports (codenamed 'Grasp') 'would be best accomplished by very large British forces being sent on board the ships in the middle of the night to take the ship's company by surprise'.[13] At Portsmouth in the small hours of 3 July the tactic proved bloodlessly successful; at Plymouth, however, two British officers, a rating and a French rating were killed or mortally wounded in a fracas on board the submarine *Surcouf*. While 'Grasp' had certainly delivered the French ships in British ports into the hands of the Royal Navy, the timing and mode of its execution, along with the death of the French rating, appeared to the French (and not least to Admiral Gensoul in Mers-el-Kebir, when the news reached him in the forenoon of 3 July) to display Albion at its most '*perfide*'.

At Alexandria Admiral Sir Andrew Cunningham, the Commander-in-Chief, Mediterranean Fleet, robustly signalled the Admiralty that he was 'most strongly opposed to [the government's] proposal for forcible seizure of ships in Alexandria', adding that 'he could not see what benefit is to be derived from it'.[14] He expressed himself equally opposed to the use of force at Oran, contending that such actions would alienate the French throughout the French Empire. In reply the Admiralty told him that he could offer Godfroy the alternatives of demilitarisation in Alexandria harbour or being sunk. By the late hours of 4 July, and despite the repercussions from events at Oran on the 3rd, Cunningham had succeeded by patient, personal, courteous and understanding diplomacy in reaching an agreement with Godfroy by which the French admiral demilitarised and immobilised his ships by surrendering the breech-blocks of the guns, discharging fuel oil, and reduced manning to skeleton crews. Cunningham was not helped by Pound's (and Churchill's) prodding signal halfway through the negotiations instructing him to tell Godfroy to reduce his crews 'at once', nor encouraged by its nagging conclusion: 'Do not (Repeat) NOT fail.'[15]

But at least London allowed Cunningham extra time to negotiate, while he also enjoyed the decisive advantage of having Godfroy's squadron already under his guns in Alexandria harbour. It was otherwise with Somerville and Admiral Gensoul at Oran, for Gensoul's powerful battle squadron supplied the main focus of the Cabinet's anxieties over the French Navy. Somerville was accorded little time in which to achieve his mission and little latitude in negotiation, being instead whipped along by Churchill's and Pound's urge to impose a quick, even if violent, solution. Somerville's command, Force H, the 'detached squadron' (in the Admiralty's phrase) formed to fill the vacuum in the Western Mediterranean and the waters off Africa created by the defection of the French Navy, was not even activated until just five days before the date set for 'Catapult'. Only on 30 June, three days beforehand, did the Naval Staff signal the War Cabinet's instructions to Somerville. He was to offer Admiral Gensoul four options with a six-hour time limit for acceptance:

1. Put to sea and join forces with the British;
2. Sail to a French West Indian port, there to demilitarise his ships;
3. Sail with reduced crews to any British port;
4. Scuttle all his ships within six hours of the offer of the British ultimatum.[16]

Failing Gensoul's acceptance of one of these choices, Somerville was ordered 'to endeavour to destroy ships at Mers-el-Kebir but particularly *Dunkerque* and *Strasbourg*', using 'all means at your disposal'.[17] Somerville was further ordered to destroy the warships in the port of Oran itself 'if this will not entail any considerable loss of civilian life'. One way or another, 'Catapult' was to be completed by the end of 3 July.

In the evening of 30 June Somerville held a meeting in his flagship HMS *Hood*, then moored with the rest of Force H at Gibraltar, in order to hammer out how best to sink Gensoul's ships if this after all had to be done. Present were Admiral Sir Dudley North, Flag Officer, North Atlantic (headquarters at Gibraltar), Vice-Admiral Wells (Flag Officer, Aircraft Carriers, flying his flag in *Ark Royal*, part of Force H) and Captain C. S. Holland, a strongly Francophile officer who had until recently been naval attaché in Paris and who was highly knowledgeable about the French Navy and its leaders. Wells, for his part, ruled out an attack by torpedo aircraft as being 'difficult and unproductive' unless anti-aircraft fire could be silenced first. Torpedo attack by destroyers was also ruled out because of net defences round the French heavy ships and the restricted space in the basin. It was finally decided, according to Somerville's later report on 'Catapult', that in the case of Mers-el-Kebir

> a round or two should be fired to show that we were in earnest, and if this failed to bring acceptance of our terms, a limited period of gunfire and/or bombing should be used to cause evacuation of ships, final sinking being effected by torpedo-bomber attack or demolition, according to circumstances.
>
> It was thought that to complete destruction by gunfire would require a great deal of ammunition and cause very great loss of life.
>
> In the case of Oran, it was agreed that gunfire would cause very severe civilian casualties and it was hoped that the action taken at Mers-el-Kebir would induce the French to scuttle their ships at Oran.[18]

This evident operational lukewarmness towards a violent solution merely reflected a deeper personal repugnance. As Somerville records: 'After the conclusion of this meeting, Admiral North, Vice-Admiral Wells and Captain Holland all expressed themselves as strongly opposed to the use of force. They considered that there was little fear of the French allowing their ships to fall into German hands.'[19] Moreover, the view held by Somerville 'and which was shared by others present . . .' was that it was 'highly improbable that the French would use force to resist our demands'. Next day Somerville signalled his doubts to the Admiralty about the use of force, putting forward an alternative suggestion of giving Gensoul advance warning of British action. But Churchill and Pound proved implacable; back came the signal:

It is most undesirable that you should have to deal with French Fleet at sea and consequently about twelve hours' warning, as suggested in your 0812 of 1st July, is not repetition not acceptable. Hence, you should arrive in the vicinity of Oran with your force at whatever time you select, and send your emissary ashore, subsequently taking such action as you consider fit with your force before time limit expires.[20]

On 2–3 July, around midnight and after (their favourite time for drafting important operational signals: hence their naval staff nickname of 'the Midnight Follies') Churchill and Pound drew up the final text of the ultimatum which Somerville was to present to Gensoul. For all the florid language about Britain being committed to restoring 'the greatness and territory of France', the four options remained as drafted on 30 June. They did not include demilitarisation of French ships on the spot, as offered to Godfroy, nor did they permit of any postponement beyond 3 July in the execution of 'Catapult', nor any extension of the six-hour time limit of the ultimatum.

In this haste may be detected a characteristic Churchillian impatience for ruthless action, especially in the present case against the French who had in his view so shamefully dropped out of the war, together with an understandable wish to impress world (and especially American) opinion in the most dramatic possible fashion with Britain's resolve to fight on. Nor should be forgotten the sheer pressure on the Prime Minister of grappling with calamity on the grand scale. When in the forenoon of 3 July ('Catapult' day) Pound in fact drafted a signal to Somerville permitting him to offer Gensoul demilitarisation of his ships where they were, the War Cabinet turned down his draft on the score that 'this would look like weakening'.[21]

At 0135 on 3 July, as the great ships of Force H were steaming for Oran under shroud of night, the final signal from the Admiralty before the loosing of 'Catapult' reached Somerville: it reminded him that it was 'very important' that the operation be completed during daylight that day. But, thanks to the wonder and the curse of modern radio communications, Somerville was to hear from London again and again during the long, hot hours to come, while he himself waited anxiously for news from Captain Holland in Mers-el-Kebir.

At 0810 Holland was met outside the boom by Gensoul's barge bearing his flag lieutenant, 'an old friend of mine', recorded Holland.[22] Now came the first setback: Gensoul refused to see Holland personally, so making it impossible for Holland to open a friendly preliminary softening-up discussion before presenting the War Cabinet's written ultimatum. Instead the flag lieutenant took the ultimatum to Gensoul, delivering it to him in his flagship *Dunkerque* at 0935. 'At this point,' according to Holland, 'it was observed that the battleships were furling awnings and raising steam.'

Some two and a half hours now passed while Holland in *Foxhound*, Somerville in *Hood* and the War Cabinet in London all waited for Gensoul's response. At around noon Somerville signalled London that he was giving the French admiral until 1500 (later extended to 1530) to reply to the British terms. At 1232 London signalled Somerville that if he thought the French were preparing to leave harbour he 'should inform them that if they moved, he would open fire'.[23] This crossed a signal from Somerville: 'Am awaiting reply to letter before opening fire.'[24] At 1236 he signalled to Holland asking whether he reckoned there was now any alternative to bombarding the French ships. But Holland recommended that the French should be asked for a final reply before fire was opened, his appreciation of the French character being that 'an initial refusal will often come round to an acquiescence'. Holland himself 'felt most strongly that the use of force, even as a last resource, was fatal to our object'. He therefore used 'every endeavour to bring about a peaceful solution' even at the cost of delaying the carrying out of the War Cabinet's orders.[25]

At around 1500 Gensoul at last consented to meet Holland in person on board *Dunkerque*, which encouraged Somerville to postpone action yet again: as he signalled to London, 'I think they are weakening.' At 1615 Holland was piped over the side of the French flagship and ushered into Gensoul's cabin, where he found the Admiral 'clearly extremely indignant and angry at the course of events'.[26] As they talked, it seemed gradually to dawn on Gensoul that the British might actually use force. But in any event he was playing for time; British Intelligence decrypts in London of French cypher traffic that afternoon revealed that the French Admiralty had signalled him that all other French naval forces in the Mediterranean had been ordered to his support and that he was 'to answer fire with fire'.[27] Passing this intercept on to Somerville at 1614, London added: 'Settle this matter quickly, or you may have reinforcements to deal with.' But Somerville was still awaiting further news from Holland or his return. Meanwhile in *Dunkerque* Holland convinced himself that 'we had won through and he [Gensoul] would accept one or other of the proposals'. What he could not know, and what the Admiralty omitted to pass on to Somerville, was that the decrypt of the French Admiralty signal to Gensoul revealed that Gensoul had misrepresented the British terms to his superiors as consisting only of two alternatives – join the British fleet or scuttle – rather than the actual four (see above, p. 175). At 1715, just about the time when Gensoul was finally rejecting the ultimatum, a signal reached him from Somerville stating that unless he accepted by 1730 Force H would sink his ships.

When the crestfallen Holland left the *Dunkerque* after a 'friendly' leavetaking he noted that the French battleships were in 'an advanced state of readiness for sea', with control positions manned, range-finders trained on Force H, and tugs at their sterns. But although Action Stations was being sounded, there was little bustle among the crews, many of whom remained on the upper decks. As Holland passed on his way back to *Foxhound* the officer of the watch in the *Bretagne* saluted smartly. It seemed as if the French could not really believe that they were about to be victims of British broadsides.

At 1755 (*Foxhound* having got clear after laying magnetic mines across the harbour entrance) *Hood*, steaming at the head of Somerville's line at 17 knots, opened fire at 17,500 yards, quickly followed by *Resolution* and *Valiant*. So at long last, and for the first time in the Second World War, there was taking place that collision of battle squadrons on which the Admiralty's mind had been so focused in the peacetime years. Yet by a sad irony the British line was not engaging the Japanese Fleet, as the Admiralty had always imagined, nor even the German or Italian capital ships, but the Royal Navy's old eighteenth-century enemy and twentieth-century ally.

Owing to the continuing haze and the smoke pouring from French ships raising steam, the upper works of *Hood*'s target, a ship of the Dunkerque class lying northernmost of the battleships anchored abeam bows to the mole, 'were indistinct and difficult to range on; in consequence the nearby lighthouse of MERS-EL-KEBIR was used for ranging'.[28] The other two British capital ships were also using the lighthouse as an aiming mark, content to make, as *Resolution*'s report put it, 'a general shoot into the area of the anchorage'.[29] The same haze and smoke made it difficult for Somerville's ships to observe the fall of shot, but a Swordfish from *Ark Royal* saw from a height of 7,000 feet the first salvo burst in a line across the *Commandante Teste* (the seaplane carrier), the *Bretagne* and the quarter deck of the *Strasbourg*. 'The second salvo,' according to the report of the Swordfish crew, 'hit the *Bretagne* which blew up immediately and enveloped the harbour in smoke.'[30] From the *Valiant* the death of the *Bretagne* at 1758 (hit in the after magazines) appeared as 'a thick, slowly rising mushroom of smoke ... behind the breakwater reaching to a great height'.[31] When the smoke cleared, the Swordfish crew could no longer see the *Bretagne*, but observed a fire aft on the *Commandante Teste*, while the

Dunkerque appeared to have grounded bows on shore opposite to her berth, after hitting a mine. It was learned later that the *Provence* too had beached (see pp. 171, 174).

The French ships, caught in confined waters with fields of fire partly masked by their neighbours, replied as best they could, their shells throwing up – to the curious interest of the unscathed British – pink and green water splashes. The dye in the nose-cones of the shells served to identify each ship's fall of shot. At 1804 Somerville ordered a cease-fire to give the French crews an opportunity to leave their vessels. By now more than 1,250 French sailors lay dead under the water or beneath the reeking smoke, most of them in the *Bretagne*. In the British heavy ships the cease-fire was welcome enough; so sulphurously hot was the evening that in HMS *Resolution* the temperature in the magazines and shell-handling rooms rose to 96°F, and the crews began to suffer from contaminated air as well as the heat.[32]

At 1812 the Swordfish sighted five destroyers followed by the *Strasbourg* leave the harbour and head along the coast, the report being received in *Hood* at 1820. However, Somerville did not, in his own admission, 'attach sufficient weight to this report' – partly because he had been so certain that the French would leave their ships once the British bombardment opened, and partly because of earlier but false reports of French movements towards the open sea.[33] Only after a confirming report at 1830 did he steer to the east in pursuit. At 1838 he altered course to 080° and at 1902 increased speed to 25 knots (the best that *Hood* could manage) in an effort to bring the *Strasbourg* to action, but then ceased fire and turned away to avoid a torpedo attack by the French destroyer escort. Somerville was to acknowledge that his general dispositions for 'Catapult' 'did not make sufficient provision for dealing with any French ships that might attempt to leave harbour . . .'

Now it was the turn of six Swordfish from HMS *Ark Royal* to try to stop the *Strasbourg*, crossing ahead of her and attacking from the landward side with the French ship (which was making enormous quantities of black smoke) silhouetted against the afterglow. At 2055 the Swordfish came in at a height of twenty feet with 300 yard intervals between them, torpedoes dropping from beneath their fixed undercarriages into a calm sea. But although the crews believed they might have scored two or three hits, the *Strasbourg* got clear away under cover of darkness (Somerville deciding against a night action) to reach safe haven in Toulon.

Three days later the *Ark Royal*'s aircraft attempted to finish off the *Dunkerque* in Mers-el-Kebir, flying from 7,000 feet down the path of the rising sun after its rays had lit up the ship. The crews reported that five out of six torpedoes had struck home and one had failed to explode.

On 8 July, far off in Dakar in West Africa, the battleship *Richelieu* was attacked by a force composed of the small carrier *Hermes* and the cruisers *Dorsetshire* and *Australia* under Captain R. F. J. Onslow, RN. In the small hours a motor boat penetrated the harbour defences and dropped depth-charges under her stern: they failed to detonate. Three hours later torpedo-bombers obtained one hit which distorted a propeller shaft and flooded three compartments – enough to give the French a year's repair work to render her fully seaworthy, although the ship could still have put to sea in an emergency.

So in blood and destruction, to the accompaniment of anguish beneath the White Ensign and abiding hostility beneath the Tricolor, Britain had largely eliminated the French Navy as a factor in the strategic balance of the war. But even as one alliance at sea was foundering in bitterness, Britain was seeking to construct another to replace it. And, by an irony, the most important lever in her diplomacy lay in the disposition of the British Fleet, should Britain follow France into defeat and surrender.

On 11 September 1939 President Roosevelt had written to Churchill to suggest that he keep in touch personally by diplomatic bag 'with anything you want me to know about'.[34] In expressing gladness at seeing Churchill back in his old job of First Lord of the Admiralty, Roosevelt reminded him that during the Great War the two of them had occupied similar posts, Roosevelt then being Assistant Secretary of the Navy. This letter marked the beginning of what was to swell into a copious and ever more intimate exchange between Roosevelt and 'Former Naval Person', as Churchill dubbed himself after becoming Prime Minister. But from September 1939 until Churchill's appointment to this office the correspondence had remained scanty and intermittent, just as Britain's general relations with America while Chamberlain remained head of government were characterised by a mutual distance and even suspicion.[35]

Yet Roosevelt himself wished to help the Allies as far as American opinion in Congress and at large made possible while at the same time keeping America out of the war. In October 1939 a Western hemisphere Neutrality Zone was proclaimed, a maritime extension of the Monroe Doctrine, warning belligerent ships to keep out of a sea area 300 miles wide drawn round the Americas, with the exception of Canada and European colonies. Roosevelt hoped that this zone, patrolled by the US Navy, would deter German warships and so enable the Royal Navy to conserve escort ships for service elsewhere, but in fact it brought little operational relief.[36] In November a revised Neutrality Act ended the American embargo on supplying arms to the belligerents in favour of trade equally with them all on a cash and carry basis, which in fact heavily favoured France and Britain because of their command of the sea lanes to America. So began to swell an immense tide of Allied orders for arms of every kind, including aircraft, which steadily helped to lift American industry out of the Depression. After the fall of France Britain took over French orders as well, pinning faith in America's willingness to continue deliveries even when the money ran out. Thus Britain's expiring wealth laid the foundation for America's colossal wartime technological expansion.

It was the collapse of France and with her the disappearance of that key piece of strategic furniture, the Western Front, which altered everything for Roosevelt as it had for Churchill. No longer could America enjoy the profitable security of being the 'arsenal of demo-cracy' while Britain and France waged and won the actual war against Nazi Germany. Indeed, it was possible – and some Americans, like Joseph Kennedy, the ambassador in London, deemed it highly likely – that Britain herself would soon succumb to Germany's overwhelming might. This would leave the United States without a foreign shield between herself and a Europe dominated by Germany, and at a time when she also had to watch Japanese ambitions in the Pacific. In particular, the British Fleet could well pass under Axis control if Britain had to make peace, for the Fleet would constitute Britain's only bargaining counter in seeking to soften German terms. In that eventuality the United States Navy would be hard put to defend both the Atlantic and the Pacific.

To keep the British going was therefore perceived by Roosevelt as an American interest, providing it could be done without compromis-ing the US's neutrality or affronting isolationist opinion. But were the British able and willing to keep going? In May and June 1940 Roosevelt himself expressed some doubts, although they were partly dispelled by Churchill's ruthless solution of the problem of the French Navy.

Churchill for his part recognised all too clearly that, in the words of the Chiefs of Staff, Britain's long-term chance of survival absolutely depended on American willingness 'to give us full economic and financial support, *without which we do not think we could continue the war with any chance of success*'.[37] For the next eighteen months he was to strive with consummate persistence and skill to draw America step by step into the war. Moreover, from the 1930s to the end of his life he was inspired by a romantic vision of a world free and at peace under the guardianship of the English-speaking peoples; and as an Englishman half-American by birth he saw a 'special relationship' between Britain and America as fundamental to the realisation of his vision.

Nevertheless the vision did not blind him to the present realities of power and necessity. He bargained as toughly as a man could from the weakness of an imperial power past its zenith, its financial and strategic foundations crumbling, with the new imperial power which, in all its young strength and with no enemies at its throat, was supplanting the old. Over relations with the United States as in the other grand issues bearing on Britain's survival in the desperate summer of 1940, Churchill was at his best: far-sightedness rooted in faith and resolution; driving will to win tempered by understanding and patience; grasp of the fundamental strategic simplicities born of long ministerial experience and a high sense of history.

The first test case for his American policy was provided by the Royal Navy's desperate need for escort ships. The new class of vessel specially designed for convoy work, the Hunt class of 900–1,000 ton destroyers, were not due to be commissioned until 1941, yet the attrition of war had reduced the Navy's strength in fleet and escort destroyers from the already insufficient number of 202 at the outbreak of war to a mere 74 out of the dockyards by June 1940 – far too few to guard the vital Atlantic convoys, provide screens for Britain's main fleets and also to supply the Navy's principal instrument for striking at a German invasion armada. On 15 May, in his first letter to Roosevelt as Prime Minister and 'Former Naval Person', Churchill therefore asked for 'the loan of forty or fifty of your older destroyers to bridge the gap between what we have now and the large new construction we put in hand at the beginning of the war'.[38]

Roosevelt, however, turned down the request, preferring to wait upon events. Stalemated negotiations dragged on into August.[39] The Americans sought to elicit from the British a firm promise that the British Fleet would be transferred to North American bases in the event of Britain having to sue for peace, while Churchill endeavoured to twang American nerves with hints that in such a circumstance his successor as Prime Minister might have to surrender the Fleet in order to obtain better terms from Germany: the implication being that it was in America's interest to lend Britain's present leadership all possible support in order to avert such a dire happening. In late August, a further modest step towards Anglo-American naval understanding was made when Admiral Robert L. Ghormley led a three-man delegation to London to hold staff talks; the Americans listening, the British expounding. Ghormley himself thereafter stayed on in London as 'Special Naval Observer' in close, but still one-way, liaison with the Admiralty. In the later months of 1940 he was to urge Washington to permit full mutual discussions of common strategic problems, but in vain. Nonetheless, he did succeed in establishing a cordial personal relationship with the British naval staff; the modest beginning of what eventually was to become the closest cooperation in history between two national navies.

On 2 September 1940 a deal was at last struck over Churchill's request for the transfer of American destroyers. Britain obtained fifty 'moth-balled' Great War American vessels, while in a *quid pro quo* Britain granted the United States 99-year leases of land on eight British possessions in the Caribbean and western Atlantic on which to establish naval and air bases, and also undertook to make a public declaration that the Royal Navy would not be scuttled or surrendered if the waters around the British Isles became untenable. It was a highly unequal exchange which illustrated the weakness of Britain's position and America's determination to exploit it (as Churchill himself well recognised). Nevertheless the British government could comfort itself that the 'destroyers-for-bases' deal marked for the first time an open official American commitment to Britain's cause, as distinct from mere commercial sales of arms; a significant step along the path towards direct American involvement in the war. And there was an uncovenanted advantage, in that American bases in this key strategic region necessarily meant the deployment of American armed force, so serving in the future to lighten Britain's own global burdens a little.

Yet these dearly bought destroyers did not in the event bring swift relief to the Royal Navy. Quite apart from requiring radical alterations to their armament and the fitting of modern sonar, they proved to be in such poor shape mechanically that months of work were needed to fit them for sea service. According to Rear-Admiral Stuart Bonham-Carter, writing from the dockyard at Halifax, Nova Scotia, to the Assistant Chief of Naval Staff (Foreign) in October 1940, the destroyers appeared at first sight 'to be in a fairly good shape but, after taking them over, one could see they may have to have a lot done to them before becoming really efficient', and he explained that in particular they had developed engine-room defects which could only have been found out in advance by complete stripping down.[40] Only nine of these ancient four-funnel destroyers were in service by the end of the year and only 30 by May 1941.

Shortage of escort ships of all kinds, but especially destroyers, therefore supplies the leitmotiv of the Royal Navy's operations in home waters and the Atlantic throughout the second half of 1940 and on into 1941. For in escorts lay the key to the Navy's two most urgent problems – that of defeating a German attempt to invade England, and that of guarding the convoys which carried home the steel and machine tools and weapons, the foodstuffs and the fuel oil, without which British resistance to Nazi power would in any case swiftly wither.

Kepe then the sea that is the wall of England:
And then is England kept by Goddes hande.

So adjured Bishop Adam de Moleyns in 1436. Time and again since then great enemies had mustered their power beyond that 'wall', determined to surmount it and subdue the islanders to their will. In 1588, when the Royal Navy was still small and young, the Spain of Philip II, then the world's greatest seapower, had posed the most dangerous threat of them all, seeking with the Armada to land a great army on the English shore, only to be thwarted by England's fledgling navy. In 1803–5 (the intervening centuries being studded with invasion scares that had come to nothing in the face of wind, tide and the Royal Navy) it was the turn of Bonaparte, the self-styled 'Napoleon, Emperor of the French', to puzzle how to pass his Grande Armée over the English Channel, which he regarded as 'a ditch which will be leaped whenever one has the boldness to try'.[41] The First Lord of the Admiralty of the time, Admiral Lord Barham, had assured his anxious Cabinet colleagues: 'I do not say the French cannot come; I only say they cannot come by sea.' So, in the zenith of the Royal Navy's size and fighting efficiency, it proved.

From the 1840s onwards, however, the coming of the steamship had posed a new kind of threat to 'England's wall'. No longer would an invader be dependent on the vagaries of wind, but be able to steam across the Channel at will, choosing his own moment to slip past the Royal Navy's guard and land an army by surprise. So was born the fear of the 'bolt from the blue' invasion: in the Victorian era, invasion by the French, the traditional enemy; and after 1900 by the Germans. Yet the Admiralty remained confident that in the face of British seapower Germany with her much smaller High Seas Fleet would be unable to do more than sneak small landing forces through to the British coast. In the event, during the Great War, Germany mounted no invasion attempt of any kind although the British government held back troops from the Western Front just in case.

[185]

Now it was the summer of 1940, and Hitler's victorious army stood along the cliffs and dunes where Philip II's *tercios* and Bonaparte's Grande Armée had waited in vain for safe passage to England. To the islanders themselves, as they erected pill-boxes and tank-traps and strung barbed wire along the beaches and between the ice-cream kiosks of seaside resorts, it was therefore a situation rendered familiar enough by their history – bracing rather than frightening. Who could really imagine that soldiers in coal-scuttle helmets and field grey would be seen marching through the gentle and hitherto inviolate landscapes of Sussex and Kent, or Norfolk and Suffolk? This was the kind of thing that only happened to other nations.

For Britain's political and military leadership too – and for none more than Churchill, with his vivid sense of the English story – 1588 and 1803–5 lived again in 1940; but in their case it conferred no comfortable feeling of immunity. Not only was the British Army after Dunkirk virtually unarmed (there was only enough equipment for two divisions in the whole United Kingdom) but this time there existed an altogether new dimension to the threat of invasion – airpower.

On 25 May, even before the lesson of Norway had been driven home by the Luftwaffe over Dunkirk, the Chiefs of Staff reported to the Cabinet that the Royal Navy's ability to defeat an invasion force while at sea depended on its power to operate in the face of heavy air attacks. They went on to state that the Royal Navy could not count on operating surface forces in strength in the southern part of the North Sea and the English Channel at all – the very seas that the Germans must be expected to try to cross.[42] After studying this report Churchill posed the Chiefs of Staff the direct question: 'Can the Navy and the Air Force hold out reasonable hopes of preventing serious invasion . . . ?' The Chiefs of Staff replied that for as long as the Royal Air Force remained 'in being', then the Navy and the Air Force between them 'should be able to prevent Germany carrying out a serious sea-borne invasion of this country'.[43] But if Germany obtained air superiority, then the Navy could hold up an invasion 'for a time', but not 'for an indefinite period'. Once a large-scale invasion began, Britain's land defences would not be strong enough to prevent the German Army establishing a firm beach-head, nor from then success-fully exploiting inland. Therefore, they concluded, 'the crux of the matter is air superiority'.

Thus the decisive role, the task of delivering a victory that would save the island from the invader, which in 1588 and 1803–5 had belonged to the Royal Navy, now in 1940 fell to the Royal Air Force.[44] Yet it would still fall, as in Nelson's and Barham's day, to the Royal

Navy, whether operating beneath the cover of British air superiority or, if need be, without it, to make plans to destroy the enemy's invasion flotilla once it set course for England. The Admiralty and the naval staff addressed themselves to this traditional problem in a novel guise.

As in 1803–5 the enemy controlled the entire Continental coast opposite England from Denmark to Finisterre; an invasion force might venture across the North Sea from the Low Countries or the North German and Danish ports to East Anglia, or it could follow the Bonapartian plan of a short passage across the Straits of Dover. But unlike in 1803–5 – or 1914–18, for that matter – the enemy in 1940 possessed only a negligible surface fleet, for the German Navy, even at the outbreak of war a fraction of the size of the old Imperial High Seas Fleet, had been drastically written down in the Norwegian campaign. British Intelligence reckoned that its operational strength in the summer of 1940 comprised the two fast battleships *Scharnhorst* and *Gneisenau* (in fact both damaged and unfit for sea), two old, slow and weak pre-Great War battleships, two heavy and at least two – possibly four – light cruisers (in fact only two cruisers in all were fit for sea), between seven and ten destroyers, 40 to 50 U-boats (whereas in July only 28 were actually operational), a similar number of torpedo boats and some twenty or so lighter craft.[45] As the German naval leadership bleakly recognised, this was a pitifully inadequate force with which to cover a vast invasion flotilla of transports and barges against the Royal Navy. No wonder Grand Admiral Raeder demanded as an essential prerequisite for an invasion that Germany enjoy absolute control of the air over the Channel.[46]

It was at the end of May, while 'Dynamo' was in full spate, that the Admiralty sent a directive to all home Commanders-in-Chief outlining its anti-invasion strategy: one little altered in the course of the summer and autumn, and which broadly followed the precepts laid down by the Admiralty in 1803–5, and, for that matter, by Lord Howard of Effingham, Raleigh, Drake and Hawkins in the 1580s. Believing that the enemy would choose the shortest crossing and be prepared to accept 'catastrophic losses' in order to land an army in England, the Admiralty stressed the importance of 'attack before departure' (shades of Drake's successful raid on the Spanish Armada in Cadiz in 1587), which therefore demanded 'early indication of assembly by our intelligence and reconnaissance'.[47] When the assembly of an invasion fleet had been detected by these means, it was to be bombed, mined and shelled in its anchorages. If it nevertheless proved impossible to destroy the invasion fleet before it put to sea, then it would be attacked 'at the point of arrival' (shades of the English fireships after the

Armada's arrival at Gravelines in 1588). Since the exact point of landing could not be known in advance, the Admiralty judged that 'our forces must be disposed to cover the area Wash to Newhaven as a whole'.

The directive then turned to a third eventuality – 'the happy possibility that our reconnaissance might enable us to intercept the expedition on passage'. It reckoned that to destroy the expedition at sea would demand four destroyer flotillas (36 ships at full strength), their firepower being further strengthened by cruisers. These flotillas were to be based in the Humber, Harwich, Sheerness and Portsmouth or Dover, where they would be well placed to attack the expedition on arrival no matter what the point of landfall. The Admiralty proposed in addition that 'the maximum number . . . of destroyers, escort vessels, corvettes, etc, as can be spared from escort duties should be allotted to the area'. On top of all this, small craft were to be 'collected immediately for watching close inshore and hampering the enemy's operations'. The Admiralty thought that the transit of the invasion fleet might be accompanied by a diversionary sortie of the two German fast battleships in northern waters, perhaps also by a foray into the southern North Sea by the two old battleships *Schlesien* and *Schleswig-Holstein* and up to five cruisers, and it therefore appreciated that the Royal Navy would have to hold ready sufficient heavy ships and cruisers to deal with these threats.

Comprehensive though these plans were, they committed virtually half of Britain's remaining destroyer strength to a defensive screen widely spread round England's south-eastern shores, so inevitably denuding Western Approaches Command (responsible for the Atlantic convoys) and the Home Fleet. By the end of July there were 32 destroyers and five corvettes in the Nore Command alone. What was more, six cruisers were also removed from the Home Fleet, already weak enough in this class of ship, and similarly dispersed to south-eastern naval bases. This provoked Admiral Forbes tartly to request the Admiralty to inform him which Home Fleet cruisers could still be considered as coming under his command. Nor was this all: as early as 17 May the Admiralty (and this really meant Pound) had suggested to Forbes that the Home Fleet's battleships too should come south to Plymouth.[48] At the other end of the scale, anti-submarine trawlers were taken away from escort duty and sent to join the new 'Auxiliary Patrol' of some 1,000 armed trawlers and drifters, of which about a third were always on patrol watching for an invasion fleet.

Admiral Forbes himself vigorously opposed this draining of strength away from his fleet and from the task of protecting merchant shipping, for he believed that no invasion attempt was possible until and unless Fighter Command was decisively beaten by the Luftwaffe. He judged that there would then be time enough to redeploy the Home Fleet for a last battle to prevent a successful invasion. In May he successfully resisted a proposal that he should bring his fleet down to Plymouth; in July he likewise opposed a suggestion that he should detach two of his battleships to Liverpool. He did, however, agree that if there were signs that the enemy was preparing to invade across the North Sea, he would transfer the Fleet from Scapa southwards to Rosyth. The dispute was finally resolved on 20 July when an Admiralty directive laid down that British heavy ships should not move into the southern North Sea unless German capital ships were being used to cover an invasion force, in which event 'our own heavy ships are to engage them at the earliest opportunity'.[49]

Needless to say, the Commanders-in-Chief whose commands covered the possible invasion coasts (Portsmouth, Dover, The Nore) took a very different view; they wanted to have and to hold all the destroyers and cruisers that the Admiralty was good enough to send them. In the words of Admiral Sir Reginald Plunket Ernle-Erle-Drax, C-in-C, The Nore (the command stretching from the Dover Strait to Flamborough Head on the east coast), 'to destroy an invading force we need gunfire and plenty of it'.[50]

But the key to this whole argument over the Royal Navy's correct deployment lay in the degree of advanced warning of invasion that might be expected. As experience during 'Dynamo' had shown, reinforcements could reach Dover from Rosyth within 24 hours. Even ships escorting convoys in the Western Approaches were within a few days' recall. Was the Admiralty really justified in reckoning on such short notice of an invasion attempt that it was right to keep so many of the Navy's precious destroyers and cruisers week after week along England's south-eastern shores? The answer to this question lies in the Intelligence data available to the Admiralty at the time.[51]

Although the Government Code and Cypher School at Bletchley Park had begun to break the Luftwaffe Enigma-machine cypher regularly during the Norwegian and French campaigns (yielding by inference useful information about the operational plans of the German Army and Navy as well), it was still to be months before the German Navy Enigma could be similarly read reliably and in quantity. After the French campaign even the Luftwaffe Enigma traffic slackened off because of increased use of landlines. However, in late June and early July, it did yield references to the forward deployment of aircraft and other preparations indicating a major offensive effort by the Luftwaffe; references also to the installation of long-range artillery to command the Straits of Dover. In London the Joint Intelligence Committee (JIC) was alarmed enough by these decrypts to give mid-July as the date from which onwards 'a full-scale invasion' might be expected. In fact the decrypts related to the Luftwaffe's coming attempt to smash the Royal Air Force as the essential preliminary to an invasion; and the opening phase of this air battle, in the form of fighter sweeps over the Channel and southern England, actually began on 10 July. Yet the JIC might surely have guessed that the Enigma decrypts pointed towards a Luftwaffe offensive rather than an invasion, for photo-reconnaissance showed that no assemblage of barges and other sea transport had yet taken place in Channel and North Sea ports. Moreover, it was unrealistic to credit even German staff work with the ability to organise a massive tri-service operation like an invasion within less than a month of the ending of the strenuous French campaign.

Unfortunately, Military Intelligence (MI) made its own contribution to this scare by arguing that an invasion might take such unorthodox forms as tanks ferried in motor boats to a wide frontage of coast, rather than the traditional pattern of a fleet of transports and barges carrying an expeditionary force together with all its stores and equipment, and escorted by warships. The Naval Intelligence Department (NID), for its part, regarded MI's concept as fanciful, not least because there was no evidence that the necessary pool of motor boats existed. But unfortunately the naval staff itself (this again really means Pound, abetted by the VCNS, Rear-Admiral T. S. V. Phillips) believed in this figment of MI's imagination – hence the haemorrhage of ships away from the Home Fleet and the Western Approaches to picket the invasion coasts.

As Pound explained to the Prime Minister early in July, possibly with the success of 'Weserübung' in mind, '. . . we cannot therefore assume that special craft will not have been provided, or that past military rules as to what is practicable and what is impracticable will be allowed to govern the action taken'. He encouragingly added that the Germans might get as many as 100,000 men ashore with little or no warning by making a number of separate attacks and feints at widely dispersed points in a carefully chosen combination of calm weather and low visibility, from ports as far apart as Biscay and Norway. This could be achieved by means of hundreds of fast motor boats previously assembled but undetected by reconnaissance in French and Dutch ports, and expeditions using larger vessels and tank-landing craft assembled beyond the range of reconnaissance in Biscay and the Baltic.[52] Thus, by an irony, the First Sea Lord accepted the possibility of that 'bolt from the blue' which his predecessors before the Great War had so derided. It must be said that Pound's picture of German strategy, for which no supporting evidence existed at that time or later in the year, was more worthy of the author of *The Riddle of the Sands* than the professional head of the Royal Navy. Churchill himself in commenting on Pound's memorandum found it 'very difficult to visualise' an invasion by means of swarms of small motor boats.

It was after the middle of August that Sigint started to pick up reliable evidence that German preparations for an invasion were indeed now in progress, although neither then nor later was any reference to an exact date or place of invasion ever detected by it. From the beginning of September photo-reconnaissance provided confirmatory proof of the assemblage of barges and other craft in Ostend, Dunkirk and Calais. This evidence hardened day by day until on 7 September the Photographic Reconnaissance Unit (PRU) warned that a well-organised and large-scale movement of barges to forward Channel bases was taking place; it noted that moon and tide on the south-east coast of England would be favourable to an invasion attempt between 8 and 10 September (dates also currently coming up in reports from diplomatic and Special Intelligence Service sources). The JIC therefore advised the Chiefs of Staff that an invasion might be attempted at any time, and at 2007 on 7 September 1940 GHQ, Home Forces, issued the codeword 'Cromwell', the signal to bring all the home defence forces to a state of readiness.

In fact Hitler had directed at the end of July that all preparations for 'Sealion' (British Sigint only picked up this codename for the invasion on 21 September) must be completed by the middle of September, but, as with his earlier contingency plans for risky forward moves, such as against Czechoslovakia in 1938 and Poland in 1939, he left himself free to choose at the last moment whether to launch his forces or not. By 7 September, when GHQ, Home Forces, signalled 'Cromwell', he had still not made up his mind, for although there were signs that Fighter Command might be beginning to weaken, the outcome of the attrition battle waged by the Luftwaffe against Fighter Command since 8 August ('Adler Tag') still lay in doubt.

Thus the invasion scare of early July, causing the premature and prolonged deployment of so many of the Navy's stretched resources round the south-eastern coasts, was not really warranted by the available and broadly accurate Intelligence data on the progress of

German preparations. In the light of that data, mid-August was the very earliest when all those cruisers and destroyers needed to be drawn away from the Home Fleet and the Western Approaches, although Forbes was probably correct in judging that that decision could even wait until the air battle was lost and won.

The Admiralty was now to prove no less tardy in perceiving that the invasion threat had passed – again despite cumulative and reliable data from Intelligence sources. On 14 September Hitler postponed for the third time his decision to order the ten-day count-down period for 'Sealion', which meant that the operation could not now be launched until 27 September, that being the last day of favourable moon and tide before 8 October. On 15 September Fighter Command crushingly defeated the Luftwaffe's climactic mass attack in the Battle of Britain. Two days later Hitler postponed the count-down for 'Sealion' yet again, this time also ordering some of the invasion barges to be dispersed. Even by 15 September British analysis of the volume of German naval radio traffic was already suggesting that invasion preparations had begun to wane, while on 20 September photo-reconnaissance confirmed this with proof that five destroyers and a torpedo boat had been withdrawn from Cherbourg and that assemblies of barges were beginning to thin out. At the end of September the PRU reported that the number of barges in the main invasion ports from Flushing to Boulogne had fallen by nearly a third within less than a fortnight.

Puzzlingly, however, Sigint and SIS sources also yielded clues at this time suggesting that 'Sealion' was still alive and preparing to pounce.[53] Once again Forbes, that commonsensical sailor, got it right, judging as early as 15 September that Fighter Command's successes 'had removed the threat of invasion completely'; he therefore pressed a reluctant and obstinate Admiralty to redeploy ships back to the Home Fleet and the Atlantic. On 28 September he sent a powerful letter to the Admiralty in which he summed up the strategic view he had held throughout the invasion summer, and urged that

> . . . the Army, assisted by the Air Force, should carry out its immemorial role of holding up the first flight of an invading force and that the Navy should be freed to carry out its proper function – offensively against the enemy and in defence of our trade – and not be tied down to provide passive defence to our country, which had now become a fortress.[54]

On 31 October at a meeting of the War Cabinet Defence Committee the Prime Minister directly asked Admiral Forbes whether he believed that an invasion was still possible. Echoing Barham in 1804 Forbes robustly answered that 'while we are predominant at sea and until Germany has defeated our fighter forces invasion by sea is not a practical operation of war'.[55]

Nearly three weeks earlier Hitler had himself come to the same conclusion, putting off 'Sealion' on 12 October until spring 1941; in fact for good. Like Bonaparte he was turning his back on the stubborn islanders behind their 'ditch' and preparing to march his army off eastwards to attack a more accessible Continental victim. So Britain would survive to serve as the catalyst for ever greater American involvement in the war and eventually as the base for an Anglo-American grand-strategic counter-offensive against Hitler's Europe. The Royal Navy's mastery of the Narrow Seas, protected this time by the Royal Air Force's hard-won victory in the Battle of Britain, had once again preserved the cause of freedom, once again decided the course of history.

Now winter was coming on with its short days and bad weather. At the 31 October meeting of the War Cabinet Defence Committee Forbes advised his colleagues that this rendered an invasion even less possible. By this time, in the light of fresh and clinching evidence from Enigma decrypts and other sources, others in high places were ready to agree with him. The Defence Committee concluded that an invasion had become 'relatively remote' and that it was now 'essential to reduce to a minimum' the light naval forces allotted to anti-invasion duties, and redeploy them to protect British trade routes.[56] For meanwhile the U-boats had been enjoying what their crews dubbed 'the happy time', prowling seas largely emptied of British men of war and preying virtually unscathed on defenceless merchant shipping.

On 23 June, immediately after the Franco-German armistice, Karl Dönitz, now a Rear-Admiral and C-in-C, U-boats, had arrived on the French Atlantic coast to carry out a tour of inspection of ports as suitable U-boat bases. On 7 July the U-30 became the first U-boat returning from an Atlantic voyage to replenish with fuel and torpedoes at Lorient, and by 2 August the dockyard there was ready to undertake U-boat repairs. From then on U-boats no longer returned to German bases for replenishment and shore leave, but only to French Biscay ports. On 29 August Dönitz transferred his headquarters from near Wilhelmshaven to Paris in an interim move while a new command centre with elaborate signals links was installed at Kerneval near Lorient.[57] The dockyard at Lorient proved in the event to be more efficient than Germany's own overworked yards in servicing and repairing U-boats, so that whereas in September 1939 to July 1940 the proportion of boats on offensive sorties to the total number of operational boats was 1 to 2.35, in the period July 1940 to July 1941 the proportion improved by almost a quarter to 1 to 1.85.[58] This was by no means the only factor in raising the operational productivity of the U-boats. As Dönitz wrote later:

> Before July 1940 the U-boats had to make a voyage of 450 miles through the North Sea and round the north of Great Britain to reach the Atlantic. Now they were saving something like a week on each patrol and were thus able to stay considerably longer in the actual area of operations. This fact, in turn, added to the total number of U-boats actively engaged against the enemy.[59]

In directing his U-boats to rich hunting areas Dönitz enjoyed the colossal advantage up to August 1940 that the German Navy's B-Dienst could read up to 50 per cent of the Royal Navy's signals, though not the cyphers used by Cs-in-C and flag officers. Even after the cyphers were changed in August B-Dienst found Merchant Navy radio traffic almost as rewarding. On the other hand, and fortunately for the desperately pressed Royal Navy, Dönitz still suffered from crippling handicaps which prevented him from unleashing what at that period might easily have proved a war-winning offensive. Owing to the mistaken earlier priority given to surface ships in the German Navy's construction programme and the current need to allot more boats to training he was still very short of operational U-boats, able only to keep a maximum of eight or nine at sea at any one time. Moreover, German torpedoes had proved a technological disaster. Inaccurate depth-setting caused them to run too deep, while they were also highly prone to failing to detonate because of the faulty design of the magnetic pistol (supposed to fire in response to a ship's magnetic field).[60] In June 1940 the U-boat arm was even compelled to revert to primitive 1914–18 contact pistols while a new and effective magnetic pistol was developed.

Yet after weighing handicaps against advantages Dönitz, the most formidably intelligent, resourceful and relentless opponent that the Royal Navy had had to fight since the Dutchmen de Ruyter and van Tromp in the seventeenth century, decided to launch a major U-boat offensive – in fact, the first phase of what in March 1941 Winston Churchill was to dub 'the Battle of the Atlantic'. Dönitz's opening offensive proved, he wrote in his memoirs after the war, 'particularly successful', and mostly because of the shortage of British escort ships in the Atlantic, as he himself acknowledged: 'The U-boats encountered a large number of vessels sailing independently while convoys were weakly escorted . . .'[61]

It was the heyday of the individual hunt for victims by U-boat aces such as Kretschmer and Prien, heroes to the German public. In June 1940 they sank 58 ships of 284,113 tons; in July, 38 ships of 195,825 tons.[62] Even though in July the Admiralty responded to the establishment of U-boat bases on the Biscay coast by switching the main British convoy route from the south to the north of Ireland, the enemy soon discovered the new routing, and in August (the month when Hitler declared a total blockade of Britain, even neutral ships now being liable to be attacked on sight) sank 56 ships of 267,618 tons, plus another fifteen of 53,283 tons by Luftwaffe long-range bombers now based on French Atlantic coast airfields as well as on Norwegian.[63]

For the British government and naval staff these were worrying enough figures, far outstripping the rate of output of new merchant tonnage by British shipyards. Yet in September Dönitz introduced a new and much more sophisticated system of U-boat warfare – attack on a convoy by a 'wolf pack' of several boats, coordinated by U-boat Command by radio and employing the tactic already well tried at the end of the Great War whereby the boats ran in on their targets at night on the surface, and so outwitted the British under-water sound detection gear.

In order to concentrate a 'wolf pack' Dönitz needed advance warning of a convoy's location and course, either from B-Dienst intercepts or from a Luftwaffe aircraft, or a U-boat on patrol. Once a U-boat had reported the presence of a convoy, it would remain with it as a radio 'marker' on which the 'wolf pack' could home before deploying ahead of the convoy and astride its course. Whether Dönitz received the necessary advanced warning therefore partly depended on luck. In September luck – in the shapes of a chance encounter of a convoy by a U-boat and a revealing B-Dienst intercept – favoured Dönitz, enabling his 'wolf packs' to make a brilliant début. On the 10th of the month four U-boats attacked a homeward-bound convoy from North America in a Force 8 gale and sank five ships.[64] On the 21st–22nd five boats ambushed a convoy of fifteen ships, sinking eleven and damaging a twelfth. These successes helped to lift the September total of sinkings to 59 ships of 295,335 tons, with another fifteen of 56,328 tons falling victim to the Luftwaffe.[65] Next month saw the 'wolf packs' sink 38 ships belonging to three different convoys on three consecutive nights. The deadly pattern of the Battle of the Atlantic had now been established – not only for those in war rooms responsible for its strategic conduct, but also for those in the front line at sea, as the war diary of Lieutenant-Commander Kretschmer of the U-99 for the night of 18–19 October 1940 starkly recorded:

> 2330. Now attacking right wing of the last line [of the convoy] but one. Bow shot at a large freighter. The vessel zig-zagged, with the result that the torpedo passed in front of her and hit instead her even bigger neighbour after a run of 1,740 yards. The ship, about 7,000 tons, was hit below the foremast and sank quickly by the bows with, I presume, two holds flooded.

> 2358. Bow shot at large freighter approx 6,000 tons. Range 750 yards. Hit below foremast. The explosion of the torpedo was immediately followed by a high sheet of flame and an explosion which ripped the ship open as far as the bridge and left a cloud of smoke 600 feet high. Ship's forepart apparently shattered. Ship still burning fiercely, with green flames.[66]

In this month the U-boats alone sank a record total of 63 ships of 352,407 tons including, on the 26th, the 42,348-ton Canadian Pacific ship *Empress of Britain*, the only one of the great British liners to be lost during the war.[67]

This was a total so worrying as to bring about the War Cabinet Defence Committee's decision on the 31st to transfer the maximum number of escorts from anti-invasion duties back to trade protection. Fortunately, however, ferocious and continual Atlantic storms brought some relief in November and December by hampering U-boat operations, and the tonnage of ships lost in these two months dropped to 146,613 tons and 212,590 tons.[68] But while the U-boats were struggling against gales and raging seas, the German surface raiders were enjoying their own 'happy time'.

Since the spring the enemy had despatched six long-range armed merchant raiders, much more strongly built and gunned than British 'armed merchant cruisers', to roam the South Atlantic and the Indian Ocean (and even the Pacific, where some of them were replenished by the Japanese) in search of lone and helpless victims. By the end of the year the six ships – *Atlantis, Orion, Widder, Thor, Pinguin* and *Komet* – had destroyed 54 ships totalling 366,644 tons.[69] For the Admiralty the problem here lay not only in the extra loss of shipping in itself but also, as with the *Graf Spee* and the *Admiral Scheer* in 1939, in the immense disruption and uncertainty caused by the raiders' far-spread exploits, to counter which demanded the deployment of a disproportionate (and ill-spared) number of British warships.

But this was not all. On 5 November the Admiralty received the chilling report by radio from a homeward-bound Halifax convoy

(HX84) of 37 ships that it was being attacked by the *Admiral Scheer* – the first the Admiralty knew that the pocket battleship had broken out into the North Atlantic via the Denmark Straits without being detected by aircraft of Coastal Command or by surface patrols. The convoy's only escort was the 14,000-ton armed merchant cruiser *Jervis Bay* (Captain E. S. F. Fegen, RN), another of those weakly armed and vulnerable ex-liners with which the Royal Navy had had to make up the shortfall in heavy ships and cruisers bequeathed by the disarmament policies of the 1920s and early 1930s. Nevertheless Fegen, like Kennedy of the *Rawalpindi* the previous year, unhesitatingly steamed to engage the enemy, 6-inch guns against 11-inch, thin plating against thick armour, while signalling his convoy to disperse. Within twenty minutes the *Jervis Bay*, a shattered hulk with her bridge aflame, had capsized, taking Captain Fegen down with her. Yet Fegen's self-sacrifice (for which he was awarded a posthumous Victoria Cross) had won enough time for all but five ships of the convoy to escape. That night, in an episode later celebrated in a feature film, the crew of the tanker *San Demetrio*, having taken to the boats when the *Admiral Scheer* set her on fire, later reboarded her and put the fires out, bringing her eventually safely home to England.

But disruption rather than tonnage was the *Admiral Scheer*'s aim, and this she had achieved. In vain hope of catching her if she were on a short raid or on her way back to port Admiral Forbes deployed the battlecruisers *Hood* and *Repulse*, three cruisers and six destroyers from Scapa across the approaches to the French Atlantic ports of Brest and Lorient, while he himself took *Nelson* and *Rodney* to cover the Iceland–Faeroes gap. At this point, however, Pound intervened directly in the C-in-C's dispositions, despatching part of the battle-cruiser force to the point where the *Scheer* had last been sighted, and allotting the *Rodney* to the task of escorting homeward-bound convoys.[70] Yet all this was groping in the blind, for the *Scheer* had vanished far into the South Atlantic, to reappear at widely different points, snapping her jaws on unwary merchant ships, and so keeping the naval staff's nerves freshly rasped.

On 24 November the Admiralty ordered the formation of three hunting groups to track down the pocket battleship and the disguised merchant raiders – Force K, consisting of the recently commissioned new aircraft carrier *Formidable* and the cruisers *Norfolk* and *Berwick*, to be based on Freetown; the small carrier *Hermes* and a cruiser on St Helena; and the cruisers *Cumberland* and *Newcastle* to reinforce the South American Division. Yet this too was groping in the blind, for so few ships could not effectively trawl such a vast area of sea. Then, in December, to add to the Admiralty's problems and cause yet further British redeployment, the cruiser *Admiral Hipper* also escaped into the Atlantic and attacked a convoy. Fortunately her voyage proved a brief one since she lacked the endurance of a pocket battleship, and on 27 December she returned to Brest, the first large German warship or merchant raider to use a French base. On the same day the *Scharnhorst* and *Gneisenau*, now repaired at last, themselves set course for the Atlantic but – even more fortunately for the Admiralty – both ships returned to port after the *Gneisenau* had been damaged by seas off the Norwegian coast.

But the *Admiral Scheer* and the six disguised merchant raiders (the latter heavily armed, adept at adopting the identity of some innocent vessel, and soon to be augmented by others) would remain at sea for many months yet – the effective and highly economical means whereby Grand Admiral Raeder could keep tweaking and straining the tightly stretched net of British seapower, while his C-in-C, U-boats, got on with the main battle of attrition against Britain's shipping capacity.

In combating the U-boat the Royal Navy and Royal Air Force Coastal Command suffered the disadvantage of having to respond defensively to the initiative which Dönitz had so boldly seized. Yet they were just as starved of resources as Dönitz and perhaps even more crippled by defective or unsuitable equipment. And whereas Dönitz had begun to implement a thoroughly pondered strategy with proven tactical systems, the Royal Navy and Coastal Command were still feeling their way from pre-war false doctrine towards effective anti-U-boat tactics and an integrated air/sea command.

For the ill effects of the 1918 separation of the air and surface dimensions of seapower between two services had only been partially remedied by the 1937 compromise by which the Royal Navy got back control of carrier aviation while the Royal Air Force retained responsibility for the land-based maritime air operations. It helped that the primary role of such operations was freshly defined as 'trade protection, reconnaissance and cooperation with the Royal Navy'.[71] But like all compromises its success depended on the spirit in which it was worked. Fortunately Air Chief Marshal Sir Frederick Bowhill, Air Officer Commanding-in-Chief, Coastal Command, from 1937 onwards, was no Trenchardite airpower fanatic, but a former naval officer who had volunteered for the Royal Naval Air Service in 1913, commanded a seaplane carrier in the Great War, and had undertaken a permanent commission in the new Royal Air Force in 1919. Under his leadership, and thanks to his deep-rooted understanding of sea warfare, Coastal Command faithfully interpreted its task as serving the operational needs of the Navy, especially in regard to protection of trade. By 1940 close cooperation already existed between Coastal Command headquarters and the Admiralty's Submarine Tracking Room, while the techniques of combined operations between aircraft sweeping ahead on a convoy and the surface escorts were beginning to evolve in the hard school of experience.

It was therefore by no means helpful when in November 1940 Lord Beaverbrook, the Minister of Aircraft Production, proposed a typical press-baron's short-cut answer to the question of integrated air-sea warfare: nothing less than a return to the pre-1918 situation, with Coastal Command handed over to the Navy. It would be hard to imagine a more ill-timed and disruptive proposal, or one more likely to reawaken maximum ill-feeling between the Air Force and the Navy. So once again, but now in the midst of war, Whitehall pondered this stale and poisonous issue. Nevertheless, in the face of the organisational complications of carving up the Royal Air Force and of the Admiralty's own tribute to 'the already excellent cooperation which exists between Coastal Command and the Navy', the Cabinet Defence Committee (advised by Churchill that it would be disastrous at that stage of the war 'to tear a large fragment from the Royal Air Force')[72] agreed on 4 December not to disturb the existing good relationship between the services.

A joint report in March 1941 closed the matter by reaffirming 'the predominance of the naval element in the existing operational partnership for the protection of sea-borne trade'. In effect this meant that the Admiralty exercised overall direction of the employment of Coastal Command, even though actual command of air operations remained vested in the Coastal Command hierarchy and the AOC-in-C. On 7 February 1941 a fully integrated joint headquarters for the Navy's Western Approaches Command (formerly at Plymouth) and Coastal Command's No. 15 Group had been opened in Derby House, Liverpool, to conduct the Battle of the Atlantic. The new headquarters, with its operations room and telephone, radio and teleprinter links, was Britain's answer to Dönitz's command centre at Kerneval; its location in the north-west of the country resulting from the switch of the main Atlantic convoy route from the south to the north of Ireland in response to Dönitz's offensive from Biscay ports.

Coastal Command was thus willing enough to help the Navy combat the U-boat; its weakness in 1939–41 lay in sheer shortage of aircraft and adequate equipment, which paralleled the Navy's own dearth of escort vessels. The Command particularly lacked modern long-range aircraft suitable for air-search and attack far over the Atlantic. The Saro Lerwick flying-boat, intended to replace the Short Sunderland, had proved by the spring of 1940 to be yet another of the aircraft industry's turkeys, its handling characteristics so bad as to render it unfit for operational service. The Sunderland therefore had to be put back into production, at the cost of several months of worryingly slow deliveries. Meanwhile Coastal Command was forced to keep flying its antique biplane flying-boats, the Saro London and the Supermarine Stranraer. The bulk of the Command's land-based aircraft still consisted of ten squadrons of Avro Ansons, an adaptation of a civilian airliner: reliable enough (hence the nickname 'Faithful Annie'), but armed with only two .303 machine-guns, able to carry no more than four 100-pound bombs and with a range of only 660 miles. The Command's sole resources in up-to-date land-based aircraft consisted of a single squadron of Lockheed Hudsons.

This paucity of long-range aircraft meant that even after the establishment of air bases in Iceland (occupied by British and Canadian troops in May 1940) Bowhill's efforts to extend British air cover further over the convoy routes were frustratingly cramped. Meanwhile the Luftwaffe's four-engined Focke-Wulf Condor reconnaissance bombers could sweep the Atlantic as far out as to the westward of Iceland, thanks to their range of over 2,000 miles, and could sink a merchant ship with just one of their four 550-pound bombs.

By contrast even a direct hit by the 100-pound bomb carried by most Coastal Command aircraft could not even harm a U-boat, while even the heavier Coastal Command standard bombs, of 250 pounds and 500 pounds, could only damage a U-boat's pressure hull if they exploded no further distant than six and eight feet respectively. That Coastal Command was equipped with these squibs was the fault of the pre-war Admiralty which had specified them in the face of experience in the Great War that bombs of at least 500 pounds were required to kill a U-boat.[73] What was more, in 1939–40 Coastal Command aircraft lacked an efficient bombsight, forcing crews to attack from such low levels as to risk destruction by the explosion of their own bombs (as indeed happened to several aircraft in 1939).[74]

In any case, for Coastal Command to attack U-boats it first had to find them. But it had been trained and equipped instead to search for enemy battle squadrons and surface raiders – the result of the pre-war Admiralty's obsession with heavy ships and also its smug conviction that sonar provided such a complete answer to the U-boat that there would be little role for aircraft in anti-submarine warfare. To locate battleships or cruisers by visual sighting from a patrolling altitude was one thing; to spot a U-boat's slim and almost awash hull and tiny conning-tower in a waste of moving water was quite another, even in clear daylight, let alone in murky weather or darkness. Yet when Coastal Command began to redirect its operations towards the sub-marine, it found itself blinkered by want of modern electronic search aids. Neither its own aircraft nor ships of the Royal Navy were equipped with direction-finding apparatus for fixing the position of U-boats by their radio signals, a particularly regrettable lack in view of the copious radio traffic generated by Dönitz's centralised deploy-ment of wolf packs. By late 1940 only a dozen Coastal Command aircraft had been so far equipped with the first airborne search radar, the heavy and unreliable ASV (Air-to-Surface Vessel) Mark I, which demanded that the aircrew fly at a height of only 200 feet if the radar operator were to distinguish a U-boat from the 'clutter' of the sea's moving surface; a height that gave a maximum search range of only three and a half miles.[75] In spring 1940, 4,000 improved Mark II sets designed for mass production were ordered, but such were the technological shortcomings of the British radio and precision engineering industries that by October 1940 only 45 sets had reached the squadrons. In any case, even when radar enabled an aircraft to locate a U-boat down to within half a mile, Coastal Command had as yet no flare or other illuminant capable of lighting up the target for the final sighting and attack, for the pre-war design of flares had proved next to useless for the purpose.

All these deficiencies in aircraft and equipment would be gradually – far too gradually – made good in the course of 1941–43, but meanwhile Coastal Command remained a sea bird weak on the wing, short of sight and blunt of beak.

By the end of 1940 the year's total of shipping losses had mounted to 3,991,641 tons, of which the U-boat alone had accounted for 2,186,158.[76] And of this horrific total no fewer than 3,599,242 tons had been sunk in the Atlantic and home waters.[77] No wonder Churchill told Roosevelt in a year's-end letter surveying the state of the war that, though the danger of invasion had receded, an 'equally deadly danger' lay in 'the steady and increasing diminution of our shipping tonnage':

... The decision for 1941 lies upon the seas. Unless we can establish our ability to feed this Island, to import the munitions of all kinds which we need, unless we can move our armies to the various theatres where Hitler and his confederate Mussolini must be met, and maintain them there, and do all this with the assurance of being able to carry it on till the spirit of the Continental Dictators is broken, we may fall by the way, and the time needed by the United States to complete her defence preparations may not be forthcoming.[78]

To the Royal Navy, then, had fallen the fundamental role in Britain's war. Yet Churchill recognised that keeping the seas open (and above all the Atlantic) was in itself a purely defensive function, forced on the Royal Navy by the onslaught of the enemy. So even amid the perils and calamities of 1940 he pined as strongly as ever to use seapower offensively in order to hurt the enemy in his turn. While the evacuation from Dunkirk was still running its course he had urged on the Chiefs of Staff the importance of not allowing 'the completely defensive habit of mind . . . to ruin all our initiative'.[79] 'We ought,' he went on, 'to organise raiding forces and keep the Germans guessing at what points along the hundreds of miles of coast under their control we should strike them next. Plans should be made for transporting and landing tanks and for the raising of 5,000 parachute troops.' In June a new Directorate of Combined Operations was created, first under Lieutenant-General A. G. B. Bourne, Royal Marines, and then from 17 July Admiral of the Fleet Lord Keyes, one of Churchill's favourite veteran heroes from the Great War. From this humble beginning in the midst of defeat was to grow the expertise, the operational doctrine and the specialised equipment which eventually made possible the D-Day landings in 1944.

But in the summer of 1940 Churchill's mind was already vaulting towards 'specially trained troops of the hunter class who can lead a reign of terror' up and down the coasts of Europe, at first by what he called a 'butcher and bolt policy', but later, he hoped, by the surprise capture of places like Calais and Boulogne.[80] His aggressive spirit in a desperate situation was admirable, but these projects boded a repetition of the futile 'descents' on the French coast so beloved of Pitt the Elder in the Seven Years' War and Pitt the Younger in the French Revolutionary War. Worse, his two particular pet projects in late 1940 for seaborne expeditions display him relapsing from grandeur of vision as a national leader into his old failing of stubborn refusal to take note of operational realities.

In the case of 'Operation Workshop' (originally conceived by Keyes at the end of October), a project for the capture of the Italian island of Pantellaria, about 150 miles north-west of Malta, the Chiefs of Staff were unenthusiastic (to say the least). Admiral Sir Andrew Cunningham, the C-in-C, Mediterranean (backed by the First Sea Lord) was forcefully opposed to it, on the grounds that Pantellaria was of little strategic value and that 'Operation Workshop' would lay a needless extra burden on the Mediterranean Fleet. Nevertheless, the Prime Minister kept plugging it week after week, even asking the Chiefs of Staff in January 1941 to consider the project yet again. It was not until April that 'Workshop' was formally abandoned. But despite the time-wasting staff study and argument, 'Workshop' at least never got as far as sucking in scarce troops, shipping and warships. It was otherwise with 'Menace', the operation to occupy the naval base of Dakar in French West Africa, which in terms of basic political and military misjudgment, hasty improvisation and humiliating failure, was to be a replay of the landings in Norway.

The concept originated at the beginning of July 1940 with enticing promise of much strategic reward for a minimal and risk-free British military investment. Nine days before his expulsion by the French the British Consul-General in Dakar averred to London that many of the local civil and military leaders were so keen to continue the war at Britain's side that an early appearance by the Royal Navy would lead to a bloodless coup d'état. His report served to confirm earlier optimistic reports via the Colonial Office by British liaison officers still in French West Africa. On 5 July Churchill minuted that the Consul-General's suggestion 'appears to be of the utmost importance'.[81] General Ismay thereupon banged back a sober military appreciation of the strength of Dakar's defences (including the battleship *Richelieu*), indicating that caution was called for.

This exchange established the pattern, familiar enough, of the developments which now ensued: demands for action as soon as possible from an enthusiastic Churchill; operational difficulties fully spelt out by the unhappy military, who nonetheless complied with the Premier's wishes. Indeed, at the beginning Churchill even bypassed the Chiefs of Staff machinery altogether in favour of consultation with an informal clique of advisers in touch with de Gaulle,[82] who together cooked up the first operational plan, code-named 'Scipio', in which de Gaulle's Free French forces were to play the active role. On 4 August the COS gave their reluctant support to 'Scipio' on the clear understanding that the British role was to be limited to providing equipment and the naval escort. Within three days – for this time Churchill was, as the record shows, truly bulldozing the project through – it had become accepted that British troops too would be involved. Impatient with the COS's caution, Churchill instructed them: 'Let a plan be prepared forthwith . . .'[83] The resulting plan called for an assault landing on Dakar by more than five battalions of Royal Marines, the date being then set for 8 September. On 13 August

Churchill successfully sold 'Menace' (as it was now retitled) to the War Cabinet.

Detailed preparations against the clock now began, the professionals asking in vain for a month's postponement in order to remedy all kinds of shortcomings and properly to organise and rehearse a tricky combined operation; Churchill chafing at every delay. The force commanders, Vice-Admiral J. H. D. Cunningham and Major-General N. M. S. Irwin, both able and forceful professionals, and their staffs fully shared the COS's (and Joint Planning Staff's) pessimism, leaving London for Dakar with the belief that 'unless received with open arms we were in for a defeat, ships' guns being no match for shore guns'.[84] The First Sea Lord and the Board of Admiralty, for their part, regarded 'Menace' as an unacceptable diversion of over-stretched naval resources, but did not choose to push their objections to the point of threatening resignation.[85] Intelligence about the French defences, about the attitudes of the local French authorities, even about the nature of the beaches at Dakar, was vague, misleading or nonexistent.[86] During the voyage to Dakar Cunningham and Irwin discovered to their chagrin that the War Office had failed to make available to them a copy it possessed of the complete up-to-date French defence scheme for West Africa. They now learned that these defences were in all respects very much stronger than they had planned for.[87] By contrast, gross security leaks in London by the careless Free French had turned the 'Menace' expedition into something of a coming public event.

The expedition finally arrived off Dakar at about 0500 on 23 September 1940, a morning of thick fog. It consisted of the carrier *Ark Royal*, the battleships *Barham* and *Resolution*, the cruisers *Devonshire*, *Australia* and *Cumberland*, nine destroyers, together with two troopships carrying 4,270 British soldiers, as well as Free French troopships and 2,400 soldiers.[88]

In execution 'Menace' provided a perfect illustration of Murphy's Law that everything which can go wrong, will. De Gaulle's emissaries were received with gunfire rather than rapture by the local French authorities, compelling the 'Menace' commanders after all to resort to force in obedience to their directive. But while a hundred 15-inch shells from the British battleships inflicted no damage on Dakar's shore batteries, the French counter-bombardment by those same batteries and by the battleship *Richelieu* damaged the *Cumberland* and lightly damaged two destroyers.[89] An ill-coordinated landing attempt by the Free French on Rufisque beach on the opposite side of the bay to Dakar harbour dismally failed. It had not been a good first day.

At 2105 the joint commanders received the signal from the Prime Minister: 'Having begun we must go on to the end. Stop at nothing.'[90] In the following forenoon the British squadron therefore resumed the process of emptying its magazines, again without result, while aircraft from *Ark Royal* launched dive-bombing and torpedo attacks on the *Richelieu*, but missed her. Eight British aircraft were lost. The French vigorously returned the British fire, straddling *Resolution* and hitting *Barham*.

That evening de Gaulle, ever a realist, advised the British commanders that '*l'affaire de Dakar est terminée*'. But after he returned to his cabin Cunningham and Irwin decided to have one more try on the morrow, signalling this intention to London at 0147 on the 25th. Already, at 0005, Churchill had sent one of his back-seat driver's signals, long and peevish, to the force commanders, demanding 'full and clear' reports on all that was going on, questioning why the bombardment had not inflicted 'grave damage', and asking why they did not 'force a landing' on Rufisque beach.[91] In the brilliant sunshine of the forenoon of the 25th the British squadron tried again to crush the French shore defences and ships by bombardment. The *Richelieu* and the *Barham* hit each other without inflicting serious damage. The *Resolution* was torpedoed by the sole remaining French submarine at Dakar, the *Beveziers*, which hit her amidships while she was under full helm, flooding her port boiler room and causing a 12½ degree list to port. *Resolution* was compelled to withdraw at 12 knots behind a smoke screen laid by destroyers. The crippling of *Resolution* settled the matter, not only for Cunningham and Irwin, but even for Churchill in London: '. . . Unless something has happened which we do not know which makes you wish to attempt landing in force, you should forthwith break off . . .'[92]

'Operation Menace' had cost the Royal Navy one battleship put out of action for a full year and one cruiser for six months (*Fiji*; torpedoed by a U-boat on the outward voyage), and nineteen aircraft destroyed.[93] The cost in terms of Britain's prestige, especially in regard to American opinion, was dear enough. The American military attaché in London, General Raymond E. Lee, all too accurately regarded 'Menace' as 'probably another of Churchill's military inspirations, like Antwerp', writing that it 'appears to have been as great a mistake as the attempt upon Norway'.[94] Yet, as similar exercises with similar results in the years to come were to demonstrate, 'Menace' even when coming on top of Norway, had taught the Premier nothing; his enthusiasm for quickly cobbled up combined operations still remained quenchless.

But in any case by the time 'Menace' took place he had already lighted upon the theatre of war where on the grandest scale seapower could take the offensive in conjunction with the British Army and so seize back the initiative from the enemy. It was that classic scene of the past triumphs of British 'blue water' strategy forever associated with Nelson's immortal memory: the Mediterranean and its shores.

8

'Blue Water Strategy': The Mediterranean, 1940

In 1937, confronting the problem of the triple German–Italian–Japanese threat to the British Empire and the worst possible case of simultaneous wars against all three powers, the Chiefs of Staff had been quite certain that conflict with Italy in the Mediterranean and the Middle East came third in order of strategic priority. In their view the United Kingdom and Singapore constituted 'the keystones' of British world strategy.[1] Any reinforcement of Egypt weakened Britain in the face of Germany, while lack of strength in the Mediterranean would not be nearly so serious as the surrender of British seapower in the Far East. The COS therefore pronounced: 'This situation demands recognition of the principle that no anxieties and risks connected with our interests in the Mediterranean can be allowed to interfere with the despatch of a fleet to the Far East.'[2] Since to pass convoys through the Mediterranean to the Suez Canal (the traditional imperial lifeline) in the face of the hostility of the Italian Navy would entail major fleet operations, the COS judged that the consequence of war with Italy must be the diversion of this lifeline to the Cape route – thus, although the COS did not say so, vitiating the whole traditional purpose of the sprawling British involvement in Egypt and the Middle East built up since the early nineteenth century.

However, by 1939 the order of strategic priority had begun to shift and blur. In April British and French staffs pondered the prospects of a long war against Germany and Italy. Although this must begin with an initial defensive while the Allies gradually mobilised their resources, the two staffs saw the hope of taking the offensive against Italy even in this opening phase – in their words, 'holding' Germany and 'dealing decisively' with Italy.[3] Moreover, Chamberlain's efforts in the spring and summer of 1939 to build up a Balkan diplomatic front against German and Italian expansion in any case necessitated the maintenance of a show of naval strength in the Mediterranean.[4] And yet on the other hand the Chiefs of Staff were still reckoning in June 1939 that 'if Japan joined our enemies, a British Fleet would have to be despatched to the Far East, and only very reduced British light naval forces would remain in the Mediterranean. In consequence the control of sea communications in the East Mediterranean would pass to Italy . . .'[5]

In the event, during the first nine months of the war when both Italy and Japan happily remained neutral, the demands of operations against the German Navy alone in home waters, the Atlantic and Indian Ocean proved sufficient to drain away the fighting power of the Mediterranean Fleet – all three of its battleships (including *Warspite*, the flagship), the single aircraft carrier (*Glorious*), the 1st Cruiser Squadron, the depot and repair ships, many destroyers. By December 1939 the Mediterranean Fleet had been reduced to four small cruisers, one Australian flotilla leader, four Australian destroyers and two submarines.[6]

When from March 1940 onwards signs accumulated that Mussolini might after all be girding himself to enter the war on Germany's side, Britain began steadily to reconstitute her Mediterranean Fleet and reinforce her air and land forces in Egypt – partly as a deterrent, partly as a precaution. On 27 March the Admiralty despatched the submarine depot ship *Medway* and the repair ship *Resource* to Alexandria, and ordered ten submarines from the Far East to the Mediterranean; on 3 May the battleships *Royal Sovereign* and *Malaya* reached Alexandria after release from North Atlantic convoy duties; and on 14 May the C-in-C, Mediterranean, Admiral Sir Andrew Cunningham, was able to hoist his flag again in the battleship *Warspite* on her return from operations off Narvik. Later in the month the battleship *Ramillies* and the aircraft carrier *Eagle* joined the Fleet from the Indian Ocean. As May turned to June cruisers too sailed in from the far distant stations: the *Orion* from the American and West Indies, *Neptune* from the South Atlantic, *Gloucester* from the East Indies, HMAS *Sydney* from Australia, and *Liverpool* from the China Station.[7] In addition there had been placed under Cunningham's command the French squadron under Vice-Admiral Godfroy consisting of the battleship *Lorraine*, four cruisers and three destroyers.

Meanwhile the Allies had been debating their strategy for the Mediterranean theatre should Italy enter the war. It had to be broadly defensive, with the principal objectives of securing French and British controlled territories along the North African and Levant shores from Italian invasion, and keeping open essential Mediterranean communications. Nevertheless the French command also invoked splendid visions of attacks on the Italian Dodecanese Islands in the Aegean, the occupation of Crete, even an expedition to Salonika, just as in the Great War, in order to open up a Balkan Front. But in any case both Allies concurred in seeing the Mediterranean in the event of Italian belligerence as a major theatre of war rather than a side show – a theatre in which the key factor must lie in seapower.

On 10 June, as the German Army swept the wreckage of the French Army past Paris in final rout, Mussolini duly declared war; on 22 June, the signing of the Franco-German armistice confronted Churchill and his strategic advisers in London and the three British service Commanders-in-Chief in the Middle East with the collapse of all previous assumptions and strategies with regard to a conflict with Italy. Now two out of the three threats to the British Empire had become actual instead of potential; worse, Britain had to contend with them both without an ally, and while still remaining alert to the third and as yet still quiescent threat, Japan.

Given this catastrophically altered situation, should Britain attempt to go on alone with the strategy of trying to damage Italy in the Mediterranean and Middle East (and in her empire in East Africa) while holding fast against Germany? Or should she revert to her pre-war global order of strategic priority, and evacuate the Mediterranean, perhaps even Egypt, in order to concentrate her available strength on the German war (indeed, her own survival) and at the same time provide forces in hand to defend her empire in the Far East and Pacific against Japan if need be? For the Royal Navy, appallingly overstretched as it already was, and with the vital Atlantic sea lanes already in jeopardy, the dilemma was particularly acute.

The First Sea Lord and Chief of Naval Staff, Admiral of the Fleet Sir Dudley Pound, and his Deputy Chief of Naval Staff, Rear-Admiral T. S. V. Phillips, were convinced that 'Atlantic trade must be our first consideration', as Pound put it to Cunningham on 16 June,[8] six days before the Franco-German armistice came into effect. On 17 June Pound therefore circulated a draft memorandum by the Director of Plans to the Chiefs of Staff formally recommending 'the withdrawal of the Eastern Mediterranean Fleet to Gibraltar as soon as it is apparent that French control of the Western Mediterranean is about to be lost to us'.[9] The draft, which enjoyed Pound's blessing, argued that the reasons given by the COS as recently as 27 May for keeping the Fleet in the eastern Mediterranean – to maintain economic pressure on the Axis, to secure Egypt and act as a stabilising influence on Turkey and other countries of the region – were all now invalidated. It was apparent that Turkey 'has little or no intention of honouring her obligations [under a Treaty of Mutual Assistance signed by her, France and Britain in 1939]; that Egypt is also equally dilatory and that the setbacks which the allied cause has suffered during the last few weeks have so shaken the confidence of the smaller nations in our ability to achieve victory that the presence of a British Fleet in the Eastern Mediterranean can do little to influence the political situation'. Moreover, the purposes of blockade could be fulfilled merely by blocking the Suez Canal.

The Director of Plans went on to urge strongly that from the point of view of 'purely naval strategy the position of the Mediterranean Fleet at Alexandria is unsound for the following reasons':

(a) It does not lie between the Italian Fleet and our vital Atlantic trade routes.
(b) With France out of the war, an increasingly heavy scale of Italian and German air attack can be brought to bear on the Fleet both at sea and in harbour.
(c) Alexandria lacks adequate repair facilities; our Fleet will be a wasting asset and will not be available to reinforce our forces in the vital areas at home and in the Atlantic.

The Chiefs of Staff referred this hottest of strategic potatoes to the Joint Planning Sub-Committee for urgent report.[10] By an irony it was the naval member of this committee, Captain C. S. Daniel, who had in his other capacity as Admiralty Director of Plans drafted the memorandum for Pound, albeit reluctantly.[11] Now he concurred with his fellow members of the Joint Planning Sub-Committee in submitting a report which effectively torpedoed Pound and Phillips.[12]

This report conceded that the German occupation of French Atlantic ports (and possibly of Spanish too) would heavily increase the scale of attack on Britain's Atlantic trade; that extra battleships for escorting Atlantic convoys could only come from the Mediterranean Fleet; and that there was 'from the purely naval point of view in relation to the war at sea as a whole . . . a strong case for withdrawing our Fleet from the Eastern Mediterranean at once . . .' But it pointed out that there were highly important military, economic and political factors to be weighed also. The British army in Egypt was designed to defeat the Italians in the Western Desert; it was not strong enough to defend the coast from Mersa Matruh to Haifa against seaborne landings. The withdrawal of the Fleet 'would be interpreted throughout the Middle East as a sign of weakness. It would probably involve, almost at once, an internal security problem in Iraq . . .' It would leave Turkey more open to German pressure. Moreover, 'a military withdrawal from the Middle East (which might ultimately be forced on us if the Fleet were withdrawn for a long period) would lose us our position in South East Europe, in Palestine and Transjordan and throughout the Middle East. It would complicate our position in India and would increase the temptation to which Japan was subject to attack our Far Eastern possessions . . .' Then again, the effect of a withdrawal on South Africa, Australia, New Zealand and India 'might be discouraging'. And the loss of control over Egypt and Iraq would mean that the blockade of the Axis would be 'seriously prejudiced'. Since the Joint Planners did not consider that 'the withdrawal of the Fleet is, at present, a vital necessity from the naval point of view', they came to the conclusion that the political, economic and military reasons for keeping the Fleet in the eastern Mediterranean outweighed the purely naval arguments for pulling it out.[13]

It will be seen that whereas for the Admiralty Britain's own survival as a European island in a death grapple with Germany constituted the supreme question, the Joint Planners were overwhelmingly concerned with Britain's traditional world-wide imperial position and obligations.

The Joint Planners' report was naturally not at all to Pound's liking, and after 'a full discussion' on 18 June,[14] the COS instructed the Joint Planners to give it further consideration, especially in regard to the future of the French Fleet, the implications of Spain turning hostile, and the oil position in the Middle East; in particular the security of the Haifa and Syrian pipeline terminals. In the meantime Cunningham had replied personally to Pound's signal of 16 June advocating withdrawal of his Fleet to Gibraltar in characteristically forthright terms:

that although I considered it feasible to move the faster portion of the fleet westward from Alexandria through the Mediterranean and the rest through the Suez Canal, the effects of this withdrawal would mean such a landslide in territory and prestige that I earnestly hoped such a decision would never have to be taken. As already pointed out, the Commander-in-Chief, Middle East [General Sir Archibald Wavell] considered Egypt would become untenable soon after the departure of the fleet. Added to that Malta, Cyprus and Palestine could no longer be held, while the Moslem world would regard it as surrender . . . I was fully aware of the paramount importance of our Atlantic trade and home defence, but . . . I felt that with our present forces we should be able to safeguard these in addition to maintaining the Eastern Mediterranean. The Italian battle fleet had so far shown no signs of activity, and from all the indications available to me it did not seem that they were yet considering serious fighting. I was of the opinion that the battleships we had were sufficient to contain the Italian heavy ships with something in hand, and that the route to Malta could be opened when required.[15]

The Prime Minister, for his part, would have none of Pound's and Phillips's doubts. For him it went without saying that the present British position in the Mediterranean and Middle East must be maintained and strengthened; after all, here remained the only land fronts where British armies could meet the enemy in battle. In his view the theatre presented splendid opportunities for taking the offensive by land and sea against Italy just as soon as her expected invasion of Egypt had been defeated; it offered the hope of early victories to encourage an embattled British nation. It could eventually serve as the base for grander strategic combinations against the Axis powers. After all, the Mediterranean had for centuries offered inspiration to British 'blue water' strategists seeking to exploit sea-power as an alternative to a Continental commitment. Here Nelson's fleet had enabled British armies to inflict their first defeats on Bona-parte's troops – in Palestine in 1799, Egypt in 1801 and southern Italy in 1806. Here Churchill himself as First Lord of the Admiralty in the Great War had pursued his vision of beating Germany via the back door of the Dardanelles by means of Allied seapower; and it was here too that Lloyd George had wanted to use seapower to establish fighting fronts in the Balkans and Anatolia; here at Salonika where the Allies had in fact established such a front in 1916–18, yet another scene of Great War stalemate.

On 23 June, in his capacity of Minister of Defence, Churchill formally vetoed the proposal to withdraw the Fleet from the eastern Mediterranean; and on 3 July the Chiefs of Staff drafted a memor-andum (later endorsed by Churchill and the Defence Committee and despatched to Cs-in-C and British representatives abroad) confirming the intention to hold the Middle East, and especially Iraq, Palestine, Aden, Egypt and Sudan, and stating: 'It is intended to retain the fleet in the Eastern Mediterranean as long as possible.'[16]

In this way a fundamental, even if in the circumstances probably inevitable, grand-strategic choice came to be made – bearing out Lord Kitchener's dictum in 1915: 'We cannot make war as we ought; we can only make it as we can.'[17] The decision reversed the pre-war order of global priorities, and opened the way for the Mediterranean and Middle East to become the main focus of the British Empire's war-making for nearly four years, thereby sucking in an ever-swelling military and logistic investment. By this grand-strategic choice Britain committed herself to fighting Italy in defence of an imperial lifeline which in any case she could no longer use; a war in direct defence of no economically or sentimentally important part of the British Empire; a war unrelated to the United Kingdom's own direct strategic interests as an island 22 miles off the north-western coast of a European continent occupied by Nazi Germany, and dependent for life itself on the North Atlantic sea lanes. Thus it was that Britain, unable in her present impotence to slug it out with Hitler, found herself reduced to trying to kick his dog Mussolini – the inglorious dénouement of British 'total strategy' pursued during the two decades since the victorious days of 1918 when Field-Marshal Haig with an army of more than 50 divisions on the decisive front of the Great War had played the major part in driving Imperial Germany to sue for an armistice.

A month after the commitment to the Mediterranean and Middle East had been made Churchill spelt out the implications for the Far East and Pacific in letters to the Prime Ministers of Australia and New Zealand. In the first phase of an Anglo-Japanese war, he wrote:

> . . . we should of course defend Singapore, which if attacked – which is unlikely – ought to stand a long siege. We should also be able to base on Ceylon a battle-cruiser and a fast aircraft-carrier, which, with all the Australian and New Zealand cruisers and destroyers, which would return to you, would act as a very powerful deterrent upon the hostile raiding cruisers.
>
> We are about to reinforce with more first-class units the Eastern Mediterranean Fleet. This fleet could of course at any time be sent through the Canal into the Indian Ocean, or to relieve Singapore. We do not want to do this, even if Japan declares war, until it is found to be vital to your safety. Such a transference would entail the complete loss of the Middle East, and all prospect of beating Italy in the Mediterranean would be gone . . .[18]

For the British Empire in the Far East and Pacific, for the Royal Navy wherever its ships floated, but above all for the Mediterranean

Fleet, it now only remained to live with the consequences of Churchill's choice of grand-strategic priority.

In the thick heat of evening on 7 July 1940, the Mediterranean Fleet slipped its moorings in Alexandria harbour, slid past Vice-Admiral Godfroy's disarmed French ships, and headed for the open sea. Its purpose was to sweep into the central Mediterranean in order to cover the passage of two convoys from Malta back to Alexandria, taking it into waters which for Mussolini must be a most sensitive area of his proclaimed 'Mare Nostrum'. Cunningham, flying his flag in the battleship HMS Warspite, had with him the battleships Malaya and Royal Sovereign, the aircraft carrier Eagle, the 6-inch gun cruisers Orion, Neptune, Sydney (Australian), Gloucester and Liverpool, and seventeen destroyers. A little after 0800 on 8 July – an ultramarine sea a-glitter in bright sunshine, the customary Mediterranean escort of plunging dolphins and leaping flying-fish – Cunningham received a report from a British submarine, HMS Phoenix, that at 0515 she had sighted two Italian battleships and four destroyers some 200 miles to the eastwards of Malta, and steering south. Cunningham guessed that these ships were escorting a convoy from Italy to Tripolitania; he therefore instructed the Vice-Admiral, Malta, to despatch flying-boats to shadow them, and himself steered to the north-westwards at 20 knots.

All too soon the new nature of sea warfare declared itself – first the Italian reconnaissance aircraft glinting high up in the blue; then, within around an hour, the bombers, flying at around 12,000 feet, and soon after that, the erupting foam of bomb explosions round the British men of war. Through the day bombers from Dodecanese airfields came and went; but mercifully only hit the cruiser Gloucester. As Cunningham reported to Pound in a private letter on his return to base, 'GLOUCESTER took a bomb on her compass platform. Such bad luck! Killed everyone on the bridge and some below it. She can steer from for'ard but has to control her fire from aft. The fore director circuits were just mashed up.'[19]

At 1510 a Malta flying-boat also reported seeing two enemy battleships steering southwards, now in a position about a hundred miles north-west of Benghazi, in Cyrenaica, and accompanied by six cruisers and seven destroyers – almost certainly covering an important convoy. Cunningham swung his fleet on to a course towards the Italian fleet base at Taranto, in the toe of Italy, in order to get between the enemy and his base. At dawn on the following day, 9 July, the Eagle flew off three reconnaissance aircraft. During the forenoon these aircraft and the Malta flying-boats confirmed that an enemy fleet of at least two battleships, twelve cruisers and many destroyers was at sea some 50 miles off Cape Spartivento (the 'toenail', as it might be said, of Italy), and some 90 miles to the westward of the British Fleet. Although Cunningham had with him only four 6-inch gun cruisers, including the damaged *Gloucester*, and was handicapped by the slow speed of his unmodernised Great War battleship *Royal Sovereign*, he steered to engage.

Towards 1500 – a north-easterly breeze, a Mediterranean summer sky lightly stippled with high cloud, visibility ten to fifteen miles – the *Orion* and *Neptune*, scouting ahead of the battleships, sighted Italian cruisers and destroyers. At 1508 the *Neptune* (Captain Rory O'Connor, RN) became the first British warship in the Mediterranean since Nelson's time to make the signal: 'Enemy battle fleet in sight.' At 1513 a column of four 8-inch gun enemy cruisers opened fire on the 7th Cruiser Squadron (Vice-Admiral J. C. Tovey). Soon *Warspite*'s 15-inch guns were firing at a range of 26,000 yards in support of Tovey's hard-pressed ships. At 1530 the Italian cruisers turned away behind a smoke screen. At 1553 *Warspite* opened fire on the leading Italian battleship. Shortly afterwards both Italian heavy ships were in action, their salvoes straddling the British flagship at extreme range. But Cunningham enjoyed the satisfaction of watching 'the great splashes of our 15-inch salvoes straddling the target', and then, at 1600, of seeing 'the great orange-coloured flash of a heavy explosion at the base of the enemy flagship's funnels. It was followed by an upheaval of smoke, and I knew she had been hit at the prodigious range of thirteen miles.'[20]

Following the precedent of so many enemy admirals down the centuries in the face of the Royal Navy's broadsides, the Italian flag officer, Admiral Riccardi, now sought refuge in escape, retiring behind a smoke screen that drifted in a dense pall across the western horizon. A spotting aircraft from *Warspite* reported that the Italian fleet was making for the Straits of Messina at high speed and in great confusion, their disarray heightened by being bombed by mistake by their own shore-based aircraft. Cunningham attempted to work round behind the enemy smoke screen, but by the time his destroyers got clear, the Italian fleet had disappeared. For the next two and three-quarter hours the Italian Air Force (Regia Aeronautica) carried out mass attacks on Cunningham's fleet, concentrating on the flagship with her distinctive slab-sided bridge structure and the carrier *Eagle*. Each were bombed five times, but without damage.

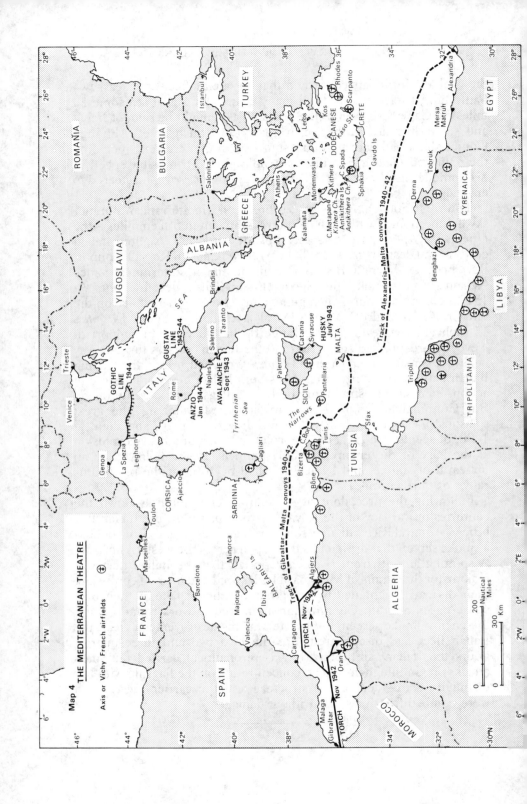

Map 4
THE MEDITERRANEAN THEATRE

Axis or Vichy French airfields ⊕

It was most frightening [Cunningham wrote later]. At times a ship would completely disappear behind the great splashes, to emerge as though from a thick, dark wood of enormous fir trees. I was seriously alarmed for the old ships *Royal Sovereign* and *Eagle*, which were not well protected. A clutch of those eggs hitting either must have sent her to the bottom.[21]

Small and old though Cunningham's only carrier, HMS *Eagle* (Captain A. R. M. Bridge, RN) was, with only seventeen Swordfish and two Gladiators aboard, it gave a convincing demonstration of the potential of seaborne airpower in fleet operations by launching invaluable air searches and by hitting a cruiser and sinking a destroyer. Cunningham reported to the First Sea Lord in a personal letter on 3 August 1940:

EAGLE's work has been above all praise. The greatest credit naturally goes to Bridge, the Captain . . . Quiet, imperturbable and thorough, he has carried out his flying programmes to the minute whether bombs were falling thick about him or not.

To me EAGLE's survival unhit is nothing short of a miracle as she has been a special object of attack.

[Commander] Keighley Peach is in charge of flying, but when we got a brace of Sea Gladiators, he volunteered to go up himself and, although shot through the leg the first day, brought down two Italian planes the second. Not bad for a man of 38 years old.[22]

In the evening of 9 July Cunningham steamed to within 25 miles of the Calabrian coast before abandoning the chase and making for the waters south of Malta in order to fulfil the original purpose of the sortie, that of covering the movement of two convoys, one fast and one slow, from Malta to Alexandria. In one of these were travelling the C-in-C's own wife and two daughters. During the return voyage from 9 to 12 July Cunningham took his ships far to the southward of the enemy air bases in the Dodecanese, only to run into relentless attack instead from bombers based in the Italian colony of Libya. At one moment on 12 July 24 heavy bombs fell along the port side of *Warspite* simultaneously, and another twelve on her starboard bow, all of them mercifully just out of line. Cunningham records that on the same day he saw the *Sydney* 'completely disappear in a line of towering pillars of spray as high as church steeples. When she emerged I signalled: "Are you all right?" to which came the rather dubious reply from that stout-hearted Australian, Captain J. A. Collins, "I hope so." '[23] In Cunningham's words in his letter to Pound, 'Literally we have had to fight our way back to Alexandria against air attack.'[24]

To Cunningham the sortie to Calabria and back had therefore

offered a grimly sobering tutorial on the impact of land-based air power on naval operations, and on the technological shortcomings of his own fleet, the legacy of the years of faith in disarmament as a means of imperial defence. Of his four battleships only the flagship *Warspite* had been modernised in terms of armament, propulsion and armoured protection. In his private letter to the First Sea Lord summing up the lessons of the action, he drew attention to what he called a 'serious thing': 'Their [the enemy's] battleships and 8-inch cruisers straddled us comfortably at 26,000 yards and more and I don't think any ship but WARSPITE crossed the target. Neither MALAYA nor ROYAL SOVEREIGN ever got into range, the latter's full speed being 18 knots!'[25] This was 6 knots slower than *Warspite*'s maximum of 24 knots – a speed itself 3 knots slower than Italy's reconstructed older battleships and hopelessly outstripped by the 30 knots maximum of Italy's two new ships, *Vittorio Veneto* and *Littorio*, now coming into service. Moreover, the *Royal Sovereign*, the least modernised of Cunningham's battleships, was also particularly vulnerable to bombing because of insufficient deck armour. Wrote Cunningham in his letter to Pound:

> My heart was in my mouth lest ROYAL SOVEREIGN should be hit, as if she had taken one of the nests of bombs that were dropping about, I think she'd have gone to the bottom or, at any rate, as we were only 25 miles from the Calabrian coast we should have had to sink her. In fact I don't think it is a bit of good taking these unprotected old battleships up the coast unless we are fully prepared to lose one.
>
> Don't think I am discouraged. I am not a bit, but with our facilities at Alexandria also within bombing range, the damaged ship is a nightmare, especially one 900 miles away from her base.[26]

When it came to cruisers, the pre-war Admiralty's decision to spread its ration of tonnage under the 1930 London Naval Treaty over more 6-inch gun cruisers rather than fewer and bigger 8-inch ships now put Cunningham at a further disadvantage. As he explained to the First Sea Lord:

> Tovey was also up against six to seven 8-inch cruisers and about four to five 6-inch cruisers and, of course could make no headway [to get within range] as they [the Italians] obscured themselves in smoke at about 22,000 yards. I know I said I could do without 8-inch cruisers, but I would dearly like the YORK and EXETER [32 knot ships of around 8,400 tons armed with six 8-inch guns].[27]

These cruisers so wished for by Cunningham dated from 1928–

29; three further vessels of the same class had, however, been cancelled in 1930 by MacDonald's Labour government.[28]

And the little aircraft carrier *Eagle* (first commissioned in 1923), despite all her enterprise off Calabria, could not provide the effective air cover and strike force of which Cunningham stood in such urgent need. 'We want some fighters badly,' he told Pound. 'At the moment EAGLE carries two Gladiators on her upper deck – Fleet Air Arm spares – and one of them brought down a bomber two days ago, but died in doing it.'[29]

Cunningham concluded this letter to Pound by summing up his weaknesses and his needs in terms which demonstrated that the action off Calabria had indeed taught him sobering lessons:

(i) With my force as at present constituted I do not say that I cannot go and command the Central Mediterranean, but there is considerable risk of losing an old battleship and, unless the object to be attained is worth losing a battleship, I do not feel we should approach, or even engage the enemy fleet under, their coast in daylight.

(ii) I feel I must have some fighters in a good and, if possible, armoured carrier for the protection of the fleet.

(iii) I must have at least one more capital ship and a cruiser or two, which can reply to the enemy's fire at his own range.[30]

Nevertheless, though he did not say so, even these additions to his strength – should he be accorded them – would not redress his sheer inferiority of numbers in all classes of vessel except battleships. In round terms he was at present outnumbered by the Italian Navy by seven heavy cruisers to none, by twelve light cruisers to nine, by 59 fleet destroyers to 25, and by 98 submarines to 24.[31]

And yet Cunningham enjoyed some advantages. The first of them – the ability to read the high-grade Italian naval cyphers – proved alas shortlived. These had been broken as far back as 1937.[32] Thanks to the British ability to read signals sent in the general Italian Navy codebook, no fewer than ten Italian submarines were located and sunk or captured between 10 June and 5 July 1940 – a major blow to the morale of the Italian submarine arm, helping to account for its poor subsequent achievement despite its numbers.[33] On 29 June the Royal Navy recovered the new naval codebook for the Italian equivalent of the 'Enigma' machine (less complex than the German, with four rotors and no plug board) from the submarine *Uebi Scebeli* west of Crete. This ability to read the enemy's high-grade cyphers, coupled with monitoring of his radio traffic by direction-finding stations and low-grade Sigint, had enabled Cunningham clearly to recognise the Italian plan for the action off Calabria for what it was: a trap in which the British fleet was supposed to be destroyed by submarine and bombing attack, but one into which the British admiral deliberately walked 'with his eyes open'.[34] In Cunningham's own words: 'We intercepted most of the Italian Admiral's signals as we had the decode on board from one of the sunk submarines and most interesting they were.'[35]

Unfortunately this priceless source of Intelligence dried up from July 1940 onwards. On 5 July the Italians introduced a new cypher for submarines, and on 17 July new cypher tables for their surface navy, and on 1 October new tables for their top secret naval cyphers. Moreover they also changed their low-grade codes and cyphers, making even these more difficult to break. Never again, except for a brief period in 1941, were the British able to read Italian signals traffic; henceforward the Mediterranean Fleet, like the Home Fleet in 1939–40, had to sweep the seas virtually blind,[36] guided only by low-grade Sigint's radio traffic analysis, which was 'at best inadequate and on occasions led to false conclusions'.[37] This frustrating blindness was worsened by the severe shortage of photo-reconnaissance aircraft in the Mediterranean theatre.[38]

The collapse of British Intelligence with regard to the Italian Navy enabled the enemy to pass 690,000 tons of shipping in fast convoys to Libya between June and December 1940 with only two per cent loss,[39] while between June and October the Mediterranean Fleet itself made no fewer than sixteen sweeps in search of the enemy but only sighted his ships three times.[40]

Another factor lay behind these figures: Italy's own Intelligence services and aerial reconnaissance enabled her naval high command to keep continual tabs on British fleet movements, and in this way time and route their own convoys and fleet sorties accordingly.[41] 'Our principal trouble,' wrote Cunningham to Pound on 3 August 1940, 'is that we cannot move without our movements being known. There is no doubt that the Italians have now got a very efficient reconnaissance going. They send planes over Alexandria every day and no force in the last three weeks has been at sea without being discovered and bombed, in some cases very heavily.'[42]

However, although the superlative Intelligence Cunningham had enjoyed at the time of the action off Calabria had proved so brief an asset, others of his advantages endured throughout the Mediterranean war. The first lay in the professional efficiency and fighting spirit of his Fleet, hastily reassembled though it had been. In contrast to the *arriviste* Italian Navy, with its scant history of battle (even if it could

look back to the naval traditions of Italian city states like Genoa and
Venice) and its tendency to spend too much time in port rather than
at sea, the Mediterranean Fleet embodied a tradition of seamanship
and victory in close-quarters attack that went back through its triumphs
under Nelson, its greatest ever commander, through the sea fights
against the royal French Navy in the wars of the eighteenth century,
to the Commonwealth's 'General at Sea', Blake, in his 1654 cruise
against the Barbary pirates. The Royal Navy had asserted its moral
domination in that first major encounter off Calabria, when Cunningham's ships, for all their technical inferiority, steamed straight
for an enemy, who, in the C-in-C's words, 'as soon as WARSPITE
hit him in the ribs at 26,000 yards . . . screamed for a smoke screen,
ordered 25 knots and turned 90 degrees away'.[43] On 19 July, the
Australian cruiser *Sydney* repeated the lesson by attacking two Italian
cruisers north of Crete and reducing one of them, the *Bartolomeo
Colleoni*, to a hulk dead in the water, later sunk by British destroyers.

Cunningham's second greatest asset – and certainly his Fleet's
greatest asset – lay in his own qualities of leadership. During the
Napoleonic Wars old Lord St Vincent had pronounced that the
Mediterranean command required 'an officer of splendour';[44] and in
1940 this is exactly what it had.

Cunningham had been appointed in May 1939 in succession to Sir
Dudley Pound on the latter's elevation to First Sea Lord. The voyage
out from Marseille to Alexandria in the cruiser *Penelope* had come as
a welcome liberation from his job as Deputy Chief of the Naval Staff
to the centralising Backhouse.

> I felt great joy at being at sea again steaming at high speed in perfect
> weather to what I have always considered as the finest appointment the
> Royal Navy has to offer [he remembered later]. I probably knew the
> Mediterranean as well as any naval officer of my generation. Of my
> forty-one years' sea-going service since leaving the *Britannia*, I had spent
> about ten-and-a-half years there in different ships, a goodish slice of a
> lifetime.[45]

In the forenoon of 5 June 1939 he had hoisted his flag (the St
George's Cross of England) in HMS *Warspite*, and all the responsibilities of a great fleet with a war in the offing had now become his; the
top of the ladder he had started to climb in 1893 when he first donned
the uniform of the Royal Navy as a cadet in the training ship *Britannia*.

Cunningham was 56 years old. A stern visage ruddy from the sun
and salt-laden winds; a grim mouth and a jawline like a battleship's

bow; a searching stare – all expressed a formidable authority. Yet it was a visage saved from arrogance or pomp by a hint of humour and kindliness about the eyes. Cunningham stood some 5 feet 10 inches: a spare and muscular body tense with a Nelsonian impatience for action; an impatience often manifested to his wary staff by a tigerish pacing of the deck. Cunningham's impact on the Fleet after Pound's somewhat reserved personality and bureaucratic methods had been drastic and immediate. When his staff presented him with elaborate Pound-style draft orders for a six-day exercise, he wrote across the draft in red ink: 'Too long, too complicated. Cut.' The staff obediently reduced the orders to fifteen pages, a fraction of their original bulk. This time Cunningham wrote in the margin: 'I agree with the second sentence of paragraph 29, and little else.' When the staff looked up the paragraph, they found that the sentence in question read: 'The Fleet will be manoeuvred by the Commander-in-Chief.' And it was – without any written orders at all, and entirely by visual signals.[46]

For Cunningham, like Nelson, was a superb handler of ships and squadrons. Lord Mountbatten later recorded his impression (when a captain) of Cunningham as Rear-Admiral, Destroyers, in the Mediterranean in 1934 personally manoeuvring 36 ships: 'In spite of his rather red and watery eyes he always saw everything first, long before the officer of the watch, the look out, or the Yeoman of Signals. No move escaped his eagle-eye. It was the greatest one-man performance I have seen on the bridge of a ship . . .'[47]

Yet this tactical skill in controlling many vessels did not mean a rigid and remote Jutland-style central direction of the Fleet in action. Cunningham wrote later:

> The time for central direction is in previous exact and detailed tactical training, so that every commander will know, should he be in doubt, exactly how the Commander-in-Chief is thinking. Nelson's instructions – drafted eleven days before Trafalgar – 'in case signals cannot be seen, or clearly understood, no captain can do very wrong if he places his ship alongside that of an enemy' is a nice case of a simple direction covering all eventualities.[48]

Nelson's restless urge to lay his ships alongside the enemy and destroy him utterly spoke straight to Cunningham's own temperament. A colleague recalled that 'A.B.C's most conspicuous quality was his intense spirit of attack – or the offensive, if you prefer it – which he brought to bear on whatever he undertook. He could be, and often was, the most biting driver; but never without acute perception that the thing could be done the way he wanted it, and, what is more, would be done.'[49]

An amendment made by Cunningham to the draft Mediterranean Fleet Tactical Instructions breathes this ruthless spirit of aggression. As drafted by the staff, one paragraph prescribed (because the Italians were laying mines from their coast out to the 200 fathom line): 'If the enemy Fleet is damaged and retires, the British Fleet is to pursue relentlessly until the 200 fathom line is reached.' The C-in-C scrawled a correction in the margin: '. . . until the enemy is sunk. Damn the 200 fathom line! Where the enemy battle fleet can go, we can follow.'[50] Here was an echo down two centuries of Hawke chasing Conflans into Quiberon Bay in 1759 despite a following gale and a lee shore.

Cunningham believed that moral dominance over the enemy was fundamental to success. Soon after the Calabria action, when ships' companies were tired and boilers were due for cleaning, a report came in that a very old and feeble Italian torpedo boat was on passage from Taranto to Tobruk in Libya. Cunningham ordered: 'Send out a division of destroyers and sink her.' When his staff protested on the grounds that the destroyers should be cleaning boilers and that anyway the torpedo boat presented no threat, Cunningham replied: 'We must never let the enemy think that it is safe to go to sea; we must make him think that he is only safe when in harbour. Contrariwise, our Fleet must feel that it is natural for them to be at sea. Go on, send the destroyers and sink the poor inoffensive bugger!'[51]

Cunningham, Scots by descent, came of the middle class, a son of the Professor of Anatomy at the Royal College of Surgeons in Dublin, a dedicated professional through and through. Long service in destroyers rather than battleships, the more usual and fashionable avenue to flag rank, had fostered and formed his special qualities as a leader. As he himself wrote in 1930 when he was actually commanding the new battleship HMS *Rodney*:

Big ship time is said to be necessary to us all. I have never found it so. What I do know is that any captain will tell you that the best officers to be found in big ships have come from submarines or destroyers. It is my experience here. I would far rather be first lieutenant of a destroyer than about tenth down the list in a battleship.

I have always maintained there is more real discipline in destroyers than big ships, and of course we are always in so much more touch with our men. The skipper of a destroyer gets soaked to the skin on the bridge just the same as any sailor, but his opposite number [in a battleship] walks dry-skinned from his luxurious cabin where he has been sitting aloof from all goings on, to an equally luxurious bridge.[52]

[223]

Years later men were vividly to remember the young Cunningham in his early destroyer commands – 'the red-faced Lieutenant-Commander on the *Scorpion*'s bridge', with 'markedly penetrating blue eyes',[53] is the recollection of Captain Francis Flynn. His reputation as a martinet given to terrifying explosions of anger and luridly Anglo-Saxon language whenever disappointed in his expectation of faultless performance became a legend in the Navy. And yet there was another side to him, as his Gunnery Officer in the *Rodney* remembered: 'Behind all his ferocity there was the kindest heart imaginable. I think it was these two "opposites", laced with an almost boyish sense of humour, that captivated and bound us to him.'[54]

Cunningham was no C-in-C to do his own staff work, an aspect of his profession which bored him vastly; rather he was happy to delegate the detailed working out of operational plans and administrative arrangements, in particular to his extremely able and hard-working Chief of Staff, Rear-Admiral A. U. Willis, slight, sharp-nosed, quick-minded. It was a relationship between executive commander and senior staff officer not unlike that customary in the old German Army of the Great War.

As early as 1922, when Cunningham was commanding a destroyer flotilla, he had formulated for himself three principles of conduct, expressed in phrases which he would often repeat for the benefit of those about him, and which stuck in the mind of at least one of them down the years: 'Duty is the first business of a sea officer'; 'N.D.B.G.Z. (No difficulty baffles great zeal)', and 'Intelligent anticipation must be your watchword.'[55] As Commander-in-Chief, Mediterranean, in 1940, Cunningham, despite his unstinting fulfilment of the first of his maxims, was to find the other two tested to the edge of destruction.

The strategic patterns of the long struggle had been revealed in that first sortie to the Calabrian coast; patterns determined above all by the shape of the Mediterranean itself in relation to Italian territory and British bases. The Mediterranean is well over 2,000 miles long from Gibraltar in the west to Palestine and Syria in the east, but only 500–600 miles across at its widest points, from Algeria (French) to the Riviera coast of France and Italy in its western basin, and from the Libyan coast to Corfu in its eastern basin. The two basins are separated by the so-called 'Sicilian Narrows', less than 100 miles across, between Sicily and Tunisia. Italy's north–south sea routes to the Libyan ports of Tripoli, Benghazi and Tobruk were consequently short, easily covered by land-based aircraft as well as by the Italian battlefleet, and distant from the Royal Navy's main fleet base at

Alexandria by at least two days' steaming. The British line of communication through the Mediterranean, however, followed virtually the inland sea's entire length, from Gibraltar (base of Admiral Somerville's Force H) to Alexandria and Suez; and the central third of the distance lay between Libya to the southwards and Sicily and southern Italy to the northwards – well within close range of Italian air and fleet bases, and running through the particularly dangerous Sicilian Narrows, mined out to the 200 fathom line. This was why the Mediterranean had had to be abandoned as a route for normal merchant shipping by way of precaution even before Italy entered the war; this was why Pound reckoned that to pass vital military supplies right through would entail major fleet actions.

Thus from the very beginning of the campaign neither side enjoyed 'command of the sea' as formulated in the writings of naval theorists like Mahan and Corbett. Instead the Mediterranean was a disputed zone where each side sought to fulfil certain tasks – above all, the running through of essential convoys – and at the same time prevent the enemy from doing likewise. The key to the whole strategic pattern lay in the island fortress of Malta, lying some 60 miles south of Sicily and under the British flag since 1800. It supplied a refuge and refuelling point for warships or merchant ships midway between Gibraltar and Alexandria, and a staging post for the Royal Air Force aircraft in transit; it could serve as the base for submarine and light surface forces striking at Italian convoys plying to and from Libya; a base too for invaluable air searches and photo-reconnaissance. For all these reasons Malta was to remain the focus of Britain's strategy in the Mediterranean for the next three years; sometimes a great asset, sometimes a supreme problem.

As the longtime base of the Mediterranean Fleet Malta ought to have been by the summer of 1940 fully fortified and equipped with all necessary ship repair facilities, and with a powerful anti-aircraft defence and fighter cover. Thanks to the ravages of pre-war policy it was none of these things. At the outbreak of war with Italy only 34 heavy and eight light anti-aircraft guns had been installed out of an approved scale of 112 and 60 respectively. There was only one radar set, and only three fighter aircraft, obsolete biplane Gloster Gladiators nicknamed 'Faith', 'Hope' and 'Charity'.[56] Here, in Malta's vulnerability, lay therefore one of the worst and most unceasing of the anxieties crowding in on Cunningham. To run convoys in and out of Malta in order to build up its defences, reinforce it with fresh aircraft so that it could survive ever fiercer air attack, and keep it supplied with essential food, fuel, ammunition and other materials, would

[225]

demand hazardous large-scale operations by both the Mediterranean Fleet and Force H – a major commitment of naval resources.

Yet whereas Cunningham for his part could concentrate his attention and his ships on the struggle within the Mediterranean, his opposite number at Gibraltar, Vice-Admiral Sir James Somerville (Flag Officer, Force H), could be, and sometimes was, called to operate far outside that sea as well as inside. Nonetheless, his principal roles were to bar the Straits of Gibraltar to enemy or Vichy-French ships seeking to enter or leave the Mediterranean; to escort eastbound convoys to Malta or to rendezvous with Cunningham's Fleet; and conduct offensive sorties in the western basin of the Mediterranean against the Italian Navy or shore targets.

Small of stature and with open, boyish features which belied his 58 years, Somerville was renowned in the Navy for his salty – some thought coarse – sense of humour and racy speech larded with foul language. Such ebullience manifested his derisive dislike of stuffiness and pompous consciousness of rank; it enabled him to achieve an easy rapport with younger officers and the lower deck. Himself quick-thinking and impatient, he was easily irritated by minds that moved more slowly and deliberately than his. However, the bouncy bonhomie consorted with a high professionalism and technical awareness; Somerville was a very modern admiral. As the Royal Navy's Director of Signals before the war he had energetically pushed on development of the Type 271 anti-submarine search radar (see below, p. 256–7), which was to prove one of the most valuable items of equipment in the Battle of the Atlantic. Now as flag officer of a force including an aircraft carrier, he insisted on flying with his aircrews in order the better to understand their tasks and problems. Although Somerville was by instinct as much of a fighting admiral as Andrew Cunningham, he tempered pugilism with a cool operational judgment. This made him less willing to gamble than Cunningham, as had become clear during that first joint operation in July 1940 to bring the convoys back from Malta to Alexandria which resulted in the action off Calabria.

Before the operation Cunningham had urged Somerville to launch carrier air strikes on Italian ships in Naples, Trapani, Palermo or Messina, but this proposal in Somerville's estimation came into the category of what he called 'wild adventures'. He had agreed instead to attack Cagliari in Sardinia, a nearer objective, but met such ferocious bombing south of Minorca on the way out that he decided to turn back to Gibraltar, on the grounds that the *Ark Royal*, one of the Royal Navy's at present only two modern carriers, was too precious to risk for the sake of a mere diversion.[57] As Somerville expressed it in a

[226]

letter to his wife: 'Anyhow I'm quite convinced that what I did was right though the Admiralty have maintained a frigid silence on the subject.'[58] Writing again three days later, he told her that he detected 'a certain critical note that I didn't adventure enough the other day. Well it seems to me just a matter of balancing up what is worth while and what is not, and before we throw a party they must give me some idea of how much they want to spend . . .'[59] But Somerville was correct about the 'critical note': by his aborting of the mission the Admiralty and even more Churchill himself were confirmed in their impression at the time of the Oran operation on 3 July – five days before the Calabrian sortie – that the Flag Officer, Force H, lacked the right pugilistic instincts. Yet the ships' companies of Force H itself did not share such doubts. According to a private letter from a newly retired admiral to the First Sea Lord in December 1940, when Somerville was under severe criticism (see below, p. 242):

> . . . James Somerville has instilled in his command a wonderful sense of trust in himself and admiration for his leadership – if only one analyses all that he has been asked to do, he has done it really well . . .
> . . . taking it by and large, he has done damned well and has got a jolly good team working under him who have every confidence in him. I remember so well when he was RA (D) [Rear Admiral, Destroyers] how all the Destroyer Flotillas thought the world of him and he pushed them devilish hard.[60]

In the event, however, the differing professional temperaments and diverging responsibilities of the two British 'doorkeepers' (as Cunningham dubbed them) at the opposite ends of the Mediterranean did not affect their mutual respect or close and cordial working relationship; not least because even Cunningham's Drake-like raiding instincts had been somewhat cooled by the waterspouts raised by Italian bombs round his ships on his voyage home to Alexandria from Calabria. From July 1940 until March 1941 (when Britain was to send an expeditionary force to Greece) the central theme of the sea war in the Mediterranean was to be supplied by the closely coordinated joint operations by the Mediterranean Fleet and Force H to cover the 2,000 mile-long passage of vital convoys and naval reinforcements in the teeth of constant air attack and possible ambush by the Italian Fleet, a theme not however unmarred by Churchillian interventions.

On 1 August 1940, twelve Hurricane 8-gun monoplane fighters successfully landed at Malta from the ancient small carrier HMS *Argus* to reinforce the island's exiguous air defence. Yet to carry out this operation, codenamed 'Hurry', had involved almost the whole strength of the Mediterranean Fleet and Force H together. While Somerville with *Argus*, the battlecruiser *Hood*, the battleships *Valiant* and *Resolution*, two cruisers and ten destroyers sailed eastwards from Gibraltar to the flying-off position, Cunningham sought to divert the Italian Fleet and Air Force from moving to meet Force H in the western Mediterranean by a sortie from Alexandria to a position west of Crete with the carrier *Eagle* and the battleships *Malaya* and *Warspite* (flag). Cunningham also arranged for cruisers and destroyers already carrying out a sweep in the Aegean to make a well-timed feint westwards through the Kithera Channel; and for other ships to simulate an imminent attack on the island of Kastellorizo in the Dodecanese.

In the event the battleships and the *Eagle* had to return prematurely to Alexandria because of mechanical trouble with the *Malaya*. Yet this only served to heighten Italian uncertainty as to Cunningham's true intentions, so inducing the enemy to remain tucked up in harbour. In the meantime Somerville had been selling his own dummy to the enemy by detaching the *Ark Royal* (escorted by the *Hood*) to launch an air strike on Cagliari. In the early daylight of 2 August the force of eight Swordfish aircraft destroyed hangars and aircraft, started fires and laid mines inside the outer harbour. By 0445 that same morning the *Argus* reached her position for launching the Hurricanes, which, to a roar of Rolls-Royce Merlins across a quiet sea, took off for Malta. By 4 August Somerville's ships had safely returned to Gibraltar.

On 30 August was launched the next Mediterranean 'milk run' – 'Operation Hats' – this time with the object of passing major fleet reinforcements along the full length of the Mediterranean to Cunningham. For the First Sea Lord had taken due note of Cunningham's statement of his weaknesses and needs in his letter of 13 July, and had embarked on a general redeployment and strengthening of the British naval resources in the Mediterranean. Force H had been ordered back to England after 'Hurry' as part of this process; when Somerville returned to Gibraltar on 28 August, his command freshly consisted of the modernised battlecruiser *Renown*, the unmodernised battleship *Resolution*, the carrier *Ark Royal*, the cruiser HMS *Sheffield* and seven destroyers. Of these ships only the *Sheffield* was equipped with radar.[61] Cunningham himself was to be reinforced by the new armoured carrier *Illustrious*, the modernised battleship *Valiant*, and the anti-aircraft cruisers *Coventry* and *Calcutta*. *Illustrious*, *Valiant* and *Coventry* were all equipped with radar.

At 0845 on 30 August Somerville (flying his flag in *Renown*) put to sea from Gibraltar with the largest British fleet seen in the Mediterranean since the placid days of peacetime – the whole of Force H (except for *Resolution*; too slow), all the ships due to reinforce Cunningham, and seventeen destroyers of the 8th and 13th Destroyer Flotillas. Soon the great, gaunt Rock dwindled astern as Somerville shaped a course to eastwards at a speed of 15½ knots, zig-zagging as a precaution against submarines. The broad plan for 'Hats' was that Force H should accompany Cunningham's reinforcements as far as a position south-east of Sardinia before turning back to Gibraltar, whereupon the reinforcements would steam on alone through the Sicilian Narrows to a rendezvous with the Mediterranean Fleet.

Except for the destruction of two Italian reconnaissance floatplanes by Skuas from the *Ark Royal*, the day of 31 August passed quietly for Somerville's command. At 1400 clocks were advanced two hours to synchronise with the Zone 3 time kept by the Mediterranean Fleet. At 2150, when Somerville's command had reached 39° 30'N, 4° 01'E, the destroyers *Velox* and *Wishart* were detached to carry out 'Operation Squawk', another of the Royal Navy's carefully designed feints. When the two destroyers were north of the Balearic Islands and still steering to the north-east they were to make a series of radio signals during the night in order to mislead the Italians into thinking that Somerville's entire fleet was heading north-east for the Gulf of Genoa. The transmissions were also to serve the second purpose of covering the low-power signals from the *Ark Royal* during flying operations in the next phase of 'Hats', the launching of another strike on Cagliari. At 2200, under cover of dark, Somerville's force altered course without signal from north-east to south-east. At 0325 on 1 September, at a distance of 115 miles from Cagliari, the fleet altered course in order to fly off the strike force: nine Swordfish each armed with four 250lb general-purpose bombs and eight 25lb incendiary bombs. The aircraft formed up over flame floats dropped ten miles away from the fleet, and flew in to Cagliari through clear, starlit skies. At 0600 the Swordfish dropped their bombs on the airfield installations 300 feet below, lit up by drifting parachute flares. As the aircrews swung back towards the carrier they could see fires sparking and glowing behind them. By 0800 all the Swordfish had safely landed back on the carrier.

Somerville now altered course to the south-westwards with the object of deceiving the Italians into believing that the main objective of the British sortie from Gibraltar had been to attack Cagliari, and that the fleet was now returning to harbour. However, as Somerville wrote in his report later, 'As the Force was apparently not being shadowed at this time, it is probable that this ruse failed.'[62] At 1030 he changed course again to 080°. From this time onwards he maintained two fighter patrols of six aircraft each over the fleet, for he was now heading into the zone of maximum danger from the Italian Air Force. Yet the day passed without incident except for a tragic mistake whereby Fulmar fighters from *Illustrious* hit a British Hudson patrol aircraft.[63]

At 2200 on 1 September, in position 38° 06'N, 10° 51'E, roughly midway between the south-eastern tip of Sardinia and the western tip of Sicily, the reinforcements for Cunningham (designated 'Force F') parted company in the dark without signal and set course to the south-eastwards.

His principal task accomplished, Somerville now turned north and then west, increasing speed to 24 knots. In the dark small hours of 2 September the *Ark Royal*'s aircraft again attacked Cagliari – without loss but also without success because haze and low cloud obscured the target. At 0800 Somerville increased speed to 26 knots and headed westwards, reaching Gibraltar in the forenoon next day without having been attacked by Italian aircraft – much to his surprise, since he had been in effective range of the enemy's air bases for at least 48 hours, and also much to his regret, since he had prepared a welcome in the form of standing fighter patrols and a closely concentrated AA-gun defence which he had hoped would 'deliver a blow to the Italian Air Force which might have a telling and lasting effect'.[64]

In the meantime Cunningham had left Alexandria early in the forenoon of 30 August with *Warspite* (flag), *Malaya, Eagle, Orion, Sydney* and nine destroyers, his mean line of advance 310° at 16 knots.[65] At 1430 the Fleet was sighted and shadowed by an Italian Cant Z 510 aircraft, which was later shot down. Between 1650 and 1800, however, another shadower was heard high above. At noon next day the battlefleet rendezvoused with Tovey's 3rd Cruiser Squadron (*Kent, Gloucester* and *Liverpool*) south-west of Cape Matapan, on the southern coast of Greece. Cunningham had dovetailed into his movements during 'Hats' the passing of two stores ships and a tanker to Malta escorted by four destroyers, this convoy having sailed earlier. During the afternoon of 30 August Italian aircraft attacked the three merchant ships, badly damaging the steering gear of the stores ship *Cornwall* and starting a fire. Nonetheless her master, Captain F. C. Pretty, kept his station by steering with his engines. At 1600 Cunningham altered the Fleet's mean line of advance to 180° 'with the object of giving the impression that the Fleet had merely been covering an Aegean convoy, and was now returning to Alexandria . . .'

Thirteen minutes later there came a report from HMS *Eagle*'s search aircraft that the enemy battlefleet – two battleships, seven cruisers and some destroyers – lay 180 miles distant on a 210° bearing from the *Warspite* in her present position of 36° 01′N, 21° 08′E.

Cunningham now faced the dilemma of whether or not to steer to engage. It would be easy for the enemy to evade during the dark hours thanks to superior speed, while sending light forces to attack the Malta convoy. Cunningham therefore decided, in the words of his report, that 'he must return to protect the convoy during the night, ready to engage the enemy if he came on and hoping that daylight would bring a chance of action'. But next day a Royal Air Force flying-boat from Malta sighted the enemy warships at the entrance of the Gulf of Taranto heading for home, a disappointment to Cunningham, who had been looking forward to banging them about again. No Italian aircraft were seen that day, possibly because of Royal Air Force attacks on Libyan airfields or because of the destruction of the shadower the day before, while the Fleet steamed on westwards towards its rendezvous with its reinforcement ships. At 0800 on 2 September the mean line of advance was altered to 320° (position 35° 25′N, 13° 48′E), and an hour later the lookouts sighted the distinctive piled silhouette of the battleship *Valiant* and, even more welcome, the slab shape of *Illustrious* approaching after a safe passage through the Sicilian Narrows.

Now it was time to carry out the next task in this carefully welded multiple operation. While the Fleet cruised all day about 35 miles south of Malta, *Valiant*, *Coventry* and *Calcutta* put into Grand Harbour in order to land army and air force personnel and stores, including such desperately needed items as eight 3.7-inch anti-aircraft guns, predictors, height finders, replacement anti-aircraft gun barrels, 100 Bren light machine-guns and 10,000 rounds of Bofors ammunition.[66] This was the second attempt that day by these ships to enter harbour, the first being aborted because of German air attack. Midshipman Terry Lewin in the *Valiant* recorded in his journal: 'We proceeded up the Grand Harbour to the cheers of civilians and the garrison. Perhaps they realised that we brought a mail, or, more important, valuable additions to their AA defence' – to which somewhat dismissive remark his 'snottie nurse' (LieutenantCommander Michael Penton) added the marginal comment: 'I think it was a *tremendous* moral fillip. No battleship had been there for months, & the small island must have felt very lonely and in the front line.' The unloading was stopped twice by air raids.

Soon after seven o'clock [noted Midshipman Lewin], when there were still a few more stores to come inboard, we sent all visitors ashore and let go our wires. We were cheered by even bigger crowds than welcomed us. Both on our way in and out of harbour we paraded Guard and band, a touch which must have impressed the Maltese considerably. They saw us at sea, being bombed and firing at aircraft; half an hour later we were entering harbour with band playing.[67]

At 1645 Cunningham had detached the 1st Battle Squadron (Rear-Admiral H. D. Pridham-Wippell: *Malaya*, *Eagle*, *Coventry* and eight destroyers), together with the 3rd Cruiser Squadron, to steam on ahead eastwards ready for the next phase of 'Hats'. At 1945 the Commander-in-Chief turned to the eastward himself in order to pick up *Valiant* and head for Crete. However, because the *Valiant*'s departure had been delayed until 1900 by the Stuka attacks on Grand Harbour, problems occurred in making the rendezvous, and radio silence had to be temporarily breached. The *Valiant* finally joined Cunningham at 2200.

Cunningham now commanded a technologically transformed fleet. Instead of relying for warning of enemy approach on the sharp eyes of lookouts peering through sun-dazzle or haze or cloud or darkness – just like Nelson or Jellicoe – he could depend on his radar operators watching their dim screens in darkened offices to detect hostile aircraft at a distance of up to 50 miles or more. For the first time too he had a big modern armoured carrier, which, coupled with the *Eagle* in a carrier squadron under the command of Rear-Admiral A. L. St G. Lyster (the new Flag Officer, Aircraft Carriers, Mediterranean), at last gave his Fleet adequate protection against Italian air attack and also a powerful air strike force. That first day she joined, the *Illustrious* demonstrated her value in sight of the entire Fleet when her Fulmar fighters, in Cunningham's words, 'quickly tumbled' two Italian shadowing aircraft into the sea

to loud cheers of the ships' companies, who had had just about as much as they could stand of being bombed without retaliation. The tremendous effect of this incident upon everyone in the fleet, and upon the Commander-in-Chief as much as anyone, was indescribable. From that moment, whenever an armoured carrier was in company, we had command of the air over the fleet. By that I do not mean that bombing ceased. Far from it. But we felt that we now had a weapon which enabled us to give back as good as we were getting.[68]

Cunningham intended that even the homeward voyage to Alexandria with his augmented fleet should pay a further operational dividend, as he had informed the First Sea Lord in a personal letter written on 19 August:

> Returning from Malta it is my intention to pass the whole force, convoy as well [a south-bound Aegean convoy; another example of splicing a subsidiary task into the main operation] . . . north of Crete and hit Rhodes a crack with the aircraft from the two carriers. The Rhodes aircraft have been very annoying to us and I propose to give them another dose as well and probably a bombardment very soon after return.[69]

The two carriers had been ordered to fly off every available Sword-fish armed as dive-bombers except an anti-submarine patrol of four. The *Illustrious* was also ordered to fly two flights of six Fulmar fighters each to act as fighter cover over the two targets, the airfields at Maritza and Callato. In *Illustrious* the launching of the strike began at 0345, when she was in a position 35° 38′N, 26° 07′E, with the wind direction 340°, speed 18 knots; the heavy old biplanes lumbering into a moonless sky clear except for a little haze between 1,000 and 8,000 feet. Unfortunately the ninth aircraft to take off caught a wing on the island bridge structure, blocking the deck and preventing the last three aircraft from taking off – including the leader of the strike force. The attack had been carefully timed for the most favourable light over the target: just enough to see, but not enough easily to be seen.

Illustrious's aircraft began peeling off in their dive-bombing runs at around 0600, forty minutes before sunrise. As they climbed away from Callato airfield they could see explosions and fires. Meanwhile the *Eagle*'s aircraft at Maritza had hit a main hangar, whence came a series of small explosions, suggesting that ammunition had been detonated, and had also blown up and set on fire a petrol dump. It all made a good début for the Mediterranean Fleet's new carrier squadron. HMAS *Sydney* did her part too in disheartening the Italian Air Force by bombarding Scarpanto airfield, her escort destroyers sinking two torpedo boats for good measure. Next day Cunningham's fleet sailed into Alexandria – and fulfilled the final task of 'Hats' by delivering 250 tons of stores for the Army and Air Force, including 28 anti-tank guns.

For all its risks, 'Hats' had proved a totally successful experiment – not least because of the supine performance of the Italian Navy and Air Force. The Premier made haste to send a personal message of congratulation to Cunningham, but nevertheless coupled praise with a nagging remark about the importance of continuing to strike at the Italians during the winter.[70] He was not pleased with Cunningham's reply which reminded him that successful operations in the central

Mediterranean depended on ample reconnaissance by long-range Royal Air Force aircraft (of which there was still a great lack) and pointed out that his Fleet lacked enough destroyers adequately to screen it against submarines.[71] And Churchill grumpily minuted to Pound on 6 September that the success of 'Hats' showed that it would have been

> quite easy to have transported the armoured brigade through the Malta channel, and that it would now be in Egypt, instead of more than three weeks away . . . [see below] I am not impressed by the fact that Admiral Cunningham reiterates his views. Naturally they all stand together like doctors in a case which has gone wrong. The fact remains that an exaggerated fear of Italian aircraft has been allowed to hamper operations.[72]

By the second week of August 1940 the War Cabinet and Chiefs of Staff had decided to send out an armoured brigade to strengthen General Sir Archibald Wavell's undermanned and overstretched Middle East Command. The brigade's equipment would comprise much of the first fruits of British war production – 150 light, cruiser and infantry tanks, 48 anti-tank guns and 250 anti-tank rifles, 20 Bofors light anti-aircraft guns, 48 25-pounder field guns, 50,000 anti-tank mines, spare parts and radio kit.[73] Since the outcome of the Battle of Britain still lay in doubt, with German invasion preparations in full spate, this decision to send a precious armoured brigade and its weaponry out of the kingdom to Egypt must in retrospect stand as one of the greatest gambles of the Second World War. It arose in its turn from that earlier grand-strategic choice, made almost by default, to develop the Mediterranean and Middle East into a major offensive theatre of war.

Churchill himself had urged that part of the armoured brigade – and in particular the heavily armoured 'I' tanks, essential for attacking Italian defensive positions in the Western Desert – should be despatched by the direct route through the Mediterranean in four transport ships under the protection of 'Operation Hats'. Having foregone the tanks for the defence of England, he wished to see them in the field in the Middle East with the least delay, rather than uselessly packed in transports taking the long route to Egypt via the Cape and the Red Sea. However, he met with united opposition from his professional advisers. On 11 August Cunningham (who would have to bear direct operational responsibility for the safety of these ships within the Mediterranean) had signalled that the practicability of passing them through as part of 'Hats' could only be decided by actual trial and error: the tank transports might arrive unscathed, or they might be a total loss. What was certain was that their presence (with a speed of only 16 knots) must dangerously lengthen the time which Force H and his own Fleet would be exposed to Italian bombing. Nevertheless, if the urgency to get the tanks to Egypt was so great as to justify the risks both to the transports and to the Fleet, he would undertake the operation subject to certain conditions.[74]

Next day the Cabinet Defence Committee, chaired by the Prime Minister, had thrashed the matter out. The First Sea Lord warned his colleagues that the presence of 'relatively slow M.T. ships accompanying the Fleet through the Mediterranean would restrict liberty of movement and reduce its effective speed, thereby increasing its vulnerability to attack by aircraft, submarines, motor torpedo-boats and destroyers'.[75] Moreover, the Italians

> were bound to become aware of the passage of M.T. ships along the North African coast and they could not fail to deduce their destination. They would thus have at least two days' warning to prepare concentrations of aircraft, submarines and small surface craft to attack the convoy in the narrow part of the Central Mediterranean. In these circumstances [went on the First Sea Lord], the chances of the convoy getting through were remote and it was quite possible that the M.T. ships would be lost and that the warships would sustain damage. The Commander-in-Chief, Mediterranean Fleet, was of the same opinion.

At the head of the table in the bleak Cabinet War Room deep down in the bunker next to the Admiralty building, the Prime Minister listened to this exposition with thunderous impatience. When Pound finished, Churchill hastened to assert:

> ... in the light of recent experience of convoys passing between Malta and Egypt, the Admiralty appeared to take an unduly pessimistic view of the risks involved. In his opinion it should be possible to pass a convoy of three fast ships through to Egypt without great difficulty. The presence of these ships with the Fleet should act as 'bait' and should draw down upon them concentrations of Italian Naval Units, thereby affording the declared opportunity to inflict serious damage upon the Italian Navy.

But he added: 'Nevertheless he felt bound to accept the opinion of the Naval Staff although he was not in agreement with it.'

General Sir Archibald Wavell, the C-in-C, Middle East (who had flown to London in order to confer), had supported the First Sea Lord's view:

... as much as he would like the reinforcements to reach Egypt at the earliest possible date, the risks of losing them in passage through the Mediterranean, and the fact that if this equipment were lost much of it could not be replaced for several months, would not in his opinion justify the gain in time.

So the decision came to be taken – finally confirmed four days before 'Hats' began – to send the armour via the Cape route. In retrospect it is hard not to think that the success of all the complicated manoeuvres and feints during the operation might well have been compromised by the shackling presence of the transport ships and their precious cargoes – as Pound and Cunningham had feared before the event.

The movement of this armoured brigade constituted only one element in the huge investment in shipping resources during the second half of 1940 needed in order to build up the British Empire's land and air forces in the Middle East. From August to December no fewer than 76,000 men were shipped from the United Kingdom, and nearly 50,000 from India, Australia and New Zealand, together with vast tonnages of equipment and supplies, from railway engines to engineering plant.[76] To escort this endless procession of convoys laid another heavy task on the Royal Navy, and especially in the Red Sea, where the route was potentially dominated by enemy ships and aircraft based on the Italian colony of Eritrea. Fortunately they showed no more enterprise than their confrères in the Mediterranean, relapsing into quiescence after their first and only surface attack on a convoy of 20–21 October was beaten off with the loss of one out of four destroyers by the British escort.[77] Yet the Red Sea climate itself was hostile enough to the crews of escort ships constantly steaming with over-driven engines, for temperatures rose to 100°F in the living spaces and an unbelievable 170° in the engine rooms. On the other side of Africa too, many more merchant ships with Navy escorts were ferrying crated aircraft from Britain to Takoradi on the Gold Coast, there to be reassembled and flown across the continent to strengthen the Royal Air Force in Egypt. On all this unsung service of the Royal Navy in the waters from the Atlantic to the Gulf of Suez and the Indian Ocean utterly depended Churchill's Mediterranean strategy.

For Cunningham and Somerville personally there was an added strain – the Premier's enthusiasms for operational fantasies born of a gut-urge to smash at the enemy; his ruthless meddling in operational matters whenever impatience drove him to anger. In the case of Somerville and even more his colleague Admiral Sir Dudley North, the Flag

Officer, North Atlantic (headquarters, Gibraltar), the farcical expedition to Dakar in September 1940 ('Operation Menace'; see above,
pp. 203–5) saw both types of strain coincide. On 6 September, two days
after Force H returned to harbour following 'Hats', Somerville,
as instructed, despatched HMS *Ark Royal*, the battleships *Barham*
and *Resolution* and nine destroyers south to Freetown, ready to act
as the naval support to 'Menace'. This left him at Gibraltar with no
more than the battlecruiser *Renown* and six destroyers in order to fulfil his primary mission of commanding the Straits of Gibraltar, and
guarding against an Italian Fleet sortie in the western Mediterranean.
In the small hours of 11 September he received a report that six warships burning navigation lights had been sighted in the Mediterranean
some 70 miles east of Gibraltar and steaming westwards at high speed
– confirming earlier reports from the Consul-General in Tangier that
Vichy French ships might soon proceed out of the Mediterranean.

Somerville at once ordered *Renown* to one hour's readiness for full
speed. Receiving no orders from the Admiralty to move against these
technically neutral vessels, Somerville ordered *Renown* to revert to
two hours' notice for steam. Not until the early afternoon did he
receive Admiralty instructions to go to sea and make contact with the
French force. Since this entailed recalling destroyers at present out
hunting a submarine or on patrol and then refuelling them, it was
clear to him that if the French were intending to head south to
Casablanca, he was already too late to intercept them. At 1546 came
further instructions from the Admiralty: there was no objection to the
French force going to Casablanca, but they could not be permitted to
go on to Dakar. At 1600 Somerville cleared Gibraltar with *Renown*
and four destroyers, steering to the south-westward at 24 knots.
Shortly afterwards he received a report that the French ships had
entered Casablanca at 1610. Next day Somerville searched for the
French ships between Casablanca and Dakar, signalling a sighting to
the Admiralty (though without response from it in terms of further
orders). In the forenoon of 14 September the Admiralty ordered him
to return to Gibraltar.[78] In fact the French squadron, having left
Dakar, was heading for Libreville in Gabon, far to the south of Dakar.

In London there was deep anger at the failure to intercept the
French squadron during its passage of the Straits of Gibraltar; and
the Prime Minister's fury (especially after the humiliating failure of
'Menace' a fortnight later) meant that a scapegoat had to be found.
The First Sea Lord was of the same mind – selecting not Somerville,
the Flag Officer, Force H, but Admiral Sir Dudley North, the
Flag Officer, North Atlantic Station, who – though the division of

responsibility had never clearly been defined by the Admiralty – was certainly not Somerville's superior since the Admiralty issued orders direct to Somerville.

On 15 October North was accused of failure 'in an emergency to take all prudent precautions without waiting for Admiralty instructions' – i.e. by ordering Force H to sea – and relieved of his command. Yet Force H at the time when Somerville first ordered it to one hour's readiness for full speed could have only consisted of *Renown* and one available destroyer – as the *Admiral Graf Spee*'s fate suggests, not necessarily a match for three modern French 8,200-ton cruisers each with nine 6-inch guns and four torpedo tubes, and three 'super-destroyers' each displacing some 2,600 tons and mounting five 5.5-inch guns and nine torpedo tubes; and all of them faster than the *Renown* and the small British destroyers.[79] The charge against North was thus baseless on two counts: first, it did not accord with the operational facts, including the Admiralty's own sloth in issuing instructions, and secondly, because it was for Somerville rather than North to decide that Force H should go to sea. In any event North had on his own initiative ordered an air search which soon revealed that the French were heading south and not, as London most feared, north and back to France.

The true villain of 'the Dudley North affair' lay in Churchill's diversion of most of Somerville's strength to support the Dakar operation, coupled with Pound's failure to issue clear directives on operational policy towards the French Navy and on the command relationship between Force H and the North Atlantic Station.[80]

At the end of November 1940 it was Somerville's turn to be struck by a squall of the Prime Minister's and the First Sea Lord's impatient wrath, when a Board of Enquiry was set up by the Admiralty to investigate his conduct in another Mediterranean convoy operation even before he had returned to Gibraltar from the operation.

The purpose of this 'Operation Collar' (these sartorial codenames were Cunningham's invention) was to pass ships both ways between Gibraltar, Malta and Alexandria. Cunningham was relinquishing the old slow battleship *Ramillies*, together with the high-freeboard cruiser *Berwick* (9,750 tons, eight 8-inch guns; launched 1926)[81] and the 6-inch gun cruiser *Newcastle*, for service in the Atlantic against German raiders, while at the same time passing a convoy of four merchant ships from Alexandria to Malta. From Gibraltar eastbound were to sail three merchant ships (two for Malta, one for Alexandria), together with the cruisers *Manchester* and *Southampton* (9,100 and 9,400 tons respectively, each with twelve 6-inch guns),[82] four minesweeping corvettes and destroyers as reinforcements for Cunningham's fleet. Once again the safe transit of these groups of ships between the cover provided by Force H on one side of the Sicilian Narrows and the Mediterranean Fleet on the other demanded carefully planned intricate movements. Cunningham's part in these was accomplished without event when the four merchant ships, together with the three warships he was relinquishing, safely reached Malta early on 27 November. Later in the forenoon the *Ramillies*, *Newcastle*, *Berwick* and five destroyers left Malta, joined up with the anti-aircraft cruiser *Coventry* (so together forming Force D), and steamed north-westwards in company to the rendezvous with Somerville.

For Somerville, however, 'Operation Collar' proved not so smooth. When 'Collar' was still being planned, he had voiced anxiety lest the Italian Fleet should take advantage of its central position in the Mediterranean (in strategic terms, the classic advantage of 'interior lines') to concentrate its available strength (which he estimated at three battleships, five to seven 8-inch gun cruisers and several 6-inch gun cruisers) against Force H, consisting only of *Renown*, *Ark Royal* and *Sheffield*.[83] It disturbed him that the efficiency of *Ark Royal*'s torpedo strike force was 'low' owing to lack of practice and a high percentage of inexperienced air crews. He had therefore requested that he be reinforced for the coming operation by the battleship *Royal Sovereign*. However, in Somerville's own words, 'The Commander-in-Chief, Mediterranean, was frankly sceptical and considered I was unduly pessimistic. In his opinion, the probability of an Italian concentration in the Western Mediterranean was more remote now than at any time since Operation HATS [some three months earlier].'[84] In the event, the *Royal Sovereign* did not accompany Force H because repairs on her could not be completed in time. Somerville was also anxious about the combat effectiveness of the two cruisers he was escorting outwards as reinforcements to Cunningham and the other two he was later bringing back to Gibraltar. On the outward voyage *Manchester* and *Southampton* would each be packed with 700 Royal Air Force and Army personnel, so impairing their fighting efficiency, while the corvettes could only manage 14 knots. On the return voyage the *Berwick* would only be capable of 27 knots instead of 32 because of turbine troubles, while *Newcastle*'s boilers were defective and unreliable.

On 27 November 1940, midway between Cape Spartivento in Sardinia and the Tunisian coast, on a calm sea under a blue sky so clear that visibility was 30 miles at a height of 10,000 feet, all Somerville's apprehensions were fully borne out. While still shepherding his convoy eastwards and with the rendezvous with Force D still to be made, air search reports came in that a powerful Italian force of battleships and cruisers was approaching from the north. On the basis of these reports Somerville estimated the enemy to consist of one Littorio class and one Cavour class battleship, plus a group of three 8-inch gun cruisers and possibly a third group consisting of more cruisers. He guessed correctly, for in fact Admiral Angelo Campioni, the Italian C-in-C, on learning that Force D had left Gibraltar, had ordered a concentration at sea of the battleships *Vittorio Veneto* and *Giulio Cesare*, seven 8-inch gun cruisers and sixteen destroyers.

Somerville's first concern now was to link up with Force D, which was successfully accomplished before noon. He then spread his augmented cruiser strength of five ships in a screen with *Ramillies*, *Renown* and destroyers astern of them (all steering due north) to the northward of the convoy on its eastbound course. A strike by torpedo aircraft from *Ark Royal* on the Italian battleships failed to achieve a hit, owing largely to lack of training of the crews, and so the outcome of the encounter turned on the surface ships. This by now had begun with a brisk exchange of fire between the British and Italian cruisers, further enlivened by some 15-inch salvoes from *Renown* (and even two from *Ramillies*). The Italian cruisers swung to a course east-north-east in order to draw the British on to their heavy ships, which were sighted at 1300. As 15-inch shells begun to plunge among them, the British cruisers sought in their turn to draw the Italians on to the *Renown* and the *Ramillies*. However, the Italian Fleet once again flinched from engaging the enemy more closely, instead continuing on its previous course. At 1318, with the enemy out of range, the action died away.

Now Somerville confronted an urgent and tricky decision – whether to pursue the enemy, or fall back to cover his convoy and *Ark Royal*. He judged that it was not possible for *Renown*, a battlecruiser, to take on two Italian battleships, one of them a powerful new ship, while the old *Ramillies* was so slow (20.7 knots) that by the time Force H caught up with the Italians she would have still been some 30 to 40 miles away. In any case, the *Renown* had developed a hot bearing on one propeller shaft, reducing her own speed to 27½ knots at 1207 hours. Of Somerville's cruisers, two were packed with RAF and Army personnel and two more were mechanically defective. Above all, he had to consider the convoy of merchant ships with their vital supplies and the corvettes which he must pass through the Sicilian Narrows – with a cramping speed of only 14 to 15 knots.[85] Somerville therefore decided to break off the pursuit of the Italian battlefleet. As he wrote in his report to the Admiralty: '. . . I was not prepared to hazard the achievement of my main objective, the safe passage of the convoy, unless there was substantial assurance that I could inflict material damage on the enemy by the destruction of one or more of his battleships.' This was a decision very similar to that taken by Cunningham during the first phase of 'Hats' (see above, p. 231). And despite Italian air attack, that main objective of passing the convoy safely through was successfully accomplished. By 30 November all the complex transit arrangements in 'Operation Collar' had been completed, with Force H home in Gibraltar with *Ramillies, Newcastle* and *Berwick*, and the Mediterranean Fleet back in Alexandria with *Manchester* and *Southampton*; the merchant ships safe in Malta and Alexandria; and the minesweeping corvettes anchored in Suda Bay, Crete.

It therefore came as a bitter surprise to Somerville to learn on his arrival at Gibraltar that the Admiralty, without even waiting for his report on 'Collar', had ordered a Board of Enquiry into his decision to discontinue the chase of the Italian Fleet.

This Board of Enquiry was a further manifestation of Churchill's deep and unceasing urge to see the enemy's nose bleed, and of the facile belief which he shared with Pound and the VCNS, Phillips, that the primary objective of naval strategy must always be to seek out and destroy the enemy's battlefleet – what might be called 'the Jutland syndrome'. It may also be (for there are parallels in Churchill's treatment of soldiers as well as sailors) that he had by now come to see Somerville, like North, as having 'not got the root of the matter in him'.[86] He had been vexed by Somerville's agonised reluctance to sink the French ships at Oran while a chance remained of a peaceful solution; by Somerville's clear support for North over the passage of the French cruisers through the Straits of Gibraltar. And, earlier, in that same November as 'Operation Collar', a major task to be carried out by Force H within another complex trans-Mediterranean convoy operation – 'Coat' – had gone sadly wrong.

The task here was to fly twelve Hurricane monoplane fighters from the elderly small carrier *Argus* (launched 1917) to Malta as desperately needed reinforcements for the island's air defence. Somerville had gone to sea on 15 November an anxious admiral, reckoning that Force H was 'quite inadequate numerically to deal with a potential Italian concentration'. On 16 November, the day before the Hurricanes were due to be flown off, he was writing: 'I've got the blasted old *Argus* like a millstone round my neck. In this weather [a blow from the west with 'a nasty sea'] I much doubt if we can make good more than 12 knots when we turn back tomorrow . . .'[87] Keen therefore not to go further eastwards into the orbit of Italian air and surface forces than need be, especially in view of reports from Malta that an Italian battle squadron was concentrating south of Naples, he asked the professional advice of the airmen in *Argus* as to the furthest west position it would be safe to fly off the Hurricanes.

On the basis of this advice the Hurricanes were launched before dawn on 17 November 1940 when the *Argus* lay some 400 sea miles from Malta, each of the two flights being led by a Fleet Air Arm Skua. Only four Hurricanes and one Skua made safe landing – with their petrol tanks virtually dry. All the rest ran out of petrol over the sea and were lost. A Board of Enquiry subsequently attributed the loss to errors of navigation and a failure of the pilots to keep to the most economical cruising speed, the distance being well within the endurance of the aircraft.[88] Nonetheless, Somerville reproached himself on the day after the loss of the aircraft: 'I feel now that in spite of the risk of meeting superior Italian surface forces it would have been better if I had proceeded 40 miles further east . . .'[89]

Now it was the beginning of December, and Somerville was facing the Board of Enquiry into his failure to pursue the enemy fleet during 'Collar'. However, this Board did not prove a tame instrument of Prime Ministerial wrath. Its President, Admiral of the Fleet the Earl of Cork and Orrery, himself wrote to Somerville: 'I hope you do not feel I have not sympathised with you in the position in which you have been placed after your successful action last week. I do so very much.'[90] Cork asked him not to judge the Admiralty too harshly because (in his words) of the people inside and outside it (meaning, according to Somerville, Churchill and the VCNS, Phillips) who, impatient to get results and ignorant of the facts, 'will always raise their voices'. In Cork's opinion, a Board of Enquiry in fact offered the best way of disposing of their criticisms – and so it proved, for the findings of the Board completely upheld Somerville's decisions. The Commander-in-Chief, Mediterranean Fleet, for his part wrote to Pound in answer to a letter from the First Sea Lord:

> You ask me if I was surprised at the Board of Enquiry on Force H's action south of Sardinia. You will wish me to speak out quite frankly and say that I was very sorry for the decision, more specially as the Board was set up even before Force H had returned to harbour.
>
> The action was an unsatisfactory one. When one is burdened with a convoy one's hands are always tied to a certain extent. Of course the Fleet

Air Arm got no hits, although they claimed to have done so, and it is obvious that all the enemy ships had the legs of Force H.[91]

According to his memoirs Cunningham thought it

intolerable that a Flag Officer, doing his utmost in difficult circumstances, should be continuously under the threat of finding a Board of Enquiry waiting for him on his return to harbour if his actions failed to commend themselves to those at home who knew little or nothing of the real facts of the case. Such pre-judgement is not the best way to get loyal service.[92]

From 16 to 24 December Cunningham successfully carried out the last major Mediterranean transit operation of 1940; another series of interlocking movements involving convoys both ways between Malta and Alexandria, and of other convoys in the Aegean, coupled with air strikes and bombardments of Italian bases in the Dodecanese and elsewhere *en passant*. But it had been intended that before the end of the year yet a further convoy (codenamed 'Excess'), composed of five merchant ships loaded with ammunition, crated Hurricanes for Malta and other urgently needed stores, would be escorted through from Gibraltar to the eastern Mediterranean. However, at the news that the German heavy cruiser *Hipper* was at large in the Atlantic (see above, p. 198), Force H was ordered into that ocean to hunt her down. Despite an exchange of fire between the *Hipper* and the *Berwick* in appalling weather, Force H's mission proved unsuccessful; worse, *Renown* was so damaged by heavy seas as to require repairs in Gibraltar dockyard. In consequence, the passage of the 'Excess' convoy had to be postponed until 6 January 1941 – a delay that was to entail unforeseen and calamitous penalties (see below, pp. 319–21).

By this time, however, tremendous events had transformed the whole pattern of the war in the Mediterranean and Middle East. On 28 October the Italian Army in Albania (occupied by Italy since spring 1939) invaded Greece – a stroke made by Mussolini behind Hitler's back, much to the Führer's pique. Next day the Royal Navy began to establish an advanced base at Suda Bay, Crete, while Air Chief Marshal Sir Arthur Longmore, the Air Officer Commanding-in-Chief, Middle East, despatched a mixed squadron of Blenheim fighters and bombers to Athens. By 8 November the Greeks had inflicted a humiliating defeat on the invaders; by the end of November they had thrown the Italians well back into Albania, where the front was to remain largely stabilised throughout the winter. And on 11 November, while the Greeks were so spectacularly thrashing the

Italian Army, it was the turn of Cunningham's fleet to thrash the Italian Navy – and without any of his battleships firing a shot.

When Rear-Admiral Lyster arrived in *Illustrious* at the beginning of September to take command of the carrier squadron, he raised at his first interview with Cunningham the question of launching an air strike on the Italian battlefleet while it lay at anchor in Taranto harbour. Cunningham was enthusiastic; indeed he had already mentioned such an idea in letters to the First Sea Lord, who, battleship-minded as he was, conceived of the operation, in Cunningham's words, as 'the last dying kick of the Mediterranean carrier before being sent to the bottom'. However, wrote Cunningham in his memoirs, 'to Admiral Lyster and myself the project seemed to involve no unusual danger'.[93] The idea had first been mooted during the Abyssinian crisis in 1935 –36, when Admiral Sir William Fisher had been Commander-in-Chief of the Mediterranean Fleet. In 1938 it was revived when Lyster was Captain of the carrier *Glorious*, only to be squashed by the new C-in-C, the Jutland-minded Dudley Pound. Now Lyster's moment had come after all.

By mid-October plans for 'Operation Judgment' were well advanced, and the C-in-C hoped to celebrate Trafalgar Day (21 October) by repeating by novel means Nelson's annihilation of an enemy fleet, but a fire in *Illustrious*'s hangar forced a postponement to 11 November, the next suitable moon period. There followed another setback because of problems with *Eagle*'s aviation fuel system, so making it necessary to employ one carrier instead of two, even though five of *Eagle*'s Swordfish, together with experienced night-flying aircrews, were embarked in *Illustrious*. 'Operation Judgment' was spliced into yet another complex pattern of convoys and transit operations to be conducted jointly with Force H (and preceding 'Coat' and 'Collar'). By dawn on 11 November Cunningham (flying his flag in *Warspite*) with the battleships *Barham*, *Ramillies*, *Valiant* and *Malaya*, the carrier *Illustrious*, two cruisers and thirteen destroyers was steaming north-eastward away from the Malta sea area towards the position from which would be flown the first air strike in history ever to be launched on a battlefleet within a defended naval base.

Illustrious (laid down in 1937, launched in April 1939) was the first of the Royal Navy's new fleet carriers to come into service. Displacing 23,000 tons, with deck armour 2½ to 3 inches thick, and side armour of up to 4½ inches, sixteen dual purpose 4.5-inch guns in twin turrets, six 8-barrelled pom-poms, and equipped with radar, she could steam 31 knots and carry a maximum of 36 aircraft.[94] The arrival of this formidable ship in the Mediterranean had alone made the planned strike possible. A second essential factor lay in the recent re-equipment of Royal Air Force No. 431 Flight on Malta with American Glenn Martin Maryland aircraft (range 1,210 miles; ceiling 26,000 feet; speed 278 mph), able to maintain a photo-reconnaissance watch on Taranto. These aircraft provided the planners of the strike with pictures showing in comprehensive detail the layout of Taranto's defences, including anti-torpedo nets and balloon barrages. The latest photographs, flown to *Illustrious* in the afternoon of 11 November, showed five battleships at anchor in the outer harbour, while a Royal Air Force Sunderland flying-boat reported that a sixth heavy ship was joining them. The well practised aircrews therefore knew the exact positions of their targets.[95]

At 1900 Cunningham detached *Illustrious* (flying the flag of Rear-Admiral Lyster) and her screen of four cruisers and four destroyers to steam to her flying-off position about 170 miles south-east of Taranto, making the signal to Lyster: 'Good luck then to your lads in their enterprise. Their success may well have a most important bearing on the course of the war in the Mediterranean.'[96]

For all ships' companies in the Fleet there was now nothing more to do but endure the tension of waiting for news of success or disaster. On Cunningham, Lyster and their staffs bore the added strain of knowing just how strong were the defences which the Swordfish must penetrate. And for the Swordfish aircrews themselves the waiting period in the *Illustrious* before take-off – supper, a last briefing, the climb into the open cockpits of the old biplanes, the flight deck of the carrier stretching ahead in the cold gleam of the moon – was a time when the bravest might feel the mouth go dry and the palms grow damp.

At 2040 the twelve aircraft of the first wave of the strike force (drawn from Nos. 813, 815 and 824 Squadrons of the Fleet Air Arm, and led by Lieutenant-Commander K. Williamson, RN) roared away down the deck one by one and lumbered up and away. At 2057 they took up formation and headed for Taranto. By 2100 the second wave of only nine aircraft (three had force-landed in the sea during earlier flights) (from Nos. 813, 815, 819 and 824 Squadrons, led by Lieutenant-Commander J. W. Hale, RN) was waiting ranked for take-off; at 2130 they were airborne, all except for an unlucky one which suffered damage to the fabric covering of a wing in a collision while taxiing, and returned to the hangar deck for repairs. But by 2200 it too was setting its own lonely course for Taranto, for its crew was determined not to be left behind. While the pilot, Lieutenant

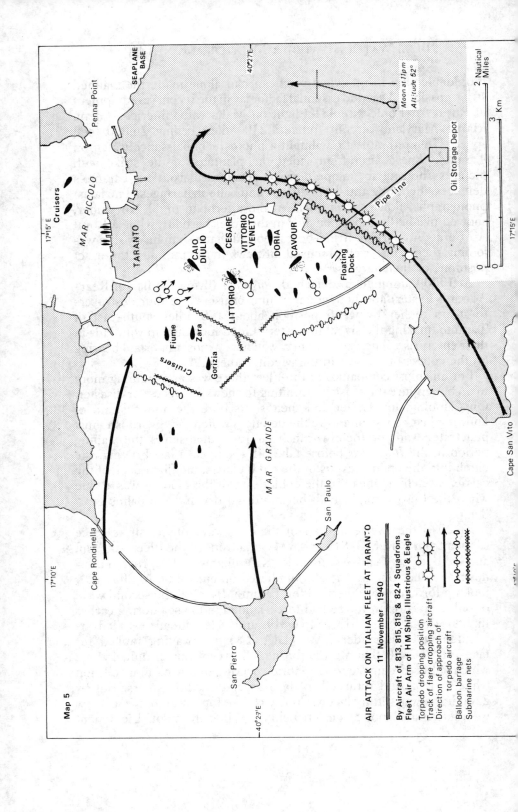

Map 5

AIR ATTACK ON ITALIAN FLEET AT TARANTO
11 November 1940

By Aircraft of 813, 815, 819 & 824 Squadrons
Fleet Air Arm of H M Ships Illustrious & Eagle

Torpedo dropping position
Track of flare dropping aircraft
Direction of approach of
    torpedo aircraft
Balloon barrage
Submarine nets

E. W. Clifford, had been urging the repair crews to do their utmost, his observer, Lieutenant G. R. M. Going, was up on the *Illustrious*'s bridge successfully persuading the captain, Denis Boyd, to allow them to go.

For the aircrew members, each solitary in his open cockpit, the flight meant time to think and think again about what lay ahead; cruising at about 130 mph at 8,000 feet through 8/10ths thin cloud under a three-quarters moon, it also meant 'the sort of cold', recorded Lieutenant Maund, 'that fills you until all else is drowned save perhaps fear and loneliness . . .'[97] Only eight aircraft made the first strike, four having got separated in cloud. It was just before 2300 that the flare-dropper broke away from the formation to make its preparatory run over Taranto, while the main force of torpedo-bombers swung westward in order to position themselves for the attack.

The climactic moment in the career of the Swordfish aircraft had now arrived. Quaintly old-fashioned though the Swordfish was, with its open cockpits and its big, ungainly biplane structure, it enjoyed the affection and the respect of its crews because of its sturdiness and capacity to take punishment, and its stability as a weapons platform. The 690 HP Bristol Pegasus IIIM3 radial engine gave it a maximum speed of 154 mph, with a service ceiling of 10,700 feet and a range of just over 1,000 miles. It could carry either one 18-inch torpedo or one 1,500 pound mine hung between its fixed undercarriage, or 1,500 pounds of bombs beneath the fuselage and wings. It was virtually defenceless, having only a single .303-inch Vickers machine-gun firing forward through the propeller hub, and a Vickers or Lewis gun mounted in the observer's cockpit. Its drawback for such an attack as 'Judgment' lay in its slow speed during the long descent and run-in to drop torpedoes, exposing it to the full storm of anti-aircraft fire.[98]

The aerial photographs had shown that the six Italian battleships and three cruisers, together with some destroyers, were moored on the shoreward side of Taranto's outer harbour, the 'Mar Grande', partly protected on the surface by a breakwater, partly by anti-torpedo nets, while three balloon barrages to the west, south and east of the ships offered partial protection against air attack. Inland from the 'Mar Grande', through a narrow entrance, lay the inner harbour or 'Mar Piccolo', where two more cruisers and four destroyers were moored. Powerful shore-based anti-aircraft batteries supplemented the warships' own anti-aircraft armaments. Taranto was no soft target. But 'Judgment' had been meticulously planned and rehearsed.

First, the flare-dropping Swordfish laid a line of twelve flares along the side of the 'Mar Grande' lying to the south-east of the anchored

Italian battleships and then went on to bomb the base's oil-storage depot. While the single dive-bomber simultaneously attacked the 'Mar Piccolo', the five torpedo-bombers now dived out of the west down from 8,000 feet towards the cluster of Italian battleships gauntly lit up by the line of parachute flares beyond them, and steered through the gap between the westernmost balloon barrage and the shore. At a height of 30 feet the Swordfish homed in on their targets through a multi-coloured storm of anti-aircraft fire, 'red, white and green onions streaming past the cockpits', and nostrils filling with the acrid powder smell of incendiary bullets.[99] Once the Mark XII torpedoes had been dropped into the water at ranges of 400 to 1500 yards and were thrusting their warheads of 388 pounds of high-explosive forward at 25 knots, at a depth setting of 34 feet, the Swordfish jinked (not their best trick) through the gunfire and over the battleships' masts into the inner harbour and then away.

As the second wave of Swordfish approached Taranto they could see flames and the huge firework display of anti-aircraft fire from 60 miles away. One observer wrote: 'I gazed down upon a twinkling mass of orange-red lights which I knew was a solid curtain of bursting shell through which we had to fly. It looked absolutely terrifying.'[100] Once again flare-dropping aircraft illuminated the target from the east while the torpedo-bombers (five in number this time) came in from the west; once again the Swordfish pilots pressed home their attacks at a height of 30 feet but this time to within 500 to 800 yards of the enemy. When this wave too had done its work and was turning for home, Lieutenants Clifford and Going arrived to finish off the night's events by dive-bombing cruisers and destroyers in the 'Mar Piccolo'. They landed back on *Illustrious* half an hour after the second wave, at around 0330 on 12 November. Only two Swordfish had failed to return; an incredibly small loss in view of the hazards – and of the achievement.

For next day photo-reconnaissance revealed the scale of the disaster which had overtaken the Italian battlefleet. One battleship, the *Conte di Cavour*, lay beached with almost all her decks under water, and two others were evidently badly damaged, with the *Italia* (as the *Littorio* had been renamed) well down by the head. In fact, the *Cavour* had suffered such serious damage from a torpedo exploding in the water beneath her keel that, though she was later raised, she never went to sea again. The *Italia* had been struck by no fewer than three torpedoes, and was to remain in the dockyard for four months, while the *Caio Diulio*, another victim of a torpedo exploding beneath her keel, was to be out of action for six months.[101] By way of bonus, the heavy cruiser *Trento*, some destroyers and the oil storage depot sustained

[248]

bomb hits. And during the night Pridham-Wippell and the cruisers *Orion*, *Sydney*, *Ajax* and the destroyers *Nubian* and *Mohawk* had raided into the Straits of Otranto and sunk all four ships of an Italian convoy. Mussolini's cup of joy was thus filled to the brim.

When *Illustrious* and her escorts rejoined the main body of the fleet that forenoon of 12 November, Cunningham signalled: 'Manoeuvre well executed.' Coming from Cunningham this was praise verging on hyperbole.

It must be left to Cunningham himself to sum up the success of 'Operation Judgment':

> Taranto, and the night of November 11th–12th, 1940, should be remembered for ever as having shown once and for all that in the Fleet Air Arm the Navy has its most devastating weapon. In a total flying time of about six and a half hours – carrier to carrier – twenty aircraft had inflicted more damage upon the Italian fleet than was inflicted upon the German High Seas Fleet in the daylight action at the Battle of Jutland.[102]

Taranto indeed marked the dethronement of the battleship as the arbiter of seapower after four centuries, and the opening of a new era of naval warfare – although diehard 'big-gun' sailors were still to blind themselves to this truth. Its immediate effect was to swing the maritime balance in the Mediterranean decisively towards the Royal Navy, and to complete the discouragement of the Italian Navy and its leaders. On 12 November every warship in Taranto capable of going to sea steamed away to safer harbours on the west coast of Italy, so leaving Cunningham master of the eastern Mediterranean and of the Aegean, where British convoys now constantly plied between Egypt and Greece. It was only a fortnight after 'Judgment', during 'Operation Collar', that the menace of attack by aircraft from the *Ark Royal* was enough to dissuade Admiral Campioni from pressing home an attack on Somerville's outweighted Force H, and encourage the Italian C-in-C to make off home instead.

Yet Taranto and the Greek Army's successes did not complete the tally of Allied triumphs in the Mediterranean theatre during the final months of 1940. On 9 December the long-cherished central purpose of Churchill's 'blue water' strategy – a major offensive by the British Army – was fulfilled at last. For on this day troops, tanks, guns, ammunition and equipment which the Merchant Marine and Royal Navy had borne to the Middle East during long months of arduous service at sea were launched into battle against the Italians in the Western Desert.

In September the Italian 10th Army in Libya had lumbered into

Egypt as far as Sidi Barrani, there to entrench itself in a chain of fortified camps. Now the 13th Corps, under the command of Lieutenant-General Sir Richard O'Connor and composed of British and Indian troops, attacked these positions from the rear and in three days consummated a staggering victory, smashing three enemy army corps and taking 38,000 prisoners (including four generals), 73 tanks and 237 guns.[103] Within a week O'Connor had expelled the Italians from Egypt and invaded Libya, laying siege to the fortress of Bardia. And the Royal Navy too was there, ferrying supplies and water to the advancing army; bombarding Italian troops in retreat along the coast road. This was the work of the new Inshore Squadron, under the command of Rear-Admiral H. B. Rawlings (Flag Officer, 1st Battle Squadron), consisting of the 1916-vintage monitor *Terror*, with two 15-inch guns and three 1915-vintage river gunboats, *Ladybird*, *Aphis* and *Gnat*, each with two 6-inch guns. From time to time the Royal Australian Navy joined in too with its destroyers *Vampire*, *Vendetta* and *Waterhen* under the command of Captain H. M. L. Waller, RAN, of HMAS *Stuart*.

On 3 January 1941 General O'Connor launched the 6th Australian Division, spearheaded by heavily armoured 'I' tanks, against Bardia's defences; by the 5th Bardia was in his hands, along with 40,000 prisoners, 128 tanks and 400 guns, and 13th Corps was already driving westwards to cut off the fortress of Tobruk, its next objective.

O'Connor's truly sensational victories sparkled against the darkest setting of the war, lifting the hearts of the British and their Allies and friends at the end of a year of disaster. They vindicated the belief of the British Chiefs of Staff in April 1939 that early successes could be won against Italy while the Allies were still girding their strength for a grand offensive against Germany – vindicated too Churchill's gamble in despatching precious tanks and personnel to the Middle East when Britain itself lay under threat of invasion.

With the triumphs of the Greek Army over the invaders of its homeland, the Royal Navy's strike at Taranto (equivalent in effect to a decisive victory in a great sea fight), and now this epic advance against heavy numerical odds by O'Connor's British Empire forces, fortune filled the sails of the Allied cause in the Mediterranean theatre and wafted it on waves of hope into 1941.

9

'Grey Water Strategy': The Atlantic, 1941

While 'blue water strategy' in the Mediterranean might at best gain some famous local victories on the periphery of the war with Nazi Germany, it could neither win that war for Britain, nor even lose it for her. Rather, Britain's fate depended – now that the danger of a German invasion of England had apparently passed – on 'grey water strategy' alone: that is, on the conduct of the month-in, month-out battle of attrition in the Atlantic wastes.

Just as with the earlier struggle with the U-boat during the Great War and the simultaneous war-deciding land battles of attrition on the Western Front, the success or failure of Britain's 'grey water strategy' was measured by a grim accountancy of comparative losses: the ratio of merchant ships sunk to U-boats destroyed or captured; the relative numbers of trained Allied merchant seamen and German submariners blown up, drowned or maimed set against the numbers of fresh volunteers coming forward to replace them; the total tonnage of shipping lost measured against the output of Britain's shipyards, and of U-boats sunk against Germany's new production; the tonnage of merchant shipping held up at any one time in British ports unloading and reloading, or immobilised in yards awaiting repair; the 'productivity' of U-boats in terms of ships sunk per U-boat per sortie.

To the opposing admirals and their staff these statistics were the equivalent of profit-and-loss accounts or monthly cash-flow figures to the directors of hard-pressed rival businesses. They were scanned with equal trepidation and hope by Grand Admiral Raeder, the head of the German Navy, in Berlin, and Admiral of the Fleet Sir Dudley Pound, the First Sea Lord, in London; by Rear-Admiral Karl Dönitz in his U-boat Command bunker at Kerneval near Lorient and Admiral Sir Martin Dunbar-Nasmith, C-in-C, Western Approaches, in Plymouth and, from 7 February 1941, in Liverpool. The statistics were no less a matter of central concern to Winston Churchill, all too anxiously aware as he was that they charted Britain's very ability to carry on the war; and on 6 March 1941 he issued a directive proclaiming that what he called 'the Battle of the Atlantic' had begun, with an enemy attempt 'to strangle our food supplies and our connection with the United States'.[1]

Yet all this cold accountancy represented an appalling human experience, as the seamen of both sides sought to survive each other's violence and the ferocity of the ocean itself – heavy-laden merchant ships labouring slowly through the huge Atlantic seas, their crews always conscious that at any moment a torpedo could consign them suddenly to those seas in frail boat or raft; the escorts plunging and rolling, their bridges swept by spray and green water, their ships' companies cold, wet and exhausted, eyes and nerves strained by unremitting watch for shadowing Focke-Wulf Condors, for the U-boat's squat conning tower amid the seaway; the crews of hunted U-boats closed up in their cramped metal capsules, listening grey-faced and silent to the thunder of depth-charges, to the drumming of their hunters' propellers overhead.

Courage, then, hardiness, and a sheer will to endure constituted the essential dynamic of the Battle of the Atlantic. But the key to the struggle between opposing sailors at sea, and to the 'grey water strategy' conducted by opposing admirals in their war rooms, alike lay in technology; in the contest between Allied and German 'boffins' in their research centres to invent new devices to find and destroy the enemy; in the competition between British and German industry to transform as quickly as possible the scientists' inventions into effective equipment in the hands of sailors and airmen. But in fact, of course, these three levels of the Battle of the Atlantic – tactical, strategic and technological – were always closely intermeshed, one reacting upon another. At the beginning of 1941 both sides were still learning through hard experience, still in a relatively early stage of evolving their techniques of attack and defence; still indeed building up their numerical strength.

For Dönitz this build-up of strength had long taken top priority, for in the U-boat itself, especially the Type VIIC, he already possessed a rugged and well-tried weapons system effectively linked to his command centre by radio. Of 753 tons displacement on the surface and 857 tons submerged, the Type VIIC enjoyed a range of 6,500 miles at 12 knots. Her 2,800 bhp diesel-electric engines gave a maximum surface speed of 17.2 knots (faster than many British escorts), while her 750 shp electric motors gave a maximum underwater speed of 8 knots, though only for a brief time before the batteries were exhausted. She was armed with one 88-mm gun, one 20-mm flak gun, and five 21-inch torpedo tubes.[2]

The U-boat's one partial weakness for the time being lay in the torpedo itself, for the unreliability of the new magnetic pistol had compelled the German Navy to revert to the Great War type contact pistol detonated by a direct hit on an enemy vessel. Such a direct hit was less destructive than the explosion beneath a ship's bottom (so breaking its back) made possible by the magnetic pistol, which (when it worked properly, as did the British version, the Duplex, at Taranto) was activated by the target vessel's magnetic field. The German Navy had also encountered difficulties with the depth setting of its torpedoes (see above, p. 194). Not until 1942 would Dönitz's Torpedo Inspectorate solve these problems, which in the meantime both reduced the effectiveness of U-boats and increased torpedo expenditure (thus sometimes leaving U-boats with no more remaining aboard with which to attack subsequent targets).

By April 1941 Dönitz's total strength in boats had for the first time passed the 100 mark, one-third of them operational, the remainder refitting, working up efficiency in the Baltic, or training relays of new crews. Of the operational boats, about twenty were at sea in April 1941; by June the figure had risen to 32.[3] Yet this was still only a tenth of the figure which Dönitz had calculated before the war would be necessary in order to achieve a decisive victory by 'wolf-pack' tactics. For U-boats came low in the scale of Nazi Germany's priorities, especially when it came to rationing out steel; a crass error of grand-strategic judgment on the part of its leadership. Moreover, Admiral Raeder still remained faithful to his concept of deploying powerful surface raiding forces against British sea communications; he cherished bright hopes of his two new 52,600-ton battleships *Bismarck* (already operational) and *Tirpitz* (still working up); and yet more heavy cruisers and an aircraft carrier were on the stocks. This programme had consumed, and was still consuming, enormous industrial resources.

Hitler himself, a Central European landlubber, took little interest in the maritime war; his mind was filled with his forthcoming project to conquer Soviet Russia, 'Operation Barbarossa' (eventually launched on 22 June 1941). Reichsmarschall Hermann Göring, for his part, regarded airpower and the Luftwaffe as his personal barony, not to be shared with anyone. It was only in January 1941, seven months after the German occupation of the French Atlantic coast, that Hitler ordered Göring to place KG [*Kampfgeschwader*] 40, a bomber group composed of Focke-Wulf Condors and based on Bordeaux, under Dönitz's operational control, in order to remedy to some extent the lamentably poor cooperation between Navy and Luftwaffe. Even so, KG 40 was only able to fly about two Condors a day, and, with the focus of the battle in the Atlantic shifting to northern waters, their range now proved insufficient despite such expedients as extra fuel tanks and flying the aircraft on to Norway at the end of a sortie. What was more, the Condor crews proved inexpert in accurately reporting the position and course of convoys when they did find them, so misleading rather than guiding the U-boats as they groped on the surface for a victim. Only nearer home, on the routes of the Freetown –Gibraltar–England convoys, were the Condors to prove a really effective help to the U-boats.[4]

Although in Dönitz's eyes the U-boat arm in 1941 was neglected, under-strength and ill-supported by the Luftwaffe, it nevertheless appeared to the British Prime Minister and the Admiralty as a lethally effective threat, especially in view of the Royal Navy's own inadequate resources. On 22 December 1940 the C-in-C, Western Approaches, Admiral Dunbar-Nasmith, wrote to the First Sea Lord on the whole topic of 'Protection of Trade in the Western Approaches', analysing the reasons, in his words, 'why the Convoy system, which achieved almost complete success in 1914–18, and again in the first half of 1940, is now failing to obtain similar results'.[5] There was the obvious factor of the installation of U-boat and Luftwaffe bases on the French Atlantic coast, which had compelled Britain to abandon the Channel and the South-Western Approaches as a convoy route and shift all convoys to the North-Western Approaches. But this factor only served to emphasise existing shortages of escort ships and weaknesses in technology. Wrote Dunbar-Nasmith: 'Our escorts have been too limited in number and ill-equipped to withstand the enemy's new method of attacking on the surface at night, particularly when the convoy is straggling and the visibility poor.'[6] Moreover: 'The majority of the officers and men of newly-commissioned ships have had no previous experience of A/S warfare, and shortage of escorts has prevented their getting the training desirable.'

The effects of this basic shortage, went on Dunbar-Nasmith, were worsened by the wear and tear caused by operating in northern waters where the winter gales were stronger; 'the greater proportion [of escorts] are out of action undergoing damage repairs'.[7] That same ferocious environment likewise curtailed the performance of the instrument of anti-submarine warfare in which the Admiralty before the war had placed its unreserved faith – sonar, or as the Royal Navy termed it at the time, Asdic. For, in Dunbar-Nasmith's words, 'The rougher weather experienced also makes the operation of the Asdic equipment less efficient.'

'*Less* efficient' was, to say the least, an understatement. The truth about Asdic is more bluntly spelt out in the Naval Staff History study, *Defeat of the Enemy Attack on Shipping 1939–1945*. In the first place, its maximum range was only 1,500 yards. Secondly:

Neither bearing nor ranges could be read accurately. For bearings there was a possible error of a few degrees – for ranges a possible error of 25 yards. It was also rarely possible to discriminate between submarine and non-submarine targets. The depth of a submerged U-boat could not be ascertained and it was not possible to detect a surfaced one. In addition very considerable skill and experience was required by the operators. The efficiency of the set rapidly fell off at speeds above 20 knots, in rough weather, and in waters with steep temperature gradients.[8]

In fact, to sum it up:

The result of the surface U-boat attack was that the Asdic was practically useless. In the vicinity of a convoy even its hydrophones, which hitherto had often been relied upon at night or in thick weather, became more generally a source of confusion.[9]

The escorts were therefore forced back on the ability of the human eye to spot a U-boat's low silhouette in all weathers and conditions of light.

But Asdic/sonar did not constitute the Royal Navy's only technical handicap in the face of the U-boat. The escort vessels themselves (fleet destroyers aside) lacked the cruising range for trans-Atlantic work, and were mostly incapable of catching a U-boat even when one was sighted; the latest types now coming out of the shipyards still being slower than a U-boat on the surface[10] – more legacies of wrong-headed pre-war decisions. While the twenty 907-ton Type I Hunt class escort destroyers of the 1938 programme (launched between December 1939 and September 1940), were certainly fast enough at 26 knots, they proved 'unsatisfactory' for ocean service, and were to be mostly employed in home waters. The 137 Flower class sloops (925 tons; later reclassed as corvettes), which had been ordered before the war for coastal work and which only came into service during 1940–41 were found as early as the end of 1940 to be 'almost useless as ocean escorts in winter owing to their excessive rolling and lack of manoeuvrability'.[11] Nonetheless, so desperately short of escort vessels was the Royal Navy that this class of ship was to supply the workhorse of the Battle of the Atlantic for years to come. Their design had to be extensively modified in order to render later ships more habitable for the overcrowded crews and give them greater firepower and endurance, but the improved versions were not to see service until 1943. Since the 'Flowers' could only make a maximum speed of 15 knots (though their designed speed was 16½), they were too slow to catch up a U-boat on the surface.

It brought some relief in the early months of 1941 that the old four-stack United States destroyers were at last being commissioned after modernisation. But in the meantime the main burden of protecting convoys fell on the Royal Navy's scarce resources of older fleet destroyers, supplemented by some sonar-equipped fleet minesweepers, enabling an average provision of two escorts per convoy of up to 40 to 50 merchant ships.

Unfortunately the principal anti-submarine weapon, the depth-charge, was technically little better than that used in the Great War, with a lethal radius of some seven yards only. The system for launching the charges – release into water from stern chutes and projection outward on both beams from throwers in a pattern of five – required that the ship had first to overrun the U-boat, so for technical reasons forcing a loss of sonar contact at close range during and immediately after the attack.[12] Although thrown-ahead depth-charges had been developed in the Great War, it was not until January 1942 that a new version dubbed the 'Hedgehog' – a multi-spigot mortar firing 24 contact-fuzed 35-pound warheads forward some 230 yards in an elliptical pattern – came into service.

All these shortcomings in vessels and equipment essentially stemmed from the pre-war Admiralty's complacent neglect of the entire problem of convoy protection and anti-submarine warfare. But already British science was working on a new means of locating the surfaced U-boat in all conditions of weather and light. By February 1941 the Admiralty Signal School had developed an experimental centimetric radar set, which, installed on a land-based tower, proved capable of following a submarine up to a range of 7½ nautical miles. The Captain of the Signal School on his own initiative ordered components for 150 of these sets (called 'Type 271'), as well as the hand-building in the laboratories of 24 copies of the prototype. By April 1941 sea trials in the new corvette *Orchis* demonstrated that the set could pick up a surfaced submarine at 4,000 to 5,000 yards and the periscope of a submerged submarine at 1,100 to 1,500 yards. By July 1941 25 corvettes had been fitted with Type 271 radars, and by the end of the year 100 sets had been manufactured and 50 ships equipped.[13]

High Frequency Direction Finders (HF/DF) for locating a U-boat by its radio transmissions offered yet another means of detection. As early as July 1940 it had been recognised that HF/DF mounted in the convoy escort could reveal the presence and bearing of a U-boat, but, owing to production delays and the need to gain experience in operating the kit, it was not until a year later that the first set came into use at sea.[14] High Frequency Direction Finders were also urgently needed for another purpose – to enable the Royal Navy to locate *British* ships in the vast spaces of the Atlantic. On 12 March 1941 Admiral Sir Percy Noble, who had just replaced Dunbar-Nasmith as C-in-C, Western Approaches on 17 February, wrote to the First Sea Lord: 'Under present conditions many hours are wasted both in the air and on the sea – tugs trying to find derelects [sic], escorts trying to meet convoys, valuable independently routed ships giving anxiety as to their position . . .'[15]

But in any event neither HF/DF nor centrimetric radar could be of much use against surface attacks by U-boats at night (their preferred tactic) because of the lack of an effective means of illuminating a U-boat once detected for the kill. Not until autumn 1941 did 'Snow-flake', a brilliant new pyrotechnic illuminant, replace the virtually useless existing star-shell.

And Royal Air Force Coastal Command too in 1941 was still striving to overcome the technical and numerical weaknesses bequeathed by past neglect, to equip itself with new types of aircraft, instruments and weapons, and to evolve new techniques of searching for U-boats and destroying them. Its old workhorses, the land-based Avro Anson and the Short Sunderland flying-boat, were being steadily supplemented by the American Lockheed Hudson and the Consolidated Catalina flying-boat. The Catalina, though lightly armed and heavy to handle, had an endurance of nearly 3,000 miles. Some squadrons of Vickers Wellington and obsolete Armstrong Whitworth Whitley bombers were transferred from Bomber Command to Coastal Command; and the robust Wellington became one of the Command's most reliable performers. The new Bristol Beaufort twin-engined torpedo-bomber was also joining the squadrons in replacement of the ancient Vildebeest.

But despite the establishment of air bases in Iceland (see below, p. 263) in order to extend air search and convoy protection as far out into the Atlantic as possible, there still remained an 'air gap' beyond the effective operational outward range (that is, allowing two hours on station) of Wellingtons (400 miles) and even Catalinas (400 to 600 miles); a gap which, as the AOC-in-C, Coastal Command, Sir Frederick Bowhill, 'stressed again and again',[16] could only be filled by very long range aircraft. In June 1941 a squadron was therefore formed of the untried Consolidated B-24 Liberator four-engine bomber, which after modification could provide protection to convoys at up to 750 miles from base. The squadron, based in Iceland and Northern Ireland, became operational in September. But its value was short-lived: by October its original strength of twenty had dwindled to only ten because of wastage and transfers to Ferry Command. By the beginning of 1942 the AOC-in-C, Coastal Command, was having to face the unwelcome fact that his single Liberator squadron 'was being allowed to die and that there was no agreed future policy for the building up of any long-range force . . .'[17]

In any event Coastal Command's means of finding and killing U-boats remained feeble enough. Although radar had been fitted experimentally in some aircraft since early 1940, development experienced 'many teething troubles',[18] and it was only in January 1941 that the first reliable ASV (Air-to-Surface-Vessel) radar began to be installed. Coastal Command's aircraft still lacked an effective bomb-sight (as well as heavy enough bombs), and they had to make do with adapted naval depth-charges, the depth-setting of which had to be fixed before take-off. This meant that if the charge was set to go off deep against a diving submarine, it would be useless against a submarine still on the surface. So Coastal Command would have to make shift as best it could while a shallower depth-charge pistol and a low-level sight were being developed.

Moreover, the Command, like the Royal Navy, possessed no effective means of illuminating a submarine at night. Not until 1943 was a slow-dropping flare to come into service. On 4 May 1941 a successful trial was held of the 'Leigh Light', an airborne searchlight proposed by Squadron-Leader H. de V. Leigh, a Great War pilot now on personnel duties at Coastal Command HQ. With the AOC-in-C's backing, Leigh had succeeded in installing a 24-inch naval searchlight in the under-turret of a Wellington equipped with ASV radar. In the trial against a British submarine, the Wellington's crew (including

Leigh in order to operate his light) first located the target by radar; after which, according to a Navy observer of the test:

> The aircraft was not heard by the submarine until it [the submarine] had been illuminated, and was able to attack down the beam for 27 seconds before being pulled out at 500 feet. This effort was most impressive, and there seems no doubt that, given an efficient aircraft crew and good team work, this weapon would be invaluable in attacking U-boats on the surface at night and in low visibility.[19]

But the Leigh Light was not to be in operational use for another year, the victim of initial opposition by the new AOC-in-C, Coastal Command, Air Marshal Sir Philip Joubert de la Ferté (who replaced Bowhill in June 1941), and of the usual problems of 'technology transfer' from the experimental stage to general installation.

All these weaknesses in equipment, when coupled with the shortage of aircraft for adequate training in ASV radar operation and marksmanship, limited the effectiveness of new tactics adopted in June 1941 whereby the Command's aircraft (now painted in white camouflage) were to approach a U-boat unseen through clouds thanks to ASV radar and attack U-boats by surprise, hoping to hit them during the 25-second interval between the time the U-boat's watch spotted the aircraft and the U-boat's complete disappearance into the depths.

Thus in the air and at sea the prospects for the Battle of the Atlantic in 1941 might be said to have turned on a balance between British and German deficiencies. Yet in command and control organisation the British had forged well ahead, especially with regard to cooperation between ships and aircraft. On 15 February 1941 Coastal Command was placed under the operational control of the Admiralty, though not under its direct command. Naval Cs-in-C in the various naval command areas would now state their operational requirements to their Coastal Command Group opposite numbers, who would then issue orders to the squadrons.[20] The closest links henceforth were to exist between Coastal Command Headquarters and the Admiralty's Submarine Tracking Room in London, while the new C-in-C, Western Approaches, Admiral Sir Percy Noble, and Air Vice-Marshal J. M. Robb, commanding No. 15 Group. Coastal Command (covering the North-Western Approaches), shared a new joint headquarters safe beneath a thick concrete roof in Derby House, Liverpool. Across one wall of the operations room was displayed the current Operational Plot of the state of the Battle of the Atlantic, based on information fed in by teleprinter from the Operational Intelligence Centre in the Admiralty 'Citadel' in

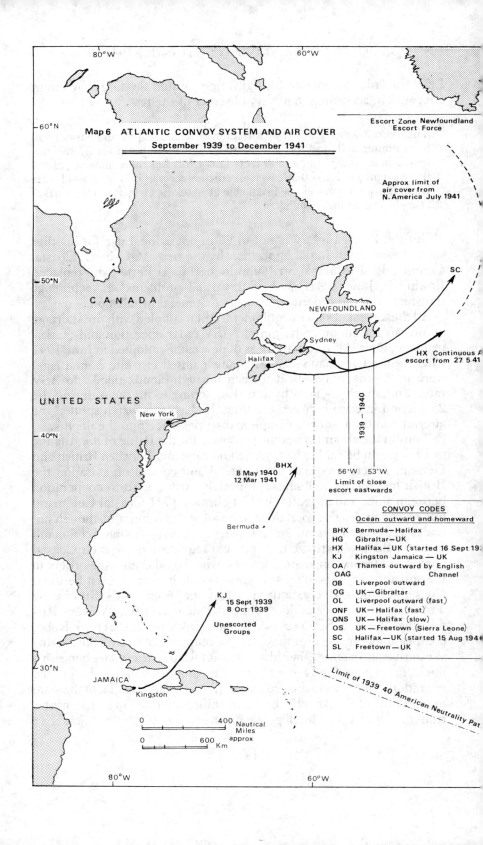

Map 6 ATLANTIC CONVOY SYSTEM AND AIR COVER
September 1939 to December 1941

Escort Zone Newfoundland
Escort Force

Approx limit of
air cover from
N. America July 1941

SC.

HX Continuous
escort from 27.5.41

CANADA

NEWFOUNDLAND

Sydney

Halifax

UNITED STATES

New York

1939 — 1940

56°W   53°W
Limit of close
escort eastwards

BHX
8 May 1940
12 Mar 1941

Bermuda

CONVOY CODES	
Ocean outward and homeward	
BHX	Bermuda—Halifax
HG	Gibraltar—UK
HX	Halifax — UK (started 16 Sept 19
KJ	Kingston Jamaica — UK
OA/ OAG	Thames outward by English Channel
OB	Liverpool outward
OG	UK—Gibraltar
OL	Liverpool outward (fast)
ONF	UK — Halifax (fast)
ONS	UK — Halifax (slow)
OS	UK — Freetown (Sierra Leone)
SC	Halifax—UK (started 15 Aug 1940
SL	Freetown — UK

KJ
15 Sept 1939
8 Oct 1939

Unescorted
Groups

JAMAICA
Kingston

Limit of 1939 40 American Neutrality Pat

0   400 Nautical
               Miles
               approx
0   600 Km

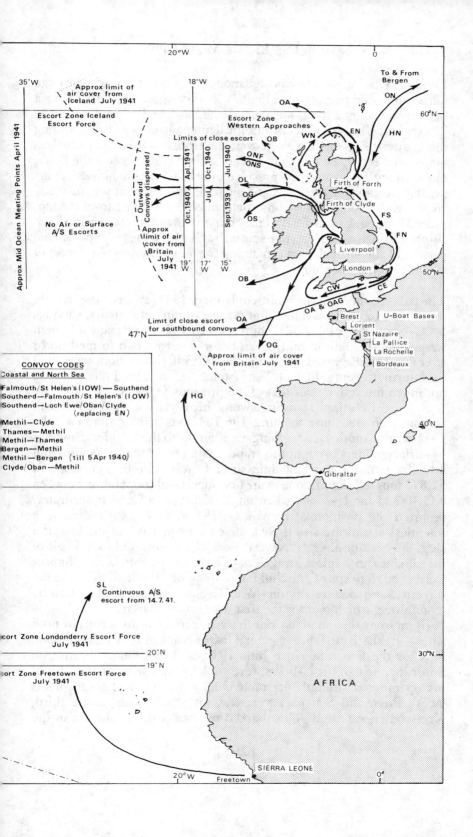

London. This highly sophisticated modern headquarters, with its large joint staffs, compared with Dönitz's 'corner shop' at Kerneval in a bunker so cramped it was nicknamed 'the Sardine Tin', and staffed by just six young U-boat officers plus the lieutenant-colonel commanding the Luftwaffe's KG 40.[21] Moreover, the British side of the battle was being overseen by no less than a War Cabinet Committee – the Battle of the Atlantic Committee – presided over by Churchill himself, comprising the chiefs of the naval and air staffs and eminent scientific advisers, while Dönitz enjoyed no such concerted backing from the top; indeed little backing at all. And the course of the year was to bring forth another British advantage, one sensed by Dönitz in the very operational pattern of the struggle, yet remaining for him a mystery the secret of which he could not plumb.

The balance sheet for the month of January 1941 favoured the British, for, thanks to winter weather and evasive routing of convoys, sinkings by U-boats dropped to 21 ships of 126,782 tons, many of them stragglers or caught in mid-ocean before convoys had formed up or after they had dispersed. Although the Luftwaffe's Condors accounted for a further twenty ships of 78,517 tons, the combined total came to not much more than half that of the previous October.[22]

But the February statistics swung heavily back in the German favour, with 39 ships totalling 196,784 tons falling victim to the U-boat, and another 27 totalling 89,305 tons to the Condor. Sinkings by surface raiders brought the grand total to more than 100 ships and 400,000 tons for the first time since October 1940. Ten ships of 52,875 tons fell victim alone to the first successful cooperation between KG 40 and the U-boats, when on 22 February a Condor accurately reported the position of convoy OB288 to U-73, so leading to a relentless assault by a wolf pack of seven boats without the loss of a single U-boat or aircraft. Nevertheless, the enemy still found half of his sinkings in hapless stragglers. The dismaying February figures were enough to spur Churchill into issuing his 'Battle of the Atlantic' directive and setting up the War Cabinet Battle of the Atlantic Committee, which met for the first time on 19 March.

By an irony the month of March was regarded as disastrous by both sides – by the British because total losses reached over half a million tons for the first time since June 1940, and by Dönitz because no fewer than five of his U-boats were sunk by convoy escorts, a fifth of his operational strength. It stung Dönitz the more that two of his 'aces', Prien and Schepke, were lost with their boats, and a third, Kretschmer, captured. This marked the final close of the era of the individual aces in the North Atlantic; henceforward Dönitz switched almost entirely to wolf packs. It was therefore in April 1941 that the true Battle of the Atlantic, the conflict of wolf pack versus the convoy system, really began.[23]

The fact was brutally signalled at the beginning of the month by an attack by seven U-boats on convoy SC26 in longitude 28°W before the anti-submarine escort had joined and when its only protection lay in the armed merchant cruiser HMS *Worcestershire* (not equipped to fight U-boats). Six ships were sunk and the *Worcestershire* herself damaged. But on the 5th, the destroyer *Wolverine* and the sloop *Scarborough* of the newly joined escort sank the U-76, whereupon the enemy gave up his attack.

Dönitz's evident strategy of pushing his U-boats further out into mid-Atlantic in search of soft targets beyond the cover of surface escorts and air patrols in turn provoked further British counter-measures. That month No. 15 Group, Coastal Command, established bases for Sunderlands of 204 Squadron and Hudsons of 269 Squadron in Iceland, while the Royal Navy opened an advanced fuelling base for escort vessels at Hvalfjord, north of Reykjavik. By mid-April convoys could be covered as far as 30°W, and by the end of the month as far as 35°W. At the same time they were re-routed nearer Iceland in order to maximise the escorts' endurance on station, while the escort forces themselves were strengthened by some sonar-equipped fleet minesweepers. Thus Iceland (first occupied by British forces in May 1940) had now fully assumed its role as the key to the struggle by the King's ships and aircraft to keep open the North Atlantic lifeline. A familiar landfall for the rest of the war to the weary men on bridge or in cockpit, it was the very embodiment of the harshness of that struggle. Captain S. W. Roskill, RN, the British official naval historian, remarks on 'its bleak and precipitous coastline, the deep inlets which formed its harbours, the poor holding ground which gave ships constant anxiety and, in particular, . . . the violence of its sudden, blinding and shifting storms'.[24]

The treachery of the Icelandic climate during the long winter months, the inhospitality of its harbours and the virtual certainty that little rest or relaxation would be possible in them soon aroused the British sailor's intense dislike of the place. To come in from fighting the enemy and the elements only to find that the fury of the latter had followed him with intensified malevolence awoke all his wide capacity for sardonic humour.[25]

The rerouting of convoys nearer to Iceland led to the uncovenanted benefit of compelling the U-boats to make longer voyages to their hunting grounds, so reducing their productive time on station. Moreover, the long spring days in this northerly latitude cramped their operational effectiveness, because it became too hazardous for them to shadow a convoy on the surface in daylight within range of British air patrols, while the night hours did not afford enough time for them to catch up and strike. In the same period Coastal Command introduced a new tactical system which rendered the role of the shadowing U-boat in daylight even more hazardous. Instead of aircraft giving only close protection to a convoy from stations on either bow as hitherto, they deployed round the convoy at considerable distances or swept well ahead of it. This surveillance and defence in depth forced attacking U-boats to submerge on approach to a convoy, so crippling their mobility, for their maximum economical speed when running on their batteries was barely five knots, and even often preventing them from developing their attacks at all.[26]

Yet Western Approaches Command, for its part, still lacked enough escort ships, especially destroyers, for which there were other urgent demands. In answer to a plea from Sir Percy Noble, the C-in-C, Western Approaches, the First Sea Lord explained on 16 April:

> The fact that I had a whip round to try and produce some more craft for the North-Western Approaches will prove that I am as keen as you are on building up your forces as much as possible.
> I have had to send Mountb's [sic] party [of destroyers] to the Mediterranean, and C-in-C, Home Fleet, had to replace them and you, I regret, must fill up C-in-C. We cannot have our capital ships risked for want of escorts.[27]

Towards the end of April submerged U-boats attacking in daylight sank four ships in convoy HX121 south of Iceland in 60°W, despite its escort. Nevertheless the corvette *Gladiolus* found one of the U-boats, the U-65, on the surface and destroyed her. It was encouraging too that in the entire month only ten ships had been sunk by U-boats while in convoy and only four of those in escorted convoys. It was the stragglers and the independent sailings that were still providing Dönitz's boats with their main stock in trade, bringing the total U-boat sinkings for April to 43 ships of 249,375 tons.

In May the accountancy of destruction swung strongly in Germany's favour, with the U-boats sinking 58 ships of 325,492 tons – half of them unescorted vessels in the Freetown area, whither the crafty Dönitz had deployed six boats in search of just such easy prey. Yet even on the trans-Atlantic route the U-boat gained two major successes. At the beginning of the month the outward bound convoy

OB318 lost five ships as against one U-boat destroyed by its anti-submarine escort. A fortnight later the homeward-bound convoy HX126 from Halifax, Nova Scotia, with only an ocean escort (i.e., to protect it against an enemy surface ship raider), was ambushed by a pack of nine U-boats south of Greenland in about 40°W, in that mid-Atlantic gap still covered neither by air patrols nor by anti-submarine escorts. Nine ships were lost, four of them after the convoy had been scattered. It was enough to induce the Admiralty, in collaboration with the Royal Canadian Navy, finally to inaugurate end-to-end surface escorts.

For that month a British-Canadian conference met to review the whole question of the air and sea defence of North Atlantic shipping. It agreed that, thanks to the arrival in service of the long-range Catalina, air cover would now be provided as far out as 700 miles from the British Isles, 400 miles from Iceland and 500 miles from Newfoundland. These arcs would, however, still leave an air gap of some 300 miles which could only be closed by very long range aircraft such as the Liberator. It was in this air gap that during the next two years Britain would come to within an ace of losing the Second World War. The conference also decided to base a powerful force of escorts at St John's, Newfoundland, and in the course of June this force reached a total of 30 destroyers, nine sloops and 24 Canadian-built Flower class corvettes. On 27 May 1941 the first convoy to enjoy the protection of an anti-submarine escort throughout its trans-Atlantic voyage, HX129, sailed from Halifax.

This inauguration of end-to-end escorts had only been made possible because at long last the shipyards of Canada and Great Britain had built enough escort vessels, supplemented by the old four-stack American destroyers and a recent transfer of ten ocean-going US coastguard cutters to the British flag. The Royal Navy's strength in destroyers and escort destroyers had now risen to 248 (of which 50 were undergoing refits), 99 corvettes and 348 assorted trawlers, sloops, coastguard cutters and anti-submarine yachts,[28] a figure which permitted the average number of escorts per convoy to be increased to five. Yet even with another 157 destroyers and 99 corvettes building (55 of them in Canada), the Admiralty still reckoned that it lacked sufficient ships adequately to protect the trade routes in the future against the enemy's own ever-increasing numbers of U-boats and also find a surplus to allow for the formation of hunting groups to destroy wolf packs once detected.

Despite the new British counter-measures the June figures again seemed to favour the U-boats, which sank sixty-one ships totalling

310,143 tons. When the Joint Planning Staff in London surveyed the cumulative overall shipping balance sheet that same month, they therefore found the arithmetic deeply discouraging. Britain and her Allies (those European states like Norway and the Netherlands which had lost their territories but retained their merchant fleets) had begun the year 1941 with shipping resources between 1.5 and 2.5 million tons smaller than at the outbreak of war. During the three months of March, April and May 1941 they had lost a total of 1,728,649 tons from all forms of enemy action and natural causes (817,887 tons from the U-boat alone): the equivalent of an annual loss of nearly 7 million tons. Moreover, well over a million tons of damaged shipping currently lay immobilised in repair yards, the victims of delays owing to antique shipyard equipment and equally antique management and trade-union practices; the equivalent of several million tons out of service annually.

Already British imports of dry cargo (including absolutely vital American technology as well as food) were running at only some 73 per cent of estimated tonnage requirements, while imports of oil were running at a tenth below. At the current rate of imports, therefore, a deficit of nearly 7 million tons of raw materials and semi-manufactured goods and two million tons of food would have accumulated by the end of 1941. Oil stocks, already dangerously low, would be down by another 318,000 tons. Certainly Britain could live for a time by running down stocks, but what then? At current rates of merchant shipping loss, calculated the Joint Planners, Britain was likely to be down another 5 million tons of shipping at the very least by the end of the year – yet the combined annual output of all the yards of the Commonwealth for dry-cargo ships came to barely 1 million tons. Britain would be fortunate if she could buy or charter as much as another half a million tons by way of supplement.

The Joint Planners therefore drew the almost despairing conclusion that 'it is only from a reduction in the rate of loss that a real margin of safety can be acquired'.[29] It was all too reminiscent of Jellicoe's doom-laden pronouncement to the Cabinet as First Sea Lord at the height of the 1917 U-boat campaign: 'It is impossible for us to go on with the war if losses like this continue.'[30]

Yet the June balance sheet was deceptive. Only thirteen ships out of the 61 lost had been sunk in convoy, while to destroy them had cost Dönitz three U-boats – two of them when an onslaught by ten boats on a single convoy off Greenland, the homeward bound HX133, was crushingly defeated by a swift and sudden British concentration of a powerful hunting group of two destroyers, ten corvettes and a sloop. And this tactical success proved to be merely the prelude to a startling shift in the strategic balance in July and August, when total U-boat sinkings dropped away to 22 ships of 94,209 tons and 23 of 80,310 tons respectively, less than a third of previous monthly totals.

The cause of these successes lay in the most astonishing, most closely guarded secret of the maritime conflict with Nazi Germany during the Second World War; one so precious that even the official naval historian writing in the 1950s was unable to refer to it. Yet it alone supplies the key to understanding the evolving pattern of the Battle of the Atlantic during the second half of 1941. For by mid-summer the Government Code and Cypher School (GC and CS) at Bletchley Park, near Buckingham (codename 'Ultra'), had broken the German Navy's 'Home Waters' Enigma, and was thus able to read Dönitz's top secret radio traffic at only short delay.

It had taken more than a year of patient analysis, of well planned captures and sheer luck – starting with luck. In April 1940 the Royal Navy had captured the German patrol boat VP2623 off Norway and retrieved Enigma settings that enabled GC and CS to read retrospectively the naval Enigma for six days, so providing important insights into the German Navy's wireless and cypher organisation.[31] GC and CS then established that the German Navy's Enigma machine now selected from a total of eight wheels instead of the five on the Luftwaffe machine – far more difficult to break – and that the Navy employed two keys, 'Home Waters' and 'Foreign', for both U-boats and surface ships, the 'Foreign' key being reserved for operations in distant waters. Over 95 per cent of all Enigma traffic was encyphered in the 'Home' key, which proved so formidably complex that GC and CS only succeeded in breaking it sufficiently to read another five days' traffic relating to April and May 1940, and then only by February 1941. It was evident that no progress could be made without important captures of code material, or, better still, a naval Enigma machine.

Naval Intelligence Division, and GC and CS, therefore decided to profit from the forthcoming Commando raid on the Lofoten Islands on 4 March 1941 by organising a special effort to seize such material – and successfully turned it up in the captured armed trawler *Krebs*. Thanks to this the Bletchley Park cryptographers managed to break the whole of the Enigma traffic for April at up to ten days' delay, and much of the May traffic at only three to seven days' delay. Moreover, the traffic read for February and April had revealed that the Germans kept one weather ship on station north of Iceland and another in mid-Atlantic, both carrying Enigma machines. On 7 May the Royal Navy captured the *München*, so enabling GC and CS to read the June Enigma traffic almost currently; and on 28 June, a date chosen because it fell just before the next month's Enigma settings came into force, the *Lauenburg* was likewise cut out, making it possible for the July traffic to be read also without delay.

Meanwhile had occurred another remarkable stroke of luck. On 9 May the captain of the destroyer *Bulldog* thought better of ramming and sinking the U-110, caught on the surface during an assault on the convoy OB318, and sent a boarding party to capture her instead. And aboard her was treasure indeed: an Enigma machine complete with a signal ready set for transmission, together with the special settings for 'officer-only' signals and the codebook for transmitting the short-range sighting reports (*'Kurzsignale'*) used by U-boats shadowing a convoy in order to call in a wolf pack.

The Bletchley Park analysts' final assault on the crumbling cryptographic fortress of the naval Enigma was further helped by flank attacks via lesser hand-codes and cyphers, in particular a dockyards hand cypher (*'Werft'*) and a meteorological cypher. Some of the traffic in these was found to be also transmitted in the Enigma, so offering valuable extra clues to the cryptographers as day by day they bent their brains and their electro-mechanical 'Bombes' to reading current Enigma traffic. By the beginning of August 1941 GC and CS had achieved complete mastery over the Enigma 'Home Waters' settings; a mastery which it was to retain until the end of the war, with a customary delay of only a few hours and a maximum of seventy-two.

Already in May the still tardy readings of the naval Enigma had permitted the Intelligence Centre (OIC) Operational to read every signal passed within Dönitz's U-boat Command and to construct a complete and constantly updated picture of Dönitz's dispositions, strategy and tactics. Then at last in June GC and CS could read Enigma fast enough to enable the Admiralty to anticipate German tactical operations. Thus it knew that convoy HX133 had been sighted by the enemy on 23 June; it knew that a wolf pack of ten boats was closing to attack it; and this was why it was able to order the escorts of two outward-bound convoys to leave their charges and reinforce HX133's own escort force to the combined total of two destroyers, ten corvettes and a sloop which in a running battle between 24 and 29 June sank the two U-boats for the loss of only five ships in the convoy.

Now came the larger strategic rewards of Bletchley Park's triumph. Since the winter of 1940–41 Western Approaches Command had resorted to the evasive routing of convoys away from suspected U-boat hunting areas, but this had been very much a matter of professional hunches and guesswork. With the new ability to read Dönitz's current

(*Above*) 'The stolid rectangular lines . . . belied their fighting effectiveness' – HMS *King George V*, name ship of the new class of battleships laid down during pre-war rearmament; 36,570 tons displacement (44,000 tons full load), ten 14-inch guns (III, I,

(Top left) Admiral Sir Max Horton *(left)*, Commander-in-Chief, Western Approaches 1942–45 – 'He matched Dönitz in ruthless will to win.' Admiral Sir John Tovey *(right)*, Commander-in-Chief, Home Fleet, 1940–43 – 'a hardened steel integrity'. (Crown copyright)
(Top, right) A. V. Alexander, First Lord of the Admiralty 1940–45, Labour MP for Hillsborough. He proved to be a staunch defender of the Navy's interest in Whitehall battles. (IWM) *(Below)* 'The vast armad of escort carriers . . . that would traverse the oceans i coming years derived from *Audacity*.' HMS *Audacity* (5,500 tons), carrying six Grumman Martlet fighters; commissioned September 1941, sunk December 1941. (IWM)

bove) 'Stout fighting ships alike in the freezing gales
the Arctic, the huge seaways of the Atlantic, and the
_ue_, brilliant, bomber-infested Mediterranean' – HMS
_effield, a 'Town' class cruiser laid down during the
_e_-war rearmament period, 9,100 tons displacement,
_el_ve 6-inch guns; here escorting convoy KMF 1 to the
_or_ch' landings in North Africa, November 1942. (IWM)

(Below) 'A new generation of bigger destroyers which
mounted eight 4.7-inch guns in twin turrets . . . on a
1,850 tons displacement' – HMS *Ashanti* of the 'Tribal'
class launched from 1937 onwards. The *Ashanti* served
with distinction escorting convoys in the Arctic (she
is pictured in Hvalfjord, Iceland, in 1942) and the
Mediterranean. (IWM)

'The new class of vessel specially designed for convoy work, the Hunt class of 900–1,000-ton destroyers, were not due to be commissioned until 1941.' HMS *Ledbury* *(above)* on completion in early 1942. (IWM) *(Below)* 'Almost useless as ocean escorts in winter owing to their excessive rolling and lack of manoeuvrability' – HMS

Bluebell, a 'Flower' class corvette (925 tons). Despite their shortcomings the Flowers were the workhorses of the Battle of the Atlantic. (IWM)

(Above) 'An entirely novel weapons system for destroying the *Tirpitz*' – X-craft midget submarine 30 tons; 51 feet long; 6½ knots on the surface and 5 knots submerged; crew of three volunteers). On 22 September 1943 three X-craft put the battleship *Tirpitz* out of action for six months. (Crown) *(Inset)* 'Their experiences might have come from a boy's adventure story.' Lieutenant B. C. G. Place, RN, commander of the X7, was awarded the VC for his part in crippling the *Tirpitz* in its Norwegian anchorage. (IWM) *(Right)* 'The same game of hunt and be hunted as in the Battle of the Atlantic, but with the roles reversed.' Lieutenant-Commander M. D. Wanklyn, VC, and crew of HMS *Upholder*, one of the British submarines preying on Axis shipping in the Mediterranean in 1940–43. (IWM)

'The loss of the *Bismarck* had a decisive effect on the conduct of the war at sea.' So wrote Grand Admiral Erich Raeder *(above, left)*, Commander-in-Chief of the German Navy, 1928–43, who pinned his hopes of cutting Britain's communications on his surface fleet. (IWM) *(Above, right)* 'The most formidably intelligent, resourceful and relentless opponent that the Royal Navy had had to fight since the Dutchmen de Ruyter and Van Tromp' – Grand Admiral Karl Dönitz in

command of the U-boat arm, 1936–43; C-in-C of the German Navy 1943–45. On the left is Albert Speer, Reichsminister for Armaments, who kept U-boat construction rising despite Allied bombing. (IWM) *(Below)* 'Oceanic submersible Volkswagens, rugged and reliable.' A 750-ton Type VII U-boat, with a range on the surface of 10,000 miles and 130 miles submerged. It carried five torpedo tubes and twelve torpedoes. (IWM)

The *Scharnhorst (above)* was brought to three hours' notice for steam.' The German fast battleship, sister ship to the *Gneisenau (below)*, carried nine 11-inch guns on 31,800 tons displacement. These formidable surface raiders shared a dramatic dash up-channel from Brest to the German ports in February 1942. *Scharnhorst* was sunk by the Home Fleet off Norway's North Cape on 26 December 1943. (IWM)

'*Bismarck*'s vast hull carried formidable weapons systems.' At 52,600 tons full load, a speed of 30.8 knots and eight 15-inch guns, she was one-fifth heavier, three knots faster, and more heavily gunned than the King George V class, but less well armoured. (IWM) (*Inset*) *Vice-Admiral Günther Lütjens, commander of her*

operational plans as if British admirals and their staffs were present beside him at his chart table in Kerneval, evasive routing of convoys became a precision exercise. Even in June the Admiralty succeeded in routing convoys so that the baffled U-boats made no sightings at all in the North Atlantic until encountering HX133. In July they patrolled in vain for three whole weeks, succeeding only once in the month in locating and attacking a convoy, OG69 – in any case not a trans-Atlantic convoy, but one proceeding through the eastern Atlantic on the run between Britain and Africa. In August, and despite a temporary slowing down in the speed of Enigma decrypts, the Admiralty was again able to steer all but one convoy clear of Dönitz's gropings for a target. When Dönitz shifted his boats to the trans-Atlantic routes (after attacking another convoy on the Britain–Africa route) they searched the wide ocean in vain for ten days.

Frustrated and perplexed, he transferred his effort to waters between Northern Ireland and Iceland, whereupon his unfortunate captains found themselves under a ferocious air and surface attack mounted by a forewarned British command. One U-boat was sunk and another, U-570, captured. The U-570, the first to surrender to an aircraft of Coastal Command, was unlucky enough to surface south of Iceland immediately beneath a Hudson of 269 Squadron on convoy patrol. The Hudson promptly depth-charged the U-boat and damaged it before it could submerge, and then persuaded the captain by machine-gun fire to raise the white flag. Later a Catalina relieved the Hudson in keeping watch on the surrendered boat until a trawler arrived to tow it back to Iceland. This capture too proved a bonus for the Bletchley Park cryptographers.

For Dönitz the dismal course of July and August meant failure in the fundamental requirement of U-boat warfare – in the location of targets, never easy at the best of times with so few U-boats and so much ocean. He could not understand why no matter how he redeployed his boats they still found themselves searching empty horizons. In his own words in his memoirs:

Time and again there occurred between one convoy battle and another a long hiatus during which the U-boats swept the seas fruitlessly in a vain attempt to find the enemy. These 'dead' periods naturally caused the U-boat sinking potential to fall. Time and again U-boat Command re-examined the whole problem in an effort to try and find some way of improving this unsatisfactory state of affairs. It was obvious that the main cause was the dearth of U-boats and the lack of 'eyes' with which to search the vast Atlantic expanses. But was it not possible that there might be other reasons to account for our meagre success in locating shipping? Was there any chance, for example, that the enemy had some means of locating U-boat dispositions and of routing his shipping clear of them?[32]

For, as he wrote at the time, 'coincidence alone it cannot be . . .'[33] He ruled out spies as the source of British information, while German cryptographic specialists were absolutely certain that Enigma was impregnable. That left High Frequency Direction Finding (HF/DF), as the most likely culprit; but unfortunately for Dönitz not the true one.

Nonetheless the fall in sinkings by the U-boats in July and August was not solely accounted for by the Admiralty's operational use of Enigma decrypts: the enhanced air and surface protection over the North Atlantic, including end-to-end escorts, provided another helpful factor; and so too did important operational changes in the Admiralty's whole convoy system. For from 18 June, five months after Admiral Sir Percy Noble had first made the suggestion, the Admiralty raised the minimum speed limit for independent sailings (those gifts to the prowling U-boat) from 13 to 15 knots, so leading to a sharp reduction in such sailings, and hence a fall in sinkings thereof from 120 ships in the three months April to June to only 25 ships in July–September.

But in September the U-boats found targets more easily again, launching mass attacks on four convoys, two of them slow homeward-bound convoys (SC42 and 44) caught south of Greenland, outside the range of Coastal Command's Whitleys and Wellingtons, and two others homeward-bound from Freetown and Gibraltar (SL87 and HG73). Convoy SC42 originally consisted of no fewer than 64 ships and was creeping across the ocean at perhaps 6 to 7 knots escorted by one Canadian destroyer and three corvettes; the whole sprawling armada reeking smoke that must have been visible, as the convoy commodore noted, 30 miles away. During the night hours of 9–10 September under a U-boat's moon a savage battle ensued with a pack of eight U-boats (no fewer than seventeen had been called in). As many as four of them were sighted on the surface running down the columns in the middle of the convoy, one of which was chased by HMCS *Skeena*. Eleven ships went down; seven more in the darkness of 10–11 September. Even though two Canadian corvettes, which had been directed by the Admiralty to the rescue, sank the U-501, and a fresh escort group from Iceland of five warships which reached the convoy at noon on the 11th sank another, the U-207, it was a thick sea mist and not the escorts which prevented the enemy from renewing his attacks the next night as well. The unfortunate SC42 had contributed half the total of 36 ships lost in these four convoys.

Of the two homeward bound convoys from Gibraltar and Freetown, HG73 was spotted by a Condor off Cape St Vincent, and shadowed for five days. On this occasion cooperation between KG 40 and U-boat Command proved all too successful: a wolf pack closed on the convoy and sank nine out of its 25 merchantmen despite a very strong escort of ten ships. There were particular reasons for the U-boats' success against HG73, reasons which also embodied an old lesson, for, as Admiral Noble reported to the Admiralty on 5 October, although the escort was strong in numbers it 'suffered from a lack of training as a team, having only recently been formed to meet the call for all-through escort to and from Gibraltar . . .' Noble suggested that it would be desirable to introduce carefully selected junior Royal Navy command-ing officers into corvette groups. He urged too that there was a 'vital need' to ensure the 'minimum dislocation of groups' and provide reasonable time for training between trips, 'since MAINTENANCE and TRAINING are the two hinge pins of success. The escort group of HG73 is an example of what we may expect if these rules are not strictly adhered to.'[34]

Dönitz's better success in September owed itself partially to the increased number of operational U-boats which the shipyards and the crew training courses had placed in his hands – now rising towards 80, as against 30 in April. Yet in fact this shift in the balance of the visible struggle out on the high seas was mainly a reflection of a further shift in the balance of the secret electronic war of Sigint, this time towards U-boat Command. For Dönitz, suspecting that HF/DF fixes were enabling the British to locate his U-boats and follow their movements, had been cutting down as far as possible on the volume of U-boat/U-boat-Command radio (and hence Enigma) traffic. Like-wise suspecting that there might be internal leaks within U-boat Command itself, he had since mid-June been introducing various coding devices to disguise the position of U-boats on the standard U-boat grid by means of 'relating positions at sea to fixed points of reference – Franz, Oscar, Herbert, etc – arbitrarily chosen and changed at short intervals'.[35] On 11 September Dönitz superseded such measures (which had only temporarily slowed the work of the Bletchley Park cryptographers) because he had found, in Professor Hinsley's words, 'that the fixed reference-point system was too cum-bersome, and the source of miscalculations by U-boats'. In the new system 'the digraphs of the naval grid squares were separately enciphered before the texts of their messages were enciphered on the Enigma machine'.[36] Although the Operational Intelligence Centre

(OIC) and GC and CS were eventually to defeat this new system to a large extent, it meant that for some weeks, in Professor Hinsley's words, 'the identification of the positions given in the instructions to the U-boats was a protracted process involving some guesswork'.[37]

But in October U-boat successes fell away again, to 32 ships of 156,554 tons; a quarter less than in September.[38] For by now GC and CS were providing the Admiralty's Operational Intelligence Centre at only 26 hours' delay with a complete picture of U-boat deployment and Dönitz's tactical instructions, enabling the Admiralty to reroute no fewer than fifteen convoys during the month. Once again Dönitz's patrol lines swept the seas in vain search for mysteriously elusive convoys, only succeeding in attacking one North Atlantic convoy (SC48) and one on the Africa–Gibraltar–England route. Moreover, the improvement in Coastal Command's air cover was also making its impact, for the U-boats sank no vessels within 400 miles of a Coastal Command base and only twelve in the range 400 to 600 miles occasionally patrolled by Catalinas.[39] There was a further factor: in September Dönitz had been ordered by Hitler and Raeder to divert six U-boats into the Mediterranean to aid the Italian Navy, so weakening his October effort in the Atlantic.

However, October 1941 is notable in the history of the Battle of the Atlantic for another reason – on 17 October the United States destroyer USS *Kearney* was torpedoed and damaged by a U-boat during a night battle against a wolf pack south of Iceland while escorting a Britain-bound convoy (SC48) of 50 ships; and on 31 October the destroyer USS *Reuben James* was sunk by another U-boat while escorting the Britain-bound convoy HX156. She was the first American warship to go down in the Battle of the Atlantic. These two events explosively drove home to the world the month-old fact that the United States of America, though still technically neutral, had joined in the battle on Britain's side.

Ever since the summer of 1940 Churchill had continued to seek by patient, well-tuned diplomacy to draw the United States, through the medium of President Roosevelt, into the fight against Nazi Germany, judging this to offer Britain's only long-term hope of survival and victory. Roosevelt himself, a crafty politician sensitive to strong isolationist opinion in Congress and the American public at large, had moved cautiously; more cautiously than the desperately pressed British wanted. Again and again he promised more than he later performed.[40] But for evident strategic reasons, the security of the Atlantic was of direct concern to the American government. On 1 March 1941 the United States Navy created the Support Force Atlantic Fleet, composed of three squadrons of destroyers and four squadrons of Catalinas and Martin Mariners, to be based on new and exclusively American bases constructed in Northern Ireland (Londonderry) and Scotland. The making of joint arrangements between an American team, led by Admiral Ghormley, and the Admiralty for setting up and operating the new bases signified another step along the road to complete comradeship-in-arms, even though Ghormley emphasised the importance politically of keeping US and British forces distinct both in organisation and tasks.[41]

In April 1941 Roosevelt extended the zone covered by the Western Hemisphere Neutrality Patrol eastwards to 26°W, which included most of Greenland where the United States had just acquired the right to establish bases. Within this zone American warships would report the position of sighted U-boats to the Admiralty but not attack them themselves. Next month Roosevelt transferred a carrier and four destroyers from the Pacific to the Atlantic via the Panama Canal, soon followed by three battleships, four cruisers and fourteen destroyers. He proposed to the British government that American forces should assume the defence of Iceland in place of British forces, although it was not until 7 July that this was carried out. That month also American forces took over the Canadian harbour at Argentia, Newfoundland, and began to develop it into a major naval base which was operational in August, when it served as the rendezvous for the first summit conference between Churchill (who had crossed the Atlantic in the new battleship HMS *Prince of Wales*) and Roosevelt (embarked in the cruiser USS *Augusta*).

At this conference Roosevelt agreed to implement the at present shelved American 'Western Hemisphere Defence Plan Number 4', by which United States warships would assume responsibility for escorting North Atlantic convoys west of 26°. Churchill in reporting this to the Cabinet described the decision as this 'unparalleled gesture of friendship by a neutral power'[42] and hoped that the measure would be implemented by the end of the month. 'The President's orders to these escorts,' he told his colleagues, 'were to attack any U-boat which showed itself, even if it were 200 or 300 miles away from the convoy. Admiral Stark [the US Chief of Naval Operations] intended to carry out this order literally, and any commander who sank a U-boat would have his action approved. Everything was to be done to force an "incident".'[43] But in the event it was German action which gave Roosevelt the political pretext finally to carry out his promise.

On 4 September the destroyer USS *Greer* was attacked by the U-boat which it had been tracking, and counter-attacked it with depth-charges. That same day Roosevelt exploited this incident in one of his famous radio 'fireside chats' to the nation as an opportunity and a justification for announcing that henceforth the US Navy would protect all merchant ships 'of any flag' within American defensive waters.[44] Although Roosevelt did not say so on the radio, 'American defensive waters' were now extended to 10°W, little more than 400 miles from the west coast of Scotland. On 16 September, and for the first time, a British convoy (the homeward bound HX150 of 50 ships) sailed under United States Navy escort.

In conformity with the newly agreed division of responsibility in the North Atlantic, the US ships took over from the Royal Canadian Navy at the 'Western Ocean Meeting Points' 150 miles south of Argentia and handed on the convoy to the Royal Navy at the 'Mid-Ocean Meeting Points' south of Iceland in about 58°N, 22°W.[45] By now too United States Navy Catalinas and the United States Army Air Corps B-24s based on Argentia were working closely with the Royal Canadian Air Force over the Western Atlantic, while other Catalinas had been stationed in Iceland to work with Coastal Command.

For the Royal Navy this final commitment of the United States Navy to the Battle of the Atlantic signified an immense lightening of the burden. As Captain Roskill, the British official naval historian, writes, what it meant 'to the Admiralty, to the Flag Officers, to the captains and crews of the ships and aircraft who had for so long fought this vital and unending struggle alone, may not be easily realised by posterity'.[46] Yet the glory and the achievement of that successful lone struggle belonged to the little but growing Royal Canadian Navy and Royal Canadian Air Force as well as to the Royal Navy and the Royal Air Force. And Canada's great port of Halifax had served – as it would continue to serve – as the rendezvous and departure point for the convoys which in constant progression bore the North American supplies across the ocean to Britain, without which she could neither wage war nor even live. Canada had been, and would remain, the essential western buttress of Britain's Atlantic bridge.

Now it was November 1941 and for two months Dönitz had been fighting three navies instead of two. His patrol lines of U-boats proved even less lucky in trawling targets than in October, no matter how he altered their search tactics, thanks to GC and CS's now complete ability to read the 'Home Waters' Enigma key at short delay. On 22 November Dönitz ordered all his Atlantic boats to concentrate in the waters off Gibraltar, thereby acknowledging the decisive defeat of his first major wolf-pack offensive in the Battle of the Atlantic. In the whole of November his boats sank only thirteen ships of 62,196 tons.

In December, when his strength in the Atlantic had been reduced to a mere 27 boats by further diversions to the Mediterranean at Hitler's insistence, sinkings in all waters stood at 26 ships of 124,070 tons – barely more than half the tonnage of December 1940, and achieved at the cost of ten U-boats.[47]

The Royal Navy had also been experimenting successfully with ingenious new means of defending convoys against the Focke-Wulf Condors of KG 40. In December 1940 the first fighter catapult ship, HMS *Pegasus*, converted from a Great War seaplane carrier, had gone to sea with a convoy. She carried three Fulmar fighters. In April 1941 she was followed by three more 'Fighter Catapult Ships' (as they were now designated), *Springbank*, *Maplin* and *Ariguani*, each converted from a merchantman to carry one fighter. A fourth conversion, the *Patria*, was sunk before she could embark her aircraft. By July all the fighter catapult ships were deployed on the Gibraltar convoy route, favourite hunting territory for the Condors, and on 3 August a Condor crew was astonished to be attacked and shot down 400 miles out to sea from the Iberian coast by a fighter whose proper habitat lay in the sky over England. The Hurricane (piloted by Lieutenant R. W. H. Everett, RNVR) had in fact been catapulted from the *Maplin*.

A start had also been made in April in fitting catapults to fifty merchantmen to be known as 'Catapult Aircraft Merchantmen' ('CAM ships'), and they began to go into service in the early summer. Unlike the fighter catapult ships, the CAM ships remained merchantmen plying under the Red Ensign, their crews merchant seamen except for the pilot (seconded from Royal Air Force Fighter Command) and for the maintenance staff of their single Hurricane. The pilots flying from both kinds of catapult ship had to be exceptionally brave men because there was no means of recovering them at the end of a sortie except by fishing them from the sea after they had parachuted from their aircraft or landed in the water – which was fortunately achieved in the case of Lieutenant Everett. Sadly the *Springbank* was sunk in September during the U-boat onslaught on convoy HG73, while in the following month the *Ariguani* was badly damaged.

In September was commissioned HMS *Audacity*, the prototype of the light escort aircraft carrier. It marked one of the most significant developments in the history of maritime airpower. The *Audacity* (5,527 tons; 15 knots)[48] had been converted from a German prize, the merchant ship *Hannover*, by installing a simple flight deck above the hull; she carried six American Grumman Martlet fighters (maximum speed at 19,400 feet, 318 mph).[49] Employed on the Gibraltar route, she provided, in Dönitz's rueful words, 'a continuous air umbrella'[50] which deprived the Condors of their ability to shadow British convoys for the benefit of U-boats or themselves bomb hapless strays. A Martlet from *Audacity* (Commander D. W. McKendrick, RN) bagged her first Condor during a major convoy battle on 20–21 September. In December *Audacity*'s aircraft played a key role in the defeat of a mass U-boat attack on convoy HG76 by driving off the shadowing Condors (downing two of them), attacking surfaced U-boats and reporting back their positions. It was thanks to the combined efforts of *Audacity*'s aircraft and the surface escorts that four U-boats were destroyed for the loss of only two merchant ships; a notable tactical victory. But she herself succumbed to a torpedo on the night of 19 December, when against the advice of the convoy escort commander, Commander F. J. Walker, RN, she was steaming outside the convoy's defensive screen.

Nevertheless *Audacity* had proved the point – the escort carrier offered the real answer to the marauding Condor. More than that, it vindicated the War Cabinet Battle of the Atlantic Committee's far-sighted judgment in May 1941 in being 'deeply impressed' with the anti-U-boat potential of the escort carrier, and in looking ahead to the day when *Audacity* (having defeated the Condor) would carry Torpedo-Spotter-Reconnaissance aircraft in order 'to provide a convoy with its own anti-submarine air patrols'.[51] In the event this development fell not to *Audacity*, but to her successors, of which five were on order in 1941 from British yards, and seven more in American yards under Lend-Lease, all bigger than *Audacity* and, unlike her, equipped with hangars. The vast armada of escort carriers, the majority of them American-built, that would traverse the oceans in coming years derived from *Audacity*. She and the other 1941 experiments in the air defence of convoys brilliantly demonstrated that the creative imagination which had inspired the Royal Navy to pioneer the aircraft carrier itself during the Great War was still in successful flight.

When the final balance sheet for 1941 in the Battle of the Atlantic came to be struck, it showed that 496 ships totalling 2,421,700 tons had been sunk by all forms of German attack – U-boat, surface raider and bomber. The total for all theatres came to 4,328,558 tons – awful enough, but far short of the Joint Planners' fear back in June that 7 million tons could well be lost by the end of the year.[52] Britain's jugular vein had been temporarily squeezed, not severed. Yet for all the endurance and professional skill of the crews of His Majesty's ships and aircraft and of the Merchant Marine on the high seas, the decisive instrument of the deliverance lay in the teams of civilians in the quiet huts of Bletchley Park who had broken Dönitz's Enigma cypher. To them for the time being belonged the place of honour on 'the right of the line'.[53]

For Dönitz himself, meditating the failure of his 1941 campaign, the only certain figure was that he had lost 35 U-boats in the course of the year. No wonder that, in his own words, 1941 came to an end 'in an atmosphere of worry and anxiety for U-boat Command'.[54]

In the meantime Grand Admiral Raeder, his Commander-in-Chief, had made his climactic effort to fulfil his own long-cherished strategy of breaking down Britain's sea communications by means of powerful raiding forces of surface warships. In contrast to the endless grinding attrition between U-boat and convoy, this had been an episode imbued with all the elements of an ancient Nordic saga – perilous questings through ice-girded and mist-shrouded seas; bloody combat and heroic death; the strivings of men and the workings of fate.

'The Bismarck *Must Be Sunk At All Costs*'

Towards noon (German time) on 18 May 1941 the battleship *Bismarck* (Captain Ernst Lindemann), flying the flag of Vice-Admiral Günther Lütjens, cast off from her moorings alongside the wharf of the Baltic naval base of Gotenhafen and moved slowly away into the roadstead. As the 150,000 horsepower Brown-Boveri turbines hummed deep down in the ship, the band on the quarterdeck played 'Muss i denn', the traditional German military song of departure on a campaign; the one sung by Ludendorff's soldiers 23 years earlier as they marched up to the line for the great 1918 March offensive on the Western Front. For an astute observer on shore here was a clue that this time *Bismarck* was sailing on more than another training exercise. During the next eight hours *Bismarck* lay at anchor out in the roadstead completing the loading of supplies and fuel. Unfortunately the rupturing of an oil fuelling pipe prevented her tanks being topped to capacity. At 0200 on 19 May, she weighed anchor and steamed westwards for the Kattegat and the North Sea, rendezvousing in the forenoon with the heavy cruiser *Prinz Eugen* (Captain Helmuth Brinkmann; 14,800 tons displacement, eight 8-inch guns) and an escort of three destroyers.

'Operation Rheinübung' ('Rhine Exercise') was under way.

Grand Admiral Raeder had been maturing the strategic concept underlying 'Rheinübung' since the Atlantic raids undertaken by the battleships *Scharnhorst* and *Gneisenau* and the cruiser *Hipper* at the end of 1940 (see above, pp. 73–6). In January 1941 he had sent the two battleships to sea on another joint foray under Lütjens's command. Baulked by British counter-moves from breaking through into the Atlantic by the direct route between Iceland and the Shetlands, Lütjens had skilfully doubled back, rounded the north of Iceland and reached the Atlantic sea routes via the Denmark Strait. His first encounter was with Convoy HX106, escorted by the unmodernised old battleship *Ramillies*. True to his instructions to avoid embroilment with British heavy ships, Lütjens fled as soon as *Ramillies*'s funnel was seen to emit dark smoke, suggesting that she was working up to full speed in order to engage. In the scornful words of a German naval historian: 'The ancient *Ramillies* had only to let off a few angry puffs of smoke and both German battleships despite their modern fire-control and the proven effectiveness of their guns, even at long range – sought safety in escape.'[1]

From then on Lütjens's ships had ranged as far south as Sierra Leone and as far west and north as waters near Halifax, and they, along with the pocket battleship *Scheer* in the Indian Ocean and the *Hipper* on the Azores route, sank or captured 48 ships totalling nearly 270,000 tons by the end of March, when they all returned to port – *Scharnhorst*, *Gneisenau* and *Hipper* to Brest; *Scheer* to Kiel. And, just as in the previous year, the disruption to British sea communications, the strain on the Royal Navy of searching for the elusive raiders and at the same time striving to protect the trade routes from attack, had been out of all proportion to the size of force employed. At this period too no fewer than six German merchant raiders were hunting as far afield as the Antarctic, East Africa and the waters between South America and South Africa, so adding enormously to the strain and disruption. All these prolonged and distant cruises of warships were made possible by the advanced posting of supply ships and oiltankers in various sea areas, at a period when the Royal Navy, lacking fleet trains, remained leashed to fixed naval bases; a heavy handicap.

Raeder now believed therefore that in the near future he could 'strike the British supply system a mortal blow'.[2] For the new battleship *Bismarck* was already nearly worked up, while her sister ship *Tirpitz* had joined her in the Gulf of Danzig in April for her own working-up. What might not be achieved by a raiding task force composed of these two ships (the most powerful in the world except for the two Japanese *Yamatos*) and the proven veterans *Scharnhorst* and *Gneisenau*? Wrote Raeder in a directive on 2 April 1941: 'As soon as the two battleships of the Bismarck class are ready for deployment, we will be able to seek engagement with the forces escorting enemy convoys and, when they have been eliminated, destroy the convoy itself.'[3]

However, he was not prepared to wait for *Tirpitz* to finish working up: 'As of now, we cannot follow this course [of deploying both new battleships], but it will soon be possible, as an intermediate step, for us to use the battleship *Bismarck* to distract the hostile escorting forces, in order to enable the other units engaged to operate against the convoy itself.'[4] Unfortunately the *Scharnhorst* and *Gneisenau* were at present in the dockyard in Brest undergoing refits – in *Scharnhorst*'s case, a major overhaul of her engines which meant that she would not be ready for sea until June. All this much reduced the scope of Raeder's plans:

> At the earliest possible date, which it is hoped will be during the new-moon period of April, the *Bismarck* and the *Prinz Eugen*, led by the Fleet Commander, are to be deployed as commerce-raiders in the Atlantic. The *Gneisenau* will also be sent into the Atlantic, but that will depend on when her repairs have been completed.[5]

At this point Royal Air Force Coastal Command intervened. On 6 April at first light a Beaufort torpedo aircraft of No. 22 Squadron, commanded by Flying Officer K. Campbell, skimming the sea below masthead level and just clearing the mole, pressed home an attack on the *Gneisenau* in the inner harbour of Brest to loose a torpedo at a range of only 500 yards. The Beaufort crashed into the ground after being riddled with concentrated anti-aircraft fire, killing the heroic Campbell and his crew of three. But even before they died, their torpedo had wrecked *Gneisenau*'s stern. Six days later, when she had been moved into dry dock Bomber Command, in one of its interventions in the naval war, hit her with four bombs. Raeder's grand design had now shrunk to the *Bismarck* and *Prinz Eugen*.

It was Lütjens's opinion, as the force commander designate, expressed to Raeder at a briefing in Berlin on 26 April, that there was 'a powerful case for waiting until at least the *Scharnhorst* has been repaired – if not until the crew of the *Tirpitz* have finished their training'.[6] Raeder disagreed: the approach of short summer nights, the danger that America might enter the war in the future, the need to keep the momentum going in the Atlantic battle, the need to divert British naval strength from the Mediterranean, all these factors argued in his view for action without delay. Convinced or otherwise, Lütjens acquiesced obediently. Hitler himself, when briefed on 5 May aboard the *Bismarck*, did not prohibit the operation even though he had his doubts, especially with regard to the danger of air attack.

Lütjens's operational brief from OKM (*Oberkommando der Kriegs-marine*) was true to the ambiguous pattern of earlier German raiding, and the very reverse of the deep instinct of the Royal Navy to 'engage the enemy more closely' whenever possible: 'Once again the primary objective is the destruction of the enemy's carrying capacity. Enemy warships will be engaged only in furtherance of this objective, and provided such engagements *can take place without excessive risk*.'[7] Lütjens finally went to sea in *Bismarck* in a mood of sombre duty, even fatalistic acceptance of death to come.[8]

For he was far from the British model of extrovert admiral exemplified by such men as Andrew Cunningham and James Somerville; rather he was a man as tightly buttoned up as his uniform jacket. His taciturn and aloof manner, severe visage relieved only by full, strongly carved lips, and intense, even troubled, gaze, all suggested a deeply serious professional; one anxious – perhaps over-anxious – not to fail in his duty. The Captain of the *Bismarck*, Ernst Lindemann, cool, competent and devoted though he was, might rather have been taken for a chief engineer or accountant in a German industrial cartel than for a fighting sailor, with sharp, pale eyes in a sharp face, grimly zealous, and his straight, oiled hair brushed flat to a narrow, big-eared head. Thus, although Lütjens's and Lindemann's mission rendered them latter-day pirates or corsairs, neither man was blessed with the adventuring temperament or the personal magic of a Francis Drake, a Bailli de Suffren or a John Paul Jones – or, for that matter, one of Dönitz's young U-boat aces.

Like every member of his ships' companies, Lütjens was very conscious that *Bismarck* and *Prinz Eugen* were about to brave the power and wrath of what was still one of the world's two greatest seapowers; aware that their first success would draw a swarm of battleships, aircraft carriers and cruisers into a hunt for them. But Lütjens and Lindemann and all their sailors put their faith in the *Bismarck* herself, as formidable a fighting ship as German technology could contrive, and, at 52,600 tons full load, a fifth heavier than the Royal Navy's new battleships *King George V* and *Prince of Wales*. From clipper bow to cruiser stern *Bismarck* was 823½ feet long; the rakish sweep of her superstructure up to her fighting top and cowled funnel the very expression of speed and power. Her beam of 118 feet compared with the 103 feet of the King George Vs and the 108 feet of the new American Iowa class battleships. A main armoured belt 12.6 inches thick, and horizontal deck armour 4½ inches thick protected her magazines and machinery, along with an internal 'bulge' of oil and water storage compartments on beams against torpedoes. *Bismarck*'s 150,000 horsepower turbines driving three shafts (uprated from an original 138,000 horsepower) gave her a maximum speed of 30.8 knots, as against *King George V*'s 27.5 knots; her range (providing that her oil tanks had been filled to the brim) was 8,000 miles at a cruising speed of 19 knots. A novel feature of her design lay in her twin rudders, but when a training exercise postulated that the rudders had been jammed by damage, it had been found to be very difficult to keep the ship on course by steering with the propellers.

Bismarck's vast hull carried formidable weapons systems. Her main battery of eight 15-inch guns in twin turrets (protected by armour up to 14 inches thick) compared with *King George V*'s ten 14-inch guns. She inherited from her Great War predecessors the proven excellence of Zeiss stereoscopic range-finders. These were mounted in revolving cupolas above the three armoured fire-control stations – forward of the bridge, in the foretop above the bridge, and aft. Attached to these cupolas were the mattress-like latticework aerials of the radar sets which could supply accurate ranges in pitch dark or foul weather. Ranges and bearings (the latter provided by the directors: periscope-like optical devices protruding through the top of the fire-control stations) were fed into a computing system comparable to the British fire-control clock, which then locked the 15-inch guns on target. Following the system employed with such success by Hipper's battle-cruisers at Jutland and since adopted by the Royal Navy too, *Bismarck*'s gunners were practised at opening fire with a 'bracketing group' of salvoes, three in the air at the same time separated by fixed range, usually 400 yards. As a gunnery officer in the ship wrote later of such training practices, 'we usually succeeded in boxing or straddling the target on the first fall of shot'[9]; the result of accurate ranging thanks to superb range-finders.

As well as her main battery, *Bismarck* was equipped with a secondary (anti-destroyer) armament of twelve 5.9-inch guns in twin turrets, a heavy anti-aircraft battery of sixteen 4.1-inch guns in twin turrets, plus sixteen 37mm anti-aircraft guns (also in twin turrets), plus again thirty-six 20mm light anti-aircraft guns.[10] Some experts have argued that *Bismarck* was old-fashioned in having both a 5.9-inch secondary armament against surface targets and a 4.1-inch heavy anti-aircraft battery, instead of a weight-saving dual-purpose secondary armament like the sixteen 5.25-inch guns carried by the King George Vs. Yet in action *Bismarck* was to use her 5.9s against aircraft as well as her 4.1s. Moreover, her anti-aircraft armament enjoyed no fewer than six separate director controls, so giving flexibility in acquiring targets.

Experts have equally argued that the designers of *Bismarck* had followed an outmoded Great War pattern of widely distributing the armour over the hull instead of the more modern 'all or nothing' technique practised by British and American designers, whereby the given weight of armour was concentrated over the vital spaces, leaving the rest of the hull unprotected (which in the case of the King George Vs, gave a maximum thickness of armour in the main belt of 15 inches to *Bismarck*'s 12.6, and 6-inch horizontal deck armour over the magazine to the German ship's 4½ inches.[11] But needless to say, no such cavils troubled the minds of Lütjens, Lindemann and the ship's company as they steamed westwards through the Baltic from Gotenhafen on 19 May 1941 in hopeful expectation of a successful foray.

Next day, shimmeringly bright, found the squadron passing through the Great Belt between Denmark and Sweden; the destroyers in the van, then the huge *Bismarck* with Lütjens's flag of a black Maltese cross on a white ground at her peak and *Prinz Eugen* (named after Prince Eugène, Marlborough's devoted Austrian comrade during the War of the Spanish Succession) following astern. On the starboard beam in clear sight lay the Swedish coast, and around the great grey ships a bright green sea bobbed with busy fishing boats. By now the ship's company of the *Bismarck* (2,200 strong, counting extra Luftwaffe personnel to operate her three aircraft) knew their mission, for Captain Lindemann had told them over the tannoy the previous day that they were setting forth on a three-month cruise in the Atlantic to devastate British convoys. He ended his address with the traditional German hunter's toast: 'Good hunting and a good bag!'[12]

At 1300 another warship appeared to starboard and for a time steamed on a parallel course: it was the Swedish cruiser *Gotland*. Lütjens therefore signalled Group North (the German naval command responsible for all operations north of the English Channel): 'At 1300 the aircraft-carrying cruiser *Gotland* passed in clear view, therefore anticipate formation will be reported.' But the C-in-C Group North, General-Admiral Rolf Carls, complacently replied: 'Because of the strictly neutral conduct of Sweden, I do not think the danger of being compromised by the Swedish warship is any greater than from the already present systematic enemy surveillance of the entrance to the Baltic.'[13]

In fact, a member of the Swedish naval staff passed the information the same day to his friend the Norwegian military attaché in Stockholm, who passed it straight to the British naval attaché, who reported it to the Admiralty at 2100 (British time) that night. The report tied in ominously with information previously derived from decrypts of the Luftwaffe Enigma that Condors had been carrying out unusually intense reconnaissance of the ice edge between Jan Mayen Island and Greenland.[14] These decrypts had already spurred the C-in-C, Home Fleet, Admiral Sir John Tovey, to instruct ships patrolling the Denmark Strait to heighten their vigilance, and in particular to order the cruiser HMS *Suffolk* specially to watch the waters along the ice edge. Now the Admiralty asked that Coastal Command photo-reconnaissance Spitfires based at Wick in northern Scotland should reconnoitre the Norwegian coast in order to locate the German squadron. Just two hours after *Bismarck* and *Prinz Eugen* anchored in Bergen fjord at 1100 hours on 21 May (British time, which will be henceforth used throughout the account of the pursuit of the *Bismarck*), one of the Spitfires, piloted by Flying Officer Suckling, was high overhead with its camera busy. At 1828 the Admiralty Operational Intelligence Centre alerted all naval commands to the discovery recorded on the returned Spitfire's film, adding: 'It is evident that these ships intend to carry out a raid on trade routes.'[15]

In Scapa Flow Admiral Sir John Tovey brought the flagship *King George V* (Captain W. R. Patterson) and the 2nd Cruiser Squadron (Rear-Admiral A. T. Curteis: *Galatea*, *Aurora*, *Kenya* and *Neptune*) to short notice for steam. He instructed Rear-Admiral W. F. Wake-Walker, commanding 1st Cruiser Squadron (*Norfolk* and *Suffolk*) to continue watching the Denmark Strait, and Vice-Admiral L. E. Holland (commanding the Battle Cruiser Force, and flying his flag in the 42,000-ton battlecruiser *Hood*) to sail with *Hood*, the battleship *Prince of Wales* and the destroyers *Electra*, *Anthony*, *Echo*, *Achates* and *Antelope* in order to cover *Norfolk* and *Suffolk*. At 0050 on 22 May *Hood* led the Battle Cruiser Force out past the Hoxa boom and set course for Denmark Strait. Tovey also ordered the cruisers *Manchester* and *Birmingham*, at present on patrol between Iceland and the Faeroes, to refuel at Skalfjord in Iceland and resume their watch. The battlecruiser *Repulse* and the new fleet carrier *Victorious* had been due to sail on 22 May as escort to the Middle East troop convoy; now the Admiralty placed them instead at the disposal of the C-in-C, Home Fleet.

While all this bustle of orders and sailings and redeployments was in train, Lütjens was oiling *Prinz Eugen* in Bergen from the tanker *Wollin*, but surprisingly failing to oil *Bismarck* herself which had sailed from Gotenhafen with tanks not completely full, and which had burnt about a ninth of her full-load capacity in the course of the voyage to Norway. It is true that Lütjens knew that there was an oiler, the

[284]

Weissenburg, waiting for him in the Arctic a day or so away; nevertheless it seems strangely neglectful not to take every opportunity to top up *Bismarck*'s tanks during so hazardous a venture. In any event, Lütjens's decision to call in at Bergen at all, overturning his previous decision to head straight for the Arctic and the *Weissenburg*, can be questioned,[16] for it lost him a day and also exposed him to possible detection by the frequent British air surveillance of the Norwegian coastline – which in the event is what happened, as Lütjens himself was well aware, the photo-reconnaissance Spitfire having been belatedly spotted by the German ships. Perhaps he had taken too much assurance from a Luftwaffe photo-reconnaissance report the previous day that three heavy ships (*King George V, Prince of Wales* and *Hood*) and a carrier (*Victorious*) were at that time all still at anchor in Scapa Flow.

At 1945 on the 21st Lütjens put to sea again and set a course due north at 24 knots, detaching the destroyers to Trondheim in the small hours of the 22nd. By 2100 that day *Bismarck* and *Prinz Eugen* were in 68°N, 3°W, in the same latitude as the Denmark Strait north of Iceland, and steaming westwards towards it. In choosing this circuitous course, he had ignored the advice of Group North to steer directly for the Atlantic between Iceland and the Faeroes; he had also decided not to go further north still in order to refuel from the *Weissenburg*. Like his predecessor Admiral Scheer on his way to Jutland in May 1916, Lütjens had no idea that strong British forces were already at sea to intercept him (in Lütjens's case, the *Hood* and *Prince of Wales*), although he did know from signals from Group North (drawing on German Intelligence sources) that his departure from Gotenhafen and passage of the Kattegat had been detected and that the British had ordered air searches for him. That very evening Group North had even confirmed to him from further Luftwaffe photo-reconnaissance that the main body of the Home Fleet still remained in Scapa Flow.

For Tovey and the Admiralty the time since the Spitfire photo-reconnaissance aircraft had radioed at 1300 on 21 May that *Bismarck* and *Prinz Eugen* were in Bergen fjord had passed in anxious and baffled waiting for news as to whether or not they had subsequently put to sea again. An attempt to find and bomb the German ships in Bergen fjord on that afternoon miscarried in dense fog. Daylight on the 22nd brought even worse weather, with cloud over the North Sea down to 200 feet. Up in the Denmark Strait the cloud was unbroken down to 300 feet, with curtains of rain closing visibility to less than half a mile, so that reconnaissance aircraft could see nothing. However, the commanding officer at the Fleet Air Arm station at Hatston in the

Orkneys, Captain H. L. S. J. Fancourt, decided on his own initiative to send a Glenn Martin Maryland twin-engined reconnaissance aircraft to look for the *Bismarck* and *Prinz Eugen* along the Norwegian coastline.

The Maryland was piloted by Lieutenant (A) N. N. Goddard, RNVR, and crewed as usual by Lieutenants Armstrong and Milne. Commander G. A. ('Hank') Rotherham (then flying a desk as second-in-command of the station) volunteered to fill the vacant job of Observer. The aircraft crossed the North Sea flying either beneath the clouds at heights down to 50 feet or above the clouds at 3,000 feet. Over the Norwegian coast the sky cleared, allowing Goddard to descend to 1,000 feet and begin his search. In Rotherham's words:

> We ran up inside the fjords to the anchorage [at Bergen], but it was bare. After we had circled to look into all of the possible holes and corners to be sure we hadn't overlooked anything I directed Noel over Bergen Harbour to see if she had moved there. This was too much for the Germans and they opened up with everything they had. We shot across the harbour and out to sea losing height as we went . . .[17]

In confirming that 'Bergen was clear' they supplied the key piece of information which the C-in-C, Home Fleet, needed; and Tovey later showed his appreciation by writing in his despatch: 'This skilful and determined reconnaissance is deserving of the highest praise, as is the initiative of Captain Fancourt in ordering it.'[18] Rotherham's report reached Tovey in his flagship at 2000 that evening of the 22nd. It then fell to Tovey, studying the charts with his staff, to guess the enemy's present course and deploy the Home Fleet accordingly.

It was the first of all the consequence-laden choices that would fall to him in the coming week as the admiral bearing the greatest single responsibility for catching and destroying Lütjens before he could disappear into the wide Atlantic. Tovey – small, lean-featured, straight of nose and mouth, eyes blue beneath hooded lids; a tough face sometimes set in resolute purpose, sometimes sparkling with humour – was well-equipped by character, experience and judgment to bear that responsibility. Like Cunningham, he had been formed by early service in destroyers, commanding HMS *Onslow* in the thick of the Battle of Jutland. Although just as deeply serious a man as his opponent Lütjens, indeed a devout Christian who prayed night and morning, he enjoyed good living and good company. He was liked for his warm and outgoing personality and respected for his forthright leadership. In 1940 Cunningham, a difficult man to please, had appointed Tovey to command all the Mediterranean Fleet's cruisers and destroyers, and later recorded his appreciation of Tovey's 'advice, outspoken criticism, loyal support, cheerful optimism and imperturbability . . .'[19]

At the core of his character lay a hardened steel integrity which forbade him to compromise with what he believed to be wrong. An admiral wrote of him when he was captain of the *Rodney*: 'Captain Tovey shares one characteristic with me. In myself I would call it tenacity of purpose. In Tovey I can only call it sheer bloody obstinacy.'[20] Tovey had demonstrated at his first meeting with the Prime Minister on appointment as C-in-C in December 1940 that his professional integrity was proof even against Churchill. As he confided in a letter to Cunningham, 'You know the PM much better than I do, and you will understand how I loved him almost at first sight, but he made some such astounding statements about naval warfare . . . [that] I still don't know if he was wanting to find out if I was prepared to applaud everything he said or whether he really believes half of what he says.'[21] But in regard to conduct of the pursuit of the *Bismarck*, Tovey was to discover that Churchill could indeed 'really believe' at least one truly astounding Prime Ministerial naval directive.

Although it was always possible that *Bismarck* and *Prinz Eugen* might be making for a port in northern Norway or even steaming to strike British bases in Iceland, Tovey was convinced that their objective must be the obvious one of the Atlantic convoy routes. Yet he had no means of judging whether the enemy ships would pass north or south of Iceland. He therefore signalled the cruiser *Suffolk* to rejoin the *Norfolk* in watching the Denmark Strait and the ice edge off Iceland, and the cruiser *Arethusa* to join *Manchester* and *Birmingham* in forming a patrol line between Iceland and the Faeroes. He requested Coastal Command to supplement these patrols by flying air searches over the Denmark Strait (180 miles across), the Iceland–Faeroes gap (255 miles wide), the Faeroes to the Shetlands (165 miles across) and also the Norwegian coast. He ordered Vice-Admiral Holland with the *Hood* (Captain R. Kerr, RN) and *Prince of Wales* (Captain J. C. Leach, RN) to cover the cruisers in the Denmark Strait north of 62°N, while he himself with the remainder of the Home Fleet would cover the passages south of 62°N.

At 2245 on 22 May 1941, an hour and a half after Lütjens, far to the north, had turned his ships westwards for the Denmark Strait, Tovey in his flagship *King George V* led the carrier *Victorious*, the cruisers *Galatea*, *Aurora*, *Kenya*, *Hermione* and the destroyers *Intrepid*, *Inglefield*, *Punjabi*, *Lance*, *Active* and *Windsor* out of Scapa Flow and headed due west.

The *Victorious* (23,000 tons displacement; 31 knots) had only just been commissioned, for, being a product of belated British rearmament, she was not even launched until eleven days after the outbreak of war. Moreover, when the Admiralty placed her at Tovey's disposal, she had been about to leave for the Middle East crammed with crated Hurricanes, and her available striking force consisted of only nine Swordfish and six Fulmars, while her aircrews lacked training and experience. Tovey's flagship *King George V* (36,750 tons displacement; 44,000 tons full load) was the first British battleship to be commissioned since the 1920s 'naval holiday', having been laid down in January 1937 at the very start of the rearmament programme and completed in December 1940. She had served as a flagship of the Home Fleet for only a month. Compared to the crew of the *Bismarck*, which had been training intensively in the Baltic since August 1940, her ship's company was still relatively raw. Furthermore, her two quadruple 14-inch turrets were of a novel design not yet tried and tested in action. The battlecruiser *Repulse* (27,333 tons displacement; six 15-inch guns), which joined the Fleet from the Clyde off the Butt of Lewis in the forenoon of 23 May, dated from 1916. Despite some strengthening of her weak armour protection in 1919–20 and new anti-aircraft batteries in the late 1930s, she remained essentially unmodernised.

It was hardly an overwhelming force, therefore, that Admiral Tovey was taking to sea to meet the *Bismarck*, either in numbers or in fighting power. Nor was the Battle Cruiser Force under Vice-Admiral Holland, now well on its way to the Denmark Strait, in better case. The battlecruiser *Hood* had been designed before the Battle of Jutland, although her armour protection was improved somewhat as a consequence of that battle. She had been due for radical reconstruction when the Second World War broke out and compelled it to be postponed. Despite her size and majestic appearance, therefore, she still suffered from fundamental weaknesses in armour similar to those of the three battlecruisers lost at Jutland – in particular, main deck armour over the magazines only three inches thick. The *Prince of Wales* (sister ship to *King George V*) had only been completed in March 1941 and still had Vickers's technicians aboard to sort out various teething troubles, especially with her 14-inch turrets.

For Tovey himself, steaming westwards through appalling weather, 23 May was a day of waiting and waiting for news of the vanished enemy. None of the intended air searches could be flown because of cloud and rain, under cover of which Lütjens's ships might have already succeeded in slipping through the Royal Navy's still wide open net. Then at 2032, when the flagship was some 230 miles northwest of the Butt of Lewis in about 60° 20′N, 12° 30′W, came a signal from the *Norfolk* (Captain A. J. L. Phillips, RN). The *Bismarck* had been sighted in the Denmark Strait.

It was in fact Wake-Walker's other ship the *Suffolk* (Captain R. M. Ellis, RN) which saw her first at 1922 as the long Arctic evening began to draw in. Above the ice edge along the Greenland coast and out across the water for some ten miles the weather was clear and bright, while the remainder of the Strait as far as Iceland seventy miles away was shrouded in dense mist. Down that corridor of bright weather (so avoiding the British minefields stretching eastwards to the north cape of Iceland) between the ice edge shining blue-white and the Greenland glaciers on their starboard beam and the abrupt wall of fog lying to port Lütjens's ships had been steaming south-westwards at 27 knots since they left the welcome cover of rain, snow and cloud astern during the afternoon. It was *Suffolk*'s starboard after lookout, Able-Seaman Newall, who spotted the *Bismarck*'s great piled shape seven miles away bearing 020° (about 55 miles north-west of Iceland's North Cape) and then *Prinz Eugen* too.

For the first time during the pursuit of the *Bismarck* the alarm bells clanged through a British warship and the crew rushed and clambered pell-mell to Action Stations, as *Suffolk* radioed her 'enemy report', turned 90° to port and headed at utmost speed for the shelter of the wall of fog. One hour later the *Norfolk*, closing to make contact with the enemy, sighted the *Bismarck* only six miles off, and for the first time *Bismarck*'s great guns boomed out in anger. The *Norfolk*, unscathed, turned away and sent her 'enemy report' at 2032. This reached the Admiralty at 2103, before *Suffolk*'s report had come through, and was immediately broadcast to all ships.

Admiral Tovey now knew that the enemy lay some 600 miles away from his flagship to the north-west; a long haul. He turned the Battle Fleet to 280° and increased speed to 27 knots. Back in London, in the spacious War Room created by knocking together several small offices, the First Sea Lord, the VCNS, (Rear-Admiral T. S. V. Phillips), and the naval staff anxiously studied the operational wall chart of the war at sea in the light of *Norfolk*'s report. No fewer than eleven convoys were at present out in the North Atlantic, six homeward bound and five outward. The most important of these was the convoy of five troopships bound for the Middle East which had left the Clyde the day before escorted by the cruisers *Exeter* and *Cairo* and five destroyers – potentially just a quick breakfast for the *Bismarck*. The

Admiralty therefore made a signal at 0050 on the 24th to Admiral Somerville (Flag Officer, Force H) at Gibraltar to rendezvous with the convoy in 47° 20′N, 26° 05′W. By 0200 Force H (which Somerville had brought to two hours' notice for steam as soon as he received *Norfolk*'s enemy report) was clear of Gibraltar harbour and steaming west at 25 knots: the battlecruiser *Renown* (flag), the carrier *Ark Royal*, the cruiser *Sheffield*, and the destroyers *Faulkner*, *Forester*, *Foresight*, *Foxhound*, *Fury* and *Hesperus*. Lütjens however had been told by Group North that Force H was safely far up the Mediterranean.

In the Denmark Strait on the night of 23–24 May – a spring Arctic night of twilight – the weather had turned foul, with squalls of rain or snow. Yet *Norfolk* and *Suffolk* hung on to the enemy as he steamed at 27 to 28 knots south-westwards, sometimes sighting him looming through the murk, only to lose him again in a squall except as glowing blips on *Suffolk*'s radar screen (*Norfolk* had no radar). As Tovey wrote in his despatch: 'With great skill in very difficult conditions, the cruisers shadowed the enemy as they followed him to the south in a momentous and persistent chase.'[22] When twilight lightened into day on the 24th, the *Bismarck* could be seen about twelve miles to the south. At 0325 she seemed to turn to starboard, so *Suffolk* turned likewise to keep her distance. As she swung it exposed the aircraft on her catapult to the half gale of wind, which caught and crumpled it. At 0445 *Norfolk* intercepted a report from *Icarus*, one of the Battle Cruiser Force's destroyer escort, giving her position: it was only a short distance astern of *Norfolk*. For the first time Rear-Admiral Wake-Walker knew that his two cruisers were no longer alone in the presence of the powerful German ships, but that Vice-Admiral Holland was close at hand with *Hood* and *Prince of Wales*; and half an hour later *Norfolk*'s lookout spotted their smoke on the port bow.

When at 2054 the previous evening Holland had received *Suffolk*'s first report that she had sighted *Bismarck* (placing her about 300 miles away, bearing 5°), he had thereupon turned to 295° and increased speed to 27 knots in order to cut the German squadron off. At 2318 he ordered his six destroyers to form a screen ahead. At midnight came a further report that the enemy was 120 miles distant, bearing 020°, and steering approximately 200°. Eight minutes later Holland reduced the Battle Cruiser Force's speed to 25 knots and altered course to due north to complete the interception. It was a night of moderate swell, the wind Force 4 to 5 from the north. Holland expected that he might make contact with the enemy at any time after 0140 on the 24th; and at 0015 the two British heavy ships hoisted their big battle ensigns and began their final preparations for battle: the transformation of wardrooms into emergency hospitals; the donning of anti-flash white hoods and gloves to protect against burns, and of clean socks and underwear in 'a ritual the British Navy has always observed before battle to prevent wounds from infection'.[23]

Throughout the ships, in hot oil-smelling engine rooms, in the shell-handling rooms and magazines closed tight shut by anti-flash doors, in the cramped 15-inch and 14-inch turrets under their cara-paces of steel, in transmitting (fire-control) rooms and high up on the bridge, the small hours were a time of dry-mouthed tension – not least when Wake-Walker's cruisers lost the enemy in a snow storm and the flow of their situation reports dried up. At 0031 Holland signalled the *Prince of Wales* that 'if the enemy was not in sight by 0210 he would probably alter course to 180° until cruisers regained touch and that he intended both ships to engage *Bismarck*, leaving *Prinz Eugen* to *Norfolk* and *Suffolk*'. However, it seems that this signal was not repeated to the cruisers.

Although the *Prince of Wales*'s Walrus biplane amphibian had been readied to take off on a reconnaissance, the weather had so worsened that it was defuelled and stored. Holland now saw little chance of engaging before full daylight and wished to give his crews a chance to rest, so at 0103 he altered away from the enemy to 200°. A mixture of relief and anticlimax swept the ships.[24] At 0247 *Suffolk* regained contact with the enemy and began to report his bearings. At 0353 Vice-Admiral Holland increased speed to 28 knots. At 0400 the *Bismarck* was estimated to lie only twenty miles to the north-west. By 0430, the eager eyes of the lookouts could see up to twelve miles across the now rough and rising sea. The order was given to refuel *Prince of Wales*'s Walrus, but the operation was held up because of water in the petrol, and the action was to begin and the Walrus itself to be damaged and jettisoned overboard before it could be flown off. *Hood* was now steaming at 28 knots on a course of 240°. At 0510 Holland ordered his force to the first degree of readiness; men began again to wind themselves up for battle. Twenty-five minutes later the *Bismarck*'s silhouette was seen on the horizon; she lay seventeen miles distant to the north-west, bearing 335°. Ahead of her could be seen the *Prinz Eugen*, a smaller but very similar silhouette.

For Vice-Admiral Holland the moment had now come to decide his mode of attack, knowing as he did that the *Hood* was vulnerable to German plunging fire smashing through her 1½–3-inch thick unhardened horizontal deck armour, and knowing too that, on the other hand, the *Prince of Wales* was so brand new that neither the ship nor her crew was nearly well enough worked up for so formidable a task as fighting the massive *Bismarck*. Holland himself, a gunnery expert, was both able and ambitious; one officer who knew him well described him as 'that very clever coolheaded Lancelot Holland'.[25] It is clear from his actions that Holland had no doubt that he must immediately engage the *Bismarck* rather than simply support Wake-Walker in shadowing her until Tovey could come up with the Home Fleet – just as Beatty had had no doubt at Jutland that he must immediately engage Hipper's battlecruisers rather than draw them on to Jellicoe and the Grand Fleet.

The parallel does not stop there: Holland like Beatty enjoyed superiority of numbers in heavy ships, but inferiority in actual fighting effectiveness (in Beatty's case, in terms of his battlecruisers). Holland's deployment too was curiously comparable to Beatty's in 1916. Beatty had attacked at high speed and with his ships on a line of bearing that placed the enemy well before the beam, where the midships and after turrets of the British battlecruisers could hardly bear at the moment when both sides opened fire;[26] Holland's final deployment similarly placed *Bismarck* and *Prinz Eugen* too fine on the starboard bow for his ships' after turrets to bear.[27] Beatty in 1916 had placed his lightly armoured battlecruisers in the van, his squadron of powerful Queen Elizabeth battleships in the rear; Holland in 1941 placed the vulnerable old *Hood* ahead of the strongly armoured new *Prince of Wales*. And, finally, Beatty in 1916 had exercised tight tactical control over his Fleet from his flagship; Holland in 1941 did likewise, manoeuvring his two ships together as a single unit in accordance with the centralising 1939 Fighting Instructions drawn up by Pound, rather than permit Captain Leach in *Prince of Wales* to manoeuvre independently and perhaps confuse the enemy by a different line of approach. Why this impetuous and ill-conceived deployment? As that fellow sailor who knew Holland well wrote years later: 'I just can't understand the tactics of the *Hood* action. It's so unlike that very clear coolheaded Lancelot Holland.'[28]

So it was that, at 0537 on 24 May, Holland turned the *Hood* and *Prince of Wales* together by blue pendant 40° to starboard towards the enemy, and four minutes later stationed *Prince of Wales* 080° from *Hood*. At 0549 he altered course to 300° by another blue pendant turn, and designated the left-hand German ship (in fact, the *Prinz Eugen*) as the target by the signal G.S.B. 337L1. The mistake was corrected by the signal G.O.B.1 ('Shift object one right') just before fire was opened. Interestingly enough, there had been comparable confusions over initial targeting in Beatty's force at Jutland. The British ships were now encountering a heavy head sea, which swept

[292]

green water over the *Prince of Wales*'s low forecastle (a weakness in the design) and spray over her fore turrets – and over *Hood* likewise, a notoriously 'wet' ship. By 0552 the range was down to about 25,000 yards and *Hood*'s 15-inch guns crashed out their first salvo. *Bismarck*, with the British ships well placed on her beam, replied with the same devastatingly immediate accuracy as Hipper's battlecruisers at Jutland (which also had their enemies well placed on the beam) and straddled *Hood* with her second or third salvo, igniting anti-aircraft rockets on deck. According to the Naval Staff Battle Summary, 'A fire broke out in the *Hood* near the port after 4-in gun which quickly spread till the whole midship part seemed to be in flames, burning with a pink glow shrouded in dense smoke.'[29]

The *Prince of Wales* opened fire at 0553 (with only six out of her ten 14-inch guns bearing), her first salvo an 'over' and only her sixth a straddle; not a good performance. But she was contending with heavy handicaps. The large 42-foot main range-finder at the back of 'A' turret and the 35-foot 'Duplex' (two-in-one) range-finder at the back of 'B' turret were both blinded by continuous streams of spray and water as the ship steamed at high speed into the strong wind and rough seas (*Hood*'s main range-finders were similarly mounted down on the turrets). This left only the 15-foot range-finders on the director control tower clear of spray and able to operate, but in terms of accuracy the range was extreme for such small range-finders. Moreover both of *Prince of Wales*'s radars (Type 284 set and Air Warning) had been kept switched off until 'Enemy in sight' as a precaution against detection by the enemy, and so they too could give no range. According to Lieutenant C. G. A. Murphy, RN, then in charge of the main armament transmitting station:

> When 'enemy in sight' was passed to the T.S. I was most anxious for a range of any description, but none was forthcoming from *any* source. The 42 foot R/F in A was largely underwater, the other in Y was not bearing, so I felt entirely dependent on radar. When nothing showed on the dials I ordered the operator to contact the 284 Radar Office by telephone and so far as I can remember from the growing tenseness he was told that Radar was jammed . . . [in fact, by the ship's high-powered radio signalling 'enemy report' to the Admiralty]. At no time during the action did I see a Radar range . . .[30]

The *Prince of Wales* therefore opened fire on the basis of a guesstimate calculated from one range obtained by the 15-foot range-finder on the director control tower.[31]

By now *Prinz Eugen* had joined in with her 8-inch guns, but *Norfolk* and *Suffolk* (also 8-inch gun ships) were too far astern to take part in the action. At 0555 Holland again manoeuvred *Hood* and *Prince of Wales* together by blue pendant, this time two points to port, a change of course which opened *Prince of Wales*'s 'A' arcs. At 0600 *Hood* hoisted a second 'two blue' pendant for another turn two points to port in order to bring the after turrets of both ships fully to bear. The signal fluttered down the halyard, the British ships began to come round, and *Bismarck* fired her fifth salvo. At least one shell, possibly more, plunged down on *Hood*, smashed through her thin deck armour and penetrated deep into her after magazine. *Hood*, for so long the very symbol of British seapower, was now rent in two by 'a huge explosion rising apparently between the after funnel and the main mast. The fore part began to sink separately, bows up, whilst the after part remained shrouded in a pall of smoke. Three or four minutes later, the *Hood* had vanished between the waves, leaving a vast cloud of smoke drifting away to leeward.'[32] She sank in 63° 20′N, 31° 50′W, taking with her Admiral Holland, her captain, Captain Ralph Kerr, RN, and more than 1,400 of her ship's company. There were only three survivors. It was an uncannily exact repetition of the last moments of the three battlecruisers lost at Jutland.

As the *Prince of Wales* violently altered course in order to avoid the wreckage the *Bismarck* swung her guns on to her. At a range now of only 18,000 yards *Bismarck*'s 5.9s were in action as well as her eight 15-inch; and within a very short time she had hit *Prince of Wales* with four heavy shells and three smaller. At 0602 a 15-inch shell (which did not explode) wrecked *Prince of Wales*' bridge, killing or wounding most of those present; at the same time another heavy shell holed her hull aft and let in 400 tons of water. At 0613 with the range down to 14,500 yards Captain Leach turned her away to 160° behind a smoke screen. As she swung, the after quadruple 14-inch turret (with a total revolving weight of about 1,500 tons) jammed on its ring; an untimely 'teething trouble' with a novel design in action for the first time. Despite the efforts of the members of the crew and Vickers's technicians to free the turret, its four guns were not all operational again until 0825.[33]

During the action – which, incredibly, had only lasted some twenty minutes – *Prince of Wales* had fired eighteen salvoes from her main armament and five from her secondary. And the *Bismarck* had not gone unscathed: one 14-inch shell passed right through her hull forward, causing her to ship 2,000 tons of water and forcing her to reduce speed, and also springing an oil leak which left a slick astern and further depleted her fuel reserves, while a second hit damaged a generator room and an engine room.

In the light of the destruction of the *Hood* both sides had now to consider their future courses of action. In the German ships there was tremendous elation; no wonder. But there was also a keen expectation that *Bismarck* would now close on *Prince of Wales* and finish her off too. Lütjens, however, with his tightly buttoned sense of obedience, would not budge from Raeder's instructions to avoid needless embroilment with the Royal Navy; especially when it might lead to further damage to *Bismarck* that could deliver him to whatever forces might already be gathering beyond the horizons to net him. In any case the damage done to *Bismarck* by *Prince of Wales*'s hits weighed heavily on him. The hit in the bows had not only led to the leak of fuel oil and the tell-tale slick far astern, but had also put oil pumps and pipeline valves out of action, so depriving the engines of 1,000 tons of oil in the forward tanks. Having neglected to fill up either from the *Wollin* or the *Weissenburg*, Lütjens now had to watch his fuel state with all the anxiety of a motorist in the midst of the Sahara. Moreover, the need to counter-flood aft in order to restore the ship's trim after the serious flooding forward through the shell-hole, coupled with the knocking out of one engine room by *Prince of Wales*'s midship hit below the armour belt, had reduced *Bismarck*'s speed to 28 knots. Lütjens therefore came to the conclusion that he must abort his mission and make for a convenient dockyard for repairs. At 0900 that morning he signalled home that he was going to take the *Bismarck* to the French Atlantic port of St Nazaire, and meanwhile detach *Prinz Eugen* for commerce raiding.[34]

For the Royal Navy the problems were more complicated. It was the Fleet radio officer, Commander Jacobs, who personally told Admiral Tovey, C-in-C Home Fleet, the news of the *Hood*'s destruction, his voice strident with the shock of it. 'All right, Jacobs,' Tovey calmly replied. 'There's no need to shout.'[35] Tovey's flagship, *King George V*, still lay 360 miles east of the scene. After discussion with his Chief of Staff, Commodore E. J. P. Brind, and his operations officer, Commander Robertson, in the plotting room next to the admiral's bridge, Tovey decided to steer just south of west. This would well place him to intercept Lütjens if the German admiral sought to double back to Germany north or south of Iceland, and equally to intercept him if he continued southwards. But he could not hope to join Wake-Walker and bring Lütjens to action until 0700 on 25 May at the earliest; a long time during which much might happen.

Upon Rear-Admiral Wake-Walker's own shoulders had suddenly

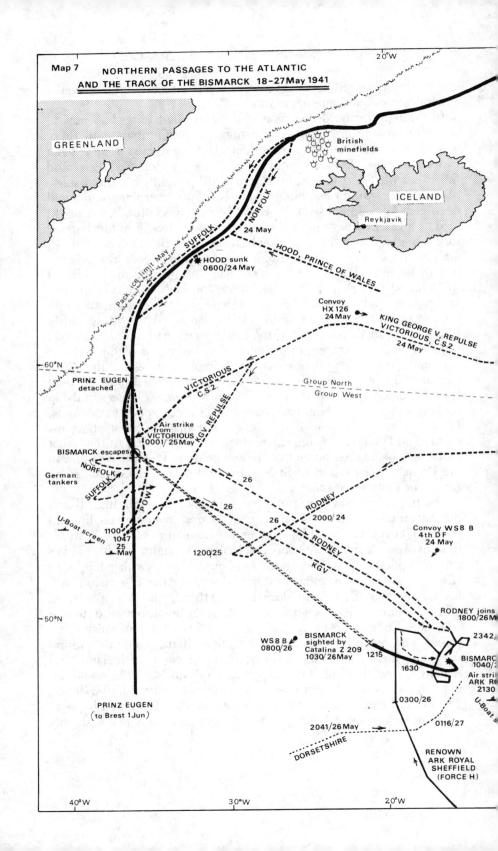

Map 7   NORTHERN PASSAGES TO THE ATLANTIC
AND THE TRACK OF THE BISMARCK 18–27 May 1941

GREENLAND

British minefields

ICELAND

Reykjavik

NORFOLK

SUFFOLK

24 May

HOOD sunk
0600/24 May

HOOD, PRINCE OF WALES

Pack ice limit May

Convoy
HX 126
24 May

KING GEORGE V, REPULSE
VICTORIOUS, C.S.2.
24 May

60°N

PRINZ EUGEN
detached

VICTORIOUS
C.S.2.

Group North
Group West

Air strike
from
VICTORIOUS
0001/25 May

KGV, REPULSE

BISMARCK escapes

NORFOLK

German
tankers

SUFFOLK

POW

26

26

RODNEY
2000/24

U-Boat screen

1100
1047
25
May

26

RODNEY

Convoy WS8 B
4th D F
24 May

1200/25

KGV

50°N

RODNEY joins
1800/26 M

WS8 B
0800/26

BISMARCK
sighted by
Catalina Z 209
1030/26 May

1215

2342

BISMARC
1040/

1630

Air stri
ARK R(
2130

PRINZ EUGEN
(to Brest 1 Jun)

0300/26

U-Boat

0116/27

2041/26 May

DORSETSHIRE

RENOWN
ARK ROYAL
SHEFFIELD
(FORCE H)

40°W

30°W

20°W

20°W

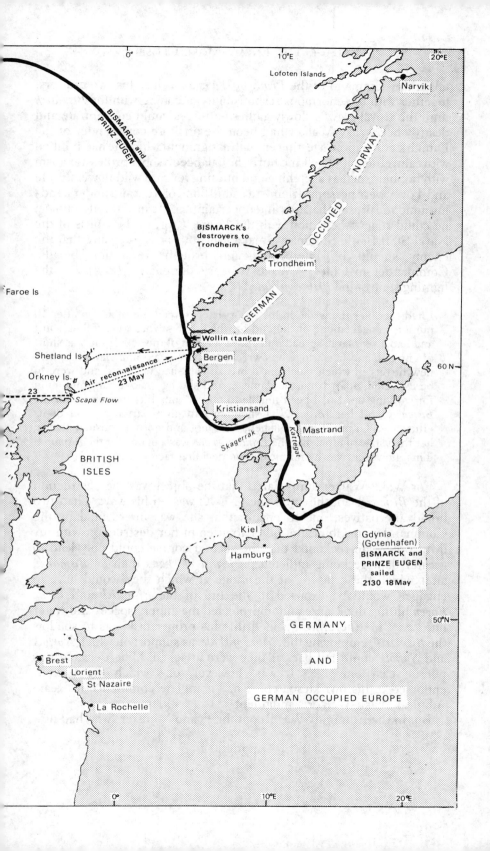

fallen the command of the *Prince of Wales* as well as his two cruisers, together with the enormous responsibility of coping with the *Bismarck* until the Royal Navy's slowly gathering forces could concentrate and destroy her. Wake-Walker had been the offshore commander of the Dunkirk evacuation, a testing enough assignment which he had fulfilled with calm efficiency. Tall and burly, he balanced a sober professionalism with hobbies such as sketching and hunting for rare wild flowers.[36] He and Tovey were personal friends; a useful bond of trust and understanding amid the present hazards and uncertainties. He now faced a choice: he could renew the action with the *Bismarck*, or, in the words of the Naval Staff Battle Summary, 'make it his business to ensure that the enemy should be intercepted and brought to action by the Commander-in-Chief'.[37] Wake-Walker's dominant worry lay in the fighting state of the *Prince of Wales*:

> I had seen her [he wrote in his report later] forced out of action after 10 minutes' engagement, at the end of which her salvoes were falling short and had a very large spread indeed. As a result of the action she was short of one gun and her bridge was wrecked. She was a brand-new ship, with new turrets in which mechanical breakdowns had occurred and were to be expected, apart from the damage, and she had had a bare minimum for working up. I had been unable to observe any hits for certain on the *Bismarck* and her [*Bismarck*'s] shooting had given striking proof of its efficiency. To put it in a nutshell, I did not and do not consider that in her then state of efficiency the *Prince of Wales* was a match for the *Bismarck*. This, however, was by no means the deciding factor . . .[38]

For Wake-Walker appreciated that the object was the destruction of the *Bismarck* and he knew the C-in-C was on his way: 'I had two broad alternatives, one to ensure that she was intercepted by the Commander-in-Chief, the other to attempt her destruction with my own force.' He reckoned that the second course could only lead to greater damage being inflicted on *Prince of Wales* than on *Bismarck*, after which the cruisers, at the range at which they would have to engage, 'would be exposed to the fire of the *Bismarck* and *Prinz Eugen* hitting their large and unprotected machinery spaces and water line . . .'[39] He therefore decided that his proper task was to shadow the *Bismarck*, employing the *Prince of Wales* as support on which *Norfolk* and *Suffolk* could fall back if they were attacked. 'The decision was not an easy one . . .'[40] It was, however, one which the C-in-C endorsed in his own despatch: 'I had complete confidence in Rear-Admiral Wake-Walker's judgment.'[41]

But in the Admiralty War Room the Prime Minister (who had now become a more or less permanent fixture there because of his anxious fascination with the hunt for the *Bismarck*) and the First Sea Lord, in the aftermath of the unimaginable loss of the *Hood*, were deeply angered at Wake-Walker's decision. Abetted and encouraged by the VCNS, Phillips, that combative little terrier, they despatched that afternoon a prodding signal to Wake-Walker of the familiar kind, asking him what his intentions were about the *Prince of Wales* re-engaging the *Bismarck*. Wake-Walker replied that he did not think *Prince of Wales* should re-engage until other heavy ships had made contact or failed to do so. He added that he doubted if she had the speed to force an action in any case.[42]

This answer far from satisfied the angry and impatient men in London; rather it excited the kind of vindictive bullying, especially on Pound's part, that had inspired the Board of Enquiry into Somerville's decision not to pursue the Italian Fleet during 'Operation Collar' in November 1940. Immediately after Admiral Tovey's return to Scapa Flow at the end of the hunt for the *Bismarck*, Pound was to telephone him to say (according to Tovey's later account) that

> . . . he wished Wake-Walker and Jack Leach brought to trial by court-martial for not re-engaging the *Bismarck*. I explained that the action taken by both these officers was exactly what I wished, the last thing I wanted was for the *Bismarck* to be pushed further to the West and away from my own force. He stated he still wished them to be brought to trial. I replied nothing would persuade me to do so. He informed me the Admiralty would order a trial. I replied that if they did I would act as Prisoner's Friend, if necessary resigning my command to do so. I heard no more about it.[43]

When the *Hood* sank, the *Norfolk* was lying about fifteen miles to the north-west, and coming up at 28 knots. Wake-Walker therefore ordered the *Prince of Wales* to follow at her best speed, so that *Norfolk* could retire on her if attacked. At 0757 the *Suffolk* reported, accurately, that the *Bismarck* had reduced speed and appeared to be damaged. A little later a Sunderland from Iceland confirmed that she was leaving a large oil slick astern. All that day *Norfolk* and *Suffolk* hung on to *Bismarck* and *Prinz Eugen*, keeping up a constant flow of enemy reports, but always on the alert lest *Bismarck* should go about and seek to attack them. Coastal Command too was keeping watch on the German ships, and at 1535 a Catalina in sight of *Norfolk* was able to report that *Suffolk* lay 26 miles distant, with *Bismarck* fifteen miles ahead and *Prinz Eugen* ahead of her.

In the afternoon a cold mist shrouded quarry and pursuer; *Suffolk* temporarily lost radar contact; and Wake-Walker, his trained professional instinct a-prickle, ordered *Norfolk* to turn 360° to port, a complete circle which lengthened her distance from *Bismarck*'s last observed position by some three miles. In fact *Bismarck* had indeed just swung to port across *Norfolk*'s bows in the mist, and but for his timely manoeuvre Wake-Walker would have encountered the German battleship at the deadly range of a mile or so.[44] At 1841 the shifting mist opened to reveal *Bismarck* about eight miles distant; her 15-inch guns crashed out, and the two British cruisers and *Prince of Wales* fired back; then the mists closed again. Once more all depended on *Suffolk*'s radar.

In the Admiralty War Room, 24 May was spent in redeploying every available unit of British seapower in order to hem in the *Bismarck* whichever course she took. Five hours before *Hood* was blown up the Admiralty had already ordered the cruisers *Manchester*, *Birmingham* and *Arethusa* to patrol north of Langanaes (the north-easterly point of Iceland) in case the German Admiral tried to double back to base via the Denmark Strait. At 1022 the battleship *Rodney* (33,950 tons displacement, nine 16-inch guns), at present escorting the liner *Britannic* with four destroyers westwards, was ordered to leave the *Britannic* and steer south-westwards on a course to intercept *Bismarck*, then some 550 miles to the north-west. Unfortunately the veteran *Rodney*, in dire need of a refit, could barely make 21 knots. The even more aged *Ramillies*, escorting convoy HX127 from Halifax, Nova Scotia, and lying some 900 miles south of the *Bismarck*, was ordered to abandon her convoy and steam northwards in order to station herself to the west of the enemy. The equally aged *Revenge* in the port of Halifax and the cruiser *Edinburgh* patrolling in the Atlantic were both ordered to close in as well. By 1800 that evening four battleships, two battlecruisers, twelve cruisers, two aircraft carriers and a swarm of destroyers were already on the move. The credit belongs to Rear-Admiral T. S. V. ('Tom') Phillips, the VCNS, who, in the words of an eyewitness, 'was right on the ball the whole time, and who took a decisive part in the coordination of all the British forces'.[45]

The First Sea Lord's own attention was – perhaps fortunately – almost entirely engrossed by the Prime Minister,[46] for in Tovey's judgment Pound was 'neither a great tactician or [sic] strategist [although] he firmly believed he was . . .'[47]

During the day Tovey himself in HMS *King George V* (110,000 horsepower steam turbines; speed 27½ knots) became more and more concerned that the *Bismarck* might outrun his attempt at interception unless she could be slowed down. Yet Tovey's only means of slowing her lay in the carrier *Victorious* (Captain H. C. Bovell) and her nine Swordfish torpedo aircraft (825 Squadron, Fleet Air Arm), and six Fulmar fighters (802 Squadron), whose pilots were desperately new to the job. Nevertheless, at 1440 he ordered Rear-Admiral Curteis (Flag Officer, 2nd Cruiser Squadron) to take *Victorious* and the cruisers *Aurora*, *Kenya* and *Hermione* to a flying-off position 100 miles east of the *Bismarck*.

As Tovey made the signal 'Good Luck', Curteis set off at 28 knots, course 280°, guided throughout by reports from *Norfolk* and *Suffolk*. However, it later became clear to Curteis from these reports that there was no hope of *Victorious* getting within 100 miles of the target before 2300 that night. He therefore decided to fly off his strike an hour earlier at a distance of 120 miles. At 2208 with the wind blowing fresh from the north-west *Victorious* turned to 330° and slowed to 15 knots in order to launch her aircraft. It was not going to be an easy first mission for the green aircrews. According to the Naval Staff Battle Summary: 'The weather was as bad as it could be. The flying deck presented a chilly prospect of dark foaming seas, rain and scudding cloud in a leaden sky, the heavily loaded planes gathered way very slowly. They were off at 2210/24 and disappeared into cloud and rain squalls.'[48]

The squadrons (led by Lieutenant-Commander (A) Eugene Esmonde) located Wake-Walker's shadowing ships by air-to-surface radar, whereupon *Norfolk* directed them on to the enemy. Just before midnight – in those latitudes, the time of sunset – Esmonde brought his lumbering biplanes down and in towards *Bismarck*, the main attack coming in on her port side, and a diversion by one aircraft on her starboard side, each aircraft carrying one 18-inch torpedo with Duplex pistol set to 31 feet. As the Swordfish rode steadily towards the *Bismarck* the length of her massive superstructure erupted in a continuous blaze of gun-flashes as every calibre of gun, from the 20mm Oerlikons up to the main armament, was brought into action. Nevertheless the Swordfish held on to drop their torpedoes.

It now fell to *Bismarck*'s captain to try with great skill to comb the torpedo tracks, the huge ship heeling at each turn, while all the Swordfish climbed away unscathed – possibly because the battleship's violent changes of course made it hard for the anti-aircraft batteries to hold their targets. A shadowing Fulmar saw one great column of smoke erupt from the *Bismarck*'s starboard side, followed by a reduction in her speed. When all the aircraft returned to *Victorious* darkness was falling and the carrier's homing beacon had failed. Esmonde's inexperienced crews had to make safe landings by means of radar and the improvised light of a signal projector. Two of the Fulmars ditched, but the crews were rescued. However, despite the aircrews' bravery, the single torpedo to hit *Bismarck* ran shallow instead of at 31 feet, and only exploded harmlessly against the battleship's armoured belt, killing one warrant officer; the ship's first fatal casualty.

In the mists of late afternoon, and under cover of *Bismarck*'s brief exchange of fire with Wake-Walker's ships, *Prinz Eugen* and the German flagship had parted company according to Lütjens's plan. As he steamed on alone in the small hours of 25 May, Lütjens knew (from a signal by Group West based in Brest) that Force H with its carrier was now in the eastern Atlantic; he knew too from the Swordfish attack that there was also a carrier some 100 miles distant from him. His greatest worry therefore lay in the uncanny ability of the shadowing British cruisers' radar to detect his every change of course. If he were to escape the powerful forces that must be closing towards him, he must find a means of dodging that unwavering electronic eye.

In the case of Tovey and the Admiralty it was exactly that constant tag by *Suffolk* on *Bismarck*'s position, course and speed which made it possible for them to deploy and direct the hunt, even though the relative speeds of hunters and hunted still rendered ultimate interception a matter of the narrowest margin.

Then, at 0306 on 25 May, *Suffolk* lost the *Bismarck*, and at once the British command was groping in the blind. According to Admiral Tovey, writing later in his despatch:

> The loss of touch, when it came, was caused primarily by over-confidence. The RDF [radar] had been used so skilfully that it engendered a false sense of security . . . The *Suffolk* was shadowing from the extreme range of her instrument, losing touch on those parts of her [anti-submarine] zig-zag which took her furthest from the enemy. The enemy altered sharply to starboard while the *Suffolk* was moving to port and by the time she got back had gone.[49]

This is a little unfair: if there was carelessness, it sprang from sheer tiredness rather than over-confidence. In any case, Lütjens and Lindemann had turned away more than 90° to the westward with the very intention of shaking off their shadowers. They now proceeded to take *Bismarck* in a complete clockwise circle, crossing their own track an hour later some 30 miles astern of Wake-Walker's ships and setting course 130° for Brest and safety. However, Wake-Walker himself wrongly guessed that the enemy had steered a westerly course, searching in vain in that direction for several wasted hours.

The day of 25 May therefore passed for the British in frantic but unsuccessful searches by sea and air for a vanished enemy; in competing guesses as to which course he might be steering; and positively misleading snippets of Intelligence. Catalinas from Iceland swept the seas all day but sighted only friendly ships. Bletchley Park could not directly help the search because it was currently taking some three to seven days to decrypt the naval Enigma signals – nothing like quick enough for a fast-moving chase where hours counted.[50] In the Admiralty War Room that day bafflement bred a mounting tension – not least because of the Premier's powerful presence and personal involvement. For so much was at stake, with the balance of attrition in the Battle of the Atlantic currently swinging towards Dönitz's U-boats, the need to avenge the *Hood*'s tragic but humiliating loss and restore the prestige of the Royal Navy in British and world opinion. Churchill himself was at first convinced that Lütjens was doubling back towards the Denmark Strait and Germany: it took much to persuade him otherwise.[51]

Tovey, for his part, continued for several hours to steer south-westwards, whereas unbeknown to him the *Bismarck* had crossed his wake about 100 miles astern at approximately 0800, steering south-east.

The only clue came from rough HF/DF fixes on *Bismarck*'s copious radio traffic with the German naval high command. For Lütjens apparently saw no reason to observe strict radio silence because he wrongly believed that he was still being closely tagged by *Norfolk* and *Suffolk*. Unfortunately misunderstandings between the Admiralty and Tovey's staff over the plotting of these HF/DF fixes misled the C-in-C into believing that *Bismarck* was indeed, as Churchill reckoned, heading for the Denmark Strait, and at 1047 Tovey reversed course and headed north-westwards at 27 knots. At noon the *Rodney* (280 miles distant from the flagship to the south-east) and *Ramillies* in mid-Atlantic conformed to this movement. Except for Force H coming up from the south-east and still 1,300 miles away, all the British forces now lay far astern of the *Bismarck* and steering 90° away from her.

As further HF/DF fixes came in during the forenoon, opinion began to harden in the Admiralty War Room that the *Bismarck* was steering for a French Bay of Biscay port.[52] As early as 1023 the Admiralty signalled Somerville (Force H) and Wake-Walker to proceed on this assumption – which Wake-Walker was already doing. At 1158 it signalled *Rodney* in similar terms. But then at 1428 it instructed *Rodney* to proceed instead on the assumption that the enemy was steering for the Iceland–Faeroes gap (a Churchillian intervention?); false guidance that was only rescinded at 1805. In the meantime, and by no means enlightened by these contradictory Admiralty signals, Tovey had continued to steer north-east, his mind nevertheless more and more uneasy as to whether this was the right course. At 1810, now convinced that *Bismarck* must be making for a French port, he turned south-east. Shortly afterwards the Admiralty confirmed to him from an Ultra decrypt of a Luftwaffe Enigma signal (to the Luftwaffe Chief of Staff, then in Athens) that such was the case.

Thanks to his almost eight-hour-long diversion in the wrong direction, Tovey now lay 150 miles astern of *Bismarck*: a colossal handicap in a race to catch her before she reached the French coast. His fleet was now desperately short of fuel after four days' hard steaming, and, lacking fleet oilers, he had to detach the battlecruiser *Repulse* to Newfoundland to refuel, the *Prince of Wales* and the cruiser *Hermione* to Iceland. He was also forced to slow his remaining cruisers to 20 knots in order to conserve oil; HMS *Victorious* and the invaluable *Suffolk* likewise. All his screening destroyers had had to leave him too. At 2238 that night Tovey signalled the Admiralty that even the flagship might have to reduce speed because of shortage of fuel.

For Force H, coming up from the south-east, it had been a day of struggle against heavy seas, wind, rain and mist. At 0900 Somerville detached three destroyers back to Gibraltar to refuel in accordance with an Admiralty signal that Force H 'might be required for extended operations . . .'[53] At 1100, when Force H was in 41° 30'N, 17° 06'W, Somerville received the Admiralty signal to proceed on the assumption 'that the enemy had turned towards Brest at 0300'.[54] Somerville therefore altered course to 000°, speed 24 knots, the north-westerly wind and sea both rising. At 1215 he altered again to 345° in order to reach a position early next day to fly air searches from the *Ark Royal* over a wide spread of the Bay of Biscay. Still the weather grew rougher and rougher, forcing him to slow to 21 knots at 2340, to 19 at 0020 on the 26th and down to 17 at 0112. Because he had heard nothing from the Admiralty concerning the whereabouts of *Scharnhorst* and *Gneisenau* since a report at 1515 on 23 May that they were still in Brest, Somerville felt 'some anxiety' on their score, 'as I could not entirely discount the possibility that one or both battlecruisers might have put to sea to support *Bismarck*'.[55] At 0300 on 26 May he altered to 000° in order to reach a flying-off position further to the east, for he reckoned that *Bismarck*, with the benefit of a following wind, would have made a better speed of advance than Force H.

But the problem for Somerville, as for Tovey, as for the Admiralty, remained that no one knew exactly where *Bismarck* was. The first, the essential, task for 26 May must be to find her.

In the *Bismarck* herself on 25 May what should have been a day of cautious hope about the prospects of reaching Brest was turned by an incredible act of poor leadership on Lütjens's part into a day when the morale of the ship's company sagged towards a sense of hopelessness. Addressing the ship's company on the tannoy Lütjens began by congratulating them on sinking the *Hood*, but then remarked – according to eyewitnesses later – that 'the enemy will try to concentrate his forces and bring them into action against us'.[56] He confirmed to them that *Bismarck* was now on its way to a French port, and went on: 'On our way there, the enemy will gather and give us battle. The German people are with you, and we will fight until our gun barrels glow red-hot and the last shell has left the barrels. For us seamen, the question now is victory or death.'[57]

The impact of this piece of libretto for a maritime *Götterdämmerung* on a ship's company of young and impressionable conscripts, many of whom had never been on the high seas before, was immediate and catastrophic. In the words of one officer, 'the high morale that permeated the ship was irretrievably lost'.[58] A petty officer recalled: 'The Fleet Commander's words had a devastating effect on us. They were taken to mean that we were sentenced to death, whereas we had been already reckoning when we would arrive in France.'[59] The tone of Lütjens's address is all too consistent with his introspective and intense temperament, not to say the fatalistic mood in which he had gone to sea. Nevertheless as an engineer lieutenant-commander put it later, 'Whether the Fleet Commander simply made a bad choice of words or whether the crew sensed his innermost fears must remain an open question.'[60] Captain Lindemann did his best to put things right by a brief and positive tannoy address of his own and by talking to members of the crew on his rounds. But although it helped a little, morale in *Bismarck* had been fatally damaged. The ship's officers and petty officers began to be seen wearing unfastened up lifejackets, a sight unlikely to raise the crew's spirits. Moreover, it is hard not to think that this lowering of morale must have had its effect on the ship's actual fighting effectiveness.

Dawn on 26 May found Force H in the latitude of Brest with half a gale blowing from the north-west. Still bothered that *Gneisenau* and *Scharnhorst* might be at sea, Somerville flew an air search to the west and north at 0716 before looking for *Bismarck* herself. At 0835, when *Ark Royal* was in 48° 26′N, 10° 13′W, ten Swordfish took off on that urgent quest. The wind was now blowing Force 7 from 320°, 'sea rough, sky overcast, visibility 10 to 12 miles', according to Somerville's report.[61] Because of the weather the Fulmars could not be employed to give greater range of search. It proved a tricky enough operation even for the robust old Swordfish, as Somerville described: 'ARK ROYAL's round down [after end of the flight deck] was rising and falling 56 feet at times, as measured by sextant. The handling of the aircraft on the flight deck was always difficult and several slid bodily across the deck which was wet with spray.'[62]

One by one the Swordfish staggered off the plunging deck into the wind; one by one an hour later they made a hazardous return landing after having seen nothing but wind-whipped sea. Could Coastal Command do better?

When late on the 25th the Admiralty liaison officer with Coastal Command, Captain Charles Meynell, took the Admiralty operation staff's proposals for the morrow's air searches to Air Marshal Sir Frederick Bowhill, the AOC-in-C, Coastal Command, Bowhill, that one-time sailor, rightly guessed (as Pound and Phillips had not) that Lütjens would not steer straight for Brest, but take a diversionary course south before bearing east. He therefore urged that there should be an extra patrol flown to cover a more southerly area than provided for in the Admiralty's existing plans.[63]

It was therefore entirely thanks to Bowhill that at 1030 on the 26th a Catalina of 15 Group, Coastal Command, from Iceland (piloted by Flying Officer Dennis Briggs, and with a neutral American 'Special Observer', Ensign Leonard Smith, USN, as co-pilot), sighted the *Bismarck* through a gap in the cloud, placing her in 49° 30'N, 21° 55'W – some 690 miles 96° from Brest. With *Bismarck* putting up a storm of fire that peppered the Catalina with shrapnel holes, Briggs and Smith found close shadowing a hazardous business, and at 1125 they lost her again. But at almost the same time two Swordfish from *Ark Royal* fitted with long-range tanks sent earlier at Somerville's order and guided by the Catalina's report also found the *Bismarck*, placing her some 25 miles further to the west than had the Catalina's crew. At noon *Ark Royal* flew off long-range shadowers, and these, regularly relieved during the day, were to send back a constant flow of precise reports until they were recalled at 2230.

Admiral Tovey himself in *King George V* received the Catalina's report at 1043. Pleased though he was that at last the *Bismarck* had been found again, he could not take comfort from the report. At *Bismarck*'s estimated speed of 21 knots, she could reach safe haven in Brest on 27 May and be under cover of powerful land-based airpower long before that. Since *King George V* lay some 130 miles to the north of her, it was highly unlikely that *Bismarck* could now be intercepted unless she was somehow slowed down. Moreover, while *Bismarck* could run home at full speed to the point of empty tanks, all the British ships had to make a long voyage home in the face of possible air and U-boat attack; and Tovey was already confronting the possibility that he might have to call off his chase for want of fuel. For the time being, however, he kept going at 26 knots, altering to 130° at 1155.

All now depended on *Ark Royal*'s Swordfish, especially since Somerville had been instructed by the Admiralty that his battlecruiser, *Renown*, 'was not to become heavily engaged with BISMARCK unless the latter was already heavily engaged with either KING GEORGE V or RODNEY'.[64] At 1315 Somerville detached the radar-equipped *Sheffield* to close and shadow the *Bismarck*, then some 40 miles south-west of his flagship. By an omission with 'serious consequences' the visual signal was not repeated to the *Ark Royal*. At 1450 fifteen Swordfish set off to attack the *Bismarck*, one of them, however, making an emergency return soon after. Owing to the foul weather a planned diversion by the Fulmars had to be abandoned. Over the target area the visibility was appalling, but one aircraft succeeded in locating a single lone ship with its air-to-surface radar. Unfortunately the ship was the *Sheffield* – which, owing to the failure to repeat to *Ark Royal* the signal detaching her, *Ark Royal*'s strike force did not know was now shadowing *Bismarck*; and at 1550 the Swordfish launched eleven torpedoes at the unlucky cruiser. Fortunately the Duplex magnetic pistols malfunctioned, two torpedoes exploding as they hit the water, three more as they crossed *Sheffield*'s wake, while the cruiser successfully evaded the rest by combing their tracks. At 1720 the strike force landed back on *Ark Royal* – and the *Bismarck* was still steaming on unscathed for Brest.

In the Admiralty War Room, anxiety and frustration fuelled the itch to intervene in both Pound and Churchill. Wrote an eyewitness: 'The staff were against sending the cautionary signal to James Somerville about not getting engaged with BISMARCK, but the First Sea Lord was insistent.'[65] The Premier himself, true to his form in both world wars, really wanted to mastermind the chase:

> As events moved towards their climax the Prime Minister took a closer interest and hardly ever left the War Room. The First Sea Lord supported by the First Lord [A. V. Alexander] did wonders in restraining him from sending impulsive signals of instructions to Tovey and others engaged in these operations ...[66]

Just as soon as the first strike force returned to *Ark Royal* at 1720, another, this time of sixteen aircraft, was put in preparation as fast as possible. At 1747 the *Sheffield* reported that she had sighted the *Bismarck* in about 48° 30'N, 17° 20'W, and was taking station about ten miles astern of her. At 1915 the second strike force (in the event, fifteen aircraft strong) roared one by one down *Ark Royal's* flight deck and away. This time great care was taken to avoid errors or failures. The torpedoes were armed with contact pistols instead of Duplex, and set to run at 22 feet. The strike force was ordered to home on *Sheffield* first by direction-finding signals, and the cruiser was then to redirect them on to the *Bismarck*.

At 2035 the strike force reached the *Sheffield*, which informed them by signal lamp that *Bismarck* bore 110°, distant twelve miles. At 2040 the Swordfish flew on towards their target in six sub-flights in line astern.

At just this moment Somerville in *Renown* received a signal from the Commander-in-Chief in *King George V* giving his position, course and speed at 1800 as 49° 48'N, 17° 33'W, 100°, 22 knots. Shortage of fuel was now causing Tovey 'grave anxiety'.[67] By noon the flagship was down to 32 per cent of capacity, while *Rodney* (which joined him at 1806) had reported that she would have to turn back to refuel by 0800 next day. At 1705 Tovey had reduced his speed to 22 knots in order to conserve fuel, which meant that it was quite impossible for him to make up the ninety miles that still separated him from the *Bismarck*. He therefore informed Somerville that 'unless the enemy's speed was reduced he would have to return in KING GEORGE V at midnight to refuel, leaving RODNEY to continue the chase'.[68] The only hope left for Tovey was *Ark Royal* and her aircraft. Then at 1830 he received a stark report from Somerville on the results of the first air strike (that on *Sheffield*): 'Estimate no hits.'[69] To Tovey and his staff this seemed to mark the end: gloom settled on the flagship. Then came a fresh signal from Somerville that *Ark Royal* had launched another strike. Hope revived; and with it the anguish of waiting.

As the fifteen Swordfish neared the *Bismarck* they ran into thick cloud banking up from 700 feet to between 6,000 and 10,000 feet and became split up. Each sub-flight took its own course through the cloud and then down under its base, there to find the *Bismarck's* great dark-grey shape beneath greeting them 'with intense and accurate fire from the first moment of sighting until out of range'.[70] The Swordfish buzzed round the stern and towards both beams of the battleship like a swarm of hornets, all but one of them making their final runs undeterred by the storm of anti-aircraft fire. Thirteen torpedoes were dropped, and two hits (possibly three) were observed – one certain

[308]

hit on the port side amidships, and the second on the starboard side well aft. At 2125 the last Swordfish climbed away to return to *Ark Royal*. The attack had lasted just half an hour, but it was one of the most decisive half hours in the history of naval warfare. For the aft torpedo hit had reduced the proud and powerful *Bismarck* to a helpless cripple.

The hit was in fact so luckily placed as truly to represent the workings of fate. For of the *Bismarck*'s 823 feet of length, the torpedo had happened to strike the one-fortieth which was the great ship's weakest and yet most vital part (apart from the actual screws and rudders) – the steering rooms where powerful electric motors operated the huge twin rudders. Moreover, at the speed *Bismarck* was steaming the torpedo would have passed harmlessly astern if it had been dropped only seconds later than it was. The effect of the hit was to jam *Bismarck*'s rudders in their existing position – which, since she had been at that moment taking violent evasive action, was 'port 12°'. *Ark Royal*'s shadowing aircraft high above observed the amazing consequences as *Bismarck* helplessly made two complete circles to port.

In the stricken ship damage-control parties and divers worked desperately to try to free the rudders, but the steering motor rooms were flooded up to the main deck, and incoming surges of sea water as the ship pitched made their work impossible. The best that could be achieved was to centre one of the two rudders; the other remained fixed immovably in its 'port 12°' position. Meanwhile Captain Lindemann tried every method of steering by the engines and propellers – but, just as on the Baltic exercise months before, it proved impossible to keep *Bismarck* on course by this means. Desperate measures such as blowing away the rudders, or taking a U-boat in tow as a steering drag, were put forward and discarded. Nothing could prevent the *Bismarck* from turning her head into the wind.

And here fate seemed to be at work again, for the wind was blowing strongly from the north-west – the direction of the pursuing Home Fleet. Moreover, in order to prevent *Bismarck* from wallowing and yawing helplessly she had to be kept under way. And so all through the night of 26–27 May 1941, she steamed at 7 to 8 knots towards her hunters, delivering herself to the kill.

But she could still fight. When, as the sun was setting on the 26th, Admiral Vian (4th Destroyer Flotilla) in HMS *Cossack*, with the Polish destroyer *Piorun* and the *Maori*, *Zulu* and *Sikh* arrived on the scene to shadow *Bismarck*, the German battleship swiftly straddled them. Vian had been ordered by the Admiralty at 0200 that day to leave the convoy he was escorting and join the C-in-C, who was now without a destroyer screen. On hearing the Catalina's sighting report, Vian on his own initiative altered to the south-east in order to close the *Bismarck*. All through the night Vian launched torpedo attacks, being determined, as he wrote to Tovey afterwards, firstly, 'to deliver to you at all costs the enemy, at the time you wished. Secondly to try to sink or stop the enemy with torpedoes in the night if I thought the attack should not involve the destroyers in heavy losses.'[71] Vian's 'Tribals', being mainly gun ships, had only four torpedo tubes instead of the usual eight, and no re-loads. Each destroyer could therefore only launch one attack with all four torpedoes fired at once to give a spread.

It proved a night of gallant but vain enterprise ('a model of its kind' according to Tovey's despatch) on the part of the British destroyers, and on the part of the *Bismarck* a night of radar-directed gunfire which although straddling Vian's ships again and again, failed to hit or sink any of them; a night lurid with gunflashes and star-shell. In the *Bismarck* members of the crew were now haplessly falling asleep at their stations in total exhaustion.

> When, after midnight [wrote one of her gunnery officers], it was announced that work on the rudders had ceased, hope evaporated. The older men took the news as a sentence of death for ship and crew. Everyone had to find his own way of dealing with the inevitable. Some fell into a mood of total indifference, in which nothing more could have any effect on them.[72]

Admiral Tovey learned of the crippling torpedo hit on *Bismarck* by a report from *Sheffield* at 2136 on the 26th that the enemy was steering 340° and then four minutes later 000°, from which it was plain that her steering was damaged. Buoyed up by fresh hope the C-in-C turned at once to the south, hoping to make contact with the *Bismarck* from the east in the failing light. At 2208 came a confirming report from Force H that *Bismarck* had been hit. By now the light was thickening, *King George* V was yawing and pitching horribly in the following wind and steep seaway, rain squalls were obscuring vision. Knowing that the crippled *Bismarck* was heading north towards him at about 10 knots, Tovey therefore decided to haul off to the east and north, and work round ahead of the German ship to attack her from the west at dawn. Later, however, Vian's night-time reports about the continuing accuracy of the enemy's fire persuaded the C-in-C to wait for full daylight before engaging from the west 'with the full advantages of wind, sea and light'.[73] Before midnight he signalled these intentions to Somerville, instructing him that *Renown* and *Ark Royal* were to keep not less than twenty miles to the southward of *Bismarck*.[74] Then, in his sea-cabin behind the flagship's bridge, he drafted a message to the ship's company:

To K.G.V.
  The sinking of the *Bismarck* may have an effect on the war as a whole out of all proportion to the loss to the enemy of one battleship. May God be with you and grant you victory.[75]

In the *Rodney*, as in the flagship, the announcement that they were going to engage the *Bismarck* at dawn was greeted with cheers throughout the ship.

Daylight on 27 May brought a heavy, sullen grey sky, a rising sea, and a tearing wind from the north-west. Tovey, back in his sea-cabin after a night of work, prayed, in his own words, 'for guidance and help', for although he had no doubt that the *Bismarck* would be sunk, he feared she might inflict heavy damage and casualties on his own ships. As he prayed his anxieties dissolved into calm. It was, he said, 'as if all responsibility had been taken from me, and I knew everything would be all right'.[76] At 0708 he signalled the *Rodney* (Captain F. H. G. Dalrymple-Hamilton, RN) to keep station six cables or more from *King George V*, and (unlike Holland with regard to Leach) gave Dalrymple-Hamilton freedom of action to adjust his own bearings as he wished. At 0737 Tovey altered to 080°, *Rodney* taking station 010° from the flagship. At 0820 the flagship's lookout sighted *Norfolk* on the port bow; the cruiser signalled: 'Enemy, 130°, 16 miles.' So at long last for Tovey the denouement had arrived. In *King George V* the order was given: 'On tin hats!' Three minutes later the squat, piled shape of *Bismarck* emerged from a rain squall on the starboard bow: 'Enemy in sight.'[77]

Because of the north-westerly gale Tovey had concluded that wind and sea made it most undesirable to attack from windward. He had therefore decided to approach the *Bismarck* on a north-westerly bearing, and then, providing the enemy continued to steer northwards, deploy to the south on an opposite course at a range of some 15,000 yards. When *Bismarck* was sighted she bore 118°, distant 25,000 yards. The two British battleships were then steering 118°, eight cables apart – in other words they were steering directly towards their victim in line abreast. At 0847 *Rodney* opened fire; *King George V* a minute later.

In the *Bismarck* the mood of officers and crew could not have made a more bitter contrast with that prevailing in Tovey's ships. Lütjens remained as ever buttoned into himself, with no heartening words to utter on the eve of action; rather an air of fatalistic melancholy. Lindemann too had capitulated to indifference and despair. His former adjutant, now a gunnery officer, found even him that morning wearing an open lifejacket:

> I had to look twice to believe it . . . he seemed strangely detached from his surroundings. He saw me coming but did not return my salute, which I held as I looked at him intently in the hope that he would say something in return. He did not say a word. He did not even glance at me. I was greatly disturbed and puzzled . . .[78]

From the very top, therefore, had seeped down the dejection that permeated the whole ship's company and seemed to rot a fighting efficiency in any case impaired by desperate tiredness; evidence perhaps of the shallowness of the young German Navy's tradition compared with that of the Royal Navy, and a consequent moral brittleness in its leadership.

The *Bismarck* opened fire at 0850 after turning as best she could to open her 'A' arcs; the salvo fell short. Her third straddled the *Rodney*, the nearest shell raising a huge column of water only twenty yards from her. She continued to straddle with succeeding salvoes, but scored not a single hit. Her constant yawing as she laboured along at 10 knots made it hard for her transmitting rooms (fire-control centres) to keep her guns accurately on target, while her inability to manoeuvre meant that she herself offered the British battleships an easy aiming mark. Moreover she was outgunned by eight 15-inch guns to nine 16-inch and ten 14-inch. It was little wonder that the speed and accuracy of her fire gradually fell away.

At 0854 the cruiser *Norfolk* joined in from the east at a range of ten miles with her 8-inch guns. At just this moment *Rodney* fired her third salvo and landed one 16-inch shell on *Bismarck*'s forecastle and another on her superstructure amidships. At 0859 the *King George V* altered to the south to bring the *Bismarck* on the beam; the *Rodney*, two and a half miles astern, followed suit although manoeuvring independently of the flagship. Clouds of cordite smoke reeking towards the enemy made spotting difficult, and the British ships had to resort to radar range-finding. Now the *Bismarck* shifted her fire to the *King George V* – again no hits.

At 0902 a 16-inch shell from the *Rodney* smashed down on to the *Bismarck*'s upper deck forward and reduced her fore turrets to a shambles of riven metal, the gun muzzles of turret 'Anton' drooping down towards the sea; those of turret 'Bruno' cocked uselessly into the air in the wrong direction. Yet somehow guns in one or other of these turrets were brought into action again later. According to an American observer in *Rodney*, Lieutenant-Commander J. M. Wellings, USN: '*Bismarck* continued to fire regularly until between 0902 and 0908 when her firing became irregular and intermittent . . . only one salvo was observed from the forward turrets after this period. This salvo was fired at 0927 . . .'[79] At 0904 the cruiser *Dorsetshire* (Captain B. Martin, RN; brought in from convoy escort duty) joined the action. In *King George V* the range remained steady at 12,000 yards between 0910 and 0915. At 0916, with *Bismarck*'s bearing drawing rapidly aft, Captain Dalrymple-Hamilton turned *Rodney* 16 points to port in order to head her off; the flagship followed suit soon after. Both ships, now steaming north in the same direction as *Bismarck*, reopened fire to starboard – *Rodney* at a range of only 8,600 yards; *King George V* at 12,000. About this time Tovey remarked to Captain Patterson, the captain of the *King George V*: 'Get closer, get closer, I can't see any hits!'[80] *Bismarck* now shifted her fire back to *Rodney*, but by now only one turret (aft) remained in action; more near misses, but still no hits. By now the German ship was ablaze amidships, her internal spaces reeking with fumes and littered with the maimed and the dead, her fire-control instruments shot away – listing to port but still crawling through the water.

At 0931 she fired her last salvo. Between 0925 and 1015 the two British battleships poured in salvoes from main and secondary armaments at ranges down to 2,900 yards, finally reducing *Bismarck* to a wreck pouring out great clouds of greenish yellow smoke lit by flame. Yet still she floated, her magazines and machinery spaces intact; a tribute to Germany's skill in building stout ships. *Rodney* had fired 380 rounds of 16-inch shell and 718 rounds of 6-inch; *King George V* had fired 339 rounds of 14-inch and 660 rounds of 5.25-inch; *Norfolk* and *Dorsetshire* 781 rounds of 8-inch – a combined total of 2,878 rounds.[81] This huge total of rounds fired, many of them at virtually point-blank range, suggests a certain lack of accuracy in British gunnery. Certainly *King George V* found ranging difficult because of cordite, smoke and water spouts concealing the target, as well as because of a breakdown in her radar. She also suffered from mechanical failures in her 14-inch turrets, just like *Prince of Wales* three days earlier, which reduced her firepower by 80 per cent for seven minutes and 40 per cent for twenty-three.[82]

At 1025, in answer to an enquiry from Somerville, Tovey signalled that *Bismarck* 'was still afloat'; three minutes later he added that 'he could not get her to sink by gunfire'; and shortly after that again that 'he had been forced to abandon the action on account of fuel'.[83] So after all Tovey had to leave it to the cruisers to finish *Bismarck* off with torpedoes. Anticipating this order, *Dorsetshire* fired two torpedoes into her starboard side and one into her port. *Bismarck*, now with a heavy list to port, began to settle slowly by the stern. About this time, according to one German witness, a scuttling party opened her sea-cocks and activated time-fused charges in the cooling water intakes. At 1036, with her flag still flying, she rolled over and disappeared in 48° 10'N, 16° 12'W, taking with her Lütjens, Lindemann and all but 110 members of her company of 2,200.

As Admiral Tovey generously acknowledged: 'She put up a most gallant fight against impossible odds, worthy of the old days of the Imperial German Navy.'[84]

In language with a true Nelsonian ring, Admiral Tovey wrote in his despatch:

> Although it was no more than I expected, the co-operation, skill and understanding displayed by all forces during this prolonged chase gave me the utmost satisfaction. Flag and Commanding Officers of detached units invariably took the action I would have wished, before or without receiving instructions from me. The conduct of all officers and men of the Fleet which I have the honour to command was in accordance with the tradition of the service.[85]

Yet it was his own style of command, so different from the centralising rigidity of Jutland as re-embodied in the 1939 Fighting Instructions, which had fostered this spirit of initiative. Tovey went on with characteristic generosity of spirit to say: 'Force H was handled with conspicuous skill throughout the operation by Vice-Admiral Sir James F. Somerville, KCB, DSO and contributed a vital share in its successful conclusion.' And, whether or not Tovey knew by this time how hard the naval staff had striven in the Admiralty War Room to keep the Prime Minister and the First Sea Lord off his back, he had praise for the Admiralty too: 'The accuracy of the enemy information supplied by the Admiralty and the speed with which it was passed were remarkable and the balance struck between information and instructions passed to forces out of visual touch with me, was ideal.'[86]

But privately he was angered by one notable exception to this ideal balance. At 1137 that forenoon of 27 May 1941 when he was steaming for home having accomplished his task, the First Sea Lord made him a signal that had in fact been drafted by Churchill and sent at his behest. It read:

We cannot visualise situation from your signals. *Bismarck* must be sunk at all costs, and if to do this it is necessary for *King George V* to remain on the scene then she must do so even if subsequently means towing *King George V*.[87]

Few will disagree with Tovey's later verdict that this was 'the stupidest and most ill-considered signal ever made'.[88]

After the killing of the shark came the hunting of piranhas – the powerfully armed raiders disguised as innocent merchantmen and the supply ships on which they depended.[89] Thanks to the picture of the deployment of the supply ships built up through Ultra decrypts of the 'Home Waters' naval Enigma, seven of these were disposed of by 21 June 1941, and another seven (including the weather ship *Lauenburg*) sunk or captured between 21 June and 11 July. But the raiders themselves when far off in the South Atlantic or beyond used the 'Distant Waters' Enigma cypher, which GC and CS never penetrated to the end of the war.[90] Nevertheless on 8 May HMS *Cornwall*, alerted by a victim's radio call, sank the raider *Pinguin* in the Indian Ocean.

On 19 December the raider *Kormoran* was caught off Western Australia by HMAS *Sydney* which incautiously approached to within 2,000 yards to identify her. On being challenged to give a secret identifying call sign, the *Kormoran* opened fire first, hitting the *Sydney* under the bridge and torpedoing her. There followed for some two hours a furious action in which the *Kormoran* was badly damaged and set ablaze, to be later scuttled by her crew. The *Sydney* herself had her two forward turrets put out of action, and when the exchange of fire ceased with the fall of night she steamed slowly away blazing furiously, later to blow up and sink with all hands; a sorry and possibly needless end for a ship which had served with such distinction in the Mediterranean in 1940.

But three days later HMS *Devonshire* avenged her by sinking the raider *Atlantis* off the Cape of Good Hope. She found the *Atlantis* thanks to GC and CS decyphering a 'Home Waters' Enigma signal instructing U-boats to rendezvous with the *Atlantis* in order to refuel from her. The remaining four raiders at large in 1941 made safe return to Germany between August and December.

Although the disguised raiders were to sneak back to the high seas in 1942, the German warships were never to return. For in hunting down and destroying the *Bismarck* the Royal Navy had sunk not just a single battleship, however formidable; it had sunk Grand Admiral

Raeder's entire strategy, so long pursued, of breaking down Britain's Atlantic communications by means of a surface fleet. When the *Prinz Eugen* returned to Brest on 1 June 1941 with engine trouble, it marked the end of all operations in the Atlantic by German battleships, pocket battleships and cruisers, even though the mere threat was to preoccupy the Admiralty and tie down British heavy ships until 1944. The death of the *Bismarck* destroyed Hitler's always lukewarm support for Raeder's strategy; it vindicated Dönitz's argument since long before the war that surface forces consumed enormous resources of material and manpower that could be far more cost-effectively employed in expanding the U-boat fleet. As Raeder was ruefully to acknowledge: 'The loss of the *Bismarck* had a decisive effect on the conduct of the war at sea.'[91]

However, by the time the Royal Navy had won this, its first strategic victory in the Second World War, Churchill's 'blue water' strategy in the Mediterranean had collapsed in catastrophe; and it had been the Mediterranean Fleet which, even more than the British and Dominion armies, had paid the gruesome price.

Greek Prelude: The Battle of Matapan

The year had begun so well. On 5 January 1941 General O'Connor's Western Desert Force completed the capture of the Italian fortress of Bardia, just across the Egyptian frontier into Libya, together with 400 guns, 138 tanks, and over 700 trucks, inflicting losses of over 40,000 men killed, wounded and prisoners. On 21 January it was the turn of the fortress port of Tobruk. After a brief Hurricane bombardment, heavily armoured 'I' tanks followed by infantry of the 6th Australian Division smashed through the defensive perimeter into the heart of the fortress. This time the bag amounted to 25,000 prisoners, 208 guns, 23 medium tanks and over 200 trucks.

Now came the bold, brilliant climax of O'Connor's campaign: an advance by his worn-out armour across abominable desert tracks to cut off the remainder of the Italian 10th Army as it retreated from Benghazi along the coast road to Tripolitania. On 6 February O'Connor closed his trap at Beda Fomm, south of Benghazi, with just half an hour to spare. All that day the desperate Italians strove to break through and escape – and failed. By the evening O'Connor had consummated that rarest of military achievements, a victory of total annihilation. In the course of his ten-week campaign he had advanced 500 miles, destroyed an army of ten divisions, taken 130,000 prisoners, 400 tanks, 1,290 guns and two major fortresses, all for the cost of 476 British Empire troops killed, 1,225 wounded and 43 missing.[1] Thanks to O'Connor's leadership and to the skill and spirit of his British,

Indian and Australian soldiers, Winston Churchill's Mediterranean 'blue water' strategy had thus been for the moment crowned with an unimagined triumph; the reward for all the effort invested in building up the Middle East forces and their base installations, all the Royal Navy's months of hazardous service along the sea lanes that led from Britain and the Empire to Alexandria and Suez.

And the Royal Navy itself had directly played an important part in the Desert offensive. On 3 January 1941 *Warspite, Barham* and *Valiant* bombarded Bardia. The elderly Great War monitor, *HMS Terror* (two 15-inch guns) and the three gunboats *Ladybird, Aphis* and *Gnat* of the Inshore Squadron (Captain H. Hickling, RN) had also bombarded the defences of Bardia and Tobruk as well; and hammered the retreating Italians as they straggled westwards on the coast road. Still more important, the flow of seaborne supplies which alone had kept O'Connor's little army in the field and able to advance depended solely upon the Navy. As Cunningham wrote to the First Sea Lord on 18 January, three days before the fall of Tobruk:

> Our commitments in support of the Army in the Western Desert grow daily and with the fall of Tobruk expected in a day or two, they will reach, I hope, a peak. Everything is going by sea including, since a few days ago, practically all the personnel. The strain on our destroyers and small auxiliary craft is tremendous and also it is very difficult to find the right type of shipping for the job. Small coastal carriers are what are required but there just aren't any.[2]

With O'Connor's final destruction of the Italian 10th Army at Beda Fomm on 6 February 1941, Tripolitania (the western province of Libya) lay open to a further British advance, for only a few demoralised, disorganised and ill-equipped Italian troops remained to defend it. O'Connor therefore planned to make an immediate advance as far as Syrte, and then, on 20 February, launch an armoured striking force along the coast road to Tripoli while the Royal Navy landed an infantry brigade from the sea. But by now it was known in London and Cairo that a new, much more formidable, foe lay just over the strategic horizon in the Mediterranean theatre – drawn in by the very brilliance of O'Connor's victories in the Desert, by the Greek Army's valiant success in throwing the Italian invader back into Albania, and by the Royal Navy's domination of the Mediterranean waters despite the Italian Navy and Air Force. For Hitler had decided to come to the rescue of his humiliated friend Mussolini.

The German forward build-up in the Balkans and Mediterranean had been steadily plotted by GC and CS at Bletchley Park through decrypts of the Luftwaffe Enigma and also the German railway administration Enigma, as correlated with other sources of Intelligence.[3] By the end of December 1940 the British knew that Germany was deploying for a major offensive in the Balkans, the tide of troops and aircraft lapping down through compliant Hungary and Romania, with the ultimate objective in all likelihood being Greece. By 9 January 1941 the Defence Committee in London had become – wrongly – convinced from the latest decrypts that the German offensive could be launched as early as 20 January. By late January further decrypts led the Director of Military Intelligence to believe that the Germans had now deployed 23 divisions in Romania, while the British embassy in Bucharest reported that the Germans would march into Bulgaria on 17 February. Military Intelligence therefore now calculated that the Germans could be on the Greek frontier with five divisions by 12 March and reach Athens with ten divisions from mid-April onwards. Here then was a colossal new weight poised to drop into the delicate balance of British 'blue water' strategy in the Mediterranean and Middle East theatre, and especially General Wavell's finely calculated deployment of his scanty land forces, already stretched from the Western Desert to East Africa.

Yet it was Cunningham's Fleet rather than Wavell's land forces which first took the shock of the German advent in the Mediterranean theatre. By 15 December 1940 Air Intelligence (AI) and GC and CS had accumulated evidence from the Luftwaffe Enigma and other sources that the Luftwaffe's 'Fliegerkorps X' (including a squadron specialising in attacks on shipping) was being moved south to Italian bases. By the first week of January 1941 it was known that the Luftwaffe had set up bases in Sicily, whence it could command the passage between the western and eastern basins of the Mediterranean, through the Sicilian Narrows and the skies over Malta only some 60 miles away. London and Cairo also took note of an Italian broadcast on 2 January welcoming the Luftwaffe to the Mediterranean war. By 10 January the strength of 'Fliegerkorps X' in Sicily had actually risen to 96 bombers and 25 twin-engined fighters.[4]

But regrettably the available Intelligence about 'Fliegerkorps X's' arrival and its estimated strength (put at 80 aircraft) were not passed to either the Mediterranean Fleet or Force H, although whether this omission is to be blamed on the Air Ministry or the Admiralty cannot now be established.[5] The omission was the more regrettable because, from 6–7 January, the Mediterranean Fleet and Force H were at sea engaged in yet another complicated trans-Mediterranean operation, covering the passage of the convoy (codenamed 'Excess') postponed from December 1940. Apart from one hour's warning from a radio intercept by the 'Y' officer ('Y' = interception of enemy radio traffic) in HMS *Warspite*, the Fleet's first intimation that the Luftwaffe had arrived over the Mediterranean in force took the form of Stukas screaming down on it in relays shortly after noon on 10 January.

Four days earlier the four merchant ships to be convoyed – one bound for Malta with 4,000 tons of ammunition, 3,000 tons of seed potatoes and a deck cargo of twelve crated Hurricanes; the three others bound for Piraeus with urgent supplies for Greece – had sailed from Gibraltar escorted by destroyers and a new radar-equipped cruiser *Bonaventure* (5,450 tons displacement; ten dual-purpose 5.25-inch guns; eight 2-pounder anti-aircraft guns; eight 0.5-inch machine guns).[6] Early next morning Admiral Somerville followed with the main body of Force H: HMS *Renown* (flag), the battleship *Malaya*, *Ark Royal*, *Sheffield* and six destroyers. Meantime Admiral Cunningham had despatched Rear-Admiral E. de F. Renouf from Alexandria to Malta with the cruisers *Gloucester* (flag) and *Southampton* and two destroyers with 500 soldiers and airmen aboard. On 7 January Cunningham followed with the main body of the Mediterranean Fleet – *Warspite* (flag), the battleship *Valiant*, the carrier *Illustrious* and seven destroyers. At first all went well. In the evening of the 9th Somerville safely handed over his convoy off Bizerta to Renouf after Italian high-level bombers had scored the usual alarming near-misses, but no hits; he then turned back for Gibraltar; an uneventful home voyage. Cunningham's light forces meanwhile successfully covered the movements of two merchant ships westwards to Malta and two small convoys eastwards from Malta, the C-in-C himself steering to a rendezvous with the 'Excess' convoy. At dawn on 10 January, to the west of Malta, he received a report from *Bonaventure* that she had sighted two enemy destroyers; and almost at the same time gun flashes could be seen ahead. Cunningham increased to full speed ahead, and reached *Bonaventure* to find her and the destroyer *Hereward* firing into a blazing Italian destroyer, which soon blew up. The united fleet now turned to follow the convoy eastwards.

However, almost at once the destroyer *Gallant* in the Fleet's screen had its bow blown clean away by a mine; the first bad news. While she was being towed into Malta under escort, two Italian torpedo bombers came in low to attack the *Valiant*, but both torpedoes passed astern. The four Fulmar fighters patrolling high above the Fleet dived down to chase the Italians away. Almost immediately radar picked up a large formation of enemy aircraft approaching from the north, and the *Illustrious* turned into the wind to fly off more fighters. Too late: before these aircraft or the original four Fulmars could regain sufficient height 43 Junkers Ju 87 Stuka divebombers were over the Fleet and diving to the attack.[7]

The Mediterranean Fleet had grown accustomed enough to attacks by Italian bombers from heights of up to 10,000 feet, even though its ships' companies found it cumulatively wearing to be near-missed again and again. The margin of bomb-aiming error from this height with so small and elusive a target as a ship violently altering course was such as to make very long odds against direct hits as opposed to near-misses. But a Stuka attack was altogether different, as Cunningham and his fleet quickly discovered:

> We opened up with every AA gun we had [wrote Cunningham] as one by one the Stukas peeled off into their dives, concentrating the whole venom of their attack upon the *Illustrious*. At times she became almost completely hidden in a forest of great bomb splashes. One was too interested in this new form of dive-bombing attack really to be frightened, and there was no doubt we were watching complete experts. Formed roughly in a large circle over the fleet they peeled off one by one when reaching the attacking position. We could not but admire the skill and precision of it all. The attacks were pressed home to point-blank range, and as they pulled out of their dives some of them were seen to fly along the flight-deck of the *Illustrious* below the level of her funnel.[8]

At this range there could be no mistake. 'I saw her [the *Illustrious*] hit early on just before the bridge,' wrote Cunningham later, 'and in all, in something like ten minutes, she was hit by six 1,000-lb bombs, to leave the line badly on fire, her steering gear crippled, her lifts out of action, and with heavy casualties.'[9] Just like the *Bismarck*, the wounded *Illustrious* turned helplessly in circles until, after three hours, she was able to steer by her main engines. As she struggled towards the shelter of Malta harbour escorted by the Fleet, the bombers came back four more times – the Stukas twice, and Heinkel 111 medium bombers twice – hitting her with another 1,000-lb bomb. At 2100 she finally limped into the Grand Harbour, her survival being, as Cunningham wrote to the First Sea Lord, 'a fine advertisement for British shipbuilding'.[10] Nonetheless, she had been so severely damaged as to require long months in a main dockyard – if she could be safely got away from Malta.

The Mediterranean Fleet had suffered its most serious setback in the war so far. 'We had plenty to think about,' was how Cunningham drily summed it up:

In a few minutes the whole situation had changed. At one blow the fleet had been deprived of its fighter aircraft, and its command of the Mediterranean was threatened by a weapon far more efficient and dangerous than any against which we had fought before. The efforts of the Regia Aeronautica were almost as nothing compared with those of these deadly Stukas of the Luftwaffe.[11]

Now, more than ever, the Mediterranean Fleet was to suffer from the pre-war Admiralty's decision to adopt the inferior and inaccurate High Angle Control System (HACS) instead of tachymetric fire-control. The harsh lesson taught by the knocking out of the *Illustrious* was repeated at 1500 next day when Admiral Renouf, with the cruisers *Gloucester* and *Southampton* (neither fitted with radar), was jumped by twelve Stukas attacking out of the sun. *Gloucester* was hit in the director tower by a bomb which then penetrated five decks. Although it mercifully failed to explode, it nevertheless inflicted severe local damage and killed nine members of the crew. The *Southampton*, however, was hit by two or three bombs which started raging fires that could not be quenched. Shortly after 1900 she had to be abandoned and sunk by torpedo.

With the Fleet back in Alexandria, Cunningham's immediate anxiety lay in the need to get *Illustrious* away from Malta, where she was being subjected to constant further German air attack, which inflicted yet further damage, and more casualties than she had suffered in the earlier attacks at sea. The dockyard staff worked frenziedly under fire to make her sufficiently seaworthy to make a dash for Alexandria, and on the night of 23 January she slipped away and set course at 24 knots. At noon on 25 January *Illustrious* steamed into Alexandria to roaring cheers from the ships' companies of the Fleet.

Already, on 12 January, the Admiralty had decided to send Cunningham the new carrier *Formidable* (then in the South Atlantic) as a replacement. But it would be well into March before she could arrive via the Cape of Good Hope and the Suez Canal. But then came a further complication: from late January onwards the Canal itself was recurrently blocked by wrecks caused by mines dropped from the air, often of the acoustic type to which there was no available technical answer. This closure of the Canal impeded the exchange of *Illustrious* and *Formidable* as well as the routine traffic of warships and merchant vessels between the Red Sea and the eastern Mediterranean. For the Royal Air Force the new need to strengthen the air defence of the Canal against the minelayers meant yet a further stretching of scarce resources already pulled as far apart as Greece, Malta, Libya and East

Africa. And for the Army it meant a recurrent throttling of its supply line from the outside world to the Mediterranean and Middle East theatre's main arrival ports, Alexandria and Port Said.

At the other end of the Mediterranean, however, Admiral Somerville and Force H had provided welcome compensation for Cunningham's setback at the hands of 'Fliegerkorps X'. On 6 February 1941 Somerville sailed from Gibraltar with the *Renown* (flag; Captain R. R. McGrigor), *Malaya* (Captain A. F. E. Palliser), *Ark Royal* (Captain C. S. 'Hooky' Holland), *Sheffield* (Captain C. A. A. Larcom) and ten destroyers with the aim of bombarding Genoa, Italy's largest port (where it was believed one of the battleships damaged at Taranto was being repaired), and of launching air strikes against La Spezia and Leghorn.[12] The operation entailed an outward voyage of 700 miles, the final leg lying in the enemy's own home waters and within easy range of his land-based aircraft. Somerville's best protection lay in the very boldness, not to say cheek, of the enterprise. For the Italians never expected a British task force to flaunt the White Ensign in the Gulf of Genoa itself, and they had taken no measures to prevent such an incursion.

Between 0600 and 0707 on 9 February spotting aircraft were catapulted from *Renown*, *Malaya* and *Sheffield*. Landfall was made off Portofino at 0649, the shoreline shrouded in mist, the mountains behind silhouetted against the sky. At 0710 *Renown*'s spotter reported that no battleships were present in Genoa; an error, for *Diulio* lay in the dry dock, unrecognised.

> The scene off Genoa was almost dramatic in its contrasts. It was a calm Sunday morning, the foreshore hidden from view in the haze, above which the mountains stood out, turning from grey to rose in the rising sun; there was nothing to break the peace and silence. Suddenly at 0714 the *Renown* opened fire.[13]

At a range of ten to fourteen miles 15-inch and 6-inch salvoes smashed on to industrial targets and the dry docks, while HMS *Renown*'s secondary armament fired on the waterfront itself. At 0745 the British ships ceased fire and turned away to the south, leaving astern the gratifying sight of flames, explosions and billowing smoke on the Genoa shoreline that indicated (correctly) that much destruction had been inflicted, although the battleship *Diulio* in dry dock was not hit. However the *Ark Royal*'s air strike against an oil refinery at Leghorn caused only slight damage, although others of her aircraft successfully laid mines in both entrances to the La Spezia naval base.

Somerville safely reached Gibraltar on 11 February, the Italians having missed their chance of intercepting him partly because of poor visibility which hampered air reconnaissance, but even more because of poor liaison between their naval and air commands.

Somerville's raid was celebrated by the British press as a Drake-like singeing of Mussolini's chin-stubble; and for the same reasons it caused lively dismay in Italy. Yet such a hit-and-run raid, however successful, could not alter the fact that the début of 'Fliegerkorps X' in Sicily had transformed the naval prospects in the central Mediterranean. Churchill's long-cherished project of capturing the Italian island of Pantellaria in the Sicilian Narrows ('Workshop') had to be postponed again for a month on 18 January and finally cancelled two days later.[14] Cunningham wrote to the First Sea Lord that he was 'indeed thankful that WORKSHOP was not being carried out. I don't think there is much doubt we should have lost both the Glen ships [fast troop carriers] and anything else lying off the island.'[15] The Prime Minister himself had drawn the opposite conclusion from the crippling of *Illustrious* on 11 January and the loss of *Southampton*. Regretting 'bitterly'[16] that he had been persuaded [in December 1940] to postpone 'Workshop', he minuted for the Chiefs of Staff on 13 January that it was 'necessary now that "Workshop" should be reviewed . . . I should be glad if revised and perfected plans would be ready by today week . . .'[17] It was only at the Defence Committee meeting on 20 January that he at last gave way to the united opposition of the Chiefs of Staff and accepted 'Workshop's' abandonment.[18]

Yet 'Workshop' was not the only gleaming strategic trinket to catch Churchill's eye at this period in spite of the pervasive British weakness in the Mediterranean theatre and the ominous German build-up. At the same Defence Committee on 20 January he told his colleagues that he wanted a plan studied 'to capture Sardinia', a project involving 40,000 troops and all the requisite transports and powerful escorting naval forces.[19] Yet another plan – 'Mandibles' – was afoot for invading the Italian Dodecanese islands and seizing the main island of Rhodes, in this case a plan actually enjoying the support of the three service Cs-in-C in the Mediterranean. In February 1941 two separate preliminary attempts were made to land forces on the outlying islands of Kaso and Kastellorizo. Both attempts failed, partly because of tactical and command errors on the British side, partly because of unexpectedly vigorous Italian counter-action;[20] two more examples to add to the long historical tally of botched British combined operations.

It was the very flexibility of seapower that made it possible for Churchill to espouse such schemes as 'Workshop' and 'Mandibles' –

a flexibility no less seductive to him than to his predecessor Pitt the Younger in plotting similar 'descents' here and there along the coasts of Bonapartian Europe. Yet it was Greece which, in the early months of 1941, presented the Prime Minister and his colleagues with the overriding choice in Mediterranean 'blue water' strategy. For Ultra decrypts and other Intelligence made it more and more plain that she was almost certain to fall victim soon to a German 'blitzkrieg'.

Should a large (in British terms) expeditionary force be transported to Greece by the Royal Navy in order to fight alongside the Greek Army against the invading Germans? Such an expeditionary force could of course only be found from the veteran troops and the tanks of O'Connor's Western Desert Force. Or should the Royal Air Force squadrons (some 80 serviceable aircraft[21]) already in Greece remain the limit of British aid? These questions aroused the same kind of argument in the Cabinet Defence Committee as that over intervention in Scandinavia in 1939–40. On the one hand there was a debt of honour to do all that lay in Britain's power to save a brave ally; and coupled with that, the political need (especially vis-à-vis the United States) not to be seen callously to abandon the Greeks. On the other hand there was the cold accountancy of available divisions, tanks, guns, aircraft and stocks of ammunition on each side; and so far as German figures were concerned, accountancy largely derived from decrypts of Enigma traffic.

By 10 January accumulating evidence from the Secret Intelligence Service (SIS) and diplomatic sources as well as from Ultra had convinced the War Cabinet Defence Committee (see above, p. 319) that Germany would invade Greece as early as 20 January. A sense of urgency now impelled the Committee to instruct the Chief of Air Staff to signal Air Marshal Sir Arthur Longmore, the AOC-in-C, Middle East, that he was to fly to Athens to offer immediate help to the Greeks. Since O'Connor was at that time preparing his onslaught on Tobruk, Wavell, on behalf of all three Middle East Cs-in-C, replied to the CIGS, Dill, that the signal to Longmore

fills us with dismay. Our appreciation here is that German concentration is move in a war of nerves with the object of helping Italy by upsetting Greek nerves, inducing us to disperse our forces in Middle East and to stop our advance in Libya. Nothing (*repeat* nothing) we can do from here is likely to be in time to stop German advance if really intended, it will lead to most dangerous dispersion of force and is playing the enemy's game . . . I am desperately anxious lest we play enemy's game and expose ourselves to defeat in detail.[22]

[325]

But the Prime Minister implacably replied through the Chiefs of Staff that the evidence showed the enemy was not bluffing:

> Destruction of Greece would eclipse victories you have gained in Libya and might affect decisively Turkish attitude, especially if we had shown ourselves callous of fate of allies. You must therefore conform your plans to larger interests at stake. We expect and require prompt and active compliance with our decisions for which we bear full responsibility.[23]

Mercifully, however, the Greek government at this time declined the British offer of an expeditionary force, while Intelligence sources had now come to suggest that it would after all take the Germans some two months to deploy against Greece. O'Connor was thus granted a reprieve – fruitfully employed by him in completing the destruction of the Italian 10th Army and clearing Cyrenaica.

Three days after O'Connor's climactic victory at Beda Fomm Wavell signalled London: 'The extent of Italian defeat at Benghazi [sic] seems to me to make it possible that TRIPOLI might yield to small force if despatched without delay.'[24] This was certainly O'Connor's appreciation (see above, p. 318). If successful such an advance would end the war in North Africa, so permanently securing Egypt and the Suez Canal from land attack; it would provide the Royal Air Force with air bases from which to cover the central Mediterranean. Indeed, the fundamental military principle of 'the maintenance of the aim' suggested that O'Connor's victory should be exploited to the uttermost. Nevertheless, Churchill successfully swayed a meeting of the Defence Committee on 10 February in favour of his own view that O'Connor should be halted for the sake of aiding Greece. According to the minutes the Prime Minister

> ... did not think that it was necessarily impossible for the Greeks and ourselves to hold the Germans, who would be advancing down the Struma valley. The Greeks might be able to disengage a few Divisions in time, and if we could support them with air and mechanised forces, we might delay them long enough to encourage the Turks, and possibly the Yugoslavs, to join in the battle.[25]

The Committee agreed that Britain should send aid to the Greeks if asked, and 'that no serious operation should be undertaken beyond Benghazi [sic] which should be held as a secure flank for Egypt'; that therefore 'we should shift the largest possible force from Egypt to the European Continent, to assist the Greeks against a probable attack through Bulgaria'.[26]

The record makes clear that, just as in the case of Norway, Churchill urged this fateful strategic choice in defiance of the military accountancy. On 11 February, in a further Defence Committee discussion on the question, General Sir John Dill, the CIGS, pointed out that it would be difficult for Wavell to find four divisions for Greece in the immediate future, because – except for the 'green' 2nd Armoured Division (still forming) – all his troops were engaged in operations. To this Churchill retorted: 'We would have to intervene with at least 4 divisions, rising to 6 or 10 in the summer. Out of the great mass of men accumulating in the Middle East, great efforts must be made to produce more mobile formations.'[27]

Yet such a massive build-up and continuing campaign thereafter would require a proportionate logistical effort, especially in terms of ammunition, not only for the British Empire troops but also for the Greek Army, and at a time when such resources were desperately scarce in the Middle East theatre. As the Chiefs of Staff pointed out in a paper on 10 February, Britain could only supply a proportion of the Greek Army's ammunition requirements, while 'the artillery weapon situation is still more difficult', not least because the Greeks needed 350 (mule) pack artillery equipments, which Britain did not even manufacture.[28]

Nevertheless such key considerations never came under discussion in the Defence Committee when the crucial decision was being reached to stop O'Connor in his tracks.

On 11 February Wavell was instructed:

> You should therefore make yourself secure at Benghazi and concentrate all available forces in the Delta in preparation for a movement to Europe ... Our first thoughts must be for our ally Greece, which is actually fighting so well. If Greece is trampled down or forced to make a separate peace with Italy, yielding also Air and naval strategic points against us to Germany, effect on Turkey will be very bad. But if Greece with British aid can hold up for some months German advance, chances of Turkish intervention will be favoured. Therefore it would seem that we should try to get in a position to offer the Greeks the transfer to Greece of the fighting portion of the Army which has hitherto defended Egypt [i.e. O'Connor's Western Desert Force] and make every plan for sending and reinforcing it to the limit with men and material.[29]

The burden, risk and likely cost to the Royal Navy in the Mediterranean in particular of the proposed grand exercise in 'blue water strategy' could not have been more plainly spelt out than it was in a joint telegram by the three Commanders-in-Chief in the

Mediterranean and Middle East theatre, Wavell, Cunningham and Longmore, about the weakness of their resources in terms of existing or projected tasks.

> From the naval point of view the new policy creates a heavy commitment in safeguarding the line of supply through Aegean, and will entail establishing bases in Greek Islands and in Turkey ... We are already completely extended in so far as our present resources are concerned in covering the long lines of sea communication on Libyan coasts and in dealing with protection of Libya in addition to our own Mediterranean bases. Admiralty are meeting our requirements in cruisers and light craft for this purpose ... but this programme does not complete until May. If the Balkan situation develops meanwhile, the present acute shortage in light craft escorts, local defence units and personnel for shore bases will become critical unless our resources continue to be built up as rapidly as possible ...[30]

The telegram went on to note the shortages of anti-aircraft guns and aircraft, and tellingly to express the three Commanders-in-Chiefs' general misgivings:

> Finally we feel there may be a tendency at home to over-estimate our actual resources in Middle East when assessing our ability to meet the varying commitments.[31]

On the same day Admiral Cunningham signalled to the Admiralty:

> If the Germans operate air force from Bulgaria, as appears to be their obvious intention, shipping in North Aegean will be gravely threatened by bombing and in ports such as Salonika and their approaches by aircraft minelaying ... obviously it will be a task of considerable magnitude to provide and organise this protection [of convoys by fighters] from Greece, which has few developed landing grounds and where scale of air attack will be high. We shall do our best to get convoys through, but we must be prepared for casualties to ships and troops.
> The magnetic and acoustic mine threat is, however, more serious because it is not possible with existing resources to keep clear yet more areas such as Salonika, its approach and island harbours ...[32]

But Churchill brushed aside such considerations – just as he did the heavily adverse military odds on land as calculated at this time from the latest Ultra Intelligence and other sources. According to these calculations German strength in Romania now stood at 23 divisions, while five German divisions could be on the Greek frontier by 12 March and ten divisions in Athens between mid-April and mid-May. The most that Britain could send to Greece, as Churchill was aware, was three infantry divisions and one armoured brigade; and only exiguous air cover could be provided for them against the Luftwaffe. Indeed the Premier actually opted for the Greek adventure in the face of apparent odds far more adverse than in reality, for German strength in Romania then stood at nine divisions, not 23. O'Connor's excellent if fleeting chance of taking Tripoli, so pre-empting a German intervention in Africa, had therefore been sacri-ficed to what was in all military respects another unrealistic gamble. Churchill chose Greece over Tripoli primarily for political reasons, if not simply moral ones, telling the Defence Committee on 10 February that it would be 'wrong to abandon the Greeks, who were putting up a magnificent fight, and who were prepared to fight the Germans, so that we could later help Turkey, who was shirking her re-sponsibilities . . . .'[33] He added that 'we could not blame the Greeks if they bowed to the superior force of the Germans if we refused them help'.

On 12 February the Foreign Secretary, Anthony Eden, and the Chief of Imperial General Staff, General Sir John Dill, were de-spatched to the Middle East to concert plans with the three Cs-in-C and the Greek government, and seek to drum up active support from Turkey and Yugoslavia – the old Great War fantasy again of a Balkan coalition, for which Eden was to find no takers either in Ankara or Belgrade. On the same day Major-General Erwin Rommel arrived in Tripoli in advance of the German field force that he was to command. During the following week Churchill too late began to have second thoughts about the Greek adventure, and on 20 February he signalled Eden in Cairo: 'Do not consider yourselves obligated to a Greek enterprise if in your hearts you feel it will only be another Norwegian fiasco. If no good plan can be made please say so. But of course you know how valuable success would be.'[34]

Unaccountably Wavell now expressed the opinion that there was a fair military chance of stopping the Germans in Greece; Dill somewhat wanly concurred; and Eden signalled home on 24 February that all three of them advised the government to despatch the 'maximum' British military and air support at 'the earliest possible moment'.[35] In London, the Director of Military Intelligence, drawing on the latest clues from Enigma – which indicated that the German attack was going to be on a formidable scale – gloomily noted that 'we must be prepared to face the loss of all forces sent to Greece'.[36] A memor-andum by the Chiefs of Staff on 24 February, drawing up a balance sheet of resources and prospects, also vented the deepest misgivings.

'We are undertaking a commitment,' they wrote, 'of which we cannot foresee the extent.'[37] It noted again 'the acute shortage of artillery and equipment for the Greeks', as well as the risk to Egypt from an enemy counter-stroke in the desert. As for the Royal Navy, on which this fresh adventure in 'blue water' strategy totally depended, the Chiefs of Staff noted that there 'would be a considerable air menace to our lines of communication to Greece, and the reduction of the Dodecanese becomes urgent. It must be repeated that, if the war spreads to the Far East, the position of our forces in Greece will be precarious if we withdrew important units of the Mediterranean Fleet to go eastward . . .' Their advice to the government hardly amounted to enthusiastic endorsement of the adventure:

> It goes without saying that the expedition must be a gamble, but our representatives on the spot, after conference with the Greeks, and full examination of the Greek plan, evidently think there is a reasonable prospect of holding up a German advance. We feel we must accept their opinion.[38]

That day the Cabinet debated the telegrams from Eden and Dill, together with the Chiefs of Staff report. Despite his belated second thoughts about the risks and costs, Churchill said 'he was himself in favour of going to the rescue of Greece, one of the results of which might be to bring in Turkey and Yugoslavia, and to force the Germans to bring more troops from Germany. The reaction of the United States would also be favourable . . .' Despite this dream of a Balkan coalition, the Prime Minister did acknowledge on the other hand, that 'the difficulties of maintaining an army on land must not be under-rated, for it would have to be supplied by ships going round the Cape of Good Hope'.[39]

Others too expressed concern about the problem of seaborne supply. The Australian Prime Minister, Robert Menzies, who was present (Australian forces forming so large a part of the expeditionary force), asked: 'Could our shipping maintain the strain of the operation?' The Minister of Aircraft Production, Lord Beaverbrook, likewise thought that 'the effect of the enterprise on our shipping resources should be closely examined'.[40] Nevertheless, the Cabinet decided to approve the despatch of forces to Greece, and in a further meeting next day the Prime Minister remarked that he 'felt no doubt' that the decision was right despite the shipping problem.[41] The Cabinet took note that German troops had been encountered for the first time in the Western Desert clash at El Agheila, on the border between Tripolitania and Cyrenaica.

On 4 March 'Operation Lustre' – the transport of the British Commonwealth expeditionary force to Greece – duly began. As the first ships were about to sail, Admiral Cunningham signalled the Admiralty that he wished to make it clear that a big risk was being taken, principally because of the weakness of the convoys and the ports of disembarkation against air attack. Apart from a run to Malta with one convoy after *Formidable* had arrived, he went on, the moves to Greece would absorb the whole energies of the Fleet for the next two months at least. Meanwhile the Cyrenaican supply line to the Desert Army would go almost unprotected, and the proposed landings in the Dodecanese would have to be postponed.[42]

This same day Dill in Athens learned from the Greek Commander-in-Chief, General Papagos, that no preparatory work had been done as promised on the defensive position to be occupied by the British expeditionary force along the River Aliakmon, and that only much smaller Greek forces than promised could now be redeployed alongside the British. Meanwhile in a Chiefs-of-Staff meeting in London the Minister of Shipping said he was 'very concerned' about the number of ships to be held in the Middle East for 'Lustre', evoking the retort from the Prime Minister (and Minister of Defence) that extra shipping must be found from the 2,200,000 tons at present 'lying idle under repair' [in the United Kingdom].[43] The Chiefs of Staff noted that Dill's disquieting news, coupled with the likely timing and weight of the German onslaught, meant that the hazards of the enterprise had been greatly increased.[44]

Next day, 5 March, the First Sea Lord, as spokesman for the Chiefs-of-Staff, told the Defence Committee that the three Middle East Cs-in-C had been asked for an appreciation of the time it would take the Germans to reach the Aliakmon line, also for a report on the Suez Canal situation (i.e., the effects of aerial mining of the Canal on the vital line of communication to the Mediterranean and Greece) and 'a report on the probable ammunition situation during the proposed campaign. [The ammunition aspect had tended to disappear into the background] . . .'[45] The First Sea Lord added that until answers were received to these queries, the Chiefs-of-Staff were not in a position to revise their previous views.

But it was far too late to ask these questions, and no answers in fact were ever received. However, on 8 March the British military mission in Athens reported that the Greek Army's artillery ammunition in the present war against the Italians would only last until mid-April

– just about the time the German invasion could be expected.[46]

By now even Churchill, in the face of all this rising doubt, had become fully seized by a belated realism; and on this same day, with the agreement of the Defence Committee, he signalled Eden in Athens to express their heavy misgivings concerning the Greek C-in-C's failure to implement his promises, with regard to the state of the Greek Army, and with regard to the political complications in respect of the Dominions of Australia and New Zealand over risking their divisions in Greece. All this, he told Eden in a telegram:

> ... makes it difficult for Cabinet to believe that we now have any power to avert fate of Greece unless Turkey and/or Yugoslavia come in, which seems most improbable. We have done our best to promote Balkan combination against Germany. We must be careful not to urge Greece against her better judgement into a hopeless resistance alone when we have only handfuls of troops which can reach the scene in time . . .[47]

It must be said that all these were considerations which were equally valid on 10 February, when the Prime Minister persuaded his colleagues to take the original and now irrevocable decision to halt O'Connor in favour of the Greek adventure. Moreover, in a remarkable volte-face, Churchill had by now changed his entire view of the strategic and political value of going to Greece anyway, telling Eden in the same telegram that 'loss of Greece and Balkans by no means a major catastrophe for us provided Turkey remains honest neutral . . .'; and he alluded to the possibility of instead resuming 'Mandibles' (the Dodecanese operation) or, of all things, an advance on Tripoli.[48]

However, Eden replied next day that the three theatre Cs-in-C remained of the opinion that 'Lustre' should continue. On 7 March the War Cabinet argued long and hard for the last time about the Greek enterprise, but finally 'confirmed the decision to give military assistance to Greece, and agreed that all arrangements to this end should proceed'.[49]

Just four days later Cunningham was writing to the First Sea Lord: 'I hope it will turn out that our policy of helping Greece is the right one. To me it is absolutely right [on grounds of politics or honour?] but I much doubt if our resources, particularly naval and air, are equal to the strain.'[50] Cunningham was especially worried about the weakness of the Royal Air Force in the theatre, now that air power had become the key to operations on sea and land:

> There seems to me some bad misunderstanding about the state of our Air Force out here. I feel the Chiefs of Staff are badly misinformed about the

number of fighter squadrons available. Longmore is absolutely stretched to the limit and we seem to have far fewer than is supposed at home. We are getting sat on by the Germans in Cyrenaica, the figures there are over 200 German and Italian fighters against 30 of our own. It seems to me that if the fighter situation is not taken in hand drastically and speedily we are heading straight for trouble – not only in Greece but if the Germans advance in Libya we have no air forces to stop them and actually very little else either.[51]

Throughout March 1941 warships plied between Alexandria and Port Said and the Greek port of Piraeus, taking the soldiers of the New Zealand Division, 6th Australian Division and 1st Armoured Brigade (the élite of Wavell's forces) from the palm trees, the ancient stinks and clamorous humanity of Egypt to the thyme-scented rocks tumbling down the northern slopes of Mount Olympus where they were to meet the expected German invasion. On disembarkation at Piraeus the troops were counted off by the German military attaché (Germany and Greece not of course yet being at war). Until after 24 March the movement of the merchant ships which transported the guns, tanks, trucks, ammunition and other supplies could be protected against attack by the Italian Fleet only by Vice-Admiral Pridham-Wippell's Light Forces (or Force B), consisting of the cruisers *Orion* (flag), *Ajax*, HMAS *Perth* and *Gloucester*, and four destroyers – because Cunningham himself with the battlefleet had been busy running the second supply convoy of the year into Malta by the customary feat of operational juggling. Two days after he returned to Alexandria came the bad news that his ill-protected forward base at Suda Bay, Crete, had been daringly attacked by six aquaplaning Italian motor boats loaded with explosives, and HMS *York* (his only 8-inch gun cruiser) so badly damaged that she had to be beached: a novel turn in the remorseless grind of attrition.

Early in the forenoon of that same day Cunningham received from the Admiralty various Ultra decrypts of Luftwaffe and Italian Navy Enigma signals which the Admiralty believed must point to a major enemy operation soon in the Aegean or eastern Mediterranean.[52] On 25 March a Luftwaffe signal had ordered all twin-engined fighters in Libya to fly to Palermo for 'special operations', and an Italian Navy signal had stated that the 25th was D − 3 for an operation involving Rhodes Command. On 26 March further signals revealed that air reconnaissance and air attacks on Allied airfields in the Aegean were to precede and accompany a certain operation; also that information had been requested about British convoys plying between Egypt and

Greece. Yet these somewhat mysterious clues could not even guide the C-in-C as to whether the impending attack on his convoys was going to be launched by air or surface forces. It was therefore in the usual sea-mist of uncertainty that Cunningham issued his first orders that evening in what was to be the climactic battle of his career as C-in-C of a fleet. He stopped a south-bound convoy from sailing from Piraeus, ordered a north-bound convoy to reverse course (under cover of darkness), and signalled Pridham-Wippell (already in the Aegean) to be south-west of Gavdo Island (south of Crete) at daylight on the 28th.

At 1230 next day came hard news at last, when a Royal Air Force flying-boat based in Crete reported three Italian cruisers and a destroyer 75 miles east of Sicily and steering towards Crete. Cunningham thereupon decided to put to sea with the battlefleet after nightfall. He intended that in the meantime the fleet lying at anchor in harbour should present a misleading picture of inactivity to the enemy air reconnaissance – which it successfully did, for at 1900 an Italian aircraft reported home that the British Fleet was still at Alexandria. In a personal deception plan to hoodwink the Japanese consul in Alexandria, a keen golfer suspected of spying for his Axis friends (and, in Cunningham's words, 'with a southern aspect of such elephantine proportions when he bent over to putt that the irreverent Chief of Staff had nicknamed him "the blunt end of the Axis"'),[53] Cunningham went ashore that afternoon to play golf, conspicuously carrying a suitcase as if he meant to spend the night ashore. He returned to his flagship after dark, and at 1900 the Fleet slipped its moorings and headed westwards course 300°, 20 knots: the *Warspite* (Captain D. B. Fisher; flag), *Barham* (flag of Rear-Admiral 1st Battle Squadron, Rear-Admiral H. B. Rawlings; Captain G. C. Cooke), *Valiant* (Captain C. E. Morgan), the carrier *Formidable* (Captain A. W. La T. Bisset) and the destroyers *Jervis*, *Janus*, *Nubian*, *Mohawk*, *Stuart*, *Greyhound*, *Griffin*, *Hotspur* and *Havock*.[54] By a mischance the flagship passed too close to a mudbank on the way out of harbour, so filling her condensers with mud and reducing her speed to 20 knots.

At dawn on 28 March an air search by four Albacores and a Swordfish was flown from *Formidable*. At 0722 one of them reported sighting four cruisers and four destroyers in 34° 22′N, 24° 47′E, steering 230°; twenty minutes later a second aircraft reported four cruisers and six destroyers in 34° 05′N, 24° 26′E. Since these fixes roughly corresponded with Pridham-Wippell's expected position, it was first believed that the aircraft had sighted him rather than the enemy. All doubt was, however, dispelled when at 0827 the C-in-C received a signal from Pridham-Wippell's flagship *Orion* (sent 0802) that she had sighted three enemy cruisers bearing north, distant eighteen miles, course eastward. Yet even now Cunningham could not be sure whether or not any enemy battleships might be present, because in the past British lookouts had taken battleships to be cruisers. He could only increase speed to 22 knots, the best that *Warspite* and *Barham* could manage, and alter course to 310° to support Pridham-Wippell.

In fact Admiral Iachino had sailed from Naples at 2100 on 26 March with the modern battleship *Vittorio Veneto* (flag; 41,377 tons displacement; nine 15-inch guns; 30 knots) and four destroyers, later to be joined from other Italian bases by the six 10,000-ton 8-inch gun cruisers *Trieste*, *Trento*, *Bolzano*, *Zara*, *Fiume* and *Pola*, the two 6-inch gun cruisers *Abruzzi* and *Garibaldi* and nine destroyers. This formidable striking force's task, undertaken in response to pressing German requests, was to attack the convoys carrying the British expeditionary force to Greece. At dawn on 28 March Iachino's fleet was deployed in three separate groups, course 130°: *Vittorio Veneto* and four escorting destroyers on the starboard station, with a group of three cruisers (*Trieste*, *Trento* and *Bolzano*) and three destroyers some ten miles on the flagship's port bow, and the third group (the remaining five cruisers and six destroyers) some twenty miles further still to port. At 0643 the flagship's spotter aircraft sighted four cruisers and four destroyers steering south-east at 18 knots only 50 miles distant – in fact, Pridham-Wippell's Force B. Judging that the presence of this cruiser squadron must signify that a convoy was near, Iachino increased to 30 knots in happy anticipation of a fruitful forenoon of destruction. At almost the same moment that the *Orion* sighted an Italian cruiser (in fact, *Trieste*) the *Trieste* herself sighted the British cruisers.

With four 6-inch gun ships Pridham-Wippell was confronting three 8-inch gun cruisers. As he wrote in his report of proceedings later: 'Knowing that vessels of that class could outrange my squadron and that, having a superior speed, they could choose the range, I decided to try to draw them towards our own battlefleet and carrier.' He therefore swung his ships to 140° and increased to 28 knots. At 0812 the Italian ships opened fire at a range of thirteen miles; at 0829, with the range down to twelve miles, *Gloucester* fired back, but her salvoes fell short. The Italian ships ceased fire and altered to the westward, Pridham-Wippell conforming in order to keep touch. But although he could not know it, he now stood in real danger of being cornered between the *Trieste* group and Iachino's other cruiser group, to say nothing of *Vittorio Veneto* herself. At 1058, when the *Orion*'s guncrews were sitting out on the turrets in the morning sunshine, an officer on the bridge paused in munching a sandwich to remark to Pridham-Wippell's Staff Officer (Operations): 'What's that battleship over there? I thought ours were miles away.'[55] Almost immediately the first of *Vittorio Veneto*'s salvoes whistled down round the British cruisers.

Back in the *Warspite*, Cunningham and his staff read the intercepts of Pridham-Wippell's next signals to his ships with a surge of excitement:

'Make smoke by all available means.'

'Turn together to 180°.'

'Proceed at your utmost speed.'

To Cunningham, the old destroyer commander, the import of these signals was immediately plain enough – Pridham-Wippell had sighted the enemy battlefleet. The *Warspite* was, however, still some 80 miles away from the scene; her maximum speed still down from 24 knots to 22 knots, which was in any case the very best the unmodernised old *Barham* could manage. So once again Cunningham had to endure the teeth-grinding frustration of trying with old, slow heavy ships to bring to action a modern enemy battlefleet several knots faster. It was a time for the 'caged tiger act' as his staff colloquially called it:

> He would pace the one side of the Admiral's bridge, always the side nearest the enemy; the speed of advance of the battleship was never fast enough for him and every second was grudged when a turn from the main line of advance was required for operating aircraft . . . we adjusted our actions accordingly.[56]

Cunningham was particularly annoyed by the reduction in *Warspite*'s speed. Aware that the Fleet Engineer Officer, Engineer Captain B. H. H. Williams, was on board, he sent for him, and, in his own laconic words, 'told him to do something about it'.[57] The flagship's speed duly rose. Cunningham's anxiety was the greater because the previous night the cruiser *Gloucester* in Force B had reported that engine trouble had cut her speed to 24 knots, which could imperil Pridham-Wippell's escape from danger. But as Cunningham put it in his memoirs, 'the sight of an enemy battleship had somehow increased the *Gloucester*'s speed to 30 knots'.[58]

The C-in-C, pacing his bridge, knew that 'something had to be done',[59] and quickly, to save Pridham-Wippell from destruction. That 'something' could only be a carrier air-strike. Cunningham had intended to delay such a strike until the Italian fleet was close enough for his battleships to come up and finish off any crippled vessels. Now he felt he had no alternative but to send in HMS *Formidable*'s torpedo aircraft (already airborne) straight away. At 1127 Lieutenant-Commander Gerald Saunt, commanding officer of 826 Squadron, led the strike force of six Albacores in two sub-flights in an attack on *Vittorio Veneto*'s starboard side. All six torpedoes missed: two ahead, four astern. Nevertheless, the attack sufficed to induce Iachino to break off his pursuit of Pridham-Wippell's Force B and turn for home (course 300°) at 25 knots, such was now Italian fear of British carrier aircraft.

With Force B safely taking station ahead of his heavy ships, Cunningham now faced the familiar problem of how to catch an Italian battlefleet legging it home much faster than his own best speed. 'It was a bitter anti-climax,' wrote the fleet gunnery officer, 'and no prudent staff officer approached the "caged tiger" without good cause . . .'[60] As it had been in past actions in the Mediterranean and as it was to be again with the *Bismarck* in two months' time, the one hope lay in the Fleet Air Arm, that pre-war naval orphan. But HMS *Formidable* (23,000 tons displacement; 32 knots; launched less than three weeks before the war broke out) had only 27 serviceable aircraft on board, of which thirteen were Fulmar fighters. Her total strike force amounted to ten of the new Fairey Albacore torpedo-bombers (maximum speed at 4,000 feet 161 mph; cruising speed 126 mph; range 820 miles)[61] and four Swordfish – a derisory strength compared with the mass carrier air groups now training for war in Japanese and American carriers, and quite insufficient to swamp the powerful anti-aircraft defence of a modern fleet. In the event the second strike force flown from the *Formidable* at Cunningham's orders only consisted of three Albacores and two Swordfish of 829 Squadron escorted by three Fulmars of 803 Squadron. While these were searching for the *Vittoria Veneto*, Royal Air Force Blenheim medium bombers from Crete bombed Iachino's ships from high altitude, causing alarm but no damage; the first time the Royal Air Force cooperated with the Navy in attacking an enemy fleet at sea in the Mediterranean.

For Cunningham the early afternoon of 28 March was still 'caged tiger' time, as *Warspite*, *Barham*, *Valiant* and *Formidable* steamed on across a flat calm sea, white bow waves cutting through purple-blue silk; black, grey and white dazzle paint, White Ensigns and the C-in-C's St George's flag of England at *Warspite*'s mainmast brilliant in the afternoon sunshine against a cobalt sky. Then, at 1510, one of *Formidable*'s aircraft reported the *Vittorio Veneto* as lying about sixty-five miles ahead, in 34° 50'N, 22° 10'E, and still steering westward. At 1519 Lieutenant-Commander J. Dalyell-Stead took his three Albacores down out of the sun and in towards the battleship's bows, while the two escorting Fulmar fighters machine-gunned her bridge and superstructure in order to distract the AA batteries. Admiral Iachino later recorded his admiration for the crew of the leading aircraft (Dalyell-Stead; his observer, Lieutenant Cooke; and air gunner, Petty-Officer Blenkhorn) as he watched them approach to within 1,000 yards of his flagship before dropping their torpedo, even though they were by now flying through a hurricane of anti-aircraft fire. Badly hit, they crashed into the sea off the starboard bow. Wrote Iachino: 'And so died a brave pilot without the satisfaction of knowing that his attack had been successful.'[62]

And successful it was. As the torpedo track bubbled through the water towards *Vittorio Veneto*, the great ship swung to starboard to comb the track. Too late: the torpedo struck her aft about sixteen feet below the waterline and just above the port outer screw, making her stagger as if hit by an enormous fist. At 1530, with thousands of tons of water flooding in through the hole, the engines stopped, and the Italian flagship began to settle by the stern. It was almost an exact preview of the lucky hit on the *Bismarck* eight weeks later; a demonstration that in the most powerful of battleships there was a point which was both vital and inherently unprotectable. Although Dalyell-Stead (who was awarded the posthumous DSO) had scored the only hit even though others were claimed by his comrades, it was enough. At 1558 a shadowing aircraft reported: 'Enemy has made a large decrease in speed.'[63]

Nevertheless frantic work by damage-control parties enabled *Vittorio Veneto* within an hour to make 15 knots. Since she was still 60 miles ahead of the British fleet, this meant that Cunningham could not overhaul her before dusk. At 1644 he therefore ordered Pridham-Wippell to go ahead with Force B at full speed to regain surface touch with the enemy, the destroyers *Nubian* and *Mohawk* to act as a visual signal link between him and Pridham-Wippell.

Cunningham now needed, in his own words, 'to signal some plan for the night which was coming on', despite a situation which was still very confused for '. . . we continued to receive reports showing another enemy force containing battleships to the north-west of the *Vittorio Veneto*. These reports, as we discovered later, were incorrect. The force referred to consisted entirely of cruisers [in fact, *Zara*, *Fiume*, *Pola*, *Abruzzi* and *Garibaldi*] . . .'[64] What Cunningham urgently wanted was hard information, and at 1745 the flagship catapulted its reconnaissance aircraft with the C-in-C's own observer, Lieutenant-Commander A. S. Bolt, on board. By 1830 Cunningham was receiving from him an exemplary series of accurate reports describing how the Italian fleet had now been concentrated into a mass round the *Vittorio Veneto*, with a column of destroyers on one side of her and of cruisers on the other, with a destroyer screen ahead; course about 300°, speed 12 knots, distant from the *Warspite* some 50 miles, bearing 292°. Cunningham therefore ordered *Formidable* to launch a third air strike.

Composed of six Albacores and two Swordfish of 826 and 828 Squadrons, plus two Swordfish of 815 Squadron based in Crete, and led once again by Lieutenant-Commander Saunt, it went in just as the Mediterranean dusk was fast turning to dark. According to Saunt's observer in the leading Albacore, Lieutenant H. F. E. Hopkins:

> When we eventually went into the attack from the dark side with the Italians silhouetted against the last glow of light in the west, we found that we had been spotted at long range and were met with an impassable barrage of fire. We were forced to withdraw, and split up and come in again individually from different angles. The barrage of fire put up by the Italians was immensely spectacular but not very effective. A good deal of hose-piping [wild firing] went on which resulted in a number of their ships hitting each other but little damage to our aircraft.[65]

Although the strike force claimed hits, Cunningham could not be sure of this. Pridham-Wippell had now made contact with the enemy, who lay nine miles to the north-west. Cunningham faced a challenge alike to his professional judgment and to his personal mettle as a leader of a fleet.

> Now came the difficult moment of deciding what to do [he wrote in his memoirs]. I was fairly well convinced that having got so far it would be foolish not to make every effort to complete the *Vittorio Veneto*'s destruction. At the same time it appeared to us that the Italian admiral must have been fully aware of our position. He had numerous cruisers and destroyers in company, and any British Admiral in his position would not have hesitated to use every destroyer he had, backed up by all his cruisers fitted with torpedo tubes, for attacks on the pursuing fleet. Some of my staff argued that it would be unwise to charge blindly after the retreating enemy with our three heavy ships, and the *Formidable* also on our hands, to run the risk of ships being crippled, and to find ourselves within easy range of the enemy dive-bombers at daylight.[66]

As Cunningham delicately put it in his memoirs, 'I paid respectful attention to this opinion, and as the discussion happened to coincide with my time for dinner I told them I would have my evening meal and would see how I felt later.'[67] But his staff recalled the scene in rather different terms. According to the fleet gunnery officer:

> The well-known steely blue look was in A.B.C.'s eye, and the staff had no doubt that there was going to be a party ... I think that A.B.C. had probably made up his mind by about 8 p.m. to send the light forces into the attack and to follow up with the battlefleet, but he nevertheless, on this occasion, went through the formality of asking the opinion of certain staff officers. Neither the staff officer operations nor the master of the fleet liked the idea much, and said so in their very different ways. The fleet gunnery officer said he was keen to let the guns off, but the battleships hadn't had a night practice for months and there might well be a pot mess with star-shells and searchlights if we got into confused night action. A.B.C. took one look at his supposed helpers and said 'You're a pack of yellow-livered skunks. I'll go and have my supper now and see after supper if my morale isn't higher than yours.'[68]

When the C-in-C returned to the bridge after his supper, his morale was higher than theirs. At 2037 he made the executive signal to the 14th and 2nd Destroyer Flotillas:

> Destroyer flotillas attack enemy battlefleet with torpedoes. Estimated bearing and distance of centre of enemy battlefleet from Admiral 286° 33 miles at 2030.
> Enemy course and speed 295° 13 knots.[69]

In fact the Italian fleet actually lay 57 miles ahead of *Warspite*, and steaming at 19 knots – with the result that when late that evening Captain P. J. Mack, commanding the destroyers, believed that he was crossing ahead of the *Vittorio Veneto*, the battleship had already passed well clear of his intended trap and lay some 30 miles to the northward. It was by no means the only confusion and lost opportunity during a night which would fully bear out Clausewitz's dictum that 'War is the province of uncertainty'.

Less than half an hour after Mack's destroyers began to hunt ahead at 28 knots, course 300°, like a pack of eager hounds, the C-in-C received a report from Pridham-Wippell: 'One unknown ship 240° five m, apparently stopped. My position 35° 20'N, 21° 6'E.'[70] This ship had been picked up by the radars in *Ajax* and *Orion*. Pridham-Wippell, thinking that the stopped ship could be the Italian battleship herself, decided to leave her to the C-in-C to deal with while he pressed on after the enemy's main body at 20 knots. This speed was ample to catch up a foe making according to the most recent reports only 13 knots. In fact, however, *Vittorio Veneto* had just worked up to

19 knots. On receipt of Pridham-Wippell's report Cunningham altered course to 280° in order to investigate, his three heavy ships and the carrier in single line ahead at 3 cables (about 600 yards) apart. At 2203 the *Valiant's* radar (the flagship was not so equipped) located a stopped ship eight to nine miles distant, bearing 244°. According to *Valiant's* signal, which reached the C-in-C seven minutes later, the strange vessel was more than 600 feet long. 'Our hopes ran high,' wrote Cunningham in his memoirs. 'This might be the *Vittorio Veneto*. The course of the battlefleet was altered 40 degrees to port together. We were already at action stations with our main armament ready. Our guns were trained on the correct bearing.'[71]

The contrast could not have been greater between Cunningham's present eagerness for battle and the night action at Jutland in 1916, when the Grand Fleet refused to become embroiled with the High Seas Fleet and steamed on in a stately line ahead. For Cunningham was benefiting from the lessons which the Royal Navy had assimilated from Jutland and the consequent immense progress in equipment and fleet training for night fighting before the Second World War. Yet Cunningham added to the recipe his own special spice as a leader. In the words of the fleet gunnery officer, Commander Geoffrey Barnard, 'A.B.C. turned the battlefleet together to investigate, handling the fleet from this moment until midnight in the same way as he would have handled a division of destroyers.'[72] The Admiralty Fighting Instructions ordained that whenever enemy destroyers might be present at night, a battlefleet should turn away to avoid the danger of torpedo attack. On the *Warspite's* bridge, as the distance between the fleet and the stopped ship (which might well be escorted by destroyers) narrowed, Cunningham's staff therefore advised him to make the signal 'Blue Four' – a turn away. But Cunningham replied: 'If that's the enemy, we will turn towards and find out what sort they are and how soon we sink them. FOUR BLUE': i.e., a turn towards.[73] As an eyewitness commented: 'It thus occurred for the first time in a night encounter either in peace or war a battlefleet turned towards an unknown force of enemy ships.'[74]

The fleet steamed on under a moonless, clouded sky in quarter line. At 2220 the *Valiant's* radar reported the stopped ship bearing 191°, distant four and a half miles – on the fleet's port bow. Only three minutes later, however, the destroyer *Stuart* to the starboard of the fleet sighted fine on her *starboard* bow two large ships with a smaller one ahead and three smaller ones astern. Even before the *Stuart's* alarm report reached the flagship, the C-in-C and his new Chief of Staff, Commodore John Edelsten, had seen these ships for themselves through their binoculars. According to Cunningham, the Chief of Staff, scanning the horizon to starboard, 'calmly reported that he saw two large cruisers with a smaller one ahead of them crossing the bows of the battlefleet from starboard to port. I looked through my glasses and there they were . . .'[75] An ex-submariner on his staff, Commander Power, an expert on ship recognition, pronounced the larger ships to be two Zara class 8-inch gun cruisers. By radio the C-in-C now signalled his fleet to turn back into line ahead for the final approach to the enemy. Cunningham and his staff had by this time gone aloft to the small captain's bridge where he could enjoy a better all-round view of the action to come.

> I shall never forget the next few minutes [he wrote a decade later]. In dead silence, a silence that could almost be felt, one heard only the voices of the gun control personnel putting the guns on to the new target. One heard the orders repeated in the director tower behind and above the bridge. Looking forward, one saw the turrets swing and steady when the 15-inch guns pointed at the enemy cruisers. Never in my whole life have I experienced a more thrilling moment than when I heard a calm voice from the director tower – 'Director layer sees the target'; sure sign that the guns were ready and that his finger was itching on the trigger. The enemy was at a range of no more than 3,800 yards – point-blank.[76]

How had these Italian cruisers and destroyers come to be wandering so far from the main body of the Italian fleet and across the bows of the British fleet? They had been ordered back by Iachino under the command of Vice-Admiral Cattaneo to the aid of the stopped ship – which was in fact the cruiser *Pola*, crippled by a torpedo from one of *Formidable*'s aircraft during the third, dusk, British air-strike. Iachino had issued this order because he had no idea at all that the enemy battlefleet lay anywhere near the scene, and believed that his only danger lay in the British aircraft carrier and its escort.

Iachino was later to complain sourly about lack of aerial reconnaissance and fighter cover afforded him during his sortie by the Regia Aeronautica and the Luftwaffe; about the generally poor cooperation between land-based airpower and his fleet. Nonetheless, around 0900 on 28 March he had received a report from the Italian island of Rhodes in the Dodecanese that at 0745 a reconnaissance aircraft had sighted a carrier, two battleships, nine cruisers and fourteen destroyers 'in sector 3836/0 course 165° 20 knots'.[77] But since Iachino himself had been in this position at that time, he radioed back to Rhodes to accuse it of committing a crass mistake. Information as late as 2000 that evening indicated to him that Cunningham's fleet was certainly at sea, but still some ninety miles astern of him. He therefore believed that Cattaneo would run no risk. In Iachino's words, 'It never occurred to me that we were within a relatively short distance of the entire British force. I thought the British cruisers had decided to turn back leaving only two destroyers to deal with us.'[78]

Now Cattaneo and his ships' companies were about to pay a terrible price for their C-in-C's misjudgment. Moreover, since no Italian warships were equipped with radar, a grievous disadvantage at night, Cattaneo could have no advance warning of the approach of the British battlefleet; nor could he know that thanks to radar Cunningham was exactly tracking him far beyond the range of the human eye in the dark.

For Cunningham himself this was the supreme moment of his career, coming forty-four years after he first joined HMS *Britannia* as a cadet of fourteen.

It must have been the Fleet Gunnery Officer, Commander Geoffrey Barnard, who gave the final order to open fire [he was to remember]. One heard the 'ting-ting-ting' of the firing gongs. Then came the great orange flash and the violent shudder as the six big guns bearing were fired simultaneously. At the very same instant the destroyer *Greyhound*, on the [destroyer] screen, switched her searchlight on to one of the enemy cruisers, showing her momentarily up as a silvery-blue shape in the darkness. Our searchlights shone out with the first salvo, and provided full illumination for what was a ghastly sight. Full in the beam I saw our six great projectiles flying through the air. Five out of the six hit a few feet below the level of the cruiser's upper deck and burst with splashes of brilliant flame. The Italians were quite unprepared. Their guns were trained fore and aft. They were helplessly shattered before they could put up any resistance. In the midst of all this there was one milder diversion. Captain Douglas Fisher, the captain of the *Warspite*, was a gunnery officer of note. When he saw the first salvo hit he was heard to say in a voice of wondering surprise: 'Good Lord! We've hit her!'[79]

Broadside after broadside from all three British battleships smashed into the enemy cruisers – HMS *Valiant* fired five in just over three minutes, a rate faithful to the tradition of Nelson's Mediterranean Fleet at Trafalgar, and which astonished and delighted Cunningham. The *Fiume* was quickly engulfed in vivid orange flame; she sank three-quarters of an hour later. The *Zara* too, hit in the forward 8-inch turret, the bridge and the engine room, was soon ablaze and listing heavily, the belching flames fearsomely illuminating the billows of smoke rising from her into the night sky. Abandoned by her crew, she was eventually sunk at 0240 on 29 March by torpedoes from the destroyer *Jervis*.

The attack by Cunningham's fleet lasted no more than four and a half minutes, for the approach of three Italian destroyers (one of which was seen to fire torpedoes) on the port bow compelled Cunningham to turn the fleet 90° together to starboard to avoid them. But the battleships had already done their work. There now followed a chaotic mêlée between British and Italian destroyers in darkness blindingly lit by gunflashes and explosions. In the early stages of this confusion the destroyer *Havock* was straddled in error by a salvo from the *Warspite* (fortunately without damage), and the *Formidable* (which had hauled out of the line before the action) was nearly fired on by the flag-ship's secondary armament. Thereafter the C-in-C took the heavy ships eastwards clear of the scene. In the course of the night's mêlée the Italian destroyers *Alfieri* and *Carducci* were both sunk. But it was not until 0403 on the 29th that the cruiser *Pola*, the catalyst that brought about the whole battle, was sunk by torpedoes from the destroyers *Nubian* and *Jervis* after her surviving crew had been taken off.

So ended the Battle of Cape Matapan. It had cost the Italian Navy three heavy cruisers, two destroyers and the lives of 2,400 officers and seamen, Vice-Admiral Cattaneo among them.

The *Vittorio Veneto* nevertheless continued to make good her escape home to Taranto. This was partly because Captain Mack, commanding the British destroyer flotilla pursuing her, had turned across her track believing *he* was ahead of *her* when in fact *she* was by now well ahead of *him*. However, a somewhat ambiguous order by Cunningham also contributed to the *Vittorio Veneto*'s escape. At around 2300 on the 28th he ordered all ships not engaged in sinking the enemy to withdraw to the north-eastwards, which caused Pridham-Wippell to abandon his efforts to find the Italian flagship.[80] Cunningham had only intended to give the destroyers a free hand to attack any large ship they might suddenly encounter in the dark, and also to make it easier for the Fleet to reconcentrate on the morrow.

Next morning the Fleet steamed for home through the sad wrack left behind by its victory, floating on a calm, sun-bright sea filmy with oil – boats, rafts, bits of debris, corpses. In the afternoon, as Cunningham made for Alexandria, came the avenging air attacks, but these were largely broken up by *Formidable*'s fighters, although several heavy bombs fell perilously close to the carrier. In the early evening of 30 March 1941 the Mediterranean Fleet safely and triumphantly moored in Alexandria, having won the Royal Navy's greatest victory in a fleet encounter since Trafalgar; and, as it was to prove, the last in all its long history.

The Battle of Cape Matapan completed the destruction of the Italian battlefleet's will to take the offensive. And it was partly thanks to this that the British expeditionary force to Greece was not forced at the end of a disastrous campaign to capitulate with its back to the sea.

12

Catastrophe in the Mediterranean, 1941

On 27 March 1941 the pro-German government of Yugoslavia was overthrown in a coup d'état and replaced by a new leadership; an event which impelled Hitler now to regard Yugoslavia as his enemy, and to recast his offensive strategy in the Balkans to include her conquest. It was this unforeseen event – one quite unconnected with the British commitment of an expeditionary force to Greece – and the consequent need to deploy fresh German forces which led to the postponement of Hitler's attack on the Soviet Union by a month, with possibly decisive effects on its success.

At the very last moment, therefore, fortune had vouchsafed Churchill two-thirds at least of his dream of a Balkan coalition, only Turkey among his hoped-for Allies remaining both neutral and excluded from Hitler's aggressive plans. Yet the strategic outcome swiftly proved what a military fantasy it had been to expect peasant armies, however numerous, to prevail against the Luftwaffe and the panzer divisions. On 6 April the German forces struck into both Greece and Yugoslavia. Within two days they had smashed through the Yugoslav front in southern Serbia and began to swing south through the Monastir gap, so deeply turning the left flank of the Greek and British defence along the Aliakmon position. Meanwhile the German 12th Army was thrusting from Bulgaria directly into Greece with ten divisions supported by some 800 aircraft. Five of these divisions, including three panzer, were soon advancing against the British Commonwealth expeditionary force (two infantry divisions and a single armoured brigade), while the Luftwaffe, undeterred by a ten times weaker Royal Air Force, bombed and machine-gunned at will just as in Norway. As the official history of the war in the Mediterranean and Middle East tersely sums up: 'The British campaign on the mainland of Greece was from start to finish a withdrawal.'[1] In the coming days the power and weight of the German offensive, the disintegration of the Greek Army (already exhausted by its heroic winter campaign against the Italians in Albania), and the capitulation of Yugoslavia on 17 April, all served fully to bear out the deep misgivings about an expeditionary force's operational chances that had been voiced earlier in London and Cairo by the realists (including Wavell himself initially). On 21 April, with the British forces now back on the Thermopylae position covering Athens and the Greek Army of the Epirus (on the Albanian front) cut off and about to surrender, the decision was taken to evacuate. And so it again fell to the Royal Navy to save what it could of a British army at the end of a foredoomed campaign.

On the day the decision was reached, Cunningham and the main body of his fleet (three battleships, the *Formidable*, two cruisers and a destroyer screen) were actually at sea returning to base after an extraordinarily hazardous but successful 900-mile voyage to bombard Tripoli, the main Axis port in Libya (see below, p. 366). Not until 23 April was Cunningham back in Alexandria. The evacuation had been originally set for 28 April, but such was the speed of the German advance and the unfolding peril to the British expeditionary force that 'Operation Demon' (codename for the evacuation) had to be brought forward to the 24th, the very next day after Cunningham's return to harbour.

'Demon' proved a combined replay of the evacuations from Norway and Dunkirk, but even more hazardous. Just as in Norway soldiers wordless with fatigue, dazed by unceasing air attack, trudged the last sour kilometres of retreat along mountain roads and down to the sea, kept going by the hope that when they reached the coast the Navy would be there. Just as in Norway (but unlike at Dunkirk) the evacuation would have to be conducted far from British bases, without fighter cover and within easy range of German shore-based airpower. Moreover in contrast to both Norway and Dunkirk there were few available harbours with jetties or wharves capable of taking vessels as big as destroyers or passenger ships, for the main port of Piraeus itself had been totally wrecked on 6–7 April in a Luftwaffe raid which devastatingly blew up an ammunition ship. So soldiers would have to be mostly lifted from the beaches – picked up, as from the sands of

Dunkirk – by small craft and ferried out to the waiting ships off shore for the voyage to safety. And there was always the possibility that these operations, hazardous as they must be in the face of German airpower, might be further imperilled by the intervention of the Italian battlefleet.

Seven beaches were selected for the embarkation, spread all the way round the deeply indented southern coasts of Greece from Raphina and Porto Raphti on the south-eastern shore of Attica to Megara between Athens and Corinth, and Nauplia, Tolon and Monemvasia at the head of the Gulf of Nauplia in the Peloponessus.[2]

To coordinate the movements of troops down to the beaches with the arrival of the nightly lifts by the Navy demanded fast and flexible planning, the closest liaison with the military command on shore; not easy when ship-to-shore communication came to depend on unreliable field radios. Rear-Admiral H. T. Baillie-Grohman was sent to Greece to work with General Sir Henry Maitland Wilson (commanding the British Commonwealth forces) and take control of inshore operations. It was Baillie-Grohman's first task to requisition and crew local Greek fishing caiques, motor boats and other small craft. To help him and also to provide beach parties he was given the entire ship's company of the bomb-damaged cruiser *York* lying at Suda Bay, Crete. Vice-Admiral Pridham-Wippell was placed in overall command of the evacuation (Ramsay's job in 'Dynamo'), with his headquarters at Suda Bay. He had at his disposal four cruisers (*Orion*, his flagship; *Ajax*, *Phoebe* and HMAS *Perth*); the three anti-aircraft cruisers *Calcutta*, *Coventry* and *Carlisle*; some twenty destroyers; three sloops; HMS *Glenearn* and HMS *Gleneagle* ('Infantry Assault Ships' adapted from merchant vessels, carrying landing craft instead of boats); nineteen middle-sized troopships; and an assortment of small craft, including the forerunners of the tank landing craft.

On 24 April, starting day for 'Demon', Cunningham made the signal:

> The object is to embark men, if possible, with arms; but no material must be allowed to take precedence to men. Troopships with men embarked to sail direct to Alexandria, except 'Glen' ships which must unload at Suda Bay and do a second embarkation. Destroyers to take their troops to Crete, where they will be transferred later.[3]

The pattern of Namsos, Andalsnes and Dunkirk quickly re-established itself. Between the avenging enemy and the embarkation stood a resolute rearguard, this time of New Zealand, Australian and British troops, still able and willing to throw the Germans back in local counter-strokes. Under cover of night the troops for embarkation left the areas just inland where they had discharged the miserable task of wrecking their heavy equipment, and filed down to the beaches and the waiting naval beach parties. Then began the slow, frustratingly slow, work of ferrying them out to the waiting ships while the short hours of darkness hastened by. It was a scene of apparent confusion, but actual efficiency and discipline, as dog-tired beach parties coped with sudden changes of plan caused by local problems and the availability of ships. And then for the soldiers the long dusty march under the Luftwaffe's bombs and machine-gun fire was over; exchanged for the relative security of a King's ship and the comfort of strong Navy cocoa. But with daylight and the voyage back to Crete or, 400 miles longer, to Alexandria came the Luftwaffe.

On 25 April the troopship *Ulster Prince* and the transport *Pennland* both succumbed to German bombs; on 26 April the *Glenearn* was bombed and disabled on her way to Nauplia and had to be towed back to Suda Bay. On the 27th the Dutch transport *Slamat* was caught in daylight by dive-bombers with a full load of troops on her way back to Crete and set on fire. She had gallantly but ill-advisedly hung on at Nauplia an hour longer than ordered rather than leave some troops behind. As the *Slamat* sank, the destroyers *Diamond* (Lieutenant-Commander P. A. Cartwright) and *Wryneck* (Commander R. H. D. Dean) were themselves dive-bombed while picking up survivors. Early that afternoon the bombers were back to finish them off, and this time sank both ships so swiftly that only one officer, forty-one ratings and eight soldiers were saved. This same afternoon the merchant ship *Costa Rica* too was sunk, although almost all her crew and soldiers were rescued. In all the Luftwaffe sank 26 Allied ships during the evacuation, including five hospital ships.

By the 28th most of the remaining troops (except those now cut off by the enemy) lay at Monemvasia, Kalamata and on Kithera Island. Pridham-Wippell therefore ordered a cruiser and four destroyers to Monemvasia, three sloops to Kithera, and HMAS *Perth* and a force of destroyers to Kalamata. All went well on Kithera and at Monemvasia, where at 0300 on the 29th Major-General Freyberg (commanding the New Zealand Division) and Baillie-Grohman embarked in HMS *Ajax* after the last of the soldiers had been lifted. At Kalamata, however, some 7,000 soldiers were eventually left behind and forced to surrender. The destroyer HMS *Hero*, sent ahead of the force led by *Perth*, arrived off the port at 2045 to observe and hear heavy fighting going on. A signal was flashed from the shore: 'Boche in harbour.' Passing this report on to the *Perth* the captain of the *Hero* sent his first lieutenant ashore to investigate in person the true state of affairs. At 2100 the first lieutenant reported back that it was still possible to lift troops from the beach. However, owing to radio trouble this information was not received in the *Perth* until 2211: too late, because at 2129 the Captain of the *Perth* had ordered his force to withdraw. Having himself seen the tracer on shore and heard the sounds of heavy fire, and on the basis of the earlier report that the enemy had occupied the harbour, he had decided that too few soldiers could be lifted to justify the risk to his ships. In Cunningham's retrospective judgment, this was 'a most unfortunate decision'.[4] Nonetheless the *Hero*, together with the newly arrived destroyers *Kandahar*, *Kingston*, and *Kimberley*, succeeded in lifting 324 soldiers from the beach by means of their whalers. Even this effort did not mark the end of 'Demon': over the next two nights the *Hero*, *Kimberley* and *Isis* brought off another 235 soldiers.

In all the Royal and Merchant Navies rescued 50,732 soldiers (including some Greeks and Yugoslavs), of which only 14,000 were lifted from wharves or jetties, as against the 58,364 British Commonwealth troops originally transported there in the 'Lustre' convoys. Like Dunkirk, this seemed a miraculous deliverance. It owed itself partly to the Luftwaffe's failure to bomb at night; partly to the cowed Italian Fleet's supine neglect of a singular opportunity to intervene against lightly protected convoys at a time when Cunningham had had to keep his battleships in Alexandria for want of enough destroyers both to screen them and also take part in the evacuation.

Yet the main credit for the success of 'Demon' – as of 'Dynamo' – belongs to the professionalism, resourcefulness and resolve of British sailors, from Baillie-Grohman on a foreign and unfamiliar coast struggling to organise and schedule the embarkations amid all the shifting confusions of a lost campaign, to Pridham-Wippell in Crete, beset by lack of news, grappling with poor communications and redeploying his scant resources in ships at the briefest notice, and to all the ships' companies whose fortitude and zeal had made it possible for merchant ships each to lift up to 3,500 soldiers a night, cruisers up to 2,500 and destroyers to jam-pack themselves with more than 800 each.[5]

Nevertheless, thankful though this deliverance was, it could not compensate for the complete and calamitous failure in which the Greek adventure had ended; a failure that had cost the British Commonwealth forces 12,000 killed, wounded and missing, 209 aircraft, 8,000 trucks and all the expeditionary force's ill-spared tanks and artillery, plus a mass of stores of every kind.[6]

Now, with the Germans and Italians occupying all of mainland Greece and the Greek islands, plus the Dodecanese, it was evident that Crete must be a likely Axis objective; and the Ultra decrypts of Luftwaffe Enigma signals confirmed this from 26 April onwards.[7] Should the British make a major military investment in the defence of the island, at a time when the resources of Middle East Command were already worryingly stretched in meeting existing or potential crises from the Western Desert to Syria and Iraq? What were the chances of a successful defence? How strategically important was Crete? These questions were now answered or ignored in London in familiar style. The Prime Minister signalled Wavell on 28 April that Crete 'must be stubbornly defended', although he told the War Cabinet the same evening that he was 'somewhat doubtful of our ability to hold Crete against a prolonged attack'.[8] His doubts were justified. General Sir Henry Maitland Wilson reported to Wavell on 27 April on the operational chances in the light of the extreme weakness of the Royal Air Force on Crete (six Hurricanes and seventeen various obsolete aircraft); the awkward configuration of the island (160 miles long and 40 miles across at the widest point, with only a single and very bad main lateral road); the presence of a semi-circle of nearby enemy air bases from Greece to the Dodecanese; and the fact that Crete had not a single large port, while such harbours as could take even a small cargo vessel all lay on the exposed northern coast. It was Wilson's judgment that 'unless all three services are prepared to face the strain of maintaining adequate forces up to strength, the holding of the island is a dangerous commitment, and a decision on the matter must be taken at once'.[9] As the official history points out, in view of the irremediable weakness of the Royal Air Force on Crete, 'this was tantamount to saying that he did not think the island could be successfully defended'.[10]

But Wavell could only confirm the instructions he had received from London that Crete must be fought for. This decision remained unchanged despite later indications from Ultra that the scale of the German onslaught, especially in airborne forces, was going to be colossal; indications that roused serious doubts in the garrison commander himself, General Freyberg, as to whether he could hope to hold off such an onslaught with the forces at his disposal.[11] Moreover little attention was paid in London to the long-term strategic implications of holding Crete indefinitely after a German attack was defeated (as was hoped), especially in regard to the strain on, and the attrition of, warships and merchant shipping in waters utterly dominated by enemy airpower.

On 20 May, after five days of ferocious air attack on the British defences at Maleme and Heraklion, the enemy launched 'Operation Merkur' ('Mercury') – 13,000 parachute and glider troops of 'Flieger-division 7' in over 500 transport aircraft and 72 gliders; a tactical air force of 228 bombers, 205 dive-bombers, 233 fighters and 50 reconnaissance aircraft.[12] The second echelon consisted of 9,000 mountain troops to be flown in by transport aircraft as soon as Maleme airfield had been captured. Only heavy loads such as a panzer battalion, artillery and ammunition supplies were to be sent later by sea. British interpretations of the latest Ultra Intelligence, though exaggerating all the German figures, indicated clearly enough that the main weight of the attack would indeed come from the airborne rather than the seaborne forces.[13] Freyberg however believed that if the Royal Navy could prevent the passage of seaborne forces (which he in any case doubted because of German air superiority), his forces could defeat the parachute and glider troops alone.

He was not alone in this traditionalist view that the main threat lay from the sea. In the words of the unpublished Naval Staff History of the campaign, 'Airborne invasion was known to be impending, but it appeared almost inconceivable that airborne invasion alone could succeed against forewarned [through Ultra] troops'; hence a seaborne invasion was seen as essential. It followed from this belief that 'destruc-tion of the reinforcing troop convoys would eventually win the day'.[14] In other words, as the British command saw it, the key role in the coming battle to hold what Churchill described as an outpost of Egypt[15] was to fall to the Mediterranean Fleet.

It was not a role which Cunningham could contemplate with much joy. In his own words:

> . . . the main difficulty, of course, was that Alexandria was some 440 miles from the scene of action, while it was impossible to use Suda Bay because of the continuous air attacks. It was hardly to be expected that the Italian fleet would remain passive while an attack upon Crete was in progress, so this made it necessary for us to provide battleship cover off the western end of the island.[16]

But Cunningham's greatest anxiety lay in his virtually total lack of air cover. On Crete itself at Maleme were three Royal Air Force Hurricanes, three Fleet Air Arm Gladiators and three Fulmars, aircraft and crews being alike worn out after weeks of fighting against overwhelming odds in Greece; all were put out of action during the preliminary German air strikes. The carrier *Formidable* was likewise suffering from wear and tear following recent hazardous operations (see below, p. 366), and was reduced to only four serviceable aircraft; she did not join the Fleet off Crete until 25 May, five days after the German offensive began.[17]

In brief, Cunningham knew he had to pit his ships against a vast number of aircraft operating within close range of their airfields. 'The obvious policy,' he wrote, 'was not to commit our forces to the northward of Crete during daylight unless enemy forces were known to be at sea . . .'[18] He divided his fleet into four forces: Force A, with two battleships and five destroyers, was to provide general support from a position to the west of Crete, while Forces B, C and D (each composed of the two cruisers plus destroyers) were to carry out nightly sweeps in the Aegean on the northern sea approaches to the island. He held back two battleships, the *Formidable*, four cruisers and sixteen destroyers in Alexandria as a reserve. With these four widely dispersed task forces to coordinate, Cunningham reluctantly decided that for the first time he must exercise command from on shore, where he could also keep in close touch with his fellow Commanders-in-Chief.

The start of 'Operation Merkur' on 20 May announced itself to the British Empire defenders of Crete when the sky filled with hundreds of Junkers 52 transport aircraft. From these peeled away stick after stick of parachute troops, soon followed by troop-carrying gliders. That evening in the dusk, while New Zealand troops and 'Fliegerdivision 7' were fighting a brutal close-range battle for control of Maleme airfield, Cunningham's task forces steamed through the Kaso and Antikithera channels to patrol north of the island. But that night they only encountered six Italian torpedo boats (duly shot up). Meanwhile three destroyers bombarded Scarpanto airfield in the Dodecanese. The following forenoon, however, gave the first taste of what was to come, for Forces A, D and C were all heavily bombed. Force C in particular was attacked continuously from 0950 to 1350, and at 1249 the destroyer *Juno*, hit by a bomb, sank in two minutes.

During the night-time sweeps on 21–22 May the Fleet had its revenge, for at 2330 on the 21st Force D (Rear-Admiral I. G. Glennie: the cruisers *Dido*, *Orion* and *Ajax*, and the destroyers *Janus*, *Hereward*, *Kimberley* and *Hasty*) massacred an enemy convoy on passage to Crete. In two and a half hours at least twelve caiques, two or three steamers, a steam yacht and one of the escorting torpedo boats were located in the dark by radar and sunk, leaving some 4,000 German soldiers to drown. By this time Glennie's flagship, the *Dido*, had fired off some 70 per cent of her anti-aircraft ammunition, and the *Orion* and *Ajax* 62 and 58 per cent of theirs. Rather than comply with Cunningham's instruction to join Force C in a daylight northward hunt for further convoys, Glennie therefore retired southwards. The Luftwaffe's retribution fell instead on Force C (Rear-Admiral E. L. S. King; the cruisers *Naiad* and HMAS *Perth*, the anti-aircraft cruisers *Calcutta* and *Carlisle*, and the destroyers *Kandahar*, *Kingston* and *Nubian*). While King's task force was itself successfully smashing up another enemy convoy south of the island of Milo, German bombers relentlessly pounded down on his ships despite all the high explosive that the ships' anti-aircraft batteries could pump into their path.

Having lost the *Juno* only the previous day, being like Glennie low in anti-aircraft ammunition, Admiral King now decided to steer no further to the northward in pursuit of the remainder of the convoy, but instead alter westwards for the Kithera channel exit from the Aegean. It was Cunningham's very typical personal judgment later that King had failed to engage the enemy closely enough: 'It is probable that the safest place was amongst the enemy convoy, and retirement could not better the most unpleasant position in which he found himself.' Also, the destruction of that large convoy would have justified severe losses. While acknowledging that it was easy to criticise from a distance and also that King found himself in 'a cruel situation', Cunningham nevertheless held that 'if the enemy is in sight on the sea, air attacks or other considerations must be disregarded and the risks accepted.'[19] In any event King's initial attacks induced the convoy to turn back; no German troops got through.

As Force C retired it was bombed without cease for three and a half hours. The *Naiad* was badly damaged, with two turrets out of action, several compartments flooded, and her speed cut to 16 knots. The *Carlisle* too was hit, and her captain, Captain T. C. Hampton, killed. At 1321 King was all too relieved to see the battleships of Force A coming up from the westward.

Rear-Admiral H. B. Rawlings (Flag Officer, Force A), flying his flag in the battleship *Warspite*, and with the battleship *Valiant* and the cruisers *Gloucester* and *Fiji* in company, had earlier been joined by Glennie's Force D. The combined squadron was patrolling some 20 to 30 miles west of the Kithera channel when Rawlings learned that the *Naiad* had been seriously damaged and her speed reduced, so placing King's Force C in peril. He therefore decided to risk entering the Aegean in daylight and steered to King's support at 23 knots. At 1332, just as Rawlings and King joined company, three Messerschmitt ME 109 fighter-bombers roared out of low cloud to attack the *Warspite* down the fore and aft line in what a connoisseur eyewitness described as 'a beautiful attack to watch'.[20] One bomb struck home, wrecking the starboard 4-inch and 6-inch batteries and damaging the No. 3

boiler room fan intakes. *Warspite* emitted a cloud of dense smoke and her speed dropped away for a time.

The combined force (commanded by King as the senior officer present) now steered west to clear the Aegean – still under fierce air attack. The first victim was the unsupported destroyer *Greyhound*, whereupon King ordered the cruisers *Gloucester* (Captain H. A. Rowley) and *Fiji* (Captain P. R. B. W. William-Powlett) and the destroyers *Kandahar* and *Kingston* to her assistance – despite the hard lesson learned in the Mediterranean never to detach ships, but always move a force as a whole. The cruisers arrived to find the *Greyhound* sunk (she had been hit twice and went down in two minutes). While they were rescuing survivors the Luftwaffe struck at them too. At 1550 the *Gloucester* took several bomb hits and was brought to a stop badly on fire and with her upper deck a shambles of torn and mangled metal. Reluctantly the captain of the *Fiji* decided that he could not remain with her, but dropped boats and rafts for her crew. The body of the captain of the doomed *Gloucester*, Captain H. A. Rowley, was washed up four weeks later on the coast of Egypt at Mersa Matruh.[21]

Now it was *Fiji*'s turn, and for three and a quarter hours German aircraft relentlessly sought to sink her. Finally,

> after surviving some 20 bombing attacks . . . she fell victim to a single ME 109. The machine flew out of the clouds in a shallow dive and dropped its bombs very close to the port side, amidships. The ship took up a heavy list, but was able to steam at 17 knots until half an hour later when another single machine dropped three bombs which hit above 'A' boiler room; the list increased and at 2015 she rolled right over.[22]

She sank some 50 miles south-west of Gavdo Island.

The destroyers *Kandahar* and *Kingston* lowered boats and rafts for the survivors, but could not stay because of the acute danger from further air attack. Nevertheless they returned under cover of night and picked up 523 of the *Fiji*'s company: exhausted men who had lost their 'home', and who, after being adrift on a dark sea, found themselves saved after all. The two destroyers had already endured twenty-two air attacks between 1445 and 1920. At 2245 the destroyers set course to rejoin Rear-Admiral King south of Crete.

Meanwhile the *Valiant* had been hit aft at 1645 by two bombs dropped from high level, though without serious damage.

During the night the destroyers *Decoy* and *Hero* embarked the King of Greece and his suite, the British ambassador and other important personages at Agriarumeli on the southern coast of Crete – a melancholy echo of similar liftings of dispossessed monarchs by the Royal Navy in 1940.

For Cunningham in Alexandria that evening and night the strain of command was all the greater because he could no longer lead his fleet into battle, but only wait for news to reach him over a signal net that was suffering from serious lags:

> In my office ashore close to the war room where the positions of all our ships were plotted hour by hour on the large-scale chart, I came to dread every ring on the telephone, every knock on the door, and the arrival of every fresh signal. In something less than twelve hours of fighting against the unhampered Luftwaffe we had lost so much, two cruisers and a destroyer sunk, with two battleships and two cruisers damaged. Most of the ships were woefully short of ammunition, and I very well knew the anxiety and physical strain under which their devoted officers and men were working.[23]

Cunningham could only signal to all his ships: 'Stick it out. Navy must not let Army down. No enemy forces must reach Crete by Sea.'[24] It might be said that this signal was as redundant as Nelson's signals at Trafalgar ordering his fleet to engage the enemy more closely and that 'England expects . . .' The Navy did not let the Army down, and no German troops did reach Crete by sea. But to achieve this was taking what may without undue melodrama be termed the 'death ride' of the Mediterranean Fleet.

When at 2230 on 22 May Cunningham received a 'Most Immediate' signal from King reporting the loss of *Gloucester* and *Fiji* and the grim state of ammunition stocks, a 'calligraphic error' in the signal (either phonetic or in the handwriting of the draft) made it appear that the battleships were 'empty' of their pom-pom ammunition, when in fact the typed version of the signal next morning confirmed that they had 'plenty'.[25] Misled by this garbled signal, Cunningham at 0408 on the 23rd ordered Force A back to Alexandria. This – in particular – deprived the destroyers *Kelly* (Captain Lord Louis Mountbatten commanding 1st Destroyer Flotilla), *Kashmir* (Commander Henry King), and *Kipling* (Commander A. St Clair Ford) of support on their passage back to Alexandria after patrolling to the north of Canea and Maleme during the night.

At 0755 on 23 May, when the flotilla lay in 34° 50′N, 24° 05′E, some thirteen miles to the south of Gavdo Island, 24 Stukas howled down on them out of the morning sky. The *Kashmir* was hit and sunk in just two minutes. The *Kelly* was struck by a large bomb while steaming 30 knots on full starboard helm, and still had considerable way on as she capsized to port. In an episode that was later to form part of the Mountbatten legend, the *Kelly* floated upside down for half an hour before she finally sank, leaving her survivors bobbing in the water round her captain under German machine-gun fire. The *Kipling* picked up 279 men from the water, including – as the world was to be reminded – Mountbatten himself, and made course for Alexandria. Between 0820 and 1300 she was attacked by no fewer than 40 aircraft, dropping 83 bombs, but emerged miraculously unscathed. She had to be met by HMS *Protector* fifty miles from Alexandria and towed in because she was now completely out of fuel. After the event Cunningham could not make up his mind whether the two destroyers might have been saved by the presence of Force A, or whether the Luftwaffe would have overwhelmed its defences and sunk yet more ships.[26]

On this day came another of the Admiralty's direct interferences with operations at sea. Because of the scale and lethal effectiveness of German airpower in the waters south of Crete as well as north of it, Cunningham (after consultation with Wavell) had at 1130 ordered the troopship *Glenroy*, then on the way to the island with reinforcements, to turn back to Alexandria. At about 1600, 'to my amazement', according to Cunningham:

the Admiralty sent a direct message to the *Glenroy* ordering her to turn north again, and about an hour later sent me a signal urging that her reinforcements be landed if it could be done that night. Of course, it was much too late, so I ordered the *Glenroy* back to Alexandria, and informed the Admiralty that if she had proceeded north she would have arrived at daylight, the worst possible time for air attacks . . . The less said about this unjustifiable interference by those ignorant of the situation the better.[27]

On the night of the 23–24 May the destroyers *Jaguar* (Lieutenant-Commander J. F. Hine, Senior Officer) and *Defender* landed stores and ammunition at Suda and took off some 'useless military mouths'. By daylight on the 24th these two destroyers on their way back to Alexandria and the minelayer *Abdiel* on passage in the reverse direction with more supplies to be landed the following night were for the time being the only warships left at sea, for Cunningham had been compelled to withdraw all the rest in order to refuel and restock with ammunition. At this point came signals from the Admiralty saying that it was vital to stop seaborne expeditions reaching Crete in the next day or two, even at the cost of serious losses to the Fleet, coupled with a signal from the Chiefs of Staff asking for Cunningham's appreciation of the naval situation. To the Admiralty Cunningham pointed out that Crete lay 400 miles from the Fleet's base and that his ships were at present out of fuel and shells. To the Chiefs of Staff he signalled that 'the scale of air attack now makes it no longer possible to operate in the Aegean or in the vicinity of Crete by day. The Navy cannot guarantee to prevent seaborne landings without suffering losses which, added to those already sustained, could very seriously prejudice our command of the Eastern Mediterranean.'[28] But the Chiefs of Staff replied that 'the Fleet and the Royal Air Force were to accept whatever risk was entailed in preventing enemy reinforcements reaching Crete. If enemy convoys were reported north of Crete, the Fleet would have to operate in that area by day, although considerable losses might be expected . . .'[29]

Hardly surprising, Cunningham, in his words, 'found this message singularly unhelpful. It failed lamentably to appreciate the realities of the situation.'[30] Tight-lipped, he signalled back on 26 May:

> It is not the fear of sustaining losses but the need to avoid losses which will cripple the fleet without any commensurate advantage which is the determining factor in operating in the Aegean. As far as I know, the enemy has so far had little if any success in reinforcing Crete by sea . . . The experience of three days in which two cruisers and four destroyers have been sunk, and one battleship, two cruisers and four destroyers severely damaged shows what losses are likely to be. Sea control in the Eastern Mediterranean could not be retained after another such experience.[31]

In any case by this time the Fleet was at sea again. Flying his flag in the *Queen Elizabeth* Pridham-Wippell had taken the 1st Battle Squadron (*Barham*, the carrier *Formidable* and eight destroyers) on a strike against the airfield of Scarpanto. At 0330 on 26 May, when 100 miles south-south-west of the objective, *Formidable* flew off a strike force of four Albacores and five Fulmars which took the enemy completely by surprise and damaged aircraft ranged on the ground. As usual the following forenoon brought the Luftwaffe's retribution, in the course of which *Formidable*'s remaining eight serviceable aircraft made twenty-four flights, and in twenty combats shot down two enemy aircraft for certain, plus two probables, for the loss of one Fulmar. But there was still an awful long way to go to Alexandria. At 1320 when Force A was some 150 miles south-west of Kaso Island, it was attacked by twenty dive-bombers, this time coming from the direction of North Africa: another accurate attack pressed home through a dense pattern of shell-bursts. HMS *Formidable* was hit twice, blowing out her starboard side between Numbers 17 and 24 bulkheads, and putting out of action the 'X' turret and her cable and accelerator gear.

The destroyer *Nubian* (Commander R. W. Ravenhill) was struck right aft, blowing off her stern. Nevertheless she was still able to steam at 24 knots, and reached Alexandria that night escorted by HMS *Jackal*. Force A made course eastward until nightfall, when *Formidable* parted company for Alexandria with a destroyer escort.

Meanwhile the *Glenroy*, escorted by the anti-aircraft cruiser *Coventry*, and the destroyers *Stuart* and *Jaguar* had been making for Crete in order to land more reinforcements and fuel. At 1820 Stukas set ablaze the petrol cans stacked on the *Glenroy*'s decks; a grim moment with eight hundred soldiers aboard. In order to bring the wind aft to prevent the fire spreading, the *Glenroy* had to turn south, away from Crete. So much time and distance were therefore lost in putting the fire out before she could resume her course for Crete that it had become impossible to land her troops before daylight, and Cunningham therefore once again recalled her. Nevertheless, the minelayer *Abdiel* and the destroyers *Hero* and *Nizam* put troops and supplies ashore at Suda on the night of 26–27 May; the last reinforcements to be landed.

At 0859 next forenoon Pridham-Wippell with Force A (*Queen Elizabeth*, *Barham* and six destroyers) was steering northwest for Kaso Island in order to cover their withdrawal when he was jumped by fifteen twin-engined Junkers 88 divebombers and Heinkel 111 medium bombers attacking out of the morning sun. The *Barham* was struck by a bomb on 'Y' turret and had two anti-torpedo bulges flooded by near misses. A fire took two hours to extinguish. At 1230 Cunningham ordered Pridham-Wippell to turn back for Alexandria; he reached harbour at 1900.[32]

By this time the land battle for Crete had been won in any case by General Kurt Student's 'Fliegerdivision 7' backed by the close support of the Luftwaffe.[33] British preparations to defend the island had been belated and hasty; the defence was desperately short of anti-aircraft artillery as well as lacking mobility; above all, it was crippled by a virtually total want of air cover. Moreover, the garrison commander, General Freyberg, had failed to appreciate that the struggle for the island turned on the local battle for control of Maleme airfield. He shared with the rest of the British chain of command right up to the Chiefs of Staff in London a continued fixation that the real key to the struggle lay in German seaborne troop convoys following up the airborne assault. Partly because of less than quick and energetic reaction on the part of the British commanders on the spot, the Germans were able to seize Maleme and use it from 22 May onwards to fly in a constant stream of Junkers 52 transports ferrying troops of the 5th and 6th Mountain Divisions. This build-up proved decisive in overcoming a tenacious but too passive a defence. By 26 May the solidly established German invaders were launching a major offensive eastwards against the British 'stop' position, breaking through it and encircling Freyberg's force reserve. On the 27th Wavell signalled London that, in view of the collapse of the front, he had ordered Crete to be evacuated as quickly as possible; the Chiefs of Staff replied at once giving their own authorisation.

So ended for the Royal Navy the first phase of the Crete campaign, in which despite grievous loss and damage it had prevented the enemy from passing a single vessel through to the island. Cunningham knew well what it had cost his sailors in physical and mental exhaustion; how much of their store of courage had been expended in enduring for day after day the constant menace and actual terror of air attack. 'I have never felt prouder [he wrote in his despatch] of the Mediterranean Fleet than at the close of these particular operations, except perhaps at the fashion in which it faced up to the even greater strain which was so soon to be imposed on it.'[34]

For yet again – and this time within less than a month – it was to be the Navy's task to bring away a beaten British Imperial Army from a foreign shore in defiance of swarming bombers. Already Cunningham had lost in Cretan waters two cruisers and four destroyers, while two battleships, his only carrier, a cruiser and a destroyer had been put out of action.[35] Now he had to rescue as many as he could of the 22,000 soldiers of 'Creforce', the majority of them from the narrow beach and tiny harbour of Sphakia on Crete's rugged southern coast; the remainder from Heraklion on the northern coast, which, although it possessed a small harbour with a jetty, was dangerously exposed to air attack, lying as it did only 90 miles from Scarpanto airfield. Once more the Commander-in-Chief turned his worn-out and often damaged ships and his weary crews towards the enemy.

On 28–29 May, the first night of the evacuation, Force C (Captain S. H. T. Arliss) with the destroyers *Napier*, *Nizam*, *Kelvin* and *Kandahar*, safely lifted 700 soldiers from Sphakia and landed rations for the 15,000 men gathering on shore after a desperate march over mountain passes. But Force B at Heraklion, commanded by Admiral Rawlings (flying his flag in the cruiser *Orion*), with the cruisers *Ajax* and *Dido*, and the destroyers *Decoy*, *Jackal*, *Imperial*, *Hotspur*, *Kimberley* and *Hereward*, suffered calamitously. On the outward voyage from Alexandria a near miss damaged the *Ajax*, and it was decided to return her to harbour. It is possible that the damage report to the captain was exaggerated and that therefore *Ajax*'s return may not have been necessary.[36] Force B reached Heraklion at 2330, whereupon the destroyers entered the harbour to begin ferrying troops out to the cruisers. By 0245 this operation had been successfully completed, and a quarter of an hour later *Kimberley* and *Imperial* embarked the rearguard. At 0320 Rawlings's squadron steamed for Alexandria at 29 knots with all 4,000 men of the Heraklion garrison aboard. But at 0345 *Imperial*'s rudder jammed, nearly causing her to collide with the cruisers. Rawlings ordered *Hotspur* to take off *Imperial*'s load and sink her. To enable *Hotspur* to carry out this order and then rejoin him Rawlings reduced his squadron's speed to 15 knots; and just after daylight *Hotspur* with 900 men aboard caught the squadron up.

However, Force B was now some one and a half hours behind schedule, and the sun was already rising when Rawlings turned south for the Kaso Strait, the eastern passage round Crete for Alexandria. 'There on watch like birds of ill omen silhouetted against the early dawn, hung four JU 88s.'[37] Although Cunningham had arranged with Air Marshal Longmore for the Royal Air Force to fly fighters over Force B from 0630 onwards, the fighters never found the task force. From 0600 to 1500 Rawlings's unprotected ships were to be subjected to continuous and all too successful bombing. The first casualty came at 0625 when the *Hereward* (Lieutenant W. J. Munn, RN) was hit by a bomb, lost speed and had to leave her place in the destroyer screen. Since his squadron was still exposed in the middle of the Kaso Strait, Rawlings concluded that he dare not imperil it by delaying to aid the *Hereward*; a harsh and difficult decision. Force B last saw the *Hereward* making for the coast of Crete some five miles off with her guns still firing. She sank on the way.

Then at 0645 the *Decoy*'s engines were damaged by a near miss, forcing Rawlings to reduce the squadron's speed to 25 knots. At 0730 his own flagship was likewise slowed by a near miss, bringing the speed of advance down to 21 knots. At 0815 *Dido* had her 'B' turret put out of action by a bomb; threequarters of an hour later it was the turn of *Orion*'s 'A' turret. At 1045, with Rawlings's task force now some 100 miles south of Kaso, eleven Stukas screamed down on *Orion*. One bomb went through the bridge, put the conning tower out of action, and burst in the densely crowded stokers' mess deck, killing 260 men and wounding 280, mostly evacuated soldiers; an appalling scene of butchery in confined space. Clearing these decks of bodies offered one of the most unpleasant experiences of the campaign to sailors already at the limits of fatigue: an experience shared by working parties sent from other ships. Three of the *Orion*'s engineer officers were also killed, while the ship herself was grievously mauled –

communications between the bridge and the engine room destroyed; steering gear out of action; three boiler rooms damaged; oil contaminated with salt water. Henceforth the speed of Rawlings's force oscillated between 12 and 25 knots, with an average of 21 knots.

Thankfully this had been the last Stuka attack. But at 1300, 1330 and 1500 there came more bombing from high altitude. As the Naval Staff History recounts: 'The first and only friendly fighters seen were two naval Fulmars of the Fleet Air Arm. They were due at noon and were there on the stroke of the hour.'[38] Royal Air Force fighters in the course of their vain attempts to find Rawlings did nevertheless succeed in shooting down two Ju 88s for the loss of one Hurricane.

At 2000 on 29 May Rawlings brought Force B into Alexandria harbour, his flagship down to only 10 tons of fuel and only two rounds of 6-inch high-explosive ammunition. The scene was observed by the Commander-in-Chief with keen dismay:

> I shall never forget the sight of those ships coming up harbour, the guns of their fore-turrets awry, one or two broken off and pointing forlornly skyward, their upper decks crowded with troops, and the marks of their ordeal only too plainly visible. I went on board at once and found Rawlings cheerful but exhausted. The ship was a terrible sight and the mess deck a ghastly shambles.[39]

This had been only the beginning: Cunningham knew that the Navy's major effort to lift troops from Sphakia was yet to come, and it was to Sphakia that nearly threequarters of Freyberg's army had retreated. He therefore found himself, in the laconic words of the Naval Staff History, 'in a most unpleasant predicament'.[40] He was particularly worried about the fast transport ship *Glengyle*, which was already at sea and due to pick up 3,000 soldiers on the night of 29–30 May. It was a day of anxious consultation with his Army colleagues and with the Admiralty in order to establish whether he was justified, in his words, 'in accepting the anticipated scale of loss and damage to his already weakened Fleet'.[41] He assured the Admiralty that he was 'ready and willing to continue the evacuation as long as a ship remained to do so, realising that it was against all tradition to leave troops deliberately in enemy hands'.[42] And so the evacuation went on – for three more nights.

By 0320 on 30 May Force D (Rear-Admiral King, flying his flag in the *Phoebe*), with HMAS *Perth*, the anti-aircraft cruisers *Coventry* and *Calcutta*, the transport *Glengyle* and the destroyers *Jervis*, *Janus* and *Hasty*, had embarked 6,000 soldiers from Sphakia. Three Luftwaffe attacks the following forenoon succeeded only in putting one of *Perth*'s boiler rooms out of action, and with – for once – two or three Royal Air Force fighters overhead, Force D reached Alexandria unscathed. Meanwhile Force C (Captain Arliss) with the destroyers *Napier*, *Nizam*, *Kelvin* and *Kandahar* had left Alexandria for Sphakia at 0915 to carry out a further lift of troops. Unfortunately *Kandahar* had to return to harbour because of a mechanical defect. Then, at 1530, three Ju 88s attacked from astern, their dive unseen by lookouts. A near-miss so damaged *Kelvin* that her speed was cut to 20 knots, forcing her to return to port. The two surviving ships reached Sphakia at 0030 on the 31st, and in two and a half hours each took aboard 700 soldiers. On the homeward voyage twelve Ju 88s did their best to sink them, but succeeded only in slowing them by near misses.

Now Cunningham confronted yet another dilemma. He had been asked by Freyberg to make one last lift of 3,000 men from Sphakia on the night of 31 May–1 June, yet the capacity of all his remaining available ships amounted to only 2,000. Worse, Captain Arliss signalled on his way back to Alexandria that there were in fact as many as 6,500 waiting to be lifted. Cunningham therefore ordered Vice-Admiral King (he had been promoted on 30 May), who had sailed at 0600 on the 31st with the *Phoebe* (flag), the fast minelayer *Abdiel* and the destroyers *Kimberley*, *Hotspur* and *Jackal*, to increase his lift to 2,500. Later still Cunningham made a fresh signal telling him simply to fill his ships to the limit. At 0300 on 1 June King's squadron finally left Sphakia with nearly 4,000 soldiers crammed aboard.

There followed the final calamity. Cunningham had despatched the anti-aircraft cruisers *Coventry* and *Calcutta* to rendezvous with King in order to provide extra protection against the Luftwaffe on the homeward voyage. A hundred miles from Alexandria the two ships were attacked by two Ju 88s diving out of the sun. The first bomber narrowly missed *Coventry* but the second hit *Calcutta* with two bombs, and she sank in a few minutes. The *Coventry* succeeded in picking up 23 officers and 232 ratings before returning to Alexandria.

The Royal Navy had rescued from Crete as many as 16,500 soldiers out of a total garrison of 22,000. Yet the cost of firstly defending Crete against seaborne invasion and then mounting this rescue operation equalled that of a great fleet battle. Cunningham had deployed a total strength of four battleships, one carrier, eleven cruisers, a minelayer and 32 destroyers. Out of this total one battleship (*Warspite*) had been so damaged as to require 22 weeks' repair work and another (*Barham*) six weeks', while the carrier *Formidable* would require twenty weeks' repair work. As well as three cruisers sunk, five had been so damaged as to need from two-and-a-half to eleven weeks' repair; and in addition to six destroyers sunk, another seven had been so damaged as to require one to sixteen weeks in the dockyard.[43]

So, with the complete destruction as a fighting force of a second British expeditionary force on Greek soil and the effective halving of the operational strength of the Mediterranean Fleet, came to an end at last the Greek adventure and the concomitant fantasy of a Balkan front. On 30 May Cunningham unburdened himself to the First Sea Lord in a personal letter. 'There is no hiding the fact,' he wrote, 'that in our battle with the German Air Force we have been badly battered. I always thought we might get a surprise if they really turned their attention to the fleet. No A/A fire will deal with the simultaneous attacks of 10–20 aircraft.'[44] After referring to his 'very heavy losses', Cunningham went on:

> I would not mind if we had inflicted corresponding damage on the enemy but I fear we have achieved little beyond preventing a seaborne landing in Crete and the evacuation of some of the Army there. I feel very heavy hearted about it all.
>
> I suppose we shall learn our lesson in time that the navy and army cannot make up for lack of air forces. Three squadrons of long range fighters and a few heavy bombing squadrons would have saved Crete for us.

But it was not only loss of or damage to ships that disturbed Cunningham. 'I have been rather anxious about the state of mind of the sailors after 7 days' constant bombing,' he told the First Sea Lord. '. . . AJAX out of the last 60 days has spent less than 10 nights in harbour I believe. DIDO has had one in the last 21 days, and so on. The destroyers are the same – just very tired.' And with regard to the morale of his ships' companies, he proceeded tactfully to give Pound a lesson in the art of leadership: 'I had hoped that, realising the work they were doing and what they were up against, the fleet might have received a message of encouragement from the Board which I feel would have done a lot of good.' He concluded his letter by saying that if the government wished to relieve him (as it had just relieved Longmore), he would not 'feel in any way annoyed, more especially as it may be that the happenings of the last few days may have shaken the faith of the personnel of the fleet in my handling of affairs'. But Pound and the Board of Admiralty, even Churchill, retained full confidence in him.

This was perhaps surprising, because only a month beforehand Cunningham had again bluntly opposed another of the Prime Minister's operational bright ideas – an idea brought forth by the disaster which had by then overtaken the British land forces in the Western Desert as the consequence of the original decision in January 1941 to halt O'Connor in full cry of victory and despatch the best of his troops and armour to Greece.

On 31 March Major-General Erwin Rommel launched his first offensive in Libya, some six weeks earlier than either the British Middle East Command or his own high command believed feasible. Punched about by Rommel in a hurry, Neame, the inexperienced British general who had replaced O'Connor, and his raw formations (an Australian brigade group and the 2nd Armoured Division) were swiftly routed. On 6 April both Neame and O'Connor (sent up by Wavell to 'advise' Neame) were captured. On 28 April Rommel reached the Egyptian frontier. All that remained of O'Connor's conquests was the isolated fortress of Tobruk, which Wavell had ordered to be held in order to hinder a German advance to the Nile.

Suddenly the Western Desert was promoted again by the Prime Minister from a merely secondary importance to a matter of supreme concern. On the day that Rommel reached the Egyptian frontier Churchill issued a War Cabinet directive stating that the loss of Egypt and the Middle East 'would be a disaster of the first magnitude', and that 'not only must Egypt be defended, but the Germans have to be beaten and thrown out of Cyrenaica'.[45] Thus began an immense effort, enormously costly in military and logistical resources (especially shipping), to repeat O'Connor's victory from scratch and re-create the discarded opportunity of clearing Italian North Africa altogether. And every stage of the process was to make its exigent demands on the Mediterranean Fleet.

The first such demand was made even while Rommel was still hounding Neame's raw troops out of Cyrenaica. Churchill believed that the key to halting Rommel in his rush towards Egypt lay in blocking the port of Tripoli, thus – so Churchill judged – starving him of supplies sent by sea from Italy. On 15 April 1941 the Admiralty (or, rather, Pound, tamely acquiescing again in the Premier's desires) signalled the C-in-C, Mediterranean, that the battleship *Barham* and a 'C' class cruiser were to be sacrificed as blockships.[46] Cunningham, horrified at the thought of losing two of his precious ships (especially the battleship) in so questionable a venture, signalled back: 'Such a price is only justified if . . . success of operation is reasonably assured and if . . . result will be efficacious. I do not consider either condition will be fulfilled.'[47] He went on: 'Even if we are successful we shall have lost a first-class fighting unit. Rather than send in HMS *Barham* .... I would prefer attack with whole Battle Fleet and accept risk.'

It was Cunningham's opinion that what he later called 'this extraordinary message' had been 'apparently dictated by someone who appeared to know little of Tripoli or to have any true realization of our circumstances in the Mediterranean'.[48] For 'Operation Lustre' (see above, pp. 331–3) was then in full swing: there was Malta to think of; and any sortie to Tripoli would require a round trip of some 1,800 miles in the face of the Luftwaffe. Nevertheless the Admiralty passed on to Cunningham next day by way of reply the text of a Prime Ministerial directive dated 14 April:

> Every convoy which gets through must be regarded as a serious naval failure. The reputation of the Royal Navy is engaged in stopping this traffic.
> The effectual blocking of Tripoli would be well worth a battleship upon the active list.[49]

There followed more sharp exchanges between Cunningham and London in which Pound warned Cunningham that the failure of the Navy to concentrate on the prevention of convoys reaching Libya 'will be considered as having let side down'.[50] Finally, however, Cunningham's unswerving opposition to sacrificing the *Barham* carried the day. Instead, at 0700 on 18 April he sailed from Alexandria for Tripoli (flying his flag in the *Warspite*), with the *Barham*, *Formidable* (all three ships to be badly damaged off Crete a month later), the *Valiant*, *Phoebe*, *Calcutta* and screening destroyers. 'My personal fears,' wrote Cunningham many years later, 'ranged from the complete loss of a ship in a minefield to heavy damage to them all through dive-bombing.'[51] It proved a brilliantly planned and executed raid. Approaching Tripoli under cover of night, the four bombarding ships – *Warspite*, *Barham*, *Valiant* and the cruiser *Gloucester* (which had now joined) – rounded a light shown by the submarine *Truant* as a navigation mark four miles off the harbour entrance, and for three-quarters of an hour blasted the harbour installations and the shipping within. Then, 'in an anti-climax as pleasing as it was unexpected', the fleet steamed back to Alexandria without incurring the vengeance of the enemy air forces.

Yet only two enemy merchant ships and a destroyer had been sunk.[52] Cunningham signalled the Admiralty: '. . . in spite of our immunity on this occasion, I do not consider in general that the results to be expected justified hazarding the whole Mediterranean Battle

Fleet in mineable waters and exposed to potentially heavy air attacks at such a distance from its base.'[53] The argument muttered on, with Admiralty and Prime Minister favouring Cunningham with various suggestions as to how best to stop the Axis convoy traffic, including the stationing of a battleship at Malta. 'I was beginning to get seriously annoyed,' wrote Cunningham. 'This constant advice, not to say interference, in how to run our own business from those who seemed to be unaware of the real facts of our situation did not help us at all. They were a mere source of worry.'[54]

To Cunningham the key to the problem – indeed the key to the entire problem of maritime control in the Mediterranean – lay in air power and the British want of it. 'We urgently needed long-range fighters to give air cover to our convoys in every area; sufficient short-range fighters to give us control of our bases in Malta, Alexandria, Suda Bay and Tobruk; and adequate reconnaissance aircraft to give us the same information of the enemy's movements at sea as the enemy possessed of ours.'[55] And he added: 'Why the authorities at home apparently could not see the danger of our situation in the Mediterranean without adequate air support passed my comprehension. However, within about a month the bitter lesson was to be learnt, in Crete.'[56]

For the Royal Navy in the Mediterranean as for the British Commonwealth Army in the Middle East, the War Cabinet's renewed enthusiasm for achieving a decisive victory in North Africa meant having to do all over again what it did in 1940, and in the Navy's case with shrunken, not expanded, resources. It would be called upon to struggle with the enemy battlefleet and air forces for the use of the central Mediterranean as a convoy route, undertake the hazardous task of supplying Malta, and provide direct support for the Army along the coast of Libya. Even before the Greek adventure had come to an end, the pattern had begun to repeat itself. Just as the key to O'Connor's Desert offensive in 1940 had lain in the 'I' tanks shipped to Suez round the Cape, so hopes of a new offensive in 1941 depended on a consignment of nearly 300 cruiser tanks, the first batch to come off the assembly lines of Britain's belatedly expanded production. Whereas in 1940 the Admiralty and the C-in-C, Mediterranean, had successfully opposed the Prime Minister's wish to send the 'I' tanks by the direct route through the Mediterranean, in 1941 Churchill, itching to attack Rommel at the least delay, prevailed in his desire to despatch the 'Tiger' convoy (bearing the 295 'Tiger cubs', as the cruiser tanks were dubbed, plus 53 crated Hurricanes) by this route. 'Operation Tiger' entailed another complicated series of interlocking movements by the whole of the Mediterranean Fleet and Force H, whereby the five fast ships carrying the tanks could be passed from escort to escort like a game of pass-the-parcel all the way from Gibraltar to Alexandria. As usual, other operations were slotted in: a fast and a slow convoy to Malta from Alexandria; bombardments of Benghazi during the Fleet's outward and homeward voyage; the passing of the battleship *Queen Elizabeth* and the cruisers *Naiad* and *Fiji* to Cunningham as welcome reinforcements.

'Operation Tiger' began on 6 May, just after the Mediterranean Fleet had evacuated the expeditionary force from Greece and three weeks before its coming 'death ride' off Crete. Thanks above all to unseasonably bad weather in the Mediterranean – cloud, rain and fog – which largely shielded the operation from enemy air reconnaissance and attack, 'Tiger' was successfully completed by 12 May,[57] when both Force H and the battlefleet safely anchored in their base ports. Only one of the five transports, the *Empire Song*, was lost, with 57 tanks and 10 crated aircraft, and this owing to a mine in the Sicilian Narrows. Nevertheless Cunningham was well aware of how lucky he and Somerville had been.

> Unfortunately [he writes in his memoirs] the apparent ease with which a convoy was brought from end to end of the Mediterranean caused many false conclusions to be drawn at home, and I think made some people think we were exaggerating the dangers and difficulties of running convoys and operations of any sort in the face of the vigorous action of the Luftwaffe. Before long the dismal truth was painfully to be brought home to them.[58]

In the event the strategic impact of the 'Tiger cubs' on the Desert War went off at half-cock because they were used in a premature and abortive offensive in June 1941 ('Battleaxe') undertaken by Wavell at the Prime Minister's urging before the Army could be thoroughly trained and prepared. Ninety-nine tanks were lost in action.

Now began five months of preparation on a vast scale for a fresh offensive. Already in 1941, between January and July, no fewer than 239,000 soldiers and over a million tons of vehicles, fuel and stores had arrived by sea to be unloaded in Egypt. Yet the object of this colossal and ever-increasing effort was to defeat a German expeditionary force of just under-strength panzer divisions and a trucked infantry division; hardly a hundredth part of the army of the one power, Germany, which threatened the United Kingdom's own survival – barely a fiftieth of the army with which Hitler invaded Soviet Russia in 'Operation Barbarossa' on 22 June 1941. Did the swelling British military investment in the Middle East represent the rational pursuit of strategy or a growing obsession?

For the Royal Navy these months of military preparation brought no comparable respite or recuperation of strength; rather, continual service, a remorseless attrition, with the nourishing of Malta and Tobruk preoccupying Cunningham and Somerville above all else. Between April and June Force H made as many as five sorties towards Malta in order to fly off air reinforcements either from the *Ark Royal* alone or together with either *Furious* or *Victorious*. Of the 189 Hurricanes which reached the island from these carriers about half flew on to Egypt at the end of July to swell the Desert Air Force. It was between the second and third of these sorties that Force H had been summoned from the Mediterranean to join the hunt for the *Bismarck* – an illustration alike of the flexibility of seapower and of how hard the task forces of the Royal Navy were being worked.

In July and August followed two more sorties by Force H, this time to run convoys of troops and stores into Malta in the continuing effort to transform the island from a beleaguered fortress into a base for offensive operations by sea and air. For 'Operation Substance' on 20 –28 July Somerville was reinforced with the battleship *Nelson* and the cruisers *Edinburgh*, *Manchester* and *Arethusa* from the Home Fleet. Despite all his careful preplanning and attempts at diversion, he was attacked on the outward voyage by high-level and torpedo bombers. The *Manchester*'s speed was slowed by a torpedo hit, compelling her to return to Gibraltar, while the destroyer *Fearless* was so badly damaged that she had to be sunk. 'Operation Style', on 31 July–4 August, was carried out by Force X (the cruisers *Hermione* [Captain G. N. Oliver], and *Arethusa*, the fast minelayer *Manxman* and two destroyers) without loss, however, and 130 tons of stores and 1,750 soldiers and Royal Air Force maintenance personnel landed in Malta.

Thanks to these 'milk runs' by the Royal Navy, the combatant strength of the garrison had now risen to 22,000, and its defences now comprised 112 heavy and 118 light anti-aircraft guns, plus 104 guns of various calibres suitable for the field. Stocks of military stores stood at eight months' supply. Whereas in January 1941 there had been only one fighter squadron on the island, there were fifteen Hurricane Is and 60 Hurricane IIs at the beginning of August.[59] The neglect of the years of peace had at last been repaired.

On the orders of the Chiefs of Staff, Somerville ran yet another convoy to Malta in late September, this time ferrying 50,000 tons of fuel and food in eight merchant ships. 'Operation Halberd' demonstrates the scale of the naval resources required by the effort to keep Malta going. The escort all the way to Malta was provided by Force X (Rear-Admiral H. M. Burrough, flying his flag in the cruiser *Kenya*), and composed of five cruisers and nine destroyers. Somerville with Force H, reinforced from the Home Fleet to a strength of three battleships (*Nelson*, flying his flag, *Prince of Wales* and *Rodney*), the carrier *Ark Royal* and a further nine destroyers, covered the convoy against the Italian battlefleet and the enemy air forces. Further air cover was supplied by 22 Beaufighters and five Blenheims from Malta. This was not all: the Mediterranean Fleet also put to sea in order to create a diversion in the eastern Mediterranean, while submarines were posted in advance as pickets off Italian naval bases. Nonetheless, 'Halberd' did not go without loss, for *Nelson* was severely damaged by a torpedo from an Italian aircraft and her speed cut to 15 knots, and one of the merchant ships, the *Imperial Star*, had to be sunk after she too had been hit by a torpedo.

Such commitment and risk could only be justified if Malta proved a profitable investment as a base from which the flow of Axis supplies to Libya could be interrupted. Until the arrival on Trafalgar Day 1941 of Force K, commanded by Captain W. G. Agnew (of the *Aurora*), composed of two cruisers from the Home Fleet (*Aurora* and *Penelope*) and two destroyers (*Lance* and *Lively*) released from Force H, no surface ships were based on Malta. Until then the task of attacking Italian convoys had fallen to the Royal Navy's submarines and the Royal Air Force. From June to October (inclusive) the Royal Air Force sank 24 ships totalling 101,894 tons and His Majesty's submarines fourteen ships of 74,694 tons.[60] In the clear ultramarine waters of the Mediterranean was played out between submarines and escorts the same game of hunt and be hunted as in the Battle of the Atlantic, but with the roles reversed – British submariners enacting those scenes of peering into periscopes or silently listening to the thunder of enemy depth-charges rendered so familiar to cinema audiences by war films featuring German U-boat crews. On 18 September 1941 HMS *Upholder* (Lieutenant-Commander M. D. Wanklyn, later awarded the VC) bagged the biggest single prizes of all this onslaught on Italian shipping, when she sank the 19,500 ton liners *Neptunia* and *Oceania*, two out of the three ships in a fast convoy to Tripoli.

Although British submarines and aircraft were inflicting cumulative losses greater than new construction in Italian yards, two-thirds of the cargoes despatched to Libya were still getting through.[61] It took the cruisers and destroyers of Force K to bring the fraction of cargoes reaching Libya in November down to under 40 per cent of those despatched. On 9 November Force K sank or set on fire every one out of seven ships intercepted off Cape Spartivento. On 21 November the Italians aborted an attempt to run two separate convoys through from Naples under strong escort after the submarine *Utmost* had torpedoed the cruiser *Trieste* and a Swordfish of 830 Squadron, Fleet Air Arm, had performed a similar service for the cruiser *Duca della Abruzzi*, forcing both to limp back to Messina. On 24 November it was Force K's turn again, when HMS *Penelope* sank two German ships loaded with bombs, fuel and trucks. And on 30 November Force K, together with Force B (Rear-Admiral H. B. Rawlings) with the cruisers *Ajax* (flag), and *Neptune* and two destroyers, sank an auxiliary cruiser and a tanker, and blew up an escorting destroyer. Royal Air Force Blenheims also sank one merchant ship and damaged two others. Only one enemy ship in this convoy made it to Tripoli.

The decision back in April to hold the fortress of Tobruk, isolated far behind Rommel's forward troops on the Egyptian frontier, had laid on the Mediterranean Fleet the burden of another dangerous and continuing 'milk run'. During the 242 days of the siege, the Navy shipped into Tobruk 72 tanks, 92 guns, 34,000 tons of stores and 34,113 fresh troops. It shipped out 32,667 troops, plus 7,516 wounded and 7,097 prisoners – all this along an enemy coastline and within a few miles of his airfields.[62]

This very large turnover of troops is accounted for by the replacement of the 6th Australian Division in September and October by the 70th (British) Division, in compliance with the demand made by the government of Britain's Commonwealth ally, Australia; a needless extra burden on the hard-pressed Inshore Squadron and a burden to which Cunningham himself had been 'much opposed'.[63] For the ships' companies the Tobruk run meant navigating accurately at night through minefields, negotiating the harbour boom and finding a berth in a harbour littered with wrecks, also in the dark, and then completing the process of unloading and loading within an hour. When the siege finally ended in December 1941 the Royal Navy had lost twenty-five vessels sunk and nine seriously damaged; the Merchant Marine five ships sunk and four seriously damaged. Two hospital ships had also been attacked and badly damaged.[64] No wonder, then, that after the war Cunningham was to say that if Tobruk 'was rightly described as "a running sore" to the enemy, it was something equally painful for the Royal Navy.'[65]

Nevertheless, the worst attrition of all in 1941 was yet to come – worse even than the battle against the Luftwaffe off Crete, for it destroyed the very core of the Royal Navy's striking power in the Mediterranean.

On 13 November 1941, Force H, fearing U-boat attack, was zig-zagging across a smooth sea under low cloud on the last thirty miles of its return voyage to Gibraltar from yet another sortie to fly aircraft into Malta. Visibility was good except during occasional rain squalls. At 1540, when Somerville altered to 290° on the next leg of the zig-zag, speed 18 knots, the carrier *Ark Royal* (Captain L. E. H. Maund) altered to 286°, speed 22 knots, in order to leave her station to fly off aircraft. A minute later, in position 36° 03'N, 4° 40'W, she was shaken by an explosion under her bottom between keel and starboard side – whether a contact or non-contact explosion was never established[66] – caused by a torpedo from the U-81 (Lieutenant Friedrich Guggenberger), one of eighteen U-boats recently transferred from the Atlantic. According to the subsequent technical report on the loss of the ship, 'The ship whipped violently, aircraft loaded with torpedoes bouncing off the Flight Deck and spreading their under-carriages before settling again.'[67]

The *Ark Royal* immediately listed 10° to starboard and 'S' boiler room began to flood. Soon almost all power was lost. By 1602 the list had reached 18° and over the tannoy, which had been temporarily restored to life, came the orders: 'Hands to station for abandon ship', and 'Everyone over the port side.' From deep down in the machinery spaces men came clattering up ladders to the open air, not knowing how many more minutes the ship might last. But in fact there followed some fourteen hours of struggle to save the *Ark Royal*. Around 1700 all steam was lost, which killed the pumps and other auxiliary machinery, including the turbo-generators which supplied electric power. At 2055 she was taken in tow at 2 knots by the tug *Thames*. Between 1815 and 2215 devoted work by repair parties succeeded in gradually restoring steam to the port boiler room and with it, electric power. But then came further trouble – owing to the increasing list sea water spilled over into the elbow of the port boiler room funnel uptake, so blocking the escape of fumes. 'As a result,' recorded the technical report, 'boiler castings became red-hot and fires broke out.'[68]

As the flames spread the boiler room had to be abandoned, so losing all steam and hence all power in the ship for good. The *Ark Royal* was now just 22,000 tons of metal dead in the water. By 0215 on 14 November her list had reached 17°; by 0400 when Captain Maund gave a final order to abandon ship, a terrifying 27°. At 0430, with the list at 35°, the last man scrambled down the port side to be rescued by attendant destroyers. At 0613, when the list had reached 45°, the *Ark Royal* capsized and sank.

The Court of Enquiry attributed her loss partly to shortcomings in the damage-control measures taken after she was hit: 'It is considered that if, when steam finally failed, the port engine room and boiler room had been flooded to upright the ship there would have still been ample buoyancy for the ship to reach harbour.'[69] But the court acknowledged that the need for drastic counter-flooding might not have been appreciated because the book issued to the ship illustrating flooded compartments gave no examples of lists greater than 8°. The court also acknowledged the problems caused by steeply sloping decks slippery with oil, and the breakdown of the ship's communication systems for want of power: '... all messages had to be passed by messenger or human chain which slowed down all action ...'[70]

Nevertheless *Ark Royal* owed her demise primarily to flaws in her own design, which had never been rectified in the dockyard because she had been in almost continuous service at sea. She was the Royal Navy's first modern fleet carrier, designed in 1935 and built as part of the initial and modest rearmament programme aimed at remedying the accumulated deficiencies caused by the defence cuts of the 1920s and early 1930s. Her designers had routed the boiler room uptakes beneath the lower hangar deck; and this, according to the technical report, 'proved a vulnerable feature at the end, as the flooding of the port boiler room finally occurred when the angle of the heel was about 19°. This restricted the passage available for funnel gases and a fire resulted.'[71] The uptakes had been routed in this way because it was impossible to route them further up in the ship, that is, through the lower hangar deck itself, because this would have restricted the number of aircraft carried. Since *Ark Royal* was not protected by an armoured flight deck (unlike later carriers of the Illustrious class), it would have been ideally desirable to armour the funnel uptakes themselves. But, as the technical report remarked, this 'would have involved substantial additional weight of armour, which could not be accepted, as the ship's displacement was limited to 22,000 tons in anticipation of the Geneva Convention [a hoped-for but aborted fresh international agreement on the limitation of armaments] ...' As a result, some risk of flooding via the unarmoured uptakes had to be accepted.[72]

The final misfortune proved to be, in the words of the enquiry report, that this was 'the first known case' when a single torpedo blew a hole in a ship's bottom 'so large as the reported size, 130 feet long', leading to an immediate list 'much greater than anticipated'.[73] Once all steam was lost, so too was power for every piece of equipment in the ship, including the electricity supply and hence telecommunications. This was because of another basic weakness in her design, for all the auxiliary machinery in the ship was powered solely by steam from the boiler rooms, even the electricity supply by means of turbo-generators; there were no stand-by sources of power at all. Moreover, the electrical problem was worsened in the event because the main switchboard was located low enough in the ship to be itself affected by flooding even while there was still steam power available. Later aircraft carriers suffered from none of these shortcomings. The final technical flaw lay in that when portable pumps were put aboard from another ship, their plugs and sockets were not compatible with those in the *Ark Royal*.

The *Ark Royal*'s fate after such brave service (including the decisive strike on the *Bismarck*) thus exemplifies two recurring strands in the twentieth-century history of British seapower – weaknesses in the design and technology of major warships, and the pernicious influence of the inter-war pursuit of naval limitation agreements.

On 18 November, four days after the loss of HMS *Ark Royal* and nearly a year after O'Connor began his offensive at Sidi Barrani, the new 8th Army, over 100,000 strong, with nearly 700 assorted tanks, launched 'Operation Crusader'; the end product of all the resources in shipping and escorts invested in the supply and reinforcement of the Middle East theatre since the disasters in Greece and Crete; the end product too of the Royal Navy's repeated Mediterranean convoy operations and its months of unrelenting service off the Libyan coast in support of Tobruk. And while the armies collided in confused tank battles in the Cyrenaican desert, the Royal Navy once again did its part, running more supplies into Tobruk (at the cost of the fast merchant ship *Glenroy*, veteran of the Crete evacuation, torpedoed, beached, but eventually towed back to Alexandria; and the Australian sloop *Parramatta*), and bombarding the German defences at Halfaya Pass and Bardia.

On 23 November, however, a crisis in the land battle (the 8th Army had failed to relieve Tobruk, while its tank losses were apparently so high that the army commander wished to break off the offensive) evoked a signal from the Prime Minister to Cunningham that it was vitally important to stop enemy ships transporting supplies, above all of fuel, through to Benghazi: 'I shall be glad to hear through the Admiralty what action you propose to take . . .'[74] There ensued a brief but sharp exchange between the Commander-in-Chief, Mediterranean, on the one hand and the First Sea Lord and the War Premier on the other, in which the C-in-C again sought to educate the desk men in London about the operational risks and realities – not least the Fleet's current acute shortage of fuel, and 'the difficulty of intercepting a convoy by a force based 550 miles from the scene of operations and under constant enemy observation'.[75]

In the early hours of 24 November, however, Cunningham received intelligence that two enemy convoys were actually at sea heading for Benghazi. He therefore ordered the cruisers of Forces K and B to intercept them while he himself took the battlefleet (*Queen Elizabeth*, flying his flag, *Barham* and *Valiant*) to sea in order to cover the operation in case Italian heavy ships intervened. Next day, at about 1630, with the battlefleet on patrol between Crete and Cyrenaica, Cunningham was having tea in his bridge cabin when he 'suddenly heard and half-felt the door give three distinct rattles and [I] thought we had opened fire with our anti-aircraft guns'.[76]

I went quickly up the one ladder to the bridge, and then I saw the *Barham*, immediately astern of us, stopped and listing heavily to port. The thuds I had heard were three torpedoes striking her. She had been torpedoed by a U-boat. The poor ship rolled nearly over on to her beam ends, and we saw men massing on her upturned side. A minute or two later there came the dull rumble of a terrific explosion as one of her main magazines blew up. The ship became so completely hidden in a great cloud of yellowish-black smoke, which went wreathing and eddying high up into the sky. When it cleared away the *Barham* had disappeared. There was nothing but a bubbling, oily-looking patch on the calm surface of the sea, dotted with wreckage and the heads of swimmers. It was ghastly to look at, a horrible and awe-inspiring spectacle when one realized what it meant.[77]

Although Vice-Admiral Pridham-Wippell and some 450 others were rescued, 55 officers and 806 men, including the ship's captain, Captain G. C. Cooke, died with the ship.

Barham had fallen victim to the U-331 (Lieutenant Hans-Dietrich Baron von Tiesenhausen), another of the U-boats transferred from the Atlantic by the German naval command in response to British devastation of Mediterranean convoys. The Royal Navy in the Mediterranean had already paid dearly for the respite thus accorded the Admiralty in the Battle of the Atlantic (see above, pp. 274–5).

In the final month of 1941 came yet more salvoes of disaster. On 14 December the cruiser *Galatea* sank almost immediately off Alexandria after being struck by two torpedoes from a U-boat. Four days later a force of three cruisers (*Neptune*, *Aurora* and *Penelope*) and four destroyers (*Kandahar, Lance, Lively* and *Havock*) which had sailed from Malta to intercept a convoy off Tripoli ran into a minefield in heavy seas and blustering wind. The *Neptune* sank after hitting four mines, with only a single survivor, while *Aurora* was badly damaged and *Penelope* lightly damaged; the destroyer *Kandahar* also sank after her stern had been blown off. Force K, which had done such execution since its arrival at Malta in October, was now reduced to one cruiser, *Penelope*. Then, on 19 December, the remaining battleships of the Mediterranean Fleet succumbed in Alexandria harbour itself to the smallest and cheapest of conceivable weapons systems – explosive charges fixed to the ships' bottoms by two-men Italian Navy teams in diving suits riding astride 'human torpedoes'. Cunningham, standing on the quarter deck of his flagship, the *Queen Elizabeth*, himself witnessed the culminating catastrophe of 1941. Just before 0600:

> . . . there was a violent explosion under the stern of the tanker *Sagona*, lying close to the *Queen Elizabeth* with the *Jervis* [destroyer] alongside. Both the tanker and the destroyer were badly damaged, the *Sagona* badly holed aft with her rudder and screws damaged. The *Jervis*'s injuries were to keep her in dock for a month.
>
> About twenty minutes later I saw another heavy explosion under the *Valiant*'s foreturret, and four minutes after that, when I was right aft in the *Queen Elizabeth* by the ensign staff, I felt a dull thud and was tossed about five feet into the air by the whip of the ship and was lucky not to come down sprawling. I saw a great cloud of black smoke shoot up the funnel and immediately in front of it, and knew at once that the ship was badly damaged. The *Valiant* was already down by the bows. The *Queen Elizabeth* took a heavy list to starboard.[78]

Thanks to this final attack by six brave and bold Italian sailors the Mediterranean Fleet entirely ceased to exist. Cunningham's remaining strength consisted of just three light cruisers (*Naiad, Dido* and *Euryalus*) and a handful of destroyers. At the far end of the Mediterranean Somerville's Force H had been reduced by losses, damage, and Admiralty withdrawal of ships for service elsewhere to one old battleship (*Malaya*), the obsolete carrier *Argus* and one cruiser, the *Hermione*. In the course of 1941 the pursuit of an opportunistic 'blue water' strategy in the Mediterranean had cost the Royal Navy a total of one battleship sunk and four badly damaged, one carrier sunk and two damaged, seven cruisers sunk and ten damaged, sixteen destroyers sunk and twelve damaged, one monitor sunk, and five submarines sunk and three damaged.[79]

Yet at the year's end the positive results of 'blue water' strategy had hardly justified this catastrophic loss, let alone paid a dividend on the huge investment of British resources in the Mediterranean and Middle East. By this time the 8th Army's offensive in Libya – the spearpoint of 'blue water' strategy once the evacuation of Crete had closed the Greek adventure – had certainly forced Rommel into retreat, marking the first victory of British Commonwealth forces over German troops in the Second World War. The 8th Army had taken 36,000 prisoners and reduced Rommel's tank strength to only thirty. This was a welcome enough success just when the Red Army was fighting titanic battles in front of Moscow and Leningrad against the main strength of the Wehrmacht. Yet the 8th Army's own striking power had been so worn down that there could be no immediate prospect of pushing on towards Tripoli. At the beginning of 1942 the Desert campaign came to rest exactly where O'Connor had been halted at London's orders a year before, at El Agheila, on the border between Cyrenaica and Tripolitania.

Nor could Cunningham and Somerville hope for replacement of their lost or damaged ships (the latter often condemned to many weeks of repair in dockyards as far afield as North America). For in that same devastating final month of 1941 the third of the triple threats to the British Empire in its worldwide sprawl – the threat that had been smouldering ever since Britain had chosen to affront Japan in the Manchurian crisis ten years earlier; really ever since Britain failed to renew the Anglo-Japanese alliance twenty years earlier – at last exploded. On 7 December Britain found herself at war with three great powers simultaneously – the pre-war Chiefs of Staffs' ultimate nightmare. The moment of bankruptcy for British 'total strategy' since the end of the Great War had arrived.

13

The Sinking of HMS Prince of Wales *and* Repulse

On 12 August 1941 the Chiefs of Staff met to consider a telegram about future United States negotiating policy towards Japan which the Foreign Secretary had just received from the Prime Minister at the summit conference then being held with President Roosevelt aboard HMS *Prince of Wales* and the USS *Augusta,* in Placentia Bay, Newfoundland. Such was the gulf between Japan's expansionist ambitions in China and South-East Asia and America's tough conditions for a general settlement that, as Churchill reported, the negotiations 'show little chance of succeeding'.[1] In fact, in Churchill's words, the 'President's idea is . . . to procure a moratorium of say 30 days in which we may improve our position in Singapore area and the Japanese who have to stand still . . . President considers a month gained will be valuable.'[2]

For the Chiefs of Staff, for the First Sea Lord above all, the arrival of this telegram signified that the defence of the British Empire in South-East Asia and the Pacific had ceased to be an anxiety nagging continually at the back of the mind while war was being waged against Germany and Italy with all available resources, and had become instead an urgent problem demanding answer – if such could be found. The Chiefs of Staff forthwith instructed the Joint Planners to report on 'what steps could be taken in the immediate future to improve our position in the Far East'.[3]

[378]

THE SINKING OF HMS *PRINCE OF WALES* AND *REPULSE*

At the 1923 Imperial Conference, held a year after Britain had allowed the Anglo-Japanese alliance to lapse and instead signed the Washington Treaties drastically limiting the size of the Royal Navy, that shrewd Boer Jan Smuts, Prime Minister of South Africa, had doubted whether the proposed new naval base at Singapore would offer any protection to Australia and New Zealand unless Britain could send the battlefleet – and believed that Japan was unlikely to attack unless she had support in Europe. If this were so, Smuts asked, would it be feasible to divide the Royal Navy, now Britain no longer enjoyed the old huge superiority? Leo Amery, then First Lord of the Admiralty, and himself a believer in the greatness of the British Empire, had admitted in reply: 'Of course it is perfectly feasible that, if there were a European combination against us at the same moment as war was declared against us by Japan, we should be in a position of extraordinary difficulty.'[4]

From the Manchurian crisis of 1931–32 onwards the possible advent of this 'position of extraordinary difficulty' had haunted the imaginations of British policy-makers and strategists, especially at times of diplomatic crisis in Europe, and more especially still if Japan had concurrently perpetrated local acts of aggression or insult against the British presence in China. Between the summers of 1940 and 1941 the advent had grown more and more probable rather than merely possible, and in circumstances far grimmer than had been foreseen even by the most pessimistic before the war. For in the immediate aftermath of France's collapse, Marshal Pétain's government had haplessly granted Japan the right to station armed forces in the northern part of the French colony of Indo-China; and a year later, on 24 July 1941, the Japanese proceeded to occupy the whole of the colony, giving their navy a magnificent forward base in the natural harbour of Camranh Bay and their air force fields in southern Indo-China from which to dominate Siam and the South China Sea. The Royal Navy's fleet base at Singapore was no longer protected by over three thousand miles of distance from Japanese strike forces based in the home islands, but instead had become an outpost exposed to attack at relatively close range.

And by now Britain herself was not only fighting for life itself against Nazi Germany (owing to the collapse of the Western Front in May 1940 and the loss of France as an ally), but also massively committed to conducting Churchill's 'blue water' strategy in the Mediterranean and Middle East, in complete reversal of pre-war strategic priorities whereby the Mediterranean was if necessary to be abandoned in order to concentrate a great battlefleet to send to

[379]

Singapore. By August 1941, what with the twin demands of 'grey water' strategy in the Atlantic and 'blue water' in the Mediterranean already severely over-stretching the Royal Navy's resources in every kind of ship, Leo Amery's 'position of extraordinary difficulty' had already come about even without an actual Japanese attack.

The problem of over-stretch was the worse because new construction of ships since 1939 had barely kept pace with the losses sustained in two years of war, let alone enabled the Royal Navy to expand in proportion to its constantly increasing commitments. In July 1941 the First Sea Lord, in a memorandum opposing yet further allotment of industrial capacity to the aggrandisement of Bomber Command at the expense of naval construction, noted that the total strength of the Navy in ships of sizes down to sloops was now 369, as against 366 on the outbreak of war; and pointed out that in the Great War 'numbers of ships . . . had increased by some 40 per cent at the end of the first two years'.[5]

Several factors account for this failure to increase the size of the Royal Navy. In the first place, such new construction as was authorised had been delayed by the backwardness of British shipyards and the sloth and restricted practices of their workforces.[6] According to the First Sea Lord in July 1941, of the new ships expected in January 1941 to be completed by 30 June, 81,000 tons (including three cruisers, twelve destroyers and three submarines) had not yet been delivered.[7]

But secondly and more importantly, Britain was more painfully caught than ever between the scissors of her strategic obligations as the Mother Country of an Empire on the one hand, and, on the other, her own inadequate financial and industrial base which made it impossible to afford or even to build and equip the size of Navy needed to fulfil those obligations. In January and February 1940 the First Sea Lord and the naval staff had fought an unavailing battle with the War Cabinet for a major new building programme of four battleships as well as two 15-inch battlecruisers.[8] So highly did Pound and his VCNS, Rear-Admiral T. S. V. Phillips, still rate the battleship that they were even prepared to sacrifice new construction of carriers and cruisers for the sake of their proposed programme, although also, to be fair, for the sake of the largest possible expansion of the anti-U-boat and anti-mine flotillas.[9] Pound's pleas for new battleships were to no avail; the pressure on Britain's inadequate shipbuilding industry to construct new merchant ships as well as escorts was such that in March 1940 the War Cabinet decided that all long-term programmes must be abandoned.

Nevertheless in September 1940 the First Sea Lord and Phillips sought to revive the battleship programme. Pound believed that work on the *Howe* (last of the 14-inch King George V class), and on the *Lion* and *Temeraire* (16-inch gun ships of a new class already laid down) should all proceed; and that two more ships of this class, *Thunderer* and *Conqueror*, should be laid down as soon as possible. He also argued that a further ship, the *Vanguard*, making use of the 15-inch guns and turrets installed in the *Courageous* and *Glorious* before their 1920s conversion from battlecruisers to aircraft carriers, should also be built. He reckoned that all these battleships were needed to match the expected combined strength in heavy ships in 1945 of Germany, Italy and Japan. Although he thought it 'desirable' to order another fleet carrier, he told the Controller of the Navy he would not do so at the expense of a battleship. The Controller in reply had to point out to this simple sailor an industrial fact of life: the demands for armour plate of such a programme would necessitate the immediate stoppage of production of tank armour.[10]

Undaunted, the Admiralty continued to push for the resumption of a major long-term construction programme. At the beginning of 1941 their modified shopping list comprised the two 16-inch battleships *Lion* and *Temeraire*, two fleet carriers, ten cruisers and forty to fifty destroyers.[11] In view of the limited capacity for making armour plate and the continued pressure on shipyards exerted by the desperate need to build new merchant ships and escorts and repair damaged ones, the Admiralty's latest shopping list proved merely more wishful thinking. On 26 March 1941 the Prime Minister, wearing his other personality of sober and realistic judgment (it was the month when he proclaimed 'the Battle of the Atlantic'), issued an instruction that no naval vessel was to be undertaken that could not be completed by the end of 1942. The pre-war hope of a 'Two-Power Standard' fleet or even just an 'enhanced One-Power Standard' fleet (see p. 37, above) had thus finally foundered on the rock of Britain's 'less than One-Power Standard' industrial resources.

The Admiralty's problem was rendered even more acute in the latter months of 1941 because nearly a third of the Navy's ships lay immobilised in the dockyards either having battle and storm damage repaired or being refitted and modernised. In the quarter July to October 1941 the number of vessels of corvette size and above in the dockyards for major work stood at no fewer than 132 (seventeen of them in American yards).[12] The inordinate time taken by British yards to complete the work served to aggravate this drain on fighting strength at sea, and at the same time justifiably enrage the Premier.

Thus it was that, at 1 August 1941, the Royal Navy had only ten capital ships in service, though four more were due to leave the dockyards during that month and the first week of September. The *King George V, Prince of Wales* and *Malaya* were with the Home Fleet; *Barham, Valiant* and *Warspite* with the Mediterranean Fleet; *Nelson* and *Renown* with Force H, and the two unmodernised Great War battleships *Ramillies* and *Revenge* with the North Atlantic Escort Force.[13]

How then was the Admiralty to find a fleet for Singapore, as had been repeatedly promised (though with waning conviction) to Australia and New Zealand before and since the outbreak of war with Germany and Italy? It went far deeper than a mere question of naval strategy and deployment. As Sir Samuel Hoare, the then First Lord of the Admiralty, had remarked to the 1937 Imperial Conference, 'the very existence of the British Commonwealth as now constituted' rested on the ability of Britain to send a battlefleet to Singapore.[14] But this in turn posed an even more profound question about Britain's very own existence as the centre of this oceanic empire, the immediate practical implications of which were so starkly confronting her leaders in the summer and autumn of 1941. For in retrospect it can be seen that it was an illusion for the British to believe that the Commonwealth and the Empire made Britain a great world power. Rather the strategic and economic balance sheet in 1941 demonstrates that the Commonwealth and Empire (with the notable exception of Canada and perhaps South Africa) were not an asset, but a net drain on Britain's strength; a predicament. For the imperial pink splashed across the map of the world in British atlases did not represent strength, as the British romantically believed, but one of the most outstanding examples of strategic overstretch in history.

In the first place Britain, an island in the northern seas, would not already have become entangled in a war in the Mediterranean and Middle East if it had not been for the British naval and military presence developed in this theatre during the previous century and a half in order to protect the imperial route to India, the Far East, Australia and New Zealand. Yet the contributions thus far made to Britain's war with Germany (and Italy) by Australia, New Zealand and India – some five divisions and six cruisers – were too small to balance the enormous British commitment of military and material resources to the Middle East and the deployment in the Mediterranean of about a third of the Royal Navy's strength. Nor did it make up for the British troops stationed in India and further British garrisons in Burma and Malaya.

[382]

In any event, the approach of war with Japan was to draw Dominion ships and divisions back from the Mediterranean and Middle East to the defence of their own countries. The military and naval contributions of the Empire lying east of Suez to Britain's own struggle in Europe therefore did not even begin to compensate for the British obligation to wage an extra war against Japan in the Empire's defence by land and above all by sea; a huge potential burden on a nation of only 45 millions, and one impossible for the Royal Navy to bear.

Nor, in the second place, did the Empire and Commonwealth east of Suez constitute an economic asset of such value to Britain as in itself to warrant preserving at the cost of an extra maritime war. India, poverty-stricken and backward, devoid of key raw materials, actually drew on British shipping resources in order to fill her essential needs for imports. Australia and New Zealand, which had been among Britain's major peacetime sources of meat and dairy produce, had now dwindled to minor importance in this regard because it was uneconomic in shipping capacity to haul such supplies over the 12,000 miles from these dominions rather than over the much shorter Atlantic routes from North and South America. Burma and Borneo, for their part, were relatively minor producers of oil. Even Malaya, the most single valuable territory in the British Empire and a prolific earner of dollars, producing a third of the world's rubber and well over half the world's tin, was hardly worth a war with a great power on top of an existing war. And the civilian trade and supply of the whole Indian Ocean area (the core of the traditional British imperial structure) from Australasia to East Africa, from India and South-East Asia to Egypt, were swallowing by the second half of 1941 over 331,000 tons of shipping in continuous employment – enough to bring an additional 800,000 tons of desperately needed imports to Britain across the North Atlantic.[15]

But of course British policy towards the Empire and Commonwealth east of Suez was not, could not be, shaped by such cost-benefit analysis. There was the question of Britain's imperial pride and prestige, while in the case of Australia and New Zealand in particular Britain's 'alliance' with them derived from kinship, from common history and culture, and from loyalty to a common Crown, not from the logic of strategic and economic advantage. These, the dominions closest to Britain in race and sentiment, happened to be the furthest away in distance – settled in that halcyon epoch of the early nineteenth century when the Royal Navy's supremacy had turned the oceans of the world into a British pond, and when Japan had been a feudal society locked up in self-imposed isolation. The haphazard workings of history and the accidents of geography had thus bequeathed a strategic absurdity: an alliance between two vulnerable and dependent small nations in the Pacific and a protecting power in Europe already stretched to the limit in the struggle for its own survival. But ties of blood, strong feelings of family loyalty and obligation, made it unthinkable, certainly unthought, for Britain's leadership to do other than seek by all means possible to preserve Australia and New Zealand from attack.

Given Britain's own peril the most desirable means must lie in deft diplomacy aimed at averting a conflict.[16] Yet British diplomacy in the Far East had lacked essential leverage ever since the lapsing of the Anglo-Japanese Treaty in 1922, for by failing to renew the treaty Britain lost Japan as an ally but failed to gain America instead, despite periodic efforts so to do, as at the beginning of 1937 (see above, pp. 33, 55). Stanley Baldwin had warned in 1932 that Britain would 'get nothing out of Washington but words, big words, but only words';[17] and that was indeed all Britain did get from America in regard to the Japanese menace right up to, and including, 1941. Thus lacking the support of an ally in the East, Britain could only look to her own strength to back her diplomacy. Unfortunately that had been lacking too. Whereas up to the mid-1930s Britain had had available a battlefleet for deployment in eastern waters but no naval base to which to send it, after the mid-1930s – and above all in 1941 – she had the naval base, but no available fleet. It had taken remarkable conduct of grand strategy and high policy on the part of successive British Cabinets to achieve this neat but paralysing sequence.

How then could a weightless diplomacy preserve the British Empire in the East from Japanese ambition? In the 1930s Neville Chamberlain (when Chancellor of the Exchequer) and the Chiefs of Staff had advocated 'strategic appeasement' – neutralising the Japanese prong of the triple threat by means of a deal with Japan over spheres of influence in China. However, the scruples of Cabinet and public opinion alike had ruled out such a cynical exercise in *realpolitik*. After the outbreak of war with Germany, and especially in the wake of France's collapse and the addition of Italy to Britain's foes, there was renewed advocacy of strategic appeasement on the part of Sir Robert Craigie, the ambassador in Tokyo, and the Chiefs of Staff, deeply worried as the latter were about Britain's global plight. In July 1940 the Chiefs of Staff advised the Cabinet that in present circumstances British policy should aim at avoiding a clash with Japan, and not merely that: 'A general settlement, including economic concessions to Japan, should be concluded as soon as possible. Failing this settlement, our general policy must be to play for time, cede nothing till we must, and build up our defences as soon as we can.'[18]

But it was illusion to believe that Britain any longer retained even the prestige needed to promote some general settlement of Far Eastern problems. Instead of 'strategic appeasement', therefore, Britain found herself in 1940 haplessly descending into 'tactical appeasement' – a sheer giving way in the face of Japanese menaces and demands, a process which even Churchill then saw as unavoidable. Already, on 10 July (the Battle of Britain was just opening; German preparations for 'Operation Sealion' just beginning) Britain had had to agree to a Japanese demand to close the Burma Road (the route by which trucks carried American supplies into China in support of Chiang Kai Shek), although only for three months. At the end of July Britain further agreed to withdraw her garrison from Shanghai and her gunboats from the River Yangtse. Yet though such diplomatic retreats might buy time they could not buy long-term Japanese non-belligerency, for in Britain's pitiful state of weakness, Japan might simply take what she wanted by armed force whenever she wished. Appeasement out of fear and weakness was as unlikely to achieve permanent results in the Far East as it had been in Europe.

That left one other expedient, pursued in vain during the 1930s, but in Britain's desperation worth another try – that of enlisting the strength of the United States to shield the British Empire in the Far East and Pacific, just as that strength was already being enlisted in the cause of Britain's own survival. In regard to Japan, however, British policy-makers saw American strength as serving in the first place as a deterrent. Sadly for the British, however, Washington proved less interested in preserving the British Empire in the East than it did in preserving Britain herself as a convenient bulwark between Nazi Germany and the United States. Indeed, from President Roosevelt downward there was instinctive suspicion of British 'imperialism'. Moreover, the axis of American naval strategy in the Pacific lay westwards from the west coast of America through the advanced fleet base of Pearl Harbor, Hawaii, to the Philippines, now an internally self-governing Commonwealth, though America retained control over foreign affairs and defence. For the Americans the British concept (now vitiated by weakness) of a naval war against Japan in the China Sea and based on Singapore was irrelevant, peripheral.

Thus while Britain and the United States shared the broad objective of averting further Japanese expansion, their interests had little in common beyond that. It is hardly surprising that British efforts in 1940–41, either at the level of government – including Churchill himself toadying valiantly to Roosevelt – or at the level of staff talks, to induce the Americans to rescue Britain from her imperial predicament in the East came to little. In the summer of 1940 the United States declined either to threaten the Japanese with a full economic embargo, as the British wished, or make a *démarche* in regard to a general settlement of Far Eastern problems. This American inaction had led directly to the British diplomatic surrenders over the Burma Road and the garrison and gunboats in China.

In late January 1941, after cordial enough meetings and exchanges of secret information between representatives of the British and United States naval staffs, formal staff conversations were held in Washington at which the British delegation pressed again the key importance (as they saw it) of Singapore, and urged that America should base there as strong a detachment of her Pacific Fleet (including battleships) as possible. An American battlefleet to Singapore! It was a solution to the imperial dilemma that would have astonished and dismayed Beatty and Amery. It marked a tacit acknowledgment that after two decades Britain's imperial bluff had at last been called by events; and that she had reached the point of bankruptcy in terms of world maritime power. But the proposal was to no avail: the Americans declined to bail the British out. The final record of the staff conversations found a polite formula to express the deep divisions of view between the Royal and the United States Navies over Far Eastern strategy: 'It was agreed that for Great Britain it was fundamental that Singapore be held; for the United States it was fundamental that the Pacific Fleet be held intact.'[19]

When in February 1941 there occurred a brief scare that Japan was about to strike (taken more seriously in London than in Washington) Churchill sought once again to wring some kind of public guarantee out of Roosevelt that the United States would go to war if the British Empire in the East were attacked. 'I think I ought to let you know,' he wrote, 'that the weight of the Japanese Navy, if thrown against us, would confront us with situations beyond our naval resources.' He proceeded to attempt to tweak the President's nerves by pointing at the 'awful enfeeblement' of the British war effort which would be caused by Japanese belligerence, and told him: 'Everything that you can do to inspire the Japanese with the fear of a double war may avert the danger.'[20] But Roosevelt proved quite unwilling to make any such public declaration as would saddle the United States with a *de facto* alliance with Britain in the Far East.

So the British continued to squirm in their imperial dilemma, the more so because Robert Menzies, the Prime Minister of Australia,

[386]

pressed Britain to state exactly what she meant to do in fulfilment of her obligations as Mother Country to defend Australia in the event of Japanese aggression. When in March 1941 Menzies called in on Cunningham in Egypt en route for London, the C-in-C, Mediterranean, was astonished to find that the Australian Prime Minister was 'still obsessed with the idea that we should send 3 or 4 battleships to Singapore!'[21] The Chiefs of Staff bluntly informed Menzies in April that in view of Britain's existing commitments, of the potential dangers in the European theatre, and of the Royal Navy's available strength in capital ships, it would 'be misleading to attempt to lay down possible strength in the Far East in advance and propose a movement timetable. It is vital to avoid being weak everywhere. All we can say is that we should send a battle-cruiser and an aircraft carrier to the Indian Ocean. Our ability to do more must be judged entirely on the situation at the time.'[22]

At a British, Dutch, Australian and American staff conference in Singapore that same month (the second such, with the Americans this time present as participants rather than observers; a tiny advance) the American delegation still refused to agree to any joint contingency arrangements that might imply a political commitment to go to war if the Japanese violated other than American territory.

The most Admiral Harold Stark, the Chief of Naval Operations in Washington, was willing to do was to relieve the pressure on the Royal Navy in the Atlantic by transferring three battleships, an aircraft carrier, four cruisers and nineteen destroyers from the Pacific to the Atlantic, thus freeing British ships for service elsewhere. In June 1941, however, the devastation of the Mediterranean Fleet off Greece and Crete prompted Stark to ask the British Chiefs of Staff whether the Royal Navy could still find a task force for the Far East, and even suggested transferring a further three American battleships from the Pacific to the Atlantic. The Chiefs of Staff replied that until repairs to the *Prince of Wales* (damaged in the *Bismarck* chase) and refits of *Rodney*, *Renown* and *Royal Sovereign* were completed in August, it would only be possible to send two 'R' class battleships from the Atlantic to the Far East after their relief by US battleships. They added that the Royal Navy was equally strapped for cruisers. It was their advice to Stark, therefore, not to transfer more battleships from the Pacific: 'We consequently feel that at the present time the need for a deterrent against Japan is greater than it was and that it outweighs the extra effect on Germany that would be produced by [such] a move . . .'[23] So nine battleships, three aircraft carriers, twenty-one cruisers and sixty-seven destroyers remained at Pearl Harbor, while

Singapore remained a base without a fleet and without prospect of one.

By now not only the Chiefs of Staff but also the Cabinet and the Prime Minister had come to the conclusion that deterrence rather than appeasement offered the better means of preventing further Japanese expansion; a major turnabout in attitude. That deterrence, in the British view, should take the form of a clear warning to Japan from the United States, backed by the presence of the American battlefleet at Pearl Harbor, that she would respond to any Japanese aggression against British or Dutch interests in South-East Asia. The Japanese occupation of the whole of French Indo-China in July 1941 seemed to push American policy the way the British wished, for Roosevelt thereupon froze all Japanese assets in America and proclaimed a harsh economic embargo, including – the most damaging of all – oil. Though not consulted beforehand, the British and Dutch governments made haste to follow suit.

At the Atlantic Conference next month Churchill employed all his skill at persuasion, all his force of personality, to persuade Roosevelt to cap this embargo with a powerful declaration that – in the words of the British draft handed to him – 'any further encroachment by Japan in the South-West Pacific would produce a situation in which the United States Government would be compelled to take counter-measures even though these might lead to a war between the United States and Japan'.[24] Churchill, over-optimistic once again, informed his Cabinet colleagues that Roosevelt had promised him 'on more than one occasion' to use this British formula, and that he, Churchill, was 'confident that the President would not tone it down'.[25]

But Roosevelt proved as ever long on cloudy promises and short on delivery. The note actually handed to the Japanese ambassador in Washington on 17 August 1941 stated that if Japan took any further steps towards the military domination of neighbouring countries the United States 'would be compelled to take immediately any and all steps which it may deem necessary towards safeguarding the legitimate rights and interest of the United States'.[26] Far from being the deterrent declaration covering British and Dutch territories and interests, as Churchill intended, it expressly disclaimed any such American concern and involvement.

Britain now had the worst of both worlds – committed to a joint economic embargo of Japan severe enough to provoke rather than postpone Japanese aggression, yet without the protection of a United States deterrent warning to Japan and without any assurance whatever that the United States would come to Britain's aid in the event of a

Japanese attack on British interests only. It has to be asked whether British policy vis-à-vis Japan and the United States in the summer of 1941 was not ill-judged in pushing for a firm diplomatic stand against Japan, even in falling in so tamely with the American embargo, given Britain's own naval weakness and America's unwillingness to commit herself to the obligations of an alliance. It is a policy that only makes sense in the light of Churchill's and Eden's overriding objective, worth in their view all the incidental risks and setbacks, 'to get the Americans into the war';[27] and what better means than a collision in the Far East between Japan and America?

While the US Secretary of State, Cordell Hull, and the Japanese ambassador in Washington, Nomura, still talked on month by month, with the British government reduced to a poorly briefed bystander, Britain could only look to her own armed forces to deter the Japanese from directly attacking the British Empire in the Far East and Pacific, or to defend that Empire if deterrence failed. With the ultimate inability of British statesmanship to find a political and diplomatic answer to Britain's imperial conundrum, the problem became a purely strategic one, to be tackled by the Chiefs of Staff, especially the First Sea Lord, and, of course, also Churchill, wearing his other hat as Minister of Defence.

Singapore was not, had never been designed to be, a fortress capable of resisting a siege *en règle* by an expeditionary force, but instead to be a naval base for the replenishing of a battlefleet and for carrying out all but the most major repairs to damaged ships: a complex of oil storage tanks, workshops, heavy handling equipment, and a dry dock capable of taking a battleship. In any case, no location could have been more unsuitable than Singapore island and Singapore city for a fortress to be defended against close-range attack, if necessary street by street, house by house; for a fortress the garrison of which must be sustained by a resolute civilian population of high morale. For Singapore was a swarming polyglot city of Malays, Indians and Chinese, all totally unconcerned about the fate of the British Empire, and a handful of imperial rulers in white ducks or khaki drill whose minds (with rare exceptions) were ossified by the arrogance of race and empire and the hierarchical snobberies of colonial society, and whose energies had been unsprung by long service in damp heat, by a social round lubricated by an excess of gin-slings and stingahs (whiskies and soda), and by pampering at the hands of multitudes of native servants.

The planners of the naval base in the 1920s and early 1930s had taken it as a premise that the only danger to it lay in a long-distance strike by a Japanese fleet before the British battlefleet could arrive from home waters and the Mediterranean. To guard against this danger, coastal defence batteries had been installed on both sides of the eastern entrance of the Johore Strait (running between Singapore island and the southern tip of Malaya) so as to command the approach to the naval base, which was situated on the northern tip of Singapore island barely a mile across the strait from the Malayan province of Johore – three batteries each of two 6-inch guns, one battery of three 9.2-inch and one of five 15-inch. On the southern tip of the island near the city of Singapore four more batteries each of 6-inch guns and one of three 9.2-inch defended the seaward approach to, and the entrances of, Keppel Harbour. Another battery of two 6-inch guns was sited on the western point of the island to command the western entrance to Johore Strait, the entrance furthest away from a Japanese fleet's direct line of approach.[28] These batteries, being intended for use against enemy warships, were mostly stocked with armour-piercing shell, and quite unsuitable for the bombardment of troops in the field.

In May 1937, however, a report by the Chiefs of Staff had challenged the basic premise that the main danger to the Singapore base lay in Japanese attack by sea. It was possible, the Chiefs of Staff argued, and in character for the Japanese to prepare a secret expedition before war was declared. The Japanese might aim to establish air forces to operate from shore bases 'and to land army forces in the Malayan Peninsula to advance on Singapore. The Japanese may hope by the combined effect of attrition, air and land attack to force our garrison to surrender before our fleet can arrive to relieve it.'[29]

The Chiefs of Staff remarked that while the east coast of Malaya was difficult country, the west coast enjoyed good communications, although the rubber and coconut plantations offered poor visibility. They reckoned that the Japanese would need up to two divisions for the invasion of Malaya; and wrote that they could not rule out the possibility of the Japanese landing in Siamese territory at Chumpon and Singora, then moving by road to seize the airfields at Victoria Point and Alor Star. Or the Japanese might land at Penang, giving them an overland advance of some four hundred miles to Singapore. Despite the risks of such an invasion, wrote the Chiefs, 'we cannot exclude the possibility that the Japanese may attempt operations of this character . . . If they overcame the difficulties of effecting a landing in Malaya and prevented our reinforcements reaching Singapore, they might consider they had a reasonable chance of capturing the base within two months.'[30] The COS then summarised the form Japanese operations might take: convoys to Malaya, an advance through Malaya, leading to 'close investment of Singapore Island, and command of the naval base by artillery fire';[31] and they repeated that this process might be accomplished within two months of the outbreak of war.

This COS paper of 1937 constitutes a very remarkable work of accurate prophecy; its existence demolishes the post-1942 legend (largely fostered by Churchill) that no one had ever thought in terms of a Japanese attack on Singapore by the back door overland. From 1937 onwards British plans to defend the base consequently rested on the need to prevent the Japanese landing in, and advancing through, Malaya. They also rested on an understanding that the key to achieving this now lay in air power; and that therefore the land defence of Malaya must be sited far enough north to cover the airfields at Alor Star and Victoria Point. In July 1940, in one among several reassessments of the problem between 1937 and December 1941, the Chiefs of Staff reiterated that it was no longer sufficient to concentrate on the defence of Singapore alone, and that the whole of Malaya must be held; that this depended on airpower, which in turn would mean that the land forces in Malaya would have to be greatly increased in order to defend the airfields.[32]

It has to be said that despite such papers put before him as Minister of Defence and discussed in Cabinet, Churchill himself refused to accept that Singapore was incapable of surviving attack if Malaya was lost; and he believed to the last that Singapore was in itself a 'fortress'. In September 1940, for instance, having affirmed his faith that the Japanese danger to Singapore was anyway remote, he proceeded directly to contradict the Chiefs of Staff's judgment that all Malaya must be held. He urged that the defence of Singapore could be entrusted to a strong local garrison and the 'general potentialities of seapower'. The defence of the whole of Malaya, he proclaimed, 'cannot be entertained'.[33] Even as late as a week after the Japanese had actually landed in northern Malaya in December 1941, Churchill was minuting to Ismay for the Chiefs of Staff: 'Beware lest troops required for the ultimate defence Singapore Island and fortress are not used or cut off in Malay peninsula. Nothing compares in importance with the fortress.'[34]

Since Churchill had been Chancellor of the Exchequer in Baldwin's Cabinet between 1924 and 1929 when plans for the Singapore naval base and its shore batteries were being discussed and evolved, and since he had specifically studied, and replied to, the Chiefs of Staff's wartime views on the necessity of a landward defence of Singapore sited in northern Malaya covering the essential British airfields, it is astonishing to read in his war memoirs that 'it had never entered my head that no circle of detached forts of a permanent character protected the rear of the famous fortress. I cannot understand how it was I did not know this. But none of the officers on the spot and none of my professional advisers at home seem to have realised this awful need . . .'[35]

From this inexplicable delusion or *idée fixe* that Singapore was a fortress rather than merely a naval base with shore batteries against sea attack were to follow grievous consequences and tragic loss. Yet the idea that Singapore island should have been girdled with Maginot Line-like forts was anyway preposterous, because the naval base itself, lying on the northernmost tip of the island, would have been in the front line, under close-range artillery fire from the Japanese besiegers across the Johore Strait, and therefore unusable; and without use of the naval base Singapore lost all strategic importance, worth no greater military investment than Hong Kong with its six battalions.

The problem for the Chiefs of Staff, for the recently appointed Commander-in-Chief, Far East, Air Chief Marshal Sir Robert Brooke-Popham, the General Officer Commanding Malaya, Lieutenant-General A. E. Percival, and the Air Officer Commanding Far East, Air Vice-Marshal C. W. H. Pulford, in August 1941 lay in that while they were charged with fulfilling the broad plan drawn up by the Chiefs of Staff and approved by the Cabinet (with the Prime Minister in the chair) a year earlier by which Singapore was to be defended by land/air forces in northern Malaya, nothing like enough troops and aircraft had been provided. Even by the outbreak of war in December 1941, the army remained a third smaller than Percival reckoned in August to be necessary, as well as wholly without tanks, while the total of first-line aircraft in Malaya amounted to only 180, as against the target figure of 336 modern aircraft considered by the Chiefs of Staff to be the minimum required. Moreover the aircraft were in fact obsolescent or obsolete: American Brewster Buffalo day fighters, old and worn-out Blenheim I night fighters, Vildebeest torpedo-bombers.[36] These weaknesses resulted from the priority necessarily given to the defence of the United Kingdom itself and the other priority which the War Cabinet had chosen to give to the Mediterranean and Middle East since 1940.

The defence plan for Malaya and Singapore, though based on a correct reading of Japanese strategy, was thus hopelessly flawed in practice by want of resources. Yet the purpose of the whole exercise, to secure the naval base, had in any case been rendered pointless because there was no British fleet available to send there; and no likelihood of there being available in the foreseeable future one large enough or composed of modern enough ships to confront the Japanese fleet in battle.

It fell to the First Sea Lord and naval staff that August to decide what the Royal Navy could do in lieu of such a large and modern battlefleet; what strategy it should adopt in place of its pre-war vision of a new and better Jutland in the China Sea. On the day following receipt of the Prime Minister's warning telegram from the Atlantic Conference, the Joint Planners (on the advice of the Naval Staff) recommended despatching to the East by mid-September one battleship (either *Barham* or *Valiant* from the Mediterranean) and that by the end of the year four of the old unmodernised 'R' class battleships should follow. It was not proposed to send at the present time any cruisers or fleet destroyers, for the latter could not be spared from either the Atlantic or Mediterranean until the US Navy had deployed additional patrols in the Atlantic. The Joint Planners also recommended sending if possible one aircraft carrier (probably the old *Eagle*) with the battleships.[37]

A week later a meeting chaired by the First Sea Lord on his return from Placentia Bay concluded that

> should the U.S.A. provide a sufficiently strong striking force of modern battleships capable of engaging TIRPITZ [*Bismarck*'s sister ship] and be prepared to allow one of these ships to replace one of our own KING GEORGE V class if damaged, then it would be possible to send one of the KING GEORGE V Class to the Far East or Indian Ocean in addition to NELSON, RODNEY, 4 'R' Class and RENOWN.[38]

In the meantime, with *Tirpitz* to watch, Pound did not believe that any of the Royal Navy's only three modern battleships (the *King George V*, *Prince of Wales* and *Duke of York*) could be spared from the Atlantic. To give Pound due credit, his assessment of the Far Eastern problem throughout was founded on commonsensical acceptance that the lack of an available battleworthy fleet meant that the Singapore base, along with the entire strategy that had been its *raison d'être*, was now a write-off. In an appreciation written back in August 1940 he had stated: 'There is no object in sending a Fleet to Singapore unless it is strong enough to fight the Japanese Fleet. Singapore is inferior to Trincomalee as a base from which to protect our trade in the Indian Ocean.'[39] Now in August 1941 he proposed assembling a homogeneous fleet of old, slow, heavy ships capable of protecting that Indian Ocean trade, and based on Trincomalee, nearly 2,000 miles west of Singapore. But in any case even this defensive fleet could not be fully assembled before March 1942.

Churchill's diagnosis of the problem was, however, entirely different. In the first place he judged that, given a show of joint deterrence by America and Britain, Japan was very unlikely to attack at all. As late as 20 October 1941 he was averring to the COS Committee that 'he did not believe that the Japanese would go to war with the United States and ourselves'.[40] Therefore he believed that British naval strategy in the Far East should be based on the concept of deterrence. This deterrence should take the form of a British '*Bismarck*' or '*Tirpitz*' offering an elusive menace to Japanese offensive plans, and in the event of conflict tying down a disproportionate number of Japanese capital ships. On 25 August Churchill put forward his proposal to Pound in a personal minute:

> Such a force should consist of the smallest number of our best ships. We have only to remember all the preoccupations which are caused us by the *Tirpitz* – the only capital ship left to Germany against our 15 or 16 [sic] battleships and battlecruisers – to see what an effect would be produced upon the Japanese Admiralty by the presence of a small but very powerful force in Eastern waters . . .
>
> The most economical disposition would be to send DUKE OF YORK . . . to the East. She could be joined by REPULSE or RENOWN and one aircraft carrier of high speed. This powerful force might show itself in the triangle Aden–Singapore–Simonstown. It would exert a paralysing effect on Japanese naval action.[41]

But thus to snatch an analogy between the effect of *Tirpitz* on the Royal Navy and the potential effect of a King George V and an old battlecruiser on the Japanese Navy was to repeat the same mental pattern that led him to believe that Singapore was a 'fortress' – the pattern of reacting emotionally to verbal symbols rather than coldly appraising the realities. In the first instance, the *King George V* (at some 38,000 tons displacement, 44,000 tons full load, and ten 14-inch guns) was smaller and less well armed than Japan's newest battleship, the 70,000-ton, 18-inch gun *Yamato*, whereas *Tirpitz* (like *Bismarck* in its time) exceeded even the most modern British capital ships in her combination of speed, size and gunpower. Secondly, Japanese naval aviation, shore and carrier based, was far more numerous than the meagre air resources successfully employed by the British to cripple the *Bismarck*. Thirdly, unlike *Bismarck* and *Tirpitz*, none of the three King George Vs had yet had time to work up to full operational efficiency, although Churchill proposed that the *Duke of York*, if sent to the East, could work up during 'her long safe voyage'.[42] Fourthly, whereas German battleships once into the Atlantic could refuel from previously posted oilers, the British ships the Premier wished to despatch to the East would be tied to fixed bases for refuelling, given the British lack of fleet oilers. And finally German battleships were free to roam on the offensive wherever they chose, while British heavy ships in Far Eastern waters could hardly avoid being drawn into action in defence of British trade or territories – especially Malaya and Singapore.

On receipt of this minute, the First Sea Lord made haste to begin one of his devious delaying actions, minuting in his own hand to the Director, Tactical and Staff Division of the Naval Staff: 'Please let me have detailed reasons based on experience of K.G.V. and P. of W. why it would not be sound for a new ship of this class to be sent abroad before she has had a thorough working up.'[43] A brief duly supplied by the DTD enabled Pound to write to Churchill on the 28th: 'I fully appreciate the attractiveness of sending one of the KING GEORGE V class to the Indian Ocean when fully worked up, but after considering this most carefully I cannot recommend it for the reasons given in this memorandum'; and he went on in well-chosen detail about the need for time to work up the crew and the complex modern machinery and electronic gear.[44]

These proved only the ranging shots in a protracted battle. The very next day Churchill replied in a long memorandum instructing the First Sea Lord on various naval matters:

> It is surely a faulty disposition to create in the Indian Ocean a fleet considerable in numbers, costly in manpower and maintenance, but consisting entirely of slow obsolescent and unmodernised ships which can neither fight a fleet action with the main Japanese force nor act as a deterrent upon his modern fast heavy ships, if used singly or in pairs as raiders. Such dispositions might be forced upon us by circumstances; but they are inherently unsound in themselves.[45]

He did not want to employ the 'R' class battleships on convoy work in the Indian Ocean, because if so 'it would be necessary to have one or two fast heavy units which would prevent the enemy from detaching individual heavy raiders without fear of punishment' – a point which ignored the experience of 'R' class battleships on convoy work in the Atlantic, where they had succeeded in warning off German heavy ships. The Premier further proceeded:

> No doubt the Australian Government would be pleased to count the

number of old battleships in their neighbourhood, but we must not play down to uninstructed thought. On the contrary, we should inculcate the true principles of naval strategy, one of which is certainly to use a small number of the best fast ships to cope with a superior force.

The potency of the dispositions I ventured to suggest in my minute M.819-1 [of 25 August] is illustrated by the Admiralty's own extraordinary concern about *Tirpitz*. *Tirpitz* is doing to us exactly what a K.G.V. in the Indian Ocean would do to the Japanese Navy. It exercises a vague, general fear and menaces all points at once. It appears, disappears, causing immediate reactions and perturbations on the other side.[46]

He concluded this exposition by referring to Japanese hesitation about going to war against the United States, the USSR and Great Britain: 'Nothing would increase her hesitation more than the appearance of the force I mentioned in my minute M.819-1, and above all of a K.G.V. This might indeed be a decisive deterrent.'[47]

However, the Premier more than somewhat undermined his own argument by also remarking that the fact that the Admiralty considered that three K.G.Vs must be used to contain *Tirpitz* 'is a serious reflection upon the design of our latest ships, which through being undergunned and weakened by hangars in the middle of their citadels, are evidently judged unfit to fight their opposite number in a single ship action'; and by noting, with reference to the Admiralty's apprehensions about the *Tirpitz*, 'the proved power of Aircraft Carriers to slow down a ship like *Tirpitz* if she were loose'.[48]

There the matter rested for six weeks, while the Americans and Japanese negotiated on in Washington. But on 2 October the Americans handed the Japanese a note stating that a hoped-for meeting between the Japanese Prime Minister, Prince Konoye, and President Roosevelt could not take place unless Japan first accepted the basic American principles for a settlement. Since these included Japan's withdrawal from her conquests in China, this effectively torpedoed any real hope in Tokyo that a deal might be done. On 7 October the supposedly moderate Konoye resigned, to be replaced by General Tojo, a soldier still on the active list, and a notorious expansionist. On 16 October, even before Tojo's appointment had been announced, Eden was minuting Churchill that Konoye's fall was 'an ominous sign'; that the next government would be 'once more under the influence of extreme elements'; that the current Soviet defeats at German hands 'must inevitably be having their effect upon the Japanese appetite'.[49] Although Eden acknowledged that there was nothing yet to show 'in which direction Japan will jump, if any,' he averred that 'it is no doubt true that the stronger the joint front that the ABCD [America, Britain, China and the Dutch] powers can show, the greater the deterrent to Japanese action'.[50] And he went on: 'In this connection you will recall that we discussed some little time ago the possibility of capital ship reinforcements to the Far East. The matter has now become urgent, and I should be glad if it could be discussed at the Defence Committee meeting tomorrow afternoon.'[51]

It was thanks to this initiative of Eden that British naval strategy with regard to the Far East now entered its final crisis. Next day at the Defence Committee Churchill repeated his opinions that the Admiralty's proposal to send a fleet composed of half a dozen old battleships was unsound because they would be 'neither strong enough to engage the weight of the Japanese Navy, nor yet fast enough to avoid action except in circumstances of their own choosing'; and that the example of the *Tirpitz* showed that the presence of one modern capital ship in Far Eastern waters 'could be calculated to have a similar effect on the Japanese naval authorities, and thereby on Japanese foreign policy':[52]

> The *Repulse* had already reached the Indian Ocean. No time should now be lost in sending the *Prince of Wales* to join up with her at Singapore. We could afford to accept some risk of the *Tirpitz* breaking out into the Atlantic in the knowledge that we ought by air action from aircraft carriers to be able to slow her up to become a prey for the heavy metal of our capital ships.[53]

Rear-Admiral Phillips, the Vice Chief of Naval Staff, who had attended the meeting in the place of the First Sea Lord (absent on leave), reported to Pound later that the Premier 'at once raised the old question of sending out the PRINCE OF WALES and gave the Defence Committee all the arguments that he had used before. He was also scathing in his comments on the Admiralty attitude to this matter.'[54] In the absence of the First Sea Lord, it fell to the First Lord, A. V. Alexander, to point out that whereas the *Tirpitz* 'was a threat to our trade convoys in the Atlantic, our dispositions in the Far East would be governed more by the need to protect our own trade routes than to raid Japanese shipping'.[55]

Nevertheless Eden urged that

> From the point of view of deterring Japan from entering the war, the despatch of 1 modern ship, such as the *Prince of Wales*, to the Far East would have far greater effect politically than the presence in those waters of a number of the last war's battleships. If the *Prince of Wales* were to call

at Cape Town on her way to the Far East, news of her movements would quickly reach Japan and the deterrent effect would begin from that date.[56]

By an irony Eden, the man whose suave persuasion had played a key role in finally getting Britain committed to the Greek adventure, was now playing a similar role over the despatch of the *Prince of Wales* to the East, for his assurance about the deterrent effect on Japanese policy that would be exerted by her sailing thither provided just the influential backing Churchill needed to sway his colleagues. As the VCNS reported to Pound:

> The First Lord and I defended the position as well as we could, but the Prime Minister led other members of the Defence Committee to the conclusion that it was desirable to send the PRINCE OF WALES to join the REPULSE and go to Singapore as soon as possible. The Admiralty expressed their dissent.[57]

A final decision was however left until 20 October, after the First Sea Lord returned from leave. The matter was first discussed that day by the COS Committee with Churchill (as Minister of Defence) in the chair. The First Sea Lord made the Admiralty's case as fully and strongly as he could, repeating the reasons against taking any of the King George Vs away from the Atlantic, and then turning to the problem of the Pacific:

> . . . the deterrent which would prevent the Japanese from moving south-wards would not be the presence of 1 fast battleship. They could easily afford to put 4 modern ships with any big convoys destined for an attack in Southern waters. What would deter them, however, would be the presence at Singapore of a force (such as the *Nelson*, the *Rodney* and the R-class battleships) of such strength that to overcome it they would have to detach the greater part of their fleet and thus uncover Japan . . .[58]

When Churchill intervened at this point to say that he had under-stood that the 'R' class battleships would be used in the Indian Ocean for convoy escort duties, Sir Dudley Pound answered that 'this would be so until it became necessary to concentrate in the Far East. The aim had always been to constitute a battle fleet with this as a nucleus.'[59]

Pound's problem as always was that the Royal Navy was just too small to meet its commitments. On 1 October 1941 its total of capital ships available for sea had stood at only nine: four with the Home Fleet (*King George V*, *Prince of Wales*, *Malaya* and *Repulse*, although *Prince of Wales* was at that time at Gibraltar and *Repulse* on detachment in the South Atlantic); three with the Mediterranean Fleet (*Queen*

Elizabeth, Barham and *Valiant*); *Resolution* in the West Indies and *Revenge* in the Indian Ocean. For *Nelson* had been badly damaged in the Mediterranean by a torpedo on 27 September (see above, p. 370), while repairs to the *Royal Sovereign* (earmarked for the Indian Ocean) were not due for completion before 15 October and to the *Duke of York* (Home Fleet) and *Ramillies* (also earmarked for the Indian Ocean) not until the 23rd, the refit of the *Renown* not until the 30th, and major repairs to the *Warspite* in the USA not until 15 December.[60]

Confronted with such weakness, Pound was throughout thinking as best he could of likely real operational contingencies and requirements in the Far East. As a handwritten note to Alexander (maddeningly undated but certainly of early October) makes clear, he even still had at the back of his mind that it might be necessary to withdraw the Mediterranean Fleet and send it to the Far East[61] (see above, pp. 209–12). In contrast the Prime Minister's mind was dwelling on symbols and gestures, because he believed, in his own words at the time, that the Naval Intelligence Department 'are very much inclined to exaggerate Japanese strength and efficiency';[62] because, as he told the COS meeting on 20 October, 'he did not foresee an attack in force on Malaya' and because he did not believe the Japanese would go to war with the United States and ourselves.[63] Such comfortable illusions made it possible to repose faith in the deterrent value of a symbolic battleship and the gesture of sending it to the East; and in this Churchill was again backed by Eden, who repeated to the Chiefs of Staff the assurance he had made four days earlier to the Defence Committee, but in even more certain language: 'From the political point of view there was no doubt as to the value of our sending, at the present time, a really modern ship.'[64] The views of Churchill and Eden were apparently supported by the C-in-C, Far East, Air Chief Marshal Sir Robert Brooke-Popham, who had cabled on 1 October to stress 'the propaganda value of even one or two battleships at Singapore'. In fact, the signal was instigated by Duff Cooper, instigated in turn by Churchill behind the backs of the authorities in Singapore via secret Foreign Office ciphers. The COS had replied on 3 October: 'We are in general agreement.'[65]

The Prime Minister now proceeded to tell the Chiefs of Staff meeting that he 'would like to see the *Prince of Wales* sent and the situation reviewed when the *Nelson* had been repaired'.[66] The First Sea Lord, isolated and outgunned, thereupon lowered the flag in surrender:

... he fully realised the value of a report from Cape Town of the arrival there of the Prince of Wales. He suggested that she should be sailed forthwith to that destination, a decision as to her onward journey being taken in the light of the situation when she arrived at Cape Town.[67]

This was agreed by the Committee. Their decision was ratified later that day, 20 October, by the Defence Committee, on the grounds that the political need to send the ship to Singapore (the destination given in the minutes) was so urgent 'as to outweigh objections hitherto advanced by the Admiralty on strategical grounds'.[68] It was to no avail, therefore, that the C-in-C, Home Fleet, Admiral Sir John Tovey, signalled the First Sea Lord that evening:

> I wish to urge as strongly as I can that despatch of PRINCE OF WALES to Far East should not take place.
> Passage of Atlantic convoys is vital to our existence and their stoppage would rapidly result in our losing the war. There is no comparable interest in the Far East.
> [The *King George V* being the only remaining battleship capable of bringing *Tirpitz* to action] ... Damage or minor defect to KING GEORGE V would leave *Tirpitz* virtually unopposed.
> ... I am convinced this proposal involves a risk which cannot be justified under any circumstance even if Japan enters the war.[69]

For Churchill and Eden had finally had their way. On 25 October HMS *Prince of Wales* (Captain J. C. Leach), wearing the flag of (Acting) Admiral Sir Tom Phillips, Commander-in-Chief, Eastern Fleet, and escorted only by the destroyers *Electra* and *Express*, slipped her moorings in the Clyde, and, as the Royal Marine band played her away, put to sea.

For all Churchill's and Eden's confident assertions about the Japanese leadership's mental processes and intentions, the truth is that neither the British nor the American governments and their professional advisers, nor their ambassadors in Tokyo, enjoyed solid, precise intelligence about Japan's plans or their timing. This was despite the success of American cryptographers ('Magic') in breaking the Japanese diplomatic 'Purple' cypher (equivalent of the German 'Enigma' machine), so enabling them to read the traffic between Tokyo and the Japanese ambassador in Washington.[70] The revealing material thus yielded by 'Magic', together with important clues from other sources, such as radio traffic analysis, went partly to waste because Washington as yet possessed no coordinated machinery for gathering Intelligence, collating it and presenting it to the decision-makers, such as Britain had created since 1939. Some 'Purple' intercepts were never even decrypted; others simply yellowed in the pigeon-holes of the decrypters.[71] The historian of American Intelligence before the Pearl Harbor attack sums up what 'Magic' and other sources had revealed about Japanese plans:

> It is clear enough that Japan was preparing for an all-out war with England and America, but it is nowhere clear whether she intended to make the first move by attacking either power directly, or whether she was preparing to meet a sudden blow from England or America ... in response to further Japanese moves to the south ... [although 'Magic' signals were 'not unambiguous' on these questions] ... they indicated quite clearly a level of tension where an accident on either side could open a full-scale war.[72]

The British in particular, last in the line to receive gleanings from 'Magic' and then by no means all of them, could only guess, grope and argue about Japanese intentions and plans – the Joint Intelligence Committee, the Foreign Office and Sir Robert Craigie, the ambassador in Tokyo, the Foreign Secretary and the Prime Minister themselves.[73]

In point of fact the Japanese leadership had decided at an imperial conference on 2 July 1941 that Japan would expand southwards (the Imperial Japanese Navy's preferred strategy) by occupying the European empires in South-East Asia, rather than northwards against Soviet Russia from the conquered territory in China, in direct fulfilment of the alliance with Germany under the Tripartite Pact (the Army's preference). This southward expansion was nevertheless to be accomplished if possible without incurring American hostility. Thanks to 'Magic' the Americans learned the gist of this decision, soon to bear fruit in the occupation of French Indo-China. In consequence of the American (and British and Dutch) freezing of Japanese assets as a result of this occupation, oil supplies to the Japanese effectively dried up as from 26 July, which meant that the Japanese Navy's oil stocks would last no more than eighteen months and the Army's no more than a year. If Japan were ever to go to war, she must therefore do so as soon as preparations could be completed, and certainly not later than December 1941, before the monsoon broke in South-East Asia.[74]

At another imperial conference on 6 September it was decided that preparations for war must be completed by early October. If the negotiations in Washington had failed by then to achieve an acceptable settlement, Japan would take the decision whether or not to go to war. On 1–2 November, after General Tojo had replaced Prince Konoye, the Japanese leadership gave the diplomats an extension until the end of November to bring off an agreement, after which date, in the event of failure, war with the United States would automatically follow.

Meanwhile the Japanese armed forces had completed their studies of alternative strategic plans of conquest by mid-August, and had drawn up detailed operational plans and timetables for the chosen strategy by the end of September. These called for the destruction of the United States Fleet at Pearl Harbor by a surprise carrier strike without declaration of war, followed by the occupation of Hong Kong, the Philippines, Malaya and Burma, and the Dutch East Indies. The conquest of Malaya was to be completed within a hundred days of the outbreak of war. This war plan was finally approved on 5 November 1941. Two days later all Japanese forces were warned that the approximate date for the opening of hostilities would be 8 December (East Longitude Time). Landings in southern Siam (at Singora) and northern Malaya were timed for the small hours of the 8th (local time).[75]

Clearly the arrival in mid-November of one modern British battleship could have no effect either on the now predetermined course of Japan's national policy or on her war plans. Churchill's and Eden's shot in the dark could do nothing but waste the ammunition.

Mystery surrounds the reasons for choosing Sir Tom Phillips, hitherto VCNS, and without sea-going experience in the present war, to command the so-called Eastern Fleet, really only a squadron, and for the destination finally given him, because no documentation survives.[76] It is clear, however, that Phillips was Pound's enthusiastic personal choice; his protégé indeed. In a private letter of 25 February 1943, Pound wrote: 'As you know, he was extremely junior for the appointment of Commander-in-Chief, Eastern Fleet, and I daresay I have been criticised for sending him there. However, I have never for a moment regretted it as he was fitted for high command . . .'[77] Since the outbreak of war in 1939 Phillips – short, stocky, dynamic, full of terrier-like aggression – had acted as the third member with Pound and Churchill in the triumvirate of back-seat drivers continually prodding flag officers at sea to show more fight and enterprise; and the First Sea Lord had found him personally and professionally the most congenial of subordinates. As Pound expressed it in a letter to Lady Phillips in January 1943:

He had such a wonderful combination of brilliance, soundness of judgment and drive, and he was head and shoulders above his contemporaries . . .

If fate had decided to take him from us I am glad that we had been able to show what trust and confidence we placed in him by making him C-in-C, Eastern Fleet, with a double step in rank – which I think is unique in the service.[78]

The Prime Minister (who had also found Phillips's eagerness for offensive action congenial, although they had clashed over the Greek adventure) happily agreed to the proposed appointment.[79] Now, after more than two years spent navigating a desk, Phillips was commanding a 'fleet' thus far consisting of one battleship and two destroyers, with Cape Town as his immediate destination. This given destination accorded with the Defence Committee's endorsement on 20 October of the First Sea Lord's suggestion that the *Prince of Wales* should be sent there in the first instance, when a further decision could be taken as to whether or not she should go on to Singapore – almost certainly a tactic on the part of that wily old badger Pound to delay a final commitment to sending her to the Far East until and unless it could no longer be avoided. Nevertheless, the very next day the Assistant Chief of Naval Staff (Foreign) informed all naval authorities on behalf of the Admiralty: '*Prince of Wales*, wearing the flag of Admiral Sir Tom Phillips, C-in-C, Eastern Fleet, and escorted by *Electra* and *Express* will leave UK shortly for Singapore.'[80]

No intervening order has been found in the records to explain this discrepancy in the stated destinations. It may simply be that since the entire debate about British strategy in the Far East had revolved round Singapore, it was taken for granted by the naval staff and by Phillips himself that this was to be his ultimate destination unless the mission was specifically aborted at Cape Town.[81] To thicken the mystery, however, the Prime Minister in a note to the First Sea Lord on 1 November made use of the phrases 'If it is decided that *Prince of Wales* should go on to Singapore . . .' and 'assuming we go on eastward', while Pound in reply next day wrote: 'It is my intention to review the situation generally just before *Prince of Wales* reaches the Cape.'[82]

Was Churchill merely being unusually tactful in his phrasing in view of the First Sea Lord's past opposition to the whole idea? Did Pound himself really believe that he still enjoyed any choice? On 6 November, while *Prince of Wales* was still steaming south towards Cape Town on a sunny voyage complete with the traditional larkings of a 'crossing-the-line' ceremony, Phillips signalled the Admiralty about his future movements after reaching the Cape. He suggested that he should remain there from 17 to 24 November for maximum publicity, but that if 'early arrival at Singapore be more important than publicity, this time could be reduced to 48 hours at some inconvenience to engine room and store departments . . .'[83] He added: 'If earliest arrival at Singapore is desired, HMS *Prince of Wales* could arrive there 12 days after leaving the Cape, destroyers being left behind when clear of the Cape area . . . If destroyers remain in company throughout, HMS *Prince of Wales* could arrive Singapore 19 days after leaving Cape.' That Phillips by now – if not earlier – took it as read that Singapore was his destination is clinched by his proposal in this same signal that *Repulse* should arrive there in company with the flagship.[84]

Two days later he confirmed his proposal that only the battlecruiser *Repulse*, and not the old 'R' class battleship *Revenge*, should go to Singapore as well as *Prince of Wales*, on the score that a force of two capital ships 'should cause the Japanese concern but should be regarded by her more as a raiding force than as attempt to form a line of battle against her', whereas the addition of one 'R' class ship 'might give the impression that we are trying to form a line of battle, but could only spare 3 ships, thus encouraging Japan'. He thought it best for *Revenge* to remain in the Indian Ocean until joined by *Royal Sovereign* and *Ramillies*, when all three could come on to Singapore in January 1942.[85]

On 11 November the Joint Intelligence Committee took note of the recent American Sigint disclosure that Japan had fixed 25 November as the deadline for a successful outcome of the Washington talks. It appeared, therefore, that her final decision for peace or war was only a fortnight away. In the light of this Intelligence the Admiralty on this same day, 11 November, signalled to the Simonstown naval base at the Cape that the urgency of arrival at Singapore 'necessitates stay of *Prince of Wales* being as short as possible over 48 hours . . .'[86] and to Phillips: 'As it has been necessary for political reasons to announce the strengthening of our forces in the Eastern area, it is considered undesirable for capital ships to arrive at Singapore without destroyer screen . . .' and that therefore *Prince of Wales* and *Repulse* were to proceed to Singapore as soon as practicable after arrival of the destroyers in Ceylon.[87]

By the time Phillips reached Cape Town on 16 November (the day after the Japanese Southern Army had ordered its formations to make final preparations for the attack on Malaya), it had been therefore settled that he was to take only two capital ships and a meagre destroyer screen on to Singapore; an unbalanced force and therefore an unsound strategic decision. It had been intended to give him the aircraft carrier *Indomitable*, the only such ship available (*Ark Royal* had been sunk on 14 November, squeezing the Navy's resources in carriers still further, see pp. 372–4), but – mercifully for her and her crew – she had run aground off Jamaica. Nor were there any cruisers available after the Mediterranean Fleet's fearsome losses. The unfortunate Phillips and his ships' companies were now finally committed to a naval nonsense in pursuance of a futile political gesture.

For the ships' companies of *Prince of Wales* and her escorting destroyers themselves the two-day stay at Cape Town afforded the opportunity for a run ashore in a city hardly touched by war. 'We were given a wonderful reception,' remembered one officer in *Prince of Wales*. 'Officers were entertained privately, functions arranged for the men and an orgy of shopping indulged in.'[88] No record has been found to indicate that Phillips's future movements were in fact reconsidered in London during this stay. On 18 November *Prince of Wales* set course eastward for Colombo, escorted for part of the voyage by a squadron of huge albatrosses which 'came within yards to glide uncannily along beside the quarter deck, with no visible life except the blink of a yellow eye as they returned our stares'.[89]

On arrival at Colombo on 28 November Phillips flew ahead to Singapore to confer with service chiefs there. HMS *Prince of Wales* then rendezvoused south of Ceylon with the *Repulse* and her two escorting destroyers (which had already arrived at Trincomalee) for the final run to Singapore. About noon on 2 December the island appeared as a smudge on the port bow. Two great ships steamed past Singapore city's straggling waterfront, round the island to the eastern entrance of the Johore Strait lying between the powerful coastal batteries in their steel casemates, and up the strait, no wider than a river, between the swampy, jungly shorelines of Johore and Singapore island. In the thick, damp heat, the *Prince of Wales* secured alongside in the naval dockyard, while the *Repulse* came to a buoy nearby; and a reception party of service and civilian grandees processed up the brow of the flagship to welcome this 'fleet' that after two decades of talk had at last arrived at Singapore.

By this time it had become clear in London that the despatch of the *Prince of Wales* and *Repulse* was not after all acting as an effective political deterrent to Japan, and that, as the First Sea Lord had feared all along, the ships now faced real operational dangers. On 1 December 1941 (it was the day the Japanese forces were told that the decision for war had been taken) the First Sea Lord personally signalled Phillips:

You and I are in agreement that C-in-C, E.F., should normally be afloat. It is possible, however, that during the present period of uncertainty whilst conferences are in progress you might consider it desirable to send *Prince of Wales* and/or *Repulse* away from Singapore in order that the uncertainty of their whereabouts would discomfort the Japs.

Under these circumstances you might find it necessary to hoist your flag on shore temporarily.[90]

Two days later (and one day after the Japanese had confirmed the date of their attack for 8 December, East Longitude Time), came another worried personal signal from the First Sea Lord, this time conveying Intelligence that Japanese submarines were heading south from Saigon, probably to watch Singapore. He required Phillips to consider two alternatives: one, ask Admiral Hart (the C-in-C of the US Asiatic Fleet at Manila) to send eight US destroyers to Singapore on a visit so that they would be available 'if the balloon goes up'; and, two, 'To get *Prince of Wales* and/or *Repulse* away from Singapore to the Eastward'.[91]

The same day Phillips replied to Pound's first signal, explaining why the First Sea Lord's suggestions could not be immediately acted upon:

It has been necessary to put in hand retubing of distiller of HMS *Prince of Wales* today 3rd December. Work should be completed in 7 days and distiller at maximum 72 hours notice during work. Ship capable of proceeding for 48 hours on reserve feed tanks.

I intend to send HMS *Repulse*, HMAS *Vampire* and HMS *Tenedos* on short visit to Port Darwin leaving Singapore Friday 5 December.[92]

While this work was carried out, the *Prince of Wales* was dry-docked so that her bottom could be scraped free of barnacles. These were hardly the best conditions for bringing the ship's company to a peak of fighting efficiency. 'The immediate effect,' recollected one officer, 'sitting as we were in a reflecting cauldron of baking concrete, was of terrific, damp, enervating heat.'[93] The heat was especially sapping on men entirely unacclimatised to it. While the *Repulse* and her escort of destroyers steamed towards Darwin, over 2,000 miles distant, and the ship's company of the *Prince of Wales* stewed in sweat-soaked cotton rig, Phillips himself flew to Manila to confer with Admiral Hart. Hart consented to move one destroyer division to Singapore on the outbreak of a war, but otherwise the two Cs-in-C did not go beyond agreeing such general principles as that the British battlefleet based on Singapore should act as a striking force against Japanese movements in the China Sea, the Dutch East Indies or through the Malay barrier; that the joint British–Dutch–American cruiser force (USS *Houston* and

Marblehead, HMS *Cornwall*, HNLMS *Java*) should be based on the Dutch East Indies, eastern Borneo and Darwin to cover convoys in that region; and that HMAS *Australia* or *Canberra*, and HMAS *Perth* and HMNZS *Leander* should protect trade in Australasian waters.[94] Details of such cooperation were to be worked out by the two staffs.

But the most astonishing decision taken by the two admirals, in view of the history of the Singapore base and the strategic purpose it had always been supposed to fulfil, was (as Phillips reported to the First Sea Lord) that Singapore was unsuitable as a main base for future offensive operations; that Manila was the only possible alternative; and that measures were in hand to enable the British Eastern Fleet (once fully assembled) to move there by 1 April 1942.[95]

On 3 December – far, far too late to be of any help to British policy or strategy – Britain had at last obtained from the United States (by word of the President) an assurance that America would furnish armed support if British or Dutch possessions in the Far East came under attack.[96]

On 6 December two large convoys escorted by Japanese warships were sighted by a RAF Hudson from Khota Baru in northern Malaya on a westerly course off the southern tip of Indo-China, prompting the Admiralty to request the C-in-C, Eastern Fleet, to report what action would be possible if it became apparent that these convoys were heading for Siam, Malaya, Borneo or the Dutch East Indies. Phillips replied that if the relative strength of the enemy force permitted, he would attempt to attack it by night or day; if the British squadron were inferior in strength, he would attempt a raid, and the air forces would attack with bombs and torpedoes in conjunction with the surface forces.[97]

The *Repulse* was now hastily recalled, arriving back at Singapore at 1600 on 7 December (local time) to find the naval base abuzz with rumour of Japanese convoys and the C-in-C's visit to Manila. An electricity of expectancy enlivened the ships' companies that evening as they sweated below or stood about on deck in the stillness of the evening. Lights still shone out across the water, despite a supposed 'brown out' to reduce their brilliance. It hardly mattered: the island was illuminated almost to the light of day by the vast white disc of a tropical moon.

In the small hours the alarm rattles sounded and over the tannoy came the bugle call of 'Repel Aircraft'. In both heavy ships, men piled out of bunks and hammocks, grabbed tin hats and gas masks and swarmed to their Action Stations. At around 0400 on 8 December (local time), searchlights picked up seventeen aircraft flying towards the base at about 10,000 feet after having bombed Singapore and its airfields; and the Eastern Fleet fired its first salvoes in anger – from the 5.25-inch high-angle secondary armament of the *Prince of Wales* in her dry dock down to Bofors guns, the tracer of which drooped away well below the unscathed Japanese formation as it swung eastwards and disappeared. A member of a 2-pounder pom-pom crew in the *Repulse* was to record: 'It was not an impressive display of fire control discipline and a terrible waste of ammunition.'[98] Later the ship's commander broadcast over the tannoy that the aircraft had indeed been Japanese, that a Japanese carrier force had struck at the US Fleet in Pearl Harbor, that the Japanese Army was at this moment landing in northern Malaya, and that, together with the United States, Britain was at war with Japan.[99]

In the gun room of the *Prince of Wales* that forenoon, recorded another eyewitness, breakfast 'was a sombre meal'.[100] For the buck which had been fumbled, dodged or passed by the politicians for twenty years had finally stopped there with Admiral Sir Tom Phillips and his two capital ships and his four destroyers.

At 0800 on 8 December (local time) Admiral Phillips officially took over command of all HM ships in the Far East from Vice-Admiral Sir Geoffrey Layton, C-in-C, China. Layton's four 'D' class cruisers (4,850 tons displacement; launched towards the end of the Great War) were at sea on trade protection duties, and in any case unfit to serve with a battle squadron. At 1230 Phillips – having already visited RAF headquarters to discuss air support with Air Marshal Pulford – held a conference in the flagship about future operations. Present were his Chief of Staff, Rear-Admiral A. F. E. Palliser, tall and lanky in contrast to his C-in-C, 'the little Napoleon' as some dubbed Phillips; the Captain of the Fleet, Captain L. H. Bell; the commanding officers of *Prince of Wales* (Captain J. C. Leach) and *Repulse* (Captain W. G. Tennant); and staff officers. They confronted a gruesome dilemma, for the assumptions underlying the despatch of their ships to Singapore had now been blown away by the Japanese, who *had* ventured to attack America and Britain together, who *had* already mounted a major invasion of Malaya. Moreover, the other, implicit, assumption that if the worst came to the worst Britain could count on the powerful US Fleet in the Pacific had also been blown away, for the Japanese strike on Pearl Harbor had sunk four battleships, badly damaged two others, and inflicted some damage on two more. Although by sheer good fortune the two US carriers currently stationed at Pearl Harbor had been at sea and so escaped, the balance of seapower had banged down heavily in Japan's favour, and the rich lands of European empire in the East now lay open to Japanese expeditionary forces.

Since it would now be pointless to vanish among the islands exercising vague menaces, as originally proposed by Churchill, Phillips's obvious objective must be the Japanese transports pouring troops ashore at Singora (in Siam) and Khota Baru, where already the British defence was crumbling and the airfield in danger. Everyone in the cabin of the *Prince of Wales* that forenoon was well aware that in northern Malaya and its airfields lay the essential key to the survival of Singapore itself. What were Phillips's chances of pouncing on these transports and destroying them? The Japanese naval forces were estimated at one modernised old battleship (probably the *Kongo*), seven cruisers (three of them 8-inch gun) and twenty destroyers. In fact the forces in the Gulf of Siam itself numbered eight cruisers (five 8-inch, two 5.5-inch), fourteen destroyers and twelve submarines, while in support off Indo-China lay two battleships, two more 8-inch cruisers and ten destroyers.[101] Thus though Phillips had no cruisers and was outnumbered five to one in destroyers (even on British estimates), he could at least assume, though wrongly, that *Prince of Wales* and *Repulse* could comfortably outmatch a *Kongo*.

The real puzzle for Phillips and his captains and staff that morning lay in Japanese air power, about the strength and efficiency of which little was known. According to the Naval Staff History 'reports on the capability of Japanese air personnel had for a number of years been consistently adverse, and may have tended to discount the possibility of their delivering a heavy scale of attack at long range'.[102] Sir Dudley Pound himself acknowledged after the event: 'I think we all underestimated the efficiency of the Japanese air forces, and certainly did not realise the long ranges at which they could operate.'[103] In the Mediterranean and British home waters no torpedo or dive-bombing attacks had been made on ships at a range greater than 200 miles from shore airfields; and it was over 300 miles to Singora and Khota Baru from the fields in southern Indo-China. It is known (though no detailed account of the C-in-C's conference survives) that Phillips expressed anxiety about going to sea without enough destroyers to screen his heavy ships and when there was considerable doubt as to whether the RAF would be able to provide the fighter cover he had asked for. Nevertheless he decided that he must carry out a sortie against the Japanese transports in view of the desperate need to defeat the landings in southern Siam and northern Malaya. Calculating that, given fighter support and surprise, his two heavy ships would have a good chance of 'smashing the Japanese forces' at Singora and Khota Baru, Phillips told his captains that he proposed to attack those forces shortly after dawn on 10 December.[104]

The Commander-in-Chief's plan, according to Captain Bell, Captain of the Fleet, was

> to detach the destroyers, which he considered very vulnerable to air attack, at midnight on 9th/10th December, and make a high speed descent on Singora with the heavy ships, relying on surprise and the speed of the battleships' attack to avoid damage. He calculated that the Japanese aircraft would not be carrying anti-ship bombs and torpedoes, and his force would only have to deal with hastily organised bombers from Indo-China during its retirement.[105]

Thus was the decision taken that 'Force Z' (as Phillips's present nucleus of an Eastern Fleet was designated) would seek out and engage the enemy. Yet the Japanese air forces in southern Indo-China actually numbered 99 bombers, 39 fighters and six reconnaissance aircraft; the bombers' crews highly trained in the attack of ships.[106] Taking these aircraft and the numerically powerful Japanese surface and submarine forces together, 'it will be seen,' comments the Naval Staff History, 'that Admiral Phillips's chance of carrying out his raid without being brought to action by very superior forces was slender in the extreme'.[107]

At 1735 on 8 December (local time) *Repulse* 'slipped from her buoy, "pointed ship" and slowly gathered way saluting the flagship as we passed her,' recalled one of her officers. 'The thunderous vibration of the ship's propellers while turning slowed to a more rhythmic beat as we steamed down the channel to the sea, following astern of the destroyers *Vampire* and *Tenedos*. The two other destroyers of our screen, *Electra* and *Express*, were already at sea, waiting for us outside the boom. *The Prince of Wales* followed astern of us.'[108] At 1830 Force Z passed the boom and the flagship took station ahead of *Repulse*. The two ships' lack of practice of working in company soon revealed itself in difficulties in keeping station: 'The tropical night closed in quickly and the weather began to deteriorate with heavy rain squalls, which made station-keeping difficult. The faint stern light of the flagship was just visible above the pale scut of her wake, and the broad zig-zag which the force was carrying out did not make things easier.'[109]

Admiral Phillips had chosen to steer to his objective by a wide evasive detour – at first east-north-east until he cleared the Anamba Islands, and then at 0400 on 9 December altering to the north, zig-zagging at 17 knots. He had now briefed his ships' companies as to the purpose of the sortie in a long explanatory signal. He hoped, he told them, 'to surprise the enemy shortly after sunrise tomorrow Wednesday':

> We may have the luck to try our metal against the old Japanese battlecruiser *Kongo* or against some Japanese cruisers and destroyers ... We are sure to get some useful practice with the HA [high-angle anti-aircraft] armament. Whatever we meet I want to finish quickly and so get well to the eastward before the Japanese can mass too formidable a scale of attack against us, so shoot to sink![110]

Yet by this time, as Force Z ran north through a grey day of rain squalls and mist patches, Phillips knew that he would enjoy no fighter cover during his strike, and also that he faced a formidable air threat. For just before he sailed he had been told that it was doubtful whether after all the Royal Air Force could fly fighters over the Singora area on 10 December. This grim news had been confirmed by a signal received at 0125 on the 9th from his Chief of Staff (ashore at Singapore): 'Fighter protection on Wednesday 10th will not, repeat not, be possible.' Palliser added: 'Japanese have large bomber forces based Southern Indo-China and possibly also in Thailand.'[111] Khota Baru airfield had already been evacuated and the British grip on other northern airfields was slipping. In actual fact, Air Marshal Pulford was evacuating his few surviving aircraft from all the northern air bases. Nevertheless, despite Palliser's signal Phillips decided that he would still carry out his intended operation on the morrow – provided he was not spotted by Japanese aircraft that day.

Why did Phillips not call off the sortie at this point? It must be guessed that he still failed to appreciate the mortal danger posed by Japanese aircraft, even though as Vice Chief of the Naval Staff for more than two years of war he could hardly have failed to be aware of the impact of airpower on surface naval operations. Yet, unlike other admirals who might have been appointed C-in-C, Eastern Fleet, instead of him, he had never personally experienced air attack on a task force at sea. Moreover, he retained his passionate pre-war belief in the battleship and the firepower of its modern anti-aircraft armament, writing in a typically pugnacious memorandum in August 1940 in favour of a large battleship construction programme:

> The fact that the capital ship is the foundation of our naval strength has always been known to the Admiralty but as a result of the experience of the past year even those misguided persons who thought of the capital

ship as dead have come to their senses and realise that without it all other forces, naval military and air, would be of no avail to us.[112]

That Phillips did not fully comprehend the peril incurred by warships while making deep sorties without fighter cover in the teeth of enemy air power is demonstrated by Admiralty signals (in which he as VCNS certainly had a hand) prodding flag officers off Norway in 1940 and in the Mediterranean in 1940–41 (especially with regard to operations off Crete) to take greater risks. Was he even aware of the shortcomings of the High Angle Control System (HACS) and the resulting inaccuracy of British ships' anti-aircraft fire? But in any case it was profoundly contrary to his own fiery, aggressive temperament to break off an operation once begun. He had been, after all, a moving spirit (with Pound and Churchill) in setting up the Court of Enquiry into Somerville's decision not to continue pursuing the Italian Fleet off Cape Spartivento in November 1940[113] (see above, p. 241). Phillips was therefore hardly likely to emulate that prudence in others which he had perceived as faint-hearted want of enterprise.

Force Z steamed on, the rain clouds and mists providing welcome cover from prying aircraft, even though at 0620 a lookout in the Australian destroyer *Vampire* thought he had spotted one for a few seconds. At 1532 Phillips received a cautionary signal from his Chief of Staff in Singapore:

> . . . Enemy apparently continuing landing in Khota Baru areas which should be fruitful as well as Singora . . . On the other hand enemy bombers on South Indo-China aerodromes are in force and undisturbed. They could attack you five hours after sighting and much depends on whether you have been seen today.[114]

It was in fact a Japanese submarine – the easternmost of a line of six picketing the southern approaches to the landing areas – that first sighted Force Z at 1340, and reported its course and speed, so enabling the Japanese C-in-C, Vice-Admiral Kondo, to order a concentration of two battleships, six heavy cruisers and numerous destroyers to intercept the British squadron. At Saigon the Japanese 22nd Air Flotilla swapped the bombs already loaded for a raid on Singapore for torpedoes and armour-piercing bombs, and took off to find the impudent British; fortunately for Phillips, on this occasion without success. Between 1700 and 1830 the protective rain clouds over Force Z gave way to a clear sky; and at 1740 lookouts in the flagship sighted three Japanese reconnaissance aircraft (in fact flown from Japanese cruisers), which, albatrosses presaging tragedy, shadowed Force Z until dusk.

Phillips now recognised that he had lost all chance of attacking the Japanese transports by surprise, and that he himself stood in danger of violent air attack within a few hours. At 2015, under cover of night, he therefore turned south for Singapore, some 500 miles distant via the east of the Anamba Islands. The morale effect on the ships' companies of this decision resembled that produced on the *Bismarck*'s crew by Lütjens's failure to pursue and finish off *Prince of Wales* after sinking the *Hood*. According to an officer in the *Repulse*, 'The ship's company did not react at all well and were very cast down as the news filtered round, but the routine and duties of the night watches took over as we steamed south at twenty knots.'[115]

Unbeknown to Phillips he was sighted again at 0210 on 10 December by another patrolling Japanese submarine. After firing five torpedoes without a hit, she reported back Force Z's position, speed and now southerly course. As a result of this report twelve aircraft took off from Saigon while it was still dark with the task of picking up and shadowing the British ships. Just before dawn there followed no fewer than 85 twin-engined Mitsubishi G3M Naval Type 96 strike aircraft (maximum range 2,722 miles at a cruising speed of 173 mph),[116] of which 34 were high-level bombers and the remainder torpedo-carriers.

At 0035 on 10 December Phillips received a report from his Chief of Staff in Singapore that the Japanese were making a fresh landing at Kuantan, deep behind the British defence in northern Malaya, and lying more than 150 miles south of Khota Baru and a similar distance south-south-west of Force Z's present position. Phillips now had to take another hard decision. Should he hold on to the south in order to make good his escape as best he might? Or should he make a distant diversion westwards in order to attack this reported new Japanese convoy? He reasoned that it lay some 400 miles distant from Japanese airfields and that the enemy would not expect Force Z to be so far south by daylight. 'On these grounds,' writes the Naval Staff History, 'the Admiral deemed surprise probable and the risk justifiable and at 0052 10th December altered course accordingly, increasing speed to 25 knots.'[117]

Phillips aimed to be off Kuantan by 0800. But at 0645, shortly after sunrise, while he was still steering westwards, the *Repulse* signalled that she had sighted an unidentified aircraft, almost certainly hostile. Nevertheless Phillips continued to hold his course for Kuantan in his riskiest gamble so far. He did so without asking for fighter cover from the airfields in southern Johore and Singapore Island, of which he was now in range, although there was no point in maintaining radio silence now that he had been spotted. Even his patron, the First Sea Lord, was to find this omission inexplicable, writing privately to Cunningham in January 1942:

> I hold most strongly that he was absolutely right to do as he did up to a certain moment, and that was when he was sighted at 6.45 in the morning by an aircraft which was presumably an enemy one. I see no reason why he should not have asked for fighter cover, but he may well have been influenced by the fact he was 400 miles from the established enemy aerodromes . . . and that all he could ask for was a standing patrol and what they could have sent him would really have been little good.[118]

Yet in Phillips's place Somerville or Cunningham would have been only too glad to see even a few friendly fighters, and would have made every effort to ensure that the Royal Air Force sent them. Was the omission another sign of Phillips's lack of personal experience of air attack at sea and a consequent under-rating of the air threat, especially from the scorned Japanese?

One eye-witness contends that a 'brain as crystal clear as Phillips's' would not make such a mistake as to neglect the need for fighter support; but that instead Phillips believed that his Chief of Staff, Palliser, was bound to appreciate that Force Z had gone to Kuantan in consequence of the signal about the Japanese landing there, and that Palliser would therefore arrange for air cover on his behalf. Phillips himself would in consequence see no need to break radio silence.[119] But Palliser, lacking the gift of second sight, had no idea that Phillips had taken Force Z to Kuantan, or even that he had abandoned his original sortie.[120]

It turned out that the report about the Japanese landings at Kuantan was wholly false; for a Walrus seaplane catapulted from *Prince of Wales* found nothing untoward, and the destroyer *Electra*, sent ahead by the C-in-C to reconnoitre the little port, reported 'complete peace'. Now Phillips was presented with the last of his choices – whether to get away to the southwards at utmost speed before time finally ran out, or to delay in order to investigate with his two capital ships a small steamer towing a string of barges which had been observed at extreme visibility at 0700 during the run-in. Phillips chose to steer east and then north after this unidentified but in any case negligible assemblage, apparently reluctant to the last to give up his sortie as having been in vain.

Shortly after 1000 came a report from the destroyer *Tenedos* (which had been detached earlier to return to Singapore) that it was being bombed by Japanese aircraft 150 miles to the south of Force Z. The barges were now forgotten as Phillips altered to the south-west and increased to 25 knots. At 1020 a shadowing aircraft was spotted from the *Prince of Wales*, and Force Z assumed the first degree of anti-aircraft readiness: tin hats, anti-flash hoods, guns manned. The sun was now shining hot and bright out of a clear sky. Almost immediately *Repulse*'s radar picked up an aircraft bearing 220°. At 1100 Phillips altered course to 135° by blue pendant signal, bringing the two heavy ships into starboard quarter line. A few minutes later nine enemy aircraft (Japanese accounts say eight) were seen approaching on the starboard bow at a height of 10,000 feet – 'small silver aircraft flying towards us in a tight line-abreast formation'.[121] Neither now nor at any time during the action did Phillips order a smoke screen. At 1113 Force Z opened fire. The Japanese aircraft flew steadily on through the winking explosions and puff-balls of smoke and down *Repulse*'s fore-and-aft line to straddle her at 1122 with an accurate stick of bombs – one near miss to starboard, seven very close to port, and a hit on the port hangar which went through and burst on the armour beneath the marines' deck, causing a fire (soon put out) on the catapult deck.[122]

This proved merely the overture. At 1142 a group of nine torpedo-bombers in close formation came in high from the port bow, used a patch of cloud on the port beam as cover in which to execute a series of turns together; and then gradually descended towards their target, stringing out into 'a loose, staggered line ahead', before launching their attack in waves of two or three in line abreast.[123] It was, the victims quickly learned, the standard tactical pattern for Japanese torpedo-bomber pilots. They executed the attack as if they simply had not noticed the fire being blasted up at them by 66 anti-aircraft guns of 4-inch calibre and upwards (including *Prince of Wales*'s sixteen 5.25-inch) and 74 2-pounder pom-poms.[124] Captain Bell, the Captain of the Fleet, later remarked that the attack was 'very well executed and the enemy in no way perturbed by our gunfire'.[125] As the Japanese aircraft made their final run-in, *Repulse*, swinging to starboard, escaped damage, but *Prince of Wales*, swinging to port, was hit aft at 1144 on the port side abreast of 'P3' and 'P4' turrets and probably by another torpedo simultaneously abaft 'Y' (main armament) turret. These were 24-inch torpedoes with warheads of 1,210-pound, as against the 18-inch torpedoes with 300-pound warheads used by the Fleet Air Arm in their strikes against *Bismarck* and Italian battleships. The results of the first two hits on *Prince of Wales*, and particularly the one aft, proved devastating, as was finally confirmed by a Royal Navy diving team which examined the wreck of the ship in 1966.[126] This torpedo blew a hole twelve feet in circumference in the hull, smashed the 'A' bracket holding the outer port propeller shaft, and bent the shaft itself. The distorted shaft revolving at full power caused thunderous vibration throughout the ship. Worse, it thrashed open watertight bulkheads and shattered fuel and oil pipes along its length. The way was clear for water pouring in through the hole blown by the torpedo in the after end of the shaft passage to reach the vitals of the ship, rendering nought all her carefully designed anti-torpedo protection. 'B' engine room, 'Y' boiler room, the port diesel generator room and the 'Y' turret action machinery room all swiftly filled with sea water.

With some 2,400 tons of water aboard, *Prince of Wales* listed 13° to port and settled by the stern until, by 1220, the port side of the quarter deck was awash despite counter-flooding. With both port propeller shafts out of action and her steering gear crippled – very similar to the damage inflicted by the Fleet Air Arm on *Bismarck* and *Vittorio Veneto* – the *Prince of Wales* now helplessly turned in a circle at 15 knots.

This was not all. The shock of the explosion and the swift inrush of water largely knocked out her electric power supply. Five out of eight dynamos quickly succumbed, four of them those supplying the after part of the ship. The damage-control parties then failed to switch power from the remaining three dynamos to the after part by means of the ring-main breakers; a failure never explained. Instead *Prince of Wales*'s damage-control parties repeated the error of the *Ark Royal*'s by devoting their energies to running emergency lines to individual points – in this case, to the forward 5.25-inch turrets. The after 5.25-inch twin turrets, having lost power, could only be slowly operated by hand. Fan-ventilation and telephone communication in the after part of the ship were similarly dead. In the dim light of emergency lamps men sweated to the point of collapse in the remaining engine and boiler rooms as temperatures climbed to 150°F. But, far more serious still, nine out of the ship's eighteen pumps had died with loss of electric power, all of them in the stricken after part of the ship. The mass of water continuing to flood through the hole made by the torpedo could not be pumped out.

At 1210, with the ship's steering motors dead, Captain Leach had hoisted 'not under control' black balls. The pride of modern British warship design and construction had been reduced by one attack by enemy aircraft to a cripple. It was the later opinion of at least one distinguished sailor that weaknesses in her design rendered her 'not

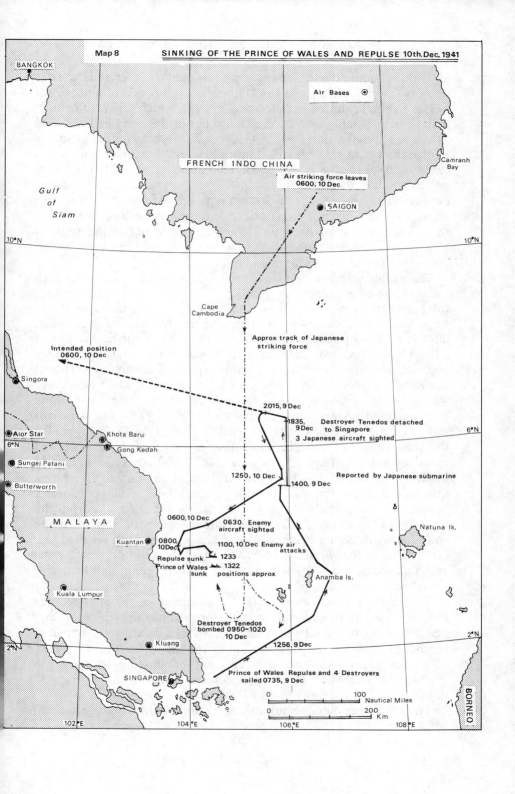

BANGKOK

Air Bases ⊙

FRENCH INDO CHINA

Air striking force leaves
0600, 10 Dec

Gulf
of
Siam

SAIGON

Camranh
Bay

10°N   10°N

Cape
Cambodia

Approx track of Japanese
striking force

Intended position
0600, 10 Dec

Singora

2015, 9 Dec

1835,
9 Dec   Destroyer Tenedos detached
to Singapore
3 Japanese aircraft sighted

6°N   6°N

Alor Star

Khota Baru

Gong Kedah

Sungei Patani

1250, 10 Dec

1400, 9 Dec   Reported by Japanese submarine

Butterworth

M A L A Y A

Natuna Is.

0600, 10 Dec

0630 Enemy
aircraft sighted

Kuantan

0800,
10 Dec

1100, 10 Dec Enemy air
attacks

Repulse sunk   1233
Prince of Wales   1322
sunk   positions approx

Anamba Is.

Kuala Lumpur

Destroyer Tenedos
bombed 0950–1020
10 Dec

2°N   2°N

Kluang

1256, 9 Dec

SINGAPORE

Prince of Wales Repulse and 4 Destroyers
sailed 0735, 9 Dec

BORNEO

| 0 | | | | | 100 | Nautical Miles |

| 0 | | | | | 200 | |
Km

102°E   104°E   106°E   108°E

as good structurally as some people thought'.[127] Certainly a later enquiry under Lord Justice Bucknill into the ship's loss found weaknesses in the layout of her electrical system, which failed to comply with principles laid down by the Controller of the Navy in 1938; and as a consequence other King George Vs were to undergo major improvements in this regard. The routing of ventilation shafts and cable ducts was also criticised (shades of *Ark Royal*). The enquiry recommended that the vulnerable stern part of the ship should be isolated by an extra, and strengthened, bulkhead. So far as her damage-control parties are concerned, there can be little doubt that they, like the rest of the ship's company, were not at the peak of efficiency simply because there had never been time to work up properly since she was commissioned.

Meanwhile Captain Tennant of the *Repulse* had sent an emergency radio signal to Singapore at 1150 that Force Z was being attacked; the only signal ever received on shore to indicate that air support was urgently needed. Six minutes after this Tennant succeeded in combing all the tracks of nine torpedoes launched by a further group of Mitsubishis, and two minutes later again *Repulse* was missed by high-level bombers while under helm at speed. Tennant now brought the *Repulse* closer to the flagship to ask if he could assist her; there was no reply. Soon it was *Repulse*'s turn again. A group of nine torpedo-bombers were spotted low on the horizon on the starboard bow. When three miles distant they split up into two sub-flights for the final run-in. The right-hand flight approached from starboard and dropped their torpedoes at a range of 2,500 yards just as the old battlecruiser began to swing to comb them. The other flight made a dummy run at the *Prince of Wales*, lying abaft the *Repulse*'s port beam, but then banked in a tight turn back to attack the *Repulse* from the port side. One torpedo struck home amidships 'with a great jarring shudder, as though a giant hand had shaken the ship', recalled one officer.[128] Yet *Repulse* still steamed at 25 knots; still her 4-inch guns and eight-barrelled pom-poms strove to put a cage of high explosive round the wounded ship.

At the same time *Prince of Wales*, incapable of manoeuvre, was attacked from starboard and hit twice forward of the breakwater and just before the bridge. Two minutes later, at 1226, she took two more torpedoes, this time aft near the 'Y' turret and abreast of 'B' turret. The consequent flooding had the effect of reducing her list to port to 3°, but the starboard outer propeller shaft was stopped, and the flagship's speed fell away to only 8 knots.

The attackers now concentrated their effort on the *Repulse*, attacking from all directions so that it was impossible for Captain Tennant to comb every track. One of the ship's officers has described what followed:

> Again the sky was blackened with shell-bursts from our fire, but the aircraft came on relentlessly to drop their torpedoes, the tracks of which could be seen heading straight for us. With the ship already committed to a swing to starboard to meet the attack from that side, the torpedoes were unavoidable and we were hit three times with only seconds separating the explosions. The first exploded near the Gunroom, the second abreast the mainmast, which shook and swayed, the heavy steel wire shrouds whipping violently. The ship seemed to stagger in her stride and I knew instinctively that this was the end, that *Repulse* was doomed.[129]

In fact she had been hit by four torpedoes, not three. Listing heavily to port *Repulse* turned 90° to starboard, which brought her fine on the *Prince of Wales*'s quarter and on a parallel course. Over the tannoy (which was fortunately still working) Captain Tennant now ordered everyone on deck:

> The decision for a commanding officer to make [he wrote later], to cease all work in the ship below, is an exceedingly difficult one, but knowing the ship's construction I felt very sure that she would not survive four torpedoes, and this was borne out, for she only remained afloat six or seven minutes after I gave the order for everyone to come on deck . . .[130]

Inexorably *Repulse* rolled to port as men scrambled up her ever more sloping decks and tilting ladders to reach the ship's side beyond the starboard rails. One survivor was to remember

> the strange sensation of walking down the ship's side just abreast of the bridge. As I reached the bilge keel the ship was still moving through the water, the ship's side was horizontal and I was standing upright . . . hundreds of men were now standing on the ship's side and bilge keel; some already sliding down the round bottom before making a last jump . . . I took my cap and shoes off and looked at the numerous heads of those who, forward of me, had already jumped, and were floating past as the ship was still moving ahead at about five knots, even though on her beam ends. It was now or never and I took a deep breath and jumped . . .[131]

Captain Tennant himself was to recollect looking over the starboard wing of the bridge when the *Repulse* had reached a 30° list and seeing the commander and two or three hundred men collecting on the starboard side of the ship:

I never saw the slightest sign of panic or ill discipline. I told them from the bridge how well they had fought the ship, and wished them good luck. The ship hung for at least a minute and a half to two minutes with a list of about 60° or 70° to port and then rolled over at 1233.[132]

The C-in-C ordered the destroyers *Electra* and *Vampire* to pick up the survivors, who numbered 42 out of 66 officers (including Tennant himself) and 754 out of 1,240 ratings. The task was accomplished without interference from Japanese aircraft, which had more important prey to kill.

The *Prince of Wales* was now steaming north at 8 knots. Soon after *Repulse* went down nine high-level bombers flew over the flagship from port to starboard, turned, and ten minutes later attacked from ahead and down the centre line as usual. From the compass platform the ship's torpedo officer watched the attack come in: 'Some guns in the forward group still going. Again steady formation of nine – waited for bombs to arrive – Captain said to Admiral "now", and we all laid flat – pattern hit ship aft.'[133] Luckily only one bomb struck home and that only caused superficial damage.

This was the last attack. But in any case *Prince of Wales* was dying minute by minute. At 1250 she signalled Singapore naval base: 'EMERGENCY. Send all available tugs . . .'[134] Eleven minutes later she repeated it. But she was beyond the succour of far-off tugs. The destroyer *Express* came alongside her starboard quarter and began to take off the wounded; the Carley floats (rafts) were launched and the gripes (bands holding the boats in place) were cast off the boom boats. By 1310 she was settling fast and listing heavily to port, a fact which impressed itself on one survivor when he 'suddenly saw that the sea was lapping at the support of the lowest pom-pom mounting. The sea near the base of the funnel! It struck me in a flash that not only was the ship heeled over but also very low in the water and the end probably a matter of minutes . . .'[135] Captain Leach now gave the order to don lifejackets and abandon ship. At 1320 *Prince of Wales* began to heel steeply, watched by appalled survivors on board the *Express*:

The great battleship continued to roll slowly away; as her upperworks dwindled and then vanished, the grey paint on her hull changed to brown as the dividing black line of her boot-topping rose out of the water, and the men at the guard rails began to climb over and slide down this treacherous slope.[136]

As they slid they had good cause to be grateful that the ship had

had her bottom scraped at Singapore, for otherwise their flesh would have been torn and ripped by a mass of barnacles.

At 1320 HMS *Prince of Wales*, flagship of Force Z and the Eastern Fleet, capsized and sank in 3° 33.6′N, 104° 28.7′E (the exact position was established when the wreck was located by HMS *Defender* in 1954), taking Admiral Sir Tom Phillips and Captain Leach with her. Ninety out of 110 officers and 1,195 out of 1,502 ratings were rescued.

To destroy Force Z had cost the Japanese only eight aircraft – another cruel demonstration of the ineffectiveness of the capital ships' anti-aircraft fire[137] and in particular of the technical shortcomings of the fire-control system adopted by the Admiralty before the war (see above, p. 47).

The *Prince of Wales* had succumbed to four, possibly six, 24-inch torpedoes with 1,210-pound warheads, and one bomb; the *Repulse* to five torpedoes and one bomb.[138] By comparison, the *Bismarck* finally sank after being hit by three 18-inch aircraft torpedoes with 300-pound warheads and five, possibly as many as twelve, 21-inch torpedoes with 600 pound warheads, together with innumerable 14-inch and 16-inch shells.[139]

As HMS *Prince of Wales* went down, eleven Royal Air Force Brewster Buffalo fighters arrived on the scene, prompting a distant group of Japanese bombers to jettison their bombs and make for home. The Buffaloes had been kept on standby at Sembawang airfield on Singapore Island to give air protection to Force Z. Tennant's emergency signal had reached the Air Operations Room at 1219, and the Buffaloes were in the air only seven minutes later. It has to be asked again: why did not the C-in-C himself ask for fighter protection – and in good time? Now the Buffaloes patrolled overhead while the survivors of both ships were being picked out of the water or from Carley floats and boats.

So all the debates about Far Eastern strategy and the dilemmas of imperial defence in Cabinet, Imperial Conference and Chiefs of Staff Committee, all the international naval conferences and naval limitation treaties, all the diplomacy in Tokyo and Washington, ended with sailors swimming for their lives in a tepid, sunlit sea 8,000 miles from England and, in the case of the survivors of the *Repulse*, giving while they did so three cheers for their captain and their lost ship.[140]

In the week following the destruction of Force Z the British defence of northern Malaya collapsed, with the consequent final loss of the airfields already abandoned by the Royal Air Force. The foundations of British strategy for securing Singapore had been swept away. The campaign now degenerated into a retreat interrupted by transient attempts at a stand by ill-equipped, under-trained and often ill-led British Imperial troops; stands in which they were swiftly out-manoeuvred and outfought by the advancing Japanese. The scenario so graphically portrayed by the Chiefs of Staff in their 1937 memorandum, of a Japanese march on Singapore overland down the west coast of Malaya, was coming true day by day. But in any case there was now no longer any point in trying to hang on to Singapore, a naval base without hope of a fleet, other than the political one of prestige. The cool strategic brain of a Moltke or a Wellington would have recognised this and begun to evacuate British civilians and military 'useless mouths' in good time, and even to thin down the fighting troops to a rearguard – not least because Burma, the eastern gate to India, was clearly the next British objective on Japan's programme of conquest, where all available forces now needed to be concentrated.

The First Sea Lord, to give credit to his common sense, warned the First Lord in a hand-written exchange of notes on 21 January 1942 (by which time the Japanese were nearing Singapore via Johore): 'If we pour reinforcements into Singapore and these reinforcements only affect the length of time Singapore can hold by a week or two we shall have squandered our reinforcements to no purpose and left Burmah [sic] very weak.'[141] For the Prime Minister, however, Singapore remained 'a famous fortress' to be defended to the last. At the turn of the year he had been instrumental in persuading the Chiefs of Staff, the Defence Committee and the Cabinet to divert major military formations into Singapore[142] – two brigades of the 17th Indian Division (previously earmarked for the defence of India) and the 18th (British) Infantry Division, then at sea en route for India. Soft and unfit for battle after a two-month voyage packed in troopships, the 18th Division arrived just in time to surrender with the rest of the garrison of the indefensible island on 15 February 1942, after the Japanese had occupied the now empty naval base and captured the water supplies on which the teeming city of Singapore depended.

Had Malaya and Singapore been evacuated in time like Greece and Crete, Britain would still have sustained – as in those cases – a disastrous defeat. As it was, by insisting that Singapore be reinforced and defended to the uttermost, Churchill inflated defeat into a highly dramatised catastrophe; a catastrophe which inflicted a mortal blow on British imperial prestige.

Now it was the turn of the Dutch East Indies and the British colony of Burma. Sir Dudley Pound had warned the First Lord in his note on 21 January the Royal Navy could do nothing to protect Burma against a Japanese seaborne expedition: 'We have not, and shall not have in the near future, sufficient naval strength in the Indian Ocean to dispute the passage of their convoys.'[143] In the event, the Japanese invaded Burma overland from Siam, and repeated their Malayan pattern of success against the British Commonwealth army defending the colony; an army weaker than need be because the formations that might have reinforced it had marched instead into Japanese prison camps in Singapore.

In the case of the Dutch East Indies the Western Allies (as they had now become by grace of Japanese aggression rather than their own will and foresight) belatedly set up a joint command (ABDA: American–British–Dutch–Australian) under a Supreme Commander, General Sir Archibald Wavell, now the British C-in-C in India. Once again the unfortunate Wavell had been handed immense responsibilities coupled with scant resources; and at this time expected to save a disintegrating situation by ad-hockery even more desperate than in the Middle East and Mediterranean in 1940–41.

The climactic moment for the naval side of this ad-hockery occurred on 27–28 February 1942, when the Dutch Admiral K. W. F. Doorman (flying his flag in the cruiser *De Ruyter*) led out the Allied 'Combined Striking Force' from Sourabaya to attack a Japanese invasion force heading for eastern Java. Doorman's command consisted of two 8-inch cruisers (HMS *Exeter* and the USS *Houston*), three 6-inch (HMAS *Perth*, HNLMS *De Ruyter* and *Java*), and the nine destroyers (HMS *Electra*, *Encounter* and *Jupiter*, HNLMS *Witte de With* and *Kortenaar*, and the USS *John D. Edwards*, *Alden*, *Ford* and *Paul Jones*). The ships lacked common signal codes and had never trained or exercised together. True to each of their naval traditions, they fought with skill and bravery as individual ships, but as a squadron were beaten by their numerically well matched but homogeneous Japanese enemy, Admiral Takagi's force of two 8-inch cruisers, two 5.5-inch cruisers and fourteen destroyers. The *Exeter* (veteran of the River Plate battle) proved the first casualty, hauling out of the line after a hit in the boiler room that brought her speed down to 15 knots. Next to go were the Dutch destroyer *Kortenaar*, torpedoed, and HMS *Electra*, repeatedly hit during an attempt by the British destroyers to attack the Japanese squadron with torpedoes. When Admiral Doorman sought to resume his attack on the Japanese convoy after dark, HMS *Jupiter* blew up, probably on a Dutch mine; and then, in a night encounter with the Japanese cruisers *Nachi* and *Haguro*, both the *De Ruyter* and the *Java* were torpedoed and sunk, Admiral Doorman going down with his flagship.

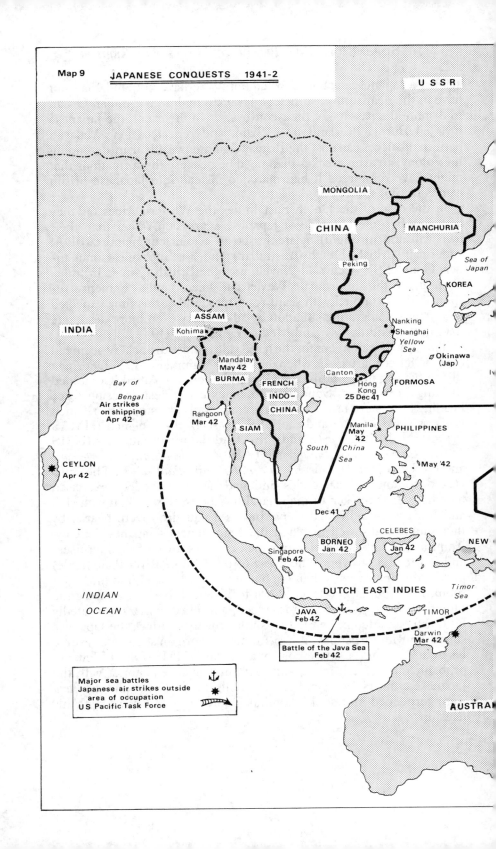

Map 9   JAPANESE CONQUESTS   1941-2

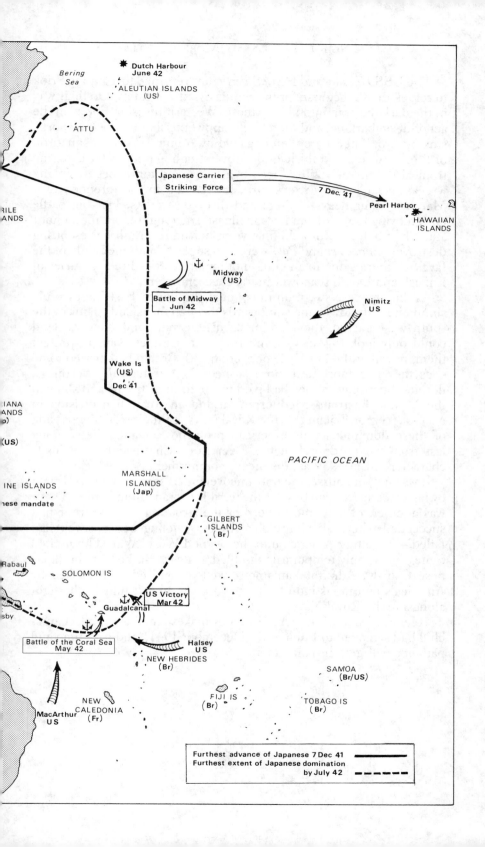

Bering
Sea

* Dutch Harbour
June 42

ALEUTIAN ISLANDS
(US)

ATTU

RILE
ANDS

Japanese Carrier
Striking Force

7 Dec. 41

Pearl Harbor

HAWAIIAN
ISLANDS

⚓ Midway
(US)

Battle of Midway
Jun 42

Nimitz
US

Wake Is
(US)

Dec 41

IANA
ANDS
p)

(US)

INE ISLANDS

nese mandate

PACIFIC OCEAN

MARSHALL
ISLANDS
(Jap)

GILBERT
ISLANDS
(Br)

Rabaul

SOLOMON IS

⚓ ✕ US Victory
Mar 42

Guadalcanal

sby

))

Battle of the Coral Sea
May 42

Halsey
US

NEW HEBRIDES
(Br)

SAMOA
(Br/US)

NEW
CALEDONIA
(Fr)

FIJI IS
(Br)

TOBAGO IS
(Br)

MacArthur
US

| Furthest advance of Japanese 7 Dec 41 | ▬▬▬▬▬ |
| Furthest extent of Japanese domination by July 42 | ▬ ▬ ▬ ▬ |

The USS *Houston* and HMAS *Perth* now returned to Tanjong Priok to refuel, then set course for the Sunda Strait and safety. On their way in the dark they ran into the Japanese 'Western Invasion Force' in the act of disembarking, and for a brief happy time shot up the transports, sinking two. They were then engaged by Admiral Kurita's squadron of three cruisers and thirteen destroyers, fighting on under a glaring tropical full moon until reduced by gunfire and torpedoes to sinking wrecks. Next it was *Exeter*'s turn, intercepted in the forenoon of 1 March by four heavy cruisers and three destroyers. Her big battle ensign flying bravely from her mainmast, she fought it out for an hour and a half before a torpedo finally put her under. Both her escorting destroyers *Encounter* and *Pope* were also sunk.[144] With the Battle of the Java Sea there came to an end – not ingloriously – three centuries of English and Dutch seapower in Far Eastern waters.

As the Japanese swept on to conquer the Dutch East Indies while simultaneously advancing southwards through the island chains of the south-west Pacific, the Dominions of Australia and New Zealand could only look to America and the United States Navy to protect them, now that the imperial connection with Britain had proved to be – as they had more and more suspected – strategically worthless, despite the premium they had paid in the form of troops and ships in the Middle East and Mediterranean and an Australian division in Malaya. Yet for Britain and the Royal Navy, on their side, the passing of these dominions into American protection meant relief at long last from what Admiral of the Fleet Lord Chatfield had so justly characterised in 1939 as 'this heavy commitment'.[145]

It was not, of course, the only uncovenanted service done to Britain by Japanese aggression besides the terrible loss and humiliation. There was another, of supreme value. For the strike on Pearl Harbor had succeeded where all Churchill's tireless cajoling of Roosevelt had failed – in getting America into the Second World War. The United States Navy, only temporarily disabled at Pearl Harbor (as the Japanese C-in-C, Admiral Yamamoto, well recognised) and backed by America's enormous industrial strength, was at last fully in the fight alongside the Royal Navy.

'The accession of the United States makes amends for all,' Churchill had signalled to Eden on 12 December 1941, 'and with time and patience will give certain victory.'[146]

PART
III

THE LONG VOYAGE HOME

14

'If We Lose the War at Sea, We Lose the War'

From the outbreak of war in 1939 to the end of April 1942 (when Japan largely attained her planned perimeter of conquest and incidentally sank an additional two British cruisers and a carrier in the Indian Ocean: see below, pp. 863–4) the Royal Navy had lost five capital ships, equal to a third of its original strength; from then on to the end of the war with Japan in August 1945, none. In fleet aircraft carriers the figures were four sunk by the end of April 1942, but only one during the rest of the war; in cruisers sixteen and twelve; in destroyers 78 and 55; and in submarines 44 and 30. Only in corvettes (the new type of escort vessel coming into service from mid-1940 onwards) and fleet minesweepers were the Royal Navy's losses heavier from the beginning of May 1942 till August 1945 than from the outbreak of war to the end of April 1942.[1]

These stark figures demonstrate a truth easily forgotten – that, with one outstanding exception, the worst of the Royal Navy's war was over before either the British Army or the Royal Air Force had got their acts together and begun to undertake operations on a grand scale.

In the case of the Royal Air Force, its single major contribution to the war, even if an historic one, so far lay in Fighter Command's victory in the Battle of Britain. Despite the personal courage of its pilots and the willingness of at least two of its leaders, Air Chief Marshals Sir Frederick Bowhill (AOC-in-C, Coastal Command, until June 1941) and Sir Arthur Longmore (AOC-in-C, Middle East, until

May 1941), to participate fully in the Army's and Royal Navy's battles, the Royal Air Force had made a feeble showing in Norway, France, Greece and Crete, and not much better over the Atlantic and the central Mediterranean. It had lacked the right kind of aircraft and, just as important, the right kind of training and doctrine for effective cooperation with the other armed services. Even by spring 1942 it remained incapable of doing for the British Army what the Luftwaffe had done for the German Army, or of doing to the enemy warships what the shore-based naval Japanese air forces had done to Force Z. This is hardly surprising in view of the air staff's long-held doctrinaire belief that the overriding priority for an air force lay in the bomber offensive aimed at destroying the enemy's industrial machine and civilian morale; and the War Cabinet's understandable decision in 1940 that in Bomber Command lay Britain's only hope of defeating Germany.

To enable the necessary mass heavy bomber force to be built up in the United Kingdom all other demands on British airpower, from the Battle of the Atlantic to the Navy's and the Army's need for support in their operations in the Middle East and Far East, had been placed a poor second. Yet it was not until May 1942 that Bomber Command launched its first effective attack on a German city, the 1,000-bomber raid on Cologne. This was laid on by the new AOC-in-C, Bomber Command, Air Marshal Sir Arthur Harris, as a public relations stunt to convince doubters that the bomber, if given absolute priority of resources, could win the war. Up till then the Royal Air Force had been learning painfully by experience, firstly, that it was impossible to fulfil its pre-war intention of bombing by daylight because of the rate of loss of aircraft, and secondly, after it had turned to night bombing in 1940, that its crews, lacking electronic navigation systems like the German X-Gerät and seeking their targets only by means of astronavigation, could not even find a German city, let alone a petrol-from-coal plant or a power station. While the Royal Navy was fighting its hard-run battles in the Atlantic and the Mediterranean through 1940 and 1941, Bomber Command, the air staff's 'war winner', was largely ploughing up German fields. Only by the beginning of 1943, with new navigational aids in quantity and new operational techniques such as the Pathfinder Force, would the great bomber offensive at last really get under way, and the Royal Air Force too enter upon its time of close engagement with the enemy and of dreadful attrition.[2]

For the British Army the period 1939 to spring 1942 had been one of hectic belated expansion from a small peacetime professional force, really an imperial gendarmerie, to a mass army based on conscription and intended ultimately for continental war; a process hindered by bottlenecks in the design, development and production of equipment, especially tanks.[3] Meanwhile it had fallen to the unlucky regulars, the Territorials and the first wave of conscripts to fight unavailingly in all the disastrous campaigns of 1940–42, from Norway to Malaya. Even the British (and Commonwealth) Army's two victories, both in North Africa – Western Desert Force's over the Italians and the new 8th Army's over Rommel in November and December 1941 in the first British set-piece offensive of the war against German troops – were no more than small-scale colonial campaigns when measured in the scale of German operations in the West in 1940 and in Russia after 22 June 1941, or British operations on the Western Front in the Great War. Not until 1944 would Britain field mass land forces in a decisive campaign against a main body of the German Army.[4]

Thus in spring 1942 the great battles of the British Army and the Royal Air Force were still to come. In contrast, the Royal Navy had been engaged at full stretch in continuous operations in all the ubiquity and variety of the sea service since the very first day of the conflict. Seapower had supplied the essential, all-pervasive element in an island nation's waging of war and indeed the sustaining of its own national life. The Navy, even more than the Army, had borne the brunt of Churchill's desperate opportunist efforts during the years of defeat to hit the enemy somewhere, somehow, and so seize back the initiative which the enemy was wielding with such assurance; his efforts to keep the war aflame so that America would believe that Britain's cause was worth backing. And for want of an air force properly designed, trained and equipped for maritime operations the Navy's ships had had to be sacrificed in unequal battles against enemy airpower – in the Far East as well as the Mediterranean.

Even for the hard-pressed soldiers there had been pauses between campaigns; periods of rest and of preparation for the next battle. But the endless round of convoys in home waters, in the Atlantic, and in the Mediterranean; the extra burden of Arctic convoys to Russia from 1941 (see below chapter 23); the repeated evacuations of vanquished expeditionary forces; the fleet battles; the bombardments of enemy bases; the support of the Army's operations ashore in Norway, Crete and North Africa; the anxious hunts for German raiders; the ambushing of Italian convoys between Sicily and North Africa by cruiser and submarine; the humdrum but vital work of laying and sweeping mines; all these had denied the Royal Navy such respites.

The theme, then, of the Royal Navy's war up to the spring of 1942, if it can be called a theme, consisted in coping valiantly, cheerfully and unceasingly in all weathers with every kind of task and challenge, often more than one at a time. But henceforward the tumult of the storm was gradually to abate. Never again – with one grand exception – were the King's ships to be required to engage the enemy so closely, so continuously and so widely against such odds. For one thing, now that America had become an ally there was no longer quite the same pressure on the Prime Minister to hazard the British armed forces on hasty opportunist strokes; instead time could be taken to forge a sound long-term Anglo-American grand strategy, time also thoroughly to prepare in adequate strength joint offensive operations in pursuance of that strategy.

For another thing, the openings for Churchillian interventions had been virtually (but, as events were to show, not entirely) exhausted by the very success of German and Japanese conquest – for where now did there remain fresh Norways or Greeces or Singapores to tempt the gambler?

Above all, the fact that the Stars and Stripes now flew alongside the White Ensign was step by step – but by no means at once – to lift from the Admiralty the near-breaking strain of 1939–41 when a 'One-Power Standard' navy had had to cope alone with the triple threat. By a decision at the Washington Conference in December 1941 the Royal Navy's responsibilities were limited to the eastern half of the North and South Atlantic, the Arctic convoy routes to Russia, the Mediterranean and the Indian Ocean. The western half of the Atlantic and the entire Pacific and Far East (including Australia and New Zealand) became the responsibility of the United States Navy, to which, therefore, now fell the task of fighting the Japanese main fleets. This was not all: American warships would eventually be made available to fill the gaps in the Royal Navy's line of battle in European waters; they would participate in strength in future Allied landings in the course of the conflict with Germany and Italy.

The global war now to be jointly waged by Britain and America would, like Britain's earlier single-handed fight, be absolutely dependent on sea communications. Although America might be a continental power in scale and geographical location she was really an island writ large, a super-Britain, in the context of fighting Japan and Germany, for her armies could only engage those of her distant enemies by grace of command of the sea. In the case of Japan, herself an island seapower whose newly acquired empire also depended on maritime communications, America would be fighting a like animal, two sharks manoeuvring for the kill in clear Pacific waters. But in the case of

Nazi Germany America faced the same problem as Britain before her, that of a seapower seeking to take the offensive against a land power. Germany could not be crippled by a maritime blockade as in the Great War because her conquests had given her overland access to all the food and raw materials she needed. Leaving aside the dream entertained by British and American airmen of victory by bombing, this meant that sooner or later the German Army in the West would have to be engaged in battle and defeated.

So to engage it would entail landings on an enemy coast: it would entail expeditionary forces despatched by sea. Yet the size of assault forces that could be put ashore would be determined by the available number and capacity of landing ships and landing craft; a cramping handicap compared with the abundant road and rail links at the disposal of a continental power deploying for an offensive on an existing land front or for an invasion across a frontier. Moreover, the overall size of the whole expeditionary force – follow-up formations as well as initial assault forces – was itself determined by the available lift of troops and supply ships across the Atlantic. Here again was a throttling disadvantage compared with a continental enemy who could freely redeploy armies on the largest scale, thanks to the carrying capacity of Europe's dense transport network.

These handicaps became quickly and dismayingly apparent in discussions between the British and American Chiefs of Staff during the Washington Conference in December 1941. For the consensus was that the maximum force that could be transported across the Atlantic in 1942 by the available shipping lift would be about fifteen divisions; hopelessly inadequate even in conjunction with British divisions in the United Kingdom to take on a defending army of the size that Germany could easily deploy at will in the West. Even in 1943 the shipping lift was only likely to permit a build-up to 40 to 50 divisions; still not enough to enable the Allies to bludgeon their way from the English Channel to Berlin in the face of the likely opposition.[5]

Thus Allied global strategy and plans for theatre operations alike were dominated from the first by the question of shipping capacity and landing-craft lift, and the consequent difficult choices and hard bargains that had to be made over priorities. 'Shipping,' wrote Churchill afterwards of this time, 'was at once the stranglehold and sole foundation of our war strategy.'[6]

At the Washington Conference Roosevelt and Churchill and their assembled Chiefs of Staff and civil servants attacked with a will the problems of framing a common grand strategy and mobilising their joint resources to provide maximum shipping capacity. The circumstances and the atmosphere were very different from the Placentia meeting only four months earlier. No longer was America an arm's-length friend prudently clinging to a formal neutrality, but, with her isolationism raped by Japanese torpedoes and her neutrality sunk in the muddy eddies of Pearl Harbor, a fully-fledged ally. The conference was held during the fleeting moment when Britain's naval and military power, now nearing its apogee of expansion, broadly matched that of the United States, which had as yet hardly begun to muster its overwhelmingly greater resources, and when the British could speak with the authority of hard-earned expertise to Americans new to the game. In forging and carrying out a common grand strategy the new allies enjoyed an advantage denied to the British and French in both world wars – they spoke almost the same language, and to some extent shared a common political heritage. Perhaps most important of all, they could enjoy the same jokes. These were the lubricants that from the start enabled the formal machinery of the alliance to function, even if a few individual senior officers on both sides were to supply the occasional grit.

The British Chiefs of Staff and the Prime Minister came to the conference comprehensively prepared; the American Joint Chiefs and the President, their minds busy with the aftermath of the catastrophe at Pearl Harbor, not so. The statement of global strategy eventually agreed by the conference, 'WW1', was an amended version of a draft tabled by the British Chiefs of Staff. It confirmed the fundamental choice that had been first agreed at staff talks in February 1941 and later reaffirmed at the Atlantic Conference in August that Germany must be beaten first: '. . . notwithstanding the entry of Japan into the war, our view remains that Germany is the prime enemy and her defeat is the key to victory'.[7] The memorandum looked ahead – very much in outline – to a return of the Allied armies to the Continent of Europe in 1943 'across the Mediterranean, from Turkey into the Balkans, or by landings in Western Europe', such operations being only 'the prelude to the final assault on Germany itself'.[8] To avoid controversy the exact nature of this assault was left for the moment undefined.

Though 'WW1' was broadly enough drafted, one thing was quite clear – its implementation utterly depended on the Allies being able to retain control of the Atlantic and having enough shipping to ferry great American armies across to Britain. On this control depended too the specific Allied operation for 1942 successfully sold to the Americans by the Prime Minister in Washington – an invasion of French North Africa, in conjunction with an offensive through Tripolitania by the 8th Army. Even this invasion (codenamed 'Gymnast') would need, so calculated the Allied staffs, the transit by sea of at least six divisions, half of them American, half British.

Yet despite the conference decision that Germany must be beaten first, the demands for shipping made by the Japanese war, a war of vast ocean distances, asserted themselves from the very beginning. The conference had to accept a proposal by General Marshall, US Army Chief of Staff, to reduce the first lift of American troops to Iceland and Northern Ireland by two-thirds in order to release ships to form a January troop convoy to the Pacific theatre.[9] This kind of seepage of shipping (and later of landing craft) from the German war to the Japanese war was to recur again and again.

To carry out the Allied grand strategy that had now been agreed between the President and the Prime Minister (acting as the 'main board' of the alliance) called for a joint 'executive board'. This machinery too the Washington Conference successfully created, in the form of the 'Combined Chiefs of Staff Committee' (composed of the chiefs of staff of each armed service of both countries). The Combined Chiefs were charged with providing the political leaders with professional advice on all strategic questions during the periodic summit conferences. In between conferences they were to act as a standing body to oversee the execution of agreed Allied strategy; they were to issue directives to theatre commanders in the name of both governments. Such a degree of integration of high command authority had never before been achieved between allies – or even between Britain and the Dominions.

In spite of the transient balance of strength between Britain and the United States in December 1941, it was plain that the centre of gravity of Allied power (especially industrial) must henceforward lie in the United States; and that the permanent location of the Combined Chiefs of Staff machine must therefore be in Washington. In consequence Britain set up in Washington an outstation of her own Chiefs of Staff Committee – the British Joint Staff Mission. Its members would sit with the American Joint Chiefs of Staff as the Combined Chiefs of Staff Committee for the transaction of regular business, except at summit conferences or other occasions when the British Chiefs would be participating in person.

The British Joint Staff Mission was to be headed by Field-Marshal Sir John Dill, until 25 December 1941 the Chief of the Imperial General Staff, a man with exactly the qualities of high professional ability, personal integrity and tact needed to create a fruitful working relationship with the leaders of the American fighting services. As the personal representative of Churchill in his capacity of Minister of Defence Dill also enjoyed direct access to President Roosevelt. The senior naval member of the Joint Staff Mission, Admiral Sir Charles Little, brought the authority of a former Second Sea Lord to the task of deputising for the First Sea Lord in discussions with the US Chief of Naval Operations (Admiral Harold E. Stark until March 1942, then Admiral Ernest J. King).

The Washington Conference proved, however, unable to agree to a civil equivalent of the Joint Chiefs; that is, a joint supply board with responsibility for planning and deploying economic resources, from raw materials and munitions to shipping. Instead it settled for two committees, one in Washington and the other in London, both to advise on the allotment of all munitions resources, which were now 'deemed to be in a common pool'.[10] The conference did, though, set up in Washington a Combined Raw Materials Board and – of key importance to a maritime alliance – a Combined Shipping Adjustment Board. On the new board sat Sir Arthur Salter, Head of the British Merchant Shipping Mission, a distinguished public servant whose experience of shipping problems in wartime stretched back to 1917, and Admiral E. S. Land of the US Maritime Commission. The new Board was directed 'to adjust and concert in one harmonious policy' the work of the Ministry of War Transport and the US Maritime Commission in maximising shipping resources, also now deemed to be pooled.[11]

A depressing balance sheet of needs and resources presented itself to these new Allied bodies responsible for conducting a joint maritime global war. In the first place the Royal Navy possessed not a single modern (or modernised) capital ship in the eastern Mediterranean or Indian Ocean. One Great War veteran, HMS *Malaya*, was with Force H at Gibraltar. The brand new battleship *Duke of York*, not yet worked up, was serving in December and January as transport for the Prime Minister to and from the Washington Conference. Admiral Tovey's Home Fleet amounted to the battleships *King George V* and *Rodney*, the battlecruiser *Renown*, ten cruisers and some eighteen destroyers; a slender enough force with which to guard against possible breakouts into the Atlantic by *Scharnhorst*, *Gneisenau* and the heavy cruiser *Prinz Eugen* from Brest or by the powerful *Tirpitz*, the pocket battleship *Scheer* and the heavy cruiser *Hipper* from the Baltic; and at the same time protect Arctic convoys from sorties by the latter ships.[12]

Of the Royal Navy's five serviceable fleet carriers, one, the new *Victorious*, was with the Home Fleet, another, the elderly *Eagle*, with Force H, and the remaining three, the large modern *Indomitable* and

Formidable, and the small old *Hermes* (the first carrier in the world to be built from the keel upward, but soon to be sunk by the Japanese) were with the reconstituted Eastern Fleet and its four unmodernised 'R' class battleships based on Ceylon. Cruisers and destroyers too were scarce after their slaughter in the Mediterranean, as the First Sea Lord explained in a letter to Cunningham at the end of 1941: 'There is nothing I should like better than to send you a present of twenty or thirty destroyers and a dozen cruisers ... You know, however, how desperately hard-pressed we are in every direction, and this will account for the smallness of our presents.'[13] And in every theatre shore-based maritime air forces remained weak and ill-equipped.[14]

After Pearl Harbor the serviceable strength of the United States Navy in battleships amounted to only three, all hitherto with the Atlantic Fleet but now transferred to the Pacific Fleet. With these ships and four fleet carriers (one of these too being transferred from the Atlantic), the Americans had to confront Japan's eleven battleships and six fleet carriers; gruesome odds.

But it was in the humble escort vessel in the Atlantic, one of the essential keys to mastering the U-boat, that the Royal Navy and the US Navy suffered from the most worrying shortages. In March 1942 the two navies calculated that they were 710 short of their operational requirements (242 British and 468 American).[15]

Only the shipyards of Britain and America could put an end to this prevailing dearth of warships of almost every kind. The US Navy Department had already embarked on a vast building programme which by summer 1945 would have completed ten battleships, eighteen fleet carriers, nine light carriers and 110 escort carriers, 45 cruisers, 358 destroyers, and 504 escorts.[16] At the end of 1941 American yards were building 300 frigates alone, of which it was hoped that 200 would be delivered by the end of 1943. On the other hand the Admiralty found itself once again baulked by Britain's limited and outdated shipbuilding capability. On the day that Pound received news of the sinking of *Prince of Wales* and *Repulse* he wrote to the Prime Minister to plead that 'in the situation created by the loss of three capital ships [i.e. including *Barham*] in a fortnight, it is important to make every effort possible to speed up the completion of the *Anson* and *Howe* [of the King George V class] and grant them 1(a) priority'.[17] Churchill consented to this, but only one further battleship was to be started by Great Britain during the war, the *Vanguard*, and she did not come into service until 1946. Only two fleet carriers, *Indefatigable* and *Implacable* (laid down in February and November 1939), were building

[437]

in January 1942, and although in the middle of that year the Admiralty drew up an ambitious programme of thirteen to twenty new vessels of this class, only one, *Audacious*, was actually laid down during the war, and even she was not completed until the year after it was over.[18] In retrospect it is remarkable that Britain did not order and complete a single fleet carrier, the new arbiter of seapower, within the compass of the Second World War, for both *Implacable* and *Indefatigable* had been ordered in 1938. For the new class of escort carrier for convoy work Britain looked almost entirely to American production.[19] Of the other new class, that of light fleet carrier, four were ordered from British yards in spring 1942 and twelve more by the end of the year, but only six of them were to come into service before the end of the German war.[20]

Britain's naval shipbuilding resources, already partly diverted to ship repair work, had been pre-empted by the essential production of escort vessels. Even so, cramped shipyard layouts, antiquated methods and obstructive trade unions[21] ensured that targets here were not met. Naval tonnage of all kinds completed in 1941 came to less than four-fifths of the expected total, while only 38 destroyers had been produced by April 1942 as against the 61 forecast in July 1941.[22]

However, the balance sheet for Allied merchant shipping at the beginning of 1942 looked much more cheerful than for warships. In the first place total sinkings in the second six months of 1941 had dropped to 1,323,276 tons, less than half those of the first six months, and December sinkings in the North Atlantic from all causes were down to a mere 50,582 tons[23] – the result of the current British ability to read U-boat cyphers and so route convoys clear of wolf-pack ambushes (see above, Chapter 9). Dry-cargo ship losses in the second half of 1941 equalled an annual rate of about 2.6 million deadweight tons, which compared with projected building programmes for 1942 of 1.5 million tons in Britain and Canada and about 7 million in the United States, of which a large share was to be allotted to Britain under Lend-Lease. If – and events were soon to make their sour comment on that 'if' – losses continued through 1942 at the same rate as in the latter part of 1941, Britain would actually see an increase in available dry-cargo tonnage of about 3 million.[24] No wonder Sir Arthur Salter could comfortably assert in December 1941: 'The shipping problem as it had been posed nine months before had been solved.'[25]

Yet paradoxically the entry of the United States into the war threw a shadow over this enticing prospect, for now her own needs for shipping were to compete with Britain's. How much of those 7 million tons of new construction would she be able and willing to spare for her ally? Moreover the patterns of the two countries' requirements differed greatly. For while the United States might be a super-island in the context of conducting a maritime war, and therefore needed an immense number of ships in order to deploy her armed forces to theatres overseas and then to nourish their campaigns, she was not an oceanic *economy* like Britain, but a self-contained continental economy with consequently small economic need for merchant tonnage. By contrast Britain needed shipping first and foremost to sustain her own national life and her war production with vital imports – as well as sustain the dependent economies of the Indian Ocean area. Thus British (really Eastern Hemisphere) *economic* requirements were to compete with American (largely Western Hemisphere; the Pacific) *military* requirements. If British demands for American ships were to be fully met, it would have to be at the expense of the American armed forces and their ability to wage war.[26]

There existed a further mismatch between the shipping and ship-building patterns of the two allies. The Americans were already getting into the swing of turning out 'Liberty' ships almost like Ford cars – well-laid-out modern yards with the latest equipment assembling prefabricated sections on the flow-line principle. In consequence their production of dry-cargo ships was to exceed their losses. But British yards, with their essentially Edwardian layouts and technology, were building far fewer than Britain was losing.[27] Nevertheless, even America's net gain of construction over loss was still not enough to meet the expanding needs of her own armed forces, let alone bail out the British. Here then were conundrums enough for the Joint Shipping Adjustment Board to solve.

Nevertheless, after much patient negotiation in Washington, a working balance was achieved between these clashing needs. As it turned out, Britain was to enjoy the use of even more American tonnage in 1942 than in 1941, equal to up to a ten per cent addition to the British merchant fleet.[28] The drawback lay in that the British could never know if and when the Americans might call some of this shipping back to meet their own military needs, so leaving Britain with a shortfall she could not possibly fill from her own resources. Yet Britain offered a trade-off for American merchant ships. America's deployment of even larger forces overseas demanded troopships, and since America in peacetime had not been a leading passenger carrier, she lacked enough suitable vessels. So most of the 27,000 American troops who crossed the Atlantic to Britain in the first quarter of 1942, plus 16,500 of those who crossed the Pacific to the Far Eastern fronts, did so in ships flying the Red Ensign;[29] and this was merely the beginning of this British service.

But all this intricate, patient Anglo-American budgeting of shipping resources could be reduced to nonsense by another factor, incalculable, unpredictable – Admiral Dönitz's U-boats and Grand Admiral Raeder's surface ships.

Dönitz knew, Sir Dudley Pound knew, Churchill knew, that in the Atlantic Britain could still lose the war despite her new alliance with the United States. In the First Sea Lord's own words in March 1942, 'If we lose the war at sea, we lose the war.'[30] As his plain sailor's mind had grasped early on and never let go thereafter, the Atlantic constituted the one decisive front for Britain, in comparison to which all else – whether 'blue water' strategy in the Mediterranean, the Army's battles in the Western Desert, the Royal Air Force's vision of a bomber offensive, or that other war in defence of Empire in the Far East – was secondary and dependent. In this centrality of the Battle of the Atlantic lay, then, the true leitmotiv of the war for the Royal Navy, even if so far overlaid by all the other episodes and encounters and dramatic losses of the conflict at sea.

Up till the moment of America's entry into the war, the Battle of the Atlantic had constituted a purely defensive campaign fought to keep open Britain's lifeline. All the resources and all the effort devoted to the battle had done nothing to inflict damage in turn on Nazi Germany's capacity to wage war, since she was a continental state whose strength resided in a great army and whose economy did not depend on sea communications. The Atlantic struggle thus serves to demonstrate the comparative disadvantage suffered by Britain by virtue of being an island state and an oceanic economy.

But the advent of America as a belligerent totally transformed the strategic significance of the Atlantic. Instead of being a *voie sacrée* maintaining the garrison of a beleaguered fortress, it became the potential route – if it could be kept open – by which great American armies could be deployed in the United Kingdom alongside the British Army for the eventual invasion of Hitler's Europe. On the Atlantic struggle now turned, therefore, not just Britain's continued survival, but also ultimate victory by the Western Allies over Germany. And this is why the Atlantic constituted the one theatre where the worst of the Royal Navy's war was still to come.

At the end of 1941 the U-boat arm had suffered, in Dönitz's own words, 'a heavy defeat', forcing him to withdraw boats from the Atlantic crossings to the sea area of Gibraltar. Though Dönitz's careful investigation of possible security leaks within his command failed to discover the fact, it was the ability of Bletchley Park to read his Enigma signals traffic that had been primarily responsible for his current setback. No wonder the year went out, as Dönitz wrote, 'in an atmosphere of worry and anxiety for U-boat Command'.[31] But paradoxically the entry of the United States into the conflict (Hitler had declared war on her on 11 December, four days after Pearl Harbor) was swiftly to revive Dönitz's fortunes, for a luxuriant, unconvoyed and hitherto inviolate traffic lay open to attack right along the east coast of the United States and down into the Caribbean.

At the beginning of 1942 Dönitz commanded a total of ninety-one operational U-boats. Twenty-three of them were now in the Mediterranean, another six posted west of Gibraltar, and four off Norway. Of the remaining fifty-eight, over half lay in the dockyards under repair. This left Dönitz with only twenty-two boats in the Atlantic out of which ten or twelve were usually in transit to and from their operational cruises.[32] It is a remarkable comment on Germany's pre-war and wartime failures to appreciate the value of the U-boat as a weapon against Britain that after two and a half years of conflict Dönitz could only deploy some ten or twelve U-boats at a time in his main offensive against Allied shipping.

Dönitz himself now urged OKM (*Oberkommando der Kriegsmarine*) to release U-boats from the Mediterranean and the Gibraltar area in order to deploy the maximum strength for the massacre of the unprotected shipping in American waters in the necessarily brief period before the United States Navy established a convoy system. At first OKM refused, and Dönitz had to launch his new offensive with only five U-boats. On 2 January 1942, at his further and urgent persuasion, OKM relented and released to him seven large long-distance boats hitherto earmarked for the Mediterranean.[33] On 13 January the first U-boats arrived off the American coast to find an almost unbelievable scene of coastal towns ablaze with lights, lighthouses and lightships sweeping their helpful guiding beams, ships with undimmed navigation lights steaming along the normal peacetime routes. So began what the U-boat arm called the second 'happy time' (the first being the autumn of 1940, the opening of the first wolf-pack offensive against British convoys).

Since this second 'happy time' belongs to the history of the United States Navy rather than the Royal Navy, it only needs to be said here that the Americans had remembered nothing from the lessons of the Great War and learned nothing from the experiences of the British in the present war. They had made no preparations for quickly setting up a convoy system. Instead they believed in the old fallacy of the 'offensive' hunting group trawling the oceans for U-boats, and even in the other old fallacy of the patrolled 'safe' shipping lane along which unconvoyed vessels sailed independently but predictably, to the jubilation of U-boat commanders. For the U-boat commanders a 'happy time' it certainly was: in the first fortnight of the campaign they sank thirteen ships totalling 100,000 tons in American and Caribbean waters, often ships bound to or from Britain. In February this figure was exceeded by sinkings within the American Eastern Sea Frontier Command alone. In March the U-boats put down twenty-eight ships of 159,340 tons in the Eastern Sea Frontier and another fifteen of 92,321 tons in the Gulf and Caribbean Commands.[34] What was even worse was that oil tankers, on the cargoes of which the conduct of modern war so utterly depended, made up 57 per cent of that lost tonnage.[35]

For the Royal Navy these U-boat successes proved especially galling. Admiral Sir Percy Noble, C-in-C, Western Approaches Command, wrote to the First Sea Lord on 8 March 1942: 'Western Approaches Command find itself in the position to-day of escorting convoys safely over to the American eastern seaboard, and then having the disappointment of finding that many of the ships thus escorted are easy prey to the U-boats which have placed themselves down the American seaboard and in the Caribbean.'[36] The Admiralty did their best to help the Americans, transferring to them ten corvettes and twenty-four anti-submarine trawlers, and by training their new American crews in the techniques of anti-submarine warfare. These were services for which on 9 May Admiral Stark (now head of the US Naval Mission in London in succession to Ghormley) warmly thanked Pound, in particular paying tribute to 'the outstanding work done by the training schools'.[37]

The British also did their best to overcome American reluctance to convoy. On 19 March the First Sea Lord told the new Chief of Naval Operations and Commander-in-Chief of the United States Fleet (COMINCH), Admiral King, that 'he regarded the introduction of convoy as a matter of urgency',[38] while Churchill personally signalled Roosevelt to express his 'deep concern'.[39] The obstinate King argued that 'inadequately escorted convoys were worse than none', which, as the British official naval historian points out, was 'the exact opposite to all that our experience had taught'.[40] On 19 June General Marshall, the US Chief of Staff, wrote to Admiral King to say that losses off the American Atlantic seaboard and in the Caribbean 'now threaten our entire war effort . . .'; in fact, he went on, '. . . I am fearful that another month or two of this will so cripple our means of transport that we will be unable to bring sufficient men and planes to bear against the enemy in critical theatres to exercise a determining influence on the war'.[41]

But by this time the lessons taught perhaps more effectively by Dönitz than by Pound had sunk in, and the US Navy had come to accept that what President Wilson back in the Great War had likened to 'chasing hornets all over the farm'[42] was useless. King was able to reply to Marshall on 21 June detailing all the emergency measures that had now been taken, including a coastwise escort system since 15 May, although he acknowledged that heavy losses were still occurring outside that zone. Wrote the now belatedly enlightened King:

> But if all shipping can be brought under escort and air cover our losses will be reduced to an acceptable figure. I might say in this connection that escort is not just *one* way of handling the submarine menace; it is the *only* way that gives any promise of success. The so-called patrol and hunting operations have time and again proved futile ... [43]

The 'happy time' along America's eastern seaboard was over, as Dönitz had to admit.[44] But it still continued in the Caribbean, where in May and June 1942 his U-boats sank 148 ships totalling 752,009 tons.[45] From the end of June, however, the convoy system was introduced in the Caribbean too, with the result that, in Dönitz's words, 'it became obvious that the main effort in the U-boat war would have to be switched back to wolf-pack attacks on convoys [in the North Atlantic]'.[46]

So the relief afforded to the Royal Navy in the Atlantic by the concentration of U-boat strength on the 'happy time' off America was now coming to an end. Moreover, Dönitz was to renew his offensive against Britain's lifeline with a colossal double advantage – for whereas since the beginning of February 1942 GC and CS at Bletchley Park had lost the ability to pinpoint U-boat deployments, the German B-Dienst had been able since December 1941 to read both the main Royal Navy cypher and also the cypher for Anglo–US–Canadian signals traffic in the Atlantic.[47]

It was therefore fortunate for the Admiralty as it faced Dönitz's renewed campaign in summer 1942 that, back in February, Hitler himself had removed one of its major anxieties from the Atlantic scene: the constant threat posed from their French base at Brest by those formidable surface raiders, the fast battleships *Scharnhorst* and

Gneisenau. For at a conference with his admirals on 12 January he had directed that the two ships plus the heavy cruiser *Prinz Eugen* should return to Germany. Sadly, however, the circumstances of their homeward voyage in February cast the bleakest light on the state of British airpower over the sea and of cooperation between the Royal Navy and the Royal Air Force in the third year of the war.

The *Scharnhorst* and *Gneisenau* had put into Brest on 22 March 1941 after an Atlantic foray but, except for one short voyage by *Scharnhorst* to La Pallice in July of that year, had thereafter remained in Brest for almost eleven months, a constant worry to the Admiralty. There they had been bombed again and again, starting with an attack by Fleet Air Arm torpedo bombers on the *Gneisenau* the very day she reached Brest which inflicted widespread damage. On the night of 10 April 1941 Bomber Command had reluctantly lent a hand, and hit her in dock with three bombs, one of them heavy, which along with near-misses on the dockside further mauled her.[48] On 1 June 1941 the *Prinz Eugen* had joined the two battleships after her short-lived sortie with the *Bismarck*. A month later it was her turn to be visited by Bomber Command, when a bomb went through her port side forward, down through the armoured deck, and exploded below to destroy the switch room, amplifier and compass compartments and gunnery transmitting station. On 24 July, while *Scharnhorst* was in La Pallice during her brief excursion, fifteen bombers scored five hits on her, causing damage to a turret, engine room machinery and fuel tanks, together with flooding of compartments, the starboard propeller shaft tunnel and dynamo room. Next day she limped back to Brest, there to remain until February 1942 except for one day at sea on gunnery exercises.

Grand Admiral Raeder perceived these ships as exercising the traditional menace of 'the fleet in being', and indeed the repeated attempts by British aircraft to destroy them offers proof of how real that menace was to the British leadership. Hitler, however, had become obsessed with the belief that Norway stood in danger of Allied seaborne invasion. After protracted arguments with his Naval Staff, Hitler provisionally decided late in 1941 that the three ships must be transferred to a Norwegian base. At the conference on 12 January 1942 he confirmed this decision, but not only on the grounds of the defence of Norway, as the record of the meeting makes clear:

> He compared the situation of the Brest group with that of a patient having cancer, who was doomed unless he submitted to an operation. An operation on the other hand, even though it might have to be a drastic one, would

offer at least some hope that the patient's life might be saved. The passage of the German ships through the Channel would be such an operation and had therefore to be attempted.[49]

Thanks to 729 photo-reconnaissance missions flown over Brest between 28 March 1941 and 12 February 1942 (costing nine Spitfires)[50] and to the watch kept by local agents of the Special Intelligence Service, the British authorities were well aware that the German ships had been damaged, but they could not exactly establish their state of fitness for operations.[51] Then in December 1941 and January 1942 Ultra decrypts of Enigma signals revealed that the gun crews of all three ships had been sent to the Baltic for firing practices in the *Scheer* and *Hipper*. As early as 24 December the Admiralty was warning Coastal, Bomber and Fighter Commands that the ships might break out of Brest at any time. By the beginning of February all Intelligence sources confirmed that the three ships were putting to sea every night for steaming trials. On 3 February the Admiralty appreciated: 'most probable course of action of enemy ships now at Brest will be to break eastwards up the Channel and so to their home ports'.[52]

Both the Admiralty and the Royal Air Force began to put into operation contingency plans matured over a whole year for dealing with a German dash up the Channel and through the Straits of Dover. Air squadrons were placed at indefinite short notice, while the C-in-C, Nore (Vice-Admiral Sir George H. D'O. Lyon), was requested to reinforce Dover Command with six destroyers and up to six motor torpedo boats. The Admiralty also placed the minelayer *Manxman* under Dover's orders.[53] The Naval Staff History rightly comments that the striking power of these naval forces 'was not great'.[54] At the request of the Vice-Admiral, Dover (still Bertram Ramsay), six Swordfish of 825 Squadron, Fleet Air Arm, at Manston in Kent were placed at his disposal. Air and sea cooperation in the Dover Command area was to be coordinated by Ramsay and the AOC, No. 11 Group, Royal Air Force (who actually shared a joint headquarters with the C-in-C, Nore).

It was not easy for Ramsay to guess the German plan and frame his own preparations accordingly. He could not expect his 'slender forces'[55] to remain on standby indefinitely, and therefore must determine as best he could the likely time of German arrival in the Straits of Dover.[56] He could not depend on air reconnaissance at night to tell him of enemy whereabouts, but he could hope for sufficient warning by daylight if the weather were fair. Since it would take the

German ships some fourteen hours to pass up Channel and through the Straits and the southern North Sea, it seemed certain to Ramsay that the enemy would time their arrival in the Dover Strait during darkness within two hours of high water, making use also of the maximum hours of darkness for their passage up Channel. He could expect that shore-based radar would give first warning of the enemy's presence when the German ships were south-west of Cap Gris Nez – about one hour's steaming from the Straits. He therefore decided that his sea and air forces must be brought to immediate notice every night for a period straddling high water at Dover. However, he appreciated on 11 February that for the next three days the times of high water were 'unsuitable in that it requires a daylight passage of the Channel or a daylight passage of the Strait'.[57]

Ramsay's plan was to launch combined attacks by Swordfish and motor torpedo boats in the Straits, in order to cripple the enemy while he was within range of British shore batteries and radar; and later to launch a destroyer attack beyond the Strait to the eastward where the destroyers would have freedom of manoeuvre unconstrained by British minefields or enemy shore batteries. Meanwhile aircraft of Bomber and Coastal Commands under fighter cover were to bomb the enemy as heavily as possible. If the enemy chose to pass the Straits by night in moonlight he was to be attacked by the six Swordfish operating as a squadron, but if during a dark period, by them singly, directed on to the target by the Royal Air Force Controller at Swingate; the target itself being lit by flares dropped by Hurricanes.

These British contingency plans were flawed by one basic miscalculation. For the German naval command did not intend the three ships to approach and run through the Straits of Dover under cover of night, but in full daylight. They reckoned that it was more important to conceal the ships' departure from Brest than their passage through the Straits, on the grounds that the Home Fleet at Scapa, if promptly alerted to the squadron's sailing, would have time to intercept it off Terschelling.

The German plan was as bold and the German arrangements were as comprehensive and effective as those of 'Operation Weserübung' back in April 1940. With the fate of the *Prince of Wales* and *Repulse* much in their minds, the Germans well appreciated the risk the *Scharnhorst* and *Gneisenau* would take in steaming for about eleven daylight hours within never more than 200 miles of London and mostly within a very short flying time of British airbases. The Luftwaffe's Third Air Fleet (Field-Marshal Hugo Sperrle) in northern France was therefore to maintain a continuous patrol of sixteen fighters over the ships during the hours of daylight, with further reserves on standby to intervene if needed. Diversionary raids were to be launched on Portsmouth and on British ships just as the operation began. Three E-boat (fast torpedo boat or '*S-boot*') flotillas and three torpedo boat ('*T-boot*') flotillas were to rendezvous with the heavy ships off Cap Gris Nez and screen them during the most dangerous passage. The ships were to sail from Brest at 1930 (BST: British Summer Time – one hour ahead of Greenwich Mean Time) on 11 February, four days before the new moon, and pass the Straits of Dover at 25 knots at about 1130 the next forenoon.

At 2245 on 11 February 1942 the *Scharnhorst* (flying the flag of Admiral O. Ciliax), *Gneisenau*, *Prinz Eugen* and six destroyers cleared the Brest net barrage at 17 knots. At 2343 Ciliax increased to 27 knots on reaching the open sea. Astern of him Bomber Command was ferociously bombing the now empty berths in Brest. Neither Enigma nor other Intelligence sources had revealed to the British the actual time and date of the German departure, or that it had taken place.[58]

Nevertheless Coastal Command had that evening mounted its regular patrol over the Western English Channel of two Hudsons equipped with airborne radar, which might have been expected to pick up the German squadron. Unfortunately the radar set of the first Hudson, which was searching the Brest area itself, broke down owing to mechanical failure. Although the crew reported this at 2113 before returning to base, no relief aircraft was despatched. The radar of the second Hudson, cruising later that evening between Ushant and the Ile de Bréhat, also broke down.[59] Regrettably no one made sure that the news of these breakdowns was passed to Vice-Admiral, Dover.

Owing, then, to a double failure of British technology, Ciliax's squadron steamed eastwards through the night entirely undetected. A dawn air search by two Spitfires as far west as Fécamp missed it too. At 0700 on 12 February the air and sea forces at the disposal of Vice-Admiral, Dover, having been at fifteen minutes' alert from 0400, reverted to four hours' readiness. Meanwhile thick snow on Norfolk airfields had prevented the planned southward transfer of fourteen Fleet Air Arm Beaufort torpedo-bombers from the Scottish station of Leuchars. The German squadron steamed on unscathed for the Dover Straits at 27 knots, the big ships' clipper bows cleaving through a slight to moderate sea, the wind astern, Force 4, the visibility some three to five miles, Messerschmitt 109s circling protectively overhead. By 1000 the British command was reckoning that, as the Naval Staff History puts it, 'the prospect of an enemy break-through had become unlikely'.[60]

[447]

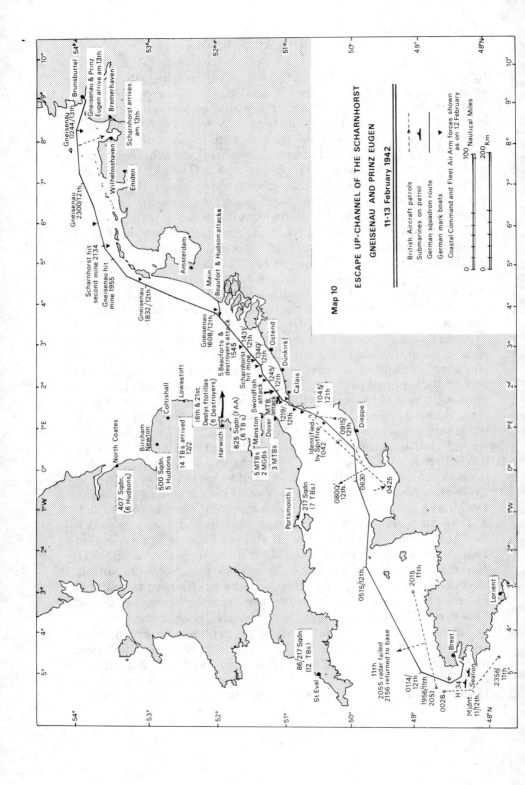

ESCAPE UP-CHANNEL OF THE SCHARNHORST GNEISENAU AND PRINZ EUGEN

11-13 February 1942

British Aircraft patrols ---→

Submarines on patrol ◄──

German squadron route ───

German mark boats ▼

Coastal Command and Fleet Air Arm forces shown as on 12 February ▼

0   100 Nautical Miles

0   200 Km

Map 10

Gneisenau & Prinz Eugen arrive am.13th

Scharnhorst arrives am 13th

Brunsbuttel

Bremerhaven

Wilhelmshaven

Emden

Gneisenau 0244/13th

Gneisenau 2300/12th

Scharnhorst hit second mine 2134

Gneisenau hit mine 1955

Gneisenau 1832/12th

Amsterdam

Main

Beaufort & Hudson attacks

Gneisenau 1608/12th

5 Beauforts & destroyers attack 1545

Scharnhorst hit mine 12th 1343/ 12th

Ostend

Dunkirk

1340/ 12th

1245/ 12th

Swordfish attack

MTB attack 1219/ 12th

Calais

Identified by Spitfire 1042

1045/ 12th

0915/ 12th

Dieppe

0800/ 12th

0630

0425

Dover attack

5 MTBs 2 MGBs 3 MTBs

Manston

825 Sqdn (FAA) (6 TBs)

16th & 21st. Desty flotillas (6 Destroyers)

Harwich

14 TBs arrived 12/2

Lowestoft

Coltishall

Bircham Newton

500 Sqdn. 5 Hudsons

407 Sqdn. (6 Hudsons)

North Coates

Portsmouth

217 Sqdn (7 TBs)

0515/12th

2015 11th

11th 2055 radar failed 2156 returned to base

St Eval

86/217 Sqdn (12 TBs)

Brest

Lorient

0114/ 12th

1956/11th 2051

0028/ 12th

H.134

Midnt J.Sealion 11/12th.

2356/ 11th

Then, at 1045, shore-based radar picked up a group of shipping 27 miles south-west of Cap Gris Nez, whereupon reconnaissance aircraft from No. 16 Group, Coastal Command, and No. 11 Group, Fighter Command, were alerted for take-off. The Swordfish crews of 825 Squadron Fleet Air Arm at Manston in Kent were brought to immediate readiness and the aircraft loaded with torpedoes set to run deep; the Beaufort torpedo-bombers of No. 16 Group, Coastal Command, likewise. At 1050 reconnaissance aircraft of Fighter Command's No. 11 Group reported sighting a cluster of 25 to 30 vessels, but made no mention of the presence of the German heavy ships or the *Prinz Eugen*. At long last at 1105 Group Captain F. V. Beamish of No. 11 Group positively identified them, reporting the fact on landing four minutes later.

But it now took nineteen minutes for this desperately urgent information to pass up through No. 11 Group to Fighter Command headquarters, across to the Admiralty and then back down to Ramsay's headquarters in Dover. And by the time that Beamish sighted the enemy ships, they were already only six miles west of Boulogne, and no more than an hour's steaming from the Dover narrows. For Ramsay and the rest of the British sea and air commands the enemy's sudden appearance came, writes the Naval Staff History with some understatement, 'as an unpleasant surprise'.[61] The British response now necessarily took the form of a scramble against time to implement the long-agreed contingency plans. At 1145 Ramsay made the first of eight emergency signals alerting the British forces to the fact that the German ships were now passing Boulogne at about 20 knots, and giving updates on their progress.[62]

At 1156 Ciliax rounded Cap Gris Nez and began to enter the Straits proper, ordering his destroyers to lay a smoke screen between him and the English coast. At 1210 British shore batteries along the famous white cliffs opened fire at maximum range. At 1245 they ceased fire, having discharged 33 rounds without scoring a hit. By now Ciliax was clear of the narrow neck between Dover and Calais.

Between 1230 and 1245 Ramsay launched simultaneous attacks with his five motor torpedo boats and the six Fleet Air Arm Swordfish. The MTB attack (led by Lieutenant-Commander E. N. Pumphrey, RN) proved another poor advertisement for British technology, this time with regard to the design and manufacture of fast motor boats, for the engines in two of them broke down, while according to Admiral Ramsay later, their best speed as well as their armaments were outclassed by those of the German E-boats.[63] For all the determination of their crews, the attempt to press home the attack to killing range was thwarted by the E-boat screen and by a well-directed fire from the German destroyers.[64] It did not help that there also occurred torpedo misfires.

The six Swordfish proved no more effective. It had been arranged that they should be protected by five squadrons of Fighter Command. At 1220 Wing-Commander J. Constable-Roberts, Air Staff Officer at Ramsay's headquarters, despatched the Swordfish because the German ships had increased to 27 knots. He was counting on the assurances of No. 11 Group, Fighter Command, that, as arranged, full fighter cover and anti-flak aircraft would be rendezvousing by now over Manston. But No. 11 Group only 'believed' that this was the case: it had in fact no accurate plot or information about the location of its aircraft, which in the event failed to turn up over Manston at 1125 as agreed.[65] At 1228 Lieutenant-Commander E. Esmonde, RN, commanding the six Swordfish of 825 Squadron, decided to fly on to attack the German ships even though only one squadron of ten Spitfires had joined him. He did so because he judged that the opportunity to attack the enemy in the Straits was so fleeting that he dare not hang about for the missing fighters. As Ramsay was to write in his report, the lack of the planned fighter cover was 'a major tragedy'.[66]

The first sub-flight of Swordfish was led by Esmonde himself, the second by Lieutenant J. C. Thompson, RN. Ten minutes out to sea from Dover they were jumped by a mass of Messerschmitt 109s and Focke-Wulf 190s which got through the outnumbered Spitfire screen and succeeded in damaging every aircraft in Esmonde's sub-flight and probably some of Thompson's as well. Undaunted, Esmonde led his squadron in towards the German squadron at around 50 feet in steady level flight, heading through the smoke and over the destroyer and E-boat screen into the winking flashes of the heavy ships' anti-aircraft fire. By this time the lower port wing of Esmonde's own Swordfish had been almost completely shot away, and yet the sturdy old biplane still flew. Some 3,000 yards from the German ships Esmonde was finally shot down by the storm of anti-aircraft fire; it is not known whether he succeeded in dropping his torpedo. He was awarded a posthumous Victoria Cross. Despite grave damage, the second Swordfish dropped its load at 3,000 yards, then crashed into the sea. Its crew were rescued by British MTBs. The third aircraft got in as close as 2,000 yards, even though the pilot (Sub-Lieutenant Rose, RN) had been badly wounded in the back, before it too crashed into the sea; the crew also to be rescued by the friendly MTBs. The second sub-flight was last seen steering a steady course for the enemy;

not one of its three aircraft survived. No British torpedo struck home.[67]

This futile attack with its tragic loss of brave men offers a bitter tactical contrast with the Japanese attacks on the *Prince of Wales* and *Repulse*. In the first place the obsolete Swordfish with their top speed of 154 mph could not compare with the twin-engined Mitsubishi G3M Navy Type 96s, with their top speed of 232 mph.[68] The belatedness of pre-war rearmament coupled with the Admiralty's and Air Ministry's peacetime neglect of maritime strike aircraft had sent Esmonde and his crews into battle against a powerful enemy squadron and swarms of enemy fighters in aircraft so slow as to render them perfect practice targets for the enemy. But Esmonde's own tactical leadership has been questioned too. Why did he elect to make a long and level approach at 50 feet when he well knew how vulnerable his sluggish aircraft were, so giving the German fighter pilots and anti-aircraft gunners an absolutely predictable aiming mark? Why did he not instead dive to the attack only at the last moment, then level out to launch torpedoes, as other Fleet Air Arm leaders had successfully done against Italian ships and he himself against the *Bismarck*? Why did he not stalk his enemy through the cloud cover, jinking and weaving as he came, like the Japanese aircraft off Kuantan? To one Fleet Air Arm veteran, Commander G. A. Rotherham, the explanation may well be that Esmonde 'believed that he was on a one-way mission. A devout Catholic, he went to confession before leaving . . .'[69]

Now it was the turn of the Royal Air Force to have a shot at sinking or crippling the German ships as they steamed up the Belgian and Dutch coasts. From 1445 to 1700, no fewer than 242 aircraft of Bomber Command took to the air in the attempt. Of this vast air fleet only 39 aircraft actually managed to locate and attack the enemy through the cloud, scoring no hits and inflicting no harm. Bomber Command lost fifteen bombers shot down and twenty damaged. Between 1540 and 1710, 28 Beaufort twin-engined torpedo bombers (the first modern British aircraft of their type, only in service since 1940: maximum speed 265 mph), together with Beaufighters and Hudsons, joined in, dropping thirteen torpedoes but making no hits. Three Beauforts were lost.

This was by no means the sum total of British airpower put up that day: Fighter Command flew 398 aircraft, of which seventeen were lost. To the destroyers of the Nore Command, operating out of Harwich to launch their own attacks on the German ships that afternoon, it seemed as if the skies above were crammed with aircraft of every shape and size – ME 109s and the occasional Beaufort at low level; Hampden and Dornier bombers and ME 110 twin-engined fighter-bombers higher up; and higher still a few four-engined Halifax heavy bombers. Also observed by the destroyer crews as taking part in this circus were Junkers 88s, Heinkel 111s, Spitfires, Wellingtons, Whirlwind fighters and Manchester twin-engined heavy bombers.[70]

While all this aerial uproar was in progress, Admiral Ciliax suffered a heart-jerking setback from another cause altogether. At 1431 his flagship struck a mine off the estuary of the River Scheldt, cutting all electric power and stopping her engines. Nevertheless her damage-control parties and engineering staff restored her to full serviceability within half an hour.[71] It was as well, because at 1517 Captain C. T. M. Pizey, RN, commanding the five destroyers from Harwich (one, HMS *Walpole*, had had to return to port with main bearing trouble), detected Ciliax's squadron by radar and steered to attack. It was now blowing hard with a heavy swell from the west, visibility about four miles, which aided the destroyers in making their approach.

At 1542 the German battleships came into sight, and Captain Pizey swung his destroyers by divisions for the final run-in. It proved yet another maritime 'charge of the Light Brigade'. The first division – *Campbell*, *Vivacious* and *Worcester* – came under accurate fire from the battleships' 11-inch main armaments, tall shell splashes straddling them again and again. Meanwhile the destroyers themselves were blazing away with their 2-pounder anti-aircraft guns at attacking German aircraft. The first division launched torpedoes at about 2,400 yards; none hit. The second division following astern – *Mackay* and *Whitshed* – launched torpedoes at 4,000 and 3,000 yards: no hits either. Meanwhile *Worcester* had been badly damaged by German fire, although she was eventually able to crawl back to Harwich.

Again unscathed, Admiral Ciliax steamed on. Pizey's gallant but vain attack offers another sour comment on the legacy of past national neglect. All his ships were of Great War design, and were completely outclassed in size (four of them some 1,000 tons displacement; two of them 1,500 tons) and armament (four with four 4-inch guns; two with five 4.7-inch) by their modern opponents, two 'Z' class destroyers of 3,600 tons and four 5.9-inch guns, and four others of 2,400 tons and five 5-inch guns.[72] Moreover, the worn-out British ships could now only steam at a maximum of 25–30 knots as against the modern German ships' designed speed of 38 knots.[73] Their normal role indeed was that of escorting coastal convoys. That they should have been called upon to try to sink the *Scharnhorst* and *Gneisenau* behind a powerful destroyer and E-boat screen was a consequence of a combination of factors: the grossly insufficient strength in destroyers with which the Royal Navy had entered the war; the loss of 107 in action since; the delays in new construction; and the necessary apportioning of scarce modern large destroyers to fleet work or ocean escort duty.

After 1700 on 12 February 1942 Admiral Ciliax steamed tranquilly north-north-east up the Dutch coast between Maas and the Texel, the crucial and most perilous part of his voyage now successfully accomplished, his ships once again under the cover of darkness. However, by an irony it was during this last lap to German ports that later that evening he sustained his worst setback, for the *Gneisenau* hit a mine off Vlieland at 1955 and the *Scharnhorst* (which had become separated) another mine in the same area at 2134; both mines having been dropped earlier by Bomber Command in its only useful contribution to the day. The *Gneisenau* suffered only minor damage and was able to steam on at 25 knots in company with *Prinz Eugen*, reaching the mouth of the Elbe at 0700 on 13 February. But the *Scharnhorst*, her engines stopped, was helplessly drifting. It was not until 2223 that her repair parties got two out of her three engines working again, and she began to limp at 12 knots towards Wilhelmshaven and safety with 1,000 tons of water sloshing about below and her turret training gear out of action.

That Bomber Command during the night of 26–27 February hit *Gneisenau* in dock at Kiel with a heavy bomb which burned her out to a useless hulk did nothing to assuage British anger and disquiet at the failure of the Royal Navy and Royal Air Force to prevent the passage of the German ships through the Channel. The cheek of it! *The Times* compared the successful Ciliax to the failed Duke of Medina Sidonia in 1588, and reckoned that this was the most mortifying affront to the pride of British seapower in home waters since the Dutch came up the Medway in 1666.[74] The government appointed a Board of Enquiry under Mr Justice Bucknill whose findings were not published until 1946;[75] and the Air Ministry requested the AOCs-in-C of its three Commands to examine the question of coordination of joint operations and make appropriate recommendations. The Bucknill Enquiry found – how could it find otherwise? – that liaison arrangements between the Royal Air Force and the Royal Navy and within each service had simply not been up to mounting a successful joint air and sea offensive operation. It noted that the training of Bomber Command, being concentrated on area bombing of German cities by night, was 'not designed for effective attack on fast-moving warships by day'.[76]

In point of fact this want of training for operations over the sea also made it even harder for Bomber Command crews to find ships in the first place and then tell friend from foe than for Coastal Command or Fleet Air Arm crews. The Harwich Force had endured some nasty moments thanks to Bomber Command during that afternoon of 12 February, and hence had good reason to be grateful for the bombers' lack of accuracy. But, to be fair, Coastal Command Beauforts also aimed a torpedo or two at the Harwich destroyers, while Fighter Command Spitfires for their part failed to locate the German squadron early in daylight on the 12th, and later, having sighted a group of ships off Cap Gris Nez, failed to identify the presence of the two battleships.

The truth is that this episode, taken as a whole, serves as an indictment of the entire British development of airpower in relation to maritime war since the founding of the Royal Air Force as an independent arm in 1918 at the expense of the old Royal Naval Air Service. On the one hand there was the under-strength and under-equipped (especially in modern strike aircraft) Coastal Command and Fleet Air Arm. On the other there was the ever-increasing force of medium and heavy bombers which, together with a powerful home fighter force, the Air Staff cherished as the foundation of its historic claim that 'airpower' was an independent entity necessarily to be wielded by central control, and capable of being switched at will from strategic bombing to operations over the sea. Yet in fact, as the passage of *Scharnhorst* and *Gneisenau* demonstrated, the belief in the all-purpose versatility of such an independent air force was fallacious, because maritime operations (and for that matter the tactical support of armies) demanded rigorous specialised training and carefully worked out tactics and integrated inter-service command and control systems.

The contrast between the sprawling organisational confusion and feeble efforts of British air operations only a few miles from the British home base itself against the two German battleships and the lethal attack on *Prince of Wales* and *Repulse* by the highly trained and specialised Japanese shore-based Naval Air Force at a range of 400 miles from advanced airfields themselves thousands of miles from Japan could not have been more glaring. How might the day of 12 February 1942 have gone if the old Royal Naval Air Service had not been abolished in 1918?

But the air staff's fallacy that airpower was an independent entity fulfilling itself through the heavy bomber had long been also exercising a just as baneful but much more dangerous effect on the Atlantic war of attrition against the U-boat. In consequence one of the two dominant themes of the Atlantic war during 1942 lay in what the First Sea Lord laconically dubbed at the time 'The Battle of the Air' – a prolonged bombardment and counter-bombardment of heavy memoranda between the Admiralty and the Air Ministry, fierce duels of debate in committee, and Jove-like – or perhaps Solomon-like – interventions by the Prime Minister.

In December 1941 total merchant shipping losses in the North *and* South Atlantic stood at a mere 56,957 tons. In July 1942, after the U-boats' 'happy time' off America and in the Caribbean had been brought to an end by convoy and Dönitz had resumed his old offensive against the main trans-Atlantic shipping route, they rose to a dreadful 513,937 tons.[77] In August the figure rose even higher to 543,920 tons, confirming that the July total was no freak; confirming too that Dönitz could now achieve devastating results even without benefit of a 'happy time'. It marked an astounding and unlooked for reversal of the position at the turn of the year when Dönitz was confessing to gloom and defeat, and the Allies were congratulating themselves that the U-boat had been largely mastered. The reversal had stemmed not from a major change in the balance of strength, armament or fighting tactics at sea, but from a victory and a defeat in the secret competition between the code-breakers of Bletchley Park and the B-Dienst for the priceless ability to read the other side's naval cyphers; the second dominant theme of the Atlantic struggle in 1942.[78]

In September 1941 B-Dienst had begun to read the main Royal Navy cypher (Naval Cypher No. 2) with an ease and speed it had not enjoyed since August 1940. In December 1941 it also began to read a special cypher (Naval Cypher No. 3) which the Admiralty had provided the previous summer for joint Allied communications in the Atlantic. Finally, in February 1942 B-Dienst completed a full reconstruction of Cypher No. 3, in which was sent most Allied signals relating to Atlantic convoy traffic. Henceforward until June 1943 and with only two short interruptions, B-Dienst was to provide Dönitz's U-boat Command with as much as 80 per cent of Allied signals about convoy movements, sometimes giving ten or twenty hours' notice of forthcoming route changes.[79] It was as if a ghostly enemy admiral were present in the Operations Room of Western Approaches Command monitoring the Allies' most secret decisions.

At almost the same moment German counter-measures made to disappear from the bunker of U-boat Command an equivalent spectral British admiral who, thanks to Ultra decrypts of the German naval

Enigma, had bent over the chart table with Dönitz during much of 1941. Although Dönitz and his experts never came to suspect that the Enigma itself had been broken, they had embarked in November 1941 on ever more elaborate coding of operational instructions to U-boats before they were even encyphered on Enigma. As the official historian of British Intelligence in the Second World War, Professor Sir Harry Hinsley, describes:

> The new system was one by which the Christian name, surname and address of an imaginary person indicated the table that was in use at any one time for encoding the large square digraphs of the [standard North Atlantic] grid. By informing the U-boats that a new address was in force, the U-boat Command could bring a new set of digraph equivalents into use at once at frequent intervals; and since it did frequently change addresses, the problem of decoding the positions given in the Enigma signal was to resist systematisation and to require continuous ad hoc research until a copy of the address book was captured from U-505 in June 1944.[80]

This made it hard enough for Bletchley Park. But then, and far worse, on 1 February 1942 U-boat Command began to make use of a fourth wheel on their Enigma machines, so immensely multiplying the complexity of the electro-mechanical encyphering; and all at once Ultra went blind. On 9 February the Tracking Room in the Admiralty Operational Intelligence Centre in its first weekly U-boat situation report since the addition of the fourth Enigma wheel acknowledged that 'since the end of January no Special Information has been available about any U-boats other than those controlled by Admiral Norway'. It went on to add: 'Inevitably the picture of Atlantic dispositions is by now out of focus and little can be said with any confidence in estimating the present and future movement of the U-boats.'[81]

Although British Intelligence had by now accumulated a vast amount of knowledge about how U-boats and U-boat Command operated, and could still draw on other sources of information such as the Secret Intelligence Service or the unaltered German Home Waters Enigma (for U-boat movements in the Bay of Biscay or off Norway), it still remained true that from now on it would be impossible for Bletchley Park and the Operational Intelligence Centre to make accurate and up-to-date plots of U-boat deployments or anticipate their tactical movements in the Atlantic. This meant that no longer could convoys be steered clear of ambushing wolf packs. It was the more worrying for the Admiralty that this crippling setback occurred

[456]

just as U-boat numbers began to rise steeply, from a daily average of 22 at sea in the Atlantic in January 1942 to 86 in August.[82]

Because Ultra had been blinded, airpower assumed an even greater, indeed decisive, importance in the Battle of the Atlantic – in the flying of protective patrols over convoys, in searching for and destroying U-boats in concert with escort ships; above all, in the form of Very Long Range (VLR) aircraft to cover the present mid-Atlantic air gap where around a third of all convoy losses occurred. And it was exactly the Admiralty's urgent need for a greater Royal Air Force effort against the U-boat, and especially for the deployment of more VLR aircraft, that fuelled the 1942 'Battle of the Air'.

'The Battle of the Air', 1942

There was, of course, no novelty in an anguished plea for more aircraft over the sea. Not only the Admiralty itself but also Air Marshal Sir Frederick Bowhill, AOC-in-C, Coastal Command, until May 1941, had constantly pressed the Air Ministry since the beginning of the war to divert more resources to the maritime war. Bowhill's successor, Air Marshal Sir Philip Joubert de la Ferté, a man whose distinguished appearance and brilliant personality (not untinged with arrogance) matched the splendour of his surname, had sent two powerful letters on 4 July 1941 to the Chief of Air Staff and on 5 September to the Air Ministry calling for Bomber Command to smash up the U-boat bases on the French Atlantic coast while they were still being built. He was crushingly snubbed by the Air Ministry, whose highest body, the Air Council, wrote to the Chief of Air Staff:

> It considered that the AOC-in-C, Coastal Command, in common with the Admiralty, had overlooked the long-term indirect contribution which the bomber offensive had made and was still making to our security at sea by attacks, not only on the main German ports, but on the German industrial effort as a whole ... The Air Ministry had accepted that the bomber force should support the naval strategy more directly when the Battle of the Atlantic was in its earlier and critical stage but there seemed no justification whatever for a return to this defensive strategy now when conditions at sea had so much improved and we were beginning to develop fully the air offensive to which we must look for winning as opposed to not losing the war.[1]

So the Todt Organisation had been left in tranquillity to complete the giant U-boat pens under their bomb-proof carapaces of reinforced concrete from which Dönitz's crews were to mount their 1942 offensive. Meanwhile all new deliveries of long-range aircraft were going to Bomber Command (to which in autumn 1941 Churchill had even suggested transferring some Coastal Command aircraft), and Coastal Command entered 1942 with only an average of 156 aircraft of all kinds available for service on any day out of a total strength of 505; a proportion that bore witness to a poor maintenance organisation, it has to be said. The Air Staff had actually even come to believe that too much of Bomber Command's effort was already being diverted from German cities to such fringe activities as attacking the *Scharnhorst* and *Gneisenau* in Brest. They itched to concentrate all their bombers on the task of, as they believed, winning the war. On 9 February 1942 (two days before these ships sailed from Brest) their case was put forward by the Secretary of State for Air, Sir Archibald Sinclair, in a memorandum entitled 'Bombing Policy'.[2] Here was the opening salvo in what the First Sea Lord would drily call 'the Battle of the Air'.

The airmen's fire was quickly returned by the First Sea Lord, who pronounced himself all in favour of the bomber offensive 'provided certain limited naval requirements are met'. He proceeded to put in orders for six and a half squadrons of Wellingtons (to be transferred from Bomber Command to Coastal Command) and for 81 American-built Flying Fortresses or Liberators to cover the mid-Atlantic air gap.[3] Since U-boats were now being built at a rate of twenty a month, the Admiralty wanted an air offensive to be mounted in the whole Bay of Biscay area by day and night, coupled with more patrols over the North Atlantic. In this regard the Admiralty noted that aircraft fitted with ASV (anti-submarine radar) and shallow-setting depth-charges with a powerful new explosive, Torpex, were at last available.

Joubert, by the nature of his job a 'navy-blue' airman, sided with the Admiralty, telling the Air Ministry on 19 February:

> . . . the prospect of Coastal Command being able to work at reasonable efficiency appeared to be becoming more and more remote. The promise of centrimetric ASV fitted Liberators had come to nothing, the one Liberator squadron was being allowed to die out and there had been a continuous change of policy with regard to this long-range aircraft.[4]

Joubert was even so blasphemous as to challenge his superiors on the fundamentals of Air Staff theology ('Theos' being the heavy bomber):

> While fully aware of the importance of the sustained bomber offensive, it

appeared to him that, if England was to survive this year, in which we were already losing shipping at a rate considerably in excess of American and British building output, some part of bomber offensive would have to be sacrificed and a long-range type such as the Lancaster diverted to the immediate threat on our Sea Communications.[5]

The Chief of Air Staff, Air Chief Marshal Sir Charles Portal, answered to the effect that the Americans would be cross if their Liberator aircraft were diverted from bombing, while he, Portal, was strongly opposed to transferring Lancasters as they were the only aircraft that could carry 8,000 lbs of bombs to Berlin.[6]

On 5 March the First Sea Lord, after much indignant internal discussion and memoranda within the Admiralty, slammed before the Cabinet Defence Committee a statement of 'Air Requirements for the Successful Prosecution of the War at Sea'. This statement, like Joubert's, went to the heart of the matter:

If we lose the war at sea we lose the war.
We lose the war at sea when we can no longer maintain those communications which are essential to us . . .[7]

The First Sea Lord went on to explain that this could happen either by 'reduction of our Merchant ship tonnage generally to such an extent that it can no longer bring us the minimum of essential supplies', or 'reduction of our Tanker tonnage to a degree which will seriously immobilise our armed forces'. In the face of the U-boat, therefore, 'we must provide the necessary shore-based aircraft for the adequate protection of our convoys and shipping'.[8] This time Pound widened the Admiralty's claims from a mere request for more airpower over the sea to a demand for control of such airpower in all theatres of war: 'If we are not to conduct the war at sea at a disadvantage we must have naval operational control of all aircraft employed on sea operations, on lines similar to those now in force with the Coastal Command in Home waters.'[9]

Moreover, he also wanted the Royal Navy to be 'intimately associated with the training in sea operations of personnel of Coastal Command aircraft'.[10] To this statement was appended another shopping list of the Admiralty's global requirements for shore-based air support, amounting to a total of 1,940 aircraft, of which 900 were needed in home waters and the Atlantic, as against Coastal Command's present strength of 519.[11]

Now it was the Air Staff's turn, through the Secretary of State for Air, to lobby the Defence Committee. In their memorandum,

'Requirements in Long-Range General Reconnaissance Aircraft'[12] they argued that

> ... our experience clearly proved that Long-Range General-Reconnaissance duties can only be usefully undertaken by aircraft fitted with A.S.V. The installation of this equipment is a lengthy process and no squadrons of Bomber Command could be modified and put into service for some months. By this time the planned expansion of Coastal Command in Long-Range G/R aircraft will already have made good the present weakness. The transfer of bomber squadrons from Bomber Command without the necessary modification would be a dispersion of our bomber resources in an attempt to contribute defensively to the control of sea communications over immense areas of ocean where the targets are uncertain, fleeting and difficult to hit ...

With tactical adroitness the memorandum did acknowledge: 'Nevertheless it is clearly encumbent on us in the Air Ministry to do our utmost to meet Admiralty requirement as expeditiously as possible ...'

Even so, and although the Air Staff had to admit that there would be no substantial improvement in Coastal Command's resources until the second half of the year, and that up to June the Command 'will be seriously under-strength in Long-Range reconnaissance aircraft',[13] it refused to transfer four Wellington squadrons from Bomber Command. In its view they were better employed over Germany. Though Coastal Command was to receive some radar-fitted flying boats, they too would only come into service between May and December. So all that the Air Staff would offer at present was a loan of one Whitley squadron (to be equipped with ASV) from Bomber Command. For the Air Staff's faith in the bomber offensive as a strategic cure-all remained unshaken:

> It remains the opinion of the Air Staff that squadrons of Bomber Command could best contribute to the weakening of the U-boat offensive by offensive action against the principal industrial areas of Germany within our range, including the main naval industries and dockyards. To divert them to an uneconomical defensive role would be unsound at any time. It would be doubly so now when we are about to launch a bombing offensive of which we have high expectations and which will enable us to deliver a heavy and concentrated blow against Germany when German morale is low and when the Russians are in great need of our assistance.[14]

The protagonists clashed in person when these papers were debated by the War Cabinet Defence Committee on 18 March,[15] Portal and

Pound arguing the toss over such matters as whether or not the Wellington had sufficient range to patrol the outer Bay of Biscay area. Portal then came to the heart of the matter – as the Air Staff perceived it:

> If the Admiralty demands were met, it would mean a considerable reduction in the strength of Bomber Command. The question was whether the war effort would be best assisted, and the maximum help to Russia given, by maintaining the maximum offensive against Germany or by diverting resources to defensive patrolling over the sea.[16]

When Portal offered the loan of two Whitley squadrons, Pound observed that two squadrons would be 'of little value';[17] he wanted a large area of the sea covered by patrols, otherwise the plan 'would fall to the ground'. After Portal had glumly remarked that this would involve 'a very great air effort', the Prime Minister intervened to say that he did not see how we could expect to patrol large areas by day and night. The only upshot of the meeting was that the Chief of Air Staff and the First Sea Lord were asked to make further proposals.[18]

By now the Army, in the person of the Chief of the Imperial General Staff, Sir Alan Brooke (who replaced Dill on Christmas Day 1941), had joined in the battle, for the Army was no less angry and anxious than the Navy about what it saw as the often ineffective and grudging air support provided by the Royal Air Force. In fact the Army and the Royal Navy were now essentially proposing that the Royal Air Force be reorganised so as to provide air forces in every theatre dedicated to land and sea operations and under military and naval control.[19] As the Chief of Air Staff bitterly pointed out in a paper on 1 April these proposals meant 'in substance if not in name the division of the Air Force into three separate services':[20] in other words, a return to the pre-1918 position.

The Chief of Air Staff now defended the present organisation of the Royal Air Force on the same grounds that the airmen of 1918 had justified its original creation – the theoretical indivisibility of airpower:

> With the help of the United States of America we are well placed to subject the Axis powers to the full rigour of an overwhelming air superiority which will be decisive in the struggle ahead. To achieve this the Royal Air Force must be held together. If we now split it up we shall at best delay victory; at worst it may elude our grasp.[21]

And again:

> The first principle of air warfare is to concentrate the maximum air

strength on whatever task may be of decisive importance at the time . . .
Only a flexible force, under commanders whose profession is air warfare,
can offer the full assistance required [by the Army and Navy] . . .[22]

The Chief of Air Staff left little doubt as to what he personally
thought constituted airpower's decisively important task, arguing that
the Army's and Navy's demands for aircraft would 'automatically
extinguish any hope of development of that Bomber offensive which
has been postulated by the British and American Chiefs of Staff as
one of the essential measures for winning the war as opposed merely
to not losing it'.[23]

These exchanges marked only the beginning of the 'Battle of the
Air', in which for the rest of 1942 each side's case was again and again
re-spliced for further use. The First Sea Lord's files for 1942 bulge
with elaborately detailed draft answers to specific points either made
by the air staff or thought likely to be made by it.[24] But at the core of
it all lay a simple strategic equation. Britain, an island seapower of
relatively small population, had not been able to engage the German
Army in the West in battle since the collapse of the Western Front in
1940. She had therefore clutched at the promise of victory through
the destruction of the German industrial economy by bombing. In
1942 Bomber Command believed itself at last ready and equipped to
achieve this. In reverse, Germany, a continental land power, had
always lacked the means directly to attack and conquer Britain, as
evidenced by the abandonment of 'Operation Sealion' in 1940. She
had therefore also resorted to an attempt to bring about the collapse
of her enemy's economy – in her case by means of the U-boat. Thus
in 1942 Germany and Britain were each pursuing the same basic
strategy against one another. The difference lay in the effectiveness
of the means the two opponents were employing.

By the beginning of 1942 Dönitz's handful of operational U-boats
had already inflicted enormous cumulative loss on British shipping
and for a period in mid-1941 caused the British government to wonder
if Britain could indeed survive (see above, Chapter 9). In 1942 his
boats, still only a fraction of the German war effort even though their
total number was now gradually rising towards 400, were sinking an
average of 450,000 tons of shipping a month in the North Atlantic,
including more oil tankers than were being built. To the British
government it seemed increasingly evident that, as things stood,
Dönitz was well on his way to achieving decisive victory in the Atlantic
and with it the collapse of the British economy. As Churchill wrote
on 24 October: 'There preys upon us as the greatest danger to the

United Nations [as the Allied countries were now collectively called], and particularly to our Island, the U-boat attack.'[25]

No such comparable peril to the German war economy was resulting from Bomber Command's efforts in 1942, even though Bomber Command and the colossal industries that supported it were engrossing a major slice of British national resources. Unkind critics pointed this out at the time – even casting doubt as to whether Bomber Command at its future point of greatest expansion could actually bring about the promised collapse of the German industrial machine. True, Lord Cherwell (the Prime Minister's personal scientific adviser, and a man whose wartime record shows him to have been more often wrong than right) was convinced that German industry would stop if the roofs were removed from workers' dwellings.[26] But in a report in April 1942 Sir Henry Tizard, a far more able scientist, demolished Cherwell's fallacious mathematical calculations and concluded that 'a policy of bombing German towns wholesale in order to destroy dwellings cannot have a decisive effect by the middle of 1943, even if all the heavy bombers and the great majority of Wellingtons produced are used primarily for this purpose'.[27]

His conclusion was endorsed by Mr Justice Singleton, appointed by the War Cabinet on 16 April 1942 to answer the question: 'What results are we likely to achieve from continuing our air attacks on Germany at the greatest possible strength during the next 6, 12 and 18 months respectively?'[28] The Judge pronounced on 20 May after pondering the evidence: 'I do not think it [the bomber offensive] ought to be regarded *as of itself* sufficient to win the war or to produce decisive results; the area is too vast for the effort we can put forth . . .'[29] In particular, he did not think that 'great results can be hoped for within six months from "air attacks on Germany at the greatest possible strength . . ."'[30] In fact post-war calculations by the British Bombing Survey Unit using German data estimated that in 1942 bombing reduced German war production by only 0.5 per cent.[31]

There was another aspect to this enormous discrepancy between the effectiveness of U-boat Command's attack on the British war economy in 1942 and Bomber Command's attack on the German war economy. On the information then available to Whitehall there was no likelihood whatsoever that Bomber Command could bring down Germany before U-boat Command brought down Britain. Thus, long before Bomber Command could mount its ultimate full-scale offensive its bombers would be, on present showing, grounded on their airfields because the U-boats in the Atlantic would have cut off their petrol supply.

None of these considerations, not even the last, were to weigh with the air staff, let alone with the new AOC-in-C of Bomber Command, Air Marshal Sir Arthur Harris, for these were men of faith, true to the gospel according to Trenchard. Naturally the reverse was true of the Admiralty, watching with something near to horror the monthly statistics (the accuracy and implications of which no one could question) of shipping losses in the Atlantic. Despite the April decision of the Chiefs of Staff that eight Liberator aircraft and four squadrons of Wellingtons and Whitleys must be lent to Coastal Command, the tonnage of merchant ships sunk in the Atlantic in May reached a staggering 585,431 tons.[32] No wonder a fresh statement of the Admiralty's case drafted on 10 May conveys a sense of near desperation:

> What the Admiralty press for now with all urgency is that:
> (a) The increased number of aircraft of the right type necessary to safeguard our vital sea communications should be provided.
> (b) The organisations of Bomber Command should be such that our bomber squadrons are capable of locating and attacking targets at sea with success.

And the First Sea Lord added a final paragraph to the draft in his own hand in pencil:

> (c) All types of aircraft which may be required to operate over the sea should receive such training as will enable them to do this with success.[33]

On 2 June Pound consulted his commanders-in-chief at the Admiralty. Afterwards Sir John Tovey, C-in-C, Home Fleet, recorded in a letter to the First Sea Lord the forthright views he had expressed at that meeting:

> ... the whole strategy of the war was governed by sea communications ... disasters had resulted and would result from our failure to protect our communications and interrupt those of the enemy. As the war progressed air co-operation had become increasingly necessary, till now the Navy could no longer carry out its much increased task without adequate air support; that support had not been forthcoming. The aircraft at the disposal of Coastal Command and of the corresponding squadrons abroad were quite inadequate to meet their commitments.[34]

Requisite air cooperation at sea meant, wrote Tovey, reducing some other air activity, and the only possible candidate lay in 'the force employed in bombing the cities of Europe':

> This force had for long enjoyed absolute priority in the design and supply of aircraft and crews and was at this time carrying out its first 1,000 bomber raids on the Ruhr. Whatever the results of the bombing of cities might be, and this was a subject of keen controversy, it could not of itself win the war, whereas the failure of our sea communications would assuredly lose it.[35]

Tovey therefore wanted Bomber Command's efforts scaled down 'enough to allow the Navy and the Army the support without which they could not play their part'. And he acidly commented: 'It was difficult to believe that the population of Cologne would notice much difference between a raid of 1,000 bombers and one by 750 . . .'[36]

Tovey concluded by reminding the First Sea Lord that he had informed the Lords Commissioners of the Admiralty that

> . . . in my opinion the situation at sea was now so grave that the time had come for a stand to be made, even if this led to Their Lordships taking the extreme step of resignation. I was supported in my contentions by Admiral of the Fleet Sir Charles Forbes and Admiral Sir Andrew Cunningham . . .[37]

Although Their Lordships were not attracted to this suggestion, it nevertheless offers proof of how deep feelings were now running in the Navy on the question of maritime airpower. Thus fortified, Pound handed a note to his fellow Chiefs of Staff at a meeting on 16 June bluntly stating that 'the present threat to our sea lines of communication, on the security of which our existence and ultimate victory depended, called for an immediate increase in the strength of the land-based air forces working with the Navy . . .'[38]

But Portal, with sublime intellectual arrogance, wrote that he was not convinced that 'the peril at sea was as great as the First Sea Lord argued'.[39] He comfortably assumed that the figures 'show that sinkings should be overtaken by new construction later this year'. Hence before a decision was taken to increase land-based air forces supporting the Navy 'our shipping position should be examined to ascertain whether our position was sufficiently serious to warrant further reduction of our bomber offensive'.[40] As it was, he found the First Sea Lord's request for more aircraft 'wholly unacceptable',[41] because in his view there was not yet sufficient evidence that the peril at sea justified what he called 'severe curtailment' of the air offensive against Germany.

He lamented that Bomber Command's operational strength had shrunk from 1,000 aircraft to 750 since the beginning of 1942 while Coastal Command's had risen from 482 to 568. It was, grumbled Portal, 'a depressing thought that after nearly three years of war so great a proportion of our effort should still be used in a defensive role (sic)'.[42]

In the absence of the Prime Minister and the CIGS in America, the Chiefs of Staff Committee chewed over the conflicting arguments again on 24 June – the month when shipping losses in the Atlantic alone reached 649,832 tons, and in all seas a truly horrifying 834,196 tons.[43] However, the Chiefs could only decide that the First Sea Lord and the Chief of Air Staff should each nominate an officer to draw up joint recommendations to the Committee on 'general policy for the employment of the air forces'.[44] These officers (Rear-Admiral E. J. P. Brind and Air Vice-Marshal J. C. Slessor, Assistant Chiefs of Naval and Air Staffs) duly reported on 2 July,[45] recommending that 54 long-range aircraft were needed for home waters, the Bay zones, the Western Approaches and for support of the Home Fleet, plus a further 72 long-range general-reconnaissance aircraft. They also recommended that two Lancaster squadrons (36 aircraft) should be transferred temporarily from Bomber Command to Coastal Command, in return for the medium bomber squadrons at present on loan.[46]

Here was essentially an endorsement of the Admiralty's case. Unsurprisingly therefore the Chief of Air Staff rejected the report out of hand. He wrote that the suggested transfer of Lancasters would only achieve results against U-boats 'at the expense of three months' work in Bomber Command'[47] where, by bombing German ports and laying mines, they would damage enemy shipping and U-boats:

I am convinced that greater value to the war effort as a whole would be obtained from these two squadrons if they remain in Bomber Command than if they are lent to Coastal Command. I am so strongly convinced of this that I regard the loss of these two squadrons to Bomber Command as unacceptable.[48]

Instead he suggested employing Bomber Command aircraft to supplement the efforts of Coastal Command by flying thirty sorties of Whitleys and twenty sorties by Lancasters over the sea each week. The Brind–Slessor report thus died the death.

On 18 July, however, the Chiefs of Staff in reporting to the War

[467]

Cabinet on the 'Provision of Aircraft for the War at Sea' seemed after all to accept the Admiralty's case:

> ... we have taken into account that the Navy is stretched to the limit and that shipping losses are dangerously high. These losses not only menace the import situation of the United Kingdom but absorb a high proportion of the productive capacity of the United Nations; they most seriously restrict our ability to nourish and reinforce our forces overseas, and also hamper dangerously our future strategy ...[49]

The Chiefs therefore agreed that Bomber Command aircraft should be used to supplement Coastal Command until that Command's strength in Liberators and Flying Fortresses had been built up to 54. Whitley training aircraft from Bomber Command would be committed to long-range anti-submarine patrols, along with some Lancasters (though still under the operational command of the AOC-in-C, Bomber Command), although the latter loan was to be less at the expense of the bomber offensive than of the far more useful activity of mine-laying at sea. Yet the Chiefs of Staff acknowledged that the number of aircraft available from Bomber Command for anti-submarine operations each week would fluctuate according to training requirements and the need to pull them back whenever 'very large-scale raids' were mounted on Germany. The Royal Navy was thus placed at the mercy of Air Marshal Sir Arthur Harris's conception of weekly operational priorities. In any event the crews of the Whitley training unit (nine aircraft) were not to prove very adept at the specialised task of U-boat hunting. All this was well short of satisfying the Navy's needs.

'The Battle of the Air' was, however, far from over. The Premier decided that the compromise proposals, though to be put in hand at once, should be discussed by the Cabinet along with a paper 'Air Against the Sea'[50] submitted by S. M. Bruce, the accredited Representative of the Australian government, who sat on occasion as a member of the British War Cabinet. At the meeting on 12 August (with Clement Attlee, the Deputy Prime Minister, in the chair, Churchill being on his way to Cairo) Bruce observed that he 'was disturbed to find that we were working on the basis of providing the minimum for the task of securing our vital communications ...'[51] He criticised the current Chiefs of Staff proposals as failing to subordinate the bomber offensive to the needs of the war at sea. But the meeting only resulted in a request to the Air Ministry for more facts and figures. All now depended on the Prime Minister descending from the clouds (quite literally, on his return from Cairo by air) to give judgment.

By this time Churchill had been got at by Air Marshal Sir Arthur Harris in a personal letter of 17 June 1942 which improperly bypassed the official chain of command. Harris was blessed with a stubborn will, high executive ability and outstanding powers of leadership. But he was so afflicted by mental tunnel vision that in regard to the wider scene of grand strategy it is fair to apply to him the epithet 'stupid'. His letter to Churchill was entirely characteristic, the pen dripping with the adrenalin of the 1,000-bomber raid on Cologne on 30 May. He assured the Prime Minister that the proper use of airpower would bring victory 'speedy and complete', and warned him against allowing that airpower to become 'inextricably implicated as a subsidiary weapon in the prosecution of vastly protracted and avoidable land and sea campaigns':[52]

> ... The success of the 1,000 Plan has proved beyond doubt in the minds of all but wilful men that we can even today dispose of a weight of attack which no country on which it is brought to bear could survive. We can bring it to bear on the vital part of Germany. It requires only the decision to concentrate it for its proper use.[53]

In Harris's thoughtful analysis Coastal Command was 'merely an obstacle to victory'.[54]

Churchill himself no longer felt quite the same enthusiasm for the heavy bomber as he had in 1940–41 when Britain stood alone and the bomber provided the only hope of ever striking directly against Germany. But although he did not now buy Harris's views in all their extravagance, he did feel a natural affinity with the pugilism innate in them and the man behind them. On 21 July, in a survey of grand strategy,[55] Churchill tolled a bell for the Admiralty's hopes:

> ... it would be a mistake to cast aside our original thought ... that the severe, ruthless bombing of Germany on an ever-increasing scale will not only cripple her war effort, including U-boat and aircraft production, but will also create conditions intolerable to the mass of the German population.
>
> It is at this point that we must observe with sorrow and alarm the woeful shrinkage of our plans for bomber expansion.[56]

He firmly placed the bomber offensive as 'second only to the largest military operations which can be conducted on the Continent' as a means of breaking the German will. He therefore called for renewed intense efforts by the Allies 'to develop during the winter and onwards ever-growing, more accurate and ever more far-ranging bomber attacks on Germany . . .'[57]

Not that he ignored the Battle of the Atlantic, so long a principal care of his. If the first main fact in the war situation lay in the 'immense power' of the German war machine, he wrote, the second lay in 'seaborne tonnage. We can only get through this year by running down our stocks heavily'; on no account must stocks be so run down as to imperil 1943. Furthermore Churchill perfectly well understood the direct relationship between the Battle of the Atlantic and the bomber offensive, acutely noting that '. . . it might be true to say that the issue of the war depends on whether Hitler's U-boat attack on Allied tonnage or the increase and application of Allied air-power reach their full fruition first'.[58]

Yet despite the clear evidence that the U-boat attack was at present well ahead in this race for full fruition, Churchill still allowed 'the Battle of the Air' to drag on without a final decision, even permitting the circulation to the War Cabinet of fundamentalist tracts by Harris and old Trenchard, the still living Messiah of strategic bombing.[59] On 17 September, however, he minuted the Secretary of State for Air on the necessity of raising Bomber Command from its present 32 operating squadrons to 50 by the end of the year – two of these to come from Coastal Command.[60]

Four days later the AOC-in-C, Coastal Command, wrote to the First Sea Lord almost despairingly about the state of the anti-submarine war.[61] U-boats now completed came to 335; those in operation to 205. Twenty-two new boats were being turned out every month, but the rate of destruction 'is not better at the moment than 6/7 a month'. Joubert pointed out that 'unless some radical change in the rate of destruction takes place we are faced with an ever increasing fleet of U-boats at sea', while on the other side of the ledger:

(i) We are losing Tankers faster than we are building them.

(ii) We are losing merchant ships at the approximate rate of building, but the immense quantities of material and valuable lives lost in the sinkings are irreplaceable.

(iii) We are unable to conduct the offensives necessary for victory at the time, and on the scale, which are desirable.

(iv) The standard of living of the people of the Allied Nations is much reduced by inability to ship required raw materials and consumption goods.[62]

The 'Battle of the Air' mounted towards another climax. On 5 October the First Sea Lord submitted to the Defence Committee the weightiest naval salvo of all, entitled 'The Needs of the Navy'.[63] He set out to prove that in all respects (and not merely in regard to airpower over the sea) the Royal Navy was playing Cinderella to the Royal Air Force's privileged ugly sister. Indeed, 'The Needs of the Navy' provides a gruesome summary of the general state of British seapower three years after the outbreak of war and two decades after the Washington Treaty. Resorting to heavy black type by way of emphasis, the First Sea Lord read the lesson:

> Since the war began, we have been struggling to build up our war production potential in men, machines and material, but daily ships are sunk with finished weapons aboard, thus losing the work of weeks, and possibly months of hundreds of workmen. The sum of such losses may cost us in equipment far more than a heavy defeat in battle . . .
> . . . we have lost a large measure of control over our sea communications. This has already had, and is having a far-reaching effect not only on the maintenance of the United Kingdom but on our ability to take the offensive . . . in fact, we have reached the point at which we are unable to carry out concurrently those operations which the present state of the war so urgently demands.

The Royal Navy had 'much less than half' the number of fleet aircraft carriers required to achieve 'the proper balance' of Britain's main naval forces, while 'another year will elapse before the proportion of obsolescent aircraft in the aircraft carriers of the Fleet is reduced to a reasonable figure'. At present, the First Sea Lord went on, the Fleet Air Arm's aircraft were almost wholly out of date: 141 Swordfish, 66 Fulmar fighters, 112 Albacores, 42 Sea Hurricanes. Of modern types, no Barracuda torpedo-bombers had yet been delivered (production delays yet again), and no Fireflies, although 54 Seafires (an adapted Spitfire) were in service.

Turning from carriers to the humble but essential escort ships, the First Sea Lord pointed out that the number available equalled only 40 per cent of those needed, 'while the minimum target figures of shore-based aircraft agreed with the Air Ministry for operations over the sea will only be met to the extent of 75 per cent by 1st November 1942'. More than that, the present Royal Air Force programme for meeting the minimum needs of the war at sea 'will not be fulfilled until the latter half of 1943'.

The Royal Navy was also, argued Pound, Cinderella in terms of manpower and industrial resources. Its personnel numbered 500,000 as of June 1942 compared with the Army's 2,428,000 and the Royal Air Force's 833,000. The industrial labour force producing for the Navy numbered 717,000 compared with 1,245,000 in the Ministry of Aircraft Production (out of the latter total, just nine per cent were producing for the Fleet Air Arm).

'The facts outlined above,' wrote the First Sea Lord, 'lead to the inevitable conclusion that the foundation upon which the whole structure of our strategy rests is in danger.'[64] He therefore urged that industrial resources be switched to the Navy, especially in regard to the production of new aircraft, and in particular that the minimum air requirements of the war at sea as agreed by the War Cabinet back in August should be met, especially in long-range aircraft and replacement of existing types with those with longer range. And he made one final, fundamental demand – that air operations over the sea should enjoy 'priority second only to the needs of the fighter defence of the United Kingdom'.[65]

Within the Admiralty, as the Naval Staff waited for the Defence Committee to give its decision on 'The Needs of the Navy', a profound gloom prevailed. The Assistant Chief of Naval Staff (Home), Rear-Admiral Brind, wrote to the First Sea Lord on 18 October that, quite apart from the forthcoming need to provide maritime air cover for convoys in transit to the invasion of French North Africa ('Operation Torch'; see below, pp. 555–6), the Battle of the Atlantic 'continues to go against us, and we have the gap between Newfoundland and Iceland in which our convoys are at the mercy of the U-boat. At the moment the main weight of the air escort work is being carried by 17 Liberators . . .'[66] He feared that the air staff's claim of priority for the bomber meant that 'we can expect no help from Bomber Command either in the offensive against submarines, the attack on blockade breakers or even in effective attack against warships . . .' Far from accepting any reduction in Coastal Command, the ACNS (H) went on, 'it is essential that our maritime aircraft should be strongly reinforced . . .'[67]

On 24 October 1942 Churchill, in his capacity as Minister of Defence, handed down in a paper entitled 'Policy for the Conduct of the War' a fresh judgment on the rival claims of the bomber offensive and the mortal struggle against the U-boat. It was not a judgment to comfort the Royal Navy; nor one which in retrospect enhances Churchill's stature as grand strategist clear-cut in decision:

There preys upon us as the greatest danger to the United Nations, and particularly to our Island, the U-boat attack. The Navy call for greater assistance from the air. I am proposing to my colleagues that we try for the present to obtain this extra assistance mainly from the United States, and that we encroach as little as possible upon our Bomber effort against Germany, which is of peculiar importance during these winter months. I have, on the contrary, asked for an increase in the Bomber effort, rising to 50 squadrons by the end of the year. Thereafter our bombing power will increase through the maturing of production. It may be that early in 1943 we shall have to damp down the Bomber offensive against Germany in order to meet the stress and peril of the U-boat war. I hope and trust not, but by then it will be possible at any rate to peg our Bomber offensive at a higher level than at present. The issue is not one of principle, but of emphasis. At present, in spite of U-boat losses, the Bomber offensive should have first place in our effort.[68]

On 30 October the Chiefs of Staff followed this up with a report on 'Anglo-American Strategy'[69] which while acknowledging the vital importance of sea communications laid the greater weight on Allied attrition of German resources and willpower. They reckoned that thanks to better accuracy and bigger bombloads strategic bombing as a means of such attrition 'is susceptible of the greatest development and holds out the most promising prospects'. They looked forward to the 'progressive destruction and dislocation of the enemy's war industrial and economic system, and undermining of his morale to a point where his capacity for armed resistance is fatally weakened . . .' The Chiefs therefore recommended that within the broad Allied strategy for eventually invading Europe the Allied bomber force 'should be expanded as rapidly as possible to a target figure of 4,000 –6,000 heavy bombers . . . by April 1944'.

This appeared to mark the Air Ministry's and the air staff's final victory over the Admiralty in the 'Battle of the Air', with all that that implied for the U-boat war. But at this point Portal committed a tactical error by putting in to the Chiefs of Staff Committee (allegedly in response to a COS request) a report[70] which spelled out in speculative statistical detail just how between 4,000 and 6,000 British and American heavy bombers could in 1944 'shatter the industrial and economic structure of Germany to a point where an Anglo-American force of reasonable strength could enter the Continent from the West'. The contribution of 58 towns to the German war effort, equalling a third of German industry, would, he asserted, be 'eliminated'. Averred the Chief of Air Staff: 'Germany is in no condition to withstand an onslaught of this character . . .'

These complacent assertions could only invite attack. This the First Sea Lord proceeded to deliver with a fearsome weight of

argumentative fire. He pointed out that the present import requirements for aviation fuel (4½ million tons for all theatres, including 1¼
million tons into the United Kingdom alone) demanded the help of
154 American tankers.[71] But the bomber programme as outlined by
Portal would require the import of another 5 million tons in 1944 into
the United Kingdom over and above the present 1¼ million. Yet,
reckoned the First Sea Lord, it was 'virtually certain' that United
States tanker building could not cope with such a load unless it was
'immensely increased'. (It should be remembered here that tanker
losses so far in 1942 had been huge, and that oil stocks of all kinds
in the United Kingdom now stood at a worryingly low level.[72]) Pound
went on to remind his colleagues of the demand for shipping space
that would also be made by the requisite imports of bombs, spares,
personnel and all kinds of equipment.

He therefore urged (just as he had in the spring) that the whole
complex issue be referred to objective scientific and technical analysis,
especially in regard to the effects of such a build-up of the bomber
force on the rest of the Allied war effort. Peevishly the Chief of Air
Staff rejected this suggestion, on the grounds that Lord Cherwell's
opinion should be good enough.

Nonetheless the 'Battle of the Air' was in flux again after all, with
the apparent unanimity of the Chiefs of Staff's decision on 30 October
in favour of priority to the bomber being now revealed as a sham. On
18 November the First Sea Lord put the Royal Navy's case yet again,
this time to the new Cabinet Anti-U-boat Committee.[73] He went
equipped with a succinct five-page brief;[74] and he made as his central
theme the need for Very Long Range aircraft to protect the North
Atlantic convoys:

> We must be able to send aircraft to any threatened Transatlantic convoys.
> Until, and even after, Auxiliary Carriers are with all convoys we need very
> long range aircraft to bridge the gap between the areas which can be
> protected by existing aircraft.
>
> Very early action is therefore required to provide these 'very long range
> aircraft'. It has been estimated that at least 40 (with the necessary backing)
> are required, divided between Newfoundland, Iceland and Northern
> Ireland.[75]

He therefore proposed:

(a) As an emergency and temporary measure comb out all resources of
the United Nations for Liberator I [range 2,400 miles] and Liberator
II [a bomber version, range 1,800 miles]. It is understood that the

latter can be converted back into Liberator I. These aircraft would not meet full requirements, but would go far towards giving the extra protection while more permanent provision is being prepared.

(b) Convert the necessary number of the most suitable bomber type into 'very long range G.R. aircraft' with an operational range of 2,500 miles with 2,000 lbs depth charge load.[76]

Pound said that the exact number of VLR aircraft could not be estimated at that stage. 'When details of the aircraft are known it can be estimated how many will be required to cover all the threatened convoys, but it is clear that the number will be small by comparison with the total production of this kind of aircraft . . .'[77] Forty VLR aircraft together with Liberator IIIs (range 1,680 miles) for 86 Squadron, Coastal Command, would enable the force available to cover North Atlantic convoys and the Bay of Biscay area to rise from the present three squadrons of Liberator IIIs to four squadrons, plus three VLR Squadrons.[78] A further squadron of LR aircraft would be wanted to escort convoys in the South-Western Approaches. Pound emphasised that 'economy in numbers of aircraft is achieved by re-equipping existing Coastal Command Squadrons with longer range aircraft. A re-equipment of Squadrons is required rather than an increase.'[79]

The First Sea Lord's brief summarises with heavy emphasis what the entire 'Battle of the Air' had been about – the switching of just 40 suitable VLR aircraft from Bomber Command to Coastal Command:

The key to the whole problem at the moment is to get at least 40 long range aircraft to re-equip selected squadrons now in Coastal Command . . . Added to this we must provide 10cm. A.S.V. for the Bay.[80]

Pound made this ultimate plea at a time when, in the words of the Assistant Chief of Naval Staff (Trade), 'our shipping position has never been tighter'.[81] In October 1942 637,833 tons of shipping had been lost in all seas and from all kinds of enemy action; of that total over 400,000 in the North and South Atlantic.[82] Since the Whitehall 'Battle of the Air' had begun in February 1942, over 4.4 million tons had been sunk in the North Atlantic alone.[83] These were the statistics of impending catastrophe.

At the meeting of the Cabinet Anti-U-boat Committee on 18 November the Chief of Air Staff at last went some way to conceding the Admiralty's case.[84] He offered to transfer 30 Halifax heavy bombers to Coastal Command to strengthen the offensive against

U-boats in transit in the outer zone of the Bay of Biscay, and to replace in December and January the Wellingtons at present patrolling the inner zone with two squadrons of more modern aircraft fitted with the Leigh Light and the new 10cm radar (see pp. 479–80, 580–2).

Yet these final concessions on the part of the Air Staff proved in the event an empty triumph for the Admiralty. For one thing, the first of the squadrons equipped with the new 10cm radar was not to come fully into service until March 1943;[85] for another, the crucial problem of the mid-Atlantic air gap remained without a solution, because at the beginning of 1943 there were still to be fewer than twenty VLR aircraft in service with Coastal Command.[86]

And meanwhile Admiral Dönitz was continuing to torpedo his way towards final victory. Over the full twelve months of 1942 his U-boats had sunk 6,266,215 tons of Allied shipping; more than 80 per cent of the Allies' total loss from all forms of enemy action of 7,790,697 tons.[87] In January 1943 imports into Britain were less than half the figure for January 1941 and nearly 42 per cent down on the figure for January 1942. In the three months November 1942 to January 1943 nearly half of Britain's consumption of raw materials – the stuff of war production – had had to come from stocks.[88] At the present rate those stocks would soon be exhausted. Then what?

At issue, then, in 'the Battle of the Air' had been nothing less than Britain's very survival. This renders it the most important single British strategic debate of the war. It is, moreover, the one case where Britain's survival was imperilled not so much by enemy action in itself as by blind folly within Britain's own leadership.

The impact of that folly on the course of the struggle out in the Atlantic was sharpened by errors in operational policy and by the shortcomings of British technology. In 1942 both Admiral Pound and Air Marshal Joubert chose to pursue an aerial version of the naval fallacy of the 'offensive' or hunting strategy against the U-boat, concentrating some two-thirds of Coastal Command's patrol effort on an attempt to find and destroy U-boats in transit across the inner and outer Bay of Biscay zones. But the so-called 'Bay offensive' proved no more than an inconvenience to Dönitz's captains. Out of 265 U-boat crossings of the Bay during the first five months of 1942 only 24 were sighted by Coastal Command, even though the boats often ran on the surface in broad daylight; and not one was sunk.[89]

In June the Leigh Light (see above, pp. 258–9), enabling an aircraft to illuminate a U-boat brilliantly at night for the final kill, at last came into service – more than a year after it had been successfully tested.

For this long delay Joubert himself was partly to blame, for when Assistant Chief of Air Staff (Radio) at the Air Ministry in 1941 he had backed the Leigh Light's rival, the Turbinlite; and then, on being appointed AOC-in-C, Coastal Command, he had returned Squadron Leader Leigh to his normal duties while development of the Turbinlite proceeded. After two months, however, Joubert realised (as he himself handsomely admitted) that he had been wrong, and that the Leigh Light was better suited to the job than the Turbinlite.[90] It was not until mid-August 1941 that Leigh resumed his development work; not until the autumn that the Air Ministry could be persuaded to approve the experimental fitting of the Leigh Light to six Wellingtons. When Joubert asked the Ministry to increase the order for Leigh Lights to 36 sets, the Whitehall desk pilots refused on the ground that the results of trials and operational experience with the first six aircraft must be awaited before a larger order was placed. In December 1941 satisfactory trials encouraged Joubert again to ask the Ministry to order 30 Leigh Lights and allocate the same number of Wellingtons to take them. The Ministry would only agree to twenty on top of the original order for six, stubbornly arguing that the equipment of further aircraft must await operational experience.

The first of the initial six operational Leigh Light Wellingtons did not reach crew training until early January 1942, though ordered in the previous autumn. Joubert had to inform the Air Ministry that as a result of this infuriating delay operational experience against U-boats was unlikely in the near future. According to the Air Historical Branch Narrative, *The Royal Air Force in the Maritime War*,[91] he pointed out to the Air Ministry that 'unless it was possible to allocate twenty Wellingtons forthwith, the continuity of fitment work would be broken and months elapse before the 20 sets of equipment on order could be installed and the completed aircraft delivered'. On 28 February 1942 the Ministry at last ordered the expansion of the existing Leigh Light flight into a squadron of twenty Wellingtons, and asked the Ministry of Aircraft Production to allocate the aircraft as they came out of the factories.[92]

Unfortunately Vickers, the manufacturers of the Wellington, were, according to a secret wartime expert report, an outstanding example of the 'British Disease', with 'no system of line production throughout the whole organisation'.[93] Thanks to this shambles of mismanagement and appalling productivity the Wellingtons to be fitted with Leigh Lights did not become available as quickly as hoped, and despite all Joubert's proddings only five of them were in service by May 1942.[94] Thus it was that failure in the aircraft factory conspired with inertia

[477]

and obstruction inside the Air Ministry to deny Coastal Command and the Royal Navy the Leigh Light aircraft they so urgently wanted. Even at the beginning of June 1942 the Air Ministry is found resisting Joubert's proposal that other types of aircraft should be fitted with Leigh Lights; it did so for the standard reason that more operational experience was needed first.[95]

In July 1942 a Leigh Light Wellington killed a German U-boat (U-502) in the Bay for the first time, its ASV II radar having first located the boat running on the surface in the pitch dark – for the German officer of the watch on his conning tower a sudden brilliant stab of light, a roar of engines overhead and then the lethal thunder of high explosive. But Dönitz quickly countered the Leigh Light offensive by instructing his captains to travel submerged at night and on the surface by day. Although a Leigh Light Wellington sank another U-boat in August, the Bay offensive continued to prove disappointing in terms of results in proportion to effort.

It is therefore somewhat surprising to find Joubert in September freshly advocating that the Bay should serve as the main focus for the Royal Air Force's and even the Royal Navy's counter-measures against the U-boat. He considered that the alternative of concentrating joint anti-submarine efforts on the open Atlantic was 'a policy to be avoided at all costs':[96]

> Scientific analysis of the situation shows that if the Allied Nations concentrate their effort at the decisive points, which are the transit areas employed by the U-boats and their bases and building yards, the prospect of victory is many times greater than if an attempt is made to protect our shipping in all possible U-boat operational areas. In the Atlantic alone there is an area of $10,000 \times 500$ sq. miles in which the U-boats can operate. The transit areas are only a fraction of this space. It seems, therefore, to be commonsense to concentrate our available A/S forces in the transit areas and on the bases and building yards.[97]

It was all specious enough, but wholly mistaken. In the first place, Bomber Command's attempts to damage Dönitz's Atlantic coast bases came to nought against their 26-feet-thick concrete roofs, while according to the official historians of the bomber offensive the effect of the numerous attacks carried out in 1942 by Bomber Command on the ports where U-boats were built was 'negligible'[98] – as indeed was accurately monitored at the time by the Ministry of Economic Warfare.[99] Secondly, it was not aircraft over the Bay area that most worried Dönitz, but aircraft over his intended victims in the open Atlantic. On 3 September he noted in the U-boat Command's war diary that two days earlier an air escort had appeared over a convoy 800 miles out from England and 400 miles from Iceland:

> By systematically forcing the boats under water [he wrote] it made them lose contact at evening twilight, thus spoiling the best prospects for attack of all boats in the first four moonless hours of the night ... The convoy operation had to be broken off in the morning of 2.9 as it no longer seemed possible for boats to haul ahead in the face of the expected heavy enemy air activity...[100]

Dönitz went on to remark that U-boat Command 'sees with extreme anxiety' the time when such air escorts 'would spread to all parts of the Atlantic', so signifying 'an unendurable reduction in prospects for success'.[101]

Ironically enough, just about the time when Joubert was urging that all efforts should be concentrated on the Bay of Biscay, Dönitz was equipping his boats with an electronic device called 'Metox' which could give warning of existing British radar transmissions so that a U-boat could dive out of harm's way. By nullifying at a stroke the effectiveness of radar-directed night attack by Leigh Light Wellingtons Metox marked the defeat for the time being of Coastal Command's Bay offensive.[102] Nonetheless Joubert still persisted with his favoured strategy. From June 1942 to January 1943 an average of 3,500 patrol hours were flown over the Bay zones each month, at a total loss of some 100 aircraft – for a bag of only seven U-boats sunk and five damaged. Meanwhile just a third of that flying time employed in escorting and supporting convoys in the North-East Atlantic had not only prevented many U-boat attacks but also had destroyed seventeen U-boats and badly damaged over twenty.[103]

The answer to Metox lay in the new 10cm radar (ASV III), its wavelength too short for Metox to pick up. Moreover, this super-accurate narrow-beam new radar could pinpoint a U-boat through all the 'clutter' of the sea's moving surface. It was indeed the complete answer to Coastal Command's problems of detection and attack. Unfortunately throughout 1942 ASV III was to be found not in aircraft but in factories in various stages of delayed assembly.

Ten cm radar required a new kind of thermionic valve, the cavity magnetron, to produce the requisite power. The magnetron had been invented by two brilliant British scientists, Dr J. T. Randall and Mr H. A. H. Boot, early in 1940, and a production prototype had been ready by the summer of that year. It was at this point that the problems began, because the British electrical industry simply lacked the technical and managerial capability to put such advanced technology as the magnetron into large-scale production and it had to be handed over to the Americans to manufacture. In any case, British production of the complete ASV III equipments was seriously held up because of shortcomings in the supply of precision-engineering components and in final assembly.[104] This was why two years after the production prototype not a single ASV III had yet seen service in a Coastal Command aircraft. Indeed such was the reigning confusion and delay in all fields of British radar and radio production in mid-1942 that the Cabinet appointed a senior judge, Lord Justice Du Parcq, to investigate the entire question and make recommendations (see below, pp. 580–2).[105]

There was a further complication. The magnetron also formed the key component in Bomber Command's new target-finding device H2S, technically very similar to ASV III. This led to keen competition between the two Commands for the dribble of hand-built production impatiently awaited in the closing months of 1942. When in November it was decided that forty H2S sets should be converted into ASV IIIs for installation in Liberators and Wellingtons, it therefore marked one of the Admiralty's and Coastal Command's more notable successes in 'the Battle of the Air'.[106] But such were the production bottlenecks that it was not to be until February–March 1943 that the first squadron equipped with ASV III actually came into service.

It was some compensation that, from mid-1942 onwards, Coastal Command aircraft began to be equipped with depth-charges filled with a powerful new explosive, Torpex, and fitted with shallow-setting pistols effective against U-boats on the surface or just diving,[107] which largely accounts for the rising number of U-boats actually destroyed in the Atlantic in the second half of the year.

The Royal Navy also was still greatly hampered during 1942 by want of the right ships and equipment for anti-submarine warfare. Its mainstay for escorting convoys remained the Flower class corvettes, of which 56 had been ordered in the summer of 1939. They rolled like barrels in a seaway and their designed speed was only 16½ knots as against the big U-boats' 18½ knots on the surface. In practice, the four-cylinder triple-expansion engines (an obsolete design adopted because it happened to be available and within the capabilities of the British marine engineering industry, as the large-scale manufacture of diesels was not) could normally manage only 14 to 15 knots.[108] The new River class frigates were still being awaited three years after the war broke out; the British shipbuilding industry lacked enough of the long building slips needed for their construction.[109] Most of the escorts in service were therefore too few and too slow to hunt detected

U-boats to death, and with a margin of only 3 to 4 knots over a 'fast' convoy's speed any prolonged diversion could easily mean losing the convoy. Escorts of all kinds were also too few to permit thorough tactical training as units.

Only in September 1942 did the Royal Navy form its first escort group with the specific task of hunting down U-boats once detected near a convoy. With ten escorts and an oiler it began work on 22 September with the slow outward-bound convoy ONS12, and although it too never operated as a tactical group it did succeed in driving two shadowing U-boats beneath the surface.[110] The demand for escort ships made by the forthcoming invasion of French North Africa in November prevented any more such escort groups being formed in the Eastern Atlantic, although a 'Western Support Force' of three destroyers based on St John's, Newfoundland, was set up to provide extra protection to convoys in the lethal mid-Atlantic air gap.[111]

It did not help that escorts, including destroyers, could run short of fuel and be compelled to leave their convoys early in order to make for port. This problem again owed itself at least partly to obsolescent British marine technology, for the Royal Navy's destroyers (even the latest) were equipped with boilers of lower steam pressure (at 300 pounds per square inch) than American destroyers (at 600 pounds per square inch) and less efficient turbines, so leading to wasteful fuel consumption and consequently shorter endurance. Whereas the Americans drew on the competitive resources of their 'land' boiler and turbine companies (i.e., those who supplied plant for such as power stations), the British shipbuilding industry relied entirely on a too cosy coterie of specialised marine engine and boiler manufacturers whose designs were essentially of 1918 vintage.[112] However, from June 1942 the practice was at last introduced of refuelling escorts from accompanying tankers.[113]

Although the escort carrier had been recognised back in 1941 as an essential tool of convoy protection, only four were in service by late 1942 and those were earmarked either for 'Torch' or for convoys to North Russia.[114] By the end of 1942 shore-based medium-range aircraft (Wellingtons, Whitleys, Sunderlands and Catalinas) could cover the Atlantic as far out as 200 miles east of Newfoundland, 500 miles south of Iceland and 600 miles west of the British Isles.[115] In the absence of escort carriers the remaining gap in mid-Atlantic could only be covered by VLR Liberator Mk I aircraft, the sticking point in 'the Battle of the Air'; and often the number of such aircraft actually available for operations in late 1942 fell to around six. The combined consequences of the grievous shortage of VLR aircraft and the complete lack of escort carriers is spelt out by the Official Naval History:

[481]

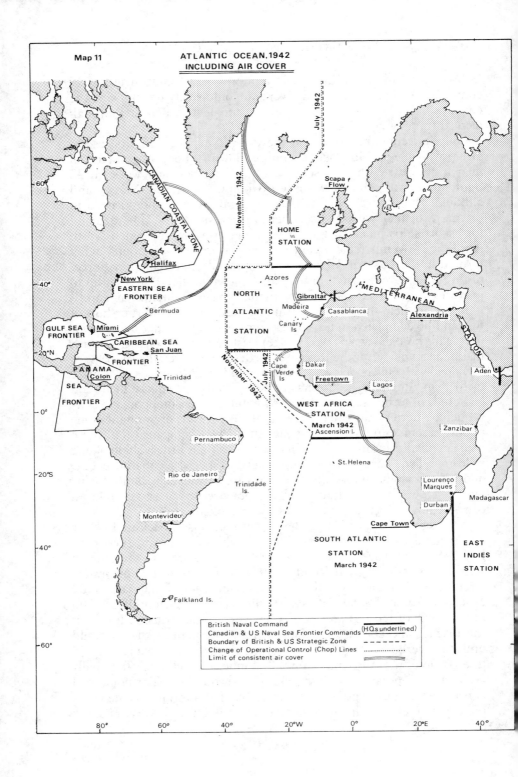

Map 11

ATLANTIC OCEAN, 1942
INCLUDING AIR COVER

Legend:
British Naval Command
Canadian & US Naval Sea Frontier Commands (H.Q.s underlined)
Boundary of British & US Strategic Zone — — — —
Change of Operational Control (Chop) Lines ⋯⋯⋯⋯
Limit of consistent air cover

Meanwhile, in mid-Atlantic, between latitude 35°N and 65°N and longitude 10°W and 50°W, ship after ship went down for lack of air cover for convoys: August, 29 ships of 156,049 tons; September, 18 ships of 108,768 tons; October, 24 ships of 172,173 tons; November, 27 ships of 166,809 tons; December, 24 ships of 127,844 tons.[116]

Utter and early disaster was alone staved off by the five Liberator Is of 120 Squadron, Coastal Command, based in Iceland, although appalling weather in December helped by greatly reducing U-boat operations. In October (first fruits of 'the Battle of the Air') one squadron of twelve Liberator Mark IIIAC was formed in England; next month a US Liberator Mark IIIA squadron was allotted to Coastal Command for operations over the Atlantic. But these measures brought no instant relief because it was to take months to convert the bombers into fully equipped VLR anti-submarine aircraft.[117]

Thus the protracted nature of the 'Battle of the Air' and the belatedness of the decision to provide Coastal Command with VLR aircraft at the expense (small) of Bomber Command caused the entire British anti-submarine effort to remain lopsided, with too much of the burden falling to the Royal Navy's escort ships. As the ACNS (H) wrote to the First Sea Lord on 20 December 1942:

> Experience shows quite clearly that surface escorts alone without air co-operation cannot give sufficient security to convoys unless in overwhelming strength; it is also clear that an air escort unaided by surface vessels is not sufficient. The most effective and economical use of our resources requires a careful balance in the combined use of surface and air escorts.[118]

Meanwhile it was the crews of the escort ships and the merchant marine who were paying the price for this lack of balance. And what that price amounted to in the iron coinage of hardship, danger and demands on human courage is epitomised by the homeward voyage in October of just one out of the 180-odd convoys which crossed the Atlantic that year, Convoy SC104.

On 10 October 1942 Escort Unit B6 of the Liverpool Escort Force rendezvoused with Convoy SC104 at 1300 in 47° 57'N, 51° 35'W, relieving Task Unit 24.18.3 of the Western Local Escort which thereupon returned to St John's. Escort Unit B6 consisted of the destroyers *Fame* (launched 1934; 1,350 tons displacement; 35½ knots; two 4.7-inch guns; four Oerlikon guns; a 'Hedgehog' anti-submarine mortar) and *Viscount* (launched 1917; 1,120 tons; 25 knots; two 4-inch guns)[119] and four Flower class corvettes (all launched mid-1941; 925 tons displacement; one 4-inch gun; one 2-pounder anti-aircraft gun).[120] Their names, evoking the gentle charms of an English country garden – His Majesty's ships *Acanthus*, *Eglantine*, and *Montbretia*, and His Norwegian Majesty's ship *Potentilla* – contrasted poignantly with the harshness of their task in war. The Senior Officer commanding B6 was Commander R. Heathcote, RN, captain of the *Fame*. Now the thirty-six merchant ships of SC104, deployed in several columns, lay in his care: his responsibility to shepherd them safely to England and home.

For two deceptive days the convoy steamed eastwards with the sweep of sea bounded by its horizon empty but for itself. The first warning that peril was beginning to encircle it came at 1624 on 12 October, when HF/DF (High-Frequency direction finding) picked up the bearing of a U-boat's radio transmission on the convoy's starboard bow. After Heathcote had ordered *Montbretia* to investigate this, a further bearing indicated that there was another U-boat prowling to port – and that the first U-boat too had moved over to port, possibly to get to windward of the convoy.[121] As dusk thickened over the grey waters B6 adopted Night Stations: *Viscount* on the starboard quarter of the convoy; *Montbretia* ahead of the starboard column; *Eglantine* to starboard of the convoy's front; *Fame* on the starboard quarter; *Potentilla* on the port bow; and *Acanthus* ahead of the port column. Heathcote had already arranged with the convoy commodore to make various evasive alterations of course during the night.

In wheelhouses and chart rooms and on open bridges in a bitter wind nerves began to tighten in the knowledge that at least two U-boats lurked behind the blank face of the sea like crocodiles awaiting their chance of meat.

Although it promised to be a dark night, owing to negligible moon and heavy clouds [wrote Heathcote in his report], bright Northern Lights kept the visibility of the convoy up to at least four miles, except during the short snow showers, and the alterations of course evidently did not pass unnoticed.

Twenty minutes before midnight three D/F bearings fixed a U-boat four and a half miles astern of the middle of the convoy. The destroyer *Fame*, on going to investigate, made radar contact at about 4,000 yards, and closed for the kill. At this point the radar broke down because of the heavy pounding of the ship. *Fame* had other problems too: 'Speed was reduced to 12 knots to reduce spray on the bridge, which made an efficient lookout impossible and the search continued for half an hour on this bearing.' She saw nothing and resumed her station at 0115 on 13 October. Shortly afterwards another HF/DF fix placed a U-boat four miles outside *Eglantine*, but she too found nothing. A night of stealthy menace ended with a false alarm at 0411. The weather was now all too favourable to the stalking U-boats: 'Conditions for R.D.F. [radar] and asdics [sonar] were very bad owing to the steep and rising sea, while spray and occasional snow showers hampered visibility.' Heathcote ordered *Viscount* ahead of the convoy, and *Acanthus* to its starboard quarter.

At 0450 SC104 took its first casualty, the Norwegian merchantman *Fagersten*, stopped and sinking astern of Column Ten. No rockets had been seen, no signals of distress received. HMS *Fame* searched for her attacker without success. At 0508 an explosion was followed by rockets arcing in the night sky, whereupon Heathcote ordered 'Operation Raspberry', a standard tactical drill for depth-charging in a pattern over the area of U-boat attack. At 0515 'Snowflake', an illuminant, was fired: a ghastly light over a desolate sea. Nothing was seen. More than an hour later Heathcote learned that three ships had been sunk and that no one had yet gone to the rescue of the crews. He ordered *Potentilla* to search for survivors at daylight and return to the convoy at dusk.

The daylight hours of 13 October brought more bearings and some sightings of U-boats; but each time the U-boat dived before an escort ship could close her. Convoy SC104 was now battling against that other Atlantic enemy – the weather. When at 0922 the convoy altered to 045° in order to regain the convoy route after evasive changes of course, the commodore reported that several of the merchantmen could not steer this course because of the heavy seas. Heathcote had to alter back to 075° as the only alternative to heaving to.

By the afternoon it had become clear from HF/DF bearings that the convoy was being shadowed by one U-boat on each quarter, with indications that a third and possibly a fourth U-boat were also around. Heathcote therefore despatched *Eglantine* to the rear to work under *Viscount*'s orders. In the evening he faced a fresh worry: although he had ordered his ships to be back in station by 2100, *Viscount* and *Eglantine* had been delayed in a hunt for a U-boat seen on the surface, while *Potentilla* was still searching for survivors who might yet be floating on the icy wind-whipped rollers and could not be back in station until 0400. This left him with only *Montbretia* on the convoy's starboard bow, *Acanthus* on the port beam and *Fame* zig-zagging across the stern.

It was the more worrying that his ships' radars and sonars were confused by the echoes of wave crests and noisy turbulence of rough seas. By around midnight two more ships, *Empire Mersey* and *Southern Empress*, had been picked off by U-boats. By this time the *Viscount* and a U-boat had had a brief but violent encounter in the darkness and atrocious weather. At 2043 *Viscount* spotted a U-boat surfacing ahead only 800 yards distant. She increased to full speed, her helm hard to port. The U-boat captain swung hard to starboard and managed to clear *Viscount*'s bow by about three hundred yards. Although *Viscount* now opened fire, her 'B' gun could only get off five rounds before the gunlayer and trainer were blinded by spray. As *Viscount*'s captain later reported:

> VISCOUNT continued her turn under full rudder and went in to ram, but heavy water coming over the bridge obscured the submarine which altered course to port and dived. A last glimpse of the conning tower, as it disappeared, was seen from VISCOUNT's bridge [about 30 yards on the port beam] . . .

With sonar rendered useless by the motion of the ship, *Viscount* had no alternative but to return to her station with the convoy.

The small hours of 14 October saw more blind gropings in the dark for elusive U-boats seen for an instant before diving; more vain chases; more ships going down as the columns steamed slowly on. In one chase by *Viscount*, 'the submarine was going down-wind and almost down-swell and was extremely difficult to keep in sight owing to the height of the swell, while the top of an occasional wave gave a very good imitation of a submarine, the white crest representing the wake'. At daylight Heathcote found that fifteen ships were now missing from his convoy, though fortunately nine of them later rejoined. It was enough, however, to have lost six vessels in two days with half an ocean still to cross. Heathcote later confessed that on this morning his own feelings 'amounted almost to despair, but these feelings did not appear to be shared by other officers and men in FAME'.

During daylight on 14 October many HF/DF fixes as well as sightings confirmed that the four U-boats were clinging persistently to SC104's flanks and rear despite all Escort Unit B6's efforts to drive them away. In the evening the favourable visibility which had helped the U-boats in stalking their prey grew mercifully worse. Commander Heathcote prearranged more evasive changes of course for the night hours with the convoy commodore, and stationed his escorts closer to the convoy than laid down in Admiralty tactical instructions. During the night of 15–16 October Heathcote's ships made no fewer than six radar contacts and succeeded in driving off all would-be attackers. And HMS *Viscount* did much more than merely drive off a U-boat after her radar picked it up 6,200 yards off the port bow at 2331. At 2342, with the range down to 2,000 yards, 'revolutions for 26 knots were ordered,' wrote her captain, Lieutenant-Commander Waterhouse in his report, 'and course set to ram.' At 2344 *Viscount*'s lookouts sighted the U-boat through the darkness fine on the port bow completely surfaced. Simultaneously the U-boat must have spotted *Viscount* because her diesels immediately thrust her to high speed while she 'snaked in line', starting with a swing to port:

VISCOUNT followed her swing to port but failed to catch her as she swung back to starboard. The U-boat Captain then 'committed suicide' by swinging back to port right across the bows of VISCOUNT who was turning under full starboard rudder. VISCOUNT struck the U-boat on her port side, about 20 feet abaft the conning tower . . . The stem hit her fairly, then lifted and crashed down on top of her, pinning her for about 15 seconds before she dragged clear to port with her back broken . . .

She passed slowly down *Viscount*'s port side as *Viscount* drew ahead; an opportunity for the British destroyer to give her broadsides from every calibre of gun. *Viscount* finished the job by placing a heavy depth-charge set to 140 feet alongside the U-boat (U-619) as she sank stern first at 2347.

But *Viscount* herself had suffered serious damage in her bows, letting in much water. Even though Commander Waterhouse had her load shifted (including fuel oil) aft in order to raise her buckled bow plates above the waterline, this proved only partially successful, and he was ordered by Captain (D), Liverpool, to make for home independently. *Viscount* reached Lough Foyle safely at 2130 on 18 October.

After the *Viscount* parted company Commander Heathcote, as Senior Officer, Escort Unit B6, found himself with just his own destroyer, *Fame*, with the requisite speed and weaponry effectively to hunt and kill his remaining pursuers. Mercifully, however, the small hours of 16 October passed quietly; the day dawned fairly calm, with gratifyingly low visibility. *Potentilla* was able to transfer to the SS *Souderoy* nearly 100 survivors who for up to two days had been packed into her cramped spaces. At sunrise came a welcome sight – a Liberator flying overhead. It reported that a U-boat had dived some five miles astern of the convoy. Heathcote now sought to shake off the enemy altogether under cover of the poor visibility by an alteration to 130° at 1220 – but to no avail, because at 1407, *Fame*, two miles ahead of Column Four of the convoy, got a clear sonar signal of a U-boat 2,000 yards distant. Heathcote increased to 15 knots and at 1413 dropped a ten depth-charge pattern set to 50 and 140 feet over the U-boat's likely position. With visibility now up to a mile, Heathcote was just preparing to use *Fame*'s 'Hedgehog' to launch more depth-charges forward over the bows when . . .

a large bubble was seen followed by the bow of a submarine breaking surface at a very steep angle. Speed was increased to 18 knots and fire opened with every weapon which would bear. By the time FAME reached the position of the submarine she was on even keel and stopped. Engines were stopped before the bow hit a glancing blow. The submarine scraped down the starboard side. A 5-charge pattern was dropped when the submarine was abreast of the stern while FAME made another circle to come up to attempt to board. The convoy were now steaming past on either side, most of them firing everything they had got. The submarine crew were now abandoning ship . . .

As the submarine settled slowly on even keel, Lieutenant P. M. Jones boarded her from *Fame*'s whaler and retrieved her documents. He scrambled back into the whaler just one minute before the U-boat sank.

Nothing could have been more true to the spirit of Nelson and his captains at Trafalgar than *Viscount*'s and *Fame*'s actions in ramming the enemy, laying themselves alongside him, and then sinking him by sheer weight of fire. But *Fame*, like *Viscount*, paid dearly for her success – ripped right along her waterline by the tin-opener of the U-boat's thick plating and hydroplanes. Her stem was twisted and her after magazine was flooded. The pumps were only just able to hold the water level steady until collision mats could be put in place. Commander Heathcote therefore stopped her and listed her to port while rags, wedges, pieces of wood, items of stores – anything that would serve – were stuffed into the rip. Heathcote himself was now overtaken by a kind of a hangover of second thoughts after the violence of the action, for he was already regretting that he had rammed the U-boat, both because of the damage to his own ship and also because he had forfeited the chance of salvaging the enemy.

'At the time, however,' he wrote in his report, 'I was faced with an apparently little damaged submarine in low visibility in the middle of a large convoy.' It is little wonder, then, that Heathcote, in his own words, 'wished to make very certain of this submarine, which proved to be U-253'. Nevertheless, he too now had to part company and make for port: 'Though loath to leave the convoy, I felt it would be foolish with a potentially dangerous leak in the engine-room to delay my arrival in Harbour . . .' At 1815 on 16 October he ordered Lieutenant-Commander C. A. Monsen, RNorN, to take command of the escort. *Fame* herself reached Liverpool safely on 19 October.

Now Commander Monsen was left with just the four 'Flowers' to guard 28 surviving ships. That same evening he demonstrated that the Viking spirit was just as much alive in Norwegian seamen as the Nelson spirit in British. When at 2140 his radar operator detected a submarine, Monsen ordered full speed. To the thunderous vibration of her reciprocating engines *Potentilla* closed on the enemy until the U-boat was sighted dead ahead 400 yards off, and steering straight for the corvette.

> We were now doing 16 knots [wrote Monsen in his report] and the submarine probably more. As a ramming ahead just would make a mess of it with more than 30 knots [combined] speed, ship was given a kick to starboard and then hard a-port. The submarine passed down our port side with a terrific speed, distance between ships less than 30 yards . . .

Potentilla opened fire with her 4-inch gun, her Oerlikons and 2-pounder pom-pom, scoring several hits. 'Helm was given hard-a-port in order to ram. By now the submarine started to dive and we passed over her swirl as she disappeared dropping the last three charges of the pattern . . .' Although further depth-charges brought up an oil slick, the U-boat had in fact escaped. Nevertheless she was the last U-boat to trouble the convoy despite unexplained bursts of fire from the convoy and the occasional false alarm on 17 October, a day blessed with thick, concealing fog; two days later Convoy SC104 and its war-sustaining cargoes made safe landfall in the Mersey. Time now for the sailor home from sea briefly to enjoy the warmth of a family welcome; the love of a lonely, anxious and for the moment thankfully relieved wife or girlfriend. For all too soon the sea service, with all its hardships and hazards, would call him back again.

It was rare for convoys in 1942 to come through with relatively light losses like SC104 and its hard-fighting escort. Later that October SC107 had fifteen ships totalling 88,000 tons sunk before an air escort arrived. Off Madeira SL125 lost thirteen ships in a seven-day battle without a single U-boat being sunk in compensation.[122] These were the kind of massacres which brought the count of merchant shipping lost in 1942 to the U-boat up to its horrifying total of 1,160 ships and 6,266,215 tons.[123]

Yet at least the fast liners – the Cunarders *Queen Elizabeth* (83,675 tons), *Queen Mary* (81,235 tons), *Aquitania* (44,786 tons), the French ship *Ile de France* (43,450 tons) and the Dutch *Nieuw Amsterdam* (36,287 tons) – succeeded in repeatedly plying the Atlantic literally stuffed with American troops (*Queen Elizabeth* was carrying 15,000 per trip) without falling victim to U-boats. Too fast at around 28 knots for surface escorts to keep up, they had to make the mid-ocean crossing entirely unprotected except by their own speed, some 10 knots more than the fastest U-boat on the surface. Despite all Dönitz's successes, 'Operation Bolero', the accelerating movement of American forces to the British Isles, succeeded to the limits of the capacity of the ships available. In the first quarter of the year 13,698 US service personnel arrived in the United Kingdom; in the second 42,314; in the third, 131,850; in the last, 63,000.[124]

So even though Britain's own survival lay in increasing jeopardy as the months of 1942 passed, the Allied leadership could nonetheless argue hopefully about where best to launch these American forces alongside the British in the first joint Allied expedition of the German war. To Churchill and the British Chiefs of Staff, though not to the Americans, the choice always seemed obvious: the Mediterranean. Yet an ultimate decision in favour of that theatre depended on the fate during 1942 of Britain's existing 'blue water' strategy there – a fate for long much in doubt.

16

The Verdun of Maritime War: Malta, 1942

Throughout much of 1942 the island of Malta served less as a British strategic asset than as a hostage to the enemy. In the face of Axis air superiority the remaining surface warships based there had to be withdrawn to Alexandria in April; soon afterwards even the submarines had to follow, because enemy bombing was so ferocious that they had been compelled to remain submerged in harbour throughout the daylight hours. They were not to return to Malta until August. With the dying away of attacks from Malta against enemy convoys plying between Italy and North Africa, Axis losses of merchant ships on this route dropped to less than one per cent in April.[1] For the foreseeable future Malta had thus ceased to function as an offensive base. Instead it was now the Verdun of maritime war. For just like Verdun and the French leadership in 1916 – or, for that matter, the besieged German Army at Stalingrad and Hitler in 1942–43 – Malta had become for the British leadership a matter of prestige and pride, a symbol of heroic resistance. This was proclaimed by the award of the George Cross to the islanders by King George VI on 16 April 1942. And like Verdun and Stalingrad the 'George Cross Island' triggered powerful emotions which dictated that it must be held no matter what the cost in resources, risk, losses, and distortion of the balance of strategy as a whole. In the case of the British leadership and the people of Malta there existed a special bond of loyalty and obligation. In Churchill's words when writing to the First Sea Lord in June to call for a fresh effort 'on the grand scale' to succour the island: 'We are absolutely bound to save Malta in one way or another'; and he asked Sir Dudley Pound to assure Field-Marshal Gort, the Governor, that 'the Navy will never abandon Malta'.[2] There was no need for such an assurance: Admiral Cunningham himself was resolved that 'we must take great risks to keep Malta supplied'.[3] As he comments in his memoirs: 'Incidentally, I am unaware if anyone had suggested abandoning the island. Certainly the Navy had not.'[4]

Yet to fulfil this commitment to Malta demanded attempt after attempt 'on the grand scale' to fight supplies and reinforcements of aircraft through to the island in the face of overwhelming Axis air superiority. Of the sixty supply ships despatched in 1942, only thirty arrived; twenty were sunk and ten had to turn back. These perilous voyages cost the Royal Navy one fleet aircraft carrier, two cruisers, one anti-aircraft cruiser and nine destroyers sunk and many other warships badly damaged.[5]

However, it was not just in regard to the Royal Navy that Malta in 1942 served as a hostage to the enemy, but also in regard to the Army's conduct of the land campaign in North Africa. For in the airfields in the northerly bulge of Cyrenaica lay the key to control of the central Mediterranean convoy routes. In British hands these airfields ensured fighter cover far to the westward over the route from Alexandria to Malta, while at the same time permitting the Royal Air Force to attack Rommel's supply ships en route between Italy and Libya. In German and Italian hands these airfields ensured the reverse – virtual free passage of stores vessels and tankers to Rommel; virtual closing of the route to Malta from the eastwards. As a consequence British military planning in 1942, and especially the timing of Desert offensives, could not be determined solely by military considerations such as the prevailing balance of land forces in numbers of troops or quality and quantity of weapons, or comparative states of training. Instead GHQ, Middle East's freedom of strategic choice was cramped by the imperative need to take or hold the Cyrenaican airfields for the sake of Malta.

In the spring months of 1942 in particular, after Rommel had forced the 8th Army back from the El Agheila defile to Gazala and recaptured these airfields, Churchill and the Chiefs of Staff were to nag away at the C-in-C, Middle East, General Sir Claude Auchinleck, to launch an offensive at minimum delay. In the words of a COS telegram to him at the beginning of March:

The dominant factor in the Mediterranean and Middle East situation at the present time is Malta . . . If we do not succeed in running a substantial convoy into Malta by May, the position there will be critical . . . A convoy can only be run [from the east] if we can use the landing grounds in Western Cyrenaica. Hence the recapture of these is vital to your whole situation.[6]

Despite Auchinleck's reluctance to commit his ill-trained and heterogeneous army with its inferior tanks to a premature offensive – and despite the Middle East Defence Committee's argument that, since Malta in its present impotence could little affect enemy supplies, its fall would not necessarily be fatal to the security of Egypt – the War Cabinet decided that the island was of such supreme importance that a battle must be fought in the Desert to save it. Auchinleck was therefore directed against his better judgment that the latest acceptable date for an offensive would be one timed to help the passage of the proposed June dark-period (little or no moon) convoy from Alexandria to Malta.[7]

When in the event Rommel pre-empted this offensive with one of his own on 26 May, Malta even played an indirect role in the crushing defeat and rout of the 8th Army that followed. For the need to protect huge dumps established just behind the 8th Army's front at Gazala for the planned British offensive, and therefore vulnerable to enemy armoured columns, shackled the British command's freedom of manoeuvre, compelling it to fight a forward battle rather than a defence in depth.

The influence of Malta on land strategy manifested itself once again in August 1942, after Auchinleck had halted Rommel and thrown him on to the defensive in the First Battle of Alamein during the previous month. For when Churchill began to press Auchinleck and thereafter his successor, General Sir Harold Alexander, to launch a fresh Desert offensive not later than September, Malta bulked large in his argument, on the familiar score that the Cyrenaican airfields must be seized back in order to provide air cover for a convoy from Alexandria that it was hoped to run in November in order to relieve the island's now desperate straits. Nevertheless Alexander – really Montgomery, the new 8th Army commander – successfully insisted that the army could not be adequately trained and equipped for an offensive until mid-October.

Even so, it was the plight of the island – along with the Prime Minister's own political need for a striking British victory[8] – which rendered it a matter of absolute necessity rather than mere choice to launch the offensive at Alamein against strong German defences at all. For it can be argued that, on purely military grounds, there would have been advantage in leaving Rommel where he was, withering on the vine of an inadequate line of communications up to 1,500 miles long, until the Anglo-American landings in French North Africa ('Torch') at the beginning of November far in his rear and threatening his main base of Tripoli eventually forced him to retreat. The costly attrition battle of Second Alamein might thus have been avoided, and Rommel might instead have been attacked in the open field in the course of a difficult retreat. But the need to have the Cyrenaican airfields in British hands by mid-November in order to cover the Malta convoy which had now been scheduled to sail in the second half of that month utterly precluded such a Wellingtonian waiting game.[9]

It is an irony that the British came close to being relieved of their liability of Malta by the Axis powers themselves, albeit the relief would have been at the cost of a moral shock as devastating as the Japanese capture of Singapore which finally resolved that particular strategic problem after twenty years. In the early months of 1942 long discussions took place within the German and Italian high commands (also involving Hitler and Mussolini) about the relative priority between an airborne operation to capture Malta, 'Operation Herkules', and an offensive by Rommel against the 8th Army in the Gazala Line. Eventually, on 4 May, Hitler issued a directive postponing 'Operation Herkules' until mid-July or even mid-August, when Rommel should have completed his Desert victory. In any case Hitler was less than enthusiastic about 'Herkules', shrewdly foreseeing 'a perpetual blood-letting' in the process of holding Malta and supplying it once taken.[10] At the end of June, after Rommel had routed the 8th Army in the Gazala battles, 'Herkules' was in fact dropped in favour of a supreme effort to conquer Egypt. The defeat of this effort in the First Battle of Alamein finally killed off 'Operation Herkules'.

So Malta remained a British problem, above all for the Royal Navy and the Merchant Marine; the epitome of the entire cost-ineffective 'blue water' strategy in the Mediterranean and Middle East by which Britain, to paraphrase Lord Kitchener, continued to make war as she must rather than as she ought.

For Admiral Cunningham, with his flagship *Queen Elizabeth* lying very low in the water in Alexandria harbour (although with decks sufficiently above the surface of the water to permit the morning ceremony of 'Colours' to be performed), the opening of 1942 marked the nadir of his command of the Mediterranean Fleet. He no longer possessed a single aircraft carrier or serviceable battleship in the face of an Italian battlefleet numbering four or five modern or modernised heavy ships and backed by very strong shore-based air forces. This weakness prompted him to protest forcefully in a letter of 9 January 1942 against the First Sea Lord's intention to deny him reinforcements of heavy ships in order to build up the Eastern Fleet.[11] In the first place, so he argued, 'the defeat of Japan will not necessarily win the war while the defeat of Germany will mean the defeat of Japan'. Secondly, shore-based bombers in the current state of Royal Air Force efficiency over the sea could not provide a substitute for battleships against enemy heavy ships.[12] 'Battleships,' wrote Cunningham, 'can only be replaced by air forces trained in sea operations consisting of adequate reconnaissance and striking forces operating under my close control . . .'[13]

This was a clear reference to the Mediterranean theatre's own 'Battle of the Air' in 1941, in which Cunningham and the new AOC-in-C, Middle East, Air Marshal Sir Arthur Tedder, had disputed about the need for a Mediterranean 'Coastal Command' consisting of squadrons specially trained for maritime warfare and under the operational control of the Royal Navy. As a compromise No. 201 Group, RAF, had been reorganised and renamed in October 1941 as No. 201 (Naval Cooperation) Group, with its primary function defined as 'the conduct of operations at sea and cooperation with the Mediterranean Fleet as required by the C-in-C, Mediterranean'. But this had far from satisfied Cunningham's wish for a shore-based naval air striking force as numerous and as effective against enemy ships as the Luftwaffe's Mediterranean Fliegerkorps or the Japanese naval air force which had so recently sunk *Prince of Wales* and *Repulse*.[14] Indeed, so he wrote to the Vice Chief of Naval Staff in the same letter of 9 January 1942, 'I fear from their last two convoy operations [attacked by the Royal Air Force without success] the enemy have learnt the utter futility of our air forces over the sea . . .'[15]

Within the next two weeks Cunningham made two successful attempts to run essential fuel oil into Malta and bring out empty merchant vessels, at a cost of one destroyer (*Gurkha**) torpedoed by a U-boat and one merchantman sunk after being set on fire by a Ju 88; and he fairly acknowledged the efficiency of the Royal Air Force's Naval Cooperation Group in flying reconnaissances and fighter cover from Malta and from airfields in the Cyrenaican bulge during the

* The second *Gurkha*, formerly the *Larne*, renamed in honour of the regiments. The first *Gurkha* had been sunk off Norway in 1940.

operations. But by the beginning of February the 8th Army had lost the latter airfields to Rommel's winter counter-stroke. On 7 February Cunningham sent a personal message to the First Sea Lord 'setting out the situation at Malta in all its grim bleakness. I pointed out in so many words the serious effect upon the island caused by our recent reverse in Libya . . .' In particular, in Cunningham's words, 'we were thus faced with a period during which the passage of convoys to Malta from the east could only be carried out at very great hazard, as there was a long stretch over which no air cover could be provided. At the same time he could provide no surface force to act as a deterrent to Italian heavy ships.'[16] On the other hand, however, Malta's general supplies could last no longer than the beginning of June, and its stock of aviation spirit no longer than the beginning of August. Cunningham therefore reckoned that he must run in a convoy before the Axis air forces could be reorganised on the captured airfields and while the enemy was still preoccupied with land operations in Libya.

And so in the afternoon of 12 February the first of the major Malta convoys of 1942 sailed from Alexandria – the fast (15 knot) big merchant ships *Clan Chattan*, *Clan Campbell* and *Rowallan Castle*, escorted by the anti-aircraft cruiser *Carlisle* and seven of the new Hunt class escort destroyers. Following in close support came Rear-Admiral Vian with the light cruisers *Naiad* (flag), *Dido*, *Euryalus* and eight fleet destroyers. Next evening after dark three empty merchant ships, the supply vessel HMS *Breconshire*, the cruiser *Penelope* and six destroyers slipped out of Grand Harbour, Valletta, and set course for a mid-voyage rendezvous with Vian.

In the event, although the *Breconshire* and the three empty ships from Malta eventually reached Alexandria safely in company with Vian's returning force, the attempt to re-supply Malta was smashed by enemy air attack. The *Clan Campbell*, badly damaged, had to be diverted to Tobruk; the *Clan Chattan* was set on fire and had to be sunk; the *Rowallan Castle*'s engines were disabled by a near-miss, and although the destroyer *Zulu* took her in tow, her speed was so slow that there remained no chance of her reaching Malta in safety. Back in Alexandria the hapless C-in-C could only order her too to be sunk. In four days of almost continuous action Vian's cruisers fired off some 3,700 rounds of 5.25-inch anti-aircraft ammunition, leaving no more than one and one-third issues for each cruiser remaining in the Mediterranean Fleet.[17]

On 27 February the Chiefs of Staff signalled Cunningham that, since it was at present impossible to supply Malta from the west via Gibraltar, Cunningham must try to run another convoy from Alexandria in March. This operation was to be regarded as the Mediterranean Fleet's primary commitment, to be discharged without regard to the risk to the ships themselves.

The resulting 'Operation MG1', the passing of convoy MW10 to Malta, was to be the last conducted by Cunningham in his present tour as C-in-C, Mediterranean.[18] He deployed his entire remaining strength in cruisers and destroyers under Rear-Admiral Vian's command. From Alexandria would sail three cruisers, an anti-aircraft ship, ten fleet destroyers and seven 'Hunts', while one cruiser (*Penelope*) and one destroyer from Malta would meet the convoy west of Crete. The convoy itself consisted of the Royal Fleet Auxiliary (supply ship) *Breconshire* and three merchantmen, the Norwegian *Talabot*, the *Pampas* and the *Clan Campbell*.

In view of the potentially overwhelming enemy strength Cunningham, Vian and the fleet staff planned MG1 with the greatest care. The 'Hunts' were to search for submarines between Alexandria and Tobruk on the night of 19–20 March (the night before the convoy sailed) and during daylight on the 20th. They would refuel in Tobruk and join the convoy in the forenoon of the 21st. The convoy itself was to sail from Alexandria with a small escort in the forenoon of 20 March, followed by Vian with the main body (Force B) in the evening. Vian would catch up the convoy next morning at the eastern end of the hazardous passage between the airfields of Crete and Libya whence ferocious bombing could be expected. In the morning of the 22nd Vian would pick up the ships from Malta and take the combined force on till dark, steering a course well to the south of the normal route to Malta. As soon as night had dropped its protective curtain over the convoy, Vian was to turn back for Alexandria with his own three cruisers and the fleet destroyers while the convoy itself sailed on to Malta under escort of the warships from Malta, together with the anti-aircraft cruiser *Carlisle* and the 'Hunts'. It was planned that the convoy should reach safe haven in Grand Harbour, Valletta, at dawn on 23 March.

In Cunningham's judgment there was great danger of attack by Italian surface forces during daylight on the 22nd or during the following night. His orders to meet this contingency were admirably clear:

Should this occur, it is my general intention that the enemy should be, if possible, evaded until darkness, after which the convoy should be sent on to Malta with the destroyer escort, being dispersed if thought desirable, and the enemy brought to action by Force 'B'. The convoy should only be turned back if it is evident that the enemy will otherwise intercept in daylight and east of longitude 18°E [some 200 miles east of Malta].[19]

Cunningham posted five submarines on patrol against such surface forces, and arranged for the Royal Air Force to conduct air searches from Malta (prevented in the event by enemy air attack) and Libya; the Royal Air Force was also to bomb the enemy's Cyrenaican airfields, fly fighter patrols over the convoy up to 300 miles from its bases, and provide strike forces of Beaufort torpedo-bombers from Malta and Libya against Italian warships.

Convoy MW10 sailed in the morning of 20 March escorted by the anti-aircraft cruiser *Carlisle* (Captain D. M. L. Neame) and six destroyers. Vian followed in the evening with Force B, the cruiser *Cleopatra* (Captain G. Grantham; flag), *Dido* and *Euryalus* and four fleet destroyers. By this time 'Operation MG1' had already suffered its first casualty – the Hunt class destroyer *Heythrop*, torpedoed by a U-boat off Tobruk, had had to be sunk while in tow. By the forenoon of 21 March Vian had joined with the convoy and the five remaining 'Hunts' from Tobruk (the sixth, delayed by a fouled propeller, joined in the evening) and the combined force was making 12 knots on a westerly course to the north of Tobruk, with relays of Royal Air Force fighters circling reassuringly overhead. At 0800 next day *Penelope* and the destroyer *Legion* joined from Malta, and the convoy (now beyond air cover) steamed on through the passage between Crete and Cyrenaica without incident. Neither inaccurate Italian high-level bombing in the forenoon nor more dangerous German attacks which followed until dusk caused damage. But now came warning via Ultra decrypts of the Italian C38M Enigma signals, confirmed by a British submarine report at 0518 on the 22nd, that an Italian heavy squadron had sailed from Taranto.[20]

For Vian – a hard, long, hatchet face; the outward visor of the ruthlessly tough fighting sailor who had boarded the prison ship *Altmark* in then neutral Norwegian waters in 1940, who had led his destroyers in persistent close-range night attack on the *Bismarck*, who had escorted Arctic convoys to Russia, and who in this same month of March 1942 had had his flagship *Naiad* sunk under him by a U-boat during an abortive sortie against an Axis convoy – for Vian this was the news which he and his C-in-C had feared the most. With just four light cruisers, eleven fleet destroyers and six 'Hunts', he now had to protect his vital convoy from an enemy force at first estimated to comprise three 15-inch gun battleships. The true odds were daunting enough – the new battleship *Littorio*, two 8-inch gun heavy cruisers, a 6-inch gun cruiser and ten destroyers, to say nothing of the enemy air forces, which could range freely over the British convoy now that it lay outside the range of Royal Air Force fighters.

But Vian had carefully worked out and thoroughly practised his tactics with his captains beforehand for just such a crisis, and in particular a manoeuvre 'to move out from a cruising disposition designed to meet air attack into a disposition for surface action with the least possible delay'.[21] In case he chose to avoid close engagement he had arranged a special signal ordering his squadron 'to carry out diversionary tactics, using smoke to cover the escape of the convoy': while the convoy itself was to turn away closely escorted by five 'Hunts' only, the cruisers and fleet destroyers (concentrated in divisions) were to lay smoke at right angles to the bearing of the enemy, but to be ready to reverse course in time to attack with torpedoes when Italian ships approached the edge of the smoke.

At 1230 on 22 March 1942 Vian made the operational signal to his striking force to steer to the north towards the enemy in six divisions (the sixth being charged with the special task of laying smoke) – the opening move in the Second Battle of Sirte.

At 1332 enemy aircraft dropped four red flares as markers ahead of the convoy. At 1410 the cruiser *Euryalus* reported seeing funnel smoke to the north and then, a quarter of an hour later, four warships bearing 015°; at the same time the destroyer *Legion* reported a ship bearing 010°, distance twelve miles. On receiving these reports Vian made his prearranged signal: the convoy hauled away to the south-west while his striking force formed into divisions in line ahead. At 1433 thick black smoke began to belch from funnels as his ships raced to lay a protective curtain between the convoy and the Italian squadron to the northward. For the next hour the four British light cruisers (three with 5.25-inch guns; one with 6-inch) and the fleet destroyers dodged in and out of the fringes of the smoke screen to engage the enemy at long range. But the Italians displayed little appetite for close action, and at 1535 Vian was able to signal Cunningham: 'Enemy driven off.'[22]

In the meantime, however, Ju 88s had been doing their determined best to destroy the convoy by high-level and dive-bombing attacks, only to fail in the face of a storm of anti-aircraft fire and skilful handling of the convoy. This was no Mediterranean summer day of white wave-crests sparkling on a copper-sulphate sea, but the winter Mediterranean – a strong and freshening breeze from the south-east; wind-torn and steeply rolling dark waters. The forecastle guncrews

[499]

of the destroyers were, wrote Commander Jellicoe of the *Southwold*, 'drenched from the start' and 'fighting their guns under most difficult conditions'.[23] Nonetheless, according to Vian in his subsequent report, the 4-inch fire from the 'Hunts' 'was most impressive, resembling continuous pom-pom fire in sound'.[24] But the cost in ammunition of repelling the Ju 88s proved to be colossal. HMS *Southwold* herself was down to only 40 per cent of 4-inch rounds, while the anti-aircraft ship *Carlisle* had fired off a third of her stocks.

Hardly had Vian come up with the convoy again when Italian ships were freshly sighted to the north-east – and this time the 8-inch gun cruisers *Gorizia* and *Trento* and the 6-inch gun *Giovanni Delle Bande Nere* had been joined by the battleship *Littorio* (45,963 tons full load; nine 15-inch guns; twelve 6-inch).

While the convoy itself steered away to the south (still under air attack), Vian's ships laid a pall of smoke from east to west between it and the enemy. In his report on the action Vian noted 'the enormous area of smoke'

> . . . which lay well in the existing weather conditions of a 25-knot wind from the south-east. The enemy tried to make touch with the convoy by passing round the western end of the smoke, to leeward, and was therefore effectively held away from the convoy, as he would not approach the smoke, which was drifting towards him.[25]

In Vian's professional judgment the Italian commander's best course would have been to pass to windward of the smoke (that is, to the east), but the enemy preferred to take the shortest course to get between the convoy and Malta.[26]

There followed a highly confused action as the British ships manoeuvred in and out of the smoke, catching short-lived sightings of the enemy, while green seas washed over fore and aft, and driving spray drenched even the cruisers' control towers when they were steaming to windward. Yet whenever possible the little British ships went for the Italians: first for the 8-inch gun cruisers and then, from 1700 onwards, for *Littorio* herself, even starting a fire abaft her after 15-inch turret. With rollers sweeping over their heaving forecastles the destroyers replied to 8-inch and 15-inch salvoes with 4.7-inch and 4-inch; torpedoes too when the Italians were close enough. It was a majestic display of tactical skill and sheer aggressive seamanship, absolutely true to the tradition of Hawke and Nelson; and it dominated and daunted the enemy. After two and a half hours the Italian squadron gave up and retired to the north-west. The British cruisers had fired between 1,600 and 1,700 rounds; the destroyers 1,300.

For Cunningham himself, back in a shore operations room in Alexandria instead of in his favourite place on the bridge in the thick of the battle, but listening in to all Vian's signal traffic, it was a time of anxiety sharpened by impotence. 'Never have I felt so keenly,' he wrote in his memoirs, 'the mortifying bitterness of sitting behind the scenes with a heavy load of responsibility while others were in action with the enemy . . . We could imagine it all, yet there was nothing we could do to help.'[27] Yet the C-in-C *was* helping Vian – in the first place by not interfering in Vian's conduct of the action with redundant advice or instructions, and secondly by simply being Cunningham. For Vian knew that stoutly supporting him in his own determination that the convoy should not turn back but (in Vian's words) 'proceed to Malta even if enemy surface forces make contact' there stood a Commander-in-Chief with a clear head, a cool nerve and a steely will. Under another Commander-in-Chief, in another desperate convoy action, Vian would find things very different (see below, pp. 509–10).

Casualties there had been, however, in seeing off the *Littorio* and her consorts. The destroyer *Havock*'s speed had been reduced to 16 knots by a near-miss from a 15-inch shell, while another shell of this calibre had crippled the destroyer *Kingston*. Reckoning that they were not fit to undertake the return voyage to Alexandria in the teeth of a rising easterly gale, Vian ordered them to go on to Malta with the convoy. His own flagship *Cleopatra* had been hit in the bridge early in the action, killing fifteen and temporarily knocking out her radio. But, wrote Vian in his memoirs, 'The damage sustained was of no importance. The leaders of the divisions of the striking force were well aware of my intentions, and communication, for the time, was unnecessary.'[28]

At 1940 on 22 March, with the convoy not yet in sight again and with darkness spreading across the wild sea, Vian turned east for Alexandria as planned with three cruisers and eight destroyers, leaving the convoy to make its own way to Malta under cover of night. At noon on 24 March Vian brought his squadron safely into Alexandria harbour despite constant air attacks on the homeward voyage (the Royal Air Force provided welcome fighter cover on the last leg). As his battered ships steamed slowly to their moorings, he and his ships' companies were, as he put it in his report, 'honoured to receive the great demonstration' for their victory given by the crowds on shore.[29] In the meantime attacks by the Royal Air Force on the homeward-bound Italian warships had proved a total failure, so bearing out

Cunningham's mistrust of its striking power over the sea. However, the submarine *Urge* (Lieutenant-Commander Tomkinson) redeemed the failure by sinking the cruiser *Giovanni Delle Bande Nere* on 1 April.

Vian's superb fight in the Second Battle of Sirte evoked a warm and generous tribute from the Prime Minister, who signalled ('Action This Day') to the C-in-C, Mediterranean:

> I shall be glad if you will convey to Admiral Vian and all who sailed with him the admiration which I feel at this resolute and brilliant action by which the Malta convoy was saved. That one of the most powerful modern battleships afloat attended by four cruisers and a flotilla should have been routed and put to flight . . . in broad daylight by a force of British light cruisers and destroyers constitutes a naval episode of the highest distinction and entitles all ranks and ratings concerned, and above all their Commander, to the compliments of the British nation.[30]

Vian himself was later rewarded with a knighthood of the Order of the Bath: 'I considered,' he wrote, 'that the honour reflected upon all who served with me.'[31]

By the time Vian had turned for Alexandria at 1940 on 22 March, Captain Hutchison of HMS *Breconshire*, the convoy commodore of MW10, had already dispersed the merchant ships for the final run-in to Malta, allotting one or two destroyers to each as escort. But now came a sad, dragging anti-climax to 'Operation MG1'. Owing to losing distance during the evasive daytime manoeuvres the merchant ships proved unable to reach safe haven during the hours of darkness as planned. In the forenoon of 23 March they were still straggling towards Malta under relentless pounding by enemy bombers every last mile of the voyage. The first two ships, *Talabot* and *Pampas*, arrived about 0915, together with their escort destroyers. According to the commander of HMS *Havock*, 'We proceeded up harbour to the cheers of the populace.'[32]

The cheers were all too soon to change to lamentation. A few minutes later the *Breconshire* got within eight miles of harbour when at last the bombers hit and disabled her. Attempts to get her in tow failed because of her deep draught and the heavy swell, and she had to be left at anchor in the open with three destroyers to protect her. At 1020 came the next misfortune: *Clan Campbell* was hit and sunk just twenty miles short of Malta by a bomb dropped from only fifty feet. HMS *Legion* was also so badly damaged that she had to be beached. And this marked only the start of the enemy's avenging of the failure of the Italian Navy. On 24 March the destroyer *Southwold* was sunk by a mine while standing by the stricken *Breconshire*. On the

26th both the *Talabot* and the *Pampas* were hit by German bombers in harbour; the *Talabot* had to be scuttled for fear that her cargo of ammunition might explode, while all but two of *Pampas*'s holds were flooded. That same day HMS *Legion* was bombed again and finally sunk in the naval dockyard. On the morrow the *Breconshire*, hit once more by bombs, sank at Marsaxlokk, whither she had been laboriously towed after three days at anchor outside Malta.

So it was that only 5,000 tons of supplies out of the 26,000 tons originally despatched in the convoy survived for the benefit of the garrison and people of Malta, along with some oil fuel salvaged from the *Breconshire*; a grimly disappointing conclusion to so great and gallant an effort. The consequences of the successful German bombing of the ships in harbour went, however, much further. In Cunningham's words it 'showed all too clearly that there was no further chance of using surface forces from the islands while that scale of attack persisted. The dockyard was a shambles of rubble and twisted girders . . . and they [the surface forces] were nearly out of fuel-oil.'[33] The Vice-Admiral, Malta, Sir Ralph Leatham, therefore began the melancholy process of evacuating to Alexandria all ships as soon as they were patched up enough to steam, starting with the cruiser *Aurora* and the Hunt class destroyer *Avon Vale* on 29 March and ending with the *Penelope* on 8 April – the latter nicknamed 'HMS Pepperpot', so riddled with holes was she.

On 1 April 1942 Sir Andrew Cunningham hauled down his flag as Commander-in-Chief, Mediterranean, on being appointed to head the British naval staff mission in Washington. He was to be replaced in two months' time by Admiral Sir Henry Harwood; in the meantime Admiral Pridham-Wippell assumed temporary command. It was a sad time for Cunningham to go, in the midst of a period of eclipse for the Mediterranean Fleet after the truly heroic days of 1940 and 1941 with their prolonged ordeals unflinchingly borne and their victories resolutely won. Nevertheless his farewell order of the day to the Fleet displayed the authentic Cunningham touch:

> The enemy knows we are his master on the sea, and we must strain every nerve to keep our standard of fighting so high that this lesson never fails to be borne in upon him . . . I look forward to the day when the Mediterranean Fleet will sweep the sea clear and re-establish an age-old control of this waterway so vital to the British Empire. I am confident that day is not far distant, and meanwhile I wish you all good fortune and God speed.[34]

The plight and problem of Malta worsened. The Navy had had to go; the Royal Air Force on the island had been virtually annihilated by the weight of enemy air attack; the future supply position was deeply worrying. In London it was decided that no convoy could be run in May from the Gibraltar direction because British seapower was being globally squeezed – in the Atlantic; in the Arctic where the battleship *Tirpitz* threatened British convoys to Russia from her Norwegian base; in the Indian Ocean where a Japanese raid by Nagumo's fast carrier force had even posed a menace to the sole surviving lifeline from Britain to Egypt up the east coast of Africa to the Red Sea (see below, p. 863). In the meantime only a trickle of vital supplies was reaching Malta by submarine.

If Malta was to survive, the first essential must be to rebuild her fighter defence; and that meant flying the aircraft in from carriers as in 1941. But the Royal Navy lacked the carriers to meet all its commitments. Churchill therefore appealed for help to President Roosevelt, who consented to the employment of the USS *Wasp* (Captain J. W. Reeves, Jr, USN: 21,000 tons full load; capacity 84 aircraft; launched 1939)[35] then already in British home waters. On 13 April 1942 she embarked 47 Spitfires in the Clyde and sailed next day escorted by the battlecruiser *Renown* (Commodore C. S. Daniel), the cruiser *Charybdis* and the anti-aircraft cruiser *Cairo*, and a mixed force of British and American destroyers. The force passed through the Straits of Gibraltar under cover of darkness in the small hours of 19 April and steamed on eastwards – the first time that the Stars and Stripes of the US Navy had flown alongside the White Ensign in the Mediterranean in this war. On 20 April the Spitfires were flown off, all but one safely reaching Malta's airfields, and many of them engaging the Luftwaffe that same day. But the enemy immediately mounted a ruthless effort to eliminate these fighter reinforcements both in the air and by smashing them on their airfields – and he largely succeeded. And so in the first week of May, with Roosevelt's further consent, the USS *Wasp* once again embarked 47 Spitfires and with the same escort as before set course for Gibraltar and the Mediterranean.

At Gibraltar on the night of 7–8 May she was joined by the old British carrier *Eagle* (with seventeen Spitfires aboard) and the fast minelayer *Welshman*, which was to go right through to Malta with a much-needed cargo of special stores and ammunition. 'We are quite likely to lose this ship,' wrote the First Sea Lord to Churchill, 'but in view of the urgency . . . there appears to be no alternative.'[36] In the event, the *Welshman* returned safely, having unloaded her stores and sailed again within seven hours. On 9 May the two carriers flew off their 64 Spitfires, only three being lost en route to Malta. Next day they fought a successful battle against the enemy; the beginning of the turning of the tide in the air over Malta.

In the middle of May the *Eagle* was back again with seventeen more Spitfires; and early in June she made two more such trips, this time ferrying a total of 55 fighters. Through such exertions Malta's fighter defence was at last made equal to its task. By this time too the island's anti-aircraft equipment, including smoke projectors to screen the harbour and dockyard, had also been cumulatively strengthened. The neglect of the inter-war years had finally been made good – but at a period when Britain had lost command of the Mediterranean, and when it looked as if Malta might soon be starved into defeat anyway.

To avert this imminent fate there had now to be mounted a complex operation of maritime war on the largest scale – two convoys to be run simultaneously to Malta from Gibraltar ('Harpoon': six merchant ships) and Alexandria ('Vigorous': eleven ships) in June, although timed to arrive at the island on successive days in order to confuse the enemy. The flying-in of the Spitfires had provided the essential air cover for the convoys during their final approach to their destination. A second serious danger lay, however, in mines, for Malta lacked the vessels and equipment adequately to sweep them.

The plan for 'Operation Harpoon', the western convoy from the United Kingdom via Gibraltar, followed the pattern of late 1941. A covering force (Force W) consisting of the battleship *Malaya*, the old carriers *Eagle* and *Argus*, three cruisers (*Kenya*, flying the flag of Vice-Admiral A. T. B. Curteis; *Liverpool* and *Charybdis*) and eight destroyers, would escort the convoy as far as the Skerki Bank, off Tunisia, then turn back. The close escort (Force X) – one anti-aircraft cruiser (*Cairo*: Acting-Captain C. C. Hardy), nine destroyers and four minesweepers – would shepherd the six merchant ships the rest of the way to Malta.[37] Yet there was a difference between the 'Harpoon' escort forces and those deployed in the late 1941 Malta convoys: the 'Harpoon' forces were much weaker because of the competing demands of the Eastern Fleet in parrying the Japanese, and also of the current Allied invasion of Madagascar (see below, pp. 864–8).

The 'Harpoon' convoy, bearing 43,000 tons of supplies, sailed from Britain on 5 June; passed the Straits of Gibraltar during the night of 11th–12th, and steamed on through a calm and sunlit Mediterranean. Next day enemy aircraft and submarines began to tag the convoy. The 14th proved another glorious – but to ships facing air attack, deadly – Mediterranean summer's day; and the convoy was now well within range of enemy air bases on Sardinia. From 1030 onwards the bombers began their persistent work: at first Italian CR42 fighter-bombers and Savoia torpedo-bombers. A Savoia inflicted the first losses with torpedoes dropped at a height of 100 feet and a range of 2,000 yards, sinking the Dutch merchantman *Tanimba* and hitting the cruiser *Liverpool* in the engine room. Now capable of only 3 to 4 knots on one shaft, the *Liverpool* had to be detached back to Gibraltar under tow by the destroyer *Antelope* and escorted by the destroyer *Westcott*, eventually making port in the evening of 17 June. Then it was the turn of Italian Cant high-level bombers approaching out of the eye of the sun and singling out the carriers, which fortunately survived without damage. So far British carrier-borne fighters had shot down three fighters and three torpedo-aircraft, which was not bad going in the light of what Captain Rushbrooke of the *Eagle* called in his report 'the most inadequate measure' of protection afforded by the two small old carriers, able to fly at most only six Hurricanes and four Fulmars at any time.[38]

The day dragged on, the convoy and its escort crawling along naked on the sea's broad surface beneath the bombers and the brilliant sky; the ships' companies sweltering in anti-flash hoods and tin hats. At 1830 the Luftwaffe joined in, ten Ju 88s coming in astern at 10,000 feet and then diving to 6,000 feet for the attack. According to Vice-Admiral Curteis in his report, 'As is usual in the Mediterranean it was very difficult to see these till they had reached the bombing position, and gunfire was ineffective.'[39] Both carriers were lucky to escape damage, especially the *Argus*, which had one bomb pitch fine on her port bow, dive beneath the ship and burst under the starboard bow.

This was merely the overture to an orchestrated onslaught of high-level bombing, dive-bombing and torpedo attacks by both Italian and German aircraft in order to overwhelm the British defences – enemy aircraft swarming round and overhead with ships' tracer curving among them, the puffballs of shellbursts drifting against the blue as thick as thistledown. Yet neither side scored a hit. Meanwhile the convoy had been manoeuvred almost as dexterously as a division of destroyers; a major reason for the enemy failure. The carrier-borne fighters that day shot down eleven aircraft for the loss of seven. As the Director of the Naval Air Division of the Naval Staff remarked later in a minute: 'The results achieved by the small force of naval fighters are most outstanding.'[40] They were the more outstanding because *Eagle* and *Argus* lacked modern fighter-direction apparatus.[41]

At 2100, when the convoy had reached the Sicilian Narrows, four welcome Royal Air Force Beaufighters turned up from Malta. Half an hour later Curteis and Force X hauled round to the west, its part completed. The merchant ships and Force Y – under the command of Captain C. C. Hardy, in the *Cairo* – stood on for Malta; the merchantmen in line ahead screened on all sides by the warships.

That evening, however, Curteis received a report that two Italian cruisers and some destroyers had left Palermo in Sicily, course undetermined. For Curteis, now some fifty miles distant from the convoy, this report presented a dilemma: should he despatch one of his two remaining cruisers to support the outgunned Hardy? His own force still lay within striking range of the enemy's Sardinian airfields, and he was worried about weakening the anti-aircraft protection of his carriers by detaching a cruiser. In any case there would be barely time for her to overtake the convoy before morning. 'With the forces available,' he wrote in his report, 'a decision either way was a gamble: if the LIVERPOOL had been present, there would have been no doubt in my mind.'[42] As it was, he decided that the convoy's own escort should prove sufficient. It was a decision that would be questioned later within the Admiralty.

Next day, 15 June, its good fortune forsook 'Harpoon'. At daybreak British submarines sighted the two Italian cruisers and five destroyers and attacked them without success. At 0620 a Beaufighter reported to Hardy that two cruisers and four (sic) destroyers lay fifteen miles distant on the port beam of the British force. The convoy was then steering south-east at 12 knots, with the merchantmen now in two columns, the *Cairo* ahead, five fleet destroyers to starboard and four 'Hunts' to port, and the four fleet minesweepers and some motor launches astern. Only a few minutes passed before the Italian ships were seen broad on the port beam and hull down against the bright eastern morning sky, and steering a slightly converging course at high speed. They were soon identified as two 6-inch gun cruisers and six destroyers. Hardy, with only an anti-aircraft cruiser, found himself heavily outweighted; a victim (like Curteis too) of the Royal Navy's sheer shortage of cruisers after the losses of nearly three years of war coming on top of crippling reductions of strength in the late 1920s and early 1930s. In previous Malta convoy operations it had been possible to provide a strong cruiser escort to send on to Malta with the merchantmen; not so this time. Hardy would have to battle his way through as best he could.

While Commander B. G. Scurfield (in the *Bedouin*) unhesitatingly led out the five fleet destroyers to attack the enemy force, HMS *Cairo* laid a smoke screen to protect the convoy, which Hardy ordered away to starboard and to shelter in Tunisian waters. At 0640 the Italian cruisers opened fire at 20,000 yards, immediately straddling the *Cairo*.

The 4.7-inch and 4-inch guns of the British destroyers were still completely outranged. In a loose line of bearing the five fleet destroyers steamed for the enemy. At 0645 they opened fire at maximum elevation. But within a quarter of an hour both leading destroyers, *Bedouin* and *Partridge*, had been badly damaged and stopped. The *Ithuriel* held her fire until she had closed the range to 15,000 yards, and succeeded in hitting one of the cruisers at 8,000 yards. The destroyer *Marne* likewise took on an Italian cruiser, and then *Marne* and *Matchless* together attacked the Italian destroyers. After the *Ugolino Vivaldi* was hit, the enemy destroyers followed the customary Italian pattern of discretion before valour, and retired. *Marne* and *Matchless* thereupon turned their guns on the cruisers, which also displayed a reluctance to engage more closely. At 0745 the Italian ships turned away to port; another success for British fighting seamanship.

However, while the bulk of Hardy's strength had been employed in driving off the enemy surface forces, enemy aircraft had taken the opportunity to savage the merchant ships. Ju 88s sank the *Chant* and disabled the *Kentucky*, which had to be taken in tow. At 0745 the convoy commodore, Commander Pilditch, decided to resume the course for Malta in order to join up with Hardy. But since the Italian surface forces were still shadowing Hardy, this could well run the convoy into fresh danger. Hardy therefore ordered the convoy to reverse course again at 0834, while the *Cairo* and the destroyers laid a protective smoke screen which successfully baffled the Italians. At this time *Cairo* took her second hit.

At 1040 the air attacks began again, although at first the enemy was driven off by long-range Spitfires from Malta. Forty minutes later, in the interval before the next relay of Spitfires arrived, Ju 88s and Ju 87s bombed from high and low, crippling the merchant ship *Burdwan*. Yet the convoy still had a hundred and fifty miles to go to Malta. Hardy therefore decided that he must sink the crippled *Kentucky* and *Burdwan* in order that the convoy could make maximum speed. In the afternoon the Italian cruisers tried again – and were driven off again. However, a torpedo-bomber succeeded in sinking the crippled destroyer *Bedouin*, which had been in tow.

The 16th June went better, thanks to constant cover by Malta Spitfires accurately directed against the foe by *Cairo*'s radar and fighter-direction centre. It seemed as though the worst must now have passed. But, by an unfortunate error of timing, the convoy reached the waters round Malta before the minesweepers. Four warships and one merchantman struck mines, although all were able to reach harbour except for the Polish destroyer *Kujawiak*, which sank.

In the evening *Cairo* and the only four undamaged fleet destroyers sailed again for Gibraltar. Back came the relentless enemy air forces, and only after what the captain of the *Ithuriel* in his report described as 'a struggle for existence' did Force Y – amazingly without further damage – rejoin Curteis for a safe return to Gibraltar.

'Operation Harpoon' had been accomplished. Its ships had been attacked by a total of about 200 enemy aircraft, of which the carriers' fighters had shot down thirteen and anti-aircraft fire another sixteen (the *Cairo* was equipped with an American fire-control system). Two destroyers had been lost, and a cruiser, three destroyers and a mine-sweeper badly damaged. And of the six merchant ships despatched, only two finally reached Malta – another disappointing pay-off.

In the meantime the Mediterranean Fleet had been mounting its even bigger operation to try to get eleven merchant ships through to Malta from Alexandria – the first to be carried out under the direction of the new Commander-in-Chief, Mediterranean, Acting-Admiral Sir Henry Harwood, who had hoisted his flag in the *Queen Elizabeth* (now being repaired in a floating dock) on 20 May. Harwood's reputation – especially with Churchill – had been made by his aggress-ive conduct of action against the *Graf Spee* in December 1939, even though he had earlier been marked down to be passed over for promotion to flag rank.[43] Since December 1940 he had served ashore in Whitehall as Assistant Chief of Naval Staff (Foreign), and therefore when he succeeded Cunningham in the enormous and complex political, strategic and operational responsibilities of the Mediter-ranean command, his previous experience as a commander had been limited to one small squadron of three cruisers. It was rather as if the owner of a corner shop had suddenly been put in charge of Harrods. No wonder that, when Cunningham heard of the Admiralty's nominee as his replacement, he had written to the First Sea Lord to express a preference for 'someone better experienced and better known to the personnel'.[44] Nonetheless Pound, A. V. Alexander (the First Lord) and Churchill all agreed that Harwood was the man.

It proved, to say the least, a mistaken choice. Harwood lacked the sheer ruthless powers of leadership of his predecessor, the certainty of mind; lacked too the matured grasp of all the problems of the theatre. For the Fleet and its flag officers, it was as if an iron grasp had suddenly relaxed; an animating fire gone cold. And almost as soon as Harwood hoisted his flag, he found himself compelled – by London's direction against his own judgment – to carry out 'Operation Vigorous', a particularly hazardous undertaking the risks of which were vastly increased by the long days and short nights of mid-June.

By 'loans' from the Eastern Fleet, the warship strength available as the main escort for 'Vigorous' was built up to seven cruisers, one anti-aircraft ship, and 26 destroyers. In addition four motor torpedo boats were to be towed by merchant ships, ready to be slipped for action when necessary, while two minesweepers and unarmed rescue ships were also to accompany the convoy.[45] It was a singular mark of the poverty of the Royal Navy's resources that in lieu of a real battleship a dummy *King George V* was to sail in the escort – the old battleship *Centurion*, launched in 1911, stripped of her guns in 1924 and later used as a radio-controlled target ship, and now put back into service again with a light anti-aircraft armament and with her superstructure unconvincingly altered to resemble a 'King George V'. Nor could a carrier be provided.

Harwood therefore looked to Royal Air Force and United States Army Air Force bombers to fill the place of heavy ships and carrier-borne aviation in preventing the Italian battlefleet from attacking the convoy. Because of this he and Tedder moved to a combined command centre in the headquarters of the Naval Cooperation Group, RAF, in Alexandria.

However, the available land-based air forces consisted of a mixed bag of only 40 aircraft: torpedo-armed Wellingtons and Beauforts from Malta, more Beauforts from Egyptian airfields near the Libyan border, and some American Liberator heavy bombers from the Suez area. The joint plan required these varied and widely dispersed forces to launch synchronised attacks on the Italian fleet once it was detected at sea by air search. In his subsequent report Harwood was to write: 'Events proved with painful clarity that our striking forces had nothing like the weight required to stop a fast and powerful enemy force, and in no way compensated for our lack of heavy ships.'[46] This was no more than Cunningham had bluntly pointed out to Pound at the beginning of the year; it hardly needed to be learned afresh by costly experience. Admiral Vian, the flag officer designated to command 'Vigorous' afloat, was of the opinion (according to his post-war recollection) that once Harwood 'accepted a weak, unescorted air striking force as a substitute [for battleships] we were sunk...'[47] Vian reckoned that it was not possible with cruisers and destroyers equipped with dual-purpose (anti-ship *and* anti-aircraft) guns to fight a fleet action from dawn till dusk on a June day with what ammunition would be left over after fending off heavy air attacks; and *then* still have enough ammunition for the return passage.[48] Vian therefore went to sea in a frame of mind very different from that in March at the start of 'Operation MG1', for, as he later confessed, he lacked confidence in the plan, in the C-in-C, and the C-in-C's ability to carry out the plan; and, because of all this, he lacked personal confidence too.[49]

In order to mislead the enemy the merchant ships were loaded in various ports between Beirut and Alexandria, and then assembled in two groups in Haifa and Alexandria. At the same time a third group of four ships sailed on 11 June (thirty-six hours ahead of the main body) as far as Tobruk in order – as it was hoped – to draw the Italian fleet to sea prematurely. This ploy failed of its purpose; and it also failed to divert the enemy air forces.

On the evening of 13 June Vian put to sea with the main body, flying his flag in the cruiser *Cleopatra* (Captain G. Grantham). From sunset until 0430 next morning enemy aircraft kept the convoy and its escort brilliantly illuminated with parachute flares. During the night the destroyer screen successfully drove off a marauding U-boat and six E-boats, which success Vian put down to the 'unattractive proposition' presented to the enemy by his dispositions for the dark hours – an anti-submarine screen ahead on the bows of the convoy, a special 'night screen' of two cruisers and four destroyers on each quarter, and a single destroyer five miles out on each bow and quarter. But Rear-Admiral Tennant (the former Captain of the *Repulse*), who was commanding the ships lent by the Eastern Fleet, recalled that 'the flares gave me a very naked feeling when dropped overhead, and it is surprising that the E-boats did not achieve a great deal more success'.[50]

Next day, the 14th – it was the day when far away to the west the enemy air forces began to attack the 'Harpoon' convoy too – the bombers arrived early, and kept it up all day, sinking one merchant ship and damaging another so badly that she had to be detached to Tobruk. Since the bottom of a third ship proved so foul that she could not keep up, the convoy's numbers had already fallen to eight. Now Vian was running the gauntlet of hostile air forces based all along the North African coast as far as Tripoli on one flank, and Crete and Sicily on the other; running deep into the zone where the Italian battlefleet would be likely to strike from its bases in Sicily and the heel of Italy. It was therefore absolutely essential that British air reconnaissance kept Harwood and Vian exactly informed about the enemy's position, course and speed. But, as the Naval Staff History remarks, 'the aircraft available for the purpose were too few to keep the enemy under continuous observation'.[51] Only confusing and sometimes incorrect reports were to reach Harwood and Tedder during the operation; an uncertainty by no means helpful to a novice of a C-in-C in his first crisis of command.

At 2215 on 14 June Vian received a signal from Harwood passing on an aircraft report that two battleships and four cruisers had sailed from Taranto and would probably encounter him on his present course at about 0700 next morning – at almost the beginning, therefore, of the long June day: the very contingency with which Vian knew he could not this time cope. He therefore signalled the C-in-C to ask: 'Do you wish me to retire?'[52] Harwood responded by ordering Vian to keep his course until 0200 (why?) and then to 'turn back along the same track'. At 0145 on the 15th Vian turned the convoy and escort – some fifty ships to manoeuvre on to a reverse course. This cumbersome process gave an opening to an E-boat to infiltrate the escort and torpedo the cruiser *Newcastle* forward, although she still remained capable of 24 knots. A little later a U-boat hit the destroyer *Hasty*, so disabling her that she had to be sunk by a consort.

At the time when Vian turned the convoy the Italian fleet, steering south to intercept, was still more than 200 miles distant to the north-west. At 0224 a further air report gave the Italian strength as one battleship, two cruisers and two destroyers, position 37° 30'N, 19° 35'E, course 190°, speed 20 knots. At 0525 Harwood was signalling once more; this time to order Vian to steer north-westwards again, on the score that 'bomb alley' between Crete and Libya would be more dangerous than the Italian ships. At 0655, Vian, having received this fresh order, duly turned the convoy back towards Malta and the approaching Italian fleet. At 0705 Harwood radioed another instruction to Vian, and not one that could have eased Vian's mind very much:

> Avoid contact until [British] aircraft have attacked, which should be by 1030. If air attack fails, every effort must be made to get convoy through to Malta by adopting offensive attitude. Should this fail, and convoy be cornered, it is to be sacrificed, and you are to extricate your forces, proceeding to eastward or westward.[53]

An hour and a half later Harwood received another air search report according to which two battleships, three cruisers and nine destroyers lay within 150 miles of the convoy, steering south-east. So Harwood signalled Vian yet again: Vian was to steer 105° – that is, eastwards once more. On receipt of the signal at 0940 Vian altered round.

With an Italian squadron including heavy ships known for certain to be at sea and steering to intercept, it was now up to the Allied bombers to fulfil their task of preventing it reaching the convoy. From 0905 to 0940 Beauforts from Malta and Egypt and Liberators from

Suez had a go; and succeeded in landing one bomb on the battleship *Littorio's* forward 15-inch turret which failed to penetrate the armour, and one torpedo on the 8-inch gun cruiser *Trento*, disabling her. She was to be sunk later that day by the submarine *Umbria* (Lieutenant S. L. C. Maydon). However, the Beauforts wrongly reported at 0944 that they had hit both Italian battleships as well as the cruiser. This apparently marvellous news encouraged Harwood at 1151 to order Vian to resume his course for Malta, although Harwood also repeated by way of caution the broad directive contained in his signal of 0705 that morning. So yet again Vian brought his sprawling and unwieldy command round: further waste of time and loss of distance.

Back in the operations room in Alexandria, Harwood waited anxiously for more aircraft reports on the whereabouts of the Italian fleet; none came. If even Cunningham had found the waiting, the uncertainty and the impotence of 'back-seat' command from on shore hard to bear, the strain on the unfortunate Harwood may be imagined. He began to worry that the Beauforts might only have hit the cruiser. He did not know whether Vian had been attacked or mauled by the Italian fleet; nor what was Vian's present ammunition state. At 1245 he signalled Vian: 'I must leave decision to you whether to comply with my 0705/15, or whether to again retire with hope of carrying out a night destroyer attack, if enemy stand on.'[54]

Vian only received Harwood's earlier signal of 1151 hours at 1345, and soon afterwards came confirmation from a report by 'Aircraft T' that the enemy was indeed standing on. The attempt to substitute bombers for battleships and carriers had thus totally failed to fend off the Italian fleet. So too had the picket lines of eight submarines, whose efforts to screen the convoy had been rendered more difficult by the convoy's changes of course.

By this time both Vian's most modern and powerful cruisers, the *Newcastle* and the *Birmingham* (both 9,100 tons displacement; twelve 6-inch guns; launched 1936 under the rearmament programme)[55] had been damaged; *Newcastle* by the E-boat on the previous day, *Birmingham* by a bomb. Vian therefore decided not to implement for the time being the C-in-C's signal of 1151 ordering him to resume course for Malta: 'My heavy striking force, the Fourth Cruiser Squadron, being somewhat under the weather, I held on to the eastward awaiting [the C-in-C's] reactions to Aircraft T's report.'[56] At 1420 he received Harwood's discretionary signal sent at 1245 hours, which only confirmed him in continuing to steer east. An hour later 30 to 40 dive-bombers escorted by Me 109s roared in from astern. Twelve of the bombers concentrated on the destroyer *Airedale* out in the air-warning screen on the starboard quarter of the convoy, and blanketed her with hits and near-misses. Disabled, she had to be sunk by a consort. Meanwhile another merchant ship had had to drop out because it could not maintain speed, so that the precious convoy was now down to only six ships.

Meanwhile, however, the Italian battle squadron had unexpectedly given up the chase when it got to within about 100 miles of the convoy. At 1515 it hauled round to the north-westward. At 1605 a British aircraft reported that it was by then well on its way to Taranto.

To Harwood this news appeared to change the situation entirely. At 1625 he signalled Vian: 'Now is the golden opportunity to get convoy to Malta. Have Hunts, *Coventry*, minesweepers and corvettes enough fuel and ammunition for one-way trip? If so, I would like to turn the convoy now, cruisers and destroyers parting company and returning to Alexandria.'[57] Two hours later he had still received no reply from Vian to this ebullient signal. For from 1720 onwards Vian was fully occupied with nearly 30 enemy bombers and ten torpedo-bombers, both German and Italian, which sought by a combination of high and low-level attack to do what the Italian fleet had failed to do. Vian wrote in his subsequent report: 'All known forms of attack were employed, the fire of the fleet being fully extended.'[58]

The high-level bombers attacked first, riding unseen at 16,000 feet in the western sun until nearly overhead: near-misses but not hits. Around 1800 it was the turn of the twin-engined Ju 88 dive-bombers. They released their bombs at 6,000 feet, slightly damaging the *Arethusa* and the ancient *Centurion* but crippling the Australian destroyer *Nestor* with a near-miss. An hour later three-engined Savoia 79s (maximum speed 267 mph; range, 1,180 miles)[59] launched torpedoes from both quarters, but again without scoring a hit. At the cost of enormous expenditure in ammunition Vian's ships shot down three Savoias and two bombers.

It was not until 1842, therefore, that Vian replied to Harwood's signal of 1625 about the golden opportunity of getting the convoy through to Malta and also enquiring about ammunition stocks. Vian reported that the destroyers had less than 30 per cent of their ammunition left, that it was being used up fast, and that he calculated it was insufficient for the passage to Malta. His report crossed another signal from Harwood sent at 1830 conveying the C-in-C's second thoughts (something to which he was rather prone) about going on to Malta: only four out of the remaining merchantmen were to continue thither, with the light cruiser *Arethusa* and two fleet destroyers as escort. But when Harwood himself received Vian's report about the depletion of ammunition, he finally ordered at 2053: 'Return to Alexandria with your whole force.'[60]

The enemy had won; the 'Vigorous' convoy had been forced to turn back; Malta would have to survive as best it might. But this did not mark the end of 'Vigorous's' travail. During the night of 15–16 June, a night of angry disappointment for Vian and his squadron, the U-205 torpedoed and sank the cruiser *Hermione* (Captain G. N. Oliver), while the damaged *Nestor* had to be scuttled at 0700 the following morning. That evening Vian's physically battered and morally bruised squadron reached Alexandria. It was some compensation that a Wellington had managed to torpedo the *Littorio* on her way home, inflicting damage that was to put her in the dockyard for several months.

No further convoy was to be run from Alexandria to Malta until November 1942.

Several factors explain this major defeat. The first was undoubtedly, as Harwood wrote (and Cunningham had well realised in his time), that the striking power of the Royal Air Force over the sea in the Mediterranean was simply not capable of stopping a battlefleet. Secondly, 'Vigorous' had to be mounted at a time when Rommel was already winning the Gazala battles – when, therefore, the Royal Air Force was deeply committed to that battle, and when even the airfields in eastern Cyrenaica could no longer be used by Beaufort torpedo-bombers. Coupled with the long June days and Vian's lack of a carrier, this meant that 'Vigorous' was more exposed to enemy air attack and for longer than any previous Malta convoy from Alexandria. Yet the clinching factor in the defeat lay in the C-in-C's dithering which led him to order Vian to turn his convoy no fewer than six times; instructions actually complied with four times, with consequent crucial loss of distance, to say nothing of the expenditure of ammunition. As Vian wrote later, his lack of confidence in the plan, in the C-in-C and in the C-in-C's ability to carry out the plan conduced to his own lack of confidence and hence, in his words, to 'its fatal corollary, irresolution'.[61] Cunningham's own retrospective judgment was that if Harwood had left Vian alone, Vian would have gone straight on; indeed Cunningham wondered why Harwood had not *ordered* him to press on.[62]

Would the convoy have got through if Cunningham had still been Commander-in-Chief? 'The reply is,' wrote Vian in 1954 in answer to this question, 'that no flag officer ever thought of not going through with a direct operation order from Andrew; but he would never issue one not capable of achievement with the forces allocated.'[63]

The end of June 1942 saw the entire Mediterranean strategy pursued by Britain since 1940 dead in the water. All the huge investment in shipping round the Cape, in the equipment, supplies (civilian as well as military), weaponry and military ration-strength poured into the Middle East in that shipping over the last two years, all the swaying Desert campaigns, had ended with a routed 8th Army preparing a last stand in defence of Egypt at El Alamein, only 60 miles west of Alexandria: with the Mediterranean Fleet's pre-war main base, Malta, neutralised; and with the Fleet itself having lost control of the Mediterranean, and even defeated outright in 'Operation Vigorous'. And now, just as the still undaunted General Sir Claude Auchinleck (who had taken personal command of 8th Army) told his soldiers that 'the enemy is stretching to his limit and thinks we are a broken army . . . He hopes to take Egypt by bluff. Show him where he gets off,'[64] his naval colleague, Admiral Harwood, precipitately ordered the Fleet to evacuate its base at Alexandria.

Although Cunningham had previously prepared a contingency plan for such an evacuation, it had taken the form of an orderly withdrawal over three weeks. Now it was carried out in 48 hours, the haste being such that the White Ensign was still flying over the deserted camp at Sidi Bishr while Egyptians looted it at their leisure.[65] The ships retired to Haifa (the submarine depot ship *Medway* being sunk en route by a U-boat) or to Port Said; Harwood himself went back to Ismailia on the Canal. In a letter to the First Sea Lord in November 1942 after his return to Alexandria Harwood claimed that he had ordered the evacuation because of the example of Singapore, where the process of withdrawal from the naval base had been left too late. 'In many ways though,' he admitted, 'I wish I had not left here [Alexandria]. . .'[66]

Yet within a month Auchinleck's hard-won victory over Rommel in the First Battle of Alamein (the first land battle to be conducted thanks to guidance by up-to-date information from Ultra decrypts of Enigma traffic)[67] had ensured that Britain's Mediterranean strategy would not after all finally founder. Hope revived. The Prime Minister (by now obsessed with beating the legendary Rommel and his three under-strength German divisions) and the Cabinet pressed on with fresh military investment in the Middle East on a gigantic scale – enough to build the 8th Army by October up to a strength of nearly 200,000 men, over 1,000 tanks (including 300 new Shermans shipped from the United States), over 900 medium field guns, over 1,400 anti-tank guns, over 8,000 (new) trucks, and more than 18,000 tons of forward stocks of medium and field artillery rounds.[68]

Such a build-up demanded yet another colossal shipping lift, both from the United Kingdom and the United States, at a time of a growing dearth of ships and of dismaying success for the U-boats in the Atlantic. In the three months July to September 1942 no fewer than 262 ships carried military cargoes to the Indian Ocean area (which included the Middle East), as against only 98 in the previous quarter.[69] And this commitment of shipping could only be at the expense of imports into the United Kingdom, both of food and of the essentials for war production, so necessitating recourse to stockpiles.[70]

Meanwhile the problem of Malta remained. Without succour the island could not survive the months that must elapse before this investment produced a victory that won back the vital airfields in the Cyrenaican bulge. Another early attempt to run a convoy to Malta in the meantime there had to be. After the experience of 'Operation Vigorous' it was clear that this attempt could only be made from the west, from Gibraltar. In the early hours of 10 August, the convoy and its escorting battlefleet reached the Straits of Gibraltar under a thick shroud of fog; 'Operation Pedestal' was about to begin.

So high did the War Cabinet place Malta in its global priorities that in order to free ships of the Home Fleet to augment the escort in 'Operation Pedestal' it decided not to run a convoy to Soviet Russia in August even though the Red Army was staggering back towards Stalingrad and the Caucasus in the face of the German 1942 summer offensive. The detachment of the battleship *Nelson*, the carrier *Victorious*, the cruisers *Nigeria*, *Kenya* and *Manchester* and eleven destroyers from the Home Fleet brought the strength of the battle-squadron escorting 'Pedestal' up to three fleet-carriers (the other two being *Indomitable* and *Eagle*), flying a total of 72 aircraft, two battleships (the other being *Rodney*), six cruisers, one anti-aircraft cruiser (*Cairo*), 24 destroyers, an ocean tug, and two fleet oilers with a corvette escort. In addition the carrier *Furious* (escorted by another eight destroyers) was to fly 36 Spitfires into Malta under cover of the main operation. In command of 'Operation Pedestal' was Vice-Admiral E. N. Syfret, flying his flag in the *Nelson* (Captain H. B. Jacomb),[71] who joined the convoy of fourteen merchantmen off the Clyde with the bulk of the escort on 3 August. On the voyage out to Gibraltar Admiral Syfret made the convoy practise emergency turns and other manoeuvres so that, in the words of his report, it 'attained an efficiency in manoeuvring comparable to that of the fleet unit'.[72] At the same time the three carriers practised air defence tactics and fighter-direction.

At Gibraltar most of the escort refuelled. Then, in the forenoon of

10 August Syfret passed the Rock into the Mediterranean, green seas mingling to blue, and set course for Malta. Thanks to fog the enemy only received news of this great armada that afternoon via a report from a Vichy-French commercial airliner. But soon after daylight on 11 August German reconnaissance aircraft were seen circling the horizon round the convoy, the familiar omen of trouble to come. They shadowed Syfret all day despite the attempts of carrier-borne fighters to drive them off. At 1230 the *Furious* (Captain T. O. Bulteel) began flying off her Spitfires to Malta at a distance of some 550 miles, a process which was to take several hours. At 1315 occurred the first disaster – from beneath the sea rather than above it. The U-73 (Lieutenant Helmut Rosenbaum) succeeded in diving undetected beneath the fleet's destroyer screen and through the four columns of merchant ships to fire four torpedoes at the carrier *Eagle* (Captain L. D. Mackintosh) on the starboard quarter of the convoy. The old ship (launched June 1918 as a Chilean battleship, completed 1923 as a carrier) suffered a huge hole blown in her port side, and sank in eight minutes in 38° 05′N, 3° 12′E. Nine hundred out of her complement of 1,160 (including Captain Mackintosh) were rescued by destroyers and the tug *Jaunty*. The four of her aircraft which were then in the air landed on other carriers.

On the evening of 11 August *Furious*, her task accomplished, turned back for Gibraltar with her escort of eight destroyers, one of which, the *Wolverine* (Lieutenant-Commander P. W. Gretton), rammed the Italian submarine *Dagabur* at high speed at 0100 next day, damaging herself badly in the process. Meanwhile the 'Pedestal' convoy and its escorting fleet steamed on towards the waiting enemy air forces. Late in the afternoon of the 11th Syfret received warning that he could expect to see these at dusk. He therefore spread out his destroyers in an all-round air-warning and anti-aircraft screen. At 2045 36 Heinkel He111 bombers and Junkers Ju88 torpedo-bombers attacked out of the setting sun: no hits, but instead four aircraft downed by the fleet's anti-aircraft fire. This was no more than the apéritif. In the bright midday of 12 August the enemy launched his first main onslaught on 'Pedestal' from his Sardinian airfields with 70 strike aircraft heavily escorted by fighters. For although Air Marshal Sir Keith Park (the airman who in command of No. 11 Group, Fighter Command, had played the leading part in defeating the Luftwaffe in the Battle of Britain, and was now commanding Royal Air Force, Malta) had done his best to suppress the enemy air forces by bombing their bases in Sardinia, Sicily and Pantellaria, he lacked the necessary weight of attack to achieve this.

This time the Luftwaffe and the Regia Aeronautica tried out a new combination of tactics in order to break up the convoy's formation and dislocate the fleet's air defence. Firstly, two Italian torpedo-bombers dropped a fearsome new product of Italian technology ahead of the convoy – the 'motobomba FF', a torpedo which ran round in circles to the bewilderment and dismay, as the enemy hoped, of British skippers. Then 42 torpedo-bombers rode in from each bow of the convoy, followed by dive-bombers and in turn by two Reggiane 2001 single-seat fighters (maximum speed 337 mph; range 684 miles)[73] each armed with an armour-piercing bomb intended for an aircraft carrier. This circus of varied turns went on for nearly two hours, but inflicted no losses beyond the merchant ship *Deucalion*, damaged and sunk later near the Tunisian coast by a torpedo-bomber. For fortunately a heavy bomb which did hit *Victorious*'s flight deck broke up harmlessly on impact.

During the afternoon 'Pedestal' had to fight and dodge its way through a massed submarine ambush. But thanks to the vigilant aggression of the escorting destroyers and frequent emergency changes of course the convoy came through unscathed, while the destroyer *Ithuriel* (Lieutenant-Commander D. H. Maitland-Makgill-Crichton) rammed and sank the Italian submarine *Cobalto*, again with crippling damage to the destroyer; in Syfret's judgment a needlessly expensive method of dealing with a U-boat surfaced after depth-charging.

At 1835 the enemy air forces tried again, this time in a strength of 100 Ju 87s, Ju 88s and Savoia 79s protected by swarms of fighters. And again they sought to confuse and overwhelm the defence by attacks from all directions and all angles – bombers from astern out of the sun, torpedo-bombers coming in from ahead and then splitting up to launch torpedoes against the convoy's starboard bow and quarter. Syfret himself was to pay tribute to the excellence of the timing of these attacks, which proved devastatingly successful. The destroyer *Foresight* (Lieutenant-Commander R. A. Fell) became the first casualty. Disabled by a torpedo, she had to be sunk later. But the onslaught focused on the carrier *Indomitable* (Captain T. H. Troubridge), lying astern of the *Rodney* on the port quarter of the convoy. Four Ju 88s and eight Ju 87s 'appearing', in Troubridge's words, 'suddenly from up sun out of the smoky blue sky' dived steeply down on the carrier from astern, the Ju 87s releasing their bombs from a height of 1,000 feet. Three armour-piercing bombs smashed into the *Indomitable*'s 2½ to 3-inch thick deck armour, wrecking her

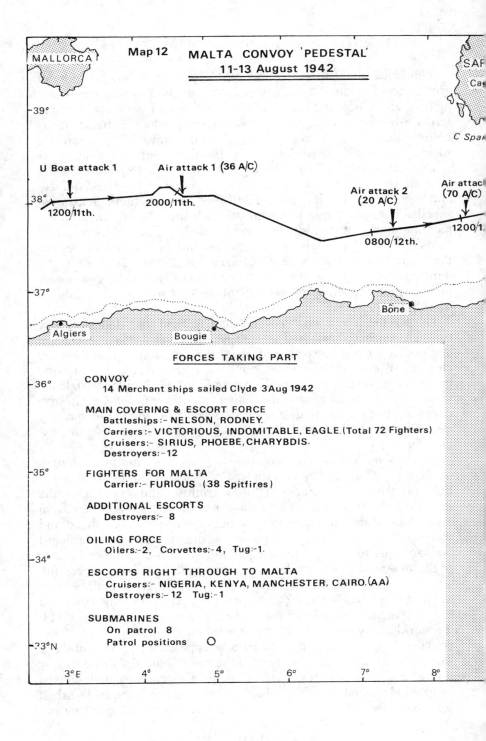

Map 12 MALTA CONVOY 'PEDESTAL'
11-13 August 1942

MALLORCA

SAR

Ca

C Spa

39°

U Boat attack 1

Air attack 1 (36 A/C)

Air attack 2
(20 A/C)

Air attac
(70 A/C)

38°

2000/11th.

1200/1.

1200/11th.

0800/12th.

37°

Bône

Algiers

Bougie

FORCES TAKING PART

CONVOY
14 Merchant ships sailed Clyde 3 Aug 1942

36°

MAIN COVERING & ESCORT FORCE
Battleships:- NELSON, RODNEY.
Carriers:- VICTORIOUS, INDOMITABLE, EAGLE.(Total 72 Fighters)
Cruisers:- SIRIUS, PHOEBE, CHARYBDIS.
Destroyers:-12

FIGHTERS FOR MALTA
35° Carrier:- FURIOUS (38 Spitfires)

ADDITIONAL ESCORTS
Destroyers:- 8

OILING FORCE
Oilers:-2, Corvettes:-4, Tug:-1.

34°

ESCORTS RIGHT THROUGH TO MALTA
Cruisers:- NIGERIA, KENYA, MANCHESTER, CAIRO.(AA)
Destroyers:-12 Tug:-1

SUBMARINES
On patrol 8
23°N Patrol positions O

3° E   4°   5°   6°   7°   8°

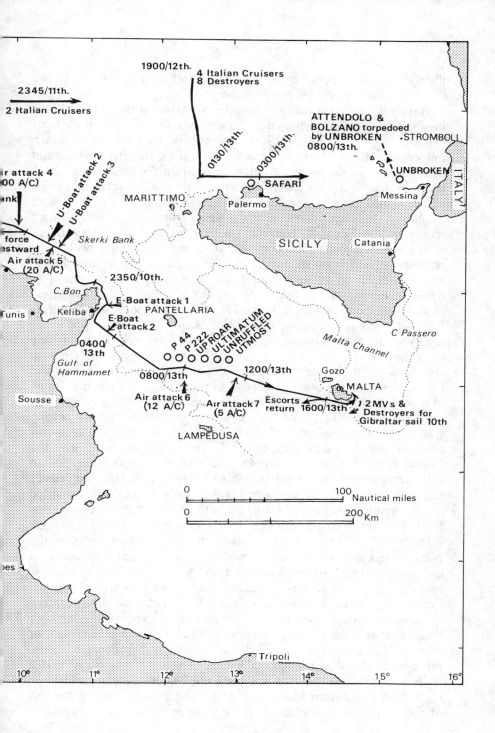

2345/11th.
2 Italian Cruisers

Air attack 4
(00 A/C)

nk

force
estward
Air attack 5
(20 A/C)

Skerki Bank

U-Boat attack 2
U-Boat attack 3

2350/10th.
E-Boat attack 1

C. Bon

Keliba

E-Boat
attack 2

PANTELLARIA

Tunis

0400/
13th

Gulf of
Hammamet

0800/13th

Air attack 6
(12 A/C)

Sousse

LAMPEDUSA

P 44
P 222
UPROAR
ULTIMATUM
UNRUFFLED
UTMOST

1200/13th

Air attack 7
(5 A/C)

1900/12th.
4 Italian Cruisers
8 Destroyers

0130/13th.

0300/13th.

SAFARI

MARITTIMO

Palermo

SICILY

ATTENDOLO &
BOLZANO torpedoed
by UNBROKEN
0800/13th.

•STROMBOLI

UNBROKEN

ITALY

Messina

Catania

C Passero

Malta Channel

Gozo

MALTA

Escorts
return   1600/13th

2 MVs &
Destroyers for
Gibraltar sail 10th

0   100 Nautical miles

0   200 Km

Tripoli

10°   11°   12°   13°   14°   15°   16°

flight deck and stopping flying operations, so that those of her aircraft then aloft had to land on the *Victorious*.

Having scored this major triumph – although at the cost of heavy losses at the hands of British fighters and anti-aircraft fire – the enemy droned away for home at 1900. The convoy now lay some twenty miles west of the Skerki Channel, off Tunisia, the customary point where the main escort of a Malta convoy from the west turned back for Gibraltar, leaving a close escort to go on with the merchant ships to the island. Syfret therefore now hauled round to the west with his heavy ships and carriers, while Rear-Admiral H. M. Burrough (commanding Force X) continued with three cruisers *Nigeria* (flag), *Kenya* and *Manchester*, the anti-aircraft cruiser *Cairo* and twelve destroyers. It had been planned that Burrough was to be met in the approaches to Malta by a flotilla of minesweepers now based in Malta, while Air Marshal Park was to have twin-engined Beaufighters (maximum speed 303 mph; range 1,470 miles)[74] and Spitfires patrolling as far out as 170 miles west of the island.

Up to this point 'Operation Pedestal' had done well, with only one merchant vessel of the convoy damaged; and in view of the strength and ferocity of the air attacks the ships' companies of convoy and escort were feeling rather pleased with themselves. This happy frame of mind was soon to change. Within an hour of Syfret parting company misfortune started to befall the 'Pedestal' convoy. While the convoy was changing formation from four to two columns in order to follow the minesweepers clearing a channel through shallow water over the Skerki Bank it ran into another underwater ambush. The Italian submarine *Axum* torpedoed Burrough's flagship *Nigeria*, the cruiser *Cairo* and the tanker *Ohio*; a brilliant triple success. The wounded *Nigeria* had to turn back to Gibraltar with an escort of two destroyers, Burrough transferring his flag to the destroyer *Ashanti* (Acting-Captain R. G. Onslow). The *Cairo* (launched 1918; veteran of the Norwegian campaign as well as the Malta convoy run), had her stern blown off and had to be sunk. And it was *Nigeria* and *Cairo* who alone had the kind of radio sets necessary to communicate with Royal Air Force fighters and so guide those from Malta on to enemy aircraft.

As the convoy altered away to the south to escape this underwater danger (at the time it was not known whether from submarines or mines), it became, in the words of naval liaison officers with the merchant ships, 'scrummed up' into a 'heterogeneous mass'.[75] Just when the convoy was in this confused and vulnerable state, and when the fighter cover from Malta had been withdrawn because of the loss of the fighter-direction ships, the enemy air forces struck again at

2030 in the deepening dusk. This time twenty Ju 88s bombed and torpedoed almost at will, sinking the merchant ships *Empire Hope* and *Clan Ferguson* and damaging another, the *Brisbane Star*, which nevertheless managed to struggle on.

Threequarters of an hour later the cruiser *Kenya* took a torpedo from a submarine in her forefoot, but managed to stay with the stricken convoy. At 0040 on 13 August German E-boats and some Italian MTBs took over with torpedo attacks in the dark lasting all the way down the Tunisian coast from Cap Bon to Kelibia. At 0120 one of them hit the cruiser *Manchester* (Captain H. Drew) and damaged her so seriously that her captain decided to scuttle her. Five merchantmen straggling behind the convoy were also hit; and four of them, the *Wairangi*, the *Glenorchy*, the American *Almeria Lykes* and *Santa Elisa* sank. The fifth, the *Rochester Castle*, managed nevertheless to rejoin the convoy.

At 0800 the Ju 88s were back again – twelve of them swooping in for a shallow bombing run to blow up and sink the merchant ship *Waimarama*. The tanker *Ohio* took more damage from a crashing enemy aircraft, but still struggled on. Although British fighters from Malta were now continuously patrolling overhead they could not prevent yet further attrition of the convoy and its escort, when at 1050 the next relay of Ju 88s and 87s arrived. The *Ohio's* engines were stopped by near-misses; the merchant ship *Dorset* was stopped by a direct hit; the *Rochester Castle* was damaged but still able to steam. Admiral Burrough had no alternative but to leave two destroyers with the cripples and press on.

At 1600 he too parted company for Gibraltar (as planned) with his two remaining cruisers and five destroyers. It was now up to the escort forces from Malta, four minesweepers and seven motor launches, under the command of Commander Jerome, to see the three merchant ships that now remained out of the original fourteen the last few miles into Malta. At 1800 on 13 August 1942 these three ships, the *Port Chalmers*, the *Melbourne Star* and the *Rochester Castle* (the latter wallowing very low in the water) steamed at last into Grand Harbour.

Meanwhile there remained the problem of the crippled *Dorset*, *Brisbane Star* and the *Ohio*. The destroyer *Penn* (Lieutenant-Commander J. H. Swain) took the *Ohio* in tow, while the Hunt class destroyer *Bramham* (Lieutenant E. F. Ramsay) stayed with the *Dorset*. However, the German bombers had not yet finished with 'Pedestal'. At about 1900 that evening they sank the *Dorset* and hit the *Ohio* yet again. At daylight on the 14th the minesweepers *Rye* and *Ledbury* arrived to help *Penn* with *Ohio*, along with some motor launches from

Malta. With the *Ohio* settling deeper and deeper in the water and German bombers complicating matters by parting the tow cable with a lucky bomb hit, this maritime cortège struggled slowly but gamely towards Malta. The tanker was brought safely into Grand Harbour in the morning of 15 August, the Maltese National Holiday, the Feast of Santa Marija. In Malta 'Pedestal' is known as the Santa Marija convoy. Meantime the damaged *Brisbane Star* had made her own way in. Thus 'Pedestal's' final tally amounted to five merchant ships arrived out of fourteen despatched.

In his subsequent report Admiral Syfret wrote:

> Tribute has been paid to the personnel of His Majesty's Ships; but both officers and men will desire to give first place to the conduct, courage, and determination of the masters, officers and men of the merchant ships. The steadfast manner in which these ships pressed on their way to Malta through all the attacks, answering every manoeuvring signal like a well-trained fleet unit, was a most inspiring sight . . .[76]

Captain D. W. Mason, the Master of the *Ohio*, was awarded the George Cross for his outstanding display of courage and seamanship.

It is noteworthy that at least the Italian surface fleet had failed to menace the 'Pedestal' convoy. Its battleships were immobilised in port for lack of fuel. Although five cruisers did put to sea, they were discouraged from energetic action by a British deception plan whereby aircraft illuminated them at night by flares, while alarming radio signals were transmitted in plain language about a forthcoming attack on them by US Liberators and British torpedo-bombers. On 13 August the British submarine HMS P-42 (Lieutenant A. C. G. Mars) torpedoed and seriously damaged the heavy cruiser *Bolzano* and the light cruiser *Muzio Attendolo* – avenging to some degree the losses suffered by 'Pedestal' and its escorting battle squadron.

From the surviving merchant ships were swiftly unloaded 32,000 tons of food and supplies, and in due course *Ohio's* vital fuel – just enough to keep Malta going on iron rations for another couple of months. As the official Naval Staff History comments: 'Five arrivals out of a convoy of fourteen ships with a powerful escort is not a large score, especially at the cost to the escort of an aircraft carrier, a cruiser, an anti-aircraft ship, and a destroyer lost, besides a carrier and two cruisers damaged.'[77]

But the First Sea Lord took a more sanguine view in a letter to Cunningham in Washington at the time: 'We paid a heavy price, but personally I think we got out of it lightly considering the risks we had to run, and the tremendous concentration of everything . . . which we had to face.'[78]

Of what utility was Malta as an offensive base after all the effort and sacrifice of the 1942 convoy operations? The 10th Submarine Flotilla returned to Malta in August and by October had reached a strength of nine boats. It took a steady toll of enemy supply ships on their way to Libya, sinking two vessels and an escort on the night of 19-20 October alone. The Royal Air Force on Malta remained limited in size because of shortage of aviation spirit, but its bombers joined with aircraft based on Egypt and even on Gibraltar in attacking Rommel's seaborne supplies. Yet recent analysis of the Axis logistic problem in North Africa has conclusively shown that British air and submarine attacks on Axis shipping from Malta and Egyptian bases together achieved no decisive effect on Rommel's ability to campaign.[79] Not even the sinking of oil tankers had the impact on Rommel that has been claimed in so many British accounts, for between 2 September and 23 October 1942 only two out of 27 Axis ships sunk were in fact tankers;[80] and Rommel actually received larger quantities of fuel in the months July to October 1942 than in February to June when he was preparing and waging his summer offensive.[81]

The choke-points for Rommel's supply throughout his campaigns from his first arrival in Libya at the beginning of 1941 onwards lay in the limited capacity of Libyan ports and the incompetence of the Italian authorities back in Italy; not in shortage of, or loss of, shipping.[82] His particular problem from July to October 1942 resulted from his own enormously lengthened land communications, which made it impossible with the available trucking lift to bring more than a fraction of the supplies stored in rear bases in Tripolitania up to the army at Alamein.[83] Therefore the damage inflicted on Rommel's communications by the relatively minor air and submarine forces able to operate from Malta in the summer and autumn of 1942 can in no sense be said to justify on objective strategic grounds the grievous losses incurred by the Royal Navy and Merchant Marine in keeping the island going, however much it was a matter of honour. Indeed, it is the judgment of one historian who has rigorously studied all the relevant statistics on Axis North African supply that, in regard to the whole period 1940–42, the importance usually attributed to the 'battle of the convoys'

is grossly exaggerated. At no time, except perhaps November–December 1941, did the aero-naval struggle in the central Mediterranean play a decisive part in events in North Africa, and even then Rommel's difficulties were due as much to his impossibly long – and vulnerable – line of communications inside Africa as to losses at sea . . . the Axis decision of summer 1942 not to occupy Malta was of far less moment to the outcome of the struggle in North Africa than the fact that the port of Tobruk was so small and hopelessly exposed to the attacks of the RAF operating from Egypt.[84]

The key to eventually winning the campaign in the Mediterranean and Middle East and reopening the long-closed imperial route to India via the Suez Canal (the historical reason for Britain's presence in the theatre at all) did not lie in Malta, that strategic burden and moral obligation glorified into a heroic myth; nor in the struggle with Rommel in the Desert. It lay in the decision finally confirmed on 30 July 1942 that the first great Anglo-American maritime expedition in the war against Germany should take the form of an invasion of French North Africa, the coastline of which commanded the sea route through the western basin of the Mediterranean, and capture of which could act as a stepping stone to Sicily and Italy.

On 21 September, D-Day for this invasion was fixed as 8 November. After more than two years of striving and setback by land and sea, and of more loss than profit on an enormous strategic investment, Churchill's Mediterranean 'blue water' strategy was about to flower anew, and on a scale grander yet.

Grand Strategy for a Maritime Alliance – I

It was neither an admiral, nor a general, nor even a Chiefs of Staff Committee who, on 30 July 1942, took the crucial decision that an Anglo-American expeditionary force should invade French North Africa as the principal operation of the year. It was a politician, Franklin Roosevelt, President of the United States; and he took it in the teeth of the objections of his own Joint Chiefs of Staff. His directive – which in fact accorded with British wishes – abruptly closed some five months of transatlantic argument over the Allied grand strategy to be pursued in 1942–43; an argument the crucial encounters of which took place between the leading actors across long tables in Washington and London.

The debate followed on from the statement of global strategy, WW1, agreed by the new Allies at the Arcadia Conference in Washington back in December 1941 and largely drafted by the British Chiefs of Staff. For WW1 had for the sake of concord deliberately left vague the actual shape of operations against Germany and her allies in the next two years. It had merely stated broadly that in 1942 a ring was to be drawn round the Third Reich and its allies, running from the Eastern Front in Russia round through Turkey and along the North African shore of the Mediterranean to the seas of Western Europe. The statement had contemplated no major land offensive by the Western Allies in that year. Rather it foresaw a preliminary phase of wearing Germany down by various means of attrition, such as blockade, the bomber offensive, support for Resistance movements, and the shipment of supplies to Soviet Russia in order to keep her going in her struggle with the main power of the Wehrmacht. WW1 looked to 1943 for the début of an Anglo-American grand offensive against the Third Reich. But even here the statement only broadly sketched with the thickest of crayons that 'the way may be clear for a return to the Continent, across the Mediterranean, from Turkey into the Balkans, or by landings in Western Europe. Such operations must be the prelude to the final assault on Germany itself . . .'[1]

WW1 therefore left it still to be decided exactly *what* the Allies should do in 1942–43. The attempt so to decide soon exposed those fundamental divergencies of approach between the Americans and the British over which WW1 had smoothly skated.

The United States was a continental power with a population of 120 million and industrial resources which dwarfed Britain's (and even Germany's). Its military leadership therefore conceived of grand strategy in classic Clausewitzian terms – the concentration of all forces at the decisive point for an offensive directed against the enemy's 'centre of gravity' (that is, his main army or one of his main armies), a decisive victory and finally the occupation of the enemy homeland, so destroying his military, industrial and moral power to resist. General George C. Marshall, the Chief of Staff, forcefully argued to the President in March 1942 that all available Allied resources in the war against Germany should be concentrated on preparing for, and launching, an Anglo-American invasion of France in 1943 (Marshall gave April as the possible month). He envisaged that this invasion would be in an ultimate strength of 48 divisions and 5,800 aircraft.

Thus in essence Marshall wished to create anew the old Western Front. To make this possible all operations elsewhere were to be closed down. In support of this strategy Marshall advanced a convincing case. He contrasted the economy of force and logistics of a cross-Channel front (as in the Great War) with the cost-ineffectiveness of distant peripheral expeditions (such as, although he did not name them, Gallipoli in the Great War and the current Middle East campaign in the Second World War). He argued that France was the only place where Allied airpower could establish overwhelming superiority, thanks to United Kingdom bases and the ability to employ the main striking power of the Royal Air Force. More, it was the only place 'in which the bulk of the British ground forces can be committed to a general offensive in cooperation with the United States forces . . .'[2]

On the other hand, Marshall strongly criticised the possible alternative strategy of attacking Germany by some back-door route – what

General J. F. C. Fuller has called 'the strategy of evasion'. For elsewhere, wrote Marshall, 'the enemy is protected against invasion by natural obstacles and poor communications leading towards the seat of hostile power . . .'[3] Moreover, it was 'impossible, in view of the shipping situation, to transfer the bulk of the British forces to any distant region, and the protection of the British Islands would hold the bulk of the divisions in England'.[4] The United States could also 'concentrate and use larger forces in Western Europe than in any other place, due to sea distances and the existence in England of base facilities'.[5]

This cogent advocacy of a Western Front to the exclusion of diversionary campaigns might have been drafted during the Great War by Field-Marshal Sir Douglas Haig or General Sir William Robertson (the then CIGS) for the enlightenment of the then Prime Minister, Lloyd George. It stood in total contrast to the strategy of evading a fight with the enemy's principal strength on the decisive front, and instead campaigning round the edges of the conflict (the Balkans, the Levant, the Middle East) which Lloyd George and Winston Churchill had urged during that war.

Yet such campaigning around the edges had been favoured since the Elizabethan age by the 'blue water' school of strategic thought in Britain as 'the British way in warfare' (in the phrase of Basil Liddell Hart, an influential military pundit of the 1930s). While some ally was left to bear the brunt of doing battle with the enemy's main army on the continent of Europe, the British (thanks to the Royal Navy) had made profitable colonial conquests at small cost in blood, carried out harmless raids on enemy coastlines, or – more effectively – fought detached portions of the enemy land forces in some secondary theatre, like Wellington in the Iberian Peninsula in 1809–14.[6] No wonder Basil Liddell Hart could contrast this relatively painless 'British way' of the Georgian era with what he saw as the futile and bloody aberration of the 1914–18 Western Front.[7]

By the mid-1930s and under the influence not only of Liddell Hart's preaching but also the harrowing best-selling novels and memoirs by literary veterans of the trenches, British Cabinets had come to accept that never again should Britain commit mass conscript armies to a Western Front, but instead return to the 'British way in warfare'. The task of confronting the German Army was firmly dumped on the French.

Yet what Liddell Hart and the Cabinets who bought his views ignored was that in the Great War the French Army had proved in the event not strong enough alone to deal with the German Army;

and that therefore the deployment of a mass British army alongside the French had proved inescapable. The failure to acknowledge this historical truth in the late 1930s greatly contributed to France's collapse in 1940, when she was left to fight the Wehrmacht virtually single-handed. Thereafter Britain was compelled *faute de mieux* to resort to the 'British way in warfare' by campaigning in the Mediterranean and Middle East – with negligible results so far.

Nonetheless, in 1942 the lure of 'the British way in warfare' and the still painful memories of the Somme and Passchendaele continued to tug powerfully at the minds and emotions of the British leadership, military as well as political.

Thus while Churchill and General Sir Alan Brooke, the Chief of the Imperial General Staff, accepted *intellectually* that Germany could only be finally defeated by an eventual return of the Western Allies to the continent of Europe, they instinctively shrank from any strategic proposal which carried with it a possibility of another prolonged slogging match with the German Army at the peak of its fighting power. In consequence their reaction to General Marshall's Continental and Clausewitzian thinking was somewhat ambiguous; and in the coming years it was to become still more ambiguous.

When in April 1942 Marshall flew to London with Harry Hopkins, the President's confidant, to put his strategy to the War Cabinet Defence Committee, the Committee therefore welcomed it in principle, and agreed that the Allies should indeed work towards an invasion of France in 1943 ('Operation Roundup').[8] But they then proceeded to smudge the black-and-white outline of Marshall's design with references to the need to allot forces to such imperial or 'blue water' concerns as the defence of India, the Indian Ocean and the Middle East. After a COS meeting the day before Marshall's departure for home Brooke confided to his diary his profound misgivings about 'Roundup': it was 'fraught with the gravest dangers' and the chances of disaster were 'great'.[9]

For it was not just a question of committing untried armies against a strongly posted enemy on an *existing front*, as in the case of the Battle of the Somme in 1916, daunting enough a prospect though this would be. 'Roundup' would first of all demand an assault landing on a hostile shore on a scale unprecedented in history, and the winning of an initial lodgement spacious enough to permit the build-up of the Allied armies for an ultimate break-out. These were the 'difficulties and dangers' (Brooke's words) which in his view appeared to be neglected in Marshall's strategic sketch. It was Brooke's standpoint then and later that he would only support an attempt at cross-Channel invasion if and when the balance of forces so favoured the Allies as to minimise the risk of failure or stalemate. But these private hesitations, however reasonable, contrast with Marshall's happy belief that the London discussions had resulted in a firm Anglo-American commitment to launch 'Roundup' in spring 1943, coupled with a renunciation of such 'dispersions' (as Marshall called them) as the Mediterranean and Middle East. Here were the beginnings of a long-festering misunderstanding between the Allies.

In any case, to reach agreement in principle about launching 'Roundup' in 1943 did not provide an answer as yet to what operations, if any, Britain and America should jointly undertake in the war against Germany in 1942. The Soviet Union was locked in struggle with some 200 German divisions; her fate still lay all in doubt; her leaders were urgently demanding a Second Front to drain away German strength. A vociferous section of British public opinion too was demanding 'a Second Front now'. It was therefore as politically unthinkable for the Anglo-Americans to do nothing in 1942 while they painstakingly prepared for 'Roundup' in 1943 as it had been for the unready British Army in France in 1916 to stand idly by while the French Army was being minced at Verdun. A joint offensive operation in 1942 of some kind there simply had to be. But what? And where?

Marshall himself had put forward the suggestion of a *limited* landing in France in 1942, but only if 'the situation on the Russian Front became desperate' or if 'the German situation in Western Europe becomes critically weakened'.[10] The first condition offered the worst possible circumstances for the Anglo-American forces to tackle the German Army in the West, and the second was in the last degree unlikely. Nevertheless 'Operation Sledgehammer' (as Marshall's proposal was somewhat ironically dubbed) was now submitted to rigorous analysis by the British, who would have to supply the bulk of the forces.

On 27 May, a meeting of the Prime Minister and the Chiefs of Staff dismissed 'Sledgehammer' on the score that the available land forces and resources of assault shipping were too small.

This however emboldened Churchill to try afresh to sell to the British Chiefs of Staff his own idea for another intervention in northern Norway, 'Operation Jupiter'. His aim this time lay in occupying the coastline from which the German Navy and Luftwaffe were devastating the Arctic convoys from Britain to Russia. As with his Norwegian schemes of 1939–40, his proposal failed to take account of the operational and logistical problems of either the initial invasion or of long-term occupation and seaborne supply. The Chiefs of Staff had not been enthused, therefore, when they received a personal minute dated 1 May from Churchill with regard to 'Jupiter', telling them: 'High political and strategic importance must be attached thereto.'[11] They had responded by resorting to the First Sea Lord's well tested strategy of procrastination and attrition by weight of detailed facts and figures.

There was left only the alternative of a joint Anglo-American operation in the Mediterranean theatre – the very 'diversion' that Marshall had most feared and which he believed he had scotched during his visit to London in April.

Back in December 1941 Churchill, in his cabin in HMS *Duke of York* plunging and rolling across a stormy Atlantic to the Arcadia Conference in Washington, had drafted a grand statement of future global strategy for the benefit of the Chiefs of Staff. This included a proposal – 'Operation Gymnast' – that American forces as well as British should invade French North Africa in 1942 in conjunction with an offensive into Tripolitania by the 8th Army (then standing on the border of Cyrenaica and Tripolitania).[12] The Allies would thus clear the whole North Africa shore (including Morocco) and open the Mediterranean through route. During the Arcadia Conference, British and American planners had studied the problems and possible timing of 'Gymnast' in detail, especially in terms of naval and shipping resources, but the prospect was put in abeyance because of more urgent needs such as reinforcement of the Far East and the shipment of American troops to Britain.[13] Nonetheless Churchill never lost sight of 'Gymnast'. With the virtual discarding of 'Sledgehammer' and 'Jupiter' by May 1942, he limbered 'Gymnast' up and began to run it again.

On 27 May Churchill telegraphed Roosevelt to inform him of British objections to 'Sledgehammer' (the limited landing in northern France), and remarked: 'We must never let GYMNAST pass from our minds. All other preparations would help, if need be, towards that.'[14] When Vice-Admiral Lord Louis Mountbatten, now an acting Vice-Admiral and Chief of Combined Operations (see below, p. 545), visited Washington in June to explain in person British misgivings about 'Sledgehammer', Roosevelt himself began to take up the 'Gymnast' idea, to the vast unease of General Marshall and also of Admiral King, US Chief of Naval Operations, who feared that it would suck in warships and assault shipping at the expense of the Pacific war, his primary concern.

On 18 June Churchill arrived in Washington with Brooke, after a gruelling 27-hour journey by flying-boat, in order to re-forge agree-

[532]

ment on future Allied strategy. It now turned out that at present the fundamental difference of opinion did not lie between the British and Americans, but between the military of both nations on the one hand and the two political leaders on the other. Brooke had for the moment ceased to be in favour of 'Gymnast' – partly because Rommel was currently defeating the 8th Army in the Gazala battles, so putting even Britain's present Middle East position in jeopardy. On 20 June the Combined Chiefs of Staff produced a report calling for the Allies to concentrate on preparations for 'Roundup' (the full-scale invasion of France) in 1943. The report argued against 'Gymnast' on the score that it would weaken the navies in all theatres, but especially the Pacific and the Atlantic; that it would slow up the flow of American troops to Britain ('Bolero'); and that it would disperse the whole Allied strategic effort. The Combined Chiefs warned that 'any 1942 operation would inevitably have some deterring effect upon Continental operations in 1943'. Their uncompromising conclusion was that '"Gymnast" should not be undertaken under the existing situation'.[15]

Meanwhile, however, the Prime Minister and the President were getting together like old cronies up in New York State at Hyde Park, Roosevelt's neo-Federal-style mansion. At Churchill's persuasion they now agreed to the very opposite to the Combined Chiefs of Staff's conclusions – that some major operation *must* be undertaken in 1942, and that in this context 'Gymnast' ought to be further studied. Next day, 21 June (the day that Tobruk fell to Rommel), the leaders in plain clothes and the leaders in olive drab, khaki and two shades of blue met in the White House to argue it out. Eventually, General Sir Hastings Ismay, the Secretary of the British Chiefs of Staff Committee and a smooth and accomplished fixer, produced a draft for another of those catch-all statements on future strategy that everyone could too easily accept. Although preparations for a cross-Channel invasion in 1943 'on as large a scale as possible' were to be pushed forward 'with all speed and energy', it was nevertheless 'essential that the United States and Great Britain should be prepared to act offensively in 1942'.[16] Therefore plans were to be studied and preparations made for a limited landing in Western Europe ('Sledgehammer') and also for an invasion of French North Africa ('Gymnast'). Even 'Jupiter' was to get a look in by being 'carefully considered'.

On 6 July, at a Chiefs of Staff meeting back in England presided over by Churchill, it was unanimously agreed that 'Sledgehammer' offered no prospect of success. Next day the War Cabinet likewise ruled that a cross-Channel attack in 1942 was 'out of the question'.[17] On 8 July Churchill telegraphed these decisions to Roosevelt, and urged that 'Gymnast' offered 'by far the best chance for effecting relief to the Russian front in 1942'. Spooning on the flattery, he added that this 'has all along been in harmony with your ideas. It is in fact your commanding idea. Here is the true Second Front of 1942.'[18]

Marshall, perceiving here the wreck at the last moment of his own Clausewitzian grand strategy and keenly remembering Churchill's Dardanelles fiasco of a sideshow in 1915–16,[19] rallied the American Joint Chiefs of Staff for a final charge. They stated their conviction to the President that 'Gymnast'

> means definitely no 'Bolero-Sledgehammer' in 1942 and that it will definitely curtail if not make impossible the execution of 'Bolero-Roundup' in the Spring of 1943. We are strongly of the opinion that 'Gymnast' would be both indecisive and a heavy drain on our resources, and that if we undertake it, we would nowhere be acting decisively against the enemy . . .[20]

The American Joint Chiefs of Staff were not alone in realising that an invasion of French North Africa in 1942 would rule out an invasion of France in 1943. On 14 July the British Joint Planners reported to the Chiefs of Staff that 'It is fairly certain that we cannot carry out "Gymnast" and "Roundup" within twelve months of each other. A properly executed "Gymnast" in fact must be regarded as an *alternative* and not in *addition* to "Roundup".'[21]

However, thanks to Auchinleck's defensive victory in the First Battle of Alamein in the first three weeks of July, which transformed British prospects in the Middle East, Brooke himself now changed his mind about 'Gymnast', reverting to his earlier belief that the clearing of North Africa and the Mediterranean was an indispensable preliminary to a cross-Channel invasion.[22] Moreover, in a rare expression of a naval view on the British side, Admiral Sir Andrew Cunningham (then a member of the Combined Chiefs of Staff in Washington) argued to the COS with all the weight of a former C-in-C, Mediterranean, in favour of 'Gymnast'. 'It would,' he wrote, 'go a long way towards relieving our shipping problem once the short route through the Mediterranean was gained.'[23] More, it would 'jeopardise the whole of Rommel's forces and relieve anxiety about Malta. It would shake Italy to the core and rouse the occupied countries . . .'.

Now it was the turn of the American Joint Chiefs to fly the Atlantic for a final attempt to trip up 'Gymnast' and instead wield 'Sledgehammer'. On 20 July 1942 Marshall put the case for seizing the Cotentin Peninsula (including the port of Cherbourg) that year and holding it as a bridgehead from which to break out into the heart of France in 1943. On 22 July the War Cabinet rejected the proposal on the advice of Brooke and Portal, who calculated that the land forces which could be put ashore and the air cover which could be provided from British bases would be quite insufficient to deal with the enemy's response.[24] Instead the Cabinet opted firmly for 'Gymnast'.

When Roosevelt learned by cable of this deadlock, he instructed his Joint Chiefs to give up 'Sledgehammer' and come to an agreement with the British on some other operation for 1942. With deep reluctance the Joint Chiefs therefore settled for 'Gymnast', the North African landings, although declaring to their British opposite numbers with some bitterness that they fully realised that this would render the invasion of France in 1943 impossible. The British did not dissent. The Combined Chiefs of Staff were therefore able to submit to the War Cabinet a joint statement on operations for 1942–43, 'CCS94'. Yet even now CCS94[25] fudged the issue. Although it recommended that 'the decision should be taken to launch a combined operation against the North and West coast of Africa at the earliest possible date before December 1942', it made this decision conditional on the news from the Russian front being so bad by 15 September 1942 as to render 'Roundup' (the full-scale invasion of France) incapable of successful execution before July 1943. The document then proceeded to recommend that 'a task force commander for the entire African operation should be appointed forthwith'. As a sop for the American Joint Chiefs it also formally recorded for the benefit of the political leaderships

> That it be understood that commitment to this operation renders 'Roundup' in all probability impracticable of successful execution in 1943 and therefore that we have definitely accepted a defensive, encircling line of action for the continental theatre, except as to air operations and blockade . . .[26]

The Prime Minister would not admit, however, that 'Gymnast' had to be at the expense of 'Roundup'. Far from it: his mind glowed with wider possibilities:

> If, however, we move from 'Gymnast' northward into Europe a new situation must be surveyed. The flank attack may become the main attack, and the main attack a holding operation in the early stages. Our second front will in fact comprise both the Atlantic and the Mediterranean coasts of Europe, and we can push either right-handed, left-handed or both-handed, as our resources and circumstances permit . . .[27]

Now, brushing aside the Joint Chiefs' condition that a decision for 'Gymnast' should only be taken if the state of the struggle in Russia by 15 September ruled out 'Roundup', he pressed Roosevelt via Harry Hopkins to decide without delay in favour of 'Gymnast'. He urged a proviso that the Anglo-American forces would invade French North Africa not later than 30 October. When Roosevelt agreed, the American Joint Chiefs could only acquiesce, albeit repeating in vain that this would kill a cross-Channel invasion in 1943. On 30 July the President told a conference in the White House that

> he, as Commander-in-Chief, had made the decision that 'Torch' [as 'Gymnast' had been renamed] was to be undertaken at the earliest possible date. He considered that this operation was now our principal objective and the assembling of means to carry it out should take precedence over all other operations as, for instance, 'Bolero' [the American build-up in the United Kingdom].[28]

So the two politicians had their way, to the delight of the British Chiefs of Staff (especially Brooke) and the deep gloom of the American Chiefs. Just as in 1940 the British had originally committed themselves to a major campaign in the Mediterranean and Middle East because at the time this theatre provided the only land front where their army could feasibly engage the Axis, so now the Americans were doing the same all over again. But already in Churchill's mind 'Torch' was no mere expedient to get the American forces into battle in 1942, no mere short-term sideshow; it had become the potential first stage in yet more distant developments of his favourite 'blue water' strategy. 'C'est le premier pas qui coûte'; and now that the Americans had made that step under pressure of circumstances, they had joined the British in making war as they must, not as they ought. They had embarked on a voyage the ultimate destination of which had yet to be charted.

18

'A Quite Desperate Undertaking': 'Operation Torch'

On 1 November 1942 the Naval Commander-in-Chief, the Allied Expeditionary Force, Admiral Sir Andrew Cunningham, Bart, GCB, reached the fortress of Gibraltar in the cruiser *Scylla* (launched July 1940; 5,450 tons; eight 4.5-inch[1] Captain I. A. P. MacIntyre), 'very comfortable but what an armament for a ship of her size',[2] after 'a bit of a volum bolum trip. N.E. gale behind us . . .'[3] Four days later Cunningham was joined by his Supreme Commander, General Dwight D. Eisenhower, who had flown from England in a B-17 Flying Fortress bomber through fog and rain. The Expeditionary Force headquarters, complete with joint Navy/Air Force operations room, was located in old tunnels cut deep into the Rock: airless, dank, dripping, but immune to the heaviest bombardment. Only three days now remained before the launching of the largest and most complicated combined operation in history to that date and in Eisenhower's judgment, an undertaking 'of a quite desperate nature'.[4]

On Eisenhower himself, who had never before commanded a major operation of war, the weight of responsibility, the burden of uncertainty, imposed a strain that tested him to proof. Quite apart from all the operational hazards, so much depended on the reaction of the Vichy French authorities and armed forces – and that lay in doubt to the last minute. Would they cooperate, as was hoped – or would they fight? And what about Franco's Spain, hitherto a neutral country but at whose mercy lay Gibraltar and its exposed airstrip and crowded anchorage, the hub of the entire enterprise? Eisenhower was to confess in a letter to Cunningham in May 1945 that

> the hours that you and I spent together in the dripping tunnels of Gibraltar will probably remain as long in my memory as will any other [episode in the war]. It was there I first understood the indescribable and inescapable strain that comes over one when his part is done – when the issue rests with fate and the fighting men he has committed to action.[5]

Yet Eisenhower, unfledged but already beginning to display the qualities that would make him an outstanding Allied supreme commander, drew strength from his Naval C-in-C, that unshakable veteran of so many desperate ventures, that ever robust optimist. Back in September Eisenhower had confided to Marshall that 'I cannot tell you how strongly and favourably I have been impressed by Admiral Cunningham . . . His frankness, his generous and selfless attitude, his obvious determination and, above all, his direct action methods and impatience with ritual and red tape all come as a refreshing breath of spring . . .'[6] To act as a staunch support to a supreme commander who was still a little unsure of himself constituted not the least of Andrew Cunningham's contributions to 'Operation Torch'.

Cunningham had shown his mettle to the American military leadership during his time as Head of the British Naval Mission (and member of the Combined Chiefs of Staff) in Washington. In particular he had seen off, and thereby won the respect of, Admiral Ernest King, the US Chief of Naval Operations and a man who believed that rudeness cost you nothing. King even regarded the other American armed forces as enemies to be sunk on sight, let alone the armed forces of allies. For the Royal Navy he entertained the underdoggish and now quite anachronistic Anglophobia so prevalent in the United States Navy in the early 1920s. Soon after Cunningham's arrival in Washington the two men engaged in what Cunningham later called 'some straight speaking'[7] over a minor matter of the requested deployment of four or five American submarines for work under British control in the eastern Atlantic. In Cunningham's recollection, King 'was offensive, and I told him what I thought of his method of advancing allied unity and amity. We parted friends . . .'[8]

At the end of July 1942 General Bedell Smith, Chief of Staff designate to the Allied Commander-in-Chief designate, privately asked Cunningham if he would be willing to serve as Naval C-in-C. Cunningham reported this to the First Sea Lord on 31 July, saying that while he did not wish to put himself forward for the post, he 'would be more than willing to serve . . .'[9] In fact, he had had enough of the committees and cocktail parties of Washington, and yearned to return to command and the sea. Pound was however thinking in terms of three separate naval commands under the Supreme Commander – covering the battlefleet, the expedition itself, and Gibraltar – plus a Naval Adviser at Eisenhower's elbow. Cunningham successfully persuaded Pound that this would be unworkable, and that the Supreme Commander must deal with a single overall naval C-in-C. It was a key contribution to Eisenhower's novel design for an integrated Allied command structure.

On 14 August Cunningham was formally appointed Allied Naval Commander, Expeditionary Force (ANCXF), with Vice-Admiral Sir Bertram Ramsay as his Deputy. Commodore R. M. Dick, a most able Deputy Chief of Staff to Cunningham in the Mediterranean in 1940–42, became Chief of Staff. Since April Ramsay had been responsible for the naval side of contingency planning for 'Sledgehammer' and in June had participated in a two-day tri-service study period on the operational problems of a large-scale opposed landing on the Cotentin Peninsula.[10] Now it was he who was to carry the main burden of planning and organising the vast interlocking naval movements involved in 'Torch'. For although Cunningham paid a twelve-day visit to England in September when key decisions were taken, he did not finally return from Washington and take up his new command full-time until mid-October. In any case, Cunningham was no man for detail, as he freely admitted, while Ramsay (as the Dunkirk evacuation proved) was a master organiser. Cunningham provided the broad direction, and also acted as 'facilitator' for Ramsay, such as when he mobilised four outstanding staff officers (including one, Commander M. L. Power, released at his request by Sir John Tovey from command of a destroyer in the Home Fleet) and eight Wren (Women's Royal Naval Service) assistants to type the final and highly complicated naval operation orders for 'Torch' in no more than a week. All the naval planning was carried out within Eisenhower's headquarters in Norfolk House, St James's Square, and in the closest liaison with the American services and the Admiralty.

Yet the meticulous routing and scheduling of the 'Torch' armada to the points of assault could avail nothing without success in the landings themselves. This time the lesson had been well learned; this time there was to be no repetition of Gallipoli or Norway in 1940, when troops untrained for landing operations had been shoved into any kind of available boat manned by bluejackets equally unrehearsed for their role, and then simply tipped out on to a hostile shore. For by 1942 the tactics, techniques and specialised craft and equipment for large-scale assault landings had at long last been evolved.

The credit belongs to relatively junior officers of the three services who had jointly studied and solved all the key problems long before the Directorate of Combined Operations was set up in June 1940, long before Churchill's protégé, the glamorous Lord Louis Mountbatten, took over the Directorate in October 1941 as a commodore or as Acting Vice-Admiral became Chief of Combined Operations in March, 1942.[11] The work began in the early 1920s, while the memory of Gallipoli was still wincingly fresh, with 'sand-table' schemes by the three staff colleges for the capture of Singapore and Hong Kong. But there was no money; little interest from on high. This was the period of tight defence budgets under Churchill's Chancellorship of the Exchequer, of the Admiralty's obsession with future fleet battles, the Army's preoccupation with the defence of India, and the Royal Air Force's dream of a strategic air offensive. Yet year by year the three staff colleges together built up a roneoed Manual of Combined Operations comprising all the basic tactical procedures and command and control techniques; the rules of the game as it was eventually to be played by immense armadas of ships and soldiers on the coasts of Africa and Europe.

Meanwhile a new inter-service Landing Craft Committee was pondering the technical problems. By 1930 just three prototype landing craft had been produced – and had proved useless because they drew four and a half feet of water, and the angle of ramp was far too steep for vehicles to negotiate. Not until 1936, and under the spur of the Abyssinian crisis, were six more ordered, but only to be delivered in the post-Munich winter of 1938.

It took the Japanese invasion of China in 1937 to shake the British armed forces into awareness of just how backward they were in developing combined operations, for at Tientsin the Japanese employed 400 landing craft and a special 10,000-ton landing craft carrier. Next year, at the suggestion of the Director of the Naval Staff College, a new Inter-Service Training and Development Centre (ISTDC) was set up, directly reporting to the Chiefs of Staff. The new Centre was modest enough, for it comprised one officer from each service: Captain L. E. H. Maund, RN (Chairman), Major M. W. M. MacLeod, RA, Wing-Commander Guy Knocker, RAF, and Captain P. Picton-Phillips, RM. A proposal that two battalions of Royal Marines should be allotted to the Centre for experimental work was not accepted, since this would cost money, and each service had its own more urgent priorities at a time of hasty rearmament.

In July 1938 (just as the ISTDC was being formed, and when Hitler was winding up the tension in the Sudeten crisis) a major combined operation exercise was mounted off the coast of Devon for which the Royal Navy supplied a battleship, a carrier, two cruisers and a flotilla of destroyers, while the Army furnished three battalions masquerading as two corps. As a gale rose, the troops were rowed to the shore of Slapton Sands by sailors in whalers and cutters in Nelsonian style. The military commander, Brigadier B. L. Montgomery, was to describe the exercise as 'a pitiful exposition of our complete neglect of landing operations'. He remembered: 'There was *one* so-called landing craft, an experimental one made many years before and dug out of some scrap-heap for this exercise . . .'[12] Of this marine demonstration of the truth of Murphy's Law Captain Maund wrote in retrospect: 'The lessons stuck out like tent-pegs. No better start could have been made.'[13]

By way of tapping in these obtrusive tent-pegs, the ISTDC now tackled and solved every kind of practical problem. In particular, it drew up common inter-service codes, procedures and signals arrangements for directing gun fire against shore targets, which were to prove invaluable in 'Torch'. By the end of 1938 the ISTDC had also worked out a complete tactical drill for assault landings – approach under cover of darkness by landing craft carriers (converted merchant ships); despatch of the landing craft to the shore under cover of smoke screens and artillery fire; a floating reserve to feed into the bridgehead in order to secure a position far enough inland to prevent enemy artillery shelling the anchorage; and finally the despatch of personnel, stores and vehicles from the transport ships to the beach in special craft.[14]

Now came the task of designing the ships, craft and equipment themselves. The ISTDC called for fast transport ships (later known as 'Landing Ships [Infantry]') capable of lowering landing craft filled with soldiers from their davits. It proposed a 'silent' armoured landing craft (the LCI or 'Landing Craft [Infantry]') to hold an infantry platoon of 31 men, together with their support weapons and also smoke-projectors; a similar craft, the 'Landing Craft (Support)' (LCS), for weapons and smoke projectors only, and a 'Landing Craft (Mechanised)' (LCM) of 12 tons for the transport of guns, vehicles and stores – all with bow ramps that could be swung down for fast disembarkation.[15] From these original sketches were to proliferate all the varied and ubiquitous vessels of 1942–45. A landing craft mock-up was built, and Authority went so far as to give sanction for £10,000 to be spent on production and trial of prototypes. This was not all; the ISTDC also tackled the problem of the water gap between a landing craft's lowered ramp and the shore, which soldiers could wade, but vehicles could not. Its answer was a design for a floating pier 150 feet long. But for want of further funding none of this inventive effort went beyond the drawing board or the prototype.

And so when in April 1939, with war in the offing, a report was carried out on Britain's present state of preparedness for combined operations it showed that, because of lack of landing craft, no operation even in the strength of one brigade would be possible for six months and no operations large enough to capture and hold territory possible for two years. The report led to a modest order for eighteen 'Landing Craft (Assault)' (LCA), twelve 'Landing Craft (Mechanised)' (LCM) and two 'Landing Craft (Support)' (LCS).

For the officers of the ISTDC this was nevertheless a time of exciting creative endeavour. In summer of 1939 they completed a survey of passenger ships suitable for conversion into 'Landing Ships (Infantry)'. They found the answers to the problems of beach organisation and of quickly laying roadways on sand or shingle; they tried out infra-red beacons for guiding assault craft at night to the correct landing point; they studied how to put tanks ashore, especially in the face of underwater obstacles; decided that a specially equipped tri-service headquarters ship would be necessary for the command and control of a major landing.

Remarkably, the outbreak of war in September 1939 led not to an expansion of the ISTDC but to its disbanding. After all, what with a new Western Front in France and the prospect of fleet battles and the bomber offensive, there was not going to be any such thing as combined operations – or so the service mandarins believed. Only MacLeod was left to carry on, simply because the War Office could find him nothing else immediately to do. Not until January 1940 (when amphibious interventions in Scandinavia and the Baltic had begun to take the fancy of the War Cabinet, and particularly the First Lord of the Admiralty) was Captain Maund ordered to rejoin MacLeod in a revived ISTDC. Further vital development work on the technical apparatus necessary to large-scale combined operations now followed. Heavy-duty davits were ordered for handling loaded landing craft. Proposals were mooted for converting two train ferries to carry LCMs ('Landing Craft [Mechanised]': a 20-ton craft for landing vehicles and stores in shallow water), and for the installation of special gantries in three Admiralty oilers for the purpose of swinging out the LCMs and lowering them into the sea. In March 1940 orders were placed with Thorneycroft shipbuilders for another 30 LCA – 'Landing Craft (Assault)': 10-ton craft able to land troops in eighteen inches of water – and eighteen LCM in addition to the 26 LCA, two LCS and twelve LCM already in production.

Then followed the Norwegian débâcle, when in the haste and muddle all the patient work of the ISTDC, all its carefully evolved rules of the game, were completely ignored. It was left to Maund and his colleagues to note the lessons so harshly taught. Firstly, the commander(s) of a combined operation must receive a clear directive from above. Secondly, the inter-service command system must be based on the precepts laid down in the Manual of Combined Operations. Thirdly (and as again laid down in the Manual) there must be thorough tri-service planning before an operation; thorough training too for the soldiers and sailors. And fourthly, there was the key importance of 'tactical loading' – stowing stores so that what was going to be needed first came to hand first.

The disappearance of the Western Front in June 1940 suddenly lent combined operations a new importance, for it now became the only means by which British forces could again fight on the continent of Europe. The Prime Minister gamely directed that raids should be launched up and down the western coasts of Hitler's empire; and a Directorate of Combined Operations was set up in the Admiralty with Lieutenant-General A. G. B. Bourne, Royal Marines, in charge, Captain Maund as the Navy's representative, and Colonel Hornby as the Army's. The Royal Air Force would send an officer to nod in as required.

Bourne's task now was to press ahead with the construction of landing craft and the conversion of fast merchant and passenger ships into 'Landing Ships (Assault)' and 'Landing Ships (Infantry)' – and recruit and train the crews. In summer 1940 total orders for craft reached 119 LCA, 31 LCM and 8 LCS(M) – as many as the available shipyard space and production resources for engines permitted. By March 1941 a follow-on order for another 104 LCA had been placed. But in this field too Britain had to turn to the vast industrial resources of the United States, placing an order for 136 of the American 'Eureka' design of landing craft. Meanwhile three of the fast 'Glen' passenger ships were being transformed into 'Landing Ships Infantry (Large)' [LSI(L)], each capable of holding three assault battalions. Two 3,000-ton, 22-knot Dutch passenger ferries were also taken up for conversion to carry 450 assault troops. These ships could each despatch 410 soldiers in the first wave with the six LCA and two LCM(I) in their davits.

In close liaison with the Director of Naval Construction a design for a specialised 'Landing Craft (Tank)' was evolved, capable of carrying a 40-ton tank and unloading it over a ramp in the bow. It was to have a speed of ten knots and a draught at the bow of 3 feet 6 inches. Thirty of these LCT(1)s were ordered, and the trial of the first was held on the Tyne in November 1940. There followed an order for a bigger version with a speed of 12 knots, the LCT(2). But here again limited British manufacturing resources imposed their handicap; for want of suitable engines, dangerous Napier Lion petrol aero-engines of 1918 vintage had to be fitted.[16]

In July 1940 the further fiasco of the Dakar expedition, equally neglecting the wisdom accumulated since the 1920s, taught the new Directorate of Combined Operations yet more valuable lessons: the need for exact information about surf conditions and about beaches and their gradients; the urgent need for a special headquarters ship (as envisaged by the old ISTDC), complete with joint operations room and elaborate radio signals equipment, which, unlike a normal flagship, would not be called upon to charge off to engage enemy warships.

Thus by the summer of 1940 the full script and stage directions for combined operations on the grand scale had been written; the production had been designed in almost every detail, and some orders for the kit had already been put in hand. What was now required was an impresario with the drive and personality to enlist the backers and launch the show. Churchill's first choice for this role was that Great War veteran, Admiral of the Fleet Lord Keyes, appointed on 17 July 1940. It proved a mistake, for Keyes, a proud and peppery man as well as an all too senior admiral, upset the three service departments rather than won them over. He did not help his cause by moving Combined Operations out of the Admiralty, its previous base, into separate offices off Whitehall, with the result that the service departments tended to ostracise Keyes's 'private navy'.

Nevertheless, he pushed on the groundwork energetically. In January 1941 a Combined Training Centre (CTC) was created under Commodore (Vice-Admiral Retired) T. J. Hallett at Inveraray (HMS *Quebec*), with another at Kabrit in Egypt in the Canal Zone. By February 1941 no fewer than 5,000 officers and ratings had been assigned to the manning of landing craft. A second Royal Navy was coming into existence – but one somewhat disdained by the sea-going Navy. Even in 1943 Admiral Ramsay was regretting in a lecture that

Service in Combined Operations is, unhappily, still regarded by many of the best Naval officers as a sideshow, and if they are temporarily employed in it their one desire is to get back into normal sea service at the earliest possible moment. This is a most undesirable state of affairs, for circumstances demand the presence in this type of operation of the best officers and men we have got, and we cannot afford always to be changing them and to be conducting operations with inexperienced personnel.[17]

The training was hard and realistic, for it was essential that the landing craft crews got to know their jobs thoroughly before they worked with soldiers on joint exercises, in order that the Army should retain its traditional unquestioning faith in the Royal Navy's seamanship. The trainees would never forget long nights and days spent chilled and wet and tired out on the waters and along the shores of Scottish lochs. Particularly important was the selection and training of naval beach parties. Theirs was the key task of going ashore with the Army's beach groups (the leading assault wave, charged with securing the immediate area of the landing) and organising the orderly flow of men and stores into the beach-head.

In October 1941 Churchill replaced the now seventy-year-old Keyes with an impresario of quite different calibre, Captain (now promoted Commodore) Lord Louis Mountbatten – young, energetic, ambitious, intelligent, charming. Here was the Sam Goldwyn of Combined Operations, eager to promote as his own production the results of twenty years of patient work. As Mountbatten's biographer remarks, by the time the first Americans came to survey his organisation early in 1942, 'they found something to admire and support. He had taken over a directorate with little executive authority and only small resources in men and material. By the spring of 1942 he controlled an important command which enjoyed a virtual monopoly in the skills of amphibious command.'[18] Mountbatten's subordinates rejoiced when Churchill appointed him a Vice-Admiral (although against the First Sea Lord's wishes)[19] and Chief of Combined Operations in March 1942, with a seat on the Chiefs of Staff Committee. Admiral Sir John Hughes-Hallett (at the time a Captain on Mountbatten's staff) was to recall: 'At one stride our organisation had penetrated the very centre and citadel of Power.'[20]

And certainly Mountbatten was blessed with both the vision of a vast expansion in the resources for seaborne invasions and the power of personality to get what he wanted. Yet it must be also said that he was fortunate in being able to ride the tide of Anglo-American grand strategy as agreed in December 1941, which pinned its hopes in the war against Germany on an eventual major Allied amphibious offensive somewhere or other.

As early as October 1941, when Churchill had first mooted 'Gymnast' to his own Chiefs of Staff, Mountbatten estimated that 16,000 men would be wanted to man the landing craft. He therefore set afoot a hugely expanded programme at the Combined Operations centres at Troon, Dundonald and Inverary. Month by month through 1942 the numbers in this second Royal Navy were to swell, while Mountbatten at the same time pressed on with providing the landing craft. In the last quarter of 1941 the number under construction in Britain totalled 348; the 1942 programme (for completion in May 1943) numbered 1,168.[21] By now Britain had had to resort to America as her main supplier of all kinds of landing craft. In January 1942 for example, Roosevelt approved the production for Britain of 200 'Landing Ships (Tank)' (capable of trans-ocean voyages) and 200 'Landing Craft (Tank)', as well as seven 'Landing Ships (Dock)' – key instruments in the ever more sophisticated orchestra of amphibious operations.[22]

It was under Mountbatten's direction too that, in spring 1942, a start was at last made on fulfilling the old ISTDC's dream of the headquarters ship by the conversion of the armed merchant cruiser *Bulolo* (9,111 tons displacement; 15 knots). This was soon followed by the *Largs* (formerly a French liner: 12,786 tons displacement; 16 knots).[23] Both ships were to make brilliantly successful débuts during the 'Torch' landings.

Most of these British developments had their parallels, of course, in the United States (where the first manual on combined landings was issued by the Joint Board of the Army and Navy in 1927, and reissued in 1935).[24] In 1934 the first major exercise had been mounted at Culebra Island, east of Puerto Rico. In 1938 there was produced the manual which laid down the American 'rules of the game' as they were to be followed throughout the Second World War – in the Japanese conflict as well as the German.[25] In January 1941 Admiral King, then the C-in-C, Atlantic Fleet, had directed another large-scale exercise at Culebra. Yet even by the time of this exercise specialised tank and vehicle landing craft were still lacking. Moreover, the Americans only came to appreciate much later than the British the need for a headquarters ship, and their own task forces in 'Torch' were to be commanded in traditional style from the fleet flagship, with exactly the disadvantages long foreseen by the ISTDC in Britain. And the United States armed forces, entering the conflict two years after their ally, still had much to learn in the unforgiving school of operational experience.

In contrast, by the time preparations for 'Torch' were well under way from the summer of 1942 onwards the British had already been taught much by two years of attacks on enemy coasts from Western Europe to Crete and North Africa. The attacks ranged in scale from small parties of Commandos to such larger raids as the highly successful sabotage mission to the Lofoten Islands off northern Norway in March 1941, the bold and gallant exploit in destroying the lock gates of the dry dock at St Nazaire in March 1942, and a botched attack on the port of Tobruk in September 1942. In May 1942 took place a major landing on the French island of Madagascar (see below, pp. 864–8). But by far the most painful and valuable lesson of all was learned in the disastrous raid on Dieppe on 19 August 1942.

This was the largest combined operation yet to be launched in the European theatre, with a landing force of two Canadian infantry brigades, a tank battalion, Royal Marine Commandos and a few US rangers – some 6,100 troops in all, most of them carried across the Channel in seven landing ships (infantry). The Royal Navy provided a supporting squadron of eight destroyers, and the Navy crews ferried the assault troops ashore in 24 LCT and 150 LCI. The Royal Air Force deployed 67 squadrons (60 of them fighters as air cover) and the United States Army Air Force seven squadrons. The ostensible aim was to take Dieppe and hold it for a few hours while everything of military value in and around the town was destroyed; the ulterior purpose was to test the German coast defence system in the West. The operation had to be called off in complete and costly failure, with the tanks baulked by a seawall and roadblocks and then knocked out by German fire, and the soldiers slaughtered on the shingle. Only subsidiary flank attacks outside Dieppe achieved any success. Among the Canadians the casualty rate amounted to 68 per cent; gruesome even by Great War standards.[26] The Royal Navy lost a destroyer and 33 landing craft; the Royal Air Force 106 aircraft.[27] The raid fully vindicated General Brooke's apprehensions about the risk of disaster involved in either 'Sledgehammer' or 'Roundup'.

The failure at Dieppe owed itself above all to a faulty plan whereby the main attacking force was committed frontally against the powerful defences of Dieppe itself rather than on the flanking beaches; a blunder for which Mountbatten and the responsible Army commander, Lieutenant-General Sir Bernard Montgomery (GOC-in-C, South Eastern Command), were jointly culpable; Montgomery much the more so.[28]

The lessons of Dieppe for 'Torch' were clear: first and foremost, that heavy and continuous bombardment of shore defences by powerful naval forces was essential during the run-in and landing of the assault waves; secondly, that the most obvious place to land was the wrong place if alternatives could be found. Moreover, Dieppe gave fresh confirmation that a headquarters ship was absolutely vital for effective command and control.[29]

Thus the planners of 'Torch' enjoyed priceless assets denied to all their predecessors in the history of amphibious operations – tactics and techniques thoroughly worked out over many years and tested under fire; a variety of craft and equipment specially developed to serve their purpose. Yet the mounting of a tri-service offensive of such complexity, on so vast a scale, and over such long sea distances presented an entirely novel challenge. General Eisenhower and his commanders and staffs had much to think about.

It hardly helped them that for six weeks, until 5 September, they had to live, in Eisenhower's words, 'under conditions of strain, uncertainty and tension'[30] while they waited for the Allied political and military leaderships to come to a final decision as to exactly how many landings there were to be in French North Africa and exactly where they were to take place. For those leaderships themselves it was six weeks of puzzling how to match desirable strategic objectives with limited available resources – above all, of warships and assault shipping. The process was tortuous and complex; the underlying issues however simple enough. The ultimate aim of 'Torch', as restated by the Combined Chiefs of Staff directive to Eisenhower of 24 August, was

> Complete annihilation of Axis forces now opposing the British forces in the Western Desert and intensification of air and sea operations against Axis installations in the Mediterranean area in order to insure communications through the Mediterranean and to facilitate operations against the Axis on the European continent.[31]

The key to achieving these objectives evidently lay in the swift occupation of Tunisia, so threatening Rommel's main base in Tripolitania at a time when he would be locked in battle with the 8th Army 1,500 miles away to the east at Alamein. To seize Tunisia and especially the ports of Bizerta and Tunis therefore constituted the immediate objective of the Allied landing in French North Africa. As the Joint Planners put it on 5 August: 'Our primary consideration must be to forestall the arrival of Axis forces in Tunisia. The defeat of the [Vichy] French is only a means to an end.'[32]

The obvious operational solution, a direct landing in Tunisia, was out of the question because of enemy land-based airpower in Sicily and Sardinia. The British Chiefs of Staff therefore proposed that

Allied forces should land at Philippeville and Bône in the east of Algeria (as well as at Oran and Algiers) and then carry out a pell-mell advance along the coast to Tunis before the Germans could get there in strength. Eisenhower agreed with this. But Marshall and Brooke both believed that it was equally essential for the Allies to land at Casablanca in French Morocco, so providing the Americans with a direct trans-Atlantic supply route from the United States, and a secure overland line of communication from the Atlantic coast to the Allied expeditionary forces in Algeria. Marshall in particular was anxious about the vulnerability of a single maritime line of communication running through the Straits of Gibraltar, fearing possible attack from Spain or Spanish Morocco. This anxiety was not shared by Cunningham or the Admiralty, who remained cheerfully confident that the Royal Navy could keep open the sea route via the Straits, as it had succeeded in doing in all Britain's previous wars for two and a half centuries.

Calculate and recalculate resources as the planners might, however, there simply was not enough of anything, especially ships and landing craft, to permit five separate landings at Casablanca, Oran, Algiers, Philippeville and Bône. The Royal Navy was already having to strip warships from the Atlantic and the Home Fleet and cancel the next Arctic convoy to Russia in order to provide cover for 'Torch' inside the Mediterranean. Could the United States Navy supply additional ships? Admiral King gave the terse answer: it could not, because it was fully stretched in current operations in the Pacific. Hard choices had therefore to be made.

Eisenhower himself, backed by Cunningham, opted for dropping the landings at Casablanca in French Morocco in order to make possible those at Philippeville and Bône. For him, 'the utmost exertion and ready acceptance of hazards' were worthwhile in order to take Tunis quickly. 'If Axis forces ever beat us to that place,' he wrote on 13 August for Marshall's benefit, 'their later capabilities for building up strength will far exceed our own and will reduce the campaign to another costly and futile defensive venture.'[33] Yet in Washington his patron Marshall and the Joint Chiefs of Staff took the opposite view, recommending to London on 25 August that in order to permit the landing in Morocco not only should the landings at Philippeville and Bône be dropped, but also even that at Algiers. Thus the Mediterranean part of 'Torch' would be restricted to Oran, in western Algeria, so rendering it out of the question to capture Tunis before the enemy.

The JCS memorandum found the British Chiefs of Staff divided in opinion. Brooke reckoned that it would be too hazardous anyway to land at Bône and Philippeville; that it would also be strategically unsound to leave Morocco unoccupied in the Allied rear. Sir Dudley Pound remained anxious about the effects of Atlantic surf on the chances of the Morocco landing; the Chief of Air Staff, Sir Charles Portal, believed like Eisenhower and Cunningham that it was vital to grab Tunis without delay. Nevertheless, the COS reached a compromise view, telegraphing the Joint Chiefs that while forestalling the Germans in Tunis came first and foremost, a landing at Casablanca was certainly desirable 'if it can be done without prejudice to the rest of the operations'.[34]

At this point the Prime Minister directly intervened by telegraphing the President on 27 August (after the Chiefs of Staff meeting) to tell him how 'profoundly disconcerted' they all were by the Combined Chiefs of Staff's proposal to drop the Algiers landing. 'It seems to me that the whole pith of the operation will be lost if we do not take Algiers as well as Oran on the first day – Not to go east of Oran is making the enemy a present not only of Tunis but of Algiers . . .'[35] He added that 'if it came to choosing between Algiers and Casablanca it cannot be doubted that the former is the more hopeful and fruitful objective . . .'[36]

But Roosevelt's reply, though constructive and conciliatory, re-affirmed bluntly that 'under any circumstances one of our landings must be on the Atlantic'.[37] A week of bargaining now ensued in which each ally rummaged again through the cupboard of its naval and military resources to see if enough could be raked together or redeployed to make possible the landing at Algiers as well as those at Oran and Casablanca. President Roosevelt, for his part, offered to reduce the strength of the American assault forces at Casablanca by 5,000 men and make them available together with their shipping for the Algiers landing. The British allotted for the same purpose the forces previously earmarked for Philippeville and Bône, plus 5,000 men from the Oran force, and offered British landing craft for the Casablanca operation. In their calculations of overall resources the British – and Eisenhower – could also now reckon on the US Navy's exact contribution to 'Torch', which had been at last revealed by Admiral King. The sums being done, the Allies decided that Algiers was 'on' as well as Oran and Casablanca. On 5 September the deal was finally struck, to a Presidential 'Hurrah' and a Prime Ministerial 'O.K. Full Blast'.[38]

Yet the deal fudged the original clear strategic axis of 'Torch' eastwards towards Tunisia, Tripolitania and the rear of Rommel's Panzerarmee Afrika. For the immediate objective had now become rather more the occupation of the western half of French North Africa – Algeria from Algiers westwards and Morocco – as a firm base for subsequent operations. This strategic ambiguity is demonstrated by the comparative weight of assault forces finally allotted to the eastern landing at Algiers and to the western in Morocco: the Eastern Assault Force numbered 20,000, whereas the Western Assault Force numbered 35,000. And in any case Tunis, 'the milk of the whole coconut' in Eisenhower's graphic metaphor,[39] lay more than 500 miles to the east of what was now to be the Allies' nearest landing point at Algiers; three times the distance from Bône.

It only remained to decide on D-Day for 'Torch'. The Prime Minister, much concerned about the timing of the next Arctic convoy to Russia in relation to 'Torch's' demand for naval forces, was at first angered when Eisenhower advised on 12 September that the existing provisional date of 31 October could not be met because of the time needed to ship certain American formations and their equipment across the Atlantic, sort them and prepare their loading schedules.[40] Eisenhower offered an earliest date of 4 November and as a latest date a 'best guess' of 8 November, but then only provisionally. Despite heavy personal pressure from Churchill, Eisenhower stoutly refused to guarantee these dates.[41] Being an American national and an Allied commander responsible in the first place to the Joint Chiefs of Staff he was better placed to resist such pressure than British commanders directly under Churchill's authority. A week later, however, he was able to fix D-Day for 8 November – falling 63 days after the final decision to undertake the three landings at Casablanca, Oran and Algiers. It did not, however, give much time in which to plan and organise the deployment of three task forces (one from the United States; two from Britain) comprising more than 70,000 soldiers, more than 400 warships and auxiliaries, and upwards of 60 merchant ships; to say nothing of finalising all the tactical plans for the amphibious assaults on the chosen beaches.

It was on 8 October that Eisenhower's headquarters issued the Outline Plan for 'Torch' incorporating all the work of the previous weeks, first in settling the integrated Allied command structure and then the deployment of forces by sea, land and air.

The land forces were divided into a Western Assault Force under Major-General George S. Patton (35,000 American troops; objective: Casablanca in French Morocco); a Central Task Force under Major-General Lloyd R. Fredendall (18,500 American troops, building up to 39,000; objective: Oran), and an Eastern Task Force under Lieutenant-General K. A. N. Anderson (20,000 troops in the first wave, half American and half British; objective: Algiers). These military commanders reported directly to Eisenhower.

Each of the three assault forces had its equivalent Naval Task Force charged with conveying it safely to the landing point and putting it ashore. The Western Naval Task Force was composed entirely of ships of the United States Navy. It was to proceed in company with the Western Assault Force to Morocco directly from the United States: 91 vessels in all, including 23 'combat loaders' (the equivalent of the British landing ship infantry), twelve of them loaded with 250 tanks, ten auxiliary combat loaders, six cargo ships and a supply train. The Western Naval Task Force itself comprised three battleships, the new *Massachusetts*, the *Texas* and the *New York*; the fleet carrier *Ranger* and four escort carriers newly converted from merchant ships (total: 171 aircraft); seven cruisers; 38 destroyers; eight fleet minesweepers; five tankers.[42] The Task Force ('Task Force 34' in the United States Navy's order of battle) was commanded by Rear Admiral H. Kent Hewitt (flying his flag in the cruiser *Augusta*, which was also to serve as improvised headquarters ship during the landings), a man of calm and massive presence, with a great hook-nosed head and a bulk that would have done credit to an eighteenth-century admiral. Since April 1942 he had been commanding the Amphibious Force, Atlantic Fleet, so he knew his business. By a reluctant concession on Admiral King's part, Hewitt was to pass from the command of Admiral R. E. Ingersoll, C-in-C, Atlantic Fleet, to Eisenhower's once his task force crossed the meridian of 40°W.[43] Although Hewitt would thereby become formally subordinate to Cunningham as Allied Naval Commander, Expeditionary Force (and Cunningham never doubted that this was so), it proved in the event something of a formality, so separate were the Moroccan operations from those along the Algerian coast.

Cunningham's own responsibility as ANCXF therefore really belonged to the Mediterranean landings, where all the naval forces were to be supplied by the Royal Navy, and where the landings stood in danger of attack by hostile heavy squadrons. When Cunningham hoisted his flag in Gibraltar on 1 November, he took over from Admiral Harwood (the C-in-C, Mediterranean) the Mediterranean command west of a line from Cape Bon in Tunisia to the northwestern tip of Sicily. Under Cunningham were the Central (Oran) and Eastern (Algiers) Naval Task Forces, together with Force H, the covering battlesquadron, and Force R, its refuelling group of two tankers and escorts.

Force H (Vice-Admiral Sir Neville Syfret) consisted of the battleships *Duke of York* (flag) and *Rodney*; the battlecruiser *Renown*; the fleet carriers *Victorious, Formidable* and *Furious* (total: 116 aircraft);[44] three cruisers; seventeen destroyers; four fleet minesweepers.[45] That Force H was to be refuelled at sea provides a mark of the Royal Navy's progress under the goad of war. The Central Naval Task Force (CNTF) (Commodore T. H. Troubridge, the latest of generations of his family to serve in the Royal Navy) comprised the headquarters ship *Largs* (Broad Pendant), the escort carriers *Biter* and *Dasher* (converted merchant ships of 8,200 tons displacement; 17 knots; 15 aircraft);[46] the cruisers *Aurora* and *Jamaica*; the anti-aircraft ships *Alynbank* and *Delhi*; thirteen destroyers; six corvettes; eight minesweepers and various ancillary craft.

The Eastern Task Force (ENTF) comprised the headquarters ship *Bulolo*; the old carrier *Argus* (completed in 1918 as the first carrier in the world with a continuous stem-to-stern flight deck; 22,600 tons displacement; 21 aircraft);[47] the cruisers *Sheffield, Scylla* and *Charybdis*; the escort carrier *Avenger* (sister ship to *Dasher* and *Biter*); the auxiliary anti-aircraft ships *Palomares, Pozarica* (each 1,895 tons displacement; 16½ knots; six 4-inch AA guns, eight 2-pounder pompoms, eight 20mm AA guns, and eight 0.5-inch machine-guns),[48] and *Tynwald* (3,791 tons displacement; 18 knots; six 4-inch AA guns, eight 2-pounder AA guns, ten 20mm AA guns);[49] the new 15-inch gun monitor *Roberts* (7,970 tons displacement; 12 knots; two 15-inch guns in a single turret);[50] thirteen destroyers; three submarines; three sloops; seven minesweepers and seven corvettes. The force was commanded by Vice-Admiral Sir Harold Burrough, a veteran of the Malta convoys and a man judged by Cunningham a few days after 'Torch' landings to be 'good but obstinate and hasn't yet realised that he is dealing with someone even more pig-headed than himself'.[51]

To find 160 warships for the 'Torch' Mediterranean operations – in particular the fleet carriers and heavy ships for Force H – did not prove at all easy for the Admiralty in the face of global commitments and especially after the loss in the 1942 Malta convoy runs of a fleet carrier, two cruisers, an anti-aircraft cruiser and nine destroyers sunk, and many other ships (including the carrier *Indomitable*) severely damaged. It was compelled to suspend convoys to Russia and also from Britain to the South Atlantic, weaken North Atlantic convoy escorts at a time of soaring U-boat success, and drastically reduce the Home Fleet. The demands of 'Torch' likewise imposed grievous extra strain on Britain's shrinking resources of merchant shipping, for quite apart from the more than 200 vessels required to convoy the Mediterranean assault forces in the first place, it was estimated that 66 ships would be needed each month thereafter up to January 1943 (when the campaign was expected to come to an end) in order to sustain the Allied army in Algeria.[52] In consequence imports into the United Kingdom would have to be still further cut: the British people at home would have to go even hungrier while at the same time drawing even faster on existing stockpiles of food and industrial raw materials in the United Kingdom.[53]

No single Allied air commander equivalent to Cunningham was appointed, but instead two separate area commands were set up directly under Eisenhower – Eastern Air Command (east of Cape Tenez in Algeria: all British aircraft) under Air Marshal Sir William Welsh, and the Western Air Command (west of Cape Tenez: all American aircraft of the 12th United States Army Air Force) under Major-General James Doolittle. In the case of the Western Air Command, Doolittle was placed under the operational control of General Patton, the Assault Force Commander, according to American practice. But in Eastern Air Command the British practice was instead followed of entrusting the effective coordination of air and ground operations to the mutually cooperative spirit of an air marshal and a general; not, as it was to prove, with the happiest results.

With the issue between 3 and 20 October 1942 of the naval operation orders for 'Torch' in eight bulky parts (short titles: 'Ton 1–8'), the planning of a maritime expedition matched for the first time in history the elaboration and exactitude that had long characterised the mounting of great offensives on land.[54] The 'Ton' orders were promulgated over the signature of the Deputy Naval Commander, Expeditionary Force, Admiral Sir Bertram Ramsay – the man who only seven years earlier had resigned as Chief of Staff to the then C-in-C, Home Fleet, Sir Roger Backhouse, because Backhouse remained loyal to the Victorian tradition of command by a one-man-band in admiral's gold sleeve rings, and could not or would not operate a modern staff system. It was another mark of how far and how fast the Royal Navy had finally emerged from the Victorian era since the outbreak of war.

'Ton 1' (issued on 3 October) outlined the strategic plan as a whole. 'Ton 2' (8 October) constituted the core document, for it laid down in detail the routing and scheduling of convoys, escorts and task forces outwards from Britain to the forward assembly area in the Bay of Algeciras; and then the final deployment via the Straits of Gibraltar to the launch points for the landings at Oran and Algiers. 'Ton 3' (also 8 October) added the detailed tactical instructions for the assault landings themselves. 'Ton 4' (issued the same day too) contained instructions for the submarine screens that were to cover the 'Torch' forces from the Italian battlefleet and the French fleet at Toulon. 'Ton 5–8' dealt with various redeployments and convoy arrangements to follow once the initial lodgement had been won.

To ensure that so many separate fast and slow groups of ships of every description (with loads ranging from specialist personnel and equipment to combat troops, tanks, guns, transport and bulk stores) arrived in the assembly area at Gibraltar at the right time and in the right sequence, Admiral Ramsay issued with the 'Ton 2' orders carefully calculated tables of convoy routes complete with lettered routing positions.

The vast, stealthy movement of darkened vessels packed with troops or cargo actually got under way on 2 October, when the first of the two advance convoys, KX1, put to sea from the Clyde with 40 vessels – a mixture of tugs, tankers, colliers and auxiliary craft with an escort of warships, and bearing with it key specialists. KX2 (eighteen vessels, including five ammunition ships, with an escort of thirteen of His Majesty's ships) soon followed. On 18 October the third advance convoy, KX3, consisting of just one ship, the 11,000-ton liner *Clanstephan Castle*, and two escorts sailed with radar, signals, anti-aircraft and other expert personnel.

Meanwhile the 50,000 British and American soldiers of the Oran and Algiers assault forces were stuffing kitbags, donning full marching order, watching their training camps recede behind them as the transport trucks carried them to railway station or straight to dockside, and climbing gangways up into the strange over-crowded, body-smelling shipboard world of messdeck, hammock or bunk, and 'heads'. On 22 October (it was the day before Montgomery launched the Second Battle of Alamein) the first of the big assault convoys, KMS1 (KM = UK to Mediterranean; S = slow) put to sea with 46 vessels escorted by eighteen warships; it was followed three days later by KMS2 with 53 vessels and ten escorts. On 26 October KMF1 (F = fast) followed with 39 ships and twelve escorts; on 31 October KX5 (32 ships and ten escorts); on 1 November, KMF2 (eighteen ships and eight escorts). The last convoy of all to arrive, KX4 (KX = Advance; i.e., first to sail), which was making the passage in two parts, was due to reach Gibraltar on 4 November.

Meanwhile the ships which were to form Force H and the two naval task forces had also been putting to sea. The carrier *Furious* and three destroyers left the Clyde on 20 October; the battleship *Rodney* and three destroyers steamed out of Scapa Flow on the 23rd; four days later the escort carriers *Dasher* and *Biter*, the cruiser *Jamaica* and the anti-aircraft ship *Delhi*, together with four escorts, departed from the Clyde; on the 30th, the main body of Force H sailed from Scapa and the Clyde, rendezvousing to the north-west of Ireland next day – the battleships *Duke of York* and *Rodney*, the battlecruiser *Renown*, the carriers *Furious* and *Formidable* and sixteen destroyers.[55]

This broad stream of convoys and task forces followed a wide sweeping course out into the Atlantic and then south and south-east through the Western Approaches, where the Admiralty knew that up to 50 U-boats could converge on the expedition by the end of October if U-boat Command once detected that it was at sea, and another 25 U-boats by 6 November.[56] The First Sea Lord therefore hardly underestimated the riskiness of the whole gamble when he warned the Prime Minister that the U-boats 'might well prove exceedingly menacing' to 'the most valuable convoys ever to leave our shores'.[57] And U-boats and German aircraft did indeed sight at least two convoys, as well as *Rodney* and two of the carriers. Yet U-boat Command failed to deduce that anything other than normal movements of convoys or warships was afoot, and consequently took no measures to concentrate against this supreme target.[58] Moreover, on 27 October, by a stroke of luck – or intervention of Providence – the U-boats in the key sea area to the west of Morocco and the Straits of Gibraltar located a north-bound convoy of merchant ships from Sierra Leone to the United Kingdom; and this thereafter served as an unwitting sacrificial decoy. Although it lost thirteen vessels, it kept Dönitz's captains entirely occupied.

In the last days of October 1942 and the first of November more than 340 ships were converging on Gibraltar through waters that had witnessed some of the greatest victories ever won by the Royal Navy – past Cape St Vincent which gave its name to Admiral Sir John Jervis's triumph over another Spanish fleet in 1797 ('If there are 50 sail of the line, I will go through them'); past Cadiz, where in 1587 Drake had singed Philip II of Spain's beard by attacking the Armada in harbour; past Cape Trafalgar itself. By 4 November 1942 the grandest assembly of merchant vessels and ships of war in all Gibraltar's turbulent history in Britain's wars since the Rock was first captured in 1704 lay at anchor in Algeciras Bay. 'The harbour is absolutely stiff with shipping, cruisers, aircraft carriers and small fry,' wrote Cunningham to Ramsay (who had remained in Britain to handle all rearward problems). 'How on earth the enemy are expected to take no notice beats me.'[59] In point of fact, the enemy's mind was dwelling on the likelihood of further major Malta convoy operations, or perhaps another attack on Dakar.[60]

On the Rock and in the ships all was now expectation, bustle and the last-minute muddles caused by inevitable human frailty; the latter topic being one on which Cunningham expressed himself with his customary salt breeziness. 'To say that things are chaotic would be an exaggeration,' he told Ramsay, 'but they are certainly a bit confused. The signalmen appear to have made everything so intricate that no one, including themselves, knows what to do.'[61] Not so much of a joking matter, however, was the careless talk about 'Torch' plans prevalent in Gibraltar, as Cunningham reported:

> The chat going on in the bars is most alarming & I have threatened to put the American colonel in *Furious* in a cell for giving the show away by chat in her wardroom. Why on earth did R.A.A. [Rear-Admiral, Aircraft Carriers] ask for them [military liaison officers] – this craze of laison [sic] officers is in my opinion getting quite out of bounds.[62]

But the trouble did not only lie with gabby liaison officers. According to Cunningham, 'a bad mistake had been that some of the Task Force commanders' orders have been distributed with no restrictions as to opening them. The fault lies with the secretariats of Burrough and Troubridge I fear. So even some of the M.L. [motor launches] are aware of the detailed orders.'[63]

For the lucky ones Gibraltar offered the last chance of a run ashore before the voyage to battle. The bars roared with song and laughter; the narrow thoroughfares beneath the Rock witnessed behaviour which aroused the wrath of that formidable disciplinarian, the Naval Commander, Allied Expeditionary Force. 'Things are damned slack in this place,' he reported to his Deputy. 'I want to lay my hands on some of the young officers to be seen in ½ dozens drunk in the streets at night. It is reported to me that they are worse than the sailors.'[64]

While the ward room, the gun room and the lower deck roistered, last-minute high-level secret diplomacy was under way in the hope – vain as it turned out – that the Vichy French administration in North Africa could be won over to the Allied cause and so avert the need for combat. It marked the climax, or rather anti-climax, of months of intrigue in French North Africa by an American diplomat, Robert Murphy (the United States having maintained diplomatic relations with the Vichy French government ever since 1940). On 23 October 1942 the Royal Navy had played its modest part in the cloak-and-dagger work by landing the American General Mark Clark near Algiers from the submarine *Seraph* for a secret meeting with General Mast, the French commander of the Algiers area. Mast was the local representative of General Henri Giraud, an antique French hero who had been captured by the Germans in 1940 but later successfully escaped to the unoccupied zone of France. It was the Allies' illusion that if Giraud could be brought to French North Africa, his prestige was such that the French civil and military authorities would rally to him. This was to be another job for HM submarine *Seraph*, this time flying the Stars and Stripes and under the nominal command of a non-submariner US officer, just in case Giraud still felt bitter about the Royal Navy's attack at Oran in 1940.

On 28 October Murphy (cloak-and-dagger name 'McGowan') signalled urgently to Eisenhower to request that the 'Torch' landings be postponed for a fortnight in order to enable General Giraud to reach Algeria and himself and General Mast, the French commander, to have time to complete their preparations for a coup. This request, with its diplomat's insouciant disregard for military practicalities, served to wind the tension in Eisenhower's headquarters even tighter. Eisenhower furiously signalled Marshall on 1 November that it was 'inconceivable that McGowan can recommend such a delay with his intimate knowledge of the operation and the present location of troops and convoys afloat . . .'[65] Cunningham in a letter to Ramsay on 3 November called Murphy 'that lunatic', and added: 'I got the wind up, not about Eisenhower, but about what might happen in the stratosphere!'[66] But nothing had happened in 'the stratosphere'; 'Torch' would be launched as planned on 8 November.

On 5 November (the first day of Rommel's retreat from Alamein) began the crux of the entire 'Torch' deployment – the passing of upwards of 340 ships through the eight-miles-wide Straits of Gibraltar into the Mediterranean in just 33 hours. According to the Naval Staff History of 'Torch' it was 'a large-scale movement of far-reaching complexity depending for its success, in the case of large vessels, on rigid adherence to a time-table . . .'[67] To complicate the problem even further, smaller vessels had to divert into Gibraltar in order to refuel, so necessitating 'the rapid and flexible execution of a fuelling programme';[68] the tricky responsibility of Vice-Admiral Sir F. Edward-Collins, Flag Officer, North Atlantic Station, and his special assistant for 'Torch', Commodore G. N. Oliver.

At 1930 the van of the armada, Force R (Force H's refuelling group), passed Europa Point. An hour later followed the carrier *Argus*, the cruisers *Sheffield*, *Scylla* and *Charybdis*, the anti-aircraft ship *Tynwald* and their escort. At 2300 it was the turn of the monitor *Roberts*. A quarter of an hour before midnight the first of the assault convoys, KMS(A)1, the slow Algiers convoy, began to head through the narrow neck of water between Europe and Africa, followed at 0100 on 6 November by the fast Algiers assault convoy KMF(A)1, and at 0300 by a group of landings ship (tank) (in this case, converted shallow-draft oilers each carrying 20 tanks or 30 trucks). An hour and a half later the great ships of Force H with their screen of cruisers and destroyers began their passage. At 0445 Force H was followed by three landing ships (infantry) (converted passenger ships) crammed with over 1,000 soldiers and carrying a total of eighteen landing craft (assault). There now elapsed an interval of nearly eleven hours while the Algiers convoys, with miles further to go than those bound for Oran, steamed ahead. At 1600 on the 6th, darkness again, the slow Oran convoy KMS(O)1 steamed eastwards through the Straits, with its fast counterpart KMF(O)1 following astern six and a half hours later. At 0400 on 7 November the Advance Carrier Force for Oran – *Furious*, the anti-aircraft ship *Delhi* and their escort – brought up the rear of the whole armada.

Meanwhile Rear Admiral Hewitt with Task Force 34 and the Western Assault Force, convoy UGF1 (94 ships in all), had safely zig-zagged the Atlantic at a steady 14 knots. In the midnight hours of 6–7 November Hewitt passed to the north of Madeira, feinting in the direction of the Straits of Gibraltar, and then altered south-east for the final approach to the Moroccan coast.[69]

Within the Mediterranean Rear-Admiral Burrough and Commodore Troubridge, in accordance with instructions, assumed on passing the meridian of 3°W the responsibility for the onward routing of their task forces to the 'release' position off Algiers and Oran from which the assault waves would be despatched to the beaches. Force H (less *Rodney, Furious* and three destroyers detached in support of the Central Naval Task Force, and the cruiser *Bermuda* detached to the Eastern Task Force) steamed eastwards to cover the landings and the follow-up convoys against attack by either Italian or French heavy ships. Admiral Syfret was under orders, however, not to proceed east of 4° 30′E unless to engage the enemy, and in any event not to jeopardise his force because upon it depended the security of the whole operation. The Malta-based 10th Submarine Flotilla (five boats) had been in place since 5 November off the northern and southern approaches of the Straits of Messina to keep watch for possible sorties by Italian squadrons from either Naples or Taranto; three boats of the 8th Flotilla (based on Gibraltar) were keeping a similar watch on Toulon. The remaining five boats of this flotilla were already on station off the landing beaches at Algiers and Oran, ready to act as rendezvous beacons for the approaching task forces.

On 7 November the Royal Air Force began to fly standing reconnaissance patrols along a line between the eastern coast of Spain and the Bonifacio Strait (between Sardinia and Corsica) in order to detect any southward movement of the French Toulon fleet; between Cape Marittimo in Sicily and Cavoli Island in Sardinia to watch for westward sorties by the Italian fleet; and north and west of Dakar in French West Africa to give early warning of any northward move towards Admiral Hewitt's task force by French warships. In addition the Royal Air Force was flying repeated reconnaissance sorties over French and Italian naval bases, while Catalinas, Hudsons and Swordfish from Gibraltar were providing anti-U-boat escorts for the invasion forces during their voyage to the Algerian coast.

Now, with the long work of preparation over and the task forces steaming eastwards through the Mediterranean, began the worst time for Eisenhower and Cunningham back at Expeditionary Force headquarters in Gibraltar, for Brooke and Churchill in London, and for Marshall and Roosevelt far off in Washington. They could only wait, and weigh again the chances of success or failure. Certainly the Vichy French forces in North Africa presented an immeasurably less daunting proposition than the German Army and the Luftwaffe. The French garrison numbered some 120,000 (about 55,000 in Morocco, 50,000 in Algeria, and 15,000 in Tunisia); and consisted of mostly native rank-and-file with French officers. Though its equipment was obsolete, its discipline was believed to be good. The French Air Force amounted to only 500 aircraft of all kinds, mostly obsolete, against 1,041 Allied aircraft – once these could be deployed forward via Gibraltar to North African bases. It was the French Navy that posed the greatest potential danger to 'Torch'. The Toulon fleet comprised three heavy ships, seven cruisers, 28 destroyers, and fifteen submarines, while at Casablanca lay a 6-inch gun cruiser, eight submarines and the battleship *Jean Bart* (not completed but able to fire her main armament), and at Dakar the modern battleship *Richelieu* and three cruisers.[70] Fortunately only destroyers and smaller craft were stationed at the Algerian base of Oran and the Tunisian base of Bizerta.

How swiftly and how effectively might Axis forces also intervene? In terms of strength in ships fit for sea the Italian fleet remained formidable enough – six heavy ships, nine cruisers, 28 destroyers and 35 submarines. Yet the recent record indicated poor morale and irresolute leadership, while the fleet's mobility was shackled by want of oil fuel. The Axis air forces were another matter, as their relentless and successful attacks on the Malta convoys in June and August had demonstrated. Allied Intelligence estimated their possible strength in Sardinia and Sicily by D-Day as 385 German aircraft (actual on the day 395) and 530 Italian (actual on the day 574),[71] so that the Allies would by no means enjoy air superiority within a radius of some two hundred miles from enemy airfields – a radius which took in Tunisia.

But at least Eisenhower and his colleagues could take comfort from the certain knowledge via Ultra decrypts of Luftwaffe and German Navy Enigma traffic that up to the last moment the enemy had failed to divine the expedition's true destination. On 4 November the enemy was reckoning that the armada now assembled at Gibraltar signified a Malta convoy rather than a landing in the Mediterranean and as late as 7 November the German Navy high command (OKM) was guessing that as well as resupply Malta it might well make a landing either in Sardinia or Sicily, or in the Tripoli–Benghazi area in Libya.[72]

Yet for Allied Expeditionary Force headquarters, uncertainties enough remained: French reactions, Spanish reactions, the surf conditions along Moroccan beaches exposed to Atlantic winds and rollers; the whole unprecedented nature of amphibious operations on the scale of 'Torch'.

'We are standing on the brink,' Eisenhower signalled privately to Marshall in the morning of 7 November, 'and must take the jump – whether the bottom contains a nice feather bed or a pile of brickbats! Nevertheless, we have worked our best to assure a successful landing, no matter what we encounter . . .'[73]

At 1800 on 7 November 1942, Rear-Admiral Burrough (Flag Officer, Eastern Task Force) swung his fast convoy, KMF(A)1, from its easterly course ostensibly for Malta round to just east of south for the Algerian coast. Away to the south-west his slow convoy, KMS(A)1 and its covering force of warships turned south-eastwards at the same time in order to join company with him off Algiers. At 1815 Commodore Troubridge began to turn the Central Naval Task Force column by column from east to south and south-east for Oran. Now ensued the final approach phase of 'Torch' in accordance with 'Ton 2': an intricate routing of fast and slow portions of Burrough's and Troubridge's commands so that they would unite at rendezvous points off the Algerian coast into landing groups ready to launch the assault waves to the beaches. For the officers of the watch and especially the navigating officers these were hours of high vigilance.

At 2145 two of Troubridge's columns were the first to home on an invisible infra-red beam from a submarine already stationed seven miles off shore to mark the rendezvous point; in this case, HMS P-54 to the west of Oran. By 2300 two more columns had picked up the beam from the submarine *Ursula* to the north-east of the port. Meanwhile sections of Burrough's fast and slow convoys had rendezvoused on the submarines P-221 and P-48 to the west of Algiers at 2230 and 2245. To the east of Algiers the remaining portion of his fast convoy homed on the infra-red beam from the submarine P-45 at 2230.

With all six landing groups now stationed on their 'release points' two miles to seaward of their beacon submarines, the work immediately got underway of deploying the assault forces in the water; a time of orderly bustle on bridges, on deck and down below, and for the individual soldier in the ranks a time, according to temperament, for quiet introspection or uneasily boisterous humour.

The product of twenty years of painstaking study by the ISTDC and then Combined Operations Command, of two years of war experience culminating in the Dieppe raid, and of three months of careful planning by Admiral Ramsay and his staff was about to be put to the proof.

At Algiers Burrough's role was to put ashore the American 34th Infantry Division (Major-General Charles W. Ryder), one brigade group of the British 78th (Infantry) Division, and the 1st and 2nd Commandos. A second brigade of 78th Division was to act as a floating reserve. The landing operations would be jointly directed by Burrough, Ryder and Air Commodore G. M. Evelegh from the headquarters ship *Bulolo*, with its elaborate radio communications facilities, ample cabin space for large tri-service staffs, and a central operations room. The invasion plan called for two landings west of Algiers ('A' or 'Apples' Sector and 'B' or 'Beer' Sector) and one to the east ('C' or 'Charlie' Sector).[74] Each sector was further subdivided into specific beaches – Apples Green and White; Beer White and Red; Charlie Green, Blue and Red. From the outer flanking lodgements at Apples and Charlie the assault troops were to drive rapidly inland to encircle Algiers and occupy the airfields at Maison Blanche and Blida.

The Apples Sector landing group consisted of 7,230 soldiers of the British 11th Infantry Brigade (78th Division) and a reconnaissance squadron, embarked in three landing ships (infantry) and four motor transport ships, with an escort of an anti-aircraft ship, two sloops, two corvettes, three minesweeping trawlers and three motor launches.[75] By 2304 on 7 November the 45 landing craft carrying the assault wave had been lowered into the water with the aid of a landing ship (gantry).

It was a dark night with a new moon, fine, a moderate swell, but with 'a very strong set'[76] which was carrying the ships westward at about 4 knots. At 2350 the assault waves chugged away for the beach led by the three motor launches bearing pilots transferred from the submarine HMS P-221, which now lay in its inner beacon position two miles off shore.

Shut within the steel walls of the landing craft, soldiers gripped their rifles in dry-mouthed tension and listened to the rumble of the diesel engines and the slap of the water against the flat sides and bow-ramps; smelt fresh salt breeze after the fug of the ships. Ahead glinted the lights of the coastal town of Castiglione. Four hundred yards from the beach a light flashed seaward from a folbot (folding boat) to guide the landing craft in. The ramps swung down, and despite a 'very bad and dangerous' beach at Apples White because of heavy surf, the troops quickly got ashore and secured a lodgement. There was no opposition from the French. Now the landing craft began to ferry in the rest of the brigade.

On Beer Sector Regimental Combat Teams of the American 34th Infantry Division and the British 1st and 2nd Commandos, 5,420 strong in all (embarked in seven landing ships [infantry] and nine motor transport ships, with an escort of four destroyers, one anti-aircraft ship, one sloop, two corvettes, three minesweepers, three trawlers and three motor launches, as well as the headquarters ship *Bulolo*)[77] had to land on five separate beaches from Sidi Ferruch round to a point just east of Algiers itself. What Clausewitz calls 'friction' soon manifested itself. For a start, an easterly Force 3 breeze pushed the ships some three miles to the west during the disembarkation and also compelled the soldiers in some ships to disembark by the lee side only. There was a failure to transfer a pilot from the submarine P-48 to a motor launch as well as other missed cues. Because of these omissions and the westerly drift, the landing craft crews found it difficult to locate their proper assembly positions for the run in, so that the assault finally went ashore on the wrong beaches, an error which would have been ruthlessly punished had this been a coast defended by German troops. But mercifully there proved to be no opposition here either. Indeed General Mast, the French commander, welcomed the Allied troops at the fort of Sidi Ferruch and even laid on a bus service to ferry them to Blida airfield, so that they could negotiate its surrender with the garrison. However, four Fleet Air Arm Martlet fighters from the carrier *Victorious* led by Lieutenant (A) B. H. C. Nation, RN, just beat them to it, taking the airfield's formal surrender at 0930.

The landing force on Charlie Sector on the opposite flank some ten miles east of Algiers (6,000 soldiers of the 39th Regimental Combat Team of the 34th Infantry Division and five troops of Commandos embarked in three American 'combat loaders', one landing ship [infantry] and one motor transport ship, escorted by an anti-aircraft ship, two destroyers, four minesweepers, two trawlers and two motor launches)[78] likewise suffered from the operation of Murphy's Law – not least because of delays in launching landing craft from the combat loader *Leedstown* and assembling them for the run-in. It did not help that a pall of fog spread from land out to sea and forced the landing craft to slow to 4½ knots in order to keep company. Troops for Blue and Red beaches finished up all on Blue, while the commandos who were to attack the coastal battery at Cape Matifou were landed nearly two hours late, if at least on the right beach. Except for a few rounds from this battery, there was no resistance on Charlie Sector either.

Only within the port of Algiers itself did fighting take place, when the destroyers *Broke* and *Malcolm* attempted to put ashore a party of American infantry to prevent the French from scuttling ships and sabotaging dock installations. At 0345 the *Broke* led the *Malcolm* in towards the harbour's southern entrance. On *Broke*'s bridge eyes dazzled by searchlights and gunflashes sought to locate the harbour entrance at the foot of the dark wall of hills that rose behind the city. At the third approach heavy shells smashed into the *Malcolm*, forcing her to limp away. At 0530, dawn now paling the sky, HMS *Broke* tried again. This time she steamed through the entrance, rammed the boom at high speed, charged through into the harbour, and disembarked her landing party. The soldiers swiftly occupied the power station and the oil storage depot. But all too soon they were pinned down by machine-gun fire, while the *Broke* herself became the sitting target for coastal batteries and field artillery. After enduring four hours of pounding she was compelled to abandon 250 American soldiers on shore and put to sea. But on her way out she was hit so heavily that she sank next day under tow.

From daylight on 8 November the carriers *Victorious*, *Formidable*, *Argus* and *Avenger* began to fly air cover over the invasion area. Troop reinforcements poured into the lodgements, while the spearheads of the assault forces thrust inland fast despite resistance by a handful of obdurate forts and coastal batteries. At 1100 Royal Air Force Hurricanes from Gibraltar flew into Maison Blanche airfield after its capture by the American 39th Regimental Combat Team – the first of many. In the afternoon General Ryder and General Juin (representing

Admiral Darlan, the Commander-in-Chief of all Vichy-French forces by land, sea and air, who happened to be in Algiers visiting a sick son) agreed a local cease-fire. At 1900 American forces rolled into Algiers. The Eastern Task Force had thus triumphed in short order, albeit against either weak opposition or none at all. But in the dusk of that successful day arrived harbingers of a different kind of opponent, in the shape of German bombers sweeping in from the east to attack shipping lying off Charlie Sector. They damaged the destroyer *Cowdray* and the combat loader *Leedstown*, the latter sinking on the morrow.

At Oran too the plan of attack relied on landings on the flanks followed by rapid advances inland to close pincers behind the city and capture the local airfields en route. The operation was to be directed from the headquarters ship *Largs* by Commodore T. H. Troubridge, RN, Major-General Lloyd R. Fredendall and Major-General James Doolittle (commanding the US 12th Air Force and the Allied Western Air Command).[79] Deployed some 30 miles off Oran in support of the landings was Troubridge's covering force: the battleship *Rodney*, the fleet carrier *Furious*, the escort carriers *Avenger* and *Biter*, the anti-aircraft ship *Delhi* and nine destroyers.

In the small hours of 8 November the weather at Oran was 'favourable, calm and dark, with good visibility'.[80] However, 'the unexpected westerly set which so seriously interfered with the landings near Algiers was equally disconcerting . . .'[81] On 'X' Sector, some 30 miles west of Oran, 'Task Force Green' (2,250 soldiers, plus tanks and trucks, of the Western Column of Combat Command B, American 1st Armoured Division) was embarked in three landing ships (infantry), four 'Maracaibo' shallow-draft motor transport vessels and one landing ship (tank), with an escort of the cruiser *Aurora*, one destroyer, two corvettes, a trawler and a motor launch. As the ships approached their 'release point' anchorage, a small French convoy straggled across their bows from starboard to port, causing a delay still further worsened when the landing group ran ahead of its minesweepers, which had also been held up by the French convoy.

As a result the landing began at 0130 instead of 0100. However, all went well, especially on 'White' beach (the westerly of the two in 'X' Sector), where the troops found themselves on a 50-yard stretch of sand in a cove well sheltered from the weather. Yet even here Murphy's Law was operating, for the sea proved so shallow that bulldozers had to be used to push the landing craft off the bottom. The consequent damage to rudders and screws left only three out of the thirteen craft that had carried the assault wave still serviceable. Nevertheless, 458 tanks and trucks and over 3,000 soldiers were to come ashore in 'X' Sector over the next three days, and most of them through that 50-yard wide sandy cove.

On 'Y' Sector, nearly 20 miles closer to Oran, 5,262 soldiers of the 26th Regimental Combat Team of the American 1st Infantry Division, embarked in three landing ships (infantry) and two motor transport ships, and escorted by two destroyers, four trawlers and five motor launches, were to land in the wide bay of Les Andalouses. Of all unlikely things, disembarkation from one landing ship (infantry) the *Monarch of Bermuda*, was seriously delayed because the rungs of the steel ladders down her sides turned out to be too far apart (at two feet) for the soldiers easily to negotiate in full combat kit. More unexpected difficulties followed. When the landing craft got within twenty feet of the shore they grounded on a submerged sand bar running the entire width of the bay, with a strip of water five feet deep inshore of it – too deep for troops to wade through. The landing craft were therefore compelled to bludgeon their way over the sand bar, thereby damaging their rudders and screws also.

By this time a northerly swell had begun to rise, causing many craft to broach to on top of the bar. With some soldiers trying to swim for the shore and with jeeps and guns submerging as soon as they left the bow ramps, it was fortunate indeed that neither a storm of fire nor a swift counter-attack descended from the rocky high ground dominating the beach on to the hapless landing forces. This potentially disastrous hold-up resulted from the Expeditionary Force headquarters' decision not to permit reconnaissance parties to land from canoes to survey beach conditions on the spot, but instead rely on observation through submarine periscopes.

Only east of Oran, in 'Z' Sector, did the landings go with complete smoothness. Here 10,472 soldiers of the 1st US Ranger Battalion, the 16th and 18th Regimental Combat Teams of the 1st Infantry Division and the Western Column of Combat Command B of the 1st Armoured Division were to disembark with their tanks and transport from nine landing ships (infantry) and two landing ships (tank), assisted by a landing ship (gantry), plus 22 motor transport ships. Because this was to be by far the largest of the Oran landings, Troubridge, Fredendall and Doolittle were themselves present offshore in *Largs*. The naval escort force comprised the cruiser *Jamaica*, the anti-aircraft ship *Delhi*, three destroyers, five corvettes, one sloop, two cutters, eight minesweepers, three trawlers and four motor launches.[82]

Punctually at 0016 the 'Z' Sector assault forces poured ashore from 68 landing craft on beaches Green, White and Red south of Arzeu, a little port nestling beneath a rocky headland and overlooked by the Fort de la Pointe, and on 'R' beach to its north. From 'R' beach the Rangers advanced swiftly overland to take the fort (it fired a few shots during the night) and Arzeu.

But the successful landings on the flanks had by now been accompanied by a bloody repulse in the centre, where (as at Algiers) an attempt had been made to rush the harbour and land a party of soldiers to prevent the French sabotaging installations or scuttling warships. At 0240 HMS *Walney* and *Hartland*, two ex-American coastguard cutters carrying Rangers and wearing both the Stars and Stripes and the White Ensign, steered for the harbour entrance starkly lit by hostile searchlights and with tracer swinging towards them. At 0310 *Walney* broke through the boom into the harbour, only to be reduced to a flaming hulk by the French sloop *La Surprise* and cross fire from submarines and the destroyer *Epervier*. *Walney* later sank. The *Hartland* fared no better, for the destroyer *Typhon* shattered her at point-blank range, leaving her to blaze from stem to stern in the middle of the harbour until she blew up after daylight. Captain F. T. Peters, RN (who planned and commanded the assault), one of the few survivors from either ship, was by a tragic irony killed a few days later in an air crash. He was posthumously awarded the Victoria Cross and the American Distinguished Service Cross. The attempts to rush the harbours at Oran and Algiers were just like the 1918 Zeebrugge raid all over again – desperate ventures, gallant and futile.

With the destruction of the *Walney* and the *Hartland* the outnumbered and outclassed French Navy, Army and Air Force now began to fight back. The destroyers *Tramontane*, *Tornade* and *Typhon* courageously put to sea to engage Troubridge's powerful task force, but the first two ships quickly succumbed to the accurate shooting of the cruiser *Aurora*, whereupon the *Typhon* temporarily sought shelter in harbour. The sloop *La Surprise* attempted to follow up her success against the *Walney* by attacking Allied shipping off 'Y' Sector, but was sunk by the destroyer *Brilliant*. Next day, 9 November, a fresh sortie by the *Typhon*, this time in company with the *Epervier*, ended with *Epervier* driven ashore engulfed in flames and *Typhon* beached after struggling back into harbour, both of them victims of the cruisers *Aurora* and *Jamaica*.

On land on 8 November a French field battery on high ground behind Arzeu shelled after first light the mass of shipping large and small lying off the shore, and hit the 17,000-ton landing ship (infantry) *Reina del Pacifico* before making off in the face of fire from the destroyer *Vansittart*. At 0900 the coastal battery Du Santon on the promontory behind the Mers-el-Kebir naval base opened accurate fire on ships lying off 'X' Sector; it took *Rodney*'s 16-inch guns to persuade it to cease fire, but then only temporarily. *Rodney* and the battery were later to resume lobbing shells at each other at extreme range, without effect. Throughout this day and the next the French field forces continued stoutly to defend the approaches to Oran from west and east.

Although it had been planned that American parachute troops should capture the airfields at Tafaraoui and La Senia at dawn on the 8th, none arrived owing to bad weather, poor visibility and errors of navigation. Albacores from HMS *Furious* escorted by Seafires and Sea Hurricanes therefore attacked both airfields, destroying some 70 French aircraft at La Senia. At noon that day the armour of Task Force Red from the 'Z' Sector beaches took Tafaraoui, and 28 British and American Spitfires from Gibraltar began to fly in. But the French Air Force was not yet finished. Dewoitine DW 520 fighters (maximum speed 332 mph)[83] attacked the last four Spitfires to arrive, shooting down one of them for the loss of three aircraft. Not until 1600 on 9 November did the armour of Task Force Green succeed in fighting its way through from 'X' Sector to take La Senia airfield. Meanwhile the American 1st Infantry Division had been slowed by tough resistance at St Cloud on the road from Arzeu to Oran. It took a general attack at 0800 on 10 November supported by a bombardment of the coastal batteries by *Rodney*, *Aurora* and *Jamaica* to bring about the final surrender of Oran to the Allies.

Back at Expeditionary Force headquarters in Gibraltar the setbacks and delays in taking the city had momentarily shaken Eisenhower, new as he was to the stress of high command in war. 'Eisenhower is good, but terribly mercurial,' wrote Cunningham to Ramsay on 12 November. 'He was in the depths of despair because Oran did not fall at once . . .'[84] It was fortunate, perhaps, that Eisenhower had 'A.B.C.', that man of battle-hardened steel, at his side.

The operations of Rear Admiral Kent Hewitt's Western Naval Task Force in landing the Western Assault Force on the coast of Morocco north and south of Casablanca belong to the history of the United States Navy.[85] Suffice to say that after incidental errors, mishaps and delays similar to those experienced in the Algerian landings, but here complicated by pounding Atlantic surf and fierce but short-lived fighting against the French Navy and ground troops, Casablanca fell early on 11 November. It is noteworthy, however, that because of the American lack of a headquarters ship General Patton (commanding the assault force) found himself carried helplessly away in Hewitt's flagship *Augusta* just as he was about to go ashore to set up his command post, simply because *Augusta* was needed to repel an attack by French warships.[86]

In hardly more than three days the Allied Expeditionary Force had thus accomplished 'Torch's' first objective of occupying French North Africa from Algiers (inclusive) westwards to the Atlantic. But now came the challenge of beating the Germans and Italians in the race for Eisenhower's 'the milk of the whole coconut' – Tunisia, and, above all, the ports of Bizerta and Tunis.

General Giraud proving on his arrival in Algiers to carry no weight at all with the French civil and military authorities, Eisenhower struck a deal with Admiral Darlan who did. By this deal the Allies recognised Darlan as the High Commissioner for North Africa. All French African territories (except Tunisia) were thereby aligned on the Allied side, including the Dakar naval base in West Africa, a strategic key to the South Atlantic, and the French battle-squadron stationed there. Nevertheless the deal was quickly criticised by prigs in the House of Commons on the grounds of having truck with a former collaborator with the Nazis and so betraying the high principles of the United Nations cause. What mattered to the pragmatic Eisenhower and his military and naval colleagues was that the deal secured the Expeditionary Force's base, and saved it from having to provide precious resources for a complete military occupation of French territories.

Darlan's defection provoked Hitler into ordering the German Army into the unoccupied zone of France, and, on 27 November, into attempting to seize the French fleet at Toulon. Nevertheless, just as Darlan had promised ever since 1940, the fleet – one battleship, two battlecruisers, four heavy and three light cruisers, 24 destroyers, sixteen submarines – scuttled itself.[87] So, after all, the French battle-fleet passed neither to the Allied side nor the Axis, but simply disappeared altogether from the naval balance in the Mediterranean.

On 15 November Admiral Syfret had taken Force H back to Gibraltar after cruising in defence of the 'Torch' landings against a possible Italian sortie that in the event never came, Force H's only victim during its patrol being the Italian cruiser *Attilio Regolo*, torpedoed and crippled by the submarine *Unruffled* (Lieutenant J. S. Stevens). The Admiralty promptly ordered the *Duke of York* and *Victorious* to return to the denuded Home Fleet. Now that the 'Torch' landings had been accomplished, the Naval Staff in London were in any case keen to strip ships away from the Mediterranean and redeploy them on the hard-pressed Atlantic convoy routes. Cunningham, however, found their keenness all too precipitate, confiding to Ramsay on 21 November:

> Not a few of the Admiralty signals are pretty futile. I got one today which indicates that someone has it in what he doubtless calls his head that you can turn Operation Torch off like a tap. Wanting to know when we can cut down on Torch commitments, when I can part with Force H destroyers and when I can part with the Gib escort force.
>
> I just sent a long signal to CNS giving our appreciation of the naval forces required but I doubt it went into his drawer and no one saw it otherwise the above signals could not have been made.[88]

The successful establishment of the Allied Expeditionary Force in Algeria added yet another continuing maritime supply route to the burdens of the Royal Navy and the merchant marine, and at the same time offered a fresh target to the U-boat. Only four days after the landings Cunningham was reporting to Ramsay: 'We have started having heavy losses from the U-boats and air attacks . . . There is I think a concentration of 20–30 of the former between here [Gibraltar] and Algiers and they are picking off our shipping rather too rapidly . . .'[89] Already picked off by the time of this letter were the 19,600-ton *Viceroy of India*, the 11,600-ton *Nieuw Amsterdam* troopships, and destroyers HMS *Martin* and HNLMS *Isaac Sweers*.[90]

In any event the race for Tunis depended on seapower because overland routes were limited to two narrow roads (only one of which was metalled), a single standard-gauge railway meandering through the hills inland and a metre-gauge line along the coast, both with worn-out locomotives and rolling-stock. It was therefore decided to land assault forces at Bougie and Bône, as staging posts along the coast to Tunis. The landing at Bougie, planned for 9 November, had to be postponed for two precious days by bad weather. Although the assault force landed safely without opposition the Luftwaffe (already operating from Tunisian airfields) proceeded ferociously to attack its shipping and escorts, sinking the landing ships (infantry) *Cathay*, *Awatea* and *Karanja* and seriously damaging the old Monitor *Roberts*. The anti-aircraft ship *Tynwald* succumbed to a mine. Where was the RAF? Its fighters were delayed in arriving at a nearby airfield because their petrol was at sea in the assault convoy.

On 12 November Bône was occupied in a joint operation by the British 3rd Parachute Battalion dropped from the air and the 6th Commando landed from the destroyers *Lamerton* and *Wheatland*. By this time the Luftwaffe in Tunisia had reached a total of 81 fighters and 28 dive-bombers, and a handful of parachute troops and panzer-grenadiers were already on the ground. Very soon the sturdy tri-motor Junkers Ju 52s began to fly in troops at an average rate of 750 a day. By sea across the narrow channel between Sicily and Tunisia (and despite British forces based on Malta) followed tanks, including the formidable new 'Tiger', 88mm dual-purpose anti-aircraft/anti-tank guns, field artillery, transport. The Italians too were moving troops and weapons in piecemeal as fast as possible.[91] The scale and pace of this enemy build-up, so much greater and faster than was expected beforehand, was fully revealed to the Allied command by Ultra decrypts of Enigma. On 16 November General Nehring (once commander of the Afrika Korps) arrived to set up a corps headquarters and direct the defence of Tunisia. With the customary German speed and enterprise, he threw forward a screen of ad hoc battlegroups of the kind which, thanks to standard tactical training, always proved so formidable. The Anglo-Americans had very little time left.

What the Allies therefore needed to lead the chase to Tunis was a Rommel or a 'Fast Heinz' Guderian who would take every risk to pre-empt and disconcert the enemy. What they had was Lieutenant-General Kenneth Anderson, a conventional British soldier judged by Eisenhower before 'Torch' to be 'straightforward, direct', but 'inclined to be too meticulous. He studies the written word until he practically burns through the paper.'[92] As early as 12 November, Cunningham, a bold enough thruster himself, was reckoning that 'we are not moving fast enough. Tunis is anyones [sic] who cares to walk in but the Huns are beating us in the race. I cannot understand why our soldiers do not embus and get on but they are methodically piling up POL [petrol, oil, lubricant] and amun [ammunition] and haven't really got going yet.'[93] Yet the logistic problems remained crippling, as even Cunningham had to acknowledge at the beginning of December: 'Rail head is choked, the wharfs are littered up all for want of transport to take the stuff away.'[94]

By the time Anderson's 1st Army (as his command had now become) and the Allied air forces were ready to launch a major offensive towards Tunis on 22 November, the German–Italian forces under Nehring were strong enough to defeat it, launch counter-strokes and throw the 1st Army back. In December the Mediterranean winter rains hosed down on the battlefield, turning roads and tracks to swamp, forcing a postponement *sine die* of a renewed Allied offensive and bogging the campaign down in stalemate. In January 1943 local Allied and German offensives equally failed to break the stalemate.

At the beginning of February (the month when, according to the original 'Torch' planning, the North African campaign was supposed to end in victory) Tunis still lay well beyond the Allied grasp behind a mountainous front strongly held by the 5th Panzer Army (created on 8 December 1942, when General von Arnim superseded Nehring). The grand strategy agreed by the Prime Minister and the President back in July 1942 had thus finished up (at least for the time being) in a cul de sac, so bearing out all Marshall's worst fears.

But much more dangerous to the Allied cause than this military stalemate was the colossal and continuing demand on shipping lift made by the campaign. It had been originally estimated that 66 ships a month would be needed until January 1943, and thereafter only a much reduced figure for the maintenance of an occupation force.[95] Even at the end of December 1942 it was still being assumed that the enemy would be thrown out of both Tunisia and Tripolitania by the end of January. But instead military demand constantly increased, so that in the event an average of 106 ships instead of 66 were despatched each month to North Africa between October 1942 and January 1943,[96] and in February 92 ships as against the original estimate of 30.[97] And it was on the Royal Navy that the strain of protecting this traffic principally fell, amounting to as many as 23 outward-bound and 22 homeward-bound convoys between 8 November 1942 and 20 February 1943 alone.[98] On top of the naval, military and air force investment in 'Torch', the total investment of merchant shipping came to 1,781,809 tons between August and December 1942[99] – all for a present strategic pay-off of a stalemated campaign against just 100,000 Axis soldiers.[100] And shipping losses on the North African route at the hands of the U-boat and the Luftwaffe amounted to 208,824 tons from October 1942 to February 1943 inclusive.[101] Taken all in all it so far hardly added up to cost-effective strategy.

But this was not the whole of it. The unexpectedly large tonnage of merchant vessels drawn into the North African campaign and the accompanying losses greatly worsened the current world shipping crisis that had been brought about by the competing demands of conducting maritime warfare against Japan as well as Germany and Italy, of supplying British war industries, of transporting American troops to the United Kingdom, and of feeding the peoples of Britain and the Indian Ocean Area countries.[102]

Such then were the costs of embarking on this grander version of Mediterranean 'blue water' strategy; costs which the Royal Navy and the Merchant Marine were having to meet just when the Battle of the Atlantic was mounting to its crisis, and when it seemed more and more possible that Britain and North Africa (and the Allied armies along with it) could be effectively cut off from the rest of the world.

19

'The Battle of the Atlantic Is Getting Harder'

In the North Atlantic the year 1942 had ended and 1943 had begun deceptively well for the Allies. Ferocious winter gales hampered the U-boats' ability to track convoys and then mass for the attack. For while cruising on the surface the U-boats were violently thrown about by huge Atlantic seas topped by breaking crests and while seeking tranquillity beneath the surface their electric motors gave them insufficient speed and range to overtake their victims. In the meantime the merchant ships steamed sturdily on though continually swept by green water. In December 1942 the Allies lost 46 ships totalling 262,135 tons in the North Atlantic as against 124 ships of 623,545 tons in the peak month of June.[1] In return the convoy escorts sank three U-boats, and shore-based aircraft another two.[2] In January 1943 the figures were even more encouraging: only 27 ships totalling 172,691 tons lost.[3]

Yet the cumulative losses of 1942 in the North Atlantic were appalling enough: 5,471,222 tons of shipping; 70 per cent of losses in all theatres of war.[4] And even though December 1942 looked so encouraging, it was ominous that convoy ONS154, although protected by six, later seven, escorts, lost fourteen out of 45 ships in a four-day battle with a pack of twenty U-boats, while the escorts sank only one U-boat and damaged another. This demonstrated that surface escorts simply could not fight off twice their own number of submarines; that the convoy system itself in these circumstances might fail. The experience of ONS154 bore out the First Sea Lord's prediction at the end of October about 'the exceedingly difficult and dangerous situation which is arising in consequence of our being unable to make the full naval provision required to tackle effectively the problem of the U-boat menace'.[5] Against a requirement of 1,050 ocean escorts of all types, only 445 were then available, and 100 of these dated from the Great War.[6] The Admiralty's Monthly Anti-Submarine Report for January 1943 therefore did well to warn that the U-boats were now deployed primarily so as 'to cut the main artery from the United States to Great Britain . . . most of them between Newfoundland and the longitude of Central Iceland . . .'; that 'the tempo is quickening, and the critical phase of the U-boat war in the Atlantic cannot be long postponed'.[7]

Nevertheless the balance sheet of the U-boat offensive against Allied shipping was much more complicated than the comparative totals of lost tonnage and sunk U-boats might indicate. In the first place shipping losses had to be set against new construction – and here the picture was very different from that during the U-boat offensive back in the Great War. As the First Sea Lord pointed out to the Prime Minister on 10 February 1943, the total tonnage of non-enemy new construction during the first 41 months of the Great War amounted to 6,840,000 tons; in the first 41 months of the present war to 10,790,000 tons.[8] Thanks to this prodigious output of new merchant ships, total *net* losses in 1942 amounted to about 700,000 tons, as against 3,700,000 tons in 1917. Better still, according to the First Sea Lord, the Allies had enjoyed an average *net* gain of something over 160,000 tons per month during the second half of 1942. 'In fact,' he told Churchill, 'despite the infinitely more difficult situation . . . [we] have brought the country through with considerable success.'[9]

That the cumulative output of new shipping in the first 41 months of the war was some 4 million tons greater than in the equivalent period of the Great War did not redound to the credit of the British shipbuilding industry, however. In fact its production and productivity record caused the government deep concern.

In September and October 1942 a small team of technical experts appointed by the Ministry of Production submitted two detailed reports on the deficiencies of the industry. The team found that with few exceptions the yards were cramped, the layouts confused, the equipment ancient, the workforce idle or strike-prone, and the whole production process slowed up by incompetent management, over-manning, and by the unions' restrictive practices and inveterate opposition to new technology and methods. The team reported that 800 new machines and nearly 200 heavy-lift cranes were needed, at a cost of over £2 million, to modernise the yards.[10] British output of merchant ships in 1942 amounted to 1.3 million gross tons – as against Allied and neutral losses of 7,790,697 tons in all seas.[11] In any case even the targets for output of new merchant ships had had to be cut back because much capacity was tied up in repairing damaged ships – and doing this so slowly and incompetently that a backlog had grown up of some 2 million tons under repair.[12]

The explanation for this hugely greater Allied output of ships in the present war lies in the American shipyards. Throughout 1942 an ever bigger procession of standardised cargo vessels, the 'Liberty ships', to a total of some 7 million tons, had been coming off the production lines of new American yards equipped with the latest technology and laid out for flow-line assembly. In 1943 American output would reach the staggering total of 13.6 million deadweight tons of dry-cargo ships.[13] American machines and American managerial excellence was therefore presenting Dönitz with the ever more difficult task of out-sinking this soaring new production.

Dönitz's answer too lay in flow-line assembly methods and standard products. From inland workshops prefabricated sections of U-boat hulls were transported by canal to Germany's excellently equipped shipyards, there to be welded together and fitted out with diesel and electric motors manufactured by great engine and electrical firms like M.A.N. and Siemens-Schuckert. Dönitz's main industrial problem lay in securing enough steel in the game of competitive scrounging which in the chaotic Nazi war economy took the place of planning. In 1942 completion of new U-boats reached seventeen per month, as against the target of twenty.[14] Meanwhile U-boat Command's training schools were batch-producing crews for the new boats. The British Monthly Anti-Submarine Report for January 1943 estimated that Dönitz now had some one hundred boats at sea, half of them in the Atlantic.[15]

However, the recent ability of Allied shipyards (above all, American) to outbuild losses of merchant ships did not mean the Allies faced no shipping crisis at the beginning of 1943 comparable to that of 1917. A further factor in a complex equation lay in the huge scale of demand for shipping in the present war.

In the first place, Britain in particular was again paying the penalty for a hundred years of Free Trade policy. This had rendered her dependent on enormous quantities of imported foodstuffs (to the ruin of British agriculture, only now being once more resuscitated in wartime by emergency measures). Free Trade had also reduced her general economic and industrial self-sufficiency by exposing her home market to massive imports of foreign technology, all of it paid for in peacetime by British exports (now reduced to only a third of the peacetime figure) or by income from foreign investments (now all liquidated). In the Victorian era this national dependence on a high volume of seaborne imports and exports had seemed the formula for unexampled prosperity. Now, in the crisis of a world war, it constituted, as in 1914–18, a strategic vulnerability that menaced the country's very survival. Britain's estimated minimum (and that meant cut to the bone) import requirements for 1943 still amounted to 27 million tons.[16]

Yet, on top of Britain's own requirements, the global civilian and strategic claims on shipping in the present war were so much larger than in the Great War. In 1917, at the height of the then U-boat offensive, the Allies were conducting a single major conflict, against a European coalition led by Germany. The overriding problem had therefore lain in supplying Britain and transporting American forces to France. The British armies on the Western Front were being maintained by the cross-Channel sea routes at maximum economy in shipping space. Large-scale military demand for merchant shipping tonnage had therefore been limited to the Atlantic and the Mediterranean (in support of the fringe campaigns against Germany's allies Bulgaria and Turkey). In 1942–43 by contrast Britain and America were fighting two separate major maritime wars at opposite ends of the globe, against Germany and Japan, while also again conducting a campaign (but even more costly in shipping than in the Great War) in the Mediterranean and Middle East.

Nor was this all. The swarming populations of India and the Middle East had to be fed (an aspect of that burden of Empire which Britain had failed to shed in the 1920s and 1930s), and in the case of India in 1942, rescued from outright famine – more heavy demands therefore for cargo ships.

It was in these vast, cumulative demands for merchant shipping, greatly exceeding available resources, that there lay the root cause of the deepening world shipping crisis at the start of 1943. Thus the rate of loss inflicted by the U-boat was not decisive in itself, as it had been in 1917 when month by month it hugely shrank the total merchant tonnage available to the Allies. Instead it was decisive in relation to the minimum amount of shipping needed by the Allies for the conduct of a global maritime war and at the same time for the civilian supply of Britain, India and the Middle East. As the British and Americans juggled their shipping budgets to make possible this campaign and that, this military build-up and another, this or that country's nourishment, Dönitz's U-boats in the Atlantic therefore supplied the marginal factor which determined whether the Allied sums would come out right or not. And herein lay the crucial significance of the Battle of the Atlantic in 1943.

The battle itself was waged at several different levels, all closely inter-connected – from the murderous front line out there in the mid-ocean spaces, through the industrial competition between the production and the sinking of merchant ships and U-boats, to the struggle for supremacy between rival technologies. This last struggle was fundamental to the outcome of the battle, for the shark, however ruthless in pursuit of prey, is impotent without lethal teeth; its hunter, however relentless, impotent without lethal harpoons; while both must have sharp eyes and acute hearing in order to track and kill – and best of all, the ability to read their antagonist's purposes in advance. In the continued striving for this ability lay the most secret technological competition of all; its swaying fortunes, indeed its very existence, unknown until 30 years after the war had ended. For in rooms quiet with mental concentration the rival cryptographers and electronics experts of the Government Code and Cypher School at Bletchley Park (GC and CS: 'Ultra') and of B-Dienst were now engaged in the climactic phase of their own battle of the Atlantic.

Back at the beginning of February 1942 GC and CS had suffered a major defeat when U-boat Command adopted a new and more complex four-rotor Enigma cypher, codenamed 'Shark' by the British (see above, p. 456).[17] It became no longer possible to divert convoys on to evasive routes away from wolf packs according to exact prior knowledge of Dönitz's instructions. Nevertheless the operational effect was less serious for several months than it might have been, because the U-boats were then concentrated along the American seaboard or working individually against ships still sailing independently.[18] When in the second half of 1942 U-boat Command again stepped up its concerted offensive against the North Atlantic convoys, the inability to read 'Shark' left the Admiralty's Operational Intelligence Centre and the tracking rooms in London, Ottawa and Washington half-blinded – but *half*-blinded only, because they now knew so much about the pattern of U-boat operations and U-boat Command's habits of mind that they could make brilliant guesses as to impending wolf-pack deployments from scraps of information from other sources, such as the German Navy Home Waters Enigma, or sightings by Allied aircraft and ships.

[577]

Nevertheless, losses to the U-boat of merchantmen in convoy had reached 50 in August 1942, 29 each in September and October, and 39 in November.[19] And it was of course in November that 'Torch' began to lay a heavy overload on Allied resources of shipping. With the prospect that in 1943 shipping available after other needs had been met would not even suffice to provide Britain with the absolute minimum level of imports needed for survival, Rear-Admiral J. Clayton, head of the OIC (Operational Intelligence Centre) on 22 November 1942 pressed GC and CS at Bletchley Park to devote 'a little more attention' to breaking the 'Shark' Enigma. He remarked that the battle with the U-boats was 'the one campaign which Bletchley Park are not at present influencing to any marked extent – and it is the only one in which the war can be lost unless BP *do* help. I do not think that this is any exaggeration.'[20]

Yet only three weeks later, on 13 December, Bletchley Park did the trick thanks to a new four-rotor electronic 'Bombe' for trial and error testings of all possible Enigma settings which had been devised by the Telecommunications Research Establishment;[21] and 'Shark' yielded the essential secret of its million-fold encyphering combinations. Yet it was still to take time before GC and CS could always read 'Shark' fast enough to enable the information to be put to immediate operational use. By the beginning of 1943 Bletchley Park had read the settings for eight days in November and also for early December, and on some occasions even the current settings. Step by step between now and August 1943 Bletchley Park, in collaboration with the US Navy Department's cryptographers, would work their way to complete and rapid mastery of 'Shark'. In the meantime they veered between periods of clear vision, when 'Shark' was being read at delays of 24 hours or less, and temporary loss of sight when the settings defied solution. Even by 17 February, for instance, the settings for the first seventeen days of January had still not been cracked, and between 10 March and 30 June settings for a further 22 days were either never broken or only at long delay.[22]

The task of decyphering 'Shark' fast enough to enable its secrets to be used operationally was rendered much harder by U-boat Command's system (introduced in November 1941) by which coded equivalents of the digraphs of the German naval grid could be frequently changed according to tables identified to the U-boats by the first name and address of imaginary persons[23] (see above, p. 456). Every time U-boat Command changed the 'address' Bletchley Park had to puzzle out the meaning by *ad hoc* brain work. And even a delay of three days in reading U-boat Command's signals directing U-boats to a new position meant that it would by then be too late to re-route a threatened convoy away from an ambush, because whereas U-boats on the surface could make 320 to 370 miles in 24 hours, a convoy could at best make only 240 miles. Add to these problems an increase in the total number of U-boats to be tracked from 212 in January 1943 to 240 in May, with some 60 usually on station in the North Atlantic, and it can be seen that the breaking of 'Shark', though a considerable help, could not yet enable the OIC and the tracking rooms promptly to locate all U-boats or route all convoys clear of them.[24]

At the same period, moreover, B-Dienst had scored its own success against the British Naval Cypher No. 3 – 'the convoy cypher'. In December 1942 the Admiralty had changed this and other cyphers, so blinding B-Dienst and leaving the U-boats groping for targets. But by February 1943 B-Dienst had broken Naval Cypher No. 3 again: once more it was as if Dönitz were present in British operation rooms, observing the flagged dispositions and routes of convoys on the wall charts, reading Admiralty movement signals in advance, and deploying his wolf packs accordingly.[25]

Yet the very sophisticated means by which Dönitz directed these far-off deployments made him peculiarly vulnerable to GC and CS's increasing mastery of 'Shark'. By 1943 Dönitz had perfected his system of detailed centralised conduct of the U-boat offensive from his command bunker near Lorient. The freebooting U-boat skippers of 1917 and of 1939–40 had now given way to captains who could hardly kill the lice in their shirts without a radio signal from U-boat Command. They had to report constantly in detail throughout their sorties – on their way out when they had cleared Biscay or (if sailing from Norway or the Baltic) 60°N; while at sea their positions and fuel states; at the end of a sortie their estimated times of arrival home. In return U-boat Command minutely directed the captains by radio in the search for convoys, in the concentration for the attack, even the time and method of attack; likewise when and where to refuel from 'milch cow' U-boats. This was how Dönitz sought to wield maximum striking power in the most effective and most economical way possible.

But this unique and unprecedented command and control system demanded an immense volume of radio traffic, handled by what one historian has called 'a signals network which for complexity, flexibility and efficiency, was probably unequalled in the history of military communications'.[26] It marked the complete reverse of the radio silence traditionally observed for security reasons by naval forces at sea, and it was founded on Dönitz's never-to-be-shaken belief that the U-boat Enigma cypher was unbreakable. But as GC and CS gradually mastered 'Shark', Dönitz's system would present his enemy with an overflowing treasure house of secrets; indeed the complete and detailed picture, constantly updated, of all U-boat operations and future tactical moves.

The escort forces too had their own means of exploiting the dependence of the Dönitz system on frequent radio-signalling back from U-boats to U-boat Command, for since July 1942 High Frequency Direction Finders (HF/DF) had been steadily fitted to more and more ships until at the beginning of 1943 this equipment had become standard. It enabled the escorts to fix the direction of a transmitting U-boat and even to estimate its range; they could then choose whether to close on the U-boat or divert their convoy clear of it.[27]

Nonetheless, even with Bletchley Park's gradually improving mastery of 'Shark' and the escorts' use of HF/DF it still needed short-wavelength radar mounted in ships and aircraft to pin-point a U-boat on the surface for the kill. The 10cm Type 271 ship's radar had been successfully tested as long ago as March 1941[28] and installation began in May that year. Able to pick up even a U-boat's periscope, it became the electronic eye of the escorts. To quote one appreciative customer, the commanding officer of HMCS *Brandon*, in a report to the Commodore (D) at Londonderry in March 1943: 'I have no hesitation in saying that the Mk IV Type 271 on the outward voyage very definitely saved some thousands of troops from an unpleasant swim . . .'[29]

However, only aircraft could speedily sweep the broad sea areas where 'Shark' decrypts or other information indicated that U-boats would be lurking; only airborne 10cm radar could enable these aircraft to pinpoint a U-boat or even just its periscope amid the clutter of the waves. Airborne 10cm radar was under development at the Telecommunications Research Establishment by mid-1941.[30] Yet the first operational sortie with ASV Mark III (the production version) did not take place until March 1943.[31] This protracted delay in bringing 10cm airborne radar into service – a delay which could have cost the Allies the Battle of the Atlantic – owed itself to a gruesome combination of bureaucratic and industrial muddle; to the priority given to Bomber Command's H2S (technically almost identical to ASV Mk III); and to the shortcomings of Britain's electronics and precision-engineering industries.[32] Two thoroughgoing reports on radio and radar production, the first by Lord Justice du Parcq (appointed by the War Cabinet) in August 1942 and the second to the Radio Board in April 1943, excoriated the wasteful overlaps in R and D and production programmes for the three services; the proliferation of different types of the same component because of the total lack of standardisation; the shortage of skilled technical personnel and managers in the radio firms; the muddles and delays in manufacture owing to the failure to plan and schedule the work properly; the 'crash' programmes by which urgently needed equipment was hand-built on benches rather than manufactured on a line.[33]

But the fundamental deficiency lay in the limited technological capabilities of the British radio and precision engineering industries. These had sufficed to produce early crude radar systems such as the 8–13 metre wavelength Fighter Command Home Chain, the 1.5 metre ASV Mark I fitted to Coastal Command Hudsons in 1940, and the 1 metre air-warning radars in warships (the early versions of the latter being 'something of a lash-up', according to one gunnery expert).[34] But the manufacture of the new 10cm radars and H2S and their sophisticated thermionic valves, the Klystron and Magnetron, presented immense difficulties because of the advanced technologies involved. The Klystron and Magnetron, British inventions, had had to be handed over to the Americans to manufacture, while the wartime development of the British electronics industry itself came to depend on American supplies of machine tools as well as components.

The Cabinet decision to give Bomber Command's H2S first call on the British radio and precision-engineering industries' limited resources meant that Coastal Command had to wait interminably for its 10cm ASV Mark III, for throughout 1942 production of H2S was held up by all kinds of teething troubles and bottlenecks.[35] Only in August 1942 (as a result of one success by the Admiralty in 'the Battle of the Air') did the government decide to divert some H2S sets into Leigh Light Wellingtons as ASV Mark IIIs. But the conversion itself presented problems because the scanner had to be redesigned for an aperture of 28 inches, instead of the 36 inches in Bomber Command's big bombers, so that it could fit under the nose of a Wellington. Other modifications were also needed because the ASV Mark IIIs would be operated at 2,000 feet instead of 20,000 as H2S.[36] It was not until December 1942 that two prototype ASV Mark IIIs could be fitted to Wellington VIIIs; not until 30 January 1943, after more technical and electronic teething troubles, that sets had been fitted to two Wellington XIIs and another Wellington VIII.[37] At this point it was found that a modification of the aerial system was urgently needed. Thanks to the zeal of the Telecommunications Research Establishment at Malvern, twelve ASV Mark IIIs had been fitted to Wellingtons by 27 February 1943, and in the evening of 1 March (a month after Bomber Command's first use of H2S) two ASV Mark III Wellingtons took off on their inaugural sortie; and on the 17th the new radar detected its first U-boat in the Bay of Biscay at a range of nine miles.[38] It enjoyed the immense extra advantage that because of its short wavelength it could not be detected by the U-boats' Metox equipment.

Yet the Wellingtons could only cover the Bay itself. Mid-ocean detection demanded VLR aircraft fitted with 10cm radars; it demanded too that aircraft from the small new escort carriers about to come into service should likewise be equipped. In January 1943 the United States began delivering to Coastal Command (by grace of the air staff and with the grudging acceptance of Bomber Command) VLR Liberators equipped with the SCR 517, the American equivalent of ASV Mark III.[39] This had been developed by the lavish human and technical resources of the Radiation Laboratory of the Massachusetts Institute of Technology and built by the US radio industry.

But fitting 10cm radar into the small single-engined aircraft that would work from the cramped flight decks of escort carriers had proved a hard technical problem to solve ever since R and D began in 1941. Most importantly the equipment for such aircraft had to be lightweight and compact; none such then existed.[40] At the end of 1941 design work was started on a set, the ASV-X, to be fitted in the Royal Navy's new carrier aircraft, the Fairey Barracuda, but since this was not yet in production the choice shifted to that old stand-by, the Swordfish. The problem of where to install the set was solved by dispensing with the third member of the aircrew and stowing the set in his place.[41] However the Swordfish was not a very suitable aircraft to work off escort carriers pitching steeply over the Atlantic, because, in the words of a report by the commanding officer of the carrier HMS *Fencer* to the C-in-C, Western Approaches, on 26 December 1943, it was 'a very tender aircraft', liable to damage throughout its fuselage in a heavy landing.[42]

The first aircraft to be fitted with a trial ASV-X set did not arrive at Faireys (the manufacturer of the Swordfish) until July 1942. The first aircraft was not fitted with a preproduction prototype set until February 1943. March passed in trials; July and August in operational trials and exercises, while in the meantime the sets were slowly being pushed out of the factories. Then came the formation of a nucleus training squadron, and finally, but finally, in November 1943 the first operational squadron of Swordfish equipped with 10cm radar was ready to embark in an escort carrier – by which date the crisis of the Battle of the Atlantic was many months past.[43] Yet had it been available in good time it would have transformed the task of the escorts and support groups, because the ASV-X Swordfish could patrol an area within a forty-mile radius of the carrier and pick up a U-boat with its decks awash or even its periscope by sweeping a lane fourteen miles wide.

But in any case there were equivalent delays in deploying the escort carriers (CVEs) that would carry the 10cm ASV aircraft. Even before the regrettably short-lived success at the end of 1941 of HMS *Audacity*, the first of all CVEs to enter service (see above, pp. 275–6), the Admiralty and the Navy Department had decided on an initial programme of building very simple carriers on existing standard American cargo-ship hulls. Four of these vessels were allotted to the Royal Navy. HMS *Archer* (the name ship of the class: 9,000 tons; diesel driven; 17 knots; 15 aircraft)[44] was completed on 17 November 1941, but did not become operational until March 1942; *Biter* (8,200 tons; 16½ knots)[45] was completed on 1 May 1942 but did not become operational until September; and *Dasher* (also 8,200 tons) was completed on 1 July 1942, but did not enter service until October. The fourth ship, *Avenger*, though completed in America on 2 March, only made her operational début with an Arctic convoy in September.[46] However, all four British CVEs were soon pulled away to provide close air support to the November 'Torch' landings in Algeria, and while escorting a 'Torch' convoy west of Gibraltar HMS *Avenger* was blown up and sunk by a torpedo from the U-155.

The United States had by now begun the series production of 11,420-ton standardised CVEs, Model Ts of the sea;[47] and Britain was provisionally to receive under Lend-Lease a total allotment of 28 vessels.[48] But whereas the United States Navy was happy to accept such CVEs into service simply equipped for the principal role of anti-submarine operations, the Royal Navy wanted them as poor man's fleet carriers. For Britain had had to abandon further large-scale construction of big fleet carriers for want of financial and industrial resources (see above, pp. 437–8). The Royal Navy therefore put their new CVEs through a three to four month refit after delivery from American yards in order to extend the flight decks, improve fire precautions, strengthen the structure, and – the most important of all – install fighter-direction radars. In the words of an Admiralty signal to the British Admiralty Delegation in Washington on 7 September 1943, 'the main cause of delay in getting our carriers into service is our endeavour . . . to get all these carriers capable of full fighter operation and not merely fit for A/S work':[49]

It must be remembered that we differ from the United States Navy since we have not in sight so large a force of Fleet and Light Fleet Types. For this reason we shall in future have to depend more than the Americans upon fighters operated from Escort Carriers in support of amphibious operations . . . We have also to consider the anti-aircraft protection of trade (e.g. in the Bay and possibly North Russian routes) . . .[50]

At the time of this signal the Admiralty reckoned that the current demands of the landings at Salerno in Italy (see below, pp. 659–60) for CVEs capable of 'full fighter operation', together with future needs in the Indian Ocean in 1944, completely justified the delays in getting them into service. Nevertheless Admiral 'Ernie' King, who at this time was providing all the CVEs on anti-U-boat operations in the Atlantic, was so incensed by British dilatoriness in getting American-supplied CVEs into service that it was formally intimated to the Admiralty that unless the delays were drastically reduced the next British allotment of seven ships would be stopped, and the ships deployed straight away in the Atlantic under the US ensign: hence the pained Admiralty signals of self-justification to Washington.[51] A report by the Allied Anti-Submarine Survey Board on 27 August 1943, signed by Rear-Admiral J. M. Mansfield, RN, and Rear Admiral J. L. Kauffman, USN, noted that out of Britain's current total of 13 escort carriers (CVEs), only six were operational; four of these allotted to the Mediterranean; and not one to anti-submarine operations in the Atlantic.[52] Little scope here, then, for Swordfish equipped with 10cm ASV, even if these had not still been in the stage of squadron training.

In the opening months of 1943 the looming crisis in the Battle of the Atlantic had consequently to be faced by the Allies without benefit of escort carriers equipped with 10cm ASV aircraft; indeed without benefit of CVEs at all to begin with, for it was not until mid-March that the first, the USS *Bogue*, joined in the battle. The Admiralty had made an ingenious attempt to fill the gap before the CVEs entered service by embarking on the construction of 'Merchant Aircraft Carriers' (MACs) – ordinary merchant ships or tankers topped by a flight deck 400 to 490 feet by 62 feet, but without hangars and able to carry only four Swordfish. The idea had been mooted in April 1942, but the first keel out of six ships was not laid until August. In November the Cabinet Anti-U-boat Warfare Committee agreed to the construction of a further twelve, possibly eighteen. It had been hoped that the initial six would be in service by the early spring of 1943, but in the event it was May before the first ship, *Empire MacAlpine*, sailed with an Atlantic convoy. The programme had miscarried in the congestion of the shipyards and because of a bottleneck over arrester gear.[53]

Eventually these invaluable escorts, flying the Red Ensign and commanded by Merchant Navy masters, were to spend 4,447 days at sea escorting 217 convoys, of which only two lost any ships while a MAC ship was in company.

But at the beginning of 1943 all this was in the future. In the meantime there were not enough destroyers or other suitable escort vessels, let alone CVEs, to enable the formation of 'support groups' for the rescue of convoys under heavy attack. Although in September 1942 an experimental 'killer group' had proved its worth in the Atlantic, thereafter the demand for destroyers on the Arctic convoy routes and then for the 'Torch' operations had taken precedence. Only in mid-February 1943 did the Admiralty judge that there were enough suitable ships to allow the C-in-C, Western Approaches, to begin planning the creation of support groups (to be titled 'Escort Groups'); and only in mid-March did the Allies decide at the Atlantic Convoy Conference in Washington that four such escort groups should be deployed as soon as possible – one American, with a CVE (*Bogue*) and five destroyers; one Canadian and two British (to include the CVEs *Dasher* and *Biter*).[54] Here was another dangerously last-minute development. On the British side, this belatedness stemmed partly from the unexpectedly long-drawn-out demands of the North African campaign, partly from shortfalls in the production of new destroyers and other escorts by British shipyards.[55]

In any case, such grim experiences as that of Convoy ONS154 in December 1942 (see above, pp. 573–4) made it all too plain that the convoy escorts themselves were not strong enough either in numbers or type of ship to fight off massed U-boats. As the commanding officer of a support group was to put it late in 1943, '. . . although the corvettes did excellent work, they were handicapped by insufficient speed, lack of plotting facilities, and their size and movement in rough weather, which imposed great strain on the personnel after long periods at sea'.[56] Only gradually in the course of that year did new classes of escort, such as the 1,350-ton, two-shaft steam turbine 'Modified' Black Swan escort sloops and the 1,370-ton River class frigates (each type with a speed of around 20 knots)[57] provide the Royal Navy in the Atlantic with vessels with the right sea-keeping qualities and the speed to chase U-boats to the death. Yet British output fell far short of the Royal Navy's needs for escorts, fewer than 50 corvettes and destroyers being completed in 1943;[58] and by now Britain had become 85 per cent dependent on North American yards for new escorts of all types.[59]

In that other technological competition to develop more and more lethal weapons, each side had so far managed to match the other in muddle, delay and designs that would not work. Dönitz's U-boats only found themselves equipped with reliable magnetic pistols for their torpedoes instead of Great War type contact pistols by the end of 1942; and only then was the problem of maintaining the torpedo's run at the correct depth also solved. It was only in September 1942 that the U-boats began to be armed with a new torpedo (FAT, or *Feder-Apparat Torpedo*) that would keep changing course according to a predetermined pattern after travelling a preset distance, and so be almost certain to hit a target within the sprawling columns of a convoy. It had therefore taken three years of war for the U-boats to come to enjoy what Dönitz called an 'unsurpassed level of excellence' in its weaponry.[60]

Why had it taken German technology, for all its resources and proven record, so long? Dönitz himself blamed it on the stultifying effects of bureaucracy within the relevant departments of the German Navy, especially the Torpedo Experimental Department that for years had been in sole charge of the whole process of torpedo development. In his view this was 'fundamentally wrong in principle':

> The Armed Forces should themselves have nothing whatever to do with the construction of the weapons they require, but should pass on their requirements to private industry. They should then submit the best weapons which emerge as the result of very keen industrial competition to most rigorous tests under as near to war conditions as possible and should then accept them only if they prove satisfactory.[61]

British experience up to 1943 in developing air and sea anti-submarine weaponry entirely bears out Dönitz's shrewd judgment. Bureaucratic rigidity of mind and structure within the various R and D departments of the Admiralty coupled with the technical conservatism of men too long in the job fouled the screws of progress. It took a year to meet a need for a shallow setting on the existing depth-charge pistol that had been first stated to the Director of Torpedoes and Mines in July 1941 – all because of lack of liaison between the development team and the end-user, lack of proper briefing as to the operational basis of the requirement, and finally to officious middle-men altering the requirement to include deep setting on the same pistol.[62] In another case, the Admiralty (and Admiral Sir Max Horton, the then C-in-C, Western Approaches) refused to believe that U-boats could dive as deep as they in fact did, well beneath the level at which the existing British 'deep' setting pistol detonated. As a result it took until June 1943 to equip the Mark X

[586]

200-pound depth-charge with a deep setting designed to detonate well below 500 feet. In any event the 200-pound Mark X depth-charge itself had not appeared until May 1942.[63]

The Air Ministry development departments proved no more fast moving. Only from May 1942 were Coastal Command aircraft equipped with Torpex-filled Mark VII 250-pound depth-charges; only from July 1942 were these depth-charges fitted with a reliable 25-foot setting pistol for destroying U-boats at the beginning of their dive to escape. It had therefore taken nearly three years of war to equip Coastal Command with a truly deadly anti-U-boat weapon.[64] But still under development at the beginning of 1943 were a 600-pound anti-submarine bomb and an air-launched rocket.[65]

However, it was the 'Hedgehog' device for throwing anti-submarine warheads forward over the bows of escorts which provides the most dismaying case-history of bureaucratic stone-headedness. By early 1940 it had already become apparent that the traditional method of discharging depth-charges over the stern suffered from the drawback that the attacking vessel necessarily lost sonar contact with her victim, often never to regain it; and that what was needed was a device for lobbing high-explosive *ahead* (see above, p. 256). A struggle now ensued between the departmental stone-heads and a group of energetic and bright-minded young officers and scientists.[66] Captain G. H. Oswald, RN, of the Department of Naval Ordnance, later recalled how a 36-year-old scientist and Fellow of the Royal Society, Charles Goodeve, then serving in the rank of Commander, RNVR, in the new Admiralty Anti-Aircraft Weapons and Devices Department, and the group of eager doers which Goodeve recruited from no matter what bureaucratic 'box'

pursued the problem with the greatest zeal and it soon became evident that a solution would be available in months. I regret to say however that others put every obstacle in the way; for example D.N.O. [Director of Naval Ordnance] said if a mortar system was adopted the whole scheme should go back to D.T.M. [Director of Torpedoes and Mines] but that the Ordnance Board must be closely associated with the ammunition; the O.B. said the required fuze was so novel that five years were required for its design and adequate test; Fairlie [the Anti-Submarine Warfare Establishment] who were busy on their own Mortar would have nothing to do with Hedgehog and would not even lend their Underwater Range in the Clyde for our trials. Incidentally we requisitioned and commissioned Western-Super-Mare Pier for this purpose.

In other words, the Obstructors were many and the Faint-hearts not a few but the enthusiasts outnumbered them.[67]

Thanks to the creative energy of these young scientists, soldiers and sailors from different departments but all working together as a team, the basic design of the Hedgehog (a ripple-firing multiple spigot mortar throwing a spread of 24 projectiles weighing 65 pounds and with 35-pound Torpex warheads) went forward well. The trouble started when the conventional departmental hierarchies took a hand, their standards of science and engineering being both second-class and out of date. The Chief Inspector of Gun Mountings designed a mounting which did not even take into account the elementary need to resist the recoil, and in his calculations used cordite tables dated 1905.[68] The Ordnance Board proposed a design for a fuze with 127 parts which, owing to inherent defects, could not possibly succeed.

The Head Scientist at the Anti-Submarine Warfare Establishment at Fairlie in Scotland, one B. S. Smith, an able man back in the 1920s in developing Asdic but now ossified into bureaucratic authoritarianism, did his best to thwart the Hedgehog team because of his own alternative project, the so-called 'Fairlie Mortar' which eventually turned out to be a complete failure.[69] Smith proposed to train his device on to its target by means of two electric motors and a differential gear box; and insisted on building a trial apparatus even though junior scientists on his staff pointed out on theoretical grounds that it could not work.[70] This was by no means the only example of Smith's opinionated mediocrity, and he eventually provoked a mutiny among the scientists drafted into his department because he took new ideas 'as criticism of existing apparatus' and therefore 'frequently discouraged' them.[71] Anyone who has worked in large bureaucratic organisations will recognise the dreary pattern. The Director of Naval Ordnance himself turned his back on the Hedgehog project, while the Director of Naval Construction gloomed fallaciously about the effect of the deck thrust.[72]

The whole Hedgehog project might well therefore have been obstructed into oblivion but for the enthusiastic backing of the Controller of the Navy, Admiral Sir Bruce Fraser.[73] Thanks to him and their own determination to succeed, the 'young Turks' finally had their way. Industry, in the form of the Hall Telephone Company, manufactured the novel hydro-dynamically armed fuze (the solution to the problem which had so baffled the Ordnance Department).[74] Hedgehog finally went to sea operationally in January 1942, nearly two years after the first gleam in its creators' eye, and by the end of the year over 100 ships had been equipped with it.[75]

In February 1942 there began a reworking of the Anti-Submarine Warfare Department's abortive 'Fairlie Mortar', this time with three

ove) Atlantic Convoy (Crown copyright)
low) Atlantic Convoy OB (Outward Bound) 331,
e 1941. '. . . the convoys which in constant progression bore the North American supplies across the ocean to Britain, without which she could neither wage war nor even live.' (IWM)

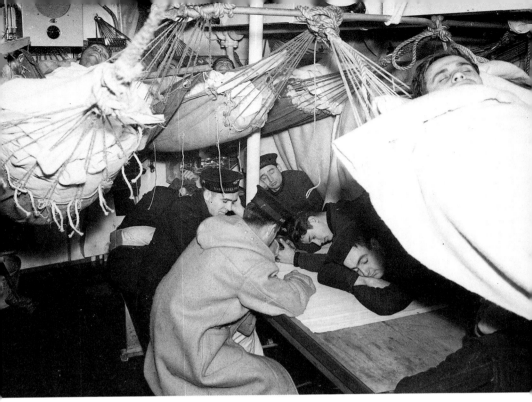

(Above) '. . . the bulkheads running with condensation; the air thick with human exhalations. . . .' A mess-deck scene typical of a destroyer or escort vessel; here the ship is the Polish-manned destroyer *Piorun*. (Crown)

(Below) A U-boat sinking. 'They felt more and more naked beneath a sky out of which an aircraft would suddenly thunder to smother their boat with 250-pou[nd] depth charges.' (IWM)

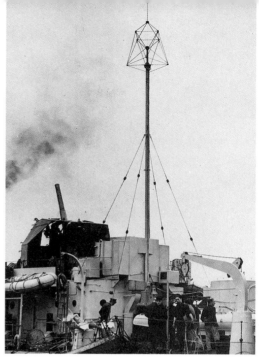

(*above, left*) 'The most secret technological competition [of them] all.' A German Enigma encyphering machine. Dönitz believed its cyphers to be unbreakable, yet the Government Code and Cypher School at Bletchley Park mastered them. But the German B-Dienst read British naval cyphers too. (IWM) (*Above, right*) 'HF/DF (High Frequency Direction Finders) mounted in the convoy escort could reveal the presence and bearing of a U-boat.' The first set came into use in mid-1941. (IWM) (*Below*) 'Across one wall was displayed the current Operational Plot of the Battle of the Atlantic.' The operations room of Western Approaches Command beneath a thick concrete roof in Derby House, Liverpool. (IWM)

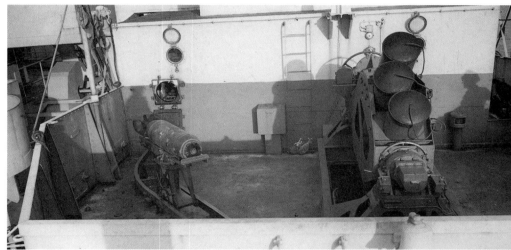

(Top) 'A new means of locating the surfaced U-boat in all conditions of weather and light.' The Type 271 radar set, installed in fifty escort ships by the end of 1941. (IWM) (Middle) The 'Squid' anti-submarine mortar. Under development from February 1942, it did not kill its first U-boat until July 1944. (IWM) (Left) The 'Hedgehog' anti-submarine mortar, housing a spread of 24 projectiles with 35-pound warheads over a ship's bow. It only saw service thanks to a protracted campaign by young scientists and serving officers against the 'bureaucratic stoneheadedness' of the Admiralty research 'establishment'. (IWM)

(*Above*) Admiral Sir Percy Noble (*left*), C-in-C, Western
Approaches, 1941–42 with Noble's opposite number,
Air Vice-Marshal J. M. Robb, Commanding No. 15
Group, RAF Coastal Command. (IWM) (*Above, right*)
'...enjoyed the affection and respect of its crews because
of its sturdiness . . . and its stability as a weapons
platform.' The Blackburn Swordfish (maximum speed
4 mph), the Royal Navy's torpedo-bomber in the early

years of the war. In November 1940, a Swordfish strike
crippled the Italian Fleet in Taranto harbour. (IWM)
(*Below*) The Fairey Barracuda Mark II (maximum speed
228 mph), the Fleet Air Arm's first monoplane torpedo
bomber, did not see action until the landings at Salerno
in September 1943. In 1944, Barracudas inflicted serious
damage on the battleship *Tirpitz*. (IWM)

(Above) 'We have the gap between Newfoundland and Iceland in which our convoys are at the mercy of the U-boat. At the moment, the main weight of the air escort work is being carried by 17 Liberators.' A Very Long Range (VLR) Liberator equipped with the Leigh Light – subject of the 'Battle of the Air' between the Admiralty and the Air Ministry. (IWM) *(Below)* The Leigh Light, which enabled aircraft to illuminate U-boats at night, had its successful trial in May 1941 but bureaucratic obstruction and technical problems delayed its first 'kill' to July 1942. (IWM)

(*Above*) 'Such desolate and dangerous voyages.' Arctic
convoy JW53 passing through pack ice on passage to
North Russia, February 1943. (Crown) (*Below*) 'All too
familiar and routine to every ship's company in the Arctic
convoys was the mustering of all hands to chip away the
enveloping crusts of ice. . . . In a small ship this could
make all the difference between capsizing or not if hit
by a torpedo.' (IWM)

'The hull was carried up to the flight deck, making an integral box-like structure of immense strength.' HMS *Illustrious* (23,000 tons displacement; designed to carry 36 aircraft), one of four new carriers laid down under the pre-war rearmament programme. (IWM)

barrels in tandem instead of five abeam. Known later as the 'Squid', it was not mounted in a ship until September 1943 and did not kill its first U-boat until 31 July 1944.[76]

All this time another 'Battle of the Atlantic' was being fought in the training schools. Since the early days of the war the Royal Navy had trained individual anti-submarine officers and lower-deck personnel in manoeuvring a ship and operating weapons and Asdic by means of the Attack Teacher House, an elaborate simulator of an escort ship at sea. Attack Teacher Houses were gradually set up at all British fleet bases and throughout the Commonwealth. In summer 1941 one was supplied to America and by June 1942 the United States Navy had put them into quantity production. The Royal Navy even installed mobile Attack Teachers in converted buses so that they could be used by smaller bases. Meanwhile the Anti-Submarine School – transferred from Portland on the south coast of England to the Clyde during the invasion months of 1940 – had grown into a great complex of training establishments for batch-producing specialist officers and ratings. The job of 'working up' such trained individuals into ships' companies who could work smoothly together to fight the ship was performed by HMS *Western Isles*, a sea training establishment at Tobermory in the Inner Hebrides. This had been opened by Commodore (Vice-Admiral retired) G. O. Stephenson in July 1940. Stephenson – 'the Terror of Tobermory' – proved a hard and brilliantly imaginative trainer, putting his fledgling crews through a relentless month of fictitious emergencies such as towing damaged ships, putting out a fire in an abandoned merchant ship or fighting their own ship with half the crew and equipment out of action.[77]

But despite all this immense and innovative training effort it had become apparent to Western Approaches Command by early 1942 that while some convoys were getting through safely or with small loss, others were sustaining heavy losses even though their escort was just as strong. This clearly indicated that wide differences existed among the escort forces in the quality of teamwork and the skill of group command.

In March 1942 Western Approaches Command therefore set up the Western Approaches Training Unit in Liverpool, followed in December by another in Londonderry. Each consisted of a large room, the floor of which represented a stretch of the mid-Atlantic, and across which Wrens moved symbols of U-boats, convoys and escorts as the training exercises proceeded. The 'U-boats' were commanded with the maximum cunning and aggression by the training officer. The escort commanders under training were shut in small cubicles off the main floor, able to see just so much of the 'Atlantic' through a slit in the wall as from the bridge of a ship. In response to U-boat attacks or sightings (either directly or as reported to them) they had to issue appropriate orders to the 'escort force' under their command. This ingenious simulator could also be used for experimental exercises in tactics and organisation.[78] In the same year the Royal Canadian Navy created its own realistic simulator for teaching night escort tactics, complete with a pitching and rolling ship's bridge and a horizon on which could be projected the silhouettes of ships, U-boats, aircraft or such illuminations of battle as star shell, searchlights and burning vessels.[79]

Nonetheless, and despite all their ingenuity, simulators could not substitute for command training at sea. In January 1943 the C-in-C, Western Approaches, therefore set up a new establishment at Londonderry round HMS *Philante*, formerly the millionaire industrialist Tom Sopwith's luxury yacht. While *Philante* served as a 'convoy' and two old submarines played the parts of U-boats, British and Canadian escort commanders in their own ships could practise escorting the 'convoy' safely through the most craftily devised attacks.[80] But only in April 1943 – as it proved, the critical month of the whole Battle of the Atlantic – was a Combined Service Anti-Submarine Training Centre set up to promote intimate cooperation between Royal Air Force Coastal Command, the Fleet Air Arm and surface escorts. The RAF stations at Eglington and Maydown in Northern Ireland were turned over to the Royal Navy for this purpose.

Yet it was beyond the reach of even sea training exercises to mimic such realities as the appalling weight of responsibility bearing down on the mind and will of an escort commander when on a night lit by the flames of dying ships he must make almost instantaneous decisions on the basis of incomplete and possibly false information; decisions which if mistaken could so easily lead to the massacre of his convoy. Nor could exercises mimic the insidious assault on the mind mounted by sheer exhaustion after days at sea and hours on the bridge; the wearing out of bodily strength by almost continuously bad weather that forced sailors to brace themselves against the violent movement of the ship 24 hours a day, waking, eating, trying to sleep. And nor could training simulate the grinding away of courage by the attrition of constant danger. In Allied escort ship and German U-boat alike duty and discipline fought a constant battle with fear – and on occasion with outright terror.

For however important were the 'battles' between rival technologies and industrial resources and cryptographic brains, the issue of the struggle out there in the Atlantic front line must in the end turn on the seamanship, the fibre and the fighting spirit of the men who crewed the merchant ships and escorts – and the U-boats. On that, and on the admiralship and willpower of those who on the opposing sides directed the battle.

Karl Dönitz, a submariner admiral to rank with the greatest fleet commanders of history, held the U-boat offensive in his single grasp. He wielded it like a cutlass, hacking relentlessly and skilfully at his enemy, thrusting swiftly through any momentary opening in his enemy's guard; a nimble killer with an incisive operational brain and a will of Krupp steel.

On the Allied side, direction of the battle remained divided – in the first place between the Royal Navy, the Royal Canadian and United States Navies, even though liaison remained close and the 'chop-lines' (marking changes in operational control) clear cut. In January 1943, in another perilously late development, the First Sea Lord and Chief of Naval Staff and COMINCH (C-in-C, US Fleet, and also Chief of Naval Operations) set up the Allied Anti-Submarine Survey Board with the task of standardising training, operational procedures and the overall deployment of the Allies' available pool of escorts. In the opinion of an Admiralty report in August 1943, the new board 'has made a great contribution in every sphere of the Anti-U-boat war . . .'[81] Nonetheless it failed to lull British suspicions that Ernie King as COMINCH (C-in-C, United States Fleet) was more concerned with finding ships for the Pacific than the Atlantic.

Nor in any case did British responsibility itself lie in single hands. At the top the War Cabinet Anti-U-boat Warfare Committee (created in November 1942) acted as a forum where major questions of policy, such as the provision of Very Long Range (VLR) aircraft, could be thrashed out and decided; it also kept a watching brief over the whole field of strategy and operations. The committee was gradually to stale into a routine chore for its members. Rear-Admiral C. D. Howard-Johnston (then Director of the Anti-U-boat Division of the Admiralty) was to recall:

> . . . the highlight of the month was the Cabinet Anti-U-Boat Meeting with the Prime Minister in the Chair. We used to lose an awful lot of time with Winston who was often miles off the point with things thought up by Professor Lindemann (later Lord Cherwell) . . .[82]

On one occasion when the Premier asked why it took so many

depth-charges to sink one U-boat, it turned out that Lindemann had simply divided the total world stocks of depth-charges at sea and on shore by the number of U-boats sunk.[83]

Under Admiral of the Fleet Sir Dudley Pound, who as First Sea Lord was in supreme executive command of all British naval operations, the day-to-day conduct of the battle against the U-boat in the Atlantic continued to lie with the Commander-in-Chief, Western Approaches, now Admiral Sir Max Horton, who had succeeded Sir Percy Noble in November 1942. Noble, an elegant, courteous, charming man, lacked aggressive drive either in regard to his own command or London's naval and political hierarchies. Horton could hardly have stood in greater contrast. Himself a veteran submariner, his last appointment that of Flag Officer, Submarines, he could match Dönitz in first-hand understanding of U-boat operations – and the psychology of U-boat crews. He no less matched Dönitz in ruthless will to win, though perhaps not in power of mind. Horton drove his command hard, his displeasure expressed in ways which reduced his less robust subordinates to nervous wrecks; and only the bravest dared approach him on days when he had lost at his regular game of golf. Every ship's company in Western Approaches Command could feel the grip and impulse of such harsh leadership.

From February 1943 the Royal Navy worked with a new Air Officer Commanding-in-Chief, Coastal Command, in Air Marshal Sir John Slessor, an able and ambitious officer, subtle of mind to the point (as some believed) of deviousness, but a committed exponent of close cooperation between the two services. From Coastal Command's operations theatre deep under a park at Northwood in the north-west London suburbs, with galleries for commander and staff facing a vast wall board where WAAFs (Women's Auxiliary Air Force) constantly updated the positions of convoys, escorts and U-boats – Slessor now directed the shore-based air offensive against Dönitz's submarines in the closest telephone and teleprinter liaison with the Naval Staff and the Admiralty Tracking Room.

Sadly, however, it was exactly in the strategy of the shore-based air offensive that the British now repeated probably their worst single misjudgment of the long Atlantic battle. For in February 1943, and once again at the Admiralty's urging though with Slessor's full concurrence, Coastal Command resumed its offensive against U-boats in transit outwards and homewards across the Bay of Biscay.

The earlier 'Bay offensive' had collapsed in October 1942 when the U-boats' new Metox device enabled them to detect an aircraft's 150-centimetre wavelength radar. But in any case the offensive had never proved cost-effective. From June 1942 to January 1943 an average of 3,500 patrol hours a month had been flown; some 100 aircraft lost; and only seven U-boats destroyed.[84] Now, it was decided to resume the 'Bay offensive' on the old fallacious supposition that it could throttle Dönitz's effort almost at source. Between 6 and 15 February 1943 eighteen U-boats were sighted out of the 40 known (thanks to Sigint) to have crossed the Bay, but only one, the U-519, sunk, and that by a US Liberator with American 10cm radar. On 20 February a Leigh Light Wellington sank the U-268. That was all. Early in March the Americans transferred the only available Liberators to Morocco in order to deal with a U-boat concentration off its coast; a serious weakening in the Allied effort. However, for eight days towards the end of March, No. 19 Group, Coastal Command, at last equipped with ASV Mark III Wellingtons, had another go. Out of 41 U-boats crossing the Bay area patrolled by the Wellingtons thirteen were sighted but only one was sunk and another seriously damaged. Meanwhile the U-333 had managed to shoot down an ASV Mark III Wellington which had attacked her, reporting back to Dönitz that her Metox had failed to give warning of the enemy's radar – Dönitz's first intimation that Allied technology had jumped past him.

The Admiralty's only response to these disappointing results was to plead in the Anti-U-boat Warfare Committee for more aircraft over the Bay – 190, no fewer. The Chief of Air Staff would only offer 70. So the 1942 'Battle of the Air' resumed in the committee. While the arguments droned on, the aircrews of Coastal Command tried again for a week in April in response to a plea from the First Sea Lord to Slessor: 'I feel that enough has been written about the poor old Bay offensive, and that what we want to do is to collect the necessary aircraft . . . and get on with the job.'[85] They had got on with the job; result: U-376 sunk and one more damaged.[86] And these were the months when the convoy system itself was coming ever closer to breakdown in the Atlantic as Dönitz relentlessly pressed his onslaught.

In December Ultra decrypts of 'Shark' signals had warned of the storm to come by revealing that U-boat Command was making radio-signalling arrangements for 'two convoy battle circuits';[87] and by 18 January Dönitz had raised the total of U-boats on the North Atlantic routes from 25 to 40.[88] Yet January like December passed deceptively well for the Allies. The weather – wild to the limits of ferocity – again played its part in hampering U-boat operations. GC and CS's partial success in reading the 'Shark' Enigma enabled the Admiralty once more to route many convoys far out of the way of Dönitz's concentrations, so that the storm-shaken U-boats searched the mountainous seascape in vain. The puzzled Dönitz and his staff sensed that the 'game of chess had become more complicated',[89] but could not make out why or how. In the whole month the U-boats sank only fifteen ships in convoy in the North Atlantic and fourteen sailing independently,[90] while one U-boat was sunk by a Coastal Command aircraft in the North Atlantic itself, and another by an American aircraft off the coast of Brazil.

And yet for the Admiralty there was a disquieting feature in the month's apparently favourable record. Of the fifteen ships lost in convoy no fewer than seven belonged to convoy TM1 of nine tankers bound from Trinidad to Gibraltar and North Africa. It is now known that the fate of TM1 had been determined by a British defeat in the covert war of Sigint. While B-Dienst had identified the convoy's course through the Admiralty 'convoy cypher', GC and CS for its part had failed to decypher fast enough the 'Shark' signals deploying the U-boat ambush, so that the Admiralty was unable to route the convoy clear.[91]

On 30 January Dönitz hoisted his flag as Commander-in-Chief of the German Navy in succession to Grand-Admiral Raeder, in whom Hitler had now lost all faith. Dönitz's new appointment did not mean a weakening in the U-boat offensive; quite the contrary, because as well as retaining his old post as *Befehlshaber* (Flag Officer), U-boats, he could now switch the balance of the whole German naval effort away from the surface fleet so prized by Raeder. To conduct day-to-day operations he appointed his former Chief of Staff, Rear-Admiral Godt. In the words of Admiralty's February report to the War Cabinet Anti-U-boat Warfare Committee, the enemy 'continued with remarkable singleness of purpose to concentrate against supplies from America to Great Britain'.[92] The daily average of operational U-boats in the entire Atlantic rose to 116, and on the northern routes to about 60.[93] In the Sigint struggle B-Dienst remained for the time being well ahead of GC and CS, able to read the British convoy cypher with such mastery that it was all too simple for Dönitz and Godt accurately to deploy their massed ambushes. Moreover they were now concentrating against eastbound convoys at the beginning of their voyage, with U-boats patrolling in a layered screen across their course.

According to the monthly Anti-Submarine Report for February 1943, nine convoys comprising 242 merchant ships suffered U-boat attack during the month; 34 ships were lost. But almost all these went down in just two convoys when GC and CS again failed to read 'Shark' quickly enough for the Admiralty to reroute them.[94]

On 4 February convoy SC118 of 63 merchantmen ran into a patrol line of 21 U-boats hastily deployed by U-boat Command according to B-Dienst decrypts of British signals in the convoy cypher. During five harrowing days of a battle fought along a track of over 1,000 miles thirteen ships went down, for the loss of three U-boats destroyed plus two more badly damaged. In Dönitz's opinion this was 'perhaps the hardest convoy battle of the whole war'.[95]

For the Allies it presented alarming portents. The convoy escort had been reinforced to a total of twelve ships, twice as strong as usual. The convoy enjoyed constant shore-based air cover during daylight hours – but this did not present surfaced U-boats, diesels pounding, from catching up the convoy and attacking it during the long winter nights. And the expenditure of depth-charges had been so colossal as almost to empty the escorts' magazines. The Admiralty drew the lessons: Leigh Lights for Liberators and Wellingtons; the importance of escorts highly trained as teams rather than spatchcocked together at the last moment; the need – long perceived but now desperately urgent – for support groups to reinforce attacked convoys and to hunt down U-boats once located. The lesson with regard to team training was rammed home by the success of the veteran escort with convoy ONS165 in mid-February, which for the loss of only two merchantmen sank two U-boats. These were the same ships of the Liverpool Escort Force – the destroyers *Fame* and *Viscount* – which had so magnificently brought SC104 through in October 1942 (see above, pp. 483–90). In Admiral Horton's words to an Admiralty conference, 'it could not be too often stressed that the trained group was the basis of protection, not mere numbers of escort vessels'.[96]

On 21 February began the second calamity of the month, when convoy ON166 ran into a U-boat ambush again deployed thanks to B-Dienst decrypts of the British convoy cypher, and when again GC and CS read 'Shark' too late to be of corresponding use to the Admiralty.[97] In another five-day span of relentless fighting convoy ON166 lost fourteen ships for only two U-boats sunk. When February closed in squalls of snow and hail, Allied losses in the month at the hands of the U-boats had reached a total of 63 ships (29 of them independents) of 359,328 tons.[98]

March brought the onset of the grand crisis of the Battle of the Atlantic. Dönitz well recognised through B-Dienst readings of Admiralty 'U-boat Situation Reports' that his enemy enjoyed an uncanny knowledge of latest U-boat deployments, but, after much cogitation, he and his staff attributed this to long-distance airborne radar surveillance for which he had no answer.[99] By an irony, however, it was during this month that GC and CS actually suffered severe setbacks in its ability to read the 'Shark' Enigma, with more than average delays for seven out of the first ten days, and a complete blank between the 10th and 19th.[100] Meanwhile B-Dienst continued regularly to place on the desks of Dönitz and Rear-Admiral Godt complete pictures of Allied dispositions and intended convoy courses and timings. This current German superiority in Sigint was the more operationally significant because of continuing Allied weaknesses out in the ocean front line.

It was only on 1 March that the British, Americans and Canadians held an 'Atlantic Convoy Conference' in Washington to sort out the organisation of the Atlantic battle and remedy the deficiencies in ships and aircraft bequeathed by earlier dilatoriness or (in the case of VLR aircraft) purblind policy. Admiral King, COMINCH and Chief of Naval Operations, now sprang an unwelcome surprise to the conference by wishing to withdraw American ships altogether from the North Atlantic convoy routes in order to concentrate them on routes further south between America and the Mediterranean theatre where the American forces, currently stuck in the Tunisian stalemate, were dependent on seaborne logistics. A bargain was eventually reached whereby the United States Navy would furnish a support group with an escort carrier (CVE) to work under British control on the North Atlantic route and also take over the task of convoying traffic between Britain and the Dutch oilfield islands in the Caribbean, while the Royal and Royal Canadian Navies would assume sole general responsibility for the North Atlantic.

The conference also agreed that the number of American and Canadian VLR aircraft based in Newfoundland should be raised to 48, as against a present operational total for the whole Atlantic of only eighteen; a dangerously belated decision. Canada agreed to create a North-West Atlantic Command (equivalent to Western Approaches Command) to control her side of the 'chop-line', which was to be shifted eastwards to 47° West. This marked the advent of Canada as a senior partner in the conduct of the 'grey water' strategy on which Allied victory in the German war so completely depended.

Yet these new command arrangements and reallotments of operational responsibility were only to come into effect on 1 April. Even by that time the number of VLR aircraft over the Atlantic had in fact risen to no more than twenty. The promised American support group (USS *Bogue* and five destroyers) did not go to sea with a convoy until the second half of March. Furthermore, it was only gradually in the course of March that ASV Mark III Wellingtons came into service over the Bay area. It was all desperately last-minute, and in the meanwhile Dönitz and his crews were inflicting savage punishment on the Allies. The March statistics starkly delineate the German success. The U-boats alone sank 108 ships of 627,377 tons in all waters; the Luftwaffe added another twelve of some 65,700 tons; the worst figure since the ghastly month of November 1942.[101] Worse, the proportion of convoyed ships lost was up 68 per cent on February.[102]

The most appalling losses fell within the first twenty days of the month. From 7 to 10 March seventeen U-boats hung on the flanks of convoy SC121 as it struggled through the storms, and picked off the stragglers one by one. In all SC121 lost thirteen ships of about 62,000 tons; not a single U-boat was sunk in return. From 7 to 14 March convoy HX228 also came under attack, but here the U-boats found no easy prey, sinking only four ships. The senior officer of the escort (Commander A. A. Tait, RN) in the destroyer *Harvester* rammed and sank the U-444 (Lieutenant Langfeld). *Harvester* having disabled herself in the process, she was torpedoed and sunk by the U-432 (Lieutenant-Commander Eckhardt), with Commander Tait lost with his ship. In turn, the U-432 was destroyed by the French corvette *Aconit*.[103]

The frantic violence of such encounters, their stabbing moments of terror, contrast strangely with the battle of brains between Bletchley Park and B-Dienst, with the wall-chart chess game between the Allied and German operation centres, or with the competition between the scientists of each side in laboratory and testing shop.

March 10, 1943 ... 30° West, 51° North [begins the war diary of Lieutenant-Commander Trojer of U-121 in describing his successful part in the attack on HX228]. In a snow squall [I] came up at right angles to course of the enemy, surfaced as soon as latter emerged from the snow squall ... 2131. Fired two torpedoes at two large, overlapping merchant ships. First torpedo hit. Ship disintegrated completely in flames and a vast cloud of smoke. Hundreds of steel plates flew like sheets of paper through the air. A great deal of ammunition exploded.

Shortly afterwards scored another hit on a freighter, which also exploded. From bows to bridge the ship was under water. Heavy debris crashed against my periscope, which now became difficult to turn. The whole boat re-echoed with bangs and crashes ...[104]

When Trojer torpedoed another freighter from periscope depth, he had to go full astern in order to avoid running into the exploding ship:

> My periscope suddenly went completely black. I could hardly see a thing, while all the time heavy fragments of debris continued to shower down on us. The noise inside the boat was terrific. It felt as though we were being hit by a stream of shells. Heard clearly the noise of a sinking ship, and then all was quiet. Tried to lower my periscope in order to clean the lens. It came down about five feet and then stuck. It was absolutely bent.

At this moment Trojer's hydrophone operator reported the sound of approaching retribution – the propellers of a destroyer at high speed. Trojer raised his periscope:

> Thanks to the swell and the smeared lens I could see very little. Then I myself heard the noise of the destroyer's propellers where I stood in the conning tower and at once gave the order: 'Dive! – full ahead! Both!' Depth charges, two patterns of four, were already falling, and pretty close to us. The conning tower hatch started to leak, and a mass of water came down into the boat. The boat plunged and jumped, but she gained depth steadily.[105]

The generally unprofitable attack on convoy HX228 was followed by complete failure against convoy ON170, which had been successfully diverted away thanks to detection of the ambush by shore-based and shipborne HF/DF. But these setbacks served only as the prelude to the U-boats' greatest single convoy victory of the whole war.

During 14–15 March 1943 the Allied command sought to reroute the eastbound convoy HX229 away from an ambush that had also been detected by HF/DF. However, U-boat Command now signalled two reserve groups of boats in mid-Atlantic to make utmost speed to reinforce the western patrol line which, thanks once again to copious B-Dienst decrypts, had already been ordered to intercept the convoy. By noon on 16 March eight U-boats were clinging to HX229 and its 38 ships, while the reserve groups had run into a slow eastbound convoy of 51 assorted vessels, SC122, then about 120 miles ahead of HX229. To complicate the battle even further, a third convoy, HX229A, composed of 25 fast ships of various types, was also making an eastbound crossing, although on a diversionary course well to the north, near Greenland; and the U-boats confused this group with HX229. As the fast HX229 closed on the slow SC122, there was to ensue a single struggle by the two escort groups to protect a vast sprawl of shipping against 38 U-boats, described by Operational

Intelligence Centre after reading belated 'Shark' decrypts as 'the largest pack of U-boats which has ever been collected together into one area for the same operation'.[106] It could be said that for the first time an encounter in submarine warfare attained the scale and decisive character of the great fleet battles of the past.

Action was joined on 16 March. Through the night of 16–17 March – nearly full moon – the convoys entirely lacked air cover, for the escort forces did not include a carrier, and nor were there shore-based VLR aircraft, which, lacking Leigh Lights, were useless in the dark. The U-boats took full advantage, hitting or sinking twelve ships in one murderous night. During daylight on the 17th three Liberators of No. 120 Squadron, Coastal Command, turned up over SC122 and attacked six out of the eleven U-boats they sighted, but without success. Only one freighter was lost. Meanwhile HX229, with no air cover, lost two ships. At dusk the Liberators had to abandon SC122. The U-boats sneaked in again in the moonlight and sank two more ships. Next day five Liberators from No. 120 Squadron were patrolling over SC122; no ships were lost. But the unfortunate HX229, still without air cover, saw two more of its freighters go down. It was during the following night that HX229 finally caught up with SC122 to form one vast area of shipping defended by a total now of eighteen escort vessels. By now the convoys had got within the operational orbit of medium-range shore-based aircraft, and so on the 19th the air cover was boosted to seven Fortresses and three Sunderlands as well as six Liberators. On this day a Sunderland of No. 201 Squadron sank the U-384 and damaged another (the first and only kill of the battle). Nevertheless the U-boats again made the most of the hours of darkness after the aircraft had returned to base, sinking two more merchantmen.

Only on 20 March, with his U-boats under heavier and heavier combined attack by Coastal Command and the escorts, did Dönitz close down the battle. It had been a triumph for him – twenty-one ships sunk in convoy for the loss of only one U-boat sunk and three badly damaged. The storms of that appalling March helped to do Dönitz's work, for another ten ships of HX229 and SC122 either foundered on passage or had to put back to port.

The disaster which had overtaken these two convoys merely formed the central episode in what had proved a catastrophic three weeks. In all waters and from all causes the Allies had lost 97 ships totalling more than half a million tons – and what was so profoundly disquieting was that threequarters of this total had been lost in convoy, the cornerstone of anti-U-boat warfare in two world wars. On 22 March, in the immediate aftermath of the disaster to HX229 and SC122, the First Sea Lord reported to the Cabinet Anti-U-boat Warfare Committee that 'we can no longer rely on evading the U-boat packs and, hence, we shall have to fight the convoys through them'.[107]

But how? For, as the Prime Minister had informed his Cabinet four days earlier, Britain's naval resources 'were stretched to the uttermost, and the strength of the escorts to our Atlantic convoys was inadequate to meet the enemy's concentration of U-boats'.[108] It was no longer a question of the U-boat eventually torpedoing the Allies' delicately balanced shipping budgets by sheer attrition; it was a question of the Atlantic soon becoming impassable. From the consequent severing of communications between North America and Great Britain – and also with the Allied forces committed to the Mediterranean – would ramify cataclysmic effects on the whole course of the war.

It was, as the Duke of Wellington said of Waterloo, a damned near run thing. But in the case of the Battle of the Atlantic relief did not arrive in the form of a single Blücher turning up at the last moment to save the day; it arrived in a cluster of operational and technical innovations, in piecemeal increases of strength on and over the ocean – though all of them just as last-minute and long-awaited in the circumstances as Blücher's appearance on the field of Waterloo.

In the final week of March 1943 the USS *Bogue* became the first of the new escort carriers to make its début in the North Atlantic, when together with two American destroyers it escorted the eastbound convoy SC123 to a position 175 miles south-east of Cape Farewell (the southernmost tip of Greenland).[109] A utilitarian ship, with all the grace of a floating coffin, *Bogue* and her aircraft signified the beginning of a new era in convoy warfare – continuous air cover even when shore-based VLR aircraft could not be present. Moreover convoy SC123 also enjoyed the protection of the first permanent destroyer escort group to be formed by Western Approaches Command. No merchant ships were lost; and only one straggler from HX230, in order to protect which the *Bogue* group turned back after escorting SC123.

By the end of the month the Royal Navy had organised its own first three escort carrier support groups round *Bogue*'s British sister ships HMSs *Biter*, *Archer* and *Dasher*. In a major setback, however, *Dasher* blew up and sank while on exercise on 27 March; probably because aviation fuel vapour had been ignited by a member of the crew smoking a cigarette or dropping a cigarette through a grating.[110] This disaster led to modifications in American dockyards to the aviation fuel system

[600]

(always regarded by the Admiralty as unsafe) in new CVEs (escort aircraft carriers) under construction.

The deployment at long last of these CVE escort groups had only been possible because for the first time since November 1942 the carriers were no longer urgently needed for 'Torch' operations in the Mediterranean. This was also true of some of the destroyers that made up the CVE escort groups and the other new escort groups. So whereas at the beginning of March 1943 the C-in-C, Western Approaches, had not a single escort group at sea, at the beginning of April he had five plus one American under command – three composed of a CVE and three destroyers each, and the remainder of five to seven destroyers or other types of small ship each. At this time too the Royal Navy began to reap the reward in operational efficiency of much more thorough group training.

A no less swift and radical revolution was taking place in the effectiveness of Royal Air Force Coastal Command and the Royal Canadian Air Force. By mid-April the available strength in VLR aircraft had risen from the winter low point of six to 41, all equipped with 10cm ASV Mark III radar. The Atlantic air gap south of Iceland and north of the Azores, so long the U-boats' rich hunting ground, was now swiftly shrinking. From 14 March Coastal Command changed the spacing of the pattern in which its aircraft dropped the 250lb Torpex depth-charge from 36 feet to 100 feet, after operational research had indicated that this wider spacing gave the optimum chance of achieving a hit or a damaging near-miss. Along with the concurrent introduction of 10cm radar this new method was in a few weeks to transform the effectiveness of air attack on U-boats. Over the Bay of Biscay too the number of ASV Mark III Wellingtons was growing rapidly from just three in March. And the airmen in the cockpits and the sailors on the bridge had now learned to work closely together in spotting and hunting U-boats.

Only in the battle of Sigint did April 1943 see little change. B-Dienst continued to supply U-boat Command with a stream of decrypted Allied secret signals. GC and CS at Bletchley Park for its part certainly read the 'Shark' Enigma much more continuously and at shorter delays than in March, but this only enabled the Admiralty successfully to reroute a few of the convoys, so numerous now were the patrolling U-boats, with as many as 98 new or refitted boats coming out from German or French bases during the month.[111]

Dönitz's total operational strength now stood at 240 U-boats;[112] the bulk of them Type VIICs (769 tons surfaced; 871 tons submerged) with a crew of 44 packed into the narrow, machinery-crammed hull.

The Type VIICs were oceanic submersible Volkswagens, rugged and reliable. On the surface their diesel-electric motors could push them to nearly 18 knots; when submerged they could manage a maximum of 7.6 knots, but only for an hour. Their range was enormous – nearly 10,000 miles on the surface at 10 knots; 3,450 miles at maximum speed. This could be extended much further by refuelling from milch-cow tanker U-boats. Beneath the surface, however, their endurance was poor – only 130 miles when creeping at 2 knots; only 80 miles at the modest speed of 4 knots. The Type VIICs could dive to 309 feet, and much deeper still in dire emergency, while later versions enjoyed a standard diving depth of 394 feet, and could actually reach well over 700 feet. The Type VIIC U-boat was essentially a platform to carry five torpedo tubes (four in the bow, one at the stern) from which to launch a maximum stock of twelve torpedoes at Allied ships. However, the boat's only protection against Allied aircraft at this time consisted of one 37mm and two 20mm anti-aircraft guns.[113]

But it would not be the shipwrights and armourers of the opposing sides, any more than the codebreakers, who would ultimately decide which way the balance of the battle would tip that critical April and May; it was the sailors ranged against each other in the Atlantic front line itself and their willingness to endure and dare. In the event the attackers, especially the novice captains and crews batch-trained in Dönitz's schools to man the new boats coming off the production lines, were the first to flinch. From the end of March onwards U-boats were signalling U-boat Command to offer ingenious excuses for failing to press their attacks or for aborting sorties; and U-boat Command was sternly signalling back to the boats to stiffen morale and resolve. All these signals were decrypted by GC and CS for the benefit of the Admiralty Operations Intelligence Centre and to the great encouragement of Western Approaches Command. The mind-numbing boredom of keeping the sea between convoy battles, the days and days spent pallid, haggard and stinking in a narrow steel tube under electric light, corroded the morale and the operational efficiency of the U-boat crews. They felt more and more helpless and naked beneath a sky out of which an enemy aircraft could suddenly thunder without warning to smother their boat with a devastating pattern of 250lb depth-charges. They had come to dread the long claustrophobic periods when lying stationary deep down, silent and listening to the screws of the hunting destroyers thrashing the water above them or to the hull-creaking thunder of the depth-charges. Dönitz's cutlass was beginning to bend in his hand.

He sustained his first major defeat at the turn of March and April when the escorts of convoy HX230 supported by the USS *Bogue*'s escort group drove off a mass attack by 40 U-boats for the loss of only one ship, and that a straggler (see above, p. 600). In the first week of April the failure by another mass U-boat ambush to sink more than six ships in convoy HX231 elicited a harsh reproach from U-boat Command. Four days later another group of U-boats managed to sink only two ships in convoy ON176. When on 11 April the next victim, convoy HX232, was sighted, a perturbed U-boat Command again signalled its suspicions to its captains that they were not pressing home their attacks as they ought. It called on the two groups now deployed against HX232 to display what it called 'the healthy warrior and hunter instincts'.[114] Nonetheless the group's instincts proved far from healthy enough, for they sank only three ships.

So it went on through the month, with some convoys successfully diverted clear of ambushes thanks to timely Ultra decrypts of the 'Shark' Enigma, and others attacked with small loss. In a combined battle against three convoys from 20 April onwards the U-boats sank only four merchantmen for the loss of three of their own number; hardly a profitable exchange rate. Already, on 19 April, the Operational Intelligence Centre tracking room on the basis of decrypts of signals traffic between U-boat Command and its boats had remarked on 'the incipient decline in U-boat morale', and particularly the crews' 'concern for vulnerability to air attack'.[115] As it happened, it was on that same day that U-boat Command conceded that it could no longer effectively employ wolf-pack tactics against convoys with air support.[116] On 26 April the OIC was stressing the success of HMS *Biter* and her escort group in completely defeating a mass attack on convoy ONS4, and reckoning that most U-boat captains had now yielded to a lack of boldness.[117]

The strengthened power of the Allied anti-submarine forces and this resultant waning in U-boat skippers' willingness to risk their boats and crews stare out of the April balance sheet of battle – 56 ships of 327,943 tons of merchant shipping sunk by U-boats in all seas; barely half the March loss.[118] 'This,' wrote the Admiralty, 'shows what our counter measures can achieve against the enemy's most strenuous efforts.'[119] It was all the more encouraging that the number of U-boats destroyed in the whole broad Atlantic or in transit through the Bay of Biscay rose from twelve in March to fourteen in April – and six of these in the last week of the month alone.[120]

Dönitz characteristically responded to these disappointing results by driving his crews still harder, his own will to victory in no degree diminished. With his numerical strength – 128 U-boats actually at sea; more than 60 of them across the North Atlantic convoy tracks – climbing to its peak,[121] he and his deputy, Rear-Admiral Godt, now launched their climactic offensive. Their purpose and strategic deployment were divined by GC and CS even though from 26 April onwards there had been great difficulty in solving the 'Shark' Enigma. The Admiralty Operational Intelligence Centre warned: 'On the basis of available information and an appreciation of the new pattern [of U-boat patrol lines] it was estimated on 1 May that by 3 May all routes would be blocked from 53°N, 48°W around to 46°N, 38°W.'[122] Two groups of seventeen and fifteen U-boats now lay spread on the western fringes of the mid-Atlantic air gap; two more of thirteen each on its eastern fringes, one of them off Cape Farewell on the northern flank of the convoy tracks, the other on the southern flank west of the Bay of Biscay.[123] On 29 April 1943 a U-boat near Cape Farewell picked up on her hydrophones the sound of the ships' screws of convoy ONS5; the decisive battles were about to be joined.

Yet the advantage in numbers of vessels, in operational technique and in technology was by this time swinging fast to the Allies. Admiral Horton, the C-in-C, Western Approaches, now disposed of six escort (support) groups, three of them with CVEs carrying a total of some 45 aircraft. At the end of May the first MAC (Merchant Aircraft Carrier, see pages 584–5), the grain ship *Empire MacAlpine* (7,950 tons), was to take her four Swordfish to sea with convoy ONS9. Thanks most of all to the prodigious output of American shipyards and the current slackening of demand from the Mediterranean for destroyers, Horton could now allot an average of eight ships to each close convoy escort, as against five in 1942. The much larger pool of such vessels had also made it possible to give more time to training captains and crews thoroughly in anti-submarine tactics, with the result that the close escorts themselves were much more effective than hitherto. In the case of convoy ONS5, now about to fight its way westwards against a swarm of U-boats, the particularly experienced escort consisted of three destroyers, a frigate, two corvettes and two rescue trawlers under a ruthlessly determined commander, Commander P. W. Gretton in the destroyer HMS *Duncan*. Moreover, the equipping of the close escorts and the escort groups alike with the Hedgehog forward-throwing anti-submarine mortar (100 ships by the end of 1942) and the new Torpex-filled depth-charge had enormously enhanced their power to kill U-boats once detected by air search or their own HF/DF, Type 271 10cm radar and sonar, or in the last resort the keen eyes of their lookouts.

But it was the advent of the escort (or support) groups, still barely a month old, which was transforming the tactical battle, and in unexpected ways. In the summer of 1943 an Admiralty Operational Research Department analysis of U-boat hunts for all 1941 and from July 1942 to March 1943 found that in the middle stage of a hunt the chances of a kill dropped away, while after the sixth attack by the escorts the chances climbed steeply to three times the average expectation.[124] The study pointed out that, following an attack by a U-boat, some 90 minutes sufficed for locating the enemy, yet the escorts had to close on their convoy again to protect it before they had time to carry out 'adequate search'. The study had ascertained that 'the number of U-boats destroyed would probably have been increased by about 30 per cent if searches up to 90 minutes could have been carried out after [initial] loss of contact. In the majority of cases contact could have been regained in a very much shorter time than 90 minutes.[125]

Thus the value of the new support groups lay in their ability to make prolonged searches and conduct protracted hunts, which served to increase the total kills by all surface ships by 30 per cent.[126] Another study, this time of support group operations between 5 May and 12 June 1943, estimated that the groups actually raised total kills by 45 per cent, even though they spent less than half their sea-time actually supporting convoys.[127] With one exception, noted this study, all kills by support groups were made in the vicinity of a convoy rather than on passage. Thus these groups of 1943, for all their offensive purpose, were in no sense successors to the 'hunter' groups which had vainly swept the seas in 1939–40 on the off-chance of encountering a U-boat (see above, pp. 68–9).

In the air dimension of what had now become a single closely integrated anti-submarine effort, the number of 10cm radar VLR aircraft available to cover a convoy for three to five hours up to 650 miles from bases in the United Kingdom, Iceland and Newfoundland had risen by 1 May 1943 to 49, out of which twelve to fifteen were operational at any one time.[128] In medium-range aircraft all Coastal Command's ageing Whitleys had been re-equipped by mid-May with Leigh Light Wellingtons (more and more of which were fitted with 10cm ASV Mk III radar) or Liberators. This changeover coincided with a mistaken new instruction by Dönitz that his boats were to evade night-time Leigh Light Wellington attacks by surfacing to charge their batteries by day.[129] Sightings of U-boats in transit across the Bay of Biscay rose from 24 in April to 100 in May;[130] sinkings from two to six. And this month, for the first time, Coastal Command and the Royal Canadian Air Force aircraft began to carry three revolutionary new items of U-boat killing technology – the new American acoustic torpedo which once in the water homed on the sound of its submerged victim's screws and motors; a 600lb-bomb (350lbs heavier than the existing standard Coastal Command bomb); and an air-to-sea rocket.[131]

Thus it was that Dönitz's supreme effort to bar the North Atlantic encountered the Allied navies and air forces when they at last enjoyed adequate strength in the right kinds of ships and aircraft, were trained to high efficiency and equipped with a comprehensive armoury for finding and destroying U-boats. The Allies – and this means above all Great Britain – had repaired two decades of neglect and mistaken policy just in time, and Dönitz was too late, thanks to Grand Admiral Raeder's and Hitler's long-standing failure to perceive that the U-boat if given sufficient industrial priority could win the war. In truth, Dönitz was too late by years, as he himself was later bitterly to admit.[132]

The turning-point arrived with the week-long effort by Commander Gretton and his eight escort ships to pass the 42 merchantmen of ONS5 through a patrol line of 31 U-boats (later 41) deployed by Dönitz to intercept the convoy. On 28 April the U-258 sighted the convoy, and Dönitz ordered his concentration against it. The weather would have done justice to January – a full gale, a colossal seaway, low cloud, squalls of rain. It was impossible for VLR aircraft to fly air cover; difficult enough for the 3rd Escort Group, which had been ordered out to the rescue from St John's, Newfoundland, even to find the convoy. Happily on 1 May the U-boats lost contact, to the lamentations next day (decrypted by Bletchley Park) of U-boat Command: 'With 31 boats something can and must be accomplished.'[133] From 1 to 3 May the U-boats searched for ONS5 and three other convoys, thus far in vain. On the 4th they managed to find ONS5 again.

By this time the 3rd Escort Group, composed of five destroyers commanded by Captain J. A. McCoy, RN, in HMS *Offa* (1,540 tons; designed 1939, launched 1941)[134] had joined the convoy. The weather was now so foul – complete with icebergs and pack-ice – that the escort ships could not be refuelled at sea. On 3 May Gretton's own ship *Duncan* (1,375 tons; 35½ knots; launched 1932)[135] had been forced to part company to St John's for oil, and command of the convoy escort passed to Lieutenant-Commander R. E. Sherwood, RNR, in the River class frigate *Tay* (1,370 tons; 20 knots; launched 1942).[136] On the morrow two ships of the 3rd Escort Group also had to make for port in order to refuel their tanks.

When the U-boat pack began its mass attack that same day, the

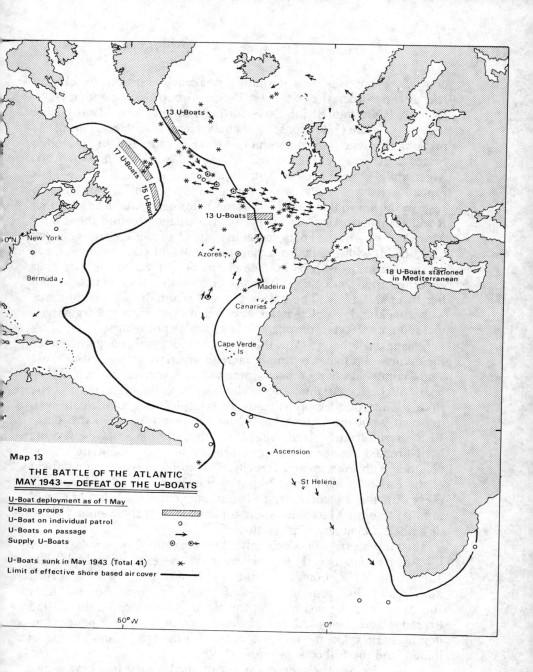

13 U-Boats

17 U-Boats

15 U-Boats

13 U-Boats

18 U-Boats stationed
in Mediterranean

New York

Bermuda

Azores

Madeira

Canaries

Cape Verde
Is

Ascension

St Helena

Map 13

**THE BATTLE OF THE ATLANTIC
MAY 1943 — DEFEAT OF THE U-BOATS**

U-Boat deployment as of 1 May	
U-Boat groups	▨▨▨
U-Boat on individual patrol	o
U-Boats on passage	→
Supply U-Boats	⊙ ⊙→
U-Boats sunk in May 1943 (Total 41)	✳
Limit of effective shore based air cover	▬▬

50° W

0°

convoy's escort was thus perilously weakened. Fortunately Horton had already ordered out the 1st Escort Group (Commander G. N. Brewer, RN) from St John's as further reinforcement. Comprising the sloop *Pelican* (1,200 tons; 19½ knots; launched 1938 as part of the pre-war rearmament programme),[137] three frigates and an ex-United States coastguard cutter, it did not join the convoy until 6 May. Meanwhile ONS5 had to fight a running battle with 30 U-boats ranged across its track, with yet another group of eleven lying in reserve further to the west. It heartened the convoy and its escort that Royal Canadian Air Force flying boats managed to find them on 4 May; and two flying boats searching ahead of the convoy sank the U-630. But with the fall of darkness over a wild sea, the convoy was on its own again with its surface escort now down to the *Tay*, four corvettes and, from the 3rd Escort Group, the destroyers *Offa* and her sister ship *Oribi*. The U-boats closed in and during a night fierce with attack and counter-attack succeeded in sinking five freighters, including a straggler, despite all the escort's endeavours.

During daylight on 5 May the weather moderated enough to enable the escorts to refuel. Four more merchantmen went down; four more ships' companies of merchant seamen to seek survival in open rowing boats in the icy Atlantic swell. However, the Flower class corvette *Pink*, having rounded up half a dozen stragglers into a little convoy of her own, sank the U-boat U-192 by way of revenge. On this day a VLR aircraft from Iceland flying at its uttermost range stayed with the hard-pressed convoy for a time. During the next night the action resumed with even greater ferocity. According to the Senior Officer of the escort in his report, 'about twenty-four attacks took place in every direction except ahead'; the fighting continued 'without a stop' until 0420 on 6 May. With some understatement the Senior Officer described the situation as 'confused'.[138]

Yet the escorts won decisively. The corvette *Loosestrife* sank the U-638; the destroyer *Vidette* (a Great War veteran, launched 1918; 1,090 tons; 24½ knots)[139] put the U-125 down with her Hedgehog mortar; the *Oribi* rammed and sank the U-531 when she suddenly slid out of the fog nearby; and the sloop *Pelican* located the U-438 by radar and destroyed her under water by repeated patterns of depth-charges. On the morning of the 6th the local Canadian escort joined, and the U-boats gave up.

In the course of their three-day assault the U-boats had sunk twelve ships, but at the cost of no fewer than seven of their own number (including one destroyed early on by a Coastal Command Flying Fortress) – five of them at the hands of the Royal Navy. Dönitz had lost some 300 of his precious highly trained submariners killed outright or trapped and drowned in the riven hulls of their boats. Five more U-boats were also badly damaged. From Dönitz's point of view this constituted a disastrous rate of exchange; a rate which, thanks to Ultra decrypts of 'Shark', was soon exactly known to his enemy.

Now the cryptographers began to take an active part in shaping the manoeuvres of the May battle. Theirs was a curious game of trick and trump. GC and CS read 'Shark' in time for Western Approaches Command to signal convoys HX237 and SC129 to alter course away from ambushes, whereupon B-Dienst in turn read these signals sent in the 'convoy cypher' and so enabled U-boat Command to redeploy the ambushes. Convoys HX237 and SC129 therefore failed to evade attack by as many as 36 U-boats between 7th and 14 May.

This time, however, the U-boats encountered the full panoply of British air and sea power over the Atlantic. HX237 enjoyed the protection of the 5th Escort Group (Captain E. M. C. Abel-Smith, RN), including the escort carrier HMS *Biter* and her aircraft, while shore-based VLR aircraft sank one U-boat and aided warships to destroy another. Despite hazardous flying conditions *Biter*'s aircraft attacked six U-boats and sank one in conjunction with surface escorts; one of her aircraft was lost, and three more damaged by forced landings. The German attack on HX237 ended in a score of three freighters sunk in return for three U-boats – another disastrous result for Dönitz.

The onslaught on SC129 fared no better. On 12 May, when the convoy was still out of range of shore-based air cover, the escort sank their first U-boat. Next day a VLR aircraft, 1,200 miles from base, attacked two U-boats patrolling ahead of the convoy (which was itself still out of air range). On the 14th the convoy came under the cover of VLR aircraft; it was also joined by HMS *Biter* with 5th Escort Group from convoy HX237. The final score of sinkings for this encounter came to two merchantmen and two U-boats, plus several other U-boats seriously damaged. Wailed U-boat Command to its captains: 'We can see no explanation for this failure.'[140] The Operational Intelligence Centre drew the cheering lesson that the failure 'provides further evidence that U-boat efficiency and morale were declining'.[141]

On 18 May began the first of the two final major convoy actions of the whole war. Guided by 'Shark' decrypts giving the secrets of Dönitz's deployment the Admiralty sought to steer convoy SC130 (38 ships) through a gap in the U-boat patrol line. It was sighted nonetheless by one of the 33 U-boats spread across its course. This time the action ended in utter failure for the U-boats. Continuous air cover was flown by Liberators of No. 120 Squadron, Coastal Command, which sank the U-954 and the U-258, and by Hudsons of No. 269 Squadron which sank the U-273. Commander Gretton (commanding the convoy's close escort) in the *Duncan* took part in destroying the U-381. And the frigate *Jed* and the escort sloop *Sennen* (ex-US coastguard cutter; 1,546 tons; 16 knots; launched 1928)[142] of the 1st Escort Group accounted for U-209. Not a single merchant vessel was lost. The convoy steamed on to Londonderry with such despatch as to fulfil the keen wish Gretton had expressed to the convoy commodore not to be late for his wedding.[143]

By this time U-boat Command had become profoundly anxious about the enemy's ability 'to deprive the U-boat of its most important attribute, its invisibility',[144] and it ordered its captains to make dummy radio signals to disguise their position.[145] Now occurred the second of the two last grand encounters of the Battle of the Atlantic; one in which all the operational and technological threads were aptly woven together. First of all B-Dienst detected the location and course of convoy HX239, so that U-boat Command was able to deploy 22 U-boats to attack it. Then GC and CS at Bletchley Park detected the ambush, thus making it possible for the Admiralty to reroute the convoy. But B-Dienst in turn decyphered the details of the rerouting, so that U-boat Command could accordingly make a fresh deployment of its boats. Now it was up to the seamen of both sides and their weaponry. On the evening before the convoy was actually sighted on 22 May U-boat Command made an almost despairing signal of supposed encouragement to its captains:

> If there is anyone who thinks that combating convoys is no longer possible, he is a weakling and no true U-boat captain. The battle of the Atlantic is getting harder but it is the determining element in the waging of the war.[146]

This signal, once decrypted, made astonishing reading for the Admiralty and for Western Approaches Command. For the first time in history the victor literally read the mind of the vanquished at that moment when hope dies and the will begins to break. In any case, U-boat Command's exhortation proved of no avail. For HX239 enjoyed powerful and continuous air cover from the USS *Bogue* and HMS *Archer*. The *Bogue* accounted for the U-569 and the *Archer* for the U-752, three of the *Archer*'s aircraft having been just fitted with the new air-to-sea rocket. Not a single merchant ship was sunk.

The very last convoy to be seriously menaced that month, SC130, arrived in the United Kingdom on 25 May also without loss. It had been continuously protected by VLR aircraft for three days and two nights, and these had made 28 sightings of U-boats, launched ten attacks on them, and sunk two.[147] By this time Dönitz's total losses for the month of May in all waters had already reached the catastrophic total of 33 U-boats; by 31 May they would rise to 41. Like Villeneuve's fleet at Trafalgar Dönitz's crews had simply been outfought and outclassed by the foe who had engaged them far more closely than they cared for.

For all his tenacity and resolve Dönitz was a cool realist. On 24 May he wrote:

In the last few days, circumstances have arisen which give a particularly strong indication of the present crisis in the U-boat war. These circumstances are:
a) The confirmation of further heavy losses.
b) The complete failure of the operation against SC130 as well as the conditions encountered during the attack on Convoy HX239 . . .
We have to accept the heavy losses provided the amount of enemy shipping sunk is proportionate. In May, however, the ratio was one U-boat to 10,000 gross tons of enemy shipping, whereas a short time ago it was one U-boat to 100,000 gross tons . . . The U-boat losses in May 1943 therefore reached unbearable heights . . .

As for the cause of these losses,

. . . the enemy Air Force therefore played a decisive part . . . This can be attributed to the increased use of land-based aircraft and aircraft carriers combined with the advantages of radar location . . . To a very great extent, the enemy aircraft brought about the failure of our U-boats against Convoys SC130 and HX239. In the former they prevented the U-boats from manoeuvring into an attacking position ahead of the enemy. In the case of HX239, the enemy aircraft precluded all contact.[148]

Although Dönitz failed to mention it in this report, the Luftwaffe had throughout wholly failed to provide the U-boats with equivalent air support, either by way of VLR reconnaissance or in cooperating in attacks on Allied convoys, or providing a defence to the U-boats against Allied aircraft. Whereas the British Air Staff had relented in its doctrinaire concentration on the bomber offensive just about in time to enable Coastal Command to become a fully effective partner of the Royal Navy, the Luftwaffe (in the ample person of Reichsmarschall Göring) remained aloof and apart from the U-boat war. Indeed Göring was openly hostile to his sister service.[149] In particular the failure of the Luftwaffe to put the Heinkel He 177 four-engined bomber into production, let alone the projected very long range 'Amerika' bomber, meant that the Luftwaffe had no aircraft to match the VLR Liberator.[150] As Dönitz was sourly to remark in his memoirs, 'In this Second World War Germany was waging war at sea without an air arm; that was one of the salient features of our naval operations, a feature that was as much out of line with contemporary conditions as it was decisive in effect.'[151]

Now, in that third week of May 1943, Dönitz had to accept that for the time being at least he had been beaten. On the 24th he wrote in his log:

> The situation in the North Atlantic now forces a temporary shifting of operations to areas less endangered by aircraft . . . the Caribbean Sea, the area off Trinidad, the area off the Brazilian and West African coasts . . . With the boats at present in the North Atlantic, operations will be made against the traffic between the U.S.A. and Gibraltar – as far as these boats are able to do with their fuel. The North Atlantic cannot, however, be entirely denuded of boats. It is necessary, by means of single boats, to leave the enemy in ignorance as long as possible of these alterations in tactics . . .[152]

However it did not at all occur to Dönitz's mind that he had finally lost the Battle of the Atlantic:

> These decisions comprise a temporary deviation from the former principles for the conduct of U-boat warfare. This is necessary in order not to allow the U-boats to be beaten at a time when their weapons are inferior, by unnecessary losses while achieving very slight success. It is, however, clearly understood that the main operational area of U-boats is, as it always was, in the North Atlantic . . . It is . . . anticipated that after equipment with quadruples [quad 20cm flak guns], i.e., from the autumn, the Battle of the North Atlantic will be completely resumed once more.[153]

So the signal went out to his captains to withdraw from the fray. The North Atlantic suddenly emptied of U-boats. The convoys began to steam across unscathed – only one ship lost in convoy between 1 June and 18 September 1943; and only fifteen ships lost in total in the North Atlantic.[154] It was as if a steel gauntlet had relaxed its grip on the Allied throat.

But this victory so hard won by the crews of the escorts and merchantmen and maritime aircraft came only just in time for the Allies. For even despite the consequent falling-off in sinkings by the enemy from June onwards, even despite the soaring output of new ships by American yards, the problem of a global deficit in shipping resources actually continued to get worse for the rest of 1943 and into 1944, so great and rising were the competitive demands.[155] And during late May and June 1943, as the U-boats slunk away from the North Atlantic, the Allies were preparing to add to these demands by embarking on a further extension of 'blue water' strategy in the Mediterranean – more amphibious landings on the grand scale (this time on a hostile shore) calling for a mass of shipping and warships; and the entire venture dependent for its continuing success on uninterrupted long-distance sea communications.

Grand Strategy for a Maritime Alliance – II

On 13 January 1943 the Prime Minister had arrived in Casablanca to join the President in another summit conference (codenamed 'Symbol') to decide the maritime alliance's global strategy for the current year and after. For Churchill and his entourage it had been a somewhat harrowing flight in a converted bomber, for he had woken up to find a heater point next to his makeshift bed so hot as to threaten to ignite the bed-clothes and after them the aircraft, whereupon he ordered the entire heating system to be turned off. The cargo of distinguished personages was left to shiver in winter skies at 8,000 feet. 'I am bound to say,' he was to record in his memoirs, 'this struck me as a rather unpleasant moment.'[1] Pleasanter ones were now to follow, as Premier and President and attendant suites of the gold-braided or merely business-suited type took up residence in luxurious villas grouped round a hotel in sub-tropical gardens, while HMS *Bulolo*, at anchor in Casablanca harbour, provided the cypher and signals facilities.

The conference sessions proved long and tough, partly because of the deep divisions of view about grand strategy between the delegations, partly because of the nature of the participants themselves: Admiral 'Ernie' King, a curmudgeon of a sailor for whom the Pacific as always took absolute priority; Marshall, still massively resolved on a cross-Channel invasion ('Roundup') in 1943; Alan Brooke, a sharp mind behind a sharp face, stubbornly in favour of pursuing still further the existing Mediterranean 'blue water' strategy; Churchill himself, resplendent in private in a dragon-embroidered silk dressing-gown and in public in the uniform of an air commodore of the Royal Air Force, by now convinced that Brooke was right, and determined to win the argument for Britain; Roosevelt, much less closely involved in the strategic argument, but a final arbiter of decisive authority. The First Sea Lord, Admiral of the Fleet Sir Dudley Pound, was of course present too; a prematurely aged man leaning on a stick and prone to doze off in committee, he was less concerned with the grand strategic issues than with the executive detail of naval operations as such, and above all the crucial Battle of the Atlantic.

The 'Symbol' Conference met when the tide of the Axis fortune had just passed high water and begun to ebb. In Russia the great German offensive of 1942 had ended in total failure with the Soviet counter-offensive at Stalingrad on 2 November 1942; and General Paulus's 6th Army, cut off in the ruins of the city, was now in the last hopeless days of its resistance (he was to surrender on 2 February with the 90,000 survivors out of his original strength of a quarter of a million). In the Pacific the United States Navy's victory over the Japanese Combined Fleet in the Battle of Midway on 3–6 June 1942 (a decisive naval battle to rank in history with Salamis, Lepanto, the thwarting of the Spanish Armada, and Trafalgar) had thrown the Japanese ineluctably on to the strategic defensive. American and Australian troops were gradually pushing back the Japanese invaders of New Guinea. Ten days before the opening of the 'Symbol' Conference the Japanese high command had ordered the evacuation of the island of Guadalcanal in the Solomons (it was completed by the end of the month), signifying America's first success on land in the Pacific theatre. In North Africa General Montgomery, plodding forward from Alamein with extreme caution (even though he was well aware through constant Ultra decrypts that Rommel was reduced to a mere handful of tanks and was shackled by dearth of fuel)[2] had now reached Buerat on the Gulf of Sirte, some 80 miles east of Tripoli. It was therefore evident that within a few weeks Rommel would have fallen back into Tunisia in order to unite with von Arnim's 5th Panzer Army in a single Axis North African perimeter. The Royal Navy had played its familiar role in the 8th Army's advance by ferrying forward supplies along the coast, and by opening the harbours of Bardia, Tobruk and Benghazi as quickly as possible after their capture despite sunken wrecks and sabotaged dockside installations.

And thanks to Royal Air Force fighter cover from Libyan bases captured by Montgomery, the first convoy to Malta from Alexandria since the June failure had been successfully run by the Royal Navy on 17–20 November 1942 – but still at a cost, for an escorting cruiser, *Arethusa*, had been torpedoed by an enemy aircraft on the outward voyage, and she only made it back to Alexandria thanks to a stern tow in heavy seas while on fire.[3] The flow of convoys to Malta continued, putting an end to her long blockade. The Royal Navy's Force K – now the cruisers *Cleopatra*, *Orion* and *Euryalus* and some four destroyers – returned to the island to savage Axis traffic between Sicily and Tunis and Tripoli in conjunction with Force Q, usually based at Bône in Algeria. In the small hours of 2 December 1942 Force Q (the cruisers *Aurora*, flying the flag of Rear-Admiral C. H. J. Harcourt, *Argonaut* and *Sirius* and the destroyers *Quentin* and HMAS *Quiberon*) sank a complete convoy of four merchant ships and four escorting destroyers off the Gulf of Tunis by point-blank gunfire in a hellish scene of ships blazing and exploding amid luridly lit billows of smoke and steam.

The 8th Submarine Flotilla continued to work out of Malta, as it had done through the worst of enemy air attack in 1942; the 10th Flotilla, now based at Algiers, also contributed to the relentless attrition of enemy convoys. This was hazardous service, for seven boats were lost between January and May 1943, including the *Turbulent*, commanded by one of the Royal Navy's veteran submarine 'aces', Commander J. W. Linton, who was awarded a posthumous Victoria Cross. The Royal Air Force too had rebuilt its striking force based on Malta, to a total of eight squadrons of torpedo bombers – Wellingtons, Beauforts and Albacores.

Now it was the Axis which had lost control of the central Mediterranean convoy routes. Tanker after tanker went down to British attack beneath the sea, on its surface and from the air, starving Rommel in particular of the fuel he needed in order freely to manoeuvre in retreat in the face of superior forces. Thus, and entirely as a consequence of the 8th Army's advance along the Libyan coast, which had evicted the Luftwaffe from the airfields in Cyrenaica that commanded the waters between Italy and Africa, and installed the Royal Air Force instead, Malta had at last become once again a strategic asset to Britain.

In Tunisia, however, as the 'Symbol' Conference met in January 1943, the stalemate still continued along the north–south front through the mountains west of Bizerta and Tunis. Enemy bombers unrelentingly attacked supply vessels and warships in the Allied advanced base of Bône, despite the efforts of the Eastern Air Command, and between 13 December 1942 and 1 February 1943 there were 68 red alerts and more than 2,000 heavy bombs dropped,[4] the most recent casualty being the cruiser *Ajax*, so badly damaged on New Year's Day as to require her to leave the station for repairs.

The land stalemate had laid a heavy and unexpected burden on the Royal Navy and the Merchant Marine, for an average of 100 ships every month was sailing from Gibraltar to Algerian ports instead of the estimated 60, all requiring defence against numerous and resolute U-boat attacks. According to the original 'Torch' calculations Tunisia was to have been occupied by the end of January 1943, so releasing Allied land, sea and air forces (and shipping lift) for other offensive projects. But now the 'Symbol' Conference had to accept that Tunisia was not likely to fall until April at the earliest. This delay bore acutely on the conference's discussions of grand strategy, which turned on two inter-related issues – the proportion of resources to be allotted respectively to the German war and the Japanese war; and the rival merits of making the main Allied effort against Germany in 1943 in the Mediterranean or across the Channel ('Operation Roundup').

The war against Japan (except for the Burma front and the Indian Ocean) had become an exclusively American preserve controlled by Admiral King as Commander-in-Chief of the US Fleet (COMINCH) and Chief of Naval Operations. Grappling as he was with the problems of 'triphibious' warfare at the end of 3,000 miles-long sea communications, King believed that the Pacific theatre was being dangerously starved of resources in favour of the German war, and that there was a consequent risk that the Japanese would be given leisure to establish a perimeter defence round their conquests so strong that the Allies might later find great difficulty in overcoming it. King therefore demanded a bigger proportion of Allied resources for the Pacific, even mentioning a figure of 30 per cent as against the present 15 per cent. This would permit him to mount a series of step-by-step or island by island offensives aimed at retaining the initiative over the Japanese and denying them the opportunity to dig in. The British, being naturally preoccupied with Germany and enjoying little or no say over operations in the Pacific, suspected King of seeking to overturn the order of strategic priority decided at the Washington Conference in December 1941 whereby Germany was to be beaten first (see above, p. 434). They wanted to see this priority clearly reaffirmed, with only minimum force going to the Pacific in the meantime. In any event, the key to Allied offensive strategy everywhere lay in landing craft lift, and thanks to American mass production of these articles, 'Ernie' King firmly held that key.

With regard to grand strategy in the German war, Churchill and the Chiefs of Staff came to Casablanca agreed that to follow the conquest of North Africa with a cross-Channel invasion ('Roundup') in 1943 (as agreed in July 1942) was not a practicable operation of war after all. But it had taken Brooke's utmost powers of persistent argument to convince Churchill that to launch 'Roundup' in 1943 would invite catastrophic failure. From the very moment when the original decision for 'Torch' was reached in July 1942, the Prime Minister had refused to accept that opting for 'Torch' in 1942 ruled out 'Roundup' in 1943, as Marshall for one had already feared must be the case. Instead Churchill had optimistically envisaged a two-handed strategy against Germany, punching with the right through the Mediterranean and with the left across the Channel.[5]

By October 1942 he had come to see 'Roundup' as following after a further development of 'blue water' strategy in the Mediterranean once the occupation of Tunisia consummated the objectives of 'Operation Torch'. The Allies, he minuted to the Chiefs of Staff, would then be in a position

> . . . to attack the underbelly of the Axis at whatever may be the softest point, i.e., Sicily, Southern Italy or perhaps Sardinia; or again, if circumstances warrant, or, as they may do, compel, the French Riviera or perhaps even, with Turkish aid, the Balkans. However this may turn out, and it is silly to try to peer too far ahead, our war until the summer of 1943 will be waged in the Mediterranean theatre.[6]

An each-way bet then – more 'blue water' strategy *and* later in 1943 a Continental campaign in France by means of 'Roundup'.

The Prime Minister was therefore much peeved when the Chiefs of Staff replied with a powerful report arguing that 'Roundup' would not be a practicable operation of war in 1943, and must wait until 1944: 'Sufficient experience has already been gained [i.e., at Dieppe] that it will not be tactically possible to establish and maintain a large Allied Army in France until German military power has been undermined . . .'[7] In the opinion of the COS, only the Red Army on the Eastern Front could achieve this: 'It cannot be too clearly recognised that it is the war in Russia which is most rapidly sapping Germany's strength.' They therefore saw the Red Army as 'the primary means by which the German army can be defeated on land'. It followed that Anglo-American operations in 1943 must be 'shaped so as to assist Russia . . .'

The COS listed the means of assistance: the bomber offensive against the German industrial machine; copious military supplies via Persia and the Arctic convoys (see below, Chapter 23); subsidiary campaigns in the Mediterranean to draw off German strength. 'In short,' summed up the COS, 'it should be possible to turn the

Mediterranean as a whole, and Italy in particular, into an immense liability for Germany . . .' Thanks to the Red Army as assisted in these ways by the Western Allies, the German Army could be weakened enough to make 'Roundup' a runner in 1944.

But Churchill did not readily give up 'Roundup' for 1943. He reminded the COS that, by the original deal with the Americans in July 1942, there were supposed to be 27 United States and 21 British divisions ready in the United Kingdom by April 1943 to launch an invasion of France, along with the necessary landing craft. Since 'Torch' had absorbed only 13 divisions, the hoped-for Anglo-American offensive effort had been effectively cut by 35 divisions. 'There is a frightful gap,' wrote the Prime Minister, 'between what the Chiefs of Staff contemplated as reasonable in the summer of 1942 for the campaign of 1943 and what they now say we can do in that campaign.'[8]

And he went on: 'We have in fact pulled in our horns to an almost incredible extent, and I cannot imagine what the Russians will say or do when they realise it. My own position is that I am still aiming at a "Roundup" retarded until August [1943] . . .'[9]

The successful Russian counter-stroke at Stalingrad in November 1942 encouraged Churchill in his hopes for 'Roundup' in 1943 for, as he pointed out to the COS, no longer would the Germans be able to transfer divisions from the East to meet an invasion in the West, 'a new fact of the first magnitude'.[10] Assuming that present operations in the Mediterranean could be wound up by June 1943, he wanted all shipping and landing craft back in Britain by the end of that month so that 'Roundup' could be launched in August and September. He counted on fifteen to twenty US and British divisions (twelve of them armoured) then being available in the United Kingdom and another fifteen (five of them armoured) in the United States. But on his reckoning no fewer than 31 divisions (including French, New Zealand and Indian) would still be required in the Mediterranean. Here was a measure of the inescapable minimum continuing cost that must result from the original Allied decision to undertake 'Operation Torch'.

The Chiefs of Staff challenged his arithmetic, however. They reckoned that only thirteen British and American divisions (or seventeen at most) would be available for 'Roundup' in July 1943, as against 40 German divisions already in France, to say nothing of reserves elsewhere.[11] The Joint Planners had already calculated that only five extra divisions could be found for 'Roundup' if all Mediterranean operations were suspended.[12]

It is certain [wrote the COS] that our resources in manpower, shipping and landing craft are wholly inadequate to build up 'Torch', re-open the Mediterranean and carry out the operations we contemplate in the Mediterranean next spring and summer, in addition to 'Round-up' in July 1943.[13]

The total Allied expeditionary force in the United Kingdom by August 1943 would be only half the size of that originally deemed necessary, while only six divisions could be organised as an assault force because of limited shipping and landing craft lift. Even this lift, they wrote, could only be found by closing down all Mediterranean amphibious operations and cancelling a cherished Allied project for a seaborne invasion of southern Burma ('Anakim'). Meanwhile the Russians would have to fight on alone for the first eight months of the year before 'Roundup' could be launched.

The Chiefs of Staff wound up their memorandum with a heavy sales pitch in favour of pursuing instead 'blue water' strategy in the Mediterranean. They laid out for the Prime Minister an enticing array of possible operations – against Sardinia, Sicily or the toe of Italy, even Crete and the Dodecanese (so encouraging Turkey to abandon her neutrality). All of these, averred the COS, would serve to drain off German strength while at the same time the mere threat of invasion kept 40 German divisions pegged down in France. Such a strategy would also allow 'Anakim' (the Burma landing) to go ahead, and permit the Anglo-American bomber force in Britain to be vastly expanded.[14]

On 16 December 1942 the CIGS, General Sir Alan Brooke, expounded this paper to a COS meeting chaired by Churchill as Minister of Defence. Brooke in fact gave the meeting a veritable staff college lecture, complete with maps and diagrams, in order to show the rate at which enemy divisions could be switched from east to west by means of the 'magnificent lateral railway system'.[15] He compared this system with 'the two vulnerable lines leading south through Italy and the single track through Nish into Greece'. The minutes do not record that he similarly dilated on the long and circuitous Allied sea communications to actual or potential Mediterranean fronts, or on the needed shipping lift and naval deployment.

If, concluded Brooke, the Allies held 40 German divisions in France by threat of a comparatively small-scale invasion, 'and could at the same time force Italy out of the war and perhaps enter the Balkans, there was no doubt that this was the better strategy, from the Russian point of view, than for us to stake everything on "Roundup", which could, at best, afford Russia no relief before August . . .'

The First Sea Lord's only contribution to this crucial meeting which so much concerned the future employment of the Royal Navy was to remark that 'it was essential that the Americans should provide a share of the Naval Forces required for amphibious operations in the Mediterranean. There was a tendency at present for all American new construction to disappear into the Pacific . . .'[16]

Churchill, for his part, at last gave way to Brooke's pertinacious argument, saying that he 'found nothing to quarrel with in the COS paper . . .' and acknowledging that 'unless the Americans could vastly improve on the estimates [of their rate of build-up for 'Roundup'] in the Memorandum, he saw no alternative to the strategy recommended by the Chiefs of Staff . . .'[17] The meeting broke up with the Prime Minister's blessing to Brooke's proposals for major operations against Sicily or southern Italy aimed at knocking Italy out of the war.

It seemed as though the Chiefs of Staff, and Brooke in particular, had won, but, a fortnight later, Churchill put in a final counter-attack which hit the very nub of the whole grand-strategic issue of the relationship between reopening a Western Front and further pursuing a Mediterranean 'blue water' strategy:

> . . . unless . . . during the summer and autumn we *also* [emphasis added] engage the enemy from the West, we shall not be able to bring the most important part of our forces into play . . . Our resources in small shipping will not be utilised. The weight of the British Home Army and of the American forces to be gathered in Britain will not count. Thus we shall have failed to engage the enemy with our full strength, and may even fail to keep him pinned down in the West while we attack in the South.[18]

Marshall himself could not have put it better. But next day, 29 December 1942, the War Cabinet Defence Committee with Churchill in the chair nevertheless approved for transmission to Washington a 'Memorandum on Future Strategy' which fully endorsed the views of the Chiefs of Staff. The Memorandum stated that the defeat of the U-boat was to remain 'first charge on our resources' and placed second on the list the expansion of the bomber offensive. Third came 'the exploitation of our positions in the Mediterranean' with a view to knocking Italy out of the war and bringing Turkey into it; and fourth the maintenance of supplies to Russia. Subject to these and other prior claims on resources, such as limited offensives in Burma and the Pacific, there was to be (according to an extra paragraph inserted by the Defence Committee) the greatest possible build-up of forces in the United Kingdom with a view to 're-entry' on the Continent in August or September 1943, 'should conditions hold out a good prospect . . .'[19]

This last inserted phrase reflected the Prime Minister's deep reluctance to abandon 'Roundup' altogether for 1943, but it was no more than a sop to him. So far as the British were concerned, 'Roundup' in 1943 was dead; the 'push' of existing commitments in the Mediterranean coupled with the 'pull' of enticing future prospects there had finally rendered the further pursuit of 'blue water' strategy irresistible.

What the prolonged debate had left almost entirely out of account, however, was the likely tonnage of merchant shipping needed to sustain extended operations in the Mediterranean; where that tonnage was to be found in the midst of a world shipping crisis; and at what cost in other directions, such as imports into Britain, the feeding of the Middle East and the averting of famine in India. To quote the official historian of merchant shipping in the Second World War, 'most of the British commitments were entered into without calculating the cost in ships . . . Yet at this time the stringency was so acute that the Ministry of War Transport was haggling over single ships on the routes to India and the Middle East . . .'[20]

The British went to Casablanca knowing that they would have a battle on their hands, for on 23 December 1942 the American Joint Chiefs of Staff had despatched to London a memorandum, 'Basic Strategic Concept for 1943', which stood in fundamental contradiction to the strategy Brooke had successfully sold to Churchill. For General George Marshall wanted even now, despite the Allied commitment to 'Torch', to arrest if he could the slide deeper and deeper into what he saw as a peripheral theatre of war. He wanted instead to pull Allied strategy back to the Clausewitzian principle of concentration of force at the decisive point. The JCS memorandum therefore called for the 'primary effort of the United Nations' to be 'directed against Germany rather than her satellite states'.[21]

This effort was to take the form of a bomber offensive 'on the largest practical scale' against German war production from bases in Britain and North Africa, coupled with building up 'as rapidly as possible adequate balanced forces in the United Kingdom in preparation for a land offensive against Germany in 1943'. The memorandum recommended closing down Mediterranean operations (except for bombers based there) once North Africa had been cleared, and transferring all surplus forces back to Britain for 'Roundup'. In short, Marshall advocated 'the strategic offensive with maximum forces in the Atlantic–Western European theatre directly against Germany at the earliest practicable date'.[22]

With so vast a gulf between the two Allies' concepts of grand strategy to bridge, it is no wonder that Brooke was to write to his wife afterwards: 'I have seldom had a harder week or one with a heavier strain.'[23] Yet in the Combined Chiefs of Staff committee sessions Marshall from the start was in the weaker position. *'C'est le premier pas qui coûte'*; and that step had been taken in July 1942 with the original decision for 'Torch'. The second step now became all too inevitable. As Marshall admitted, 'one of the strongest arguments for undertaking such an operation [as landing in Sardinia or Sicily] is that there will be an excess of troops in North Africa once Tunisia has been cleared of Axis forces'.[24] Against Brooke's eloquent repetition of the same arguments that had worn down Churchill earlier, Marshall could only fight a rearguard action, asking Brooke and his colleagues whether the Mediterranean strategy was to be a means to an end or an end in itself. Was it simply opportunism, he wished to know, or was it part of an integrated plan to win the war? Brooke had his well-rehearsed answer to this of course. He deftly soothed Marshall's fear of 'interminable operations' in the Mediterranean by warning that the Allies should be very careful about invading Italy, even in support of an anti-fascist coup. Nonetheless Churchill in the previous November had already scorned Sicily or Sardinia as an ultimate Mediterranean objective and instead looked beyond to 'a decisive attack on Italy'.[25]

And so Marshall finally came to accept Brooke's contention that the forces available for 'Roundup' in 1943 were insufficient to offer hope of success, that it was better therefore, in Brooke's words, 'definitely to count on re-entering the Continent in 1944 on a large scale',[26] and in 1943 to exploit Mediterranean possibilities instead. Of these Roosevelt for his part liked best a landing in Sicily. The conference duly settled for this operation, codenamed 'Husky'. It was Marshall himself who explained to Roosevelt and Churchill when they met the Combined Chiefs of Staff that he and his colleagues had agreed to undertake 'Husky' 'because we will have in North Africa a large number of troops available . . .'[27] – in other words that the Allies were once again to wage war as they must rather than as they ought.

Only in a later session, concerned not with grand strategy but with the particular operational problems of the war against the U-boat, did the conference touch on the implications of 'Husky' in regard to shipping and naval escorts. The First Sea Lord took the opportunity to warn his colleagues that they might be trying to have it both ways, in that the decision to go ahead with amphibious operations in the Mediterranean as well as in the Pacific was not compatible with the principle that 'the defeat of the U-boat remains first charge on resources'.[28] Pound's apprehensions were to be borne out at the end of February when Eisenhower reported that, if 'Husky' were to be launched in June, he would need enough extra shipping, including 30 merchant ships, to carry an additional 38,000 soldiers earmarked for the expeditionary force.[29]

On 24 January the 'Symbol' circus left town by aircraft and ship, the star turns generally well satisfied with the final agreed memorandum on 'The Conduct of the War in 1943', which was based on a subtle compromise drafted by that wily diplomat of an airman, John Slessor.[30] 'Ernie' King was given essentially all he needed for his Pacific theatre; Dudley Pound had the defeat of the U-boat confirmed as the Allies' first priority; 'Hap' Arnold, the US Chief of Air Staff, and Charles Portal had 'the heaviest possible bomber offensive' confirmed as the Allies' main direct mode of attack on Germany in 1943; Brooke the ringmaster carried away the strategic box-office. Marshall for his part could only stifle his mistrust of British commitment to an eventual cross-Channel invasion and resolve that, whatever happened, Brooke's 'blue water' strategy would not be allowed to wander further than Sicily.

In the meantime the Allies still remained far from even fulfilling the objectives of 'Torch'.

On 12 February 1943, the second anniversary of Rommel's arrival in Africa, the rearguards of Panzerarmee Afrika retreated across the Libyan frontier into Tunisia, so closing the Desert campaign as such. It can be said that, except for his one major error, that of trying to reach Alexandria in the summer of 1942, Rommel had mounted one of the most successful diversionary campaigns in history. He had been sent to Libya in January 1941 simply to rescue the defeated Italians and hold the British off in a passive defensive. By his genius for taking risks and leading marvellous spoiling offensives, by the power of his own striking personality, he had wonderfully played on the obsession of the British with the Middle East, inducing them (and especially Churchill) to pump ever larger forces, ever more tanks and guns and aircraft into the effort to beat him – which equally meant an ever increasing procession of convoys trundling 13,000 miles round the Cape and up the Red Sea from Britain. By his domination of the Libyan coastline (and, except for brief intervals, the Cyrenaican airbases) he had stretched the Mediterranean Fleet to the limit in its attempts to keep Malta going. Rommel had, in sum, kept in play the major active war-waging effort of the British Empire for two years – and all with a shipping lift across the Mediterranean narrows that had been the merest fraction of the comparable British shipping investment; all with just three (later four) under-strength German divisions and some largely second-rate Italian formations. This and not the equivalent British Middle East and Mediterranean campaign had proved the profitable exercise in 'blue water' strategy; an irony of which British myth takes little account.

On 14–22 February 1943 Rommel's and Arnim's now united forces launched a major offensive westwards through the Tunisian mountain passes. Though compromised by Arnim's cautious orthodoxy, the offensive dealt a heavy blow on green American formations (this was Rommel in the Battle of the Kasserine Pass), and temporarily threw the Allied armies into disarray. Up to this point, therefore, the Axis intervention in Tunisia in opposition to 'Torch' had likewise proved a profitable diversionary exercise, bogging the Allied expeditionary force down in stalemate and dislocating the Allies' timetable for the clearance of North Africa. Moreover, it had compelled them to invest nearly twice the expected monthly total of ships in order to sustain the protracted land operations; between D-Day on 8 November 1942 and 12 March 1943 'Torch' had demanded the colossal cumulative total of 8,029,929 tons of shipping.[31]

But the successful spoiling offensive of 14–22 February marked the moment when a wise Axis leadership would have decided to liquidate its investment in Tunisia before superior Allied strength by land, sea and air could trap and destroy the German and Italian armies. However, Hitler, as is the way with political leaders when wars are going badly, had already got into the suicidal habit at Stalingrad and Alamein of ordering his forces to stand fast and fight to the bitter end. From March to the beginning of May 1943 von Arnim (Rommel had gone home sick) fought on obediently while the Royal Navy sought to throttle his sea communications.

In Cunningham's judgment, the Royal Air Force in the Mediterranean was still not being as helpful or effective in supporting the Navy in this task as it ought. He reported to the First Sea Lord on 15 March 1943 that he had 'had a collision with Tedder over a sea striking force permanently attached to the Coastal Group and he gave way'. But this was not the only difficulty:

The Air have reached the decision that no reconnaissance over the

Sicilian narrows in daylight is possible with which I don't agree and the reconnaissance in the Tyrrhenian Sea is still quite inadequate.

Fortunately we get on very well with the Americans who are always ready to place squadrons at our disposal. They seem to realise the importance of sinking ships *at sea* much better than do our R.A.F.

The Coastal Group *will* function satisfactorily but it's hard slogging getting them going. Neglect to make an all weather aerodrome between Bône and Algiers is also exposing our shipping to most unnecessary risks. Yesterday, Sunday, the cruisers and the L.S.I.s carrying troops to Bône spent the day dodging torpedoes fired by T/B aircraft boldly within 10 miles of our coast. Eisenhower has got on to this himself and his Chief Engineer has orders to give this aerodrome first priority.[32]

But gradually, as the Axis air effort waned and the Allied air effort grew and the Royal Navy's little ships hunted for victims, von Arnim's shortfall of supplies of every kind grew more and more crippling. On 6 May the Allied armies (now the 18th Army Group, under the command of General Sir Harold Alexander) launched their final onslaught against the Axis bridgehead, burst through after an initial repulse, and took Bizerta and Tunis. On the 12th von Arnim surrendered with some 230,000 men (of which about 100,000 were German). Very few enemy troops had attempted to escape by sea in the face of the destroyers and light craft scraped up by Cunningham from all over the Mediterranean and deployed in 'Operation Retribution' with the order: 'Sink, burn and destroy. Let nothing pass.'[33] Nor did the Italian Navy emulate the Royal Navy's self-sacrifice off Greece and Crete in 1941 and attempt to rescue von Arnim's stranded soldiers.

So at long last, by gift of Hitler's misjudgment, had arrived the crowning triumph of 'Torch' and indeed of the entire campaign along the North African shore since June 1940; and at long last too, after all the fleet actions and all the convoy battles, the Mediterranean lay open again to through military traffic. The first such convoy passed the Straits of Gibraltar on 17 May, and steamed into Alexandria harbour on the 26th. Two days earlier the first convoy to make an unopposed voyage to Malta since Italy's declaration of war reached the island.

By now planning for 'Operation Husky', the invasion of Sicily, was well in hand; its original target date the June new moon period.

21

The Invasion of Sicily: 'Operation Husky'

The Combined Chiefs of Staff Committee had set up the higher command structure for 'Operation Husky' at the 'Symbol' Conference in Casablanca. Eisenhower was again to be Allied Commander-in-Chief, with Air Marshal Sir Arthur Tedder (previously British AOC-in-C, Middle East) as his air C-in-C, General Sir Harold Alexander (currently commanding the 18th Army Group in Tunisia) as ground forces C-in-C, and Admiral Sir Andrew Cunningham once again his naval C-in-C.

On 20 February 1943 the Admiralty had reorganised the British naval commands in the Mediterranean, with Cunningham hoisting his flag for the second time as Commander-in-Chief, Mediterranean, and Admiral Harwood becoming C-in-C of a new Levant Command. The boundary between the two commands ran north from the frontier between Tunisia and Tripolitania to 35°N, 16°E, and thence to Cape Spartivento on the toe of Italy.

In March the Admiralty in any case relieved Harwood on the grounds of ill-health, largely because of an intrigue against him by General Montgomery, the 8th Army Commander. Montgomery had conceived a spite for the corpulent Harwood, a man who – although Pound's and Churchill's choice – certainly lacked the mental and physical drive desirable for the job. Alleging slothfulness and neglect on the Royal Navy's part in opening up the port of Tripoli, and on the score that the Army had lost confidence in Harwood, Montgomery virtually demanded that he should go. As so often with Montgomery's tales out of school, the record does not bear out these allegations.[1] Nevertheless once doubts about Harwood's capacity had been conveyed to Pound via the Prime Minister, Pound was quick to sack him. As Cunningham was to write privately after the war, 'I fear D.P. was inclined to condemn officers, without hearing what they had to say, in reply to reports and rumours backstairs and otherwise.'[2]

Planning for 'Husky', from its very start in mid-February 1943, yawed rudderless while on the bridge all was argument, confusion and increasingly bad blood. Until May Eisenhower, Cunningham, Tedder and Alexander had their minds and energies almost entirely engaged in the conduct of the Tunisian campaign. This was also true of the designated military commanders of the Western and Eastern Task Forces, Generals Patton and Montgomery. Meanwhile an undirected and relatively junior team of planners, entitled 'Force 141' and set up in Algiers on 10 February, struggled on unhappily to produce an acceptable outline plan. It hardly helped that the nucleus Western Task Force headquarters lay in Rabat, Morocco, while the equivalent Eastern Task Force headquarters lay in Cairo (where the Naval Commander, Eastern Task Force, Admiral Sir Bertram Ramsay, had hoisted his flag on 2 March). Moreover, other planners in Washington and London also had their say in the steering of 'Husky' plans, because some American troops were to travel directly from the United States and some British and Canadian troops directly from the United Kingdom.

All this fell far short of an ideal way to tackle for the first time the problem of mounting assault landings on the grand scale against German and Italian opposition; a very different prospect from the Vichy French. Montgomery, a clear-headed military realist if ever there was one, was reckoning in April that they 'must plan the operation on the assumption that resistance will be fierce and that a prolonged dogfight will follow the initial assault'.[3] A month earlier Eisenhower even conveyed to the British Chiefs of Staff and the American Joint Chiefs of Staff his own and his fellow Commanders-in-Chief's convictions that 'if substantial German ground troops should be placed in the region prior to the attack, the chances for success become practically nil and the project should be abandoned'.[4] This fainthearted signal blew into flame the Premier's always smouldering fighting spirit, and he blazed out at the Chiefs of Staff:

... if the presence of two German divisions is held to be decisive against any operation of an offensive or amphibious character open to the million men now in North Africa, it is difficult to see how the war can be carried on . . . I trust the Chiefs of Staff will not accept these pusillanimous and defeatist doctrines, from whoever they come . . . I regard the matter as serious in the last degree . . . What Stalin would think of this, when he has 185 German divisions on his front I cannot imagine . . .[5]

In due course the Combined Chiefs of Staff signalled their own displeasure to Eisenhower, who meekly replied that he and his colleagues would prosecute 'Husky' 'with all means at our disposal. There is no thought here except to carry out our orders to the ultimate of our ability . . .'[6]

But fighting spirit alone did not supply answers to the problems of successfully landing in Sicily. A balance had to be struck between clashing service interests. Tedder and Cunningham both wanted the cluster of airfields in the south-western corner of Sicily to be captured early on in order to deprive the enemy of air striking power over the invasion shipping and the beach-heads. They could hardly forget that it was from Sicilian fields that the Luftwaffe had so successfully dominated the central Mediterranean since spring 1941. Moreover Cunningham wished landings to be made at widely separated points round the eastern and western coasts of Sicily in order to exploit the flexibility of seapower and so distract the enemy ground forces.

In late March 'Force 141' produced its own outline plan for landings by three British divisions at several points strung along 100 miles of the southern coast from Syracuse round to Gela, while an American division went ashore on the west coast some 60 miles distant from the nearest British beach-head. On D + 2 another American landing was to take place near Palermo in the north-west of the island, and on D + 3 a further British landing on the west coast at Catania. Because of its dispersion and its promise of early capture of enemy air fields, both Cunningham and Tedder rather liked this plan. So too did Eisenhower and Alexander. It was therefore duly approved in principle.

However, when Montgomery learned in mid-March about the plan it was the very dispersion that horrified him. He signalled Alexander: 'In my opinion the operation breaks every common-sense rule of practical battle fighting and is completely theoretical. It has no hope of success and should be completely re-cast.'[7] It was, and remained, Montgomery's conviction that 'To operate dispersed means disaster'[8]; and he began to use all the power of his ruthless will to rescue 'Husky' from being in his words 'a real dog's breakfast' and 'a very high-class mess'.

Fortunately Admiral Ramsay in Cairo and Major-General Miles Dempsey, the corps commander deputed by Montgomery to work with him, got on well, as Ramsay confided to his wife in a letter of 19 March: 'I like my general immensely and we see eye to eye on things, which makes life easier. But we don't see eye to eye in all things with those above us! . . .'[9] In particular Ramsay did not see eye to eye with his Commander-in-Chief, Andrew Cunningham, who, superb fighting sailor in command of a fleet though he was, now showed serious limitations in terms of an inter-service amphibious operation of the new kind. In brief, he revealed himself as an old-fashioned and authoritarian centraliser. As Ramsay expressed it in his letter home on 19 March:

A.B.C. has his own very definite views, which are based on wishful thinking rather than facts. His judgment is excellent but his facts are often wrong. There may be trouble later on, owing to his way of centralising command, in the same way as when he and I play together in Ping Pong he takes 4/5ths of the balls. He's very good too.[10]

The problem, exacerbated by distance and communication by signal, grew trickier. On 7 April 1943 Ramsay was writing to his wife:

I am not awfully happy about the way things are taking shape between A.B.C. and his party and myself and mine. I find him most unsympathetic towards suggestions put up to him, making it appear as though he was at pains to find an excuse to knock them down instead of a way of meeting them. The fact is that he wants to keep everything very tight in his own hands and doesn't welcome suggestion or anything that doesn't emanate from himself and his staff. It will lead to a cleavage sooner or later, which is most undesirable. It seems that he regards anything to do with Combined operations as anathema & that the R.N. must keep well clear & all to themselves. I on the other hand have had diametrically opposite views and consider the army & Navy as one for thinking, planning and action. He is of the 'true blue' school and I suppose I am not. I hope for the avoidance of trouble but am afraid it is going to be difficult.[11]

Trouble shortly arrived, when Cunningham, in Ramsay's words, allowed

the army [that is, the military staffs in Algeria] to make plans without prior consultation with the Navy and in particular accepting plans which I should have to carry out, without my knowing anything about it . . . In this respect I was confronted a few days ago with a plan which had been concocted and approved right up to the highest plane; in fact a 'fait accompli'.[12]

The plan in question represented the latest attempt by the staffs in Algeria to amend the original strategy in order to assuage Montgomery's horror of dispersion, and it too had won the approval of Eisenhower, Alexander, Tedder and Cunningham. Ramsay was so horrified at its operational implications that he protested to Cunningham, who replied that the plan had his full approval – 'meaning,' wrote Ramsay, 'that he had not properly gone into it'.[13]

> At the end of a long passage [he] added grudgingly that if I liked to try and persuade a certain prominent person [Montgomery] to change it I might do so! I did try and got his immediate & hearty consent (& almost thanks) and have just had the great satisfaction of telling him [Cunningham] so. But the work entailed in changing the plan now is almost heartbreaking to the wretched staffs. If only I'd been consulted at the right time & the plan made jointly or if A.B.C.'s staff had done their job properly the necessity would never have arisen.[14]

Montgomery, with Ramsay's full concurrence, now produced a completely novel plan by which his 8th Army was to land shoulder to shoulder in a single extended lodgement on the eastern coast of Sicily south of Syracuse. This entailed abandoning the proposed British landings in the Gulf of Gela in the south-west, aimed at quickly securing three vital airfields. Incensed by all the bumbling, Montgomery added to the brief statement of his plan a crisp ultimatum that 'I have given the orders that so far as the army is concerned all planning and work is now to go ahead along the lines indicated'.[15]

Montgomery's thinking might be clear and his action decisive, but his personality now served to obstruct rather than further his purpose, which Ramsay sought as best he could to overcome by judicious lubrication:

> Monty has thrown a spanner of considerable size into the works & in doing so has caused almost complete disruption of work besides increasing, if possible, his unpopularity. It is really most unfortunate that he should do so many things that make him unpopular and so few the contrary. It means, naturally, that I have all the time to try & modify his remarks to suit his audience & it is curious how quite unable he is to see the effect he causes or in fact to care in the least what that effect is. It requires all the tact I can gather in to deal with him in this way, though he and I are on the best possible terms. I have got him just where I want him as regards the Navy & there is complete understanding between us. I can however foresee that he will for ever be putting me in the midst of most difficult circumstances which, with someone like A.B.C., produces difficulties I would prefer to avoid. It's all a great pity for Monty is a great success.

[631]

The trouble is that he adopts the attitude that he is now omnipotent.[16]

Cunningham did indeed take exception to Montgomery's new plan, judging it to be 'unsound' partly because it left the airfields in enemy hands, 'and we are landing from a mass of shipping a mere thirty miles off', partly because it 'also seems to surrender our greatest asset – that of being able to assault the island in numerous places at once at will'.[17] Yet in his retrospective report on 'Husky' to Eisenhower in 1944 he followed Ramsay in acknowledging that the fundamental principle of amphibious warfare must be that

> . . . a combined operation is but the opening, under particular circumstances, of a purely army battle. It is the function of the navy and of the air to help the army establish a base or bases on the hostile coast from which the military tactical battle to gain the object must be developed. It is upon the army tactical plan for the fulfilment of its object that the combined plan must depend. The navy and the air commanders must join with the army commander to ensure that the base or bases for seizure are capable of achievement without prohibitive loss in their respective elements, and that, when seized, they will fulfil the requirements of the force; but it is of no use to plan on the seizure of bases unrelated to the realities of the military situation when ashore.[18]

This exactly mirrored the views of Admiral Ramsay, the acknowledged master planner of amphibious operations, who had agreed from the first with Montgomery over 'Husky'.

It was therefore entirely proper that Montgomery's clear-cut military plan should prevail; and impossible in retrospect not to applaud his insistence on concentration instead of dispersion. But the resentment which he aroused in other equally strong personalities contributed yet another complicating factor in a planning process already bedevilled by human as well as purely operational problems. On 28 April Cunningham complained to the First Sea Lord that 'Montgomery is a bit of a nuisance; he seems to think that all he needs to do is to say what needs to be done and everyone will dance to the tune of his pipings'.[19] Cunningham went on:

> But the seriousness of it all is that here we are with no fixed agreed plan, just over two months off D-day and the commanders all at sixes and sevens, and even if we do get a final agreement, someone will be operating a plan he doesn't fully agree with. Not the way to make a success of an operation . . .[20]

It worsened the impasse that Eisenhower as overall Commander-in-Chief chose to act the role of remote chairman of the board, while Alexander, his ground forces commander, was a man weak of will and dim of brain who would take no decisive lead.

This collective vacuum in leadership Montgomery took it upon himself to fill, and just as well he did. At a meeting in Algiers at the end of April he convinced Eisenhower and his Chief of Staff, Bedell Smith, of the merits of a revised version of his own plan. As Ramsay reported to his wife with qualified jubilation: 'We managed to get our way, however, in Algiers which has simplified things though causing us and everyone else an immense amount of work . . .'[21] Under Montgomery's new plan the American landings near Palermo would be abandoned altogether in favour of one in the Gulf of Gela only twenty miles distant from the 8th Army's left flank. This would make it possible to capture early the south-western airfields of so much concern to Tedder and Cunningham while, at the same time, both Allied armies would be enabled to consolidate a strong single lodgement astride the southern tip of Sicily from which to break out later. Montgomery conceived that it would be he who did this breaking out (towards Catania) with Patton acting as his left flank guard. In the event Patton's thrusting leadership was to make its own comment on this wishful thinking.

The major drawback with Montgomery's plan lay in that instead of Patton's 7th Army being able quickly to make use of the port of Palermo, it would for a time have to be supplied with 3,000 tons of stores a day over open beaches, which Admiral Hewitt (Naval Commander, Western Task Force) doubted could be done. Moreover the nature of the plan, reducing Patton to a secondary role, and the pushy manner by which Montgomery successfully sold it, left Hewitt and Patton 'very sore', in Cunningham's words.[22]

On 12 May the plan, already blessed by Eisenhower and Alexander, was formally approved by the Combined Chiefs of Staff at the Washington ('Trident') Conference – three months after the 'Symbol' Conference at Casablanca, and only two months before 'Husky's' currently projected launch date in July. With all the detailed operational plans for this daunting triphibious operation still to be worked out, time was houndingly short. Ramsay wrote that although his staff was 'excellent' it was 'proving too small and some members are grossly overworked. Compared with Monty's staff mine are in the proportion of about 1 to 8. The army doesn't know what work is for us.'[23]

In January 1943 the Joint Intelligence Committee in London had guesstimated that, after the conclusion of the Tunisian campaign, enemy strength in Sicily could rise by the time of the landings to between five and eight field divisions, of which two or three could be German, and that reinforcements by ferry across the Straits of Messina could reach a total of one German and one and a half Italian divisions per week.[24] These guesstimates governed Allied planning, which throughout was based on the need for an expeditionary force of at least eight divisions. This figure in turn determined the quantity of shipping and landing craft that would be required – no fewer than 1,365 warships and merchant ships and 715 British and 510 American landing craft; a grand total of 2,590 ships and craft of all descriptions for the operation itself and thereafter for the expeditionary force's seaborne logistics. In the event the total was to climb close to 3,000.[25]

That various portions of the expedition were to sail from the United States and Britain as well as from Mediterranean bases as widely separated as Egypt and Tunisia immensely complicated the staff problems both of concentrating the assault forces off the coast of Sicily and also of training the troops and crews. In particular, Bizerta and Tunis, the bases for the Western Task Force (American), only fell into Allied hands on 12 May, and much damage had then to be repaired. A section of the Eastern Task Force faced similar problems at Sfax and Sousse. Moreover a very large number of landing ships and craft new to the theatre had to be received and allotted base facilities, while their officers and crews (many of them newly recruited and trained) had to be put through crash training programmes in the specialised task of disembarking troops on beaches. Their initial inexperience caused some temporary wavering in the soldiers' confidence in the sailors.

The problems of training and rehearsal were worsened because vessels such as landing ships (tank) were late to arrive in the theatre, and crews had little opportunity to practise with the pontoons by which tanks were transferred to shore.[26] A further handicap to training lay in the need to employ landing craft in heavy and continuous running simply in order to transport troops, airmen and vehicles from widely scattered points round the Mediterranean to the assembly bases for the attack. Would the landing crafts' engines stand the strain? According to Cunningham later, 'These fears were happily disproved, and in fact the sea training provided by these voyages must have stood them [the crews] in good stead. That the craft themselves withstood the extra wear and tear is a tribute to those who designed and built them.'[27]

The problem of repair and maintenance of these overworked craft before the launch of 'Husky' was aggravated by what Cunningham called 'one of the most disappointing things, pre "Husky"'[28] – that 'not a single one of all the landing craft maintenance equipment, docks, slips, etc, etc, functioned before the operation . . .'

> The craft were only just got ready by suspending repairs and maintenance to every other type of vessel in every port in North Africa and Malta and Gibraltar. If it had not been for this and for a most astonishing and, to me, previously unknown tidal rise and fall of 8 ft at Sfax, which enabled us to dock the landing craft on a sand bank, we should have been badly caught.[29]

A military decision that airborne forces must serve as a key to quick seizure of lodgements ashore further complicated the task of Cunningham, Ramsay and Hewitt and their staffs. In plotting the complex routing tables for the assault convoys from their various bases they had to leave corridors clear for the flight paths of Allied transports in order to avoid confusion with enemy aircraft, and possible mistaken anti-aircraft fire by Allied ships. The intended use of airborne forces also made the navies' role more difficult in regard to the timing of the actual assaults, for while moonlit nights were needed for the parachute drops and glider landings, the navies would have preferred a new-moon period, giving them the cover of darkness against air attack during the initial run-in and on every night thereafter. On the finally decided launch date for 'Husky', 10 July 1943, there would be a waxing moon which set about 0200, with full moon on the 17th.[30] In the event, the airborne troops were not employed as originally in-tended, but the change was made too late for the timing of the landings to be altered. The navies therefore had to operate at night in disadvantageous light conditions for no good purpose. Admiral Kent Hewitt in his report on 'Husky' was to vent angry criticism of the decision to time seaborne landings according to the needs of airborne troops, and Cunningham agreed with him, writing:

> A seaborne assault is unalterably committed to a date for some days in advance of D-day. In tidal waters it is even more inflexibly bound by time and tide. It may well be that, on the selected date, airborne troops are weatherbound and cannot operate. It does therefore appear most necessary that airborne troops should be considered as a useful auxiliary rather than as a governing factor which may react to the disadvantage of other services . . .[31]

More generally, the air plans for 'Husky' appeared all along to the naval commanders to be, in Cunningham's phrase, 'somewhat nebulous'.[32] It did not help that Tedder and his HQ remained at La

Marsa in Tunisia, while the naval and ground forces Cs-in-C moved to Malta.

Also to be dovetailed into the overall plan were naval covering forces against the Italian battlefleet. Although its morale and state of training were known to be low, it still remained formidable enough in numbers – six battleships, seven cruisers, 48 destroyers and torpedo boats, 50 submarines (plus twenty German U-boats) and some 115 Italian and 30 to 35 German E-boats.[33] 'It must be recognised,' stated Cunningham's 'Husky Orders Naval', 'that if it is ever going to fight, it must fight now in defence of its country . . .'[34]

And finally all aspects of the 'Husky' deployment had to be planned so that they fitted in with the deception plan being sold to the enemy – that the Allies were intending to land in Greece.[35] Cunningham therefore instructed that in order to disguise the direction of attack the concentrating of ships in the central Mediterranean should be delayed as long as possible, while the 'approach march' of assault forces from great distances to their assembly areas were to conform with the normal pattern of through Mediterranean convoys. Yet further complications were posed to the planners by the bottleneck through the Tunisian channel, and by the need to schedule movements so that escort vessels could refuel before they finally deployed for the landings.

On 20 May 1943 Cunningham issued the bulky 'Husky Orders Naval' ('HON') which embodied the meticulously thorough answers to this whole vast and intricate strategic conundrum. In the opening words of the Introduction to 'HON', 'This is a large and complicated operation involving in all the movement of some 2500 ships and major landing craft. The operational orders are necessarily voluminous.'[36] It had taken twenty typists seven days to type the originals, after which 800 copies had to be run off.[37] In his own words in reporting to Eisenhower in January 1944:

> Very detailed orders were issued regarding the routes and timing of the approach, backed up by track charts and the inevitable 'Mickey Mouse' diagrams which are in my view essential to the clear understanding of a problem of this nature. Even so, everything depended, as always, on the seamanship and good sense of individual commanding officers and on the smooth working of the berthing and fuelling organisations of the several ports concerned. My confidence in their abilities was not misplaced. The operation ran like a well-oiled clock.[38]

The sea movements began on 28 May when the first convoy from the United States for Oran and Algiers sailed with troops and stores for the Western Task Force. Between 20 June and 1 July two slow convoys (KMS18 and KMS19) and one fast convoy (KMF18), making up Force V, steamed out of the Clyde with tanks, stores and fuel for the Eastern Task Force. Movements within the Mediterranean itself got under way on 3 June, when the 30 motor transport stores ships, fifteen landing ships (tank), and two landing ships (gantry) of convoy MWS36 put to sea from Alexandria and headed westwards at an average speed of advance of 8 knots. Three more convoys from Alexandria followed on 6–9 July. These convoys, making up Force A of the Eastern Task Force, comprised in all 60 motor transport ships and 32 personnel ships, as well as fuel carriers and the fighter direction ship *Antwerp* (see below, p. 638). Only one vessel was lost on passage, falling victim to a U-boat off Derna on the Libyan coast.

Meanwhile the American assault convoys of the Western Task Force (TJS1, TJF1 and TJM1) had sailed from Bizerta and Sousse, and the convoys from the United States (NCF1 and NCF2) had put to sea again from Algiers and Oran. More than 800 major vessels were converging on the sea area south of Malta from west, south and east at speeds varying from 6 knots to 13, bearing with them some 115,000 British Empire and 66,000 American troops, together with a mass of tanks, artillery, motor transport, ammunition and every kind of stores: their purpose the destruction of two under-strength German panzer-grenadier divisions, four Italian field divisions (only one of which was fit for battle) and five Italian coastal divisions of largely low quality and poor equipment.[39]

By way of an overture to 'Husky' the Italian island base of Pantellaria west of Malta (the object of Churchill's cherished 'Workshop' project in 1940–41; see above, pp. 202–3 and 324) was attacked on 19 June. Allied bombers had already dropped 6,400 tons of bombs on it in three weeks; a lavish expenditure of ordnance on so tiny a target. On 10 July cruisers added their mite of high explosive, watched by Eisenhower and Cunningham from HMS *Aurora* (wearing Cunningham's Admiral of the Fleet's Union Flag). Next day the garrison of 11,000 war-weary Italians surrendered even before the landing craft could reach the harbour. The only Allied casualty was a British soldier bitten by a donkey. On the 12th the neighbouring island of Lampedusa also surrendered. The capture of Pantellaria not only removed a potential menace to Allied sea communications but it also provided a much needed extra advanced airbase from which Allied fighters could cover the 'Husky' landings.[40] Already 600 Allied fighters had been concentrated on Malta and its neighbouring island of

[637]

Gozo; a further belated return on the past British strategic investment in their defence.[41]

On 1 July 1943 Admiral Ramsay sailed from Alexandria to join Cunningham in Malta. At 0630 on 9 July, the eve of D-Day for 'Husky', he put to sea from Grand Harbour in a sun-sharp Mediterranean morning, white foam sparkling against the blue, in the fighter direction ship *Antwerp* (2,957 tons gross) in order to witness the culmination of his own and his staff's labours – the rendezvousing south of Malta between Force V from Britain, Force A from Egypt and Force B from Sousse, Sfax, Tripoli and Malta. At noon he assumed operational command of all these components of the Eastern Task Force. 'After the months of tiresome planning,' he wrote to his wife two days later, 'it is a treat to *do* things instead of write or talk about them.'[42] The past irritation of signals from Cunningham 'worded most rudely'[43] gave way to the exhilaration of being at sea 'with my flag flying'[44] and in command of a great enterprise.

In the course of the forenoon the wind had freshened; the landing craft loaded with soldiers on the haul from Sousse and Sfax began to pitch sickeningly in the short, steep sea for which the Malta channel is notorious, forcing them to slow down; and the flagship groaned in its twenty-four-year-old joints as it took the strain.

Far off, the covering forces to protect the expedition against the Italian battlefleet were already on station. Five submarines of the 8th Flotilla were patrolling on a line between Corsica and the Italian mainland in order to intercept any fleet units making sorties from the bases of La Spezia, Genoa or Leghorn, while three boats of the 10th Flotilla (including the Polish *Sokol*) lay north of the Strait of Messina and five more (including the Polish *Dzik*) were off Taranto watching out for the two battleships stationed there. Well away to the east of Sicily Force H (Vice-Admiral A. U. Willis), comprising the battleships *Nelson* (flag), *Rodney*, *Warspite* and *Valiant*, the fleet carriers *Indomitable* and *Formidable*, six light cruisers of the 12th Cruiser Squadron and eighteen destroyers, had concentrated in the Ionian Sea in order to protect the eastern flank of the landings from attack by Italian ships based on Taranto. As part of the cover plan, Force H feinted towards the west coast of Greece on 9 July (D − 1); then closed the assault area by dawn on D-Day. Force Z (Captain C. H. L. Woodhouse, RN), consisting of the battleships *Howe* and *King George V*, two cruisers and six destroyers, lay to the west of Sicily with the role of reserve force. Force K (four cruisers and six destroyers under Rear-Admiral C. H. J. Harcourt) was to provide close fire support to the landing operations of the Eastern Task Force.[45] Force Q (detached from

Force H) was to provide nightly cover to the north of the British landings.

The painstaking assembly of a maritime steamhammer was thus complete. How easily would the continental walnut crack? At the end of May GC and CS (Ultra) had broken into the teleprinter link between the German high command in Italy and the German Army high command (OKH), and from now on to the end of the Italian campaign in 1945 this was to yield even more comprehensive information than the Luftwaffe or Army Enigmas.[46] Thanks to such sources the Allies calculated with fair accuracy on the eve of 'Husky' that the Axis forces defending Sicily consisted of the Hermann Göring Division (a Luftwaffe field division), and the 15th Panzer-Grenadier Division, plus four Italian field divisions and five coastal.[47] Of the Italian field divisions only the Livorno was thought to be worth much, while the coastal division on the front of the Eastern Task Force's landings was known to be poorly equipped. The two German divisions had been divided into four battlegroups to act as stiffeners to the lacklustre Italians.

The Hermann Göring Division presented neither a great advertisement for its namesake nor for the German armed forces, for it had no battle experience and in the main its leadership was slack. However, in its commander, Lieutenant-General Paul Conrath, it enjoyed a standard issue German general – that is, experienced, thoroughly well trained, tough, resourceful. The 15th Panzer-Grenadier Division had only been cobbled together since its elements arrived in Sicily, but its commander, Major-General Eberhard Rodt, was another standard issue German general with similar attributes. The liaison officer to General Guzzoni, commanding the Italian 6th Army (responsible for the defence of Sicily) was General Frido von Senger und Etterlin, an outstanding soldier against whom the Allies were to break many lances in the Battle of Cassino.

Luftwaffe strength was calculated by Allied Intelligence to amount to 135 fighters in Sicily and 130 fighters and fighter-bombers in Sardinia (actual figures: some 300 fighters in Sicily and the toe of Italy, 70 in Sardinia, together with a total of some 130 fighter-bombers in the whole region).[48] As against this the Allied air forces deployed 4,328 aircraft of all kinds, including some 700 fighters based on Malta, Gozo and Pantellaria.[49]

Sigint guided the Allies in other important respects too. It revealed that the enemy had not been deceived by the Allied cover plan of a landing in Greece, but instead was correctly expecting an attack on Sicily, and along the southern and south-eastern coasts (though the

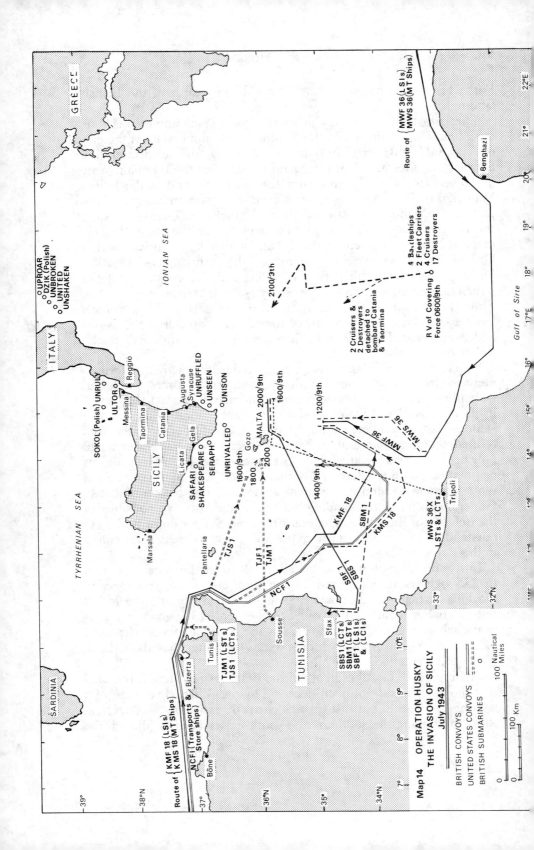

Map 14 OPERATION HUSKY
THE INVASION OF SICILY
July 1943

BRITISH CONVOYS
UNITED STATES CONVOYS
BRITISH SUBMARINES

100 Nautical
Miles

100 Km

GREECE

ITALY

SICILY

SARDINIA

TUNISIA

TYRRHENIAN SEA

IONIAN SEA

Gulf of Sirte

Benghazi

Tripoli

Sfax

Sousse

Tunis

Bizerta

Bône

Marsala

Pantellaria

Messina

Reggio

Taormina

Augusta

Syracuse

Catania

Gela

Licata

MALTA

Gozo

UPROAR
DZIK (Polish)
UNBROKEN
UNITED
UNSHAKEN

SOKOL (Polish) UNRULY
ULTOR

UNRUFFLED
UNSEEN
UNISON

SAFARI
SHAKESPEARE
SERAPH

UNRIVALLED

Route of {KMF 18 (LSI's)
{KMS 18 (MT Ships)

NCF1 (Transports &
Store ships)

TJM1 (LSTs)
TJS1 (LCTs)

SBS1 (LCTs)
SBM1 (LSTs)
SBF1 (LSIs)
& (LCIs)

TJS1
TJF1
TJM1
NCF1
SBF1
SBS1

KMF 18
SBM1
KMS 18

MWS 36X
LSTs & LCTs

1600/9th
1800
2000

1600/9th

1400/9th

1200/9th

2000/9th

MWS 36

MWF 36

2100/3th

2 Cruisers &
2 Destroyers
detached to
bombard Catania
& Taormina

R V of Covering
Force 0600/9th

4 Battleships
2 Fleet Carriers
4 Cruisers
17 Destroyers

Route of {MWF 36 (LSI's)
{MWS 36 (MT Ships)

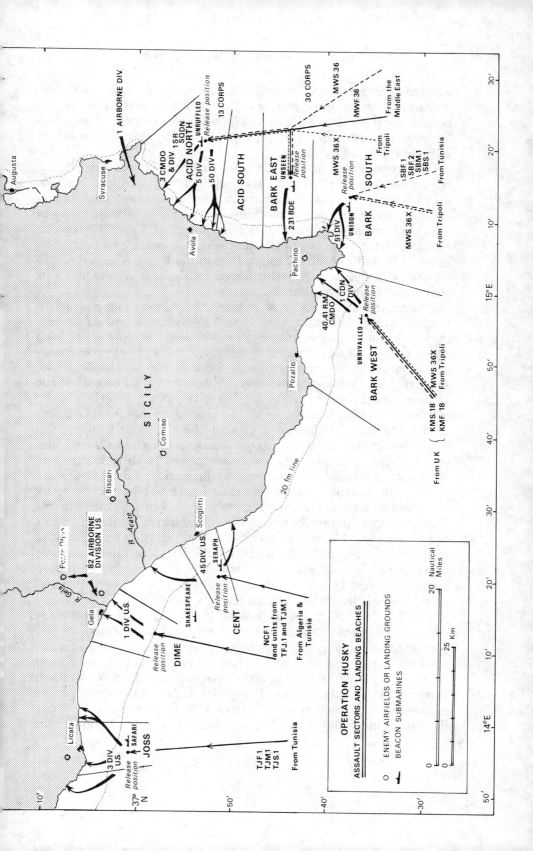

OPERATION HUSKY

ASSAULT SECTORS AND LANDING BEACHES

○ ENEMY AIRFIELDS OR LANDING GROUNDS

⚓ BEACON SUBMARINES

Nautical Miles

0 ———— 20

0 ———— 25 Km

1 AIRBORNE DIV.

3 CMDO & DIV
1 SR SQDN
UNRUFFLED

ACID NORTH
5 DIV
50 DIV

Release position
13 CORPS

ACID SOUTH

BARK EAST
231 BDE
UNSEEN

Release position

30 CORPS

MWS 36
MWF 36

From the Middle East

MWS 36X
From Tripoli

BARK SOUTH

SBF 1
SBF 2
SBM 1
SBS 1
From Tunisia

Release position

MWS 36X
From Tripoli

BARK
51 DIV
UNISON

40, 41 RM CMDO
CDN DIV
Release position

UNRIVALLED

BARK WEST

MWS 36X
From Tripoli

KMS 18
KMF 18
From UK

Syracuse
Augusta
Avola
Pachino

S I C I L Y

Comiso
Biscari
Scoglitti

Pozzallo

20 fm line

82 AIRBORNE DIVISION US

Ponte Olivo
R. Acate
Gela
R. Gela
Licata

45 DIV US
SERAPH
Release position

SHAKESPEARE

CENT

NCF1 and units from
TFJ.1 and TJM.1
From Algeria & Tunisia

1 DIV US
DIME
Release position

3 DIV US
SAFARI
JOSS
Release position

TJF.1
TJM.1
TJS.1
From Tunisia

37° N

50'

40'

30'

50'

10'

14°E

20'

30'

40'

50'

15°E

10'

20'

30'

western coast was not excluded). Allied Intelligence also knew from the latest decrypts of the medium-grade Italian C38M naval Enigma cypher that the enemy had ordered their forces to a state of readiness in the early evening of 9 July, having observed by air the approach of some of the assault convoys.[50]

Given that on top of all other deficiencies the German and Italian commands had failed to agree on a joint strategy for the defence of the island, the Axis was ill-prepared in every sense to meet an invasion of such weight and power as 'Husky'. Their one advantage lay in the classic strategic position of 'interior lines', with communications running back via the two to five-miles-wide Messina Strait and then direct road and rail links through Italy to the Reich – in contrast to the Allies' 'exterior lines', with forces and logistic communications converging from vast distances.

During the afternoon of 9 July, as the various components of the Western and Eastern Task Forces advanced according to their intricately woven net of routings towards the assembly areas from which the assault forces would be launched, the weather grew gradually worse, with the wind rising to force 6, and the landing craft struggling in a choppy sea to make 3½ knots.[51] In Force B of the Eastern Task Force the craft were driven to leeward, as well as losing formation in trying to make up for lost ground, so that the final stages of the approach 'resembled a general chase',[52] with landing craft (tank) arriving two hours late at the release position. In Force A also the majority of smaller craft were compelled to drop astern; and the Force commander, Rear-Admiral Troubridge (as he now was), resolved that even if his landing craft (tank) had had to heave to, he would launch his assault without the supporting arms. In the headquarters ship *Antwerp* and back in Cunningham's and Alexander's headquarters in Malta 'considerable anxiety' was felt on account of the plight of the small craft, especially since it was 'manifestly too late' to postpone the landings.[53] But, thankfully, the wind began to drop as the sun westered, the sea subsiding into a heavy swell that still promised thunderous surf on the beaches.

At 2030 Force A (the right flank of the Eastern Task Force) made the most dramatic landfall of any of the British or American task forces that evening as they approached their release positions for the assault – the conical mass of Mount Etna rising black against a clear starlit sky. At 2200 British and American aircraft towed gliders carrying 2,000 soldiers of the British 1st Airborne Division over the assembled ships of the waiting Eastern Task Force towards the coast. The mission of this airlanding brigade was to capture the Ponte

Grande Bridge, a key to a swift advance on Syracuse. Now, however, a tragic combination of high winds, poor navigation owing to inexperience, and the bewildering effects of Italian anti-aircraft fire and flares caused the glider formations to disintegrate into total confusion. Sixty-nine gliders crashed into the sea, ten were towed back to Tunisia, two were shot down, 59 landed in Sicily in a 25-mile scatter, of which only twelve grounded in the intended landing zones. Nonetheless, a handful of survivors took the Ponte Grande Bridge and held it until British ground forces from the beaches came to the rescue next day.

In the meantime a similar disaster overtook the drop of American parachute troops of the 82nd Airborne Division in the Gela area, when again the pilots became entirely lost in darkness and strong wind, and the soldiers landed in small parties all over the place; none of them in the designated dropping zones. With commendable leadership and enterprise these parties transformed themselves into guerrillas and for several days spread alarm among the German and Italian defenders. Nevertheless this first great Allied airborne operation of the war, the routing of which had added to the problems of the naval planners and commanders, lamentably failed to fulfil the role allotted to it.[54]

About an hour and a half after the Allied transport aircraft had rumbled overhead at 2200 on 9 July, the assault forces parted company from their parent convoys and headed off towards their release positions. This time it was hoped that the confusions and mishaps of the 'Torch' landings could be avoided. In reconnoitring the beaches in the weeks beforehand the hard lessons learned on the Algerian shore had been applied as best possible. According to Cunningham, 'the estimation of beach conditions and gradients by air photography and study of wave velocities have now reached a fine pitch of efficiency . . .'[55] Unfortunately the results of this photo-reconnaissance had not reached the staffs in time to be of much value.[56] COPP parties (Combined Operations Pilotage Parties) had this time been put ashore or had swum ashore from submarines (all of them Royal Navy, even on American beaches) and from folbots (folding boats) to obtain details of beach gradients and sand bars. As Cunningham reported afterwards, 'where sand bars exist there is no present substitute for swimming reconnaissance, so the service of these gallant parties will continue to be necessary. Their casualties in this operation were unfortunately heavy . . .'[57]

As in 'Torch', submarines (again all of them British) marked the release positions for the assault waves; their names a roll call of hazardous service: *Safari*, *Shakespeare* and *Seraph* on the Western Task Force Front; *Unrivalled*, *Unison*, *Unseen* and *Unruffled* on the Eastern Task Force Front. Sonic buoys and folbots again served to guide the landing craft into the beaches. Once more, however, the utmost care and foresight failed in the event to avert the operation of Murphy's Law. For delays caused by the bad weather and difficulties in joining separate elements of the assault waves and forming them up in correct order for the run-in caused some problems in getting craft to the right beaches on time.

In the Eastern Task Force (British) the assault on the right flank, nearest to Syracuse, touched down on Acid North beach at H-Hour + 10 minutes, and met only slight opposition, a coastal battery being soon silenced by the destroyer *Eskimo*. On Acid South everything went well even though on some stretches of beach the sonic buoys were either missed or not present. On Bark East (the southernmost beach on the eastern coast of Sicily) all flights touched down on time despite a somewhat ragged run-in, and fire from warships suppressed an attempt by an Italian coastal battery to engage the landing craft when some 200 yards out from the shore. On Bark South and West (astride the southern tip of the island) the heavy swell made it difficult to lower the landing craft (mechanised) or for landing craft to embark soldiers from the big landing ships (infantry). And despite all the efforts at accurate beach reconnaissance, surprises were sprung on Bark West by off-lying sandbanks; and an attempt to blast openings through them proved only a short-lived answer. On another stretch of Bark West, however, the swell simply heaved the landing craft over the false beach.

On every beach of the Eastern Task Force the assault forces enjoyed complete surprise and virtually no opposition. Cunningham attributed this 'unexpected success' partly to the 'little blow' during the day of 9 July, coupled with the enforced choice of an unfavourable phase of the moon. These, he reckoned, had 'actually the effect of making the weary Italians, who had been alert for many nights, turn thankfully in their beds saying "tonight at any rate they can't come!" '[58]

But the morning broke fine and calm, the prelude to a 'most lovely day', as Ramsay recounted to his wife:

It was almost unreal to find oneself off Sicily with Etna looking down on the scene of the landings. Hundreds literally of ships of the largest size down to the smallest & one had to pinch oneself to make sure one was not in a dream. The coast looked so sleepy and peaceful.
   The opposition was surprisingly poor but there was just sufficient to

make it clear that we really were undertaking a warlike operation . . .[59]

So Montgomery's army was solidly ashore; and the admiral responsible for putting it there could well write that launching 'Husky' 'has all been a great thrill and an outstanding success so far . . . I wouldn't have missed it for the world.'[60]

It was on the Western Task Force (American) front along the Gulf of Gela that the toughest opposition was encountered, as well as the worst conditions of sea and beach. In the Joss area on the left flank, even though here the Italian 207th Coastal Division offered only unenthusiastic resistance, the beaches sprang nasty surprises. Two of them combined narrow rocky entrances with shallow sand beyond, features which in conjunction with a north-westerly cross-sea left most of the landing craft stuck in the sand and impossible to pull off.[61] At another Joss beach soft sand and a difficult gradient thwarted attempts to unload tanks. On Dime beach, in the centre astride the town of Gela itself, the Americans ran into heavy fire, but here too the main problem lay in the breaking surf rolled on to a dead lee shore by a Force 4 westerly wind, causing many landing craft to broach. Only on the Cent beaches, on the right flank, did everything go smoothly.[62]

While joint army and navy beach groups sorted out the beach-heads and strove to organise the smooth inward flow of supplies, reinforcements and vehicles, the British and Canadian troops of the Eastern Task Force (now constituted as the 8th Army under Montgomery) and the Americans of the Western Task Force (now the 7th Army under Patton) consolidated their lodgements. By 2100 on D-Day the 8th Army had captured the ports of Syracuse and Augusta, and within three days Royal Navy harbour parties had put them into full working order. On the west coast the 7th Army had taken the port of Licata and the airfields behind Gela, and – thanks partly to its own stout resistance and partly to the devastating fire of the US cruisers *Savannah* and *Boise* – had repulsed a counter-attack by the Hermann Göring and Livorno Divisions which at one point almost reached the beaches.

The two navies had now done their job, landing in three days 80,000 men, 7,000 vehicles, 300 tanks and 900 guns.[63] His own task complete, Ramsay struck his flag as Naval Commander, Eastern Task Force, on 19 July and returned to the United Kingdom, while Hewitt handed over command of the Western Task Force to Rear Admiral Connolly before proceeding to Bizerta. From now on the navies' role was to provide flank guards against enemy ships and E-boats and to bombard coastal targets in support of military operations. On D + 1 the battleships *Howe* and *King George V* shelled Levanzo and Trapani on the western tip of Sicily by way of seeking to arouse enemy apprehensions that another landing was about to take place there; the cruisers *Sirius* and *Dido* performed the same service at Marsala. On 17 July HMS *Warspite*, showing a remarkable turn of speed for a veteran of Jutland, raided Catania, pouring in a storm of 15-inch shells. Her exploit elicited the appreciative signal from the Commander-in-Chief to his one-time flagship: 'Operation well carried out. There is no question that when the old lady lifts her skirts she can run.'[64]

Throughout the campaign the light forces of both Royal and US Navies fought off sorties by enemy cruisers, submarines and E-boats, sinking in all four German and three Italian submarines,[65] for the loss of only four British and two American merchantmen and two American landing ships (tank), and damage to a further three merchantmen and the cruisers *Cleopatra* and *Newfoundland*. But as during the North African campaign it was the Luftwaffe which posed the most dangerous threat to the Allied navies and shipping, arriving early on D-Day and keeping it up to the end. The first victim was the brilliantly lit hospital ship *Talamba* on the night of the 10th. The Eastern Task Force lost merchant vessels and landing craft to a total of 41,509 tons in the course of the campaign; the Western Task Force a destroyer, a minesweeper, two landing ships (tank) and one merchant vessel.[66] The Luftwaffe also seriously damaged the fleet carrier *Indomitable*, the monitor *Erebus* and two destroyers.[67]

The Allied air forces, although so numerous, failed to prevent these enemy strikes – possibly because, as the navies believed, the command and control links between sea and air forces remained slow and cumbersome.[68] And yet fresh innovations had been made in this regard, with air controllers in each headquarters ship to direct forward fighter operations, and a fighter direction ship (equipped with long-range radar) with each headquarters ship to provide the controllers with battle information. For the control of night fighters three seaborne ground control interception centres were lodged in landing ships (tank).[69] Nevertheless the navies still found that the air forces were failing to deploy aircraft quickly enough where most urgently needed.

Both navies rendered an essential if humdrum service to the developing campaign by running a dense traffic of ships and landing craft under their protection between North Africa and the Allied lodgements in Sicily. The two armies had to rely for some time partly on supplies fed through open beaches because port capacities were not large enough. The American 7th Army, with at first only the small harbour of Licata, particularly depended on the beaches; and it was here that the ingenious American invention, the DUKW or 'Duck' (DUKW stood for the factory serial letters of production: 'D' for the year of origin, 1942, the fourth year of war; 'U' for utility; 'K' for front-wheel drive; 'W' for six-wheeled) proved invaluable. The Duck was an amphibious 2½-ton truck, able to ferry stores or troops from ships off shore and then trundle straight out of the sea and up the beach to the unloading point; and it proved the key tool in keeping the 7th Army supplied and on the move. As Admiral Vian put it, 'the DUKWs first and last were the outstanding success of the operation'.[70]

Yet much reliance had also been placed on ordinary landing craft for transport, especially the big seagoing landing craft (tank). For the first time repair ships were taken to the assault area so that each beach could have its own repair and maintenance facilities for landing craft. Nonetheless Cunningham was not at all happy about working so hard as supply transport craft that were really designed for assault operations; and he drew afresh the lesson 'which we have learnt time and time again but neglected on every new occasion' that, as part of the equipment of an amphibious assault, 'one must provide an ample supply of tugs and lighters to take over from the landing craft so that they can be serviced for the next operation . . .'[71]

In 'Husky' just as in 'Torch' the complete success of the initial landings was swiftly succeeded by stalemate in the land campaign, as Hitler fed in the 1st Parachute and 29th Panzer-Grenadier Divisions as reinforcements, and Lieutenant-General Conrath sharpened up the Hermann Göring by means of ferocious orders of the day coupled with courts martial and the sacking of senior officers.[72] On 14 July Montgomery found himself blocked in his frontal push on Catania, and blocked again a week later in trying to carry out a left-hand hook round the western skirts of Mount Etna. There he stuck until a fresh push by his left wing on 29 July – also abortive. Although Rear-Admiral R. McGrigor (Flag Officer, Sicily) had available a force of small landing ships (infantry) and landing craft complete with Commando troops, Montgomery failed to make use of them to outflank the strong German defensive positions, except on one occasion (on 15–16 August) when the Commandos were anyway put in short of the by now retreating enemy. Cunningham later commented acidly in his report to Eisenhower on 'Husky':

There were doubtless sound military reasons for making no use of this, what to me appeared, priceless asset of seapower and flexibility of man-oeuvre; but it is worth consideration for future occasions whether much time and costly fighting could not be saved by even minor flank attacks which must necessarily be unsettling to the enemy. It must always be for the General to decide. The Navy can only provide the means and advice on the practicability from the naval angle . . . It may be that had I pressed my views more strongly more could have been done.[73]

It was otherwise with Patton's 7th Army and the United States Navy. Freed by Alexander on 19 July from the shackling role of flank-guard to the deliberate Montgomery, Patton thrust swiftly up into the north-western tip of Sicily, took the port of Palermo on 22 July, and swung east along the northern coastline towards Messina. All through his operations Patton sought to make use of the US Navy and its landing craft lift, as the Allied naval Commander-in-Chief was to praise in reporting to Eisenhower:

> The whole of these operations [wrote Cunningham] both before and after the capture of PALERMO was a model of amphibious tactics by the Western Task Force.
>
> In particular, after the capture of PALERMO . . . U.S. generalship showed that it had nothing to learn of the value of sea power and Task Force 86 [the US Navy component of the Western Task Force] under Rear Admiral DAVIDSON, U.S.N., that it had nothing to learn of the rapid planning and execution of outflanking operations.[74]

In point of fact Cunningham was being over-generous to Patton, possibly because Montgomery's failure to exploit seapower still rankled. Patton's navy-borne left-hooks achieved little, and on one occasion landed behind the American front, to be greeted by General Lucian Truscott's staff on the beach.

On 25 July 1943 Mussolini was dismissed from office thanks to a revolt within his own Fascist Grand Council, and replaced by an interim government under Marshal Badoglio. Hitler had now to take into account the possible defection of Italy from the Axis, and he laid long-term plans accordingly. But as an immediate consequence of Mussolini's fall OKW ordered Field-Marshal Kesselring (Commander-in-Chief, South) on 26 July to prepare to evacuate German troops from Sicily. So this time there was to be no repetition of the Tunisian débâcle; no last stand ending in a free gift to the Allies of a colossal bag of prisoners. By 1 August the plans were ready, and a preliminary evacuation began. The German forces on the ground, now constituted as the 14th Panzer Corps under General Hans Hube, and such Italian formations as still wished to fight, now carried out a characteristically skilled and stubborn step-by-step withdrawal on Messina.

On the night of 11 August the main evacuation ('Operation Lehrgang') began; it was completed on 16 August. Thanks to the efficiency with which Captain von Liebenstein of the German Navy organised the German ferry operation (mostly by Siebel ferries, mass-produced diesel-driven craft 80 feet long and 50 feet in the beam), nearly 40,000 German troops and 15,000 wounded, 10,000 vehicles, 51 tanks, 163 guns and about 20,000 tons of ammunition and equipment were safely brought back to the mainland.[75] The Italian evacuation, conducted by Admiral Barone (Naval Commander, Sicily) and Brigadier-General Monacci (land force commander) proved similarly successful, bringing away a total of 62,000 soldiers and sailors.[76] 'Operation Lehrgang' marked the model ending of what became, after a shaky start, a model defensive and delaying campaign; it rendered hollow and sour the Allies' eventual Sicilian victory. And 'Lehrgang' was carried out virtually without interference from the Allied air forces or navies – or armies, whose medium artillery had sufficient range if pushed forward. Yet the Allied command had been forewarned by cumulative indications from Sigint.[77]

Part of the problem lay in delays within the cumbersome Allied organisation in passing the Sigint indications on to the operational commands. It was only on the third day of the main enemy evacuation that Alexander signalled Tedder that 'it now appears German evacuation has really started'.[78] Even now, the Allied bomber forces (only a fraction was deployed) achieved little in the face of the immense concentration of anti-aircraft batteries organised by the enemy on both sides of the Messina Strait – 123 heavy and 102 light anti-aircraft guns in fixed batteries, plus another 150 mobile dual-purpose guns.[79] Neither was it thought possible for heavy ships, cruisers or even destroyers of the Allied navies to penetrate up the Strait, a two to five-miles-wide winding strip of water between mountainous coasts bristling with heavy cannon.[80] Certainly no such attempt was made: a unique occasion where Cunningham failed to show boldness, fiery aggressive spirit and disregard for loss. It may well be that Cunningham was remembering Admiral Sir John de Robeck's disastrous attempt to take a fleet up the Dardanelles in 1915, with the loss of three battleships. It fell to the light craft (motor torpedo boats and motor gunboats) gallantly to do what they could, which was little; and in the course of 'Lehrgang' the Axis lost only fifteen ferry craft from all causes and not a single man.[81]

On 17 August Patton consummated the Allies' conquest of Sicily after a 38 day campaign by entering Messina. What then was the final balance sheet of 'Husky'? The Allies committed nearly 3,000 warships, transports and landing craft, nearly 2,000 aircraft, and 450,000 men. These forces brought to battle a total of never more than 65,000 Germans at any one time,[82] inflicting losses of about 5,000 killed and between 5,500 and 6,600 captured, at a cost to themselves of nearly 5,000 killed and missing, and 13,083 wounded.[83] In addition the Allies inflicted on the 200,000 Italian troops on the island losses of 2,000 killed, 5,000 wounded and 137,000 prisoners.[84] By way of a benchmark as to comparative scale, in the same month of July 1943 the Red Army had defeated seventeen panzer divisions in the course of repelling the German summer offensive on the Eastern Front ('Operation Zitadelle', 5–13 July 1943), and inflicted losses of between 2,000 and 3,000 tanks and 70,000 killed.[85]

All that can be said in mitigation of the Sicilian campaign's poor return on a large investment is that it certainly helped to topple Mussolini, and thereby brought Brooke's original aim of knocking Italy out of the war a step nearer.

And now what? That had already been decided, not without acrimony, by another summit conference ('Trident'), held in Washington on 11–19 May 1943, when the North African campaign was coming to a victorious close.

The British delegation had profited by the five-day voyage across the Atlantic in the liner *Queen Mary* to agree the strategic case to be put to their allies. It was a case that was to fulfil General Marshall's glummest apprehensions, for it argued in favour of an open-ended extension of 'blue water' strategy in the Mediterranean after the capture of Sicily. In the words of a Joint Planners' memorandum, adopted almost completely by the Chiefs of Staff and the Prime Minister:

> Our final conclusion is that the Mediterranean offers us opportunities for action in the coming autumn and winter which may be decisive, and at least will do far more to prepare the way for a cross-Channel operation in 1944 than we should achieve by attempting to transfer back to the United Kingdom any of the forces now in the Mediterranean theatre. If we take these opportunities, we shall have every chance of breaking the Axis and bringing the war to a successful conclusion in 1944.[86]

During the previous month the Joint Planners, the Chiefs of Staff and the Prime Minister had revolved in detail how best to exploit these apparent Mediterranean opportunities. What about invading

Italy, not least to gain air bases from which to bomb southern Germany? The Joint Planners, much in favour of this invasion, calculated that if Italy defected from the Axis then the Germans would have to find 24 divisions to hold Italy itself, the Balkans and southern France, which they could not do 'without disastrous consequences elsewhere'.[87] The COS, however, were not yet willing at this point to buy an invasion of Italy, for they were still bothered about the cost of a protracted campaign in all kinds of resources.

What about Sardinia (and perhaps Corsica) instead, as advocated by Eisenhower and Cunningham? The case for these was well put in a paper by Eisenhower's Chief of Staff, General Bedell Smith, which criticised an invasion of Italy on the grounds that 'we might be involved in a campaign against superior German forces in a country where superiority in numbers would have full weight',[88] with a consequent heavy drain on shipping resources. To invade Sardinia, on the other hand, would only take five infantry divisions and one armoured; and only two infantry divisions to hold it afterwards. Sardinian air bases would enable the Allied air forces to dominate the whole of Italy while at the same time reducing the enemy air threat to sea communications in the western basin of the Mediterranean. But Air Chief-Marshal Tedder disagreed: an invasion of Sardinia would lie beyond the cover of shore-based fighters, while Sardinia's airfields were in any case really not needed for a bomber offensive against Italian targets, all of which could be reached from present Allied bases.[89]

Or what about the Aegean and the Balkans, the old favourites of the Great War 'easterners' like Lloyd George and Churchill, and taken up again by Churchill in 1941? This was the choice of GHQ, Middle East, although old hankerings stirred in Churchill too. An attack on the Dodecanese might bring in Turkey, might it not, and so open the way for a major offensive thrust via Greece into the Balkans. Or the occupation of southern Italy might itself serve as the preliminary to amphibious landings in the Balkans directly across the Adriatic.

Common to all this strategic picking and choosing was the conviction, just as with 'Torch' and 'Husky', that Allied forces could not simply be left idle until the launching of a cross-Channel invasion a year ahead; and hence in the present situation should be freshly employed as soon as possible after 'Husky' in further Mediterranean operations. In view of Soviet Russia's struggle with some 200 German divisions, the political and moral pressure on the Western Allies to campaign actively and on the largest possible scale somewhere during the current year was certainly enormous, perhaps irresistible; another

[651]

case of waging war as one politically must, rather than militarily ought.

Yet the drawback with all these ample gestures over the map of southern Europe was that they depended for fulfilment on long-distance sea communications and consequently major investments in assault and merchant shipping. The participants in these British discussions were more aware of this problem now than they had been when advocating 'Husky' at Casablanca. But they were quite happy that this shipping should be found at the expense of 'Bolero' (the movement of US forces across the Atlantic to Britain in preparation for the invasion of France). A paper drafted by General Ismay in the *Queen Mary* pronounced that the disadvantage of taking shipping from 'Bolero' 'will be greatly outweighed by the fact that successful Mediterranean operations, and still more the elimination of Italy, will ease the task confronting an army landing in Europe from the United Kingdom'.[90] The British delegation as a whole endorsed this. As the Prime Minister wrote in his cabin while the 81,000-ton bulk of the *Queen Mary* thrust its way towards the new world, 'We want them to agree to the exploitation of "Husky" and the attack on the underbelly taking priority of the build-up for "Bolero", as it must necessarily do for the execution of "Round-up".'[91] Brooke, for his part, although recognising that the pursuit of Mediterranean strategy would mean taking shipping from the Pacific theatre or 'Bolero', reckoned that 'Bolero' 'could afford a cut'.[92] Portal even went so far as to suggest that the British delegation should seek an agreement that the requirements of Britain's import programme and of the Mediterranean should be 'sacrosanct', after which it might be discussed whether 'Bolero' or the Pacific should suffer the necessary cuts.[93]

In total contradiction to all this renewed British enthusiasm for 'blue water' strategy General Marshall came to the Washington Conference even more strongly determined than at Casablanca to put a stop to the ever deeper slither into the mire of peripheral warfare in the Mediterranean at the expense of 'Roundup' – the direct cross-Channel invasion and the defeat in battle of the main German Army in the West. Already by the beginning of May 1943 he had seen the commitment of US forces to the Mediterranean rise to 388,000 men and 37 Combat Air Groups, while US forces in the United Kingdom had sunk from 168,000 at the beginning of the previous November to only 59,000.[94] Marshall wondered whether a cross-Channel invasion would ever be possible if such a haemorrhage continued; certainly he could not conceive how the grand ideas entertained by the British about the Mediterranean in 1943 could be reconciled with 'Roundup' in 1944.

The United States Joint Chief of Staff's policy position for the conference (endorsed by the President) therefore ruled out further operations in the Mediterranean after Sicily, except such limited ones as would enable Allied forces there to be actually reduced. It totally ruled out too adventures in the Aegean, leaving the British to have a go on their own if they were so minded. As the Joint Chiefs roundly briefed themselves for the conference:

> ... in the event the British insisted on Mediterranean commitments that in American opinion would jeopardise the early defeat of Germany and the ultimate defeat of Japan the U.S. representatives were to inform the British that the United States might be compelled to revise its basic strategy and extend its operations and commitments in the Pacific.[95]

In furtherance of these aims, the Joint Chiefs submitted a memorandum to the British Chiefs of Staff which uncompromisingly laid down:

> ... from our standpoint the concept of defeating Germany first involves making a determined attack against Germany on the Continent at the earliest practical date; we consider that all proposed operations in Europe should be judged primarily on the basis of their contribution to that end ... It is the opinion of the United States Chiefs of Staff that a cross-Channel invasion of Europe is necessary to an early conclusion of the war with Germany ...[96]

There resulted a dourly fought encounter-battle between the US Joint Chiefs of Staff and the British Chiefs of Staff and their opposed philosophies of war. The issue turned on guesstimates as to whether further Mediterranean operations in 1943 such as the invasion of Italy would weaken German forces available to meet a cross-Channel invasion in 1944 more than it would weaken the Allied forces (including assault shipping) available to launch that invasion. Marshall, for example, reckoned that every further Mediterranean operation would reduce the number of landing craft for 'Roundup' by 1,000.[97]

But there was also a clash between the Americans' Germanic preference for a clear 'overall strategic concept' and British opportunism. Thus Brooke threw in the thought that a collapse of Mussolini's régime or an invitation to the Allies by some other Italian political party to enter Italy could present the Allies 'with a decision as to what action was necessary to take advantage of this situation'.[98] But Marshall in response wondered whether the British were underestimating the likely strength of a German defence of Italy, and he uttered a prophetic warning:

[653]

In this very connection it must be remembered that in North Africa a relatively small German force had produced a serious factor of delay to our operations. A German decision to support Italy might make intended operations extremely difficult and time-consuming.[99]

There finally emerged from this collision of minds in Washington yet another fudge. On the one hand it was agreed by the Combined Chiefs of Staff in their final report to the President and the Prime Minister

That forces and equipment shall be established in the United Kingdom with the object of mounting an operation with target date 1st May, 1944, to secure a lodgement on the Continent from which further offensive operations can be carried out.[100]

The required forces were put at nine assault divisions and twenty follow-up divisions.

But on the other hand, the Combined Chiefs of Staff also resolved:

That the Allied Commander-in-Chief, North Africa, will be instructed, as a matter of urgency, to plan such operations in exploitation of 'Husky' as are best calculated to eliminate Italy from the War and to contain the maximum number of German forces. Which of the various specific operations should be adopted, and thereafter mounted, is a decision which will be reserved to the Combined Chiefs of Staff. The Allied Commander-in-Chief in North Africa may use for his operations all those forces available in the Mediterranean area except for four American and three British divisions which will be held in readiness from the 1st November onwards for withdrawal to take part in operations from the United Kingdom, provided that the naval vessels required will be approved by the Combined Chiefs of Staff when the plans are submitted. The additional air forces provided on a temporary basis for 'Husky' will not be considered available.[101]

In other words, a continuation of 'blue water' strategy but supposedly under tight rein. Even so, Brooke essentially got his way, for the Mediterranean theatre was to be left with 27 divisions (virtually equal to those at present allotted to 'Roundup' in 1944) and 3,648 aircraft.[102] This figure of 27 Allied divisions may be compared with a British Joint Planners' estimate this same month that 24 German divisions would have to be diverted from other fronts for the defence of Italy and the Balkans in the event of Italian defection from the Axis.[103]

Marshall had to draw what comfort he could from the 'Trident' conference's other decision to instruct COSSAC – the Chief of Staff to the Supreme Allied Commander designate, Lieutenant-General Sir Frederick Morgan – to prepare by 1 August 1943 an outline plan for a cross-Channel invasion with the target date of 1 May 1944.

Italy was therefore to be knocked out of the war. But the 'Trident' Conference left it to Eisenhower and his colleagues to recommend to the Combined Chiefs of Staff the appropriate means, whether direct invasion or other. The Prime Minister himself, flying to Algiers immediately after 'Trident' to confer with Marshall, Eisenhower, Alexander, Cunningham and Tedder, was 'determined to obtain before leaving Africa a decision to invade Italy should Sicily be taken'.[104] Eisenhower, for his part, advocated setting up two planning staffs, one to consider the problems of invading Sardinia, the other of the Italian mainland; a final decision to be deferred until after Sicily had fallen into Allied hands and the quality of German opposition could be gauged. This proposal was backed by Marshall and adopted by the conference. Nevertheless Churchill put in a last emotional plea in favour of invading Italy itself and seizing Rome: 'the alternative between Southern Italy and Sardinia,' he proclaimed, 'involved the difference between a glorious campaign and a mere convenience.'[105] At this Marshall raised the sordid question of shipping lifts and shipping shortages. But Churchill had his answer: he would, he averred, cut the rations of the British people in order to provide the ships.[106]

The arguments as to the best means of laying Italy low rumbled on through July, Churchill's strategic visions being given new wing by the success of the Allied landings in Sicily. He kept up relentless pressure on his own Chiefs of Staff and on Eisenhower in favour of far-reaching operations in Italy with Rome 'as the bull's eye'. Brushing aside American concerns about availability of landing craft in the context of global strategy, he asked on 13 July '. . . why we should crawl up the leg like a harvest-bug from the ankle upwards? Let us rather strike at the knees . . .'[107] He instructed the British Joint Planners immediately to 'prepare the best scheme possible for landing on the Italian west coast with the objective the port of Naples and the march on Rome . . . It would seem that two or three good divisions could take Naples and produce decisive results . . .'[108]

Here was the first sketch of what became 'Operation Avalanche', the Allied landings in the Gulf of Salerno. Churchill was resolved that in any event, as he wrote to Field-Marshal Smuts on 15 July 1943, he would 'in no circumstances allow the powerful British and British-controlled armies in the Mediterranean to stand idle . . .'[109]

His imagination flew even further: 'Not only must we take Rome and march as far north as possible in Italy, but with our right hand must give succour to the Balkan patriots ... I shall go to all lengths to procure the agreement of our Allies. If not, we have ample forces to act by ourselves.'[110] Four days later visions of marching on Vienna from northern Italy blazed before him, relegating 'Overlord' (as 'Roundup' had now been re-named) to the shadows.[111]

In any case Marshall, as well as Eisenhower, had by this time become convinced by the collapse of Italian resistance in Sicily that mainland Italy and not Sardinia should indeed be the next Allied objective; and on 18 July Eisenhower's formal recommendation to this effect was promptly approved by the two governments (hence Churchill's Napoleonic vision next day of a march on Vienna).

So by the familiar process of the 'push' of existing commitment (coupled with the pressing political need to support Soviet Russia during the current year) and the 'pull' of the next enticing prospect, the Allies finally opted for an offensive campaign in the perfect defensive terrain of Italy; another campaign to be opened by large-scale seaborne landings protected by major Allied naval task forces and thereafter nourished by ships in slow procession from Britain and the United States and back again.

Yet in their pertinacious and eventually successful advocacy of an invasion of Italy Churchill and Brooke had astonishingly ignored one key factor – German fighting prowess on land. They had reckoned without such formidable opponents as the 1st Parachute Division and the 14th Panzer Corps (already encountered in Sicily), or such redoubtable leaders as General von Senger und Etterlin, future defender of Cassino, and Field-Marshal 'Smiling Albert' Kesselring who, as Commander-in-Chief, South, and later of Army Group C, would prove himself a grandmaster of the strategic defensive. The capture of Rome, let alone the march on Vienna, might be somewhat delayed.

'Some Underbelly; Some Softest Part': The Mediterranean, 1943–1945

By the time this final decision to undertake a campaign in Italy had been taken, the implications in terms of resources had already begun to sink in. Eisenhower, in a signal to the COS and Combined COS on 30 June outlining various proposals for invading Sardinia or landing on both sides of the toe of Italy, had asked for more long-range fighters to cover the beaches; and also asked to retain thirteen American combat loaders (landing ships) and eighteen American destroyers due to depart from the theatre.[1] Three weeks later the Admiralty signalled the Chief of Naval Operations to request that the US carrier *Ranger* be lent to the Home Fleet because the Home Fleet carrier, HMS *Illustrious*, had to be sent to the Mediterranean to replace the damaged *Indomitable*. The Admiralty added that it was proposing to send out four escort carriers for the forthcoming invasion of Italy, leaving only one in the Atlantic on convoy duties – a risk that it reckoned it could now accept because of Dönitz's withdrawal of his U-boats.

Because the British COS doubted whether Eisenhower would have enough assault shipping, they now urged their American colleagues to agree that, for the time being, none should leave the Mediterranean for South-East Asia as had been decided at the 'Trident' Conference; and on 20 July the Admiralty unilaterally ordered Cunningham not to allow any shipping to leave the theatre except such as was needed for Atlantic convoys. Cunningham, conscious of his awkward position as an Allied commander, at first asked the Combined Chiefs of Staff to issue a confirming order to Admiral Hewitt but then, on 23 July, gave the order himself in accordance with his instructions from the Admiralty.[2] Meanwhile the Combined Chiefs of Staff had replied to Eisenhower's requests, telling him that he was to get no more long-range fighters even as a temporary loan, because they were needed in the United Kingdom for the bomber offensive. Nevertheless, they consented to eighteen US destroyers remaining in the Mediterranean and up to three cruisers, but reiterated that fifteen destroyers would have to leave the theatre by 31 July and another fifteen by 12 August. They also informed Eisenhower that he could retain thirteen American combat loaders, and that a total of 90 cargo ships would be allotted to support the landings. A convoy carrying extra troops asked for by Eisenhower would sail in late August.

Thus the agreement to limit resources committed to the Mediterranean, which Marshall had stitched up (as he had hoped) in Washington, was already beginning to unravel. The disputes between London and Washington began all over again, but this time not just as an intellectual debate as to the best grand strategy, but over the real material questions of quantities of shipping and troops and aircraft needed for the strategy chosen. On 22 July the COS signalled the British Joint Staff Mission in Washington that Eisenhower would need an extra 40 stores ships, as well as retaining some amphibious craft at present due to leave the Mediterranean. They recommended that he be instructed to plan the landing on the west coast of Italy on the basis that all necessary resources *would* be provided, and that he should report as soon as possible on just what resources he would require. The COS again urged the American Joint Chiefs to agree that in the meantime all movement of shipping out of the theatre be halted.

But the Joint Chiefs would have none of it. They insisted that Eisenhower must plan his landings on the basis of resources at present allocated, otherwise operations elsewhere would be prejudiced. General Arnold, Chief of Staff of the US Army Air Force, wanted the three heavy bomber groups lent to Eisenhower for 'Husky' to be returned to the United Kingdom. He did not reckon that to eliminate Italy would directly threaten Germany, and he did not consider Italian airbases would be of much help to the bomber offensive; and he thought that Eisenhower's demands for resources could compromise 'Overlord' in 1944. Arnold, King and Marshall were all agreed therefore that Eisenhower's requests were excessive, indeed would prejudice the seaborne landings in Burma (now 'Bullfrog') also decided on at the 'Trident' Washington Conference; and in this they were to be proved right enough, for 'Bullfrog' was not merely delayed until 1944 but even into 1945. In short, the Americans were prepared to take a risk over the invasion of Italy on the grounds that Italy might soon collapse, while the British, remembering such débâcles as Gallipoli, wished to be well insured against failure.

Nevertheless, the US Joint Chiefs were not to be budged further, even though the British COS played their well-worn record that 'it would be a profound mistake to allow anyone or anything, which General Eisenhower might need, to move from the Mediterranean area until we know . . . his precise requirements for whatever operation might be decided upon'.[3] And the First Sea Lord, in repeating this signal to the Commander-in-Chief, Mediterranean, added: 'In view of the effect this proposal will have on "Overlord" and "Bullfrog" there may be objections from Washington but meanwhile you should hold everybody and everything you think may be required for "Priceless" [the invasion of Italy] whatever form it may take.'[4]

No wonder, then, that an angry Marshall was reported by the British Joint Staff Mission as having expressed disquiet lest the initial landing near Naples 'might well be the first step to similar demands as success after success opened further possibilities'.[5]

From the Allied Mediterranean command itself the pleas to retain ships and aircraft or even be sent more of them still mounted. Eisenhower, like his colleagues, was worried about the weakness of the land-based air cover to be provided over the beaches. On 28 July he asked for four groups of B-17 'Flying Fortress' heavy bombers to be lent by the 8th Army Air Force in Britain in order to smash the Luftwaffe on its airfields. But the request was turned down by the COS and JCS on the score that it would enfeeble the bomber offensive against Germany, and that in any case it would take a month to transfer the 4,000 groundcrew. They similarly turned down a later proposal by Eisenhower on 10 August that he be allowed to keep the three B-24 Liberator groups lent to him for 'Husky'.

Meanwhile the Admiralty had acceded to Cunningham's request for escort carriers in order to provide seaborne air cover over the landing areas, signalling him on 25 July that as well as the fleet carrier *Illustrious* for Force H, the American-built ex-United States Navy escort carriers *Attacker*, *Battler*, *Hunter* and *Stalker* (11,420 tons displacement; 17 knots; 18 aircraft)[6] were sailing for the Mediterranean. As Cunningham explained to the First Sea Lord:

I am most unwilling to use the escort carriers for AVALANCHE but I made Tedder produce an estimate of the fighters he could maintain over the assault and found it was only nine. This miserable figure made it essential that ship-based fighters should be used . . . Although it would appear natural that they should form part of the assault force I am not prepared to put them under Hewitt's command. As the U.S.A. troops are in the majority he has been nominated task force commander.

I intend to form the escort carriers, 3 DIDO class cruisers and 8–10 Hunts, if I can collect them, into one force with the job of fighter support on the beaches. Unless you have any objections I propose to make Vian hoist his flag in command of this force . . .[7]

At Cunningham's urging the Admiralty dropped a proposal that he should return one of his only two modern battleships (*Howe* and *King George V*) in a swap with the old *Malaya*, which Cunningham argued would only prove a liability. The Admiralty also acceded to his request that the cruisers *Scylla* and *Charybdis* be sent out as replacements for the *Cleopatra* and *Newfoundland*, damaged in Sicilian waters.[8] It can be seen that the First Sea Lord and the naval staff were doing their best to meet Cunningham's wishes over naval forces for 'Avalanche'. But, after all, this was Britain's own cherished 'blue water' project, and it was being driven by the full power of the Prime Minister's enthusiasm.

On 13 August there opened yet another of the 1943 summit conferences ('Quadrant'), this time in Quebec; a fresh opportunity for General Marshall and his fellow American Joint Chiefs of Staff to restitch the limits on resources for the Mediterranean. In consequence the Combined Chiefs of Staff proceeded to revoke the British stand-still order on the movement of assault shipping from that theatre to South-East Asia. They ordered Eisenhower *not* to detain the ten landing ships (tank) due to leave Oran for India. Such decisions caused further anguish in Malta and Algiers. Cunningham in particular remained uncharacteristically gloomy, signalling the Admiralty on 29 August that, in his view, the Combined Chiefs were being altogether too sanguine about the prospects for 'Avalanche'. Had they realised how difficult the operation would be? 'I believe that we can and shall succeed but only if we go flat out. If we whittle away our resources now to build up "Overlord" our chances of success will be greatly reduced, and if "Avalanche" fails "Overlord" may be stillborn.'[9]

He particularly protested at the removal of the three groups of B-24 heavy bombers (to be followed by three Wellington squadrons on 15 September, six days after D-Day of 'Avalanche'), stressing that 'Avalanche' depended on the Allies being able to pass a mass of ships and craft right up to an enemy coast on a moonlit night, with only carrier-borne fighters for protection against the Luftwaffe. This, he remarked, was a calculated risk taken on the assumption that the Luftwaffe would have been beaten into impotence, but the removal of powerful bomber forces rendered this assumption doubtful.[10]

Cunningham was also worried about the capacity of his landing craft lift, in this case, in regard to shuttling supplies and reinforcements to the armies. He pointed out to the Admiralty that even if the Allies held every port in Italy south of Naples, it would only be possible to build up to twelve divisions by December, as against the elements of seventeen German divisions at present on Italian soil. The Admiralty having forwarded this signal on to Churchill in Quebec, the First Sea Lord signalled Cunningham the answers on 31 August: while the Premier agreed that 'nothing should be removed which is necessary for victory in "Avalanche"', it had been decided that the three B-24 groups (now in any case back in the United Kingdom) would not be made available, although the Wellingtons might be retained after 15 September if need be. But Cunningham was given discretion to retain landing craft due for withdrawal 'if this was considered essential'.[11]

Just two days before the first assault convoy was due to sail for the 'Avalanche' beaches even Marshall, that stern refuser of further resources for the Mediterranean, began to have anxious second thoughts and offered Eisenhower extra shipping. However, Eisenhower's Deputy Chief of Staff replied that the problem in speeding the build-up of Allied armies lay in port capacities rather than shipping – not Cunningham's view. On the same day the First Sea Lord (now in America) signalled the Vice-Chief of Naval Staff in London to ask if he was satisfied that the Commander-in-Chief, Mediterranean, was getting all he needed, even at the expense of other theatres.

This tug-of-war prolonged to the last minute serves to illustrate afresh the essential paradox of maritime warfare waged against a continental foe. On the one hand Eisenhower and Cunningham were perfectly justified in their calculations of the resources of all kinds needed to ensure success in a risky, opposed, large-scale amphibious operation virtually beyond the range of Allied land-based airpower; yet on the other hand the size of the total Allied commitment to the coming campaign in southern Italy was out of all proportion to the eight German divisions which according to Sigint were at present deployed in that region – two panzer, four panzer-grenadier and two parachute.[12] For the Combined Chiefs of Staff had allotted Eisenhower a total of 27 divisions (excluding seven due for return to the United Kingdom at the end of November in preparation for

'Overlord', and two British divisions earmarked for Turkey if required). The Allied Mediterranean air forces would (according to a Combined Chiefs' estimate in May) amount to 242 heavy bombers, 519 medium bombers, 296 light or dive-bombers, 2,012 fighters and 576 transport and Army Cooperation aircraft;[13] a vast margin of numerical superiority over the dwindling Luftwaffe in the Mediterranean. To deal with the Italian Navy in its present moral and professional decrepitude, the British Mediterranean Fleet alone would comprise six capital ships, two fleet carriers, five light carriers, ten cruisers, six anti-aircraft ships and cruisers, 27 fleet destroyers, 44 escorts of all kinds, 24 submarines, two headquarters ships, twelve landing ships (infantry), and well over 300 ancillary vessels and craft from minesweepers and tugs to repair and depot ships.[14] And there has also to be weighed in the balance the merchant shipping which would provide the essential foundation of a protracted campaign – no fewer than 3½ million deadweight tons or 900 ships over the remaining months of 1943, according to Ministry of Transport estimates in August.[15]

The uncertainties and disputes over resources hardly helped the Allied staffs in trying to work out in exact detail the mustering and launching of another complex 'triphibious' operation; and neither did the short span of time available. It was only seven weeks before the eventual D-Day for 'Avalanche' that Eisenhower received instructions to consider Naples as his objective, and was first told that an invasion of Italy was to follow immediately after the fall of Sicily rather than in November or even early in 1944.[16] The date of 9 September was only confirmed as D-Day for a landing on the Italian west coast at a conference between Eisenhower and his commanders-in-chief on 17 August. Since 17 August happened also to be the day that Patton's entry into Messina brought the Sicilian campaign to an end, only now could the Allied commanders and staffs free themselves from involvement in current operations and so wholly concentrate on 'Avalanche' and 'Operation Baytown' (a crossing of the Straits of Messina into the toe of Italy by the 8th Army). In any event, it was only on 19 August that 'Avalanche' took priority with the planners over 'Buttress', a now discarded project for landing on the west coast of the toe of Italy. From the very beginning the planning of 'Avalanche' therefore became a frenzied scramble.

Yet at least it looked as if the Italian Navy, Army and Air Force would be out of the fight. Already secret negotiations for Italy's surrender, clandestine meetings, were in progress between the Allies and the Italian government that had replaced Mussolini. It proved a story of remarkable muddle, sometimes farce, which dragged on until 3 September (final D-Day for 'Baytown'), when the Italians signed an instrument of unconditional surrender, to come into effect on 8 September, the night before 'Avalanche'. Here then was another uncertainty to plague the planners in the meantime.[17]

Their tasks were rendered all the harder because (just as in the case of 'Husky'), commanders, headquarters, military formations and assault shipping lay scattered at various points round the Mediterranean. Eisenhower was in Algiers and, in any case, deeply entangled in the clandestine negotiations with the new Italian government; Cunningham was in Malta; Alexander (Deputy Supreme Commander, and army group commander, Allied 15th Army Group, comprising the American 5th and the British 8th Armies) was in Syracuse; Tedder (Allied Air Commander-in-Chief) was in Tunis; Admiral Hewitt (Allied Naval Commander, Western Task Force) was at first at sea off Sicily, then in Malta and finally Algiers. General Mark Clark (commanding the 5th Army, and Ground Force Commander, 'Avalanche') was at Mostaghanem in Algeria, while Montgomery was in the field in Sicily. Commodore Oliver (Naval Commander, Northern Attack Force, 'Avalanche') was in Algiers, while his military opposite number (Horrocks; later McCreery) was in Tripoli.

It all made for severe strain on a signals net already stretched by the Sicilian campaign – as well as for intense competition for aircraft seats. As Cunningham confided to the First Sea Lord on 5 August:

> I travel madly between Malta and Algiers . . . There is a suggestion in the wind that when taken A.F.H.Q. [Allied Forces Headquarters] should move to Naples and I think this will solve the problem. Meanwhile continual air travel, in spite of the irritating difficulties and delays that appear to be inseparable from getting a plane to take you or your staff, appears to be the best we can do.[18]

The limited capacity of available ports in relation to the mass of vessels to be brought together for 'Avalanche' meant that the preliminary mustering of shipping and their loads had to be dispersed over every usable harbour on the North African coast from Oran to Alexandria – another conundrum for the staffs to solve.[19] Fortunate indeed by comparison are the commander and staff planning a classic land offensive, all tidily together in a single headquarters, and with subordinate formation commanders only a brief journey away by air, road or rail.

Because of the pressure of time, naval planning for 'Avalanche' had to proceed simultaneously at three different levels of command –

Allied Force Headquarters, Naval Commander, Western Task Force (Admiral H. K. Hewitt), and under him, the Naval Commanders, Northern Attack Force (Commodore G. N. Oliver, RN) and Southern Attack Force (Rear Admiral John Hall, USN). In Commodore Oliver's words, 'Orders were coming in from three authorities more rapidly than they could be disseminated, and, due to hurried and simultaneous production amendments and addenda kept pouring in up to the last moment . . . a most undesirable, but in the circumstances, unavoidable state of affairs.'[20]

It added to the naval staff's problems that military requirements were frequently altered, upsetting for example the tactical stowage that had been painstakingly worked out in relation to the exactly measured dimensions of vessels' internal spaces. Oliver put these alterations down to the 'inability of the Army Command to reach a final decision as to what troops should be employed in the operation and how they should be distributed between the two Task Forces . . .'[21] On 24 August General Clark made his own helpful contribution by advancing H-Hour by 30 minutes, so compelling changes to the navies' sailing and routing schedules.

It is hardly surprising that personal relations between commanders could become somewhat strained, causing more dry bearings in an already hot-running staff machine. In the case of D-Day for 'Baytown', the 8th Army's crossing of the Straits of Messina, Montgomery brought on a blazing row between himself and Cunningham by exercise of his habit of instant lying if convenient. When Eisenhower asked at a conference on 23 August 1943, why D-Day for Baytown could not be advanced to 1 September, Montgomery answered that the Navy refused to carry out the operation until 4–5 September. Montgomery also asserted that the Navy was unwilling to undertake the operation at night. As Cunningham wrote furiously to Montgomery's superior, General Alexander, three days later:

> So serious did it appear to me that I decided . . . to fly to Sicily at once as the only means of clearing up the situation. I found that, not only were the statements incorrect, but that General Montgomery had at no time been in direct touch with the Senior Naval Officer of the Expedition [Rear-Admiral R. McGrigor] and that his statements were, in fact, completely unfounded . . .[22]

Cunningham discovered that McGrigor had in fact been given the date of 4–5 September by the responsible corps commander, Lieutenant-General Dempsey, although McGrigor was instead working to the earlier date of the 3rd as decided in a staff conference (and confirmed by a signal from Alexander on 20 August). Cunningham now instructed McGrigor to advance the date to 2/3 September in accordance with Eisenhower's known wish. But, as Cunningham pointed out to Alexander, 'Had I or Rear-Admiral McGrigor been made aware some days previously that the Army could be ready on 1st September I have no doubt another valuable day could have been saved.'[23] And he also pointed out that while McGrigor had certainly told Dempsey that there were naval disadvantages in a night operation, McGrigor had also said that the final decision must rest with the Army: '. . . again a complete contradiction to General Montgomery's statement that the Navy insisted on a day assault.'[24]

While Montgomery's latest victims fumed and wasted time, the staffs toiled on with their piles of paper; and sailors, soldiers and local labour in djellaba or galabieh humped stores into ships under the keen eyes of the quartermasters, and drivers manoeuvred trucks and armour into the narrow decks of landing craft (tank). The naval planners themselves derived great help from the system of Mediterranean Naval Planning Memoranda, which were promulgated regularly by the Commander-in-Chief. As he wrote later, 'It is no exaggeration to say that without this system, these subordinate commanders could never have produced their own orders in time for the operation . . .'[25] Even so, the orders proved so voluminous, the amendments and annexes so numerous that, according to Oliver, it was only 'by superhuman efforts of all concerned and under conditions in which I hope a combined operation will never again have to be concerted', that the various commands managed to issue their final orders by 29 August.[26]

Many discrepancies and gaps still remained. Only a fortnight before D-Day for 'Avalanche' Intelligence revealed a probable enemy minefield in the assault area,[27] but in order to avoid compromising the source of the information the task forces were not told until the last minute. So the brain-weary staffs had to set to and revise the intricate landing craft schedules because the lowering points for the assault waves now had to be nine miles off shore for the British landing ships (infantry) and twelve miles for the American combat loaders. And this was not the only last-minute development demanding that schedules be rejigged. It turned out that there would be a larger number of landing craft available than expected, both because of successful repair work and because losses in 'Baytown' (launched on 3 September) were less than expected, so enabling more craft to be transferred to 'Avalanche'. No wonder Cunningham's own set of orders bears innumerable annotations; no wonder Rear Admiral Hall of the United

States Navy (Commander, Southern Attack Force) was to write in his report that even when he entered the assault area in the evening of 8 September, he still did not know the exact number of landing craft under his orders, 'the designation of the individual craft assigned, or the designation of all the units embarked therein'.[28]

On 30 August Eisenhower submitted the overall 'Avalanche' plan for approval to the Combined Chiefs of Staff and COS. Of three possible landing areas, Eisenhower and his colleagues ruled out the coast north of Naples because it lay beyond the range of land-based Spitfires and in any case the beaches were poor; and they ruled out the Bay of Naples itself because of its powerful coastal defences. Instead they selected the Gulf of Salerno, the nearest point to Naples that could be covered by fighters from Sicilian airfields, and blessed with superb beaches conveniently weak in fixed defences. Its sole disadvantage lay in that Naples, the Allies' strategic objective, lay 30 miles distant to the north on the far side of a mountain bottleneck.

According to the air plan the beaches were to be covered on D-Day by 36 land-based fighters at one time, flown in rotation by three groups of American Lightnings, one group of American Spitfires and eighteen squadrons of Royal Air Force Spitfires – a great improvement on Tedder's original offer of only nine aircraft aloft at any one time. The light aircraft-repair carrier HMS *Unicorn* (14,750 tons displacement; 24 knots; 35 aircraft)[29] and the four escort carriers of Force V (Rear-Admiral Vian, with his flag in the cruiser *Euryalus*) would keep another 22 fighters over the beaches on D-Day. However, the air plan critically depended on the soldiers capturing Montecorvino airfield, less than two miles from the sea, on the first day so that Spitfires could be flown in.

With regard to ground forces, Eisenhower estimated on the basis of Sigint that on D-Day the Allies would meet one panzer division and two to five parachute battalions; that by D + 5 enemy strength would rise to two and a half panzer divisions, one and a half motorised (panzer-grenadier) divisions and one parachute division; and by D + 22 by another panzer division, and half a motorised.[30] By the latter date Allied forces ashore would amount to one armoured division, three tank battalions, one airborne division and four infantry divisions. This was by no means a comforting balance, even allowing for the 8th Army coming up overland to the rescue from Messina.

The British return to the mainland of Europe after two and a half years, and this time to stay, began at 0430 on 3 September 1943 with a bombardment by massed artillery of the 8th Army across the Straits of Messina, augmented by the fire of fifteen warships on Reggio di Calabria at the southern end of the Straits and by strikes inland by heavy bombers. This impressive Montgomeryian overture was followed by anti-climax when British and Canadian soldiers, crossing the Straits in some 300 landing craft, found the far shore devoid of enemy, for the German forces had prudently withdrawn two days previously. In the next fortnight cunningly located demolition of bridges and the blowing of precipitous roads in the wild mountain country of Calabria effectively put the brake on the 8th Army, which now needed mules and pack artillery rather than masses of motor transport dependent on copious fuel supplies. On 8 September, when his advanced guard had got as far as the narrow neck of land where the toe of Italy joins the instep, Montgomery halted his army in order to bring up stores and fuel and put his line of communication in order.

On the same day, at Cunningham's initiative, the cruisers USS *Boise* and HMSs *Aurora*, *Penelope*, *Sirius* and *Dido*, and the fast minelayer *Abdiel* put to sea from Bizerta loaded with troops of the British 1st Airborne Division. They rendezvoused at sea with the battleships *Howe* (flying the flag of Vice-Admiral Arthur Power) and *King George V* from Malta, and on 9 September entered Taranto harbour and put the soldiers ashore to occupy the port and city. Sadly the *Abdiel* struck a mine and sank in a few minutes, with heavy loss of life.

While Power's squadron was steaming towards the 'instep' of Italy on 8 September, the 'Avalanche' convoys were approaching the 'knee', in Churchill's word – the Gulf of Salerno.[31] The first convoy, consisting mainly of landing craft (tank), had left Tripoli for the Sicilian port of Termini on the 3rd, and by dusk of the 8th all the assault convoys had been staged through Sicilian ports and refuelled as necessary. Over a calm sea under a brilliant moon the sprawl of shipping headed northwards like some giant regatta towards the waiting folbots and beacon submarines off shore. In the afternoon of 7 September Force H had steamed out of Grand Harbour, Valletta, in two divisions – *Nelson*, *Rodney* and *Illustrious*, escorted by the 4th and 24th Destroyer Flotillas; and *Warspite* (wearing the flag of Rear-Admiral A. W. de la T. Bissett), *Valiant* and *Formidable* – to take up its role of protecting Vian's Force V, the five light carriers which were to fly air cover over the beaches. During the night of 8–9 September Force V steamed north through the Straits of Messina and, as Vian remarked in his report later, 'H.M. Ships *Scylla* and *Charybdis* made a bowing acquaintance with their famous forbears.' Meanwhile the battleships and destroyers of Force H and night fighters flown by *Formidable* and *Illustrious* beat off an attack by 30 German torpedo-bombers; and by daylight on the 9th fighters from *Illustrious* and *Formidable* were circling high above Force V.

Meanwhile a swarm of British, American and Dutch small ships and craft from Palermo had been shelling and raiding islands off Naples and the Gulf of Gaeta (north of Naples) in order to deceive the enemy about the location of the Allied landing – but without success.[32] As Ultra decrypts of the Luftwaffe Enigma traffic had revealed, the German command had for some time been expecting the Allies to land near Naples; and at 2200 on the 8th it signalled '*Orkan*' ('Hurricane'), the codeword to alert its forces to repel a landing next day in the Naples–Salerno area (a signal also quickly decrypted by Ultra). This time the Anglo-American assault waves would not come ashore against little or no opposition, but would run into the 16th Panzer Division.

For while the Allies had been bumbling away at their negotiations for Italy's surrender, and dickering with a project for landing the US 82nd Airborne Division to seize Rome, Hitler and the OKW had prepared complete contingency plans to deal with Italy's likely defection and to defend Italian territory. When in August Rommel, now C-in-C of Army Group B in northern Italy, had recommended that Italy south of the River Po should be abandoned, Kesselring had successfully convinced Hitler that instead battle could and should be given to the Allies south of Rome. Kesselring's plan was that such formations as he had at hand in southern Italy should delay the Allies for as long as possible, while his engineers surveyed and constructed a formidable defence in depth (to be called the *Gustavstellung* or Gustav Line) sited in ideal mountainous country across the narrowest point of the waist of Italy, from Gaeta to the Adriatic. In parallel Hitler and the OKW had perfected arrangements for disarming the Italian forces both in Italy and Greece and the Balkans, should Badoglio's government 'treacherously' surrender to the Allies.

'Operation Axis' (as this plan was codenamed) was precipitated in the event by an ill-judged radio broadcast by Eisenhower from Algiers on 8 September announcing that Italy was surrendering. The OKW thereupon issued the prearranged signal 'Bring in the harvest' to all German units, and the Wehrmacht pounced on the Italian armed forces with all the old ruthless speed and boldness of 1940. Within two days it had disarmed them all on pain of being shot, and had occupied Rome. Only the Italian Fleet escaped, its main body sailing from La Spezia at 0300 on the 9th for a rendezvous off Tunisia with Rear-Admiral A. W. de la T. Bissett's battle squadron detached from

Force H (*Warspite, Valiant,* and five British, one French and one Greek destroyer; the old Allies). The Italian Fleet was then to be escorted into Grand Harbour, Valletta, to surrender. But events did not go entirely according to expectation.

At about 1600 on 9 September the Italian Fleet, consisting of the battleships *Roma, Vittorio Veneto* and *Italia* (formerly the *Littorio*), six cruisers and eight destroyers under the command of Admiral Bergamini (flying his flag in the *Roma*) was attacked west of the channel between Corsica and Sardinia by eleven Dornier Do-17 bombers of a special unit from an airfield in southern France. Mistaking them for Allied aircraft the Italians failed to fire on them. The attack marked the opening of a new era in the technology of naval warfare, for the Do-17s were equipped with the first ever air-to-sea guided missile – the free-falling FX-1400 radio-controlled armour-piercing bomb filled with 1,400 pounds of high explosive, released at heights of between 12,000 and 19,000 feet, and attaining a terminal velocity of 800 feet per second.[33] The FX-1400 had already been tried experimentally but unsuccessfully against Allied ships in Malta and off Sicily. Thanks to Ultra, however, neither its existence nor the enemy's intention to use it in current operations was a secret to the Allies.[34] Now a single FX-1400 smashed its way deep into Bergamini's flagship, the 41,000 ton *Roma*, blowing it up in a storm of flame with the loss of nearly all hands, including Bergamini himself.

At 0600 next morning the surviving Italian ships (*Italia* too was damaged by an FX-1400) made their rendezvous with Admiral Bissett's squadron. Cunningham was there with Eisenhower to witness this consummation of his outstanding leadership of the Mediterranean Fleet since 1940, having come out from Bizerta for the occasion in the destroyer *Hambledon*. The meeting of the two fleets was resonant with historical echoes; an occasion when even Englishmen might display their feelings. At the head of the British line steamed Cunningham's old flagship *Warspite* – 'in her appointed station', as Cunningham signalled her with pride and pleasure – the veteran not only of the victories over the Italian battlefleet at Cape Spartivento in 1940 and Cape Matapan in 1941, but also of the Battle of Jutland. And both *Warspite* and *Valiant* had been at sea that grey November day in 1918 when Beatty's Grand Fleet had conducted the Imperial German High Seas Fleet into internment. Now it was an Italian flagship, the cruiser *Eugenio di Savoia* (flying the flag of Admiral Romeo Oliva, who had taken the place of Bergamini) which led the line of a vanquished fleet astern of the same great battleships flying the White Ensign at the truck. Captain H. A. Packer of the *Warspite*, who had also served in her at Jutland, recorded the moment of meeting in his diary:

> Presently they came in sight at about 15 miles, and we steamed towards each other at 20 knots. It was in November 1940 in the Battle of Spartivento that I had last seen the Italian battleships. Our feelings were queer. Curtis, the Officer of the Watch (a South African), was mumbling to himself 'To think that I should be here to see this', and I felt the same. 'Guns' was busy comparing their silhouettes with his [identification] cards, and remembering his many tussles with them. As they took station astern the Padre said 'It's pathetic somehow'; and Pluto [the ship's dog] raced up and down the fo'c'sle barking . . .[35]

For Cunningham personally it was, in his own words 'a most moving and thrilling sight':[36]

> To see my wildest hopes of years back brought to fruition, and my former flagship the *Warspite*, which had struck the first blow against the Italians three years before, leading her erstwhile opponents into captivity, filled me with the deepest emotion and lives with me still. I can never forget it.[37]

When the British battleships escorted the Italian Fleet into Grand Harbour in the morning of 11 September, they found the Italian squadron from Taranto – the battleships *Andrea Doria* and the *Caio Duilio*, two cruisers and a destroyer – already there. Except for a few stray ships that came in to surrender in the following days, the entire Italian Navy was now moored in waters ringed by the cumulative ruin left by the Axis's three-year effort to bomb Malta into submission, and within the joyful sight of the celebrating population. Cunningham had now only one more duty to perform in the war against Italy, and that was to make this signal to the Admiralty:

> Be pleased to inform their Lordships that the Italian Battle Fleet now lies at anchor under the guns of the fortress of Malta.[38]

So, at a total cost to the Royal Navy since June 1940 in ships sunk of one battleship, two aircraft carriers, fourteen cruisers, a monitor, two anti-aircraft ships, two fast minelayers, 44 destroyers, 41 submarines, seven corvettes, eight fleet minesweepers, 94 other ships and craft of all kinds[39] and all the killed, drowned and wounded of their ships' companies, the Italian menace so quixotically and unnecessarily raised up by British diplomacy (and British public opinion) in the Abyssinian crisis of 1935–36 had at last been removed. The middle prong of the triple threat to the global sprawl of the British Empire had been broken.

The imperial lifeline through the Mediterranean to the dependent territories of the East lay open again to civilian as well as military traffic, so offering an immense economy in shipping tonnage as compared with the circuitous Cape route.

Yet how much nearer did the fall of Italy bring the defeat of Nazi Germany, the only prong of the triple threat that posed a mortal threat to the United Kingdom itself? Not much so far, to judge from the experience of the 'Avalanche' assault forces in the beach-heads of Salerno at the hands of the 16th Panzer Division.

It is important that the Military plan for the subsequent land campaign should be worked out first, and that the assaults should be solely designed to position our forces for the commencement of this. A sound Military plan subsequent to the assaults must be the basis of the whole operational plan . . .

So in September 1943 wrote Admiral Ramsay, the brilliantly successful naval planner of 'Torch' and 'Husky', and now home in the United Kingdom engaged in preliminary studies for 'Overlord'.[40]

Unfortunately General Mark Clark's 5th Army staff produced a military plan for 'Avalanche' that was flawed in overall design and defective in detail.[41] There were to be two separate landings some ten miles distant from each other; a clear invitation to a German commander to thrust in between them if the Allies failed to link up quickly. The British 10th Corps (General R. McCreery) formed the Northern Attack Force, with the British 46th and 56th Infantry Divisions, and two special brigades of Commandos and US Rangers under command. Its task on D-Day was to seize a lodgement running from the mountains fringing the northern coast of Salerno Bay (in order to command the road to Naples) and just north of the town of Salerno itself and then inland beyond the little town of Battipaglia, giving a maximum depth of about ten miles. The plan required the 46th Division to wheel north after landing in order to capture Salerno, a manoeuvre which must therefore expose its right flank to German counter-attacks; it required the 56th Division to advance inland ten miles and then extend its right flank southwards in order to link up with the American 45th Infantry Division from the southern beach-head. This would give the 56th Division a weak and vulnerable front some fifteen miles wide.[42]

Clark's plan allotted the Southern Attack Force (the US 6th Corps, with the 45th and 36th Infantry Divisions under command) a much narrower frontage both of initial landing and of objective line for D-Day, which ran from Ponte Sele some ten miles inland round to the coast just south of Paestum. However, the little river Sele and its tributary the Calore, both impassable except by bridges, sliced the hoped-for lodgement right to the sea; another opening for a German counter-attack.[43]

The 'Avalanche' lodgement area consisted of an undulating plain filled with tall crops, villages and olive groves and overlooked by a ring of mountains offering the German defenders marvellous observation and siting for artillery. In the words of two authorities on the Battle of Salerno, an invader 'was in effect thrusting his head into a bag'.[44]

The Allied landing forces appear formidable enough in numbers of men and heavy weapons – two special brigades of Commandos and Rangers, 27 battalions of infantry supported by 150 tanks, plentiful anti-tank guns, 144 field guns, 200 medium guns and howitzers, and 24 self-propelled howitzers, all to be put ashore by nightfall on D-Day. The defending 16th Panzer Division – 100 tanks, 55 assault guns, 36 medium howitzers, eight dual-purpose 88mm guns (as well as light anti-tank guns) – was therefore heavily outweighted.[45] Yet on the accepted rule-of-thumb that attackers should outnumber defenders by between 2.5 to 1 and 4 to 1 (and enjoy a faster rate of reinforcement) the Allied margin was slender, especially as the Allied infantry divisions as a whole could not compare in fighting efficiency with 16th Panzer. All four Allied divisions had originated as Territorial or National Guard civilian volunteer formations, and were now filled out with conscripts. Their own training and the quality of their officers and staffs did not always match the rigorous demands of an assault landing like 'Avalanche'. Moreover, while the two British infantry divisions (or some units within them) had had previous experience of battle (the 46th had been in the field in Tunisia from February to May), the two American divisions in the Southern Attack Force came largely new to it. The most effective arm of the Allied forces lay in their abundant and excellent artillery, and the well-trained gunners who served it.[46]

In the 16th Panzer Division the Allies confronted a veteran, if battered, formation of the Stalingrad campaign, with a core of war-hardened survivors around which a mass of new recruits had been quickly turned into competent soldiers by means of the excellent German training system and standardised tactical drills. Its officers and NCOs would know what to do, and they would do it with the customary unhesitating initiative;[47] and on the night of 8–9 September 1943 the four battlegroups of 16th Panzer were already in position around the Gulf of Salerno, watching and waiting for the Allied armada to loom into view across a moonlit sea.

The assault convoys deployed before dark for the final approach. From the British vessels of the Northern Attack Force the island of Capri could be clearly seen in the moonlight on the port beam. At 2155 the Southern Attack Force sighted the beacon light from the submarine HMS *Shakespeare*. At 2357 the moon set; by 0053 on the 9th all transports were anchored in their lowering positions nine to twelve miles off shore, and unloading began according to the now familiar routine. At 0217 the Commandos and Rangers set off for the northern shore of Salerno Bay. Soon the mass of infantry and support landing craft (many of them had voyaged from Sicily or North Africa under their own power) were heading for the beaches through enemy shell splashes with the main bodies of the two attack forces. In the vain hope of achieving tactical surprise the Allied command had decided not to lay on a preliminary naval or air bombardment of the German defences. Morning twilight was just beginning to lighten the sky behind the mountains inland when the ramps of the assault craft dropped on to the sand at about 0300.[48]

In the Northern Attack Force area (Commodore G. N. Oliver, with his broad pendant in the headquarters ship HMS *Hilary*) the Royal Navy put 10th Corps ashore with relatively few foul-ups. On the extreme left flank the Commandos and Rangers found their beaches empty of Germans, and they hastened into the mountains in order to secure the vital ground commanding the roads and railway from Naples to Salerno. On the adjacent Uncle Red beach part of the British 46th Division also came ashore free of mishap; a deceptive beginning. On Uncle Green beach the landing craft guides steered the assault wave towards a stretch of sand where rockets from support landing craft could be seen exploding. But the landing craft had mistaken the target, and the assault went ashore on the wrong part of the beach. The error led to congestion and confusion; it made it impossible to use Uncle Green for unloading that day.

The error also produced a knock-on effect on the neighbouring Sugar beaches to the south, by shouldering the assault waves of the 56th Division sideways. Nevertheless the beach parties managed quickly to sort out the resulting crowd scenes. On Roger Amber and Roger Green (the right flank beaches of the 56th Division) another error of navigation turned out to be a stroke of luck, Murphy's Law in reverse, for by landing 1,500 yards south of the correct point the first wave of landing craft evaded the fire of a German battery.

On the Southern Attack Force sector (Rear Admiral J. L. Hall,

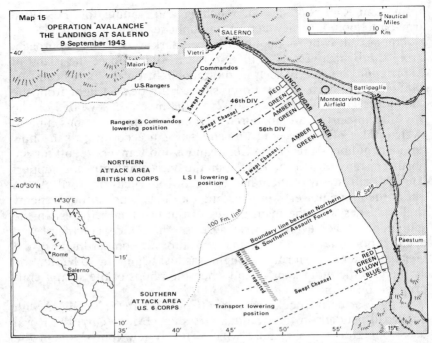

Map 15
OPERATION 'AVALANCHE'
THE LANDINGS AT SALERNO
9 September 1943

flying his flag in the transport *Samuel Chase*) the United States Navy put the US 45th and 36th Infantry Divisions (6th Corps) ashore on a narrow and continuous front without mishap except for delays in sweeping a channel through a suspected minefield. However, the very narrowness of the beach-head (the result of a shortage of landing craft) now began to cause major problems in deploying troops and feeding in supplies.

As a whole, therefore, the landings themselves had gone better than those in 'Torch' or 'Husky'. It was from now on, with the coming of daylight, that the trouble started. When Allied troops tried to push inland towards their D-Day objectives, the 16th Panzer offered the kind of resistance behind the beaches never before encountered in major amphibious operations in the Mediterranean. At the same time 16th Panzer put down a fierce bombardment on the crowded beaches themselves and on the follow-up waves of landing craft bringing in reinforcements and heavy weapons such as tanks. Luftwaffe fighter-bombers and dive-bombers roared in to make their own contribution of high explosive. The 'Avalanche' beaches all too soon presented a very different picture from the relatively undisturbed and systematic process of sorting out initial confusions that had characterised 'Torch' and 'Husky'. Instead, here was the classic picture of a battlefield – continual explosions, a litter of wrecked guns and transport and abandoned kit, damaged landing craft, corpses and wounded; frenzied, fear-driven activity.

On the Northern Attack Force sector the destroyers HMS *Laforey*, *Lookout* and *Loyal* closed the shore astern of the first assault waves according to plan in order to provide immediate floating artillery-support to the hard-pressed army, their fire called down on to specific targets by Bombardment Liaison Officers (BLOs) ashore with the troops. Direct duels took place between destroyers and German tanks and batteries, in which *Laforey* was hit five times and forced to retire temporarily for repairs. Under cover of smoke screens belched out by smoke-projectors in specially equipped landing craft, the follow-up waves continued to feed in troops, supplies, tanks and guns. By 1030 that morning the first of the big landing craft (tank) had beached; and in the next eleven hours no fewer than 38 of those valuable carriers unloaded on Sugar and Roger beaches.

On the Southern Attack Force sector no prior plans for destroyers to give the two American divisions fire support immediately on touch-down had been made, because of the US Army's mistaken hope of achieving surprise by a 'silent' landing. The green and not very well trained troops of the 45th and 36th Infantry had to struggle forward off the beaches in the face of the crackle and thunder of accurate enemy fire; a terrifying initiation to battle. But later in the day the monitor HMS *Abercrombie* (7,850 tons; two 15-inch guns),[49] the cruisers USS *Savannah* and *Philadelphia*, and several US destroyers came up to the rescue. By smothering positions held by 16th Panzer with 15-inch, 6-inch and 5-inch rounds, they decisively helped to prevent 6th Corps being trapped and destroyed on the beaches that first day.

Above this 30-mile-wide sunlit scene of smoke, fire, flashes from guns and bursting shells and bombs, packed beaches and a wide blue bay filled with shipping of all shapes and sizes, flew the Seafires from Admiral Vian's five light carriers. That day they made 265 sorties, keeping an average of 20 aircraft aloft at any one time. From bases in Sicily American Lockheed P-38 Lightnings with long-distance tanks also joined in the fight to keep the Luftwaffe away. But the Allied air plan went into a fatal spin when the British 56th Division failed to capture Montecorvino airfield as planned.

For in the course of D-Day the armies' battle had already gone desperately wrong – and with dangerous repercussions for the navies as well. On the extreme left of the landings, on the peninsula where the resort villages of Amalfi, Positano and Sorrento cling to the sides of mountains tumbling steeply into a copper sulphate sea, the Rangers and Commandos had fought their way inland and secured an objective line giving command of the key roads and the railway from Naples. But on the main British 10th Corps front, and despite the capture of the port of Salerno itself, 16th Panzer had the best of a confused 'soldiers' battle' at close quarters amid the sweetcorn and tobacco plantations, its battlegroups putting in a successful counter-attack that completely dislocated 10th Corps' plan. At the end of D-Day the Corps had been stopped well short of its objective line, and holding only a narrow lodgement less than five miles deep. The American 6th Corps (Southern Attack Force) had a truly terrible day, for the Corps attracted the heaviest German artillery fire and air attack, and its inexperience and clumsy tactics fared ill against 16th Panzer's determined battlegroups. By the end of D-Day 6th Corps too lay cramped into a narrow lodgement far short of its objectives. Most dangerous of all, the British and Americans had failed to link up their two beach-heads.[50]

The inability of the armies to get rapidly forward and the weight of enemy fire on the beaches (causing some to be closed) created a waterborne traffic jam of the big landing craft (tank) that were trying to put urgently needed armour ashore. This situation worsened the next day when enemy artillery fire forced the British to give up using the port of Salerno. By now the 14th Panzer Corps (with three panzer-grenadier divisions) was on its way to help 16th Panzer, and the 10th Army (General von Vietinghoff) had taken control of the German forces.

Between 10 and 15 September, the struggle at Salerno mounted to a crisis in which the Allied 5th Army appeared to Clark to be near to disaster. On land the enemy first fought the British and American troops to a standstill and then launched a classic counter-stroke intended to split the American 6th Corps front in two, and reach the sea. In the air the effort of carrier-borne Seafires waned each day until on 12 September Vian withdrew his light carriers to Palermo, while Admiral Hewitt ordered the remaining 26 aircraft to transfer to an improvised airstrip near Paestum. The Seafires (adapted Spitfires) were not really suitable for carrier operations, having weak undercarriages which led to 32 of those at Salerno being damaged by deck landings. At a maximum speed of 341 mph[51] they lacked the pace easily to intercept the German fighter-bombers. They also had difficulty in reaching the 19,000-feet altitude from which the special unit of Do-17s which had sunk the *Roma* were launching FX-1400 radio-guided bombs.[52]

And the radio-guided bombs once again were proving dismayingly effective. On 11 September the USS *Philadelphia* was badly shaken by a near-miss, the *Savannah* heavily damaged, and HMS *Uganda* damaged so severely as to need towing back to Malta. Cunningham forthwith ordered the cruisers HMS *Aurora* and *Penelope* to replace the damaged ships, while the US Navy sent in the cruiser *Boise*. Shortly before 1500 on 14 September Hewitt signalled Cunningham to report his anxiety about the critical military situation, and asked for heavy ships which could lay a protective curtain of fire between the recoiling Allied troops and the enemy. Cunningham immediately ordered *Warspite* and *Valiant* to sail forthwith. On 16 September the *Warspite* (which had arrived off Salerno with *Valiant* the previous day) was attacked at 1410 by an FX-1400-carrying aircraft which was neither detected by radar nor sighted. Two FX-1400s near-missed; a third penetrated to *Warspite*'s No. 4 boiler room and burst with tremendous concussion. At once five out of six boiler rooms filled with sea water, and the ship could only steam at slow speed on her starboard engines. Then at 1500 the last boiler room filled and all steam was lost. *Warspite* lay dead in the water in a crowded sea under enemy air attack; a situation which was indeed, as Captain Packer wrote in his subsequent report, 'unattractive'. Ignominiously this renowned fighting ship had to return to Malta wallowing astern of British and American tugs.

Meanwhile British and American cruisers and destroyers had been doing their own best to bloody the nose of the German offensive. Between 10 and 13 September the cruiser HMS *Mauritius* alone fired over 1,000 6-inch rounds. Nevertheless, by 14 September the Allied armies were everywhere stuck fast. Attacks rashly ordered by General Clark had been smashed by the enemy, and battlegroups of the 16th Panzer-Grenadier and 15th Panzer-Grenadier had thrown the Americans back to within three miles of the sea (this was the day that the much-needed fire of *Savannah* and *Uganda* was silenced by radio-guided bombs).

The German command believed on the 14th that the Allies were about to admit defeat and re-embark.[53] This was by no means fanciful. For that day a major crisis, even a panic, was taking place in the headquarters of General Clark's 5th Army. According to Admiral Sir Geoffrey Oliver (then Commodore Oliver, Naval Commander, Northern Attack Force):

Rather late on in the afternoon on D + 5, Hewitt asked me to come down and see him in BISCAYNE [his headquarters ship]. I duly went in the barge and found an atmosphere of intense gloom . . . To my surprise and misgiving, I was told that General Clark wanted two emergency plans immediately prepared . . . One was to withdraw the British X Corps and disembark it again through the American VI Corps beaches; the other was vice versa and was stated to be the most likely alternative. I was also asked to find room in HILARY for General Clark and his numerous Headquarters in the event of their leaving to be re-embarked, since ANCON [the big and vulnerable American headquarters ship] had departed.[54]

In other words, Clark and his staff were seriously considering giving up the American lodgement. In fact, at Clark's request Hewitt had already ordered all available craft to stand ready to lift the troops, and stopped the unloading of cargo ships in the Southern Attack Force sector. On hearing this defeatism as reported by Admiral Hewitt, Oliver was horrified:

> I protested to Hewitt that re-embarkation of heavily engaged troops from a rather shallow beach-head, followed by disembarkation again, was simply not on, quite apart from other considerations. I also said that in my view it would be suicidal to so shorten the front, which would allow enemy artillery to rake the beaches from end to end, and that we should lose an immense amount of ammunition and stores already ashore.
>
> I asked whether my Corps Commander [McCreery] had been consulted, but no one seemed to know.[55]

General Mark Clark, inexperienced as he still was, had so far proved in his first battle crisis a commander more notable for his imposing eagle profile and his personal courage under fire than his operational competence. As for Commodore Oliver, he returned to his ship 'very angry', and got in touch as soon as he could with McCreery through his liaison officer at 10th Corps headquarters. He learned later that night that McCreery knew nothing of Clark's project, 'was furious and was last seen making tracks for Army Headquarters to expostulate. I reported the position by signal to A.B.C. to enlist his support against any such plan being pursued further.'[56] McCreery himself signalled Clark and Hewitt to say that he considered there was no question of such re-embarkations taking place. Cunningham fully supported Oliver; he too perceived that if the Allied lodgement were narrowed, the enemy would be able to enfilade the entire length of shore from either flank. Nothing further was heard about the project, which would have resulted in a catastrophe of the first magnitude. As Admiral Hewitt remarked in retrospect, 'Fortunately, very fortunately I believe, subsequent developments made it unnecessary to attempt it.'[57]

Since the British 10th Corps, although stuck fast, was at this time not so hard-pressed by enemy attack as the American 6th Corps, McCreery remained confident that with the mass of reinforcements, tanks, guns and ammunition still pouring into the lodgement the Allies could stop the enemy and force him back. And so it proved. The German onslaught on the Americans faltered in the face of the immense weight of fire put down by the American gunners, supplemented by the heavy ships, cruisers and destroyers off shore. A fresh attack on the 10th Corps was similarly smashed by British artillery. By 16 September the crisis was over; the Allied lodgement was secure. Meanwhile, on the 13th, Montgomery had started off again with the main body of the 8th Army in response to anxious proddings from Alexander, at the same time sending light troops on ahead to make contact with the 5th Army and threaten the rear of the enemy. In the event, it was a party of journalists with the 8th Army who were first to penetrate through to the Salerno beachhead.[58]

Field-Marshal Kesselring was nevertheless well pleased with the performance of his 10th Army at Salerno. For eight days it had held, and even forced on to the defensive, a much more powerful Allied army backed by a fleet. Mere platoons of panzer-grenadiers had seen off whole companies of Britons and Americans. Now it was time to put into operation his well-pondered strategy for a protracted campaign. He ordered the 10th Army to wheel back, pivoting on its right (on the north coast of Salerno Bay) in order to form a front with a new 14th Army extending from the Mediterranean across to the Adriatic, and then make a step-by-step fighting withdrawal to the *Gustavstellung* (Gustav Line).[59]

The Allies took much delight in their prize of Naples, occupied on 1 October. It seemed for a happy moment that the grand hopes entertained by Churchill and Brooke of their Mediterranean strategy were now in the course of being realised. The moment swiftly passed. Instead the 5th and 8th Armies now began dragging months of dreary campaigning against a skilled and stubborn German retirement, as the weather worsened week by week; one mountain ridge after another to fight for, one river after another to battle a way across. An attempt to employ seapower to land commandos and two infantry brigades behind the German front on the Adriatic at Termoli on 3–6 October narrowly succeeded after a stiff fight against battlegroups of the 16th Panzer counter-attacking straight off the march from their rest camps;

a repetition in miniature of the lesson of Salerno that seapower is merely a defended transport service, not a magic formula of victory, and that what counts is the subsequent land battle.

In November the Allies came up against the *Bernhardstellung*, the formidable outwork of the *Gustavstellung*; more grim attrition battles and slow advances against the German 10th and 14th Armies (now constituted as Army Group C). By now the Italian winter had broken in all its bleakness, and the Allied troops began to suffer from attrition by sickness and frostbite as well as German fire. In December the 5th and 8th Armies found themselves before the *Gustavstellung* itself – the most ingenious use of ideal defensive terrain in order to create a virtually impregnable defence system since Wellington's Lines of Torres Vedras in Portugal in 1810.[60] On the Adriatic sector Montgomery's frontal pushes across the River Sangro, intended to break through the *Gustavstellung*, bogged down in mini-Sommes of clinging mud, floods, lashing rain and a tenacious German defence in depth. In the Mediterranean sector Clark's 5th Army gnawed away at a massive chain of fortified mountain ramparts largely held by an outstanding frontline soldier, General von Senger, and his valiant 14th Panzer Corps.

By the end of December 1943 the Italian front had become locked fast in a stalemate reminiscent of such earlier essays in 'blue water' strategy as Gallipoli in 1915 or the Allied Salonika front in 1916–18. Rome, the prize Churchill had dreamed of in July, still lay securely under the Swastika some 80 miles beyond the *Gustavstellung*, with far distant Vienna unimaginably out of reach. Some 'underbelly'; some 'softest part'!

As for the Royal and United States Navies, their major role in Mediterranean 'blue water' strategy had come to an end with the successful establishment of the Allied armies on the Italian mainland in September 1943. On 6 October Admiral Kent Hewitt struck his flag as Commander, Western Naval Task Force, upon the dissolution of that force. Henceforward Rear-Admiral J. A. V. Morse of the Royal Navy, flying his flag ashore in Naples as Flag Officer, Western Italy, would be responsible for naval operations in the Tyrrhenian Sea. On 14 October Vice-Admiral Sir Algernon Willis struck his flag as Flag Officer, Force H, and a few days later this famous battle squadron, whose record of battle encompassed the attacks on the French Fleet in 1940, the hunt for the *Bismarck*, the hard-fought convoys to Malta, and the 'Torch', 'Husky' and 'Avalanche' landings, was also disbanded. Its badly needed heavy ships could now be deployed against the Japanese in the Indian Ocean or brought back to England to strengthen the Home Fleet.

And at sunset on 17 October 1943 the Union Flag of Admiral of the Fleet Sir Andrew Cunningham, Bart, GCB, Commander-in-Chief, Mediterranean, was struck in HMS *Maidstone*. The Admiral had already flown back to London two days earlier to take up the post of First Sea Lord in succession to the dying Sir Dudley Pound (see below, pp. 731-4). Cunningham's departure from the Mediterranean marked the end of the sea-going career of England's greatest fighting sailor since Nelson – who, like him, was ever eager to engage the enemy as closely as possible.

> I leave you all in the Mediterranean with keen regret [he signalled in farewell]; but also with pride. It has been my privilege to command a great fleet of ships of the Allied nations of every category from battleships to the smallest craft. We may well look back with satisfaction to the work which has been performed . . . To you all who have fought and endured with such courage, tenacity and determination, I send my heartfelt thanks and appreciation . . .[61]

He was succeeded by his namesake (but no relative) Admiral Sir John Cunningham, formerly C-in-C, Levant Command, who at first flew his flag ashore at Algiers, and then, from the beginning of January 1944, at Naples. With the Mediterranean now dominated by Allied seapower from end to end, and no longer an enemy battlefleet to fight, the tasks of the Allied navies henceforward would be to protect convoys against U-boats, E-boats and the Luftwaffe ranging down from French or North Italian airfields; to run supplies up both coasts of Italy to the Allied armies; and to attack the enemy shipping that still plied in the Aegean, Adriatic and in Mediterranean waters off France and Italy. It was a war now of smaller vessels and craft instead of heavy ships and fleet carriers, of workaday but essential service instead of desperate sea fights.

However in the autumn of 1943, while the Allies were landing in Italy and struggling north towards the *Gustavstellung*, the Royal Navy had been put through an exercise in instant 'blue water' strategy in the Aegean that marked a throw-back to the Greek adventure of 1941, the trip to Dakar and the intervention in Norway in 1940, and even the expedition to the Dardanelles in 1915.

On 10-14 September 1943, British forces had landed on the Dodecanese islands of Kastellorizo, Kos and Leros. By 18 September seven of the islands were in the hands of scratch British garrisons, but not Rhodes, the biggest and the military key to all the rest. On the 13th Churchill had made a signal to General Sir Henry Maitland Wilson, the C-in-C, Middle East, which struck a familiar enough note:

> The capture of Rhodes by you at this time with Italian aid would be a fine contribution to the general war. Let me know what are your plans for this. Can you not improvise the necessary garrison out of the forces in the Middle East? What is your ration strength?[62]

The capture of Rhodes ('Operation Accolade') had been a favourite in the Prime Minister's toy-box ever since 1942, taken out and played with from time to time by him and the British Chiefs of Staff, even offered to the Americans at various summit conferences as one of the attractions for pursuing a Mediterranean strategy throughout 1943.[63] In May 1943, at the Chiefs of Staff's request, General Maitland Wilson had submitted in time for the 'Trident' Washington Conference a grand proposal by which 'Accolade' became the mere preliminary to 'possible major operations based on Salonika and Istanbul with objectives up to the line of the Danube'.[64] In July, with the fall of Mussolini, the Prime Minister took 'Accolade' out of the box again, minuting the Chiefs of Staff: 'Here is a business of great consequence, to be thrust forward by every means . . .'[65] In turn the Chiefs of Staff on 3 August prodded Maitland Wilson, authorising him to ask Eisenhower for the necessary landing craft and air cover.[66] But Eisenhower refused to divert resources from the task given him by directive of the Combined Chiefs of Staff.

> I view with considerable concern [he signalled the British Chiefs of Staff on 12 August] possibility that in practice requirements of this operation will draw on resources urgently required for main business in hand which is to knock Italy out of the war. Fact is that in Mediterranean there are many critical items such as AA, landing craft, air forces which are barely sufficient for present operations. Operations such as Accolade cannot be staged without drawing to some extent upon these resources.
>
> In my opinion, with which the D.C-in-C [Alexander], C-in-C, Mediterranean [Sir Andrew Cunningham] and Air C-in-C [Tedder] agree, we should concentrate on one thing at a time and Accolade should be abandoned for the present.[67]

Eisenhower, strong in his position as an Allied commander and an American officer, was not to be budged by further pleading and pressure from the British. If they wanted to adventure in the Aegean, they would therefore have to do it on their own resources. General Maitland Wilson therefore netted his now backwater of a Middle

East command for resources. On 9 September, D-Day of 'Avalanche' and the morrow of the Italian surrender, Churchill signalled Wilson on learning that his attack on Rhodes with improvised forces was imminent: 'Good. This is the time to play high. Improvise and dare.'[68]

But on 14 September the Italian garrison on Rhodes surrendered to the Germans. To take the island would now require a major amphibious operation and a hard fight. By no means discouraged, however, the Premier now evoked for his colleagues and Allies a vision of the Balkans set aflame by the igniting agent of an Allied occupation of Rhodes. Turkey might thereby be encouraged to enter the war; the Allies might land a small force in Greece; the Allies might then open the Dardanelles and pass ships through into the Black Sea; an Allied expeditionary force (perhaps the 80,000 strong Polish Army in exile, now in the Middle East, plus the New Zealand Division) might land on the Dalmatian coast.[69]

However, it soon became obvious that the British forces in the Aegean were neither strong enough to attack Rhodes, nor even withstand for long a German counter-offensive aimed at recapturing the other islands of the Dodecanese. In particular the Luftwaffe enjoyed complete air superiority (the Dodecanese being virtually out of range of British aircraft from the Middle East) and was using it to full effect – another throw-back to 1941.[70] From the British Chiefs of Staff, from the Prime Minister himself, there now came a succession of pleas to Eisenhower for troops, ships, bombers, transport aircraft and long-range fighters.[71]

But Eisenhower steadfastly refused more than a trickle of help. On 12 August he signalled the British Chiefs of Staff: 'In my opinion we should concentrate on one thing at a time and Accolade [the projected attack on Rhodes] should be abandoned at present.' In a further signal of 1 September he listed the 'limit of resources provide for Aegean in view of absolute necessity for concentrating on main battle in Italy . . .'[72]

This signal caused dismay among the British Middle East Cs-in-C, for they estimated that 350 German aircraft were now thrashing the weak British garrisons in the Dodecanese and the Royal Navy in the Aegean Sea. A minimum of four Lightning fighter squadrons and a heavy bombing effort against Greek airfields was required 'forthwith', they signalled London in reply to a COS signal of 20 September, 'otherwise position in Leros and Cos [sic] may become untenable . . .'[73] But on 5 October Eisenhower (backed by Tedder) insisted that likely German resistance in Italy meant that he 'must employ the whole available air effort'; and he pronounced against a major operation to take Rhodes;

> ... if Accolade is undertaken the operation however desirable in itself is bound to place calls on us for a very considerable and continuing diversion of air effort from the main operations in Italy. I consider any material diversion highly prejudicial to the success of Italian operations . . .[74]

And that was that. Eisenhower's devotion to the classic strategic principle of the concentration of force and the avoidance of dispersion (as well as his obedience to the directives of the Combined Chiefs of Staff) cannot be faulted. Now the British armed services had once again to pay the consequences of strategic opportunism. By 3 October Kos had already come under German assault, eliciting a message from the Prime Minister to the British garrison commander that might easily have been reprinted from those despatched just before the fall of Singapore or Tobruk: 'We rely on you to defend this island to the utmost limit . . .'[75] Next day Kos was overrun.

In the face of the Luftwaffe the British had to resort to the submarines *Severn* and *Rorqual* to run supplies to the British garrison on Leros from Haifa. During one trip the *Rorqual* had to dive with a jeep and six Bofors guns lashed to the casing when it was attacked by German aircraft; hardly to the benefit of the jeep's engine. Four Italian submarines were also employed to ferry stores. But such frantic improvisations proved of no avail. On 13–14 November the German Army landed on Leros supported by the Luftwaffe enjoying its brief local return to total air superiority. By the 16th Leros was in enemy hands. On the night of 19–20 November Samos was evacuated, and on the 28th Kastel/lorizo. So ended this replay in miniature of Greece and Crete in 1941.

For the Royal Navy, as it braved the Luftwaffe in order to succour the troops and then eventually bring them away, the sense of *déjà vu* was especially keen, for the Dodecanese gamble too cost them dear. The Royal and Royal Hellenic Navies suffered four cruisers damaged (one of them, HMS *Carlisle*, beyond repair), six destroyers sunk and four damaged, and ten coastal craft and minesweepers sunk.[76]

The unfolding débâcle by no means quenched Churchill's enthusiasm for maritime offensives in the Aegean. Even while the Dodecanese islands were falling to the enemy he was urging that fresh operations be mounted to retake Kos and take Rhodes. What was more, in his mind such operations remained only the opening gambit in carrying the war into the Balkans.[77] Did Brooke, that other convinced pro-

(*Above*) The fortress and harbour of Gibraltar, in 1939. It was the key to British control of the western Mediterranean and the eastern side of the Atlantic. Here the Anglo-American armada was concentrated before the 'Torch' invasion of French North Africa, November 1942. (IWM) (*Below*) 'Ark Royal owed her demise primarily to flaws in her own design. . . .' The aircraft-carrier sinking after being torpedoed by U-81 some thirty miles from Gibraltar, 13 November 1941. (IWM)

(*Left*) 'Cunningham's most conspicuous quality was his intense spirit of attack.' Sir Andrew Cunningham, Commander-in-Chief, Mediterranean Fleet, 1939–42 and 1943; Allied Naval Commander Expeditionary Force in 'Operation Torch,' 1942; First Sea Lord, 1943-45. (Hulton) (*Below*) 'The enemy was at a range of no more than 3,800 yards – point-blank.' The sinking of three Italian cruisers by the Mediterranean Fleet, 28 March 1941, in the Battle of Cape Matapan, from a painting by Roland Langmaid. (IWM)

(*Above*) 'The steadfast way in which these ships pressed
on their way to Malta through all the attacks . . . was a
most inspiring sight.' (*Below*) The oil tanker *Ohio* hit
by a torpedo in the Malta convoy 'Operation Pedestal',
August 1942. She finally reached Malta safely. (Crown)

(Above) 'The dull rumble of a terrific explosion. . . .'
The battleship HMS *Barham* blows up in the
Mediterranean, 25 November 1941, after being struck
by three torpedoes from U-331. (IWM) *(Below)* 'The
Italian Battle Fleet now lies at anchor under the guns
of the fortress of Malta.' Admiral Sir Andrew

Cunningham's signal to the Admiralty on 11 September
1943 after the surrender of the Italian Navy. (IWM)

ponent of 'blue water' Mediterranean strategy, concur? He certainly disapproved of Churchill's 'Rhodes madness', as he termed it on 7 October 1943, characterising it as 'another of those typical examples of dispersal of effort for very problematic gains'.[78] But on the much larger issue of extending the scope of present Mediterranean operations from Italy into the Balkans, he was much of the same mind as the Premier, confiding to his diary on 20 November (during another summit conference, this time in Cairo: 'Sextant') that 'the drag' of the Americans

> ... has seriously affected our Mediterranean strategy and the whole conduct of the War. If they had come wholeheartedly into the Mediterranean with us we should by now have Rome securely, the Balkans would be ablaze, the Dardanelles would be open, and we should be on the highway to get Rumania and Bulgaria out of the war.[79]

Did Brooke in his heart hanker like Churchill for a Mediterranean solution to beating Germany which would avoid the necessity for 'Overlord', that dreaded encounter with a main body of the Germany Army?[80] His biographer has to answer that this remains an enigma.[81] Certainly Brooke and Churchill fought as hard as they could with their American allies before and at the Cairo Conference to persuade them not to weaken Allied resources in the Mediterranean in order to build up strength in the United Kingdom for 'Overlord', and successfully cajoled them into allowing General Alexander (now Allied Commander, 15th Army Group, in Italy) to retain 68 landing craft due to go to England.[82] Certainly too both men (and the British Chiefs of Staff) were willing to see 'Overlord' postponed in order to ensure success in Italy.[83]

At the second plenary meeting of the Cairo Conference on 24 November 1943 Churchill put to Roosevelt 'the programme he advocated':

> Rome in January, Rhodes in February, supplies to the Yugoslavs, the opening of the Aegean subject to the outcome of an approach to Turkey, and all preparations for 'Overlord' to go ahead full steam within the framework of the foregoing policy for the Mediterranean.[84]

A paper by the British Chiefs of Staff wrapped meat round these bare bones, but no final decision was taken. That had to wait for the Teheran Conference ('Eureka') held immediately after 'Sextant'. Here Churchill presented a deftly turned sales pitch to Stalin on the next stage of Mediterranean strategy:

... we had not contemplated going into the broad part of the leg of Italy, still less of invading Germany across the Alps. The general plan was first to capture Rome and seize the airfields north of it, which would enable us to bomb Southern Germany, and then to establish ourselves on a line towards Pisa–Rimini. After that the possibility of establishing a Third Front in conformity with, but not in substitution for, the cross-Channel operation would have to be planned.[85]

This 'Third Front' might take the form, he said, of a move into southern France or 'from the head of the Adriatic north-west towards the Danube'.[86] Beguilingly he assured the conference that there was 'no question' of using large forces in the Mediterranean or the Aegean. But neither he nor Britain any longer weighed in the scales of Allied decision-making as once they had, for in different ways the war efforts of the United States and Soviet Russia, the two continental powers, now dwarfed that of Britain, an island state of only 45 millions with an industrial base too small and backward to equip her own forces, and an economy kept going by an American life-support machine. It was Stalin who – with Roosevelt's tacit support – ruthlessly decided the outcome of the conference: 'Overlord' in May 1944; a Supreme Commander for it to be nominated immediately; a subsidiary Mediterranean operation into southern France rather than towards the Danube.

The Anglo-American Combined Chiefs of Staff in their own closed sessions in Teheran did however agree that there should be a limited further offensive in Italy aimed at the capture of Rome and an advance to the Pisa–Rimini line, as well as the supply of modest rations of support for the Yugoslav partisans. So once again the Western Allies decided to take their Mediterranean strategy forward one more step, and once again supposedly under tight limits. Yet Brooke took comfort from the fact that the theatre was now going to retain landing craft for the invasion of southern France ('Anvil'); resources which he reckoned (according to his biographer) that General Alexander, 'once they were to hand, might use to better effect as the situation developed'.[87] In other words Brooke still saw a chance that the tight limits might again in the event be stretched, just as they had been stretched to General Marshall's discomfiture and dismay after 'Torch' and after 'Husky'.

In December 1943 the Prime Minister suggested to the Chiefs of Staff that the 'stagnation' on the Italian front could be ended and Rome swiftly taken if Allied seapower were used to land a powerful force behind the German front.[88] Such an operation, reckoned the COS, would require at least 88 landing craft. However, of the 102 at present in the Mediterranean, 68 (56 of them British) were due to return to England in mid-January in preparation for 'Overlord'. Could the Americans be persuaded to consent to all craft remaining in the theatre for another three weeks for the sake of a stroke which would enable the Allies to advance to the Pisa–Rimini line? They could: Roosevelt telegraphed their agreement on 28 December.[89]

On 21 January 1944 the expedition to carry out 'Operation Shingle' (a landing on the west coast of Italy astride the port of Anzio) put to sea from Naples, the force commander, Admiral F. J. Lowry (of the United States Navy) flying his flag in the headquarters ship USS *Biscayne*.[90]

The Northern Assault Force ('Peter' Force) consisted of the British 1st Infantry Division and two Commandos embarked in three landing ships (infantry), 33 landing ships (tank) and 56 infantry and other types of landing craft, all escorted by the cruisers *Orion* and *Spartan* (15th Cruiser Squadron: Rear-Admiral J. M. Mansfield), the anti-aircraft and fighter-direction ship *Palomares*, eleven destroyers, sixteen minesweepers, four anti-submarine/minesweeping trawlers, three tugs and some twenty miscellaneous smaller craft.[91] The majority of the shipping and warships were British. In command of Peter Force was Rear-Admiral T. H. Troubridge, flying his flag in the headquarters ship HMS *Bulolo*, the veteran of 'Torch'.

The Southern Attack Force ('X-Ray') comprised three battalions of Rangers and the US 3rd Infantry Division, transported in five British landing ships (infantry), 40 British and ten American landing ships (tank), and 104 assorted types of landing craft. X-Ray Force was escorted by the cruisers HMS *Penelope* and USS *Brooklyn*, thirteen destroyers (ten American, two Greek and one British), two Dutch gunboats and 23 American minesweepers.[92] The Royal Navy supplied the two beacon submarines for the landing, HMS *Ultor* ('Peter' beaches) and HMS *Uproar* ('X-Ray' beaches). In the event the expedition's strength in landing craft of all kinds had been built up to a total of no fewer than 162. 'Operation Shingle' therefore represented a very major investment of maritime resources.

From the navies' point of view the Anzio landings on 22 January 1944 (H-hour at 0200) proved much like the first day of 'Avalanche', there being few major mishaps or errors, thanks to the excellent prior reconnaissance of the beaches and painstaking staff work carried out against the clock; and even though the beaches 'with their shallow approach and offshore sandbars were,' wrote Troubridge in his report, 'the worst in my experience.' Within a week 68,886 men, 508 guns, 237 tanks and 27,250 tons of stores had been unloaded – and despite a gale which forced the closure of the beaches for two days.[93] But, again as in 'Avalanche', German fighter-bombers, torpedo-bombers and a special unit equipped with glider bombs (this time the Hs.293 radio-controlled, rocket-boosted, winged missile with a speed of 300 to 400 mph and a warhead of 1,000 pounds of explosive)[94] came early and stayed late. In that first week the destroyer HMS *Janus* was sunk and HMS *Jervis* and USS *Plunkett* badly damaged; one of three brilliantly illuminated hospital ships, the *St David*, was also sunk – a repetition of the Luftwaffe's similar feat of arms on D-Day of 'Husky'; the US destroyer *Mayo* struck a mine and had to be towed back to Naples; and, worst loss of all, HMS *Spartan* capsized inshore after being hit by a Hs.293 guided missile.

On 2 February Admiral Sir John Cunningham, C-in-C, Mediterranean, ordered Lowry to hand over command of the naval forces to Rear-Admiral Morse, Flag Officer, Western Italy, in Naples. It was a sign that the navies' principal task in landing the 'Shingle' forces was done; now began the hard grind of running in supplies and reinforcements and providing fire support to the Army. For it was on the soldiers and the land battle that depended the success of 'Shingle', as of all amphibious operations.

According to General Clark's offensive plan, the 'Shingle' forces were to strike immediately and rapidly inland to cut the communications of the German 10th Army in the *Gustavstellung* while the 5th Army attacked it frontally and broke through towards Rome. None of this happened. The 5th Army's offensive was stopped in its tracks with heavy loss, largely owing to Mark Clark's faulty planning and operational mistakes. Owing to feeble leadership on the part of the commanding general, the American John Lucas, the 'Shingle' landing forces contented themselves with establishing a defensive perimeter round their beach-head. Both he and Clark himself had strongly disliked the 'Shingle' venture; and Clark had even told Lucas to dig in rather than take risks. The initiative was promptly seized by the Germans; the invaders became the besieged and in desperate danger of being heaved into the sea – 'Avalanche' all over again. But just as in 'Avalanche', the enemy attacks were eventually held in savage fighting and partly thanks to naval gunfire, and the Allied lodgement made secure.

This time, however, no strategic retreat by the enemy followed. Instead the front at Anzio became as frozen in stalemate as the main

Italian front – a vain exercise in seapower, indeed a veritable Gallipoli. This four-month stalemate laid a severe strain on the Allied navies, for the planning for 'Operation Shingle' had originally assumed that the expeditionary force would only have to be supplied by sea for fifteen days, after which it had been expected that overland supply would be opened from the main Allied front.

On that main front, the cutting edge of Churchill's and Brooke's Mediterranean strategy, the 5th Army continued to hew in vain at the iron shield of the *Gustavstellung*. American, British, Indian and New Zealand troops in turn all pitted their military skills and military virtue in vain against the 14th Panzer Corps in a narrow killing ground around Monte Cassino, and beneath in the ruins of the town of Cassino itself (defended by the 1st Parachute Division). Here – and at Anzio – was fought the Verdun, the Stalingrad, the Passchendaele of the Italian campaign.[95] The stalemate endured through February, through March, through April and into May, despite one Allied offensive after another – and these were the months of preparation for 'Overlord', when according to Churchill's and Brooke's strategic thinking the Italian front should have been weakening the forces available to the enemy to meet a cross-Channel invasion. That, after all, had supplied them with a central argument in support of their 'blue water' strategy.

But in fact the long-drawn-out campaign in Italy was costing the Allies far more dear in resources than the enemy, not least because again they were fighting in a detached theatre of war dependent on long sea communications.

According to two authorities on the campaign, Dominick Graham and Shelford Bidwell, the Allied commitment of manpower for land and air forces (including infrastructure and logistics) was to rise by 1944 to a total of 1,677,000.[96] This figure compares with Kesselring's 195,000 men in July 1943 and 411,000 in July 1944.[97] As for the high British hopes that the collapse of Italy would force the Germans to drain away troops from their other fronts to a possibly disastrous extent in order to hold the Balkans, the truth is that the German deployment in Yugoslavia increased by a net total of only seven divisions (mostly second-class and ill-equipped) between the time of Italy's surrender up to February 1944, and only one of these divisions came originally from the Russian front.[98]

Moreover, to supply the Allied forces in the whole western Mediterranean area (including Italy) called for the commitment of over 1 million deadweight tons of British shipping alone.[99] Kesselring by contrast drew his supplies direct from Germany, only some 600 miles distant, along direct road and mainline rail links through the Alps – including the railways of neutral Switzerland. As Graham and Bidwell acknowledge: 'It could be said, therefore, that it was not Alexander who was drawing forces that would otherwise be employed against Allies in north-west Europe, but Kesselring who was containing Alexander.'[100]

On 18 May 1944 Alexander launched the 15th Army Group into a grand offensive on the front from Monte Cassino to the sea. Thanks to a brilliant plan designed by Major-General John Harding, Alexander's Chief of Staff, and the sheer weight of cleverly concentrated manpower, airpower and metal the *Gustavstellung* now gave way at last. Polish troops took Monte Cassino. Reinforced Allied forces in the Anzio beach-head broke out with the task of cutting off the 10th Army's retreat and so turning victory into total annihilation. However, General Clark, the 5th Army commander, in his vanity and egoism, diverted the Anzio forces north-westwards in order to award himself the prize of the city of Rome, rather than north-eastwards across the German lines of communication. The 10th Army escaped to fight another day. Rome fell on 4 June.

Now, while the 15th Army Group pressed on after the retreating enemy, Churchill and Brooke tried for the last time to persuade the American leadership to make a further investment in their Mediterranean strategy. They wished them to cancel the proposed seaborne invasion of the French Riviera (now codenamed 'Dragoon' instead of 'Anvil') so that Alexander could keep the two divisions and the landing craft earmarked for it. Alexander even revived Churchill's vision of marching to Vienna (and getting there before the Russians) from northern Italy via the so-called 'Ljubljana Gap' in Yugoslavia. Brooke himself, however, regarded this less as strategy than as mere 'dreams' or 'hopes',[101] since the 'Ljubljana Gap' actually consisted of a long and tortuous route with bad road and rail communications through mountain country; ideal terrain for a German army on the defensive.[102]

But the Americans would not hear of cancelling 'Dragoon'. Eisenhower (whose Allied Expeditionary Force was by now on the verge of final victory in Normandy), Marshall and Roosevelt all turned down the proposal flat, much to Churchill's chagrin.[103] 'Dragoon' duly took place on 15 August, so securing in Marseille a major and undamaged port which Eisenhower badly needed for the supply of his armies via the Rhone valley (see below pp. 842 and 849).

After the fall of Rome the elation of victory in the 15th Army Group once more gradually gave way to curdling disappointment as the retreat of Kesselring's Army Group C slowed down to another step-by-step fighting withdrawal through the mountains. It took August and September to crumble away the stubborn defence of the Gothic Line, running across Italy north of Pisa and Florence to Pesaro on the Adriatic. By December 1944 after months of grim slogging, of huge expenditure of shells and steeply mounting casualties, and despite total command of the air, the Allied armies found themselves once more stuck fast in stalemate: and still short of the wide plains of northern Italy. There they remained until April 1945.[104]

And every shell, every cartridge, every man's daily rations, every gallon of fuel or aviation spirit, every spare part and every bandage reached the Allied front by grace of the convoys still making the 8,000-mile round voyage between America and the Mediterranean ports and the 3,000-mile round voyage between Britain and those ports – and by grace also of the Allied warships that protected the merchantmen against the U-boat, the E-boat and the marauding bomber. Albert Kesselring could well smile, for his diversionary campaign was proving as profitable as Rommel's in Africa.

While the Allied armies had been hammering their way north, the navies had been keeping pace along the west and east coasts of Italy, busy with the routine tasks of ferrying up supplies, bombarding enemy troops and communications, attacking his convoys, landing raiding parties to keep alive the enemy's fear for his flanks. In the Adriatic a kind of guerrilla war at sea was fought by the Royal Navy and the French Navy, their destroyers and coastal craft sneaking into the channels running between the myriad islands strung along the Dalmatian coast in order to prey upon enemy coastal traffic. In the Aegean British and Greek ships were waging a similar buccaneering war amid the archipelagoes.

Yet it was the Russian victories on the Eastern Front in autumn 1944, leading to the collapse of the whole German position in the Balkans, which opened the way for the Royal Navy to return to the waters north of Crete for the first time since May 1941. On 5 September the Germans began to thin out their troops in southern Greece, Crete and the Aegean islands. On 3 October they decided to pull out of Greece altogether, although they still left reduced garrisons in Crete, Rhodes and elsewhere to fight it out to the last. Next day British commandos landed at Patras in the Peloponnese; the first British troops to stand on the Greek mainland since the débâcle of 1941. On 13–14 October parachute troops seized Athens airport in the wake of the decamping Germans and entered Athens. On the

15th a task force of two British infantry brigades escorted by the 15th Cruiser Squadron and two escort carriers commanded by Rear-Admiral J. M. Mansfield, flying his flag in HMS *Orion*, arrived in the Gulf of Athens; and by sunset, after a mass of shallow mines had been swept, Mansfield brought his ships to anchor off Piraeus. So after three and a half years the Royal Navy and the British Army returned again to Greece by the grace of the continental victories of the Red Army; and two veterans of the desperate evacuation of April 1941, HMS *Orion* and her sister ship *Ajax*, lay moored amid a mass of British and Greek ships of war beneath a sky whence never again would Stukas howl down to loose their bombs.

On 8 April 1945 the 8th Army in Italy in a new offensive smashed through the Adriatic sector of the German front; on the 14th (it was two days before the Red Army opened its final offensive across the Oder towards Berlin) the 5th Army Group pursued a disintegrating Army Group C to the foothills of the Alps. On 29 April (far away to the north the Russians were now fighting in the very heart of Berlin) was signed the unconditional surrender of Army Group C, to come into effect on 2 May. It marked the final consummation of the 'blue water' strategy espoused by the British since June 1940.

Yet after all the land campaigning from the Nile to the Po and beyond, all the Royal Navy's fleet actions and convoy struggles, all the sunk and shattered ships, all the arguments in London and Washington, this strategy had ended in a cul-de-sac. For ahead of 15th Army Group towered the barrier of the Alps, stretching in a vast semi-circle from the French Riviera round to Trieste on the Adriatic. This barrier German soldiers could have defended indefinitely if there had not been already behind it in southern France the forces of the Anglo-Americans, and behind it in northern Yugoslavia and Austria the forces of the Yugoslavs and Russians – and if the Third Reich had not itself been within six days of extinction when the surrender of Army Group C to Alexander came into effect.

For the ultimate victory in the Mediterranean was a mere by-play in the conclusion of a war that had been won in mass battles on the Eastern and Western Fronts. And the Western Front owed its existence to what remains to this day by far the grandest amphibious operation ever, and one executed under the command of an admiral of the Royal Navy.

23

'Such Desolate and Dangerous Voyages': the Arctic Convoys, 1941–1945

Ever since 22 June 1941, when 143 German divisions (including seventeen panzer) launched 'Operation Barbarossa' – Hitler's war to conquer and colonise the Soviet Union west of the Urals – it had been clear to the British leadership that in the Red Army lay the one potential means of tearing the guts out of German military power. For in contrast to the Great War the Eastern Front now constituted the *only* front in the present war where mass battles of attrition were taking place; it would remain the only one until the Western Front could be eventually reopened by an Anglo-American landing in France. At first, during the initial German onrush into the Soviet Union in the summer of 1941, British military opinion doubted the Red Army's ability to survive. Nevertheless, in order to help the Soviet Union as best she could, Britain quickly began to despatch aircraft, tanks, trucks and other war supplies which she could ill spare at this time of her own weakness. In August 1941 the first convoy to Russia (codenamed 'Dervish'), sailed for Archangel with seven freighters, followed by a second in September (PQ1). By the end of the year eight outward convoys had been despatched, all arriving without loss; a short-lived 'happy time'.

When the successful Soviet counter-offensive during the winter of 1941–42 proved that Hitler was after all not going to win his Russian war outright, the Western Allies (America by now having been bombed into the war by the Japanese attack on Pearl Harbor) came to base their entire grand strategy against Germany on the Red Army. As the British Chiefs of Staff summed it up in October 1942: 'It cannot be too clearly recognised that it is the war in Russia which is most rapidly sapping Germany's strength.' In their view, the Red Army constituted 'the primary means by which the German army can be defeated on land'. Only when the Red Army had finally undermined German military power would it be possible 'to establish and maintain a large allied army in France . . .'[1] It therefore followed, according to the COS, that the Western Allies must shape their own war-making first and foremost 'so as to assist Russia'.

The postponement of 'the Second Front' from 1942 to 1943 and then to 1944, meant, however, that there was relatively little that Britain and the United States could do militarily to take the pressure off the Red Army – only the bomber offensive and the secondary campaigns in North Africa and Italy. The Western Allies' most useful direct contribution therefore took the form of sending copious military supplies, the bulk of them American (and including thousands and thousands of trucks to move and supply the Red Army in the vast campaigns of movement that sprawled across the Russian plains). Although the overland route through Iran from the Persian Gulf ports carried some of this material, capacity was restricted by poor road and rail links, and most of the supplies had to go by sea from Britain through the Arctic to North Russian ports.

From August 1941 to the end of the war a total of 40 outward convoys were despatched on what was probably the most hazardous and horrible convoy route of them all – Arctic pack ice; fog; ferocious storms; perpetual night in winter, perpetual day in summer; compasses, even gyro compasses, unreliable because of the high latitudes, so making large navigational errors an extra hazard; all this plus the constant menace of attack by the Luftwaffe, the U-boats and the German heavy ships (including the *Tirpitz*, sister ship of the *Bismarck*) from their strategically dominating Norwegian bases. A total of 811 merchant ships sailed from Britain to Russia, the majority of them American or Panamanian-registered; 33 returned to port for various reasons such as weather or damage from ice; 58 were sunk by the enemy (plus another five lost in the Kola Inlet after arrival); and 720 arrived safely. The convoys carried a total of 4 million tons of supplies, including 5,000 tanks and over 7,000 aircraft; of that huge total despatched only about 300,000 tons (7.5 per cent) went down with sunken ships. The return journey was made by 35 convoys of 717 ships in all; eight ships had to return to harbour, while 29 ships were sunk, including one foundered and four lost in British minefields. Of thirteen ships which sailed independently to Russia from Iceland, five were sunk, and three had to turn back; in the reverse direction, 28 independents sailed, but only one was lost. Given all the dangers, these are remarkably small losses.

From start to finish the Arctic convoy shuttle cost the Royal Navy two cruisers, six destroyers, two sloops, one frigate, two corvettes, four minesweepers and one armed whaler; a Polish submarine was also lost.[2] Although American warships served with the Home Fleet during certain operations to support convoys, and Russian destroyers occasionally met convoys on their arrival, almost all the escorts and covering forces were furnished by the Royal Navy, which also carried the sole operational responsibility.

This heavy new burden began to fall on the Royal Navy when its resources were already painfully stretched by Dönitz's 1941 offensive in the Atlantic and by the battles that year to run convoys through the Mediterranean; when the Admiralty was also having to take anxious note of the growing Japanese menace. In 1942 the strain was to grow worse. The war in Russia still lay in the balance, for this was the year of the second great German summer offensive, which by September had reached the Volga at Stalingrad and the foothills of the Caucasus. The Western Allies consequently tried their uttermost to swell the flow of supplies to Archangel and Murmansk, with no fewer than twenty outward convoys despatched in the course of the year. The Germans equally recognised in 1942 how important these convoys had become to the issue of the campaign on the Eastern Front, and this year they mounted their most ferocious and sustained attack on the Arctic traffic. Yet 1942 saw the Admiralty even more hard pressed for ships than 1941. There were Dönitz's mounting successes in the Atlantic. There was the need to reconstitute British seapower in the Indian Ocean after the destruction of the *Prince of Wales* and *Repulse*. There were the most desperate of all the Malta convoy battles. And finally, from October onwards the demands of the 'Torch' expedition and the subsequent campaign in North Africa had to be met. As the Admiralty juggled its resources as best it could between all these urgent requirements, the same ships were to see service in turn in the Arctic, the Atlantic and the Mediterranean.

If the Arctic convoys added enormously to the Admiralty's global strategic problems, they presented Sir John Tovey, the Commander-in-Chief, Home Fleet, the admiral responsible for routing and protecting the convoys, with a baffling operational conundrum. In the first place, Tovey had to face both ways – to cover the convoys to the eastward while at the same guarding against a breakout westward by the German heavy ships. For from the end of February 1943, as Ultra decrypts recorded, Hitler moved both the *Tirpitz* and the pocket battleship *Admiral Scheer* to Trondheim in Norway. Parrying the threat of so formidable a battleship as the *Tirpitz* – in view of what it had taken to trap and sink her sister ship *Bismarck* – became a major preoccupation, not only for Tovey but also for the Admiralty and the government. In the second place, the Arctic convoys' Russian destination lay 2,000 miles distant, yet exposed to U-boat attack all the way, while the convoys' sea-room was restricted to a relatively narrow corridor by ice to the west and north and by the German-held coast of Norway to the south and east. This coast was blessed with numerous anchorages and well-placed airfields. From the airfields the Luftwaffe could dominate 1,400 miles of the voyage, while British shore-based aircraft were limited to bases no further to the north and east than Iceland and Sullom Voe in the Shetlands. The Luftwaffe also kept the ports at both ends of the route under constant surveillance. It is hardly surprising in the circumstances that differences of professional judgment should sometimes arise between Tovey and the First Sea Lord, Sir Dudley Pound, or that the latter, the arch-centraliser in the old naval tradition, should sometimes directly intervene in operations – on one occasion with catastrophic results.

Nevertheless at the beginning, from August 1941 to the end of February 1942, the Arctic convoys encountered small enemy opposition and sustained only minor loss. At this period the German Army hoped to take Murmansk, which would have effectively put a stop to the convoys. The failure to take the port compelled the German high command to look to its air and naval forces in Norway instead to stop the traffic of goods to Russia. It was from March 1942 onwards, with both sides coming fully to recognise the relevance of the convoys to the now protracted struggle on the Eastern Front, that Tovey's troubles really commenced. All factors were against him. The *Tirpitz* and *Scheer* lay at Trondheim ready to strike. The hours of daylight – the Luftwaffe's hunting time – were lengthening, and yet the pack ice still lay at its furthest extent southwards, so compelling convoys to pass south of Bear Island and therefore within 250 miles of the Norwegian coast. From 19 April to 6 May there would be no hours of darkness, only all-night twilight; between 6 May and 5 August the sun would always remain above the horizon.[3]

On 26 February, with an outward and a homeward convoy (PQ12 and QP8) due to run shortly, Tovey submitted his general proposals to the Admiralty for the future protection of the Arctic traffic. Firstly the voyages of the PQ and QP convoys were to be synchronised so that they passed together (on opposite courses) through the area of greatest danger of attack by German warships between longitude 5°W and 14°E; convoys were therefore to sail on the same date at minimum intervals of fourteen days.

'Such a programme,' Tovey wrote, 'would involve Home Fleet forces being in northern waters about five days in every 14; and it cannot be managed with the present number of destroyers, if a proper screen is to be provided for capital ships and an escort of two destroyers for each convoy. Another four destroyers will be required.'[4]

Tovey informed the First Sea Lord that he intended 'normally to cover these convoys with two capital ships, and sometimes with a carrier as well'. He accordingly proposed sending his second-in-command, Vice-Admiral A. T. B. Curteis, with the battlecruiser HMS *Renown* and the modern battleship HMS *Duke of York*, together with a cruiser and a destroyer screen, to support the convoys between 5°W and 14°E. He himself would remain at Scapa Flow with HMS *King George V*, the fleet carrier *Victorious* and another cruiser, ready either to join Curteis if necessary or to deal with a German attempt to break out into the Atlantic. Tovey acknowledged that the protection of the Arctic convoys constituted 'a major commitment for the Home Fleet, but in it lies the hope of bringing enemy surface ships to action'.[5] He nonetheless pronounced himself against employing the whole of the Home Fleet in this role, on the grounds that it would 'lead to a steady decline in efficiency' by interrupting the cycle of refits and leave.[6] But Pound and the Naval Staff overruled him. He was instructed instead to concentrate his entire fleet in support of the convoys – *King George V*, *Duke of York*, *Renown*, *Victorious*, the cruiser *Berwick* and nine destroyers. 'Their Lordships,' Tovey was informed on 3 March 1942, 'took full responsibility for any breakout of German ships which may occur while you are covering PQ and QP convoys.'[7]

On 1 March 1942, PQ12 (fifteen freighters and one oiler) left Reykjavik and QP8 (fifteen freighters) the Kola Inlet.[8] In the afternoon of the 5th a Luftwaffe Focke-Wulf Condor located PQ12 and reported its course and position; as it was to prove, the last useful reconnaissance by the Luftwaffe during this particular convoy action. On receipt of the Condor's report the *Tirpitz* (flying the flag of Vice-Admiral Ciliax) and three destroyers put to sea from Trondheim. Ciliax's orders were to avoid action with superior enemy forces but to engage equal British forces if need be in order to accomplish his main task of destroying the convoy.[9] *Tirpitz*'s departure escaped the vigilance of Coastal

Command reconnaissance patrols; nor did Sigint give the British any warning.[10] However, at 1730 on 6 March, Lieutenant I. F. Raikes, RN, in the patrolling submarine *Seawolf* sighted a faint smear of smoke to the south, and then the foretop and funnel of a large warship steaming fast up the Norwegian coast. According to his later report, 'I was certain in my own mind that it was the *Tirpitz*.'[11] But whereas Tovey now knew that *Tirpitz* was hunting for the convoy, Ciliax still had no idea that the Home Fleet was at sea.

The *Tirpitz* presented one lethal hazard; another lay in the ice encountered by the convoy that evening, causing it to alter from north-east to south-east. Even though this was only loose pack ice the experience led Captain M. M. Denny of the cruiser *Kenya* to conclude that 'I would never take a convoy anywhere near ice, accepting almost any other risk in preference'.[12] During the night, as vessels butted their way through the heaving islets of ice, the *Oribi* (Commander J. E. H. McBeath, RN) sustained considerable damage to her destroyer's light hull. (As destroyers went in for a refit, they had their hulls strengthened forward by lining with wood, and the whole hull lined with sprayed limpet asbestos in order to insulate against the cold and prevent condensation, which was a curse in closed down mess decks full of men.)

Next day, while Arctic fog rose eerily from the icy sea like a special effect in a horror film, the two sides played hide-and-seek with each other, the *Tirpitz* and her destroyers hunting for QP8 and PQ12, and especially PQ12 (crammed with supplies for the Red Army), but fortunately always to the south of the convoy's track; the Home Fleet in turn hunting for *Tirpitz*, but always to the south-west of her. Even so, all four groups of ships were steaming within 100 miles of one another for most of the day, and the convoys only narrowly escaped discovery. Because of poor visibility and icing *Victorious* was unable to fly air searches as intended to the south of the convoys which would in all likelihood have picked up the *Tirpitz*, while the *Tirpitz* herself was similarly unable to use her four Arado reconnaissance aircraft. The only contact of the day, a violent one, took place between a German destroyer and a Russian straggler from QP8, sunk by the destroyer.

The Russian's garbled and unintelligible distress signal, coupled with HF/DF bearings of an enemy ship which might be the *Tirpitz* (in fact it was a U-boat), persuaded Tovey that the enemy would now regard his position as being compromised and would be making for home. Tovey therefore altered to the east at 1750 and then north-east at 2000 in order to intercept him, ordering six destroyers to sweep

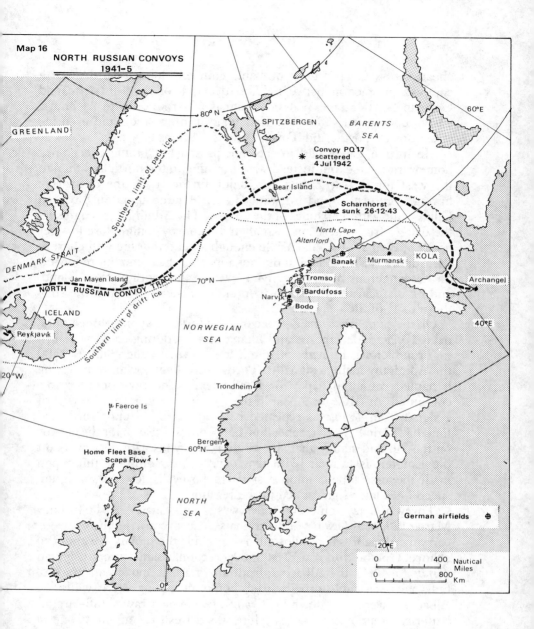

Map 16

NORTH RUSSIAN CONVOYS
1941–5

GREENLAND

80° N

SPITZBERGEN

BARENTS SEA

60°E

✳ Convoy PQ 17
scattered
4 Jul 1942

Southern limit of pack ice

Bear Island

Scharnhorst
sunk 26·12·43

North Cape
Altenfiord

Banak ⊕

Murmansk

KOLA

DENMARK STRAIT

Jan Mayen Island

70°N

Tromso

Archangel

NORTH RUSSIAN CONVOY TRACK

Southern limit of drift ice

⊕ Bardufoss

Narvik

Bodo

40°E

ICELAND

NORWEGIAN SEA

Reykjavik

20°W

Trondheim

Faeroe Is

Bergen

60°N

**Home Fleet Base
Scapa Flow**

NORTH SEA

German airfields   ⊕

20°E

| 0 | 400 | Nautical Miles |
| 0 | 800 | Km |

0°

ahead across Ciliax's most probable course. There now followed a complex interaction between Ultra decrypts of the Luftwaffe and German Navy 'Home Waters' Enigmas (at around 16 to 24 hours' delay), consequent Admiralty signalling of information and even instructions to Tovey, and Tovey's own evolutions at sea.[13]

Meanwhile Ciliax had in fact not passed the Home Fleet on a homeward course, but instead was searching to the north and then to the west for PQ12; *Tirpitz* now being on her own, the destroyers having to return to port for want of fuel. Around noon on 8 March Ciliax came within 80 miles of the convoy. The Admiralty, recognising the danger from intercepts, signalled the convoy commodore to steer north of Bear Island. A sensible enough solution on the wall chart in the Admiralty War Room, it did not appeal to the commodore in view of the dangerous mass of ice lying even to the south of Bear Island, and he disregarded the order, continuing instead to follow the southern edge of the ice.

On the same day came a stroke of good fortune: at only three hours' delay GC and CS cracked an Enigma signal ordering Ciliax to return to Trondheim if he had not found the convoy by nightfall. At 1500 the Admiralty made a signal to Tovey accordingly, who on receiving it hauled round to make for Bear Island. The flow of intercepts continued. At 0102 on 9 March the Admiralty received a decrypt of a signal from *Tirpitz* as repeated back to her by Group North and timed 2232 on 8 March, cancelling her proposed search for the convoy on the 9th and stating that she would rendezvous with destroyers off the Lofoten Islands at 0700 that day.[14] The Admiralty thereupon made the terse and peremptory signal to Tovey: 'Steer 120° maximum speed'.[15] A later signal filled in the reasons.

Tovey now lay some 200 miles west of his quarry. At 0640 on 9 March *Victorious* flew off her reconnaissance aircraft. To the torpedo-carrying Albacores that followed, Tovey made the signal: 'A wonderful chance. God be with you.'[16] At 0800 a reconnaissance aircraft sighted *Tirpitz*; at 0840 the Albacores rode in to attack her great, graceful bulk. Yet not a single torpedo struck home, all passing astern, while two Albacores were shot down by *Tirpitz*'s fearsome array of anti-aircraft batteries of assorted calibres. Here was a fresh repetition of one of the oldest lessons of war – that success demands more than courage and determination; it demands group training to the highest standards of performance. The Albacore crews were relative novices, and the flight commander himself new to his squadron, having never flown with it before. By attacking from astern and into the wind rather than ahead and from windward the aircrafts' speed relative to the battleship was much less than it might have been, so giving the enemy time to take effective evasive action. Never again was the opportunity to occur for carrier aircraft to slow *Tirpitz* in the open sea so that the Home Fleet could bring her to action and destroy her like her sister ship.

In the evening of 9 March *Tirpitz* reached harbour in Narvik; on the following day Tovey brought the Home Fleet into Scapa Flow. Despite all the gropings and confusions Convoys PQ12 and QP8 had made safe passage in the face of the first sortie by the German heavy squadron now based in Norway.

Nevertheless the episode caused Tovey to think again about the whole problem of covering the Arctic convoys; and on 14 March he signalled a new appreciation to the Admiralty. In particular he now expressed pungent dissatisfaction with the Admiralty's directive of 3 March (see above, p. 697). In the first place Tovey was convinced that the German policy for their heavy ships must be to avoid at all costs action with British heavy forces:

> The *Tirpitz*, by her existence, contains very large British and United States forces and prevents their transfer to the Far East or the Mediterranean. She is so valuable an asset to all the Axis Powers that I am convinced that the enemy will not willingly expose this unique and irreplaceable asset to any unnecessary risk. The promptitude with which she entered the nearest harbour when attacked by aircraft from the *Victorious* . . . supports my conviction . . .[17]

In this Tovey guessed exactly right: in their own post-mortem on the PQ12 and QP8 operation the enemy were ruefully acknowledging that only 'sheer good fortune' had saved *Tirpitz* from damage, and both Ciliax and Raeder were determined in future to husband rather than hazard the ship.[18] On the assumption that the enemy would not risk the *Tirpitz* in future Tovey wrote that he preferred his own original suggested disposition of his resources. He argued that the Admiralty instructions of 3 March compelled him to operate his three capital ships and his carrier as a single unit in far-distant U-boat ridden waters where his destroyers' lack of endurance (for refuelling at sea remained in 1942 a relatively limited practice in the Royal Navy) would force him to keep the sea for long periods without a screen. All of this amounted in his view to 'a risky proceeding'.[19] He also bluntly stated to the Admiralty – really to Pound himself – that throughout the recent operation he 'had been seriously embarrassed' by the Admiralty's instructions. He reckoned that to sink the *Tirpitz* was 'of incomparably greater importance to the conduct of the war than the safety of any convoy'.[20] He claimed that if it was known that she was at sea he must be at liberty to take her destruction as his object. And he requested an assurance that the Admiralty agreed with this analysis, adding that in any case he believed that it was the U-boat that offered 'by far the most serious threat' to the convoys.

This was not all Tovey had to say. He strongly complained about the Admiralty signalling to him 'detailed instructions for the handling of his forces'. However here, in this particular case, he was on unsafe ground, because the Admiralty had known much more about Ciliax's intentions and movements thanks to Ultra than Tovey had at sea, while because of signalling difficulties on a secure link Tovey himself had at one point to ask the Admiralty to manoeuvre his cruisers and destroyers for him.

The First Sea Lord and the naval staff still believed, for their part, that two battleships, as proposed by Tovey, did not constitute enough force to cover a convoy against the *Tirpitz*, especially in view of experience with the *Bismarck*. Nonetheless, they did agree that the Home Fleet should not go east of 14°E without a destroyer screen; and also that Tovey's main objective should be to destroy the *Tirpitz*. But they considered that the best way of bringing this about was to provide a strong escort to the convoys. It is not clear whether they actually conveyed these views back to Tovey, for no reply to the latter's letter remains on the file.[21]

In the last week of March it was the turn of PQ13 and QP9, each of nineteen ships, and again supported by the whole of the Home Fleet during the most dangerous part of their passage. This time, however, the German heavy ships stayed in harbour – even though they had now been reinforced by the heavy cruiser *Hipper* – leaving the convoys to the Luftwaffe, the U-boats and the big German destroyers. All went well with QP9, but not so with PQ13, which on 24 March ran into a storm so violent that by the 27th not one merchantman remained within sight of the escort. Next day, with the convoy scattered along 150 miles of sea south of Bear Island, offered the Luftwaffe a superb opportunity to massacre the defenceless, and yet it only managed to destroy two vessels.

On the 29th German destroyers from Kirkenes took a hand, encountering the British escort at around 0900 in appalling weather. At 0922 the cruiser HMS *Trinidad* (flying the flag of Rear-Admiral S. S. Bonham-Carter: 8,000 tons; twelve 6-inch guns; launched March 1940)[22] fired torpedoes at the German destroyer Z26, but two of them failed to leave the tubes because of icing. With ships looming momentarily out of the snowy murk, two British destroyers even fired at each other. The report of proceedings by the captain of HMS

Eclipse (1,375 tons; four 4.7-inch guns; launched 1934)[23] described how spray sweeping over the guns and bridge froze instantly; how the gun decks became a sheet of ice; how the gun wells filled with sea water and ice. It was almost impossible to use binoculars because frozen spray immediately obscured the lenses.[24]

When the action petered out Z26 had been sunk, but HMS *Trinidad* herself had been seriously damaged by a torpedo. She finally struggled into Murmansk on 30 March. Here on 7 May a stoker fished out of a boiler furnace part of a torpedo pistol identifiable as belonging to *Trinidad*. She had thus torpedoed herself owing to the effect of intense cold on the oils in the torpedo's motor and gyroscope.[25] This was unique. But all too familiar and routine to every ship's company on the Arctic convoys was the mustering of all hands to chip away the enveloping crusts of ice on decks and gear and guns with pick and maul, in order to reduce the top weight of ice. In a small ship this could make all the difference between capsizing or not if hit by a torpedo. Only later in the war were technical measures introduced to keep the working parts of deck machinery, the muzzles and chases of guns, and the torpedo tubes free of ice, such as a coating of special grease, steam or electric heating, and insulating jackets.[26]

The attacks on PQ13, costing five merchantmen, convinced Tovey that the enemy was 'determined to do everything in his power to stop this traffic. The U-boat and air forces in Northern Norway had been heavily reinforced, the remaining three destroyers were disposed offensively at Kirkenes and the heavy forces at Trondheim remained a constant, if reluctant, threat.'[27] At his request the Admiralty transferred sufficient destroyers, corvettes and trawlers from Western Approaches Command to bring the close escorts of each convoy up to ten. The Russians were asked again and again, even at the highest level, to supply air and naval support, but so pressed were they that in Tovey's words 'little was forthcoming'.[28] Nonetheless two Russian destroyers did join the escort of the next outward convoy, PQ14, for the last few days before arrival in Murmansk.

With the arrival of the season of perpetual sunlight in the Arctic Tovey urged that the convoys should be run less frequently. His view was shared by the First Sea Lord, who submitted a memorandum on 8 April 1942 to the War Cabinet Defence Committee listing the threats to the convoys from German air and naval forces in Norway. He argued: 'Geographical conditions are so greatly in favour of the Germans that losses . . . may become so great as to render the running of these convoys uneconomical.'[29] Indeed the Naval Staff wanted to stop the traffic altogether during the summer months. Yet April was the month when the Russians launched a series of spring counter-offensives in the Crimea and Ukraine, while at this same period the British government knew from Ultra decrypts that the German Army was preparing its own summer offensive on the Eastern Front in prodigious strength. The Prime Minister had already assured Stalin in the previous month that he had given 'express instructions' that supplies to Russia 'shall not in any way be interrupted or delayed'.[30]

But now occurred a near-disaster to the joint passages of PQ14 and QP10, which left their departure ports on 8 April. PQ14, enlarged to 24 freighters in response to pressure from Roosevelt on Churchill, ran into a maze of thick drifting ice and became hopelessly scattered as each ship sought its way out through channels of clear water, only to find themselves blocked ahead or with ice closing in astern. Forepeaks crumpled against the jagged shelves; propellers and rudders were damaged and distorted by submerged ice. Several ice-damaged escorts had to return to Iceland, while only eight out of the 24 freighters were eventually able to make their way on towards Kola. Then came the Luftwaffe. The convoy commodore's own ship, *Empire Howard*, succumbed to two torpedoes, and the commodore himself, Commodore Rees, RN, was lost with her. Seven ships out of the original 24 reached harbour on 19 April. The commander of the escort, Rear-Admiral Bonham-Carter, who was flying his flag in the cruiser *Edinburgh* (10,000 tons displacement; twelve 6-inch guns; a 'rearmament' ship launched in March 1938)[31] explained in his report of proceedings why the enemy only managed to sink the *Empire Howard*:

> The remains of PQ14 were extremely lucky in the weather in that when the first heavy air attack developed on Friday, 17th April, fog suddenly came down ... on the following day ... when a combined surface, submarine and air attack was expected, the weather again was on our side, fog and snow showers persisting all day, and on the final run into the Kola Inlet a strong gale from the north-west sprang up. I consider it was due to the fine work of the Anti-Submarine Escort Force (under Commander M. Richmond) that only one ship was lost.[32]

Bonham-Carter could only draw a depressing lesson from the experience of the PQ14:

> Under present conditions with no hours of darkness, continually under air observation for the last four days, submarines concentrating in the bottlenecks, torpedo attacks to be expected, our destroyers unable to carry

out a proper hunt or search owing to the oil situation, serious losses must be expected in every convoy.[33]

Yet the political pressures to continue the convoys, even increase the traffic, were mounting. When on 26 April Churchill sought to make Roosevelt understand 'the serious convoy situation' Roosevelt replied that any stoppage of supplies, 'for any reason', would have 'a most unfortunate effect'.[34] Although the Prime Minister explained how short the Royal Navy was of escorts and that each convoy meant a major fleet operation, the President remained adamant that Britain must recognise 'the urgent necessity of getting off one more convoy in May in order to break the log-jam of ships already loaded or being loaded for Russia'.[35] Courteously but unshakably Churchill answered on 2 May: 'With very great respect what you suggest is beyond our power to fulfil.' After going on to list all the operational problems, he concluded: 'I can assure you, Mr President, we are absolutely extended and I could not press the Admiralty further.'[36] The question being then referred to the joint professional opinions of the First Sea Lord and COMINCH (Commander-in-Chief, United States Fleet), the latter agreed with his British colleague; whereupon Roosevelt at last accepted the British view.[37]

By this time, however, further calamities had befallen the Royal Navy on the Arctic route while escorting PQ15 (of fifteen merchant-men) and QP11 (of thirteen). From 29 April onwards the homeward-bound QP11, with a strong close escort of six destroyers, four corvettes and a trawler under the command of Rear-Admiral Bonham-Carter (again flying his flag in HMS *Edinburgh*), came under heavy attack by U-boats, destroyers and aircraft. *Edinburgh*'s stern was blown off and her steering wrecked by two torpedoes from the U-456. For 23 hours she steered back to Murmansk in the company of two British and two Russian destroyers on her engines only at about two knots average speed of advance, all the time swinging from port to starboard and back. According to her engine-room register no fewer than 64 engine orders were issued in one watch on one propeller shaft alone.[38] On her way she still managed to hit and stop the German destroyer *Hermann Schoemann* in a fight with three enemy destroyers hungry for an easy victim, but sadly then succumbed to another torpedo which almost cut her in two. *Edinburgh* was finally sunk by a torpedo from HMS *Foresight* (Commander J. Salter) after the minesweepers *Harrier* and *Gossamer* had rescued all 790 survivors. In the same fight the destroyers *Forester* and *Foresight* (each 1,350 tons displacement; four 4.7-inch guns; launched 1934)[39] were in turn hit, stopped and badly damaged by the big German destroyers with their 5.9-inch guns. Fortunately the remaining two enemy ships chose to go to the aid of their wounded sister rather than finish off their enemies. Once the *Hermann Schoemann* had sunk, they withdrew; another German case of not engaging the enemy more closely. The British destroyers now slowly got under way again.

On 1 May the three German destroyers before turning their attention to the *Edinburgh* had tried five times to break through QP11's weakened escort and get at the convoy – and each time were foiled by the aggressiveness of the British escort, even though the German ships mounted a total of ten 5.9-inch guns and five 5-inch to the six 4.7-inch and three 4-inch in the four smaller British ships remaining with the convoy. The convoy itself sought refuge within the pack-ice, picking its way in single file through heavy drifting slabs. According to the report of Commander Richmond, commanding officer of the escort, in HMS *Bulldog*: 'in order to maintain touch the destroyers were led through lanes of open water as opportunity offered, bearing in mind that sufficient sea-room to manoeuvre in action must be maintained. This presented a nice problem.'[40] The enemy destroyers finally gave up and disappeared behind a smoke screen as the British ships headed towards them. When Commander Richmond signalled his congratulations to his little force, one captain instantly replied: 'I should hate to play poker with you!'[41]

The outward convoy, PQ15, supported by the Home Fleet and with a strong close escort, proved to have better luck. Although aircraft and U-boats attacked it from 2 to 4 May only three merchantmen were lost, victims of torpedo-bombers. Then on the 4th dense fog closed protectively round the convoy and shrouded it for the rest of the voyage. The total losses in both convoys amounted therefore to no more than four out of 38 ships. But the Royal Navy's own losses had been dismayingly high. In addition to the cruiser *Edinburgh* sunk and the destroyers *Forester* and *Foresight* damaged, the destroyer *Punjabi* was rammed and sunk by HMS *Duke of York* in fog on 1 May and the Polish submarine *Jastrzab* destroyed in error by British warships when she was suddenly encountered 100 miles away from her expected patrol area. Nor was this all. On 14 May the damaged cruiser *Trinidad* was hit by a bomb while on her way home from Murmansk and set on fire. The fire spread out of control and she had to be sunk by a British torpedo. Rear-Admiral Bonham-Carter thus lost two flagships in succession. In his report of proceedings he drew an even more sombre lesson from the experiences of PQ15 and QP11 than from those of PQ14 and QP10:

I am still convinced that until the aerodromes in North Norway are neutralised and there are some hours of darkness that the continuation of these convoys should be stopped. If they must continue for political reasons, very serious and heavy losses must be expected. The force of German attacks will increase not diminish. We in the Navy are paid to do this sort of job, but it is beginning to ask too much of the men of the Merchant Navy. We may be able to avoid bombs and torpedoes with our speed, a six or eight knot ship has not this advantage.[42]

Tovey fully endorsed these views in conveying them to the Admiralty. In any case the First Sea Lord was of the same mind, writing to COMINCH, 'Ernie' King, on 18 May that the Russian convoys 'are becoming a regular millstone round our necks and cause a steady attrition in both cruisers and destroyers'. He added that 'the whole thing is a most unsound operation with the dice loaded against us in every direction . . . but I do . . . recognise the necessity of doing all we can to help the Russians at the present time'. 'Ernie' King answered on 21 May: 'I am very much in sympathy with your views . . .'[43] The political pressure to continue, even to enlarge, the operation proved irresistible. By now the Russian spring offensives on the Eastern Front had become stuck, and on the very same day that the First Sea Lord was writing to COMINCH the Germans launched a smashing counter-stroke in the Ukraine which threw the Russians back in disorder. And all the time, as the Western Allies well knew through Ultra, the Germans were slotting into place the panzer armies for their own coming summer offensive on the Eastern Front. The Arctic convoys would have to go on, as the Red Army would have to go on.

On 21 May 1942, now the most unfavourable season of the year with perpetual Arctic daylight, the largest ever outward convoy to Russia, PQ16 of 35 merchantmen, put to sea from Iceland. Although the Commander-in-Chief, Home Fleet, had asked for Royal Air Force reconnaissance aircraft and fighters to be stationed in North Russia to provide air cover over the Barents Sea, Coastal Command simply could not find the resources.[44] The Arctic skies would therefore belong to the Luftwaffe 24 hours a day. It was known through Ultra that the two pocket battleships *Scheer* and *Lützow* now lay at Narvik, in addition to *Tirpitz* and *Hipper* at Trondheim. Tovey therefore deployed four cruisers, HMS *Nigeria*, *Norfolk*, *Kent* and *Liverpool*, and three destroyers under Rear-Admiral H. M. Burrough as close cover while the whole Home Fleet provided distant cover against the German heavy ships, especially the *Tirpitz*. As was usually the case, submarines were also deployed as cover for the convoy in the hope that they might intercept and sink the German heavy ships if they should put to sea to attack it. The escort of PQ16 comprised HMS P-614, the Dutch submarine 010, HMS P-46 (*Unruffled*), HMS P-37 (*Unbending*) and the Norwegian *Uredd*. Serving as close escort to the convoy were HMSs *Trident* and *Seawolf*, the former submarine firing off all her ammunition in the course of the convoy's fight against enemy air attacks.

On 25 May a Luftwaffe shadower appeared on the horizon, and for the next five days the merchantmen were never without a watcher circling maddeningly out of gun range; as always, an experience cumulatively depressing to morale. After the homeward convoy QP12, of fifteen ships, had passed safely to the westward of PQ16, the Luftwaffe started work on PQ16 and kept it up almost without pause throughout the remaining five days of the voyage, Heinkel He 111 torpedo-bombers alternating with Ju 88 dive-bombers in the tactics already so familiar in the Mediterranean. Their first victim was the freighter *Carlton*, which suffered a fractured steam pipe from a bomb hit; she had to be detached to Iceland under tow by the *Northern Spray*. The commander of the close convoy escort, Commander R. G. Onslow, RN, was to write in his report: 'I was greatly impressed by the spirit and determination of the Master and crew of the *Carlton*, also by the calm acceptance by *Northern Spray* of a long and difficult voyage with no hope of support against air attack.'[45]

Early on 26 May came the convoy's first loss – a freighter torpedoed by a U-boat. Then it was the Luftwaffe's turn again, only to be thwarted by the storm of fire put up by the combined close and cruiser escort forces. Making her début on the Arctic run was the catapult aircraft carrier *Empire Lawrence*, whose single Hurricane shot down one enemy aircraft and damaged another.

Next day, however, after Burrough had turned back with his cruiser force according to instructions, the Luftwaffe hammered the convoy with unrelenting strikes, the German aircraft giving their customary but unadmired imitation of a swarm of furious hornets buzzing round the head of an intruder. The anti-aircraft ship *Alynbank* counted attacks by 108 aircraft. Six ships went down, including the *Empire Lawrence*. The convoy commodore's own ship, the *Ocean Voice*, received a direct hit from a bomb which set her on fire and stripped away about twenty feet of side plating abreast of No. 1 hold within two feet of the waterline. Two other ships and the Polish-manned destroyer *Garland* were badly damaged. Fortunately for the *Ocean Voice* the sea remained calm. Yet Commander Onslow, the escort commander, later confessed that he 'had little hopes of her survival, but this gallant ship maintained her station, fought her fire, and with God's help arrived at her destination'.[46]

Nevertheless it had been a terrible day. 'With another three days to go', wrote Onslow,

... and 20 per cent of the convoy already lost, I felt far from optimistic. I ordered all ships to exercise strict economy [of ammunition] and restricted controlled fire in *Ashanti* to one mounting at a time. We were all inspired however by the parade ground rigidity of the convoy's station-keeping, including *Ocean Voice* and *Star Bolshevik* who were both billowing smoke from their holds.[47]

Thankfully this proved to have been the worst day. Only an already damaged ship was lost on 28 May, while the escort was strengthened by three Russian destroyers. In the evening of the 29th six British minesweepers also joined, and next day Russian Hurricanes flew in to provide air cover. That afternoon the convoy passed Toros Island into the Kola Inlet, 'reduced in numbers,' wrote Onslow, 'battered and tired, but still keeping perfect station'.[48] That PQ16 had got through without disaster in fact owed much to Onslow's own leadership as an outstandingly skilful and resolute close escort commander. The two previous convoys had had a cruiser and an admiral in their close escorts, and lost both cruisers.

He now had his own recommendations to make to his superiors: the importance of including an escort carrier or a catapult aircraft carrier in the escort in order to deal with shadowing aircraft; likewise an anti-aircraft ship; the need for stronger anti-aircraft armament in the destroyers and for reserves of ammunition to be held in the convoys and at Kola; the desirability of as many long-range radar sets as possible.[49] Onslow also suggested that convoy escorts should include a high-powered salvage tug with good fire-fighting appliances which could save damaged ships; special rescue ships as well. But how was the Royal Navy, with its desperately straitened resources, to honour these requests?

The Commander-in-Chief, Home Fleet, gave vent to immense relief that PQ16 had completed its passage with such small loss:

This success was beyond expectation; it was due to the gallantry, efficiency and tireless zeal of the officers and men of the escorts and to the remarkable courage and determination of those of the merchant ships. No praise can be too high for either.[50]

Dönitz, for his part, could only confide glumly to his war diary that the attacks against the convoy 'must be accounted a failure'.[51]

Thus Tovey's and Pound's forebodings about the appalling risks being incurred in continuing to run the Arctic convoys had so far failed to be borne out in the event. They could only pray that the next outward convoy, PQ17, would be equally fortunate.

Convoy PQ17, of 36 merchantmen, did not sail for Russia from Iceland until 27 June 1942. The Admiralty had been compelled to suspend the Arctic convoy traffic for a month because the cruisers *Kenya* and *Liverpool* and eight destroyers had had to be despatched to the Mediterranean for 'Harpoon', the hazardous operation to run a convoy through to Malta from Gibraltar in order to relieve Malta's now extreme plight (see above, pp. 505–9). This redeployment of ships serves as a demonstration both of the flexibility of seapower and of the Home Fleet's role as the Royal Navy's central strategic reserve. Unfortunately *Liverpool* and the destroyer *Matchless* were reduced to dockyard cases by enemy action during 'Harpoon', and the destroyer *Bedouin* (Commander B. G. Scurfield, a close friend of Onslow) was sunk. The Mediterranean Fleet also lost a destroyer and had two destroyers and a minesweeper damaged. Such weakening of resources could only sharpen Pound's and Tovey's anxieties about the prospects for the next convoy to North Russia. As Tovey was to write in his despatch, the strategic situation

> . . . was wholly favourable to the enemy. His heavy ships would be operating close to their own coast, with the support of powerful shore-based air reconnaissance and striking forces, and protected, if he so desired, by a screen of U-boats in the channels between Spitzbergen and Norway. Our covering forces, on the other hand, if they entered these waters would be without shore-based air support, one thousand miles from their bases, with their destroyers too short of fuel to escort a damaged ship to harbour.[52]

Tovey wished to solve the problem by means of deceptive manoeuvre rather than simply trying to fight PQ17 through the enemy's ambushes. Reckoning that 'a more favourable disposition could be brought about only by inducing the enemy heavy ships to come further to the westward to deliver their attacks',[53] he proposed that when PQ17 reached longitude 10°E it should put back for twelve to eighteen hours, unless the German heavy ships were known to be still safely in harbour or unless the weather proved thick enough to prevent enemy aircraft from shadowing. Tovey hoped that 'this temporary turn back would either tempt the German heavy ships to pursue, or cause them to return to harbour, or cruise for an extended period among our submarines . . .'[54]

The Admiralty – the First Sea Lord and the naval staff – disagreed with Tovey's proposal, issuing instructions to Tovey on 27 June which, in the words of the Naval Staff History, 'envisaged the possibility, under certain circumstances, of the convoy being temporarily turned back by the Admiralty; but not of this turn being timed to achieve [Tovey's] object'.[55] Instead the Admiralty instructions laid down that British surface forces were to defend the convoy against enemy heavy ships to the west of Bear Island, but not beyond, where the task would fall to submarines alone. The Admiralty emphasised that even the cruiser covering force was not intended to go east of Bear Island unless the convoy was threatened by surface forces capable of being fought by cruisers, and in any case not beyond 25°E.

This was not the only point of disagreement between the Admiralty and the Commander-in-Chief, Home Fleet. The other related to contingency plans should German heavy ships attack the convoy when it was no longer supported by the Home Fleet. On 16 March 1942 Tovey had issued a new directive, subsequently incorporated into the Home Fleet's 'Instructions for Escorts of North Russian Convoys',[56] in which he stated:

> I wish it to be clearly understood that in the event of a Russian convoy being attacked by a force overwhelmingly superior to the escort, the primary object of the escort is to ensure the enemy being shadowed to enable them to be brought to action by our heavier forces or submarines or to be attacked after dark, or under more favourable conditions, by the escort itself.[57]

The Atlantic Convoy Instructions (ACIs) of April 1942 indeed specifically forbade scattering in the face of attack, 'until or unless the escort is overwhelmed'; and on 21 June, a week before PQ17 put to sea, Tovey issued a Home Fleet memorandum that Arctic convoys were to follow ACIs.[58]

Tovey was therefore seriously perturbed to learn, during a telephone conversation with Pound, that the Admiralty now contemplated ordering PQ17 to scatter under certain circumstances. Tovey pointed out to Pound how recent operations had shown the importance of convoys remaining concentrated for the sake of mutual support against aircraft. According to the Naval Staff History, Tovey 'strongly deprecated such an order being given, except as a last resort in the actual presence of attack by overwhelming surface forces'.[59]

The deployment of warships in support of PQ17 and QP13 followed the pattern for PQ16 and QP12. PQ17's close escort, all British or French ships, consisted of six destroyers (plus the US destroyers *Wainwright* and *Rowan*, which joined on 4 July), the anti-aircraft ships *Palomares* and *Pozarica*, four corvettes and two submarines under the command of Commander J. E. Broome, RN, in the old destroyer *Keppel* (1,480 tons displacement; two 4.7-inch guns; four 20mm anti-aircraft guns).[60] Three rescue ships also accompanied the convoy, which initially numbered 36 merchantmen. Commander Jack Broome was one of the Royal Navy's colourful characters, an able and witty cartoonist, a man with a sense of humour buoyant even in the most hazardous of circumstances; a skilled and resolute fighting sailor in the best tradition of convoy escorts. Close cover to PQ17 as far as Bear Island would be provided by the 1st Cruiser Squadron, composed of the cruisers HMS *London* (flag), HMS *Norfolk*, USS *Tuscaloosa* and USS *Wichita*, and three destroyers under Rear-Admiral L. H. K. Hamilton. Tovey, with two battleships, HMS *Duke of York* (flag) and USS *Washington* (flying the flag of Rear Admiral R. C. Giffen, commanding the United States Navy's Task Force 39), the fleet carrier *Victorious*, the cruisers *Nigeria* and *Cumberland* and fourteen destroyers (including the USSs *Mayrant* and *Rhine*), would give distant support against the German heavy ships to the north-east of Jan Mayen Island. In addition, thirteen submarines were now patrolling off the exits to the bases of German surface forces.

Rear-Admiral 'Turtle' Hamilton, 'a fighting puckish little bachelor' according to his Staff Officer (Operations), 'a destroyer officer in the classic mould',[61] all too soon found himself having to manoeuvre to the whistles of two masters. Around noon on 4 July, when PQ17 had been at sea for a week and had already passed east of Bear Island into the zone of greatest danger, Hamilton received a signal from the Admiralty that 'unless otherwise ordered by the C-in-C, HF, you may proceed eastward of 25°E [NB: five degrees east of Bear Island] should the situation demand it. This is not to be taken by you as urging you to proceed eastwards against your discretion.'[62] The C-in-C, Home Fleet, thereupon signalled Hamilton with his own gloss on this Admiralty instruction: 'Once the convoy is to the eastward of 25°E or earlier at your discretion you are to leave the Barents Sea unless assured by the Admiralty that the *Tirpitz* cannot be met.'[63] Longitude 25°E runs almost exactly through Norway's North Cape, where the jagged coastline bends from a SW–NE alignment to NW –SE towards Russia, and some 2° east of Altenfiord.

The C-in-C's signal to Hamilton crossed one from Hamilton to him at 1520 stating that he, Hamilton, would remain with the convoy until the situation with regard to enemy surface forces had been clarified, but certainly no later than 1400 on 5 July.[64] At 1809 Hamilton informed the C-in-C that he intended withdrawing the 1st Cruiser Squadron to the west about 2200 that evening after refuelling his destroyers. But about 1930 Hamilton received a fresh order from the Admiralty telling him to remain with the convoy pending further instructions. It could not be said therefore that Hamilton was enjoying a Nelsonian standard of decisive leadership from above. But the explanation alike for these uncertainties of mind and for the 'second-guessing' of the C-in-C by the Admiralty is to be found in the amount and reliability of the available Sigint (and especially Ultra decrypts) about German movements and intentions. In the first place, the Admiralty – that is, the Operational Intelligence Centre, the War Room, the Naval Staff, the First Sea Lord himself – enjoyed the fullest first-hand access to Ultra decrypts, which Tovey at sea to the north-west of Bear Island did not, so providing in this case a powerful and genuine justification for Pound's own temperamental itch to centralise decision in his own hands. In the second place, Sigint – even Ultra – was failing to give a clear and certain picture of the most dangerous single threat facing PQ17, that of the *Tirpitz*.[65]

By the time PQ17 sailed, GC and CS at Bletchley Park had certainly provided full information about the intended deployment of U-boats against the convoy and also about the Luftwaffe's operational plans. As for the German surface forces, decrypts of the naval Enigma had provided no evidence that the *Tirpitz* had left Trondheim for the north; they also indicated that it was 'probable' that the pocket battleships *Scheer* and *Lützow* were still in Narvik.[66] In the afternoon of 1 July the Admiralty informed Tovey and Hamilton that, while it was known that the enemy expected the convoy to pass Jan Mayen Island about this time, 'on negative evidence it would appear that there had been no movement of main units and no sighting of PQ17 up to 1200 on 1 July'.[67] At 1900 that day the Admiralty was able to report further to the C-in-C and the Flag Officer, 1st Cruiser Squadron, that the convoy had now been sighted by the enemy; and that at 1313 on 2 July a torpedo-bomber attack had been ordered. At 2349 the Admiralty confirmed to the two flag officers that there was still 'no direct indications of movements of enemy main units', but only possible inferences to be drawn from the fact that the Luftwaffe had located the Home Fleet (it soon lost it again).[68]

Next day, 3 July, however, it became clear through Ultra that the *Scheer* was now on the move to some base north of Narvik, probably

Altenfiord, and that the *Tirpitz* and *Hipper* too were steaming north from Trondheim, though it seemed that *Lützow* was not in company with *Scheer* (in fact, the *Scheer* and three destroyers ran aground and took no further part in the operation).

Now, just as German movements were under way, there occurred a tantalising delay in decrypting the naval Enigma, for not until 1837 on 4 July were the signals for the period 1200 on 3 July to 1200 on 4 July read by GC and CS. To fog the situation still further, Coastal Command reconnaissance patrols off the North Cape were interrupted by an accident to an aircraft. Only two pieces of Ultra guidance reached Tovey in *King George V* during this lapse of time – confirmation that the *Scheer* was moving to Altenfiord; and that an hourly sequence of indecipherable Enigma signals 'may indicate the commencement of a special operation by main units'.[69] Tovey was thus for the moment reduced to the same kind of anxious guessing as his predecessors as fleet commanders in earlier wars such as Jellicoe steaming towards the High Seas Fleet in 1916, or Nelson hunting for Villeneuve in 1804–5. This accounts for Tovey's signal to Hamilton ordering him to leave the Barents Sea when the convoy was east of 25°E or earlier at his discretion, unless the Admiralty could assure him that the *Tirpitz* could not be met.

During the afternoon of 4 July a Luftwaffe Enigma decrypt indicating that aircraft from Bardufoss airfield were preparing to attack the convoy led the Admiralty to signal directly to Commander Broome (commanding PQ17's close escort), who was not in on the Ultra secret, in plain language: 'Most immediate. Blue Pendant', Blue Pendant in the signal code meaning air attack imminent.[70]

In the warren of fusty offices adjacent to the Admiralty War Room in 'the Keep' (the huge block-house on the corner of Horse Guards' Parade and the Mall) uncertainty was winding nerves taut, sharpening minds. Since the convoy had put to sea, Commander Norman Denning, the officer in the Operational Intelligence Centre responsible for reading the intentions of the German surface fleet, had been visited ever more frequently by various members of the Naval Staff – the Assistant Chief (Rear-Admiral E. J. P. Brind), the Director of Operations (Home) (Captain John Eccles); and the Vice Chief (Vice-Admiral Henry Moore). Not until late on 3 July, however, did the First Sea Lord and Chief of Naval Staff, Sir Dudley Pound, himself limp into Denning's room for the first time.

Now, 24 hours later, as the Naval Staff waited eagerly and in trepidation for the latest Enigma decrypts to come through, Pound's homely face and bent figure of a weather-worn old sailorman came through Denning's door again. With him were Brind and Eccles. Rear-Admiral Clayton, the Director of the OIC, was already in the room with Denning, who recalled:

> Pound sat down on a stool in front of the main plotting table. The plot showed the planned convoy route, the position of the convoy, our own forces and as far as was known or estimated, the position of U-boats and German surface forces.
>
> Bletchley had not yet broken the new keys.
>
> Luftwaffe reconnaissance had still not relocated Tovey's force, and had not yet located Hamilton's cruiser force.
>
> Almost immediately Pound asked what would be the farthest on position of TIRPITZ assuming she had sailed direct from Trondheim Fjord to attack the convoy . . . someone – I think it was Brind – plotted a rough course and estimated that she could then be within striking distance of the convoy.
>
> I interjected that it was unlikely in any event that she would have taken a direct course from Trondheim Fjord as she would almost certainly have made as much use as she could of the Inner Leads and proceed via Vest Fjord: I also considered that she would put into Narvik or Tromso to refuel her escorting destroyers before setting out on a sortie.[71]

The roomful of officers fell silent while Pound 'gazed at the plot for some time but said very little'.[72] Denning then broke into 'his apparent reverie' to say that within a few hours Bletchley Park would probably have broken the naval Enigma for the previous twenty-four hours. Pound then left the room. Shortly afterwards Denning was telephoned from Bletchley Park by Dr (now Professor Sir Harry) Hinsley of the Naval Section of GC and CS with the news that a break was imminent. This prompted the signal, drafted by Eccles and presumably approved by Pound, to Hamilton (and repeated to Tovey at 1930): 'Further information may be available shortly. Remain with the convoy until further instructions.'

At 1900 the teleprinter began to clack out two decrypts: a report timed 0040 that morning that the Luftwaffe had located a force composed of a battleship and three cruisers (which the Admiralty knew from the position given must be Hamilton's 1st Cruiser Squadron); and an order timed 0740 that morning from Grand Admiral Raeder to the Admiral Commanding Cruisers. This read:

> Immediate. Arriving Alta [Altenfiord] 0900. You are to allot anchorage to TIRPITZ . . . Newly arrived destroyers and torpedo boats to complete with fuel at once.[73]

Denning was in the midst of drafting a signal to convey this information to Tovey and Hamilton when Pound came in with several members of the Naval Staff, followed shortly by the VCNS and the Assistant Chief of Naval Staff (Trade), Vice-Admiral E. L. S. King. 'I was immediately asked,' writes Denning,

> what I was proposing to say. I gave the gist of the two intercepts and a proposed comment that all indications pointed to TIRPITZ and ac- companying ships still being in harbour at Alta. Pound apparently con- sidered the comment premature and my proposed 'Ultra' was whittled down to the bald facts that TIRPITZ had arrived at Alta at 0900 that morning and that Admiral SCHEER was already there.[74]

All decisions now turned on whether the *Tirpitz* was or was not by now at sea heading for PQ17. These decisions Pound, the executive head of the Navy, took upon himself in the most critical hour of his entire service as First Sea Lord. He suffered from the handicap that he had never flown his flag at sea in the present war, and knew nothing of modern naval operations at first hand; from the further handicap that his habits of mind had been shaped by the rigidities and artificiality of peacetime fleet manoeuvres. Now he had to resolve an operational puzzle on the basis of negative rather than positive Intelligence indications.

> Pound resumed the seat on the stool at the head of the plotting table and enquired how long it would take for the destroyers to top up with fuel. I had already mentally calculated this as about three hours. Then he asked what was likely to be the speed of TIRPITZ. I replied probably 25 or 26 knots provided the weather was favourable for the destroyers but two or three knots less if pocket battleships were also in company.
>
> Taking up the dividers and using a smaller chart of the area for plotting, Pound remarked that if TIRPITZ had sailed from Alta that morning, she could be up with the convoy about midnight. He then asked me why I thought TIRPITZ had not yet left Alta?[75]

In reply Denning drew Pound's attention to the cautious pattern of *Tirpitz*'s sortie against PQ12; noted that up to noon that day no decrypt had been received ordering U-boats to keep clear of the convoy (in order to avoid possible mistaken attack on *Tirpitz*), and that HF/DF showed that the U-boats were still clinging to the convoy. Moreover, the Luftwaffe had not yet relocated Tovey, while its having reported Hamilton's cruiser squadron as including a battleship could only increase the German naval command's apprehensions. The Luftwaffe had also reported seeing an aircraft in the vicinity of Hamilton's force, so probably raising the spectre for the German command that a British carrier might be present. Then again, the pattern of German naval radio signalling showed none of the characteristics typical of surface ships at sea. Finally, no sighting report of enemy heavy ships had been received from the British submarines patrolling off the North Cape.

Though other members of the Naval Staff made comments or put questions to Denning, Pound himself 'spoke very little and played idly with the dividers, and apparently sunk in thought'.

> After a time Pound got up to proceed to the U-boat tracking room but before leaving he turned to me and asked: 'Can you assure me that TIRPITZ is still in Altenfjord?'
> My reply was to the effect that although I was confident she was, I could not give absolute assurance but fully expected to receive confirmation in the fairly near future when Bletchley had unbuttoned the new traffic.[76]

At 2031 the teleprinter clattered out a fresh decrypt of a signal timed 1130 that forenoon from Admiral Commanding Group North to the U-boats operating against PQ17: 'No own forces in operational area. Position of heavy enemy group not known at present but is main target for U-boats when encountered . . .'[77]

This new decrypt resolved all possible doubts in Denning's mind; in his own words, 'Clearly TIRPITZ had not sailed that morning.'[78] He hastened to find Clayton, only to bump into him in the corridor while he was on his way to a meeting called by Pound. They exchanged a quick word, and Clayton took the teleprinter message with him to the meeting. Back in his own room, Denning 'tried to sum up the situation as it appeared in the eyes of the German Naval Staff from such information as was available to them . . .' Denning came to the firm conclusion that with Tovey's heavy ships and the possible carrier still not relocated, with the chance that there might be a second British heavy group with a carrier at sea (that is, Hamilton as reported by the Luftwaffe), he as a German admiral would judge that 'it would be taking an unjustifiable risk to commit our only worthwhile surface force to attack the convoy at present. Thus for the time being we will continue to attack and harass the convoy by U-boat and aircraft.'[79]

This appreciation chimed, of course, with Tovey's general judgment in his letter to the Admiralty on 14 March that the Germans would take no risks with so precious and irreplaceable an asset as the *Tirpitz*.

Denning now began to draft a signal to Tovey and Hamilton based on his appreciation. The draft stated, according to Denning's recollection, that 'it was considered TIRPITZ and accompanying ships were still in Altenfjord at 1200/4. Indications strongly pointed to them not having yet sailed. It was unlikely they would sail until Germans have located and established location and strength of the forces in support of the convoy.'[80]

Tovey back in March and Denning now had in fact accurately read the enemy's mind. For although Admiral Raeder had ordered the movement of the heavy ships to northern Norway, Hitler consistently refused to allow them to go to sea to attack the convoy until and unless the whereabouts of British aircraft carriers had first been established.

In the normal course of events Denning would have despatched his signal on his own responsibility. This time he felt he must await Clayton's return from a meeting with the First Sea Lord. Meanwhile he was visited by Commander Rodger Winn, RNVR, in charge of the U-boat tracking room, who on reading Denning's draft remarked that he understood from discussion going on in his room that 'the TIRPITZ was already at sea and there was talk of dispersing the convoy'.[81] It did not relieve Denning's 'grave concern' at such a decision being taken, and on unsound grounds, when Clayton returned at about 2130 and confirmed that 'because of the U-boat threat Hamilton had been ordered to withdraw to the westward at high speed and because of the possible threat of attack by surface forces on the convoy, Pound had decided to disperse it'.[82]

Denning now showed his draft signal to the equally perturbed Clayton, who fully agreed with its contents. With some hesitation he fell in with Denning's suggestion that he should take it to Pound. All too soon, however, Clayton was back again: 'Father says he's made his decision and is not going to change it now.'[83]

Three fateful signals resulted from Pound's irrevocable decision, each bald of language and without explanatory comment, certainly without the comment Denning had wished to include, that is, to the effect that the *Tirpitz* was most probably still in harbour.

Most Immediate. Cruiser force withdraw westward at high speed. (Despatched at 2111.)

Immediate. Owing to threat from surface ships, convoy is to disperse and proceed to Russian ports. (Despatched at 2123.)

Most Immediate. My 2123/4. Convoy is to scatter. (Despatched 2136.)[84]

It cannot be doubted that in the absence of positive Intelligence as to whether the *Tirpitz* was or was not at sea, the First Sea Lord had confronted an unpleasantly hard choice, and one fraught with heavy consequences. Nevertheless Pound's performance during this crisis

[718]

shows up his characteristic limitations. Why did he not allow Denning to send his signal to Tovey and Hamilton as drafted, complete with Denning's appreciation that the balance of the evidence indicated that *Tirpitz* had not left Altenfiord – and then leave it to the responsible Commander-in-Chief at sea to act as he judged best? Instead Pound had arrogated operational direction to himself once again, despite Tovey's vehement objections to such interference after the PQ16 episode in May. Why did Pound during his first meeting with Denning already find it easier to think that *Tirpitz* might be at sea heading for the convoy than not? Why did he thereafter close his mind firmly to the later Ultra evidence that she was still at Altenfiord? And why, even given his own assumption that she might well be heading for the convoy, did he order Hamilton so urgently to withdraw at high speed simply because of U-boats? This order stood in glaring contradiction to Tovey's own directive in March that in the face of enemy heavy ships convoy escorts should remain in the vicinity to shadow and even to attack the enemy if opportunity should serve.

And why also, given again Pound's assumption that *Tirpitz* could well be at sea, did he order the convoy first to disperse (meaning spread out) and then, a quarter of an hour later, to scatter? These orders stood in contradiction to both Atlantic Convoy Instructions and Tovey's own directive, which alike stated that a convoy was only to scatter if the escort had been overwhelmed. Why in any case was Pound so much more concerned with the danger posed by the *Tirpitz* to the convoy while concentrated than with the danger from U-boats and aircraft once it was scattered? Yet Pound's decision only fulfilled what had already been in his mind when he first mentioned scattering to Tovey on the telephone between Whitehall and Scapa before PQ17 sailed, and to which Tovey had then objected so strongly.

It is not unjust to see in all this a combination of Pound's old-fashioned naval authoritarianism and his well-known stubborn closed-mindedness – coupled with a lack of that imaginative insight into the enemy's mind which is the mark of great commanders. After all Tovey, long before the sailing of PQ17, and Denning, at the critical hour, both rightly divined that the Germans would not hazard the *Tirpitz* in waters where she might encounter unlocated British heavy forces.

Nor did the very language of the three signals, with their almost panicky tone of imminent emergency, do Pound any credit as a leader in a crisis. He, or his staff, ought to have realised the impact such signals must have on the recipients at sea.

Thus far PQ17 had come through almost unscathed and in high fettle. Two merchantmen had dropped out because of ice damage and grounding. On 1 July the escort beat off U-boat attacks without loss to the convoy; on 2 July PQ17 and the homeward QP13 passed each other in 73°N, 3°E, and that evening torpedo-bombers attacked PQ17, which again sustained no loss. By now Rear-Admiral Hamilton's 1st Cruiser Squadron had caught up with the convoy, and was steaming some 40 miles off its port beam (that is, on the far side from a likely approach by German surface ships). Early on 4 July a torpedo-bomber suddenly swept out of a hole in the then prevailing fog to inflict PQ17's first casualty, an American freighter. At about 2000 came a determined attack by some 20 torpedo-bombers (as Broome had been forewarned by the Admiralty thanks to Ultra), which were welcomed with heavy anti-aircraft fire by convoy and escort, in which the USS *Wainwright* (Captain R. H. Gibbs, USN) played a particularly effective part. Three ships were hit, and two of them had to be scuttled. The third, a Russian tanker, survived 'holed but happy and capable of nine knots', as Commander Broome expressed it in his later report of proceedings. That evening of 4 July a feeling of elation buoyed up the ships' companies of PQ17 and its escort. 'My impression,' recorded Broome, 'on seeing the resolution displayed by the convoy and its escort was that, provided the ammunition lasted, PQ17 could get anywhere.'[85]

Then, at around 2200, with the convoy in 75° 55'N, 27° 52'E, arrived the Admiralty's 'Most Immediate' order to scatter the convoy. Just as Denning and Clayton had feared back in Whitehall, the urgency of the language led Broome to expect to see at any moment Hamilton's cruisers open fire and the enemy's masts appear on the horizon.[86] Fifteen minutes later Broome passed on the order to scatter the convoy, and he himself steered to join Hamilton in compliance with Tovey's standing instructions. His decision to do so was later approved both by Hamilton and Tovey. At 2230 Rear-Admiral Hamilton, on receipt of the Admiralty's order to him to 'withdraw westward at high speed', turned south-west to get between the convoy and the apparent enemy. 'Assuming as we all did assume,' he later wrote, 'that the scattering of the convoy heralded the imminent approach of enemy surface forces, we were – in the eyes of all who did not know the full story – running away, and at high speed.'[87]

The commodore of PQ17, Commodore J. C. K. Dowding, RNR, on receiving the order to scatter signalled Broome in HMS *Keppel*: 'Many thanks, goodbye and good hunting.' Broome could only reply: 'It is a grim business leaving you here.'[88] The convoy then proceeded to scatter, in Dowding's words, 'as laid down . . . in perfect order, though it must have been apparent to the ships that had to turn to the south-west that they were heading towards where trouble might be expected'.[89] So the defenceless merchant ships steamed away, each on her lonely course under the Arctic summer daylight, the numerous patches of fog 'made all the more interesting by the presence of growlers [small icebergs]'.[90] The nearest Russian landfall lay 600 miles distant.

The Commander-in-Chief, Home Fleet, was to write in his despatch:

> The order to scatter the convoy had, in my opinion, been premature . . . its results were disastrous. The convoy had so far covered more than half its route with the loss of only three ships. Now its ships, spread over a wide area, were exposed without defence to the powerful enemy U-boat and air forces. The enemy took prompt advantage of this situation, operating both weapons to their full capacity.[91]

Tovey also retrospectively criticised Rear-Admiral Hamilton for failing to release Broome's escort force back to the merchant ships once he, Hamilton, was clear of the convoy 'and in default of information that the *Tirpitz* was near'.[92] Tovey judged that the value of Broome's destroyers 'for anti-U-boat purposes, for rounding up scattered ships, and, if the *Tirpitz* had appeared, for diverting and delaying her, would have been considerable . . .'[93] This was hardly fair on Hamilton, for the destroyers' oiler had been sunk, leaving them without fuel for extended operations in the Barents Sea.

In the event, the *Tirpitz* did put to sea next day, 5 July, only to be quickly recalled by the German naval command (as revealed to the Admiralty by Ultra), and for the very reason guessed by Denning on the 4th: a decision to leave the convoy to the U-boats and the Luftwaffe. And for these to massacre the scattered merchantmen in the following days proved as easy as shooting rabbits in a stubble-field. Twenty-three ships went down, including the Commodore's ship *River Afton*, although happily Dowding and her master survived. The rescue ship *Zaafaran* was also sunk.[94]

That eleven merchantmen still managed to reach Kola owed itself to the courage of their crews and the cunning of their masters in navigating along unlikely shores and exploiting the recurrent fogs – as well as to the devotion of Allied escort ships in defending small groups against the Luftwaffe. Lost with the sunk ships were 210 crated aircraft, 430 tanks, 3,350 vehicles and nearly 100,000 tons of stores.[95] This huge loss was the more serious because on 18 June the

German Army had begun its summer offensive on the southern half of the Eastern Front with the first of a succession of grand attacks over the next two weeks that smashed the Russian defence to fragments. On the very days that PQ17 was scattering in obedience to the Admiralty's order the German panzer armies reached the River Don at Voronezh. Once again battle had been joined on a scale and of a savagery not experienced by armies of the Western democracies since the Great War.

On 1 August the First Sea Lord reported to the War Cabinet on the disaster to PQ17. His version of events was, to say the least, somewhat disingenuous. He alleged (according to the minutes of the meeting) that the Admiralty 'had had information on the night before the order to disperse was given that the TIRPITZ, having eluded our submarines, would, if she continued on her present course, be in a position to attack the convoy early the following morning...'[96] Of the three forms of attack, air, U-boat or surface ships, proceeded Pound, 'the most dangerous threat' if the convoy remained concentrated 'appeared, in the circumstances as then known to the Admiralty, to be from surface ships'; hence the order to scatter.

The massacre of PQ17 aroused the Prime Minister's pugilistic instincts, and on 12 July he urged on the Admiralty that 'assuming all goes well in Malta' the Mediterranean Fleet's two modern fleet carriers *Indomitable* and *Victorious*, the older carriers *Argus* and *Eagle*, at least five of the new escort carriers, all the Dido class cruisers (5,450 tons displacement; ten 5.25-inch dual-purpose guns; 33 knots)[97] and at least 25 destroyers should be concentrated to protect PQ18. This vast concourse of ships should, he suggested, proceed to Archangel 'keeping southward, not hugging the ice, but seeking the clearest weather, and thus fight it out with the enemy'.[98] With the supply ships moving 'under an umbrella of at least 100 [carrier] aircraft,' wrote Churchill, 'we ought to be able to fight the convoy through and out again, and if a Fleet action results, so much the better.'[99]

Neither the First Lord, A. V. Alexander, nor the First Sea Lord were attracted to this grandiose concept, especially at the price of denuding the Mediterranean Fleet at a time when all was *not* going well in Malta. Next day the Defence Committee agreed to the recommendation of the Chiefs of Staff that 'convoys should not be run to North Russia in present circumstances' – no attempt therefore to fight PQ18 through by means of a great fleet; indeed, no further convoys at all for the remainder of the Arctic summer of 1942.[100] It fell to Churchill himself to telegraph this disagreeable news to Stalin at a time when the Russian defence in the Ukraine had already crumbled under the weight and power of the German summer offensive.

In the event, instead of the Mediterranean Fleet releasing major ships for the Arctic in August, the Home Fleet had to release the battleship *Nelson*, the carrier *Victorious*, the cruisers *Kenya*, *Nigeria* and *Manchester* and eleven destroyers to the Mediterranean for another Malta convoy – 'Pedestal' (see above, pp. 517–25), the supreme effort which alone enabled Malta to survive into the autumn. Of these Home Fleet ships, the *Manchester* and a destroyer were sunk during 'Pedestal', and *Nigeria* and *Kenya* damaged, so materially adding to Admiral Tovey's troubles. The anti-aircraft cruiser *Cairo* had also been sunk. In mid-July the battleship *Washington* and four American destroyers were withdrawn from service with the Home Fleet, Admiral Giffen transferring his flag to the heavy cruiser *Wichita*. In August the *Wichita* and then the *Tuscaloosa* also departed. 'Task Force 39' thus came to an end, much to the regret of the Home Fleet and of Tovey, its Commander-in-Chief, who was to pay a heartfelt tribute in his despatch:

> This force had provided a welcome reinforcement to the Home Fleet of a time when its strength was much reduced. The conduct of officers and men had been admirable, and the ships displayed a very high degree of weapon efficiency. In Admiral Giffen I had a loyal and enthusiastic colleague whose tact and good humour never failed. I was very sorry to see them go.[101]

To fill the place of the departing *Washington* there had already arrived HMS *King George V*, fresh from a refit. In August the recently worked-up new battleship *Anson* (another 'King George V': 38,000 tons displacement; 29 knots; ten 14-inch guns; launched February 1940)[102] joined the Fleet, bringing its strength in heavy ships up to three battleships and the battlecruiser *Renown*.

To Churchill's news that no further convoys were to be despatched to North Russia during the summer and the concurrent and equally unpalatable news that the Western Allies had finally decided that a 'Second Front' in France in 1942 was not a feasible operation of war, Stalin objected furiously on 23 July, pointing out the present critical position on the Eastern Front (where German panzer forces had now got as far as the southern reaches of the River Don). In the course of August these forces were to hammer their way closer and closer to Stalingrad and to the Volga crossing, while a second army group was to drive deep into the Caucasus. With the Red Army fighting desperately to slow and stop these divergent offensives and in ever more urgent need of tanks, trucks, aircraft and ammunition from the Anglo-Americans, it was therefore decided after all that PQ18 must be run in September.

Although the Admiralty had torpedoed the Prime Minister's suggestion of escorting the convoy all the way through with a great fleet, nevertheless arrangements for protecting PQ18 were on an unprecedented scale. Accompanying the convoy (of 39 merchantmen, a rescue ship, an oiler, three minesweepers for Russia and two fleet oilers) would be a close escort of two destroyers, two anti-aircraft ships, two submarines, four corvettes, three minesweepers and four trawlers. This in itself was not very different in strength from PQ16's or PQ17's close escorts. But this time there would be two other escort forces with the convoy as well during the most dangerous stretches of the passage – a Carrier Force comprising the escort carrier *Avenger* (Commander A. P. Colthurst, RN: American-built; 8,200 tons displacement; Diesel motors giving 17 knots; 15 aircraft),[103] making her operational début, and two destroyers; and a Fighting Destroyer Force consisting of no fewer than sixteen fleet destroyers and the light cruiser *Scylla* (5,450 tons displacement; 33 knots; eight 4.5-inch dual-purpose guns; launched August 1940).[104] Rear-Admiral R. L. Burnett (flying his flag in *Scylla*) was to command all three escort forces.

As in previous operations there was to be a cruiser covering force, this time made up of the *Norfolk* (flag of Vice-Admiral S. S. Bonham-Carter, recently promoted), *Suffolk* and *London*. The distant covering force of heavy ships would be based on Akureyri in northern Iceland and commanded by Vice-Admiral Sir Bruce Fraser, Second-in-Command, Home Fleet, flying his flag in the new battleship *Anson*. With him would be one other battleship (*Duke of York*), the cruiser *Jamaica* and five destroyers, all of the latter being of limited range because the fleet destroyers had been allotted to the Fighting Destroyer Force.

This time the homeward-bound convoy (QP14) was not to pass the outward convoy just west of Bear Island, but in the Barents Sea where, as experience had painfully taught, both would stand in the greatest need of protection.

With so many warships therefore going so far, elaborate arrangements had to be made to fuel them *en passage*. As well as the two fleet oilers sailing with the convoy, two more were to be sent under escort by four destroyers to a rendezvous in Lowe Sound, on the coast of the island of Spitzbergen. The Royal Navy had indeed come a long way since Admiral Sir Charles Forbes's operations during the Norwegian campaign in 1940 had been shackled by the need frequently to return ships to Scapa to refuel. One further force was also involved: the cruisers *Cumberland* and *Suffolk* and one destroyer were to carry reinforcements and stores to the Allied garrison on Spitzbergen.

By the beginning of September 1942, at long last, and by dint of much effort – not least in eliciting the necessary Russian cooperation – Royal Air Force Coastal Command had been able to set up an advanced striking force in North Russia, the necessary ground staff and equipment being transported by the USS *Tuscaloosa* (on her last operation in Arctic waters) and three destroyers in August. The force, under the command of Group Captain F. L. Hopps, consisted of 24 Hampden torpedo-bombers of Nos. 144 and 455 Squadrons, four photographic reconnaissance (PR) Spitfires and long-range reconnaissance Catalinas of No. 210 Squadron. A joint Navy–Air Force Combined Area Headquarters was created at Polyarnoe on the Kola Inlet leading to Murmansk, the Navy's representative being Rear-Admiral D. B. Fisher, the Senior British Naval Officer in North Russia.[105] No longer would the Luftwaffe enjoy that undisputed mastery of the Arctic skies which it had wielded with such success against previous Allied convoys.

In the air as well as on the surface, therefore, PQ18 was to be immensely better protected than the unfortunate PQ17 or the triumphant PQ16 and its gallant escort. And this time Sigint posed no taxing operational puzzles for the Admiralty or the Commander-in-Chief, Home Fleet (who coordinated his different task groups from a shore headquarters at Scapa). The British Naval Attaché in Stockholm, the able and assiduous Captain H. M. Denham, was receiving through the Deputy Chief of the Swedish General Staff information derived from the tapping of the supposedly secure teleprinter landline through Sweden from Berlin to the Wehrmacht in Norway.[106] From this source and from Ultra it was known that the pocket battleship *Lützow* had been withdrawn from Norway and the 6-inch cruiser *Köln* transferred from the Baltic to Trondheim, and then, later in August, to Narvik. The Admiralty also knew the location of the twenty U-boats deployed to attack the convoy; it estimated the Luftwaffe's strike forces at 65 torpedo-bombers (actually 92) and 120 bombers.[107] On 11 September (eight days after PQ18 put to sea from Iceland) Ultra decrypts confirmed sightings by British submarines on the day before that the *Scheer*, *Hipper* and *Köln* had been moved north to Altenfiord. From hints in Enigma signals and the results of photo-reconnaissance by Spitfires from North Russia the Operational Intelligence Centre concluded that *Tirpitz* probably remained in Narvik. Later photo-reconnaissance confirmed that the three smaller ships remained in Altenfiord, while on 15 September Ultra decrypts revealed that on the previous day the *Tirpitz* had still been in Narvik. On the 16th came fresh news from Captain Denham's impeccable source that the German naval command only proposed to employ the three smaller ships against PQ18 and that *Tirpitz* was suffering from a technical defect (later confirmed through decrypts as bearing trouble). By this time, as it happened, the enemy had in any case decided not to take unnecessary risks even with the smaller ships in view of their importance to the defence of Norway.[108]

Yet for all the strength of PQ18's covering forces under the command of no fewer than three admirals afloat and one ashore, the Luftwaffe and the U-boats gave the convoy as hard a time as PQ16, which had nevertheless finally reached its destination with the loss of only seven ships out of 35.

The air attacks on PQ18 began at 1530 on 13 September 1942, after the convoy emerged from the cover of fogs and snowstorms. Over 40 twin-torpedoed Ju 88s and He 111s flying in the 'Golden Comb' formation line abreast came in, according to Commodore (Rear-Admiral, retired) E. K. Boddam-Whetham, the convoy commodore, like 'a huge flight of nightmare locusts'.[109] At the time HMS *Avenger*'s aircraft were all chasing shadowers and high-level bombers, so that in less than ten minutes the 'locusts' succeeded in sinking eight ships.[110] The experience decided the captain of *Avenger*, Commander A. P. Colthurst, that

> ... with the small number of obsolete fighters at our disposal, and with their slow operation in an auxiliary carrier, we must use them only to break up large attacking formations rather than to destroy individuals; further we must endeavour to maintain a continual cycle of sections taking off, landing to re-arm and re-fuel, and taking off again. The achievement of this would avoid congestion in the carrier and ensure that there were always some fighter sections available ready to counter-attack striking forces.[111]

Next day *Avenger* was to live up to her name – partly owing to Colthurst's revised operations system, partly owing to the 'Headache' party installed in Rear-Admiral Burnett's flagship *Scylla*. 'Headache' was the codename for the shipborne sections of 'Y' Intelligence (charged with intercepting and reading the enemy's low-grade radio-telephone traffic) which had been steadily introduced since 1941.

Now 'Headache' gave *Avenger* advanced tactical warning of impending Luftwaffe attack.[112] The combined results of 'Headache' and Commander Colthurst's change of method proved impressive, as Rear-Admiral Burnett recounted:

> It was a fine sight to see *Avenger* peeling off Hurricanes, whilst streaking across the front of the convoy from starboard to port inside the screen with her destroyer escort [HMS *Wheatland* and *Wilton*] blazing away with every gun that would bear, and then being chased by torpedo-bombers as she steamed down on the opposite course to the convoy to take cover . . . Altogether a most gratifying action . . .[113]

That day, 14 September 1942, *Avenger*'s Hurricanes and the guns of the escorts shot down 22 enemy aircraft for the loss of three Hurricanes – and even those three in fact fell victim to their own pilots' courage in flying through the ships' anti-aircraft fire to reach the enemy. Happily all of the pilots were rescued from the icy water. For the next five days the Luftwaffe tried again and again, though not on the same scale, despite the fact that the *Avenger* and other covering forces turned back on the 16th to protect the homeward QP14 convoy. The Luftwaffe's final attack coincided with a full gale. When the battle died down at last on 20 September, the enemy had lost 33 torpedo-bombers, six dive-bombers and two long-range reconnaissance aircraft – 41 in all, one of them falling to the Hurricane pilot from the Catapult Aircraft Merchant Ship *Empire Morn*. Thus the introduction of the CVE began to close the air gap over the Arctic in 1942 six months before it served the same vital purpose in the Atlantic in March 1943; and the Luftwaffe in northern Norway was left permanently winged.

Nor were the U-boats successful against PQ18, partly because of the presence of patrolling Catalinas from Russia from 18 September onwards. They sank only three ships for the loss of three of their own number. Of the 40 ships which had set out, 27 reached safe haven in Russia after eighteen days of constant strain, exertion and peril. For the ships' companies of the merchantmen, there was (as in all convoys) the added stress occasioned by the often hazardous nature of their cargoes. As Commodore Boddam-Whetham remarked in a private letter later to Rear-Admiral Burnett:

> It's a funny feeling to realise one is sitting on top of 2,000 tons of T.N.T., but we nearly all carry between that and 4,000 tons. I don't think the bigger amount would make much more than a tiny fraction of a second difference to the time one entered the next world . . .[114]

PQ18's escort and covering forces had not merely got the convoy through without crippling losses (though they were still greater than those of PQ16), but also scored a damaging victory over the Luftwaffe. Nevertheless Burnett reckoned that they had been lucky. In his report of proceedings he wrote: 'I do not know how far this operation may be considered a success or a failure, but I am convinced that had any of six circumstances been otherwise it must have been a tragic failure . . .'[115] For instance, if the weather had been bad, no oiling at sea would have been possible, forcing the escorts to turn back – as would also have happened if one or two of the oilers had been torpedoed early on. Delays in refuelling part of the Fighting Destroyer Escort at Spitzbergen or delays if it had had to be oiled at sea would have meant its absence during the crisis of the battle. Burnett also pointed out that had the enemy synchronised his air and sea attacks the losses would have been heavy. Then again, if the enemy had kept up his torpedo-bomber attacks, the stocks of anti-aircraft ammunition would have become critical, with little left with which to defend the homeward QP14.[116]

QP14 (fifteen merchant ships) in any case ran into trouble – partly because en route Burnett detached *Avenger* for home rather than expose her to further risk of U-boat attack. Although he asked for shore-based air cover, Coastal Command was too stretched by simultaneous demands in the Battle of the Atlantic and too hampered by bad weather to provide more than intermittent protection. This time it was the U-boats that did the damage, sinking three merchant ships and a fleet oiler. The Tribal class destroyer *Somali* also took a torpedo from a U-boat, but was taken in tow by her sister ship *Ashanti*. Thanks to prodigious seamanship they made 420 miles westwards in eighty hours before that ever-present enemy, the weather, intervened with a full gale. *Somali*, her weakened hull severely stressed by motion through huge seas, broke in two and sank.

Taken together, the battles of PQ16/QP12 and PQ18/QP14 mark the turning point for the Arctic convoys, for with the exception of the heavy ships the German forces in northern Norway had done their utmost to stop the traffic, and yet failed first against PQ16 and then, after a misleadingly easy triumph over PQ17, failed once more against PQ18. Henceforward the German effort would wane. In particular the Luftwaffe's strike forces were drawn away to the Mediterranean in November 1942 to deal with the Anglo-American 'Torch' landings (an uncovenanted benefit of that operation to the Royal Navy in the Arctic), and were never fully rebuilt.

Yet it was the demand of 'Torch' for warships from the Home

Fleet that prevented any further outward convoy to Russia until 15 December, despite renewed attempts by Stalin and Roosevelt to bully Churchill. In fairness to Stalin, this was another time of crisis on the Eastern Front. In October the German offensive against the Soviet garrison of Stalingrad was entering its final and appalling phase of street-fighting amid the ruins. On both flanks of the German 6th Army, Red Army reserves were moving into place in readiness for the coming Soviet counter-offensive. This was launched on 19 November 1942, leading within a week to the encirclement of the 6th Army.

On 15 December – by now the trapped 6th Army under General Paulus was dying fast of hunger and frostbite – the Royal Navy resumed the Arctic convoys with JW51A (first of a new numerical series in replacement of the PQ/QP series) of fifteen ships; at Tovey's insistence half the size of the last three PQs. The threat of the German heavy ships remained, but their sorties proved to be rare and timid. On 30 December 1942, for instance, Vice-Admiral Kummetz put to sea with the pocket battleship *Lützow* (six 11-inch guns), the 8-inch gun cruiser *Hipper* and six destroyers to attack outward convoy JW51B south-east of Bear Island in the Barents Sea. In a confused sequence of encounters amid snow storms the German squadron was seen off by the convoy's escort of destroyers and two 6-inch light cruisers, all of which steered to engage closely a cringing enemy whenever he was sighted; a familiar enough pattern. The close escort of five destroyers under Captain R. St. V. Sherbrooke in HMS *Onslow* themselves held off the German heavy ships for an hour in yet another unhesitatingly aggressive destroyer action. Sherbrooke himself, badly wounded, later received the Victoria Cross. As Admiral Tovey remarked in his despatch:

> . . . that an enemy force of at least one pocket battleship, one heavy cruiser and six destroyers, with all the advantages of surprise and concentration, should be held off for four hours by five destroyers and two 6-inch cruisers without any loss to the convoy is most creditable and satisfactory.[117]

In March 1943, after two more outward convoys had been despatched, the current danger of catastrophe in the Atlantic at the hands of the U-boat, with the Royal Navy desperately short of escort vessels to take on the wolf packs, compelled the War Cabinet to cancel the next two Arctic sailings. Even Roosevelt had to agree when Churchill told him that the disasters to the Atlantic convoys HX229 and SC122 (see above, pp. 598–600) offered a 'final proof that our escorts are everywhere too thin. The strain upon the British Navy is becoming intolerable.'[118] It was thanks to the cancellation of further Arctic convoys that the Home Fleet was able to release enough destroyers and corvettes to enable the creation of the new 'escort groups' in the Atlantic which helped so much in April and May 1943 to break Dönitz's U-boats.

The hiatus in the Arctic convoy traffic also simplified the Home Fleet's role as the Admiralty's central strategic reserve, enabling it to release the new battleship *Howe* (another 'King George V') and the *King George V* to the Mediterranean for 'Husky', the invasion of Sicily, in June 1943 (see above, Chapter 21). In return the elderly *Rodney* and the Great War veteran *Malaya* came home. To augment the Home Fleet's strength in the face of the modern German heavy ships still based in northern Norway – *Tirpitz*, *Scharnhorst*, *Lützow* – the United States Navy again contributed a task force, this time composed of the battleships *Alabama* and *South Dakota* and five destroyers under Rear Admiral O. M. Hustvedt.

On 8 May 1943 Admiral Sir John Tovey struck his flag as Commander-in-Chief, Home Fleet. He was later appointed C-in-C, The Nore. No diplomat but a forthright sailor of unbendable integrity, he fell into that same category as Generals Wavell and Auchinleck of commanders-in-chief serving in the most difficult period of the war whom the Prime Minister found uncongenial in their stubborn realism. Churchill had indeed manoeuvred to oust Tovey as long ago as April 1942 when Cunningham had been called home at short notice from the Mediterranean Fleet ostensibly to become head of the British Naval Mission in Washington. On Cunningham's arrival Churchill told him that he wanted him to relieve Tovey, to which 'A.B.C.' had angrily retorted: 'If Tovey drops dead on his bridge I will certainly relieve him. Otherwise not.'[119] So Cunningham went to Washington after all, before returning to the Mediterranean as Naval Commander, Allied Expeditionary Force (see above, pp. 538–9).

The new Commander-in-Chief of the Home Fleet, previously its Second-in-Command, Admiral Sir Bruce Fraser, had no doubt that the Russian convoy traffic should not be resumed even in September (the earliest feasible month in terms of ice and light) unless German surface strength could be reduced, or unless to operate this route in addition to the trans-Iranian route was considered 'vital to the prosecution of the war', which he wrote in a letter to the First Sea Lord on 30 June he had 'no reason to suppose'.[120] In fact by this time the danger that Soviet Russia might collapse had passed for good with the destruction of the German 6th Army at Stalingrad (Paulus and the remnant of his army had surrendered on 2 February 1943) and the sweeping Russian advances in the Ukraine and the Caucasus which had followed. The German Army on the Eastern Front had now been forced ineluctably on to a strategic defensive which was to end two years later in the ruins of Berlin. Moreover, Russia's own factories were now pouring out crude but effective weapons to equip her massed soldiery – T.34 tanks, heavy artillery and 'Katushka' rocket batteries, Stormovik ground-attack aircraft. The British and American Armies were beginning to take some of the weight off the Red Army by their campaign in the Mediterranean, for von Arnim surrendered in Tunisia on 13 May and the invasion of Sicily was scheduled for July. The possible invasion of Italy thereafter was already under debate. There was no longer, therefore, the hounding need of 1941–42 to keep the Arctic convoys going at any hazard; and in the event no further convoy was to be run until November 1943.

Yet the existence of the German heavy ships as a 'fleet in being' – and especially the *Tirpitz* – continued to weigh on the Admiralty. It was only partial comfort that Fraser, like his predecessor, judged that these ships would not put to sea 'unless they either could attack a convoy while it was not covered by British heavy forces', or unless those forces 'suffer damage from underwater or air attack'.[121] The German heavy ships, enjoying as they did the choice of the time and direction of a sortie, compelled the Admiralty to keep a disproportionate number of capital ships at Scapa and preferably a fleet carrier as well in order to parry a breakout into the Atlantic. This in turn affected the Admiralty's entire global deployment. And so during the months April to September 1943 the Royal Navy was patiently, thoroughly, preparing an entirely novel weapons system for destroying the *Tirpitz* and the other two heavy ships; one which for success merely required superlative skill and dauntless audacity on the part of its operators. On 11 and 12 September the task force put to sea to launch 'Operation Source'.

One day earlier, on 10 September, Admiral of the Fleet Sir Dudley Pound had ceased to be First Sea Lord. So long an evidently very tired man prone to drool down his pipe in a doze during Chiefs of Staff meetings, worn down by the ceaseless pain of his arthritic hip, Pound suffered a stroke while in Washington with the Prime Minister after the Quebec ('Quadrant') summit conference. By the night of 9 September, when he was being questioned by the Premier and President Roosevelt after dinner in the White House Pound showed clear signs of being, in Churchill's words, 'very ill'.[122] Next morning Pound went to see Churchill in his bed-sitting room, and told him: 'Prime

[731]

Minister, I have come to resign. I have had a stroke and my right side is largely paralysed. I thought it would pass off, but it gets worse every day and I am no longer fit for duty.'[123] Brought home in HMS *Renown* he was reduced by a second stroke to total paralysis. He lingered on until 21 October, Trafalgar Day, 1943.

Unlike his opposite numbers, the Chiefs of the Imperial General Staff and Air Staff, Pound had carried a double burden and had done so for four years of war. As well as bearing in his capacity as Chief of Naval Staff a responsibility similiar to theirs in terms of general policy and strategic advice to the Prime Minister, Pound in his other capacity as First Sea Lord was also supreme commander of the Royal Navy. For the Admiralty – unlike the Army and Air Councils, which were purely administrative bodies – was an operational headquarters, its radio net giving it direct access to British fleets, squadrons and individual ships in all oceans. To discharge effectively these twin roles called for high managerial talent, not only for delegation, but also especially for selecting the big questions from the detail. This talent Pound sadly lacked. He ran the Navy as if he were the executive officer of a ship, endlessly prying into and arranging matters of detail, drafting signals himself, second-guessing his staff and commanders-in-chief; even on one occasion, when on passage home from the first Washington Conference in August 1941 in the *Prince of Wales*, signalling a rebuke to two escorting destroyer captains for failing to carry out a minor evolution according to the book.[124] Admiral Sir Ralph Edwards, then, as a Captain, the Deputy Director of Naval Operations (Home), was to bear witness after the war:

> He was an arch meddler and I could not have believed that any Admiral could interfere with his Commanders at sea as the First Sea Lord then did. Over and over again I was instructed by him to make signals to the Fleets and ships how fast to go and where to put the Cruiser screen . . . I do not agree that Winston was invariably the nigger who interfered. Far from it; I regard his interference as negligible when compared with Dudley Pound.[125]

Pound's direct order to PQ17 to scatter stands as the supreme case of such operational intervention – and not least because of his rigid refusal to change his mind about scattering in the face of new evidence from Ultra that *Tirpitz* was not at sea (see above, pp. 717–8).

The double functions of First Sea Lord and Chief of the Naval Staff as Pound chose to interpret them could only be discharged by unceasing desk work; and in accomplishing this the elderly admiral simply wore himself out. Happiest when immersed in administrative and operational detail, Pound allowed the larger issues of grand strategy in a maritime war to become dominated by soldiers in the shape of the Chiefs of the Imperial General Staff. For all his sense of duty he was therefore far from being another Lord Barham or a Beatty (in the latter's full professional maturity as First Sea Lord after the Great War); rather an industrious journeyman, a narrow professional sailor, not very well informed about wider issues.[126] Nonetheless, he did grasp a single simple truth, one which cleverer minds in high places lost sight of from time to time – that Britain's survival and the Western Allies' ultimate victory alike depended totally on keeping the Atlantic convoy routes open; and that therefore the defeat of the U-boat ought to override all other considerations in framing grand strategy.

It is possible to admire Pound's devious tactics in handling his headstrong Prime Minister and putting to sleep some of his wilder schemes, such as 'Operation Catherine' (see above, pp. 93–5). Thereby he never incurred the smouldering hostility that Churchill evinced towards those who openly crossed him, such as Wavell and Auchinleck among soldiers and Tovey and Cunningham among sailors. However it also meant that Pound never enjoyed the independent stature of his predecessor, Admiral of the Fleet Lord Fisher, as First Sea Lord during the Great War (which Churchill all too keenly remembered), or of General Sir William Robertson, the Chief of the Imperial General Staff during the same conflict, or Alan Brooke in the present one. Too often Pound acquiesced in Churchill's interventions, such as the signals to Warburton-Lee and Lord Cork during the Narvik operation in April 1940 (see above, pp. 114–116 and 124), or the fatuous order (on the face of it issued by the Admiralty) to Tovey during the *Bismarck* chase to the effect that *King George V* was to continue to pursue even if it meant towing her home later for want of fuel.

This compliance with Churchill's wishes, coupled with a manner towards subordinates that varied between aloofness and bullying ill-temper, meant that Pound by no means enjoyed wide trust and confidence among his flag officers and staff, although he always remained on cordial relations with Andrew Cunningham. There was a feeling that he was too ready to listen to criticisms of naval officers via the backstairs or from outsiders such as the Prime Minister, as in the case of the enquiry into Somerville's conduct in the face of the Italian Fleet while escorting a Malta convoy in November 1940 (see above, pp. 241–3), or the precipitate relief of Harwood in 1943 on the basis of Montgomery's tittle-tattle. Some even suspected that

Pound was not always quite 'as high principled' in his dealings as could be wished.[127] If so, was this unwitting? It is curious that he once wrote to Churchill that he could 'quite definitely' tell his critics in the Navy that the *Prince of Wales* and *Repulse* had been sent to Singapore 'in accordance with my advice',[128] whereas the documentary record clearly shows that Pound opposed the move but allowed himself to be overborne (see above, pp. 393–400).

Thus, taking Pound's record as First Sea Lord all in all, there is an unintended resonance in Churchill's tribute in his war memoirs when he writes that Pound 'had been a true comrade to me, both at the Admiralty, and on the Chiefs of Staff Committee'.[129]

Churchill wanted Admiral Sir Bruce Fraser to replace Pound, out of fear of getting Andrew Cunningham instead, whose powerful and independent character he had encountered since 1940 in the course of Mediterranean operations. But Fraser told the Prime Minister that whereas he believed he enjoyed the confidence of his own fleet 'Cunningham has that of the whole Navy'.[130] So for the second time Cunningham struck his flag as C-in-C, Mediterranean, and returned to London (see also above, p. 681). In the Chiefs of Staff Committee and the War Cabinet Defence Committee Churchill no longer looked across the table at an admiral content to be his loyal sea-dog, but one with the high stature conferred by victorious command of a fleet in battle; a man of dominating presence, well able with his blue-eyed glare to outface even the Prime Minister.

Between 1600 on 11 September 1943 and 0100 on the 12th the submarines *Thrasher*, *Truculent*, *Stubborn*, *Syrtis*, *Sceptre* and *Seanymph* put to sea from Loch Cairnbawm on the north-west coast of Scotland in the first phase of 'Operation Source'. Each towed an 'X-Craft', the Royal Navy's latest technological innovation: a 51-foot-long midget submarine of only some 30 tons, with a beam of only 5¾ feet and a height from upper deck to keel also of only 5¾ feet. A 42 brake-horsepower diesel engine gave her a maximum speed of 6½ knots on the surface; a 25 horsepower electric motor a maximum speed of 5 knots submerged. Cruising on the surface at a speed of 4 knots the X-Craft had a maximum range of 1,500 miles.[131] Each operational crew consisted of three officers and one engine room artificer, all volunteers, who were expected to endure in the tiny coffin-like interior for up to a fortnight if need be. During the outward voyage the boats were manned by a 'passage crew' of three. The X-Craft's armament consisted of two 1-ton high-explosive charges carried on each side of the hull. These could be either detached on to the seabed beneath an enemy ship or be fixed to the enemy's hull with magnetic clamps and lines by a diver exiting from the submarine from a special chamber. After the X-Craft had been released by the towing submarines off the enemy coast, it would be the task of the four-man crews to navigate through confined and tortuous rocky channels towards their victims, penetrate through elaborate net defences, dive under the enemy's hulls, detach the charges, and then make good their escapes before the charges were blown by clockwork time-fuzes.

Three prototypes had been successfully tested in 1942.[132] In April 1943 the 12th Submarine Flotilla was formed under Captain W. E. Banks, RN, to train the crews of the six operational X-Craft. All that summer the crews rehearsed and rehearsed again what they would have to do. Thanks to three photo-reconnaissance Spitfires temporarily based in North Russia at the end of August the planners of 'Operation Source' possessed complete and detailed pictures of the location of the German ships and the protective measures round them.[133] At the last minute Ultra decrypts of the naval Enigma together with air reconnaissance by Catalinas gave confirmation that *Tirpitz*, *Scharnhorst* and *Lützow* should indeed all be present as expected in inlets off Altenfiord rather than in some alternative base such as Narvik or Trondheim.

Yet the voyage from Scotland to Norwegian waters proved tricky enough in itself. Tows parted; the X9 tragically foundered in unknown circumstances; the X8 had to be scuttled after damage from the premature explosion of her charges, ditched because of leaks; a third (X7) impaled herself on a mine, and was only safely got free by a gambler's kick against the mine-casing by the boat's commander. In the small hours of 20 September 1943 the crews who were to carry out the attacks took the place of passage crews in the four X-Craft that remained. Between 1830 and 2000 that day X5 (Lieutenant H. Henty-Creer, RVNR), X6 (Lieutenant D. Cameron, RNR), X7 (Lieutenant B. C. G. Place, RN) and X10 (Lieutenant K. R. Hudspeth, RANVR) parted from the parent submarines and began the run-in through Sorby Sound between the outer Norwegian islands and thence deep into Altenfiord.

X10, detailed to attack the *Scharnhorst* in Kaa Fiord, off Altenfiord, fell early victim to Murphy's Law, for technical troubles left her without effective compass or periscope and lying low on the bottom of the fiord while the crew tried to remedy the defects. As it happened, however, the *Scharnhorst* had anyway gone to sea for firing practice, a fact revealed by Ultra too late for the news to be relayed forward to the task force. Lieutenant Hudspeth nevertheless managed to get X10 to sea again, but took six uncomfortable days to locate one of the parent submarines. On 3 October, when on tow within 400 miles of the Shetlands, X10 had to be scuttled because of an imminent gale; a sad end to a gallant effort.

Of the three X-Craft making for the *Tirpitz*, X5 simply disappeared, her fate unknown, although it is possible that she fell victim to German gunfire outside the net defences. As for the surviving midget submarines X6 and X7, their experiences might have come from a boy's adventure story. After slipping past the anti-submarine boom in Kaa Fiord on the surface early on 22 September Lieutenant Place in X7 was forced to dive when a patrolling German motor boat neared him, only to become tangled up in defensive nets. It took him two hours to get his boat free. Lieutenant Cameron in X6, for his part, had to creep his way through the German defences with a periscope operated by hand because the electric motor had burnt out. When X6 accidentally broke surface at 0707 that morning of the 22nd on going aground, she was sighted from the *Tirpitz*, becoming the target for frenzied small-arms fire. By this time Cameron was feeling his way blind because his periscope and compass had both failed. Nevertheless he managed to surface alongside the battleship, detach his explosive charges and scuttle his boat. He and his crew were picked up from the water by a German motor boat and taken on board the *Tirpitz*, there to await the detonation of his own charges.

Meanwhile Lieutenant Place in X7, with his compass too now useless, had continued to struggle through one entangling net after another. He finally bumped into *Tirpitz*'s towering side before diving beneath her to drop his charges. When all four charges exploded shortly afterwards X7 was temporarily trapped nearby in yet another net, and the shock of the explosions damaged her controls. After helplessly plunging and surfacing like a porpoise while under heavy fire, X7 finally ran alongside a German gunnery practice target, then sank. Lieutenant Place and one other officer survived to be taken prisoner.

On board the *Tirpitz* the shock of sighting the approaching X-Craft close by within her supposedly impenetrable anchorage caused near panic. Even though the battleship was winched on her cables away from the point where the X6 had sunk, at least one charge dropped by X7 went off exactly beneath the battleship's engine rooms. According to one report, the force of the explosion caused 'the whole ship to heave several feet . . .' The lights went out; unstowed or unsecured gear crashed about; hatches jammed. But these were only the immediate and outward signs of the crippling inner blow which the *Tirpitz* had sustained, for inspection was to discover that her main turbines and her fire-control system had been put out of action.

Although Ultra decrypts were not able to tell the Admiralty the exact nature of the damage, they did make it clear that the enemy expected it to take until mid-March 1944 to repair the ship, and that the work was going to have to be carried out in Norway rather than back in Germany.[134] On 2 January 1944 a further decrypt was to specify 15 March as the date when the work on the hull, machinery and electrical systems would be completed.[135] Thus although *Scharnhorst* and *Lützow* had escaped attack and *Tirpitz* had not actually been sunk, 'Operation Source' had nonetheless achieved a stunning success. For their audacity, courage and skill in the face of such immense hazards, Lieutenants Place and Cameron were both awarded the Victoria Cross.

By putting the German Navy's most valuable single asset out of action for six months, 'Operation Source' had also transformed the whole strategic situation in home waters and the Arctic. The Admiralty and the Commander-in-Chief, Home Fleet, could now contemplate reopening the Russian convoy traffic, the more so as the enemy brought the *Lützow* back to Germany in the last week of September. *Lützow*'s homeward voyage, however, occasioned yet another demonstration of the limited effectiveness of Britain's shore-based maritime airpower in attacks on enemy surface ships. Just as with the escape of the German battleships up Channel in 1942 the strike force against the *Lützow* had to be cobbled together at the last moment from such aircraft as were serviceable. The Fleet Air Arm and Coastal Command crews enjoyed no common doctrine and had never worked together. To mount and carry out the operation itself called for much telephoning between the C-in-C, Home Fleet and his Chief of Staff, the AOC, No. 18 Group, Coastal Command, and Headquarters, Coastal Command; another case of clumsy and creaking liaison links instead of a proper joint command organisation. Despite advance warning from Ultra and an SIS agent that *Lützow* was about to move, and then was on the move, the small strike force failed even to locate the pocket battleship, let alone attack her, let alone sink her – not least because a wrong guess by Admiral Sir Henry Moore, Chief of Staff, Home Fleet, led the force to search too far to the north, and actually astern of the pocket battleship on her voyage south.[136]

These fresh muddles and confusions in shore-based air operations against an enemy surface ship provoked a report by yet another heavyweight Navy and Air Force Committee in November 1943.[137] This recommended that Coastal Command's strike forces be expanded to three strike wings, each of twenty torpedo-bombers and twenty twin-engined fighters; and that Coastal Command and the Fleet Air Arm should hammer out a common operating procedure and tactical doctrine. Would this report, coming as it did at the end of the fourth year of war, have been needed if all air operations over the sea had continued to be vested in the old Royal Naval Air Service? Coastal Command under its successive Air Officers Commanding-in-Chief had certainly done its loyal best to become an effective all-purpose maritime air force, but the Command had always been, and still was, shackled by lack of resources in numbers and modernity of aircraft, thanks to an Air Staff doctrinally committed to putting the bomber offensive first and foremost and to the War Cabinet's endorsement of this priority. It is a depressing irony, therefore, that just at this period, autumn 1943 into winter 1943–44, Sir Arthur Harris's heavy bombers were in the course of being defeated in the Battle of Berlin by the Luftwaffe's night-fighter defence, as well as suffering insupportable losses in the bomber offensive as a whole without commensurate effect on German war production.[138]

The renewal of the North Russia convoy traffic after the crippling of the *Tirpitz* and the departure home of the *Lützow* would no longer represent – as in the past – the Western Allies' principal effort to save Soviet Russia from defeat, but instead an investment in her victorious forward march. Since smashing the German summer offensive at Kursk ('Operation Zitadelle') in July 1943 the Red Army had re-covered about half the Soviet territory initially conquered by the Germans in 1941. The first of the new series of convoys to sail, the homeward-bound RA54A of thirteen empty ships marooned at Archangel since traffic was suspended in the spring, made a safe voyage at the beginning of November. On 15 November the first outward convoy (JW54A, of eighteen merchantmen) followed, with close escort and covering forces of the well-established pattern. Neither JW54A, nor its successor JW54B sailing a week later, suffered any form of enemy attack.[139] In the middle of December Admiral Fraser even took his flagship *Duke of York* all the way through to Kola with convoy JW55A, so insignificant now was the German air threat owing to the demands of the Eastern Front; and there conferred with the Soviet Commander-in-Chief, Admiral Golokov.

Sir John Tovey had vainly hoped during his command of the Home Fleet that the passage of an Arctic convoy would give him an opportunity to bring German heavy ships to action. Now the opportunity was to fall to his successor, for the enemy had come to the decision to send out the *Scharnhorst* to attack the renewed Arctic traffic when the time seemed ripe. This decision had been maturing for almost a year. On 26 February 1943 Dönitz had successfully persuaded Hitler to delegate to himself the responsibility for choosing whether or when to risk the heavy forces against convoys. In April Hitler had sanctioned the transfer of *Scharnhorst* to northern Norway in order to 'provide a significant reinforcement', so ran the German Naval Staff directive, 'for attacking the convoys running to North Russia. This task is to be given priority, and it is not to be hampered by the secondary considerations of the defence of Norway.'[140] As Commander-in-Chief of the German Navy Dönitz remained committed to keeping the heavy ships in Norwegian bases in order either to induce the British to suspend the convoys (as they did from May to November 1943) or to attack the convoys should they still continue to run.

On 20 November 1943 the German Naval Staff in a new directive appreciated (a little late) that the British might resume the traffic to Russia in the dark winter season, even if only in the form of single ships: 'Against this traffic both the Northern Task Force and the U-boats are to be operated.'[141] According to the directive such deployment compelled the Royal Navy to hold capital ships in home waters, and so took the pressure off Germany's Japanese ally.[142] After B-Dienst decrypts and air and U-boat sightings confirmed that in November the Arctic traffic had indeed been resumed, Dönitz reaffirmed his decision to send the Northern Task Force into action, not least because supplies were being sent to Russia 'under our very noses' at a time when the German Army on the Eastern Front was under heavy pressure. Dönitz rated the chances of success as 'not inconsiderable'.[143]

From 22 December U-boats and Luftwaffe reconnaissance repeatedly reported sightings of the outward convoy JW55B (22 ships), which had left Loch Ewe on 20 December. On the 22nd *Scharnhorst* was brought to three hours' notice for steam. Late on Christmas Eve Group North at Kiel asked Dönitz for a decision by noon on Christmas Day as to whether *Scharnhorst* should be ordered to attack the convoy. The German naval hierarchy being in fact riven with dissent over the question, the teleprinters clattered with last-minute argument. Admiral Otto Schniewind, Fleet Commander and Flag Officer, Group North, remained (as previously) sceptical of *Scharnhorst*'s chances of braving the escorts' torpedoes and then cutting up the convoy at a season when there was only one hour of maximum visibility for gunfire in the day: 'On the whole the chances of a major success are slender, and the stakes high.'[144] Admiral Erich Bey in Altenfiord, the Flag

Officer, Northern Task Force, was of the same mind; himself a destroyer man, he agreed with Schniewind that the convoy should be attacked by destroyers only. In any case he was very unhappy about the 'completely inadequate' air reconnaissance, and wanted a further search to establish whether or not the British heavy ships were covering the convoy.[145]

Nevertheless Dönitz (who had returned to Berlin from Paris on Christmas Day) completely overruled his subordinates, so demonstrating that he yielded nothing to Dudley Pound when it came to taking operational decisions into his own hands. At 1412 (actually before Dönitz himself arrived back in Berlin) the naval staff passed on his instructions to Admiral Bey to take the *Scharnhorst* and six destroyers to sea.

At 1900 the *Scharnhorst* (Captain Fritz Hintze) weighed anchor in Altenfiord and headed for the open sea, her mess decks still festive with Christmas trees, her ensign a tiny splash of red, white and black against the snowbound granite cliffs. Her ship's company were in high spirits at the prospect of action at last. But even in the deep shelter of the fjord the wind howled in the rigging, a witness to the accuracy of the latest weather forecasts:

> Southerly gale, Force 8–9, increasing sea 6–7. On 26.12. veering south west 6–8, with heavy S.W. swell. Overcast with rain, visibility 3–4 miles, only intermittingly improving to 10 miles. Snow-falls in Barents Sea.[146]

Rightly fearful of the effects of such weather on the destroyers, Schniewind (as Flag Officer Group North and Fleet Commander) telephoned the Naval Staff in Berlin to ask that 'Operation Ostfront' be cancelled while the task force was still within the fjords. But the Naval Staff adamantly ordered that even if heavy seas prevented the destroyers from keeping station, *Scharnhorst* was to carry out the attack in the form of 'cruiser warfare', that is, as a lone raider. The final decision as to how to operate was left to Bey. It seems clear that Dönitz stuck to his resolve largely because of the current plight of the German Army on the Eastern Front. In the words of his signal to Bey earlier for benefit of ships' companies: 'In sending an important convoy of supplies and weapons to Russia the enemy hopes to increase the difficulties of the heroic struggle of our Eastern Army. We must help.'[147]

In its report later on *Scharnhorst*'s sortie, the German naval staff justified the decision to carry 'Ostfront' through on the grounds that there was a chance of surprising the British after two convoys had gone through unmolested, and that 'No heavy ships had been reported among the enemy's covering force, either by air reconnaissance or by other sources . . .'[148]

But in point of fact Admiral Sir Bruce Fraser was at sea with the *Duke of York* (flag), the cruiser *Jamaica* and four destroyers, in addition to the cruiser covering force under Vice-Admiral R. L. Burnett (*Belfast*, *Sheffield* and *Norfolk*). The outward convoy JW55B and the homeward RA55A themselves each enjoyed a powerful escort of ten destroyers and several smaller vessels.

The *Scharnhorst* (32,000 tons displacement; 39,000 tons full load)[149] with her nine 11-inch guns could therefore find herself fighting the heavily armoured *Duke of York* (38,000 tons displacement; 44,460 tons full load)[150] with ten 14-inch guns, as well as one 8-inch cruiser and three 6-inch cruisers. She would also face the hazard of torpedo attack by the cruisers and by up to 24 destroyers.

Throughout the coming action the German command ashore and Bey himself remained in a complete fog as to British strength and movements – partly because of the poor liaison between the Luftwaffe and the naval headquarters, leading to a failure to pass on news of a sighting of a force of several ships, including 'a big one', by reconnaissance flying boats on the 26th. B-Dienst indications that a British heavy force might be at sea were also ignored.[151] GC and CS on the other hand provided the Admiralty with the texts of all signals between the German naval command and *Scharnhorst* at relatively short delay. Thus it was that at 0217 on 26 December the Operational Intelligence Centre issued the urgent Ultra signal: 'Emergency: *Scharnhorst* probably sailed 1800 25 December.'[152]

At 0339 and for the benefit of the convoy escort and other ships not in receipt of Ultra, the OIC broadcast the general message: 'Admiralty appreciates *Scharnhorst* at sea.'[153]

Thereafter the flow of Ultra decrypts, coupled with intercepts of low-grade Luftwaffe radio traffic by airborne Royal Air Force 'Y' parties, kept Admiral Fraser fully informed about his enemy's intentions and – just as useful – the enemy's current state of knowledge about British strength and movements. This invaluable Intelligence, undreamt-of by admirals in earlier wars, enabled Fraser to manoeuvre his own force, the cruiser force and the convoy escorts as components in a single evolving operational design. In order to coordinate the operation in this way Fraser took the risk of breaking radio silence, so that he could signal instructions and also so that his separate groups could be kept fully informed as to each other's current positions.[154]

In the early hours of 26 December the enemy and the British forces were converging within the sea area between Bear Island and the North Cape – Admiral Bey in *Scharnhorst* coming up from the south, Burnett and his cruisers down from the north-east in order to intercept Bey; convoy JW55A steaming from the west; and Fraser in the *Duke of York* from the west also, but still some 200 miles distant from the convoy. In order to narrow the gap Fraser ordered the convoy to put about for three hours before resuming course eastwards; he also ordered it to steer further north away from the *Scharnhorst*. It would be a day of virtual darkness, with Arctic twilight providing the merest paling on the horizon between 0830 and 1530. The wind was now blowing hard from the south-west, the sea rough and rising. Fraser's and Bey's destroyers alike were having a particularly uncomfortable time, the following wind and sea making it hard for their helmsmen to keep them on course. An officer in HMS *Scorpion* describes how the destroyer

> . . . running downwind of a gale broached to at 24 knots, and charged along a giant trough with her funnel nearly in the water. Thank God the Quartermaster kept hold of the wheel which of course had full opposite rudder on. I tried to hold on to the binnacle but was flung down on my back in one corner of the bridge . . .[155]

The big German destroyers, being not such good sea-boats, generally suffered worse than the British. At about 0730 Bey spread them to the south-west to search for the convoy, so plunging them straight into a head sea. In the event they found nothing thanks to Fraser's diversion of the convoy to the north; and Bey later ordered them back to base. So *Scharnhorst* steamed on alone while Admiral Fraser drew his net round her.

At 0840 Burnett's cruisers picked up the distant battleship by radar; at 0921 *Sheffield* (Captain C. T. Addis) sighted her at 12,000 yards in the faint twilight. Three minutes later Burnett's flagship *Belfast* (Captain F. R. Parham) fired a starshell; at 0939 the *Norfolk* (the only cruiser that could bear, the others being masked by their fellows in quarter line) crashed out a salvo. Like a silent ghost in the shadows *Scharnhorst* immediately hauled round to the south without returning the fire and at 30 knots soon outran the British cruisers struggling at 24 knots against wind and sea. She had been hit at least once.

Burnett now steered to place himself ahead of the convoy in order to guard against any enemy attempt to work round and attack it. He was reinforced by Fraser with four destroyers switched from the escort of the homeward RA55A, which was now out of the danger zone to the westward. Fraser himself was now coming up in *Duke of York* at 24 knots, the flagship taking as usual in a sea-way masses of water over her flat forecastle (the lack of sheer in her bows being a fault in the design of this class of ship).

For the Commander-in-Chief the worry now lay in that his destroyer screen might run short of fuel before *Scharnhorst* could be brought to action, so giving him the difficult choice of turning back or running all the way on to Kola. The German admiral solved his problem for him, however, by turning north in the hope of finding the convoy – only to run into Burnett's cruisers again. Just after noon the *Belfast* detected the *Scharnhorst* on her radar, and twenty minutes later the *Sheffield* reported: 'Enemy in sight'. For Fraser this was glad news indeed, for he now lay only 160 miles distant from the scene to the west. At a range of about 11,000 yards Burnett's three cruisers opened fire. As the *Scharnhorst* turned south and sped for home she smashed back with 11-inch salvoes, putting out of action one of *Norfolk*'s main turrets and all but one of her radar sets.

Burnett now shadowed the enemy by radar just out of visibility range, secure in the knowledge that *Scharnhorst*'s southerly course was delivering her to Admiral Fraser as he came up on a converging course from the west. At 1617 *Duke of York*'s own radar picked up *Scharnhorst* at 20 miles range, and the C-in-C deployed his force for action. At 1650 the flagship and *Belfast* fired a starshell; a lurid white glare in a charcoal sky. An eye-witness in HMS *Scorpion* was to recall:

> . . . when the starshell first illuminated *Scharnhorst*, I could see her so clearly that I could see her turrets were fore-and-aft (and what a lovely sight she was at full speed). She was almost at once obliterated by a wall of water from the *Duke*'s first salvo – quite like the spotting table! When she re-appeared her turrets wore a different aspect![156]

For the next two and threequarter hours *Scharnhorst* twisted and turned in her attempts to shake off her hunters while steering for home, her guns again and again straddling *Duke of York* without inflicting damage. In this war, unlike the Great War, it was German shells that proved unreliable, too often failing to explode at all. Not least owing to the superior British gunnery radar the *Duke of York* scored probably as many as thirteen 14-inch shell hits on her enemy in the course of the battleship action – and yet still the German ship floated and steamed. At 1830 the *Scharnhorst*'s guns stopped firing. At about 1850 HMS *Scorpion* and the Norwegian destroyer *Stord*, labouring in the heavy seas, at last gained enough bearing to launch torpedoes. Just at that moment *Scharnhorst* sighted them in the light of starshells, and her captain put his wheel over in an instinctive but fatal evasive move, so that, in the words of an officer in *Scorpion*, 'an onrushing target at a fine inclination became a sitting bird'.[157] *Scorpion*, *Stord*, *Savage* and *Saumarez* were able to fire a total of twelve torpedoes at the *Scharnhorst*'s beam, of which probably three struck home.

With her speed down to only five knots, *Scharnhorst* now became merely a hapless target for more torpedoes, for 8-inch and 6-inch salvoes from the cruisers and 14-inch salvoes from *Duke of York* at a range of only 10,000 yards. Last seen as a dim red glow within a pall of smoke, the *Scharnhorst* finally succumbed to torpedo attack from all sides by the cruisers and destroyers. She went down with Admiral Bey and Captain Hintze in 72° 16′N, 28° 41′E. Only thirty-six survivors from her complement of 2,000 were plucked from the ice-cold rollers.

Scharnhorst's lone fight for so long against such odds reflects the greatest credit on her ship's company and also on her designers and builders, who enabled her to withstand hits from some thirteen 14-inch shells, about a dozen 8-inch or 6-inch shells and at least eleven torpedoes before foundering. But her fight reflects little credit on liaison between the German Navy and the Luftwaffe, nor on the German ability to make good operational use of available Sigint; and it reflects none at all on Dönitz's strategic judgment and exercise of command.

Henceforward it was left to the U-boats virtually alone to try to interrupt the Arctic traffic. But in the face of very large escorts that included on occasion as many as two escort carriers and two of the Western Approaches Escort (Support) Groups, they could achieve little. In a battle in March 1944 with outward convoy JW58, of 49 ships, closely escorted by the light cruiser *Diadem*, twenty destroyers, four corvettes, five sloops and the CVEs *Activity* and *Tracker*, the enemy lost six shadowing aircraft and four U-boats without sinking a single ship. Here was a very different scene from the desperate convoy fights of 1942 against great odds above and below and on the surface of the sea.

Yet the *Tirpitz* still remained a potential menace, her wounds slowly healing. In January and February 1944 Intelligence from Ultra and other sources indicated that she could be seaworthy by mid-March.[158] By mid-March further decrypts of Enigma revealed that she was undergoing sea trials. On 21 March the Operational Intelligence Centre suggested that because of the worsening plight of the German

Army on the Eastern Front (during the previous five weeks the Russians had smashed through in the Ukraine towards the Carpathians), the enemy might risk the *Tirpitz* against an Arctic convoy if it were not covered by heavy forces. The Admiralty therefore decided that the Home Fleet should cover JW58, strongly escorted as it in any case would be (see above). Admiral Fraser would have with him the battleships *Duke of York* and *Anson*, the fleet carriers *Victorious* and *Furious*, and the escort carriers *Emperor*, *Searcher* and *Pursuer*. But the carriers were to operate as a separate task force with the separate mission of crippling the *Tirpitz* in her anchorage in Altenfiord.[159]

In the small hours of 3 April 1944 the task force (under Vice-Admiral Sir Henry Moore) had reached the launching point 120 miles from Altenfiord. By 0437 the bombers and fighters of the first strike were aloft and heading for *Tirpitz*; at 0525 the second strike followed: a total of 42 bombers and 80 fighters. The bombers, Fairey Barracudas (cruising speed 172 mph; range 1,150 miles; the Fleet Air Arm's first monoplane torpedo-bomber)[160] were all flown from the two fleet carriers. The fighter cover, American-built Grumman Wildcats and Hellcats (maximum speeds respectively 318 and 380 mph; armament six forward-firing 0.5-inch Browning machine-guns, or, in the case of the Hellcat, two 20mm cannon plus four 0.5-inch machine-guns)[161] was largely provided by the three escort carriers.

The *Tirpitz* presented a difficult enough target, ensconced as she was behind torpedo nets close under the cliffs of the fjord and heavily defended by her own 68 anti-aircraft guns of various calibres and by numerous shore batteries tactically sited round the fjord. However, thanks to detailed photo-reconnaissance pictures and repeated rehearsal of the attack with uttermost thoroughness by the strike forces, both attacking waves swept in and over and out in just a few minutes with the loss of only three aircraft. As they flashed over the ship they dropped a mixture of ten 1,600-pound armour-piercing bombs (from a height of 3,500 feet), sixty-six 500 pound semi-armour-piercing bombs (from a height of 2,000 feet) and some high-explosive and anti-submarine bombs for good measure. The first wave swept in before smoke from smoke candles had time to shroud the ship, even before all *Tirpitz*'s water-tight doors could be closed.[162] By attacking from port and starboard simultaneously, the Barracudas confused a defence already taken by surprise. As the German battle report later ruefully described:

> ... The aircraft flying in to port (about 20 in number) flew along the ridge of the mountains, making use of every dip, and so low parallel to

the ship that they themselves could only see the Foretop, thus making it impossible for the lower lying guns and controls to fire at them. When these aircraft were in a position between 220° and 240° from the ship, they suddenly (from a distance of 6,560 feet), 'hedge-hopped' over the mountains and dived on to the ship, firing with all their guns. The bombs were released from a height of 600–1,000 feet. At this time the main Flak battery with both Forward Flak fire controls had already been put out of action by gunfire . . . [163]

Tirpitz took a total of fifteen bomb hits, causing internal fires and widespread damage, some of it structural,[164] putting her out of action again for three months.

The Fleet Air Arm was to attack her four more times, on 17 and 22 July and 24 and 29 August 1944, with varying success. However, carrier aircraft could not carry an armour-piercing bomb of sufficient weight to penetrate the *Tirpitz*'s main armour and so inflict mortal damage. It finally took four-engined Lancasters of Bomber Command to do the trick with their recently developed ability to hit small targets.[165] On 15 September 1944, 28 Lancasters took off from North Russian airfields, dropped their own number of monster 12,000-pound armour-piercing bombs, and flew on to Britain. One direct hit and two near-misses left *Tirpitz* with severe damage to her bow. Dönitz now decided that her sea-going days were finally over, and he ordered her to be moved to Tromsö harbour to serve as a floating coastal defence battery. Here the German naval authorities sought to find shallow water with a suitable bottom for her berth so that she could not capsize even if badly holed, but simply settle on even keel. They failed, for calculations showed that the depth of water under her, according to a German report, 'would not give complete security against capsizing, but that safety was likely'.[166]

Before the unfavourable contours of the bottom could be filled by dredger Bomber Command struck again on 12 November with 32 Lancasters, with results tersely summarised in the report of the Sea Defence Commandant at Tromsö, Captain Krüger:

Eye-witness accounts reveal that the port-side outer hull was ripped open by a direct hit and several near-misses. This caused heavy inrush of water. The Captain's order for counter-flooding could not be carried out. As a result of the explosion [in her magazines] when the ship heeled over 60–70°, C turret [the after turret] shifted 20–25 metres from its mounting – confirmed by divers. This immediately caused heavier inrush of water and further rapid heeling over of the ship, resistance to further heeling over was small, so that, in spite of the bilge keel, which broke off, the ship finally turned over.[167]

Of the 1,000 members of her ship's company trapped in the capsized hull, 85 were rescued thanks to the prompt initiative of an engineer captain and his men in at once cutting a hole through the plating of the bottom.

With the capsizing of the *Tirpitz* was finally ended that menace from the German heavy forces that had weighed so much on the minds of the Admiralty and the Commanders-in-Chief, Home Fleet, ever since the outbreak of war, with consequent ramifying effect on the global deployment of Britain's inadequate resources of capital ships and fleet carriers. Only the pocket battleships *Scheer* and *Lützow* were now left to Dönitz, and henceforward they were to be fully committed in the Baltic in support of the struggling German troops on the northern flank of the Eastern Front as they fell back into Germany itself.

For the Arctic convoys and their escorts the principal enemies in 1944 and 1945 were therefore the U-boats – and the weather and the latitude, both particularly hard on the ships' companies and the flying crews of the escort carriers that now often sailed with the convoys. The Arctic run meant operating aircraft on a gruelling schedule of twelve hours flying and twelve hours maintenance, in light conditions ranging from perpetual daylight to perpetual dark, in extreme cold with deck gear frozen, and in seas that could be gigantic. Some escort carriers buckled the fore-ends of their flight decks 60 feet above the waterline, and one even recorded a green sea rolling the full length of the flight deck.[168] Convoy RA64 in February 1945 met constant gales of up to 80 knots from dead ahead, and Rear-Admiral McGrigor, the covering force commander, reported '. . . much difficulty in keeping stragglers with the convoy. Engine troubles, defective steering, ice-chipped propellers, shifting cargoes, and splitting decks were among the very genuine reasons for dropping astern and at times stopping.'[169]

During this particular but by no means untypical passage the escort carrier HMS *Campania* (12,450 tons displacement)[170] was compelled to heave to after rolling 45° each way; and the convoy's average speed of advance dropped to 3½ knots.[171]

For the ships' companies – Merchant Marine as well as Royal Navy – life on the mess deck of a closed-up vessel in such weather was wearing enough in itself to body and spirit, just as it was on the North Atlantic too. Packed into the steel box of the mess deck, deadlights screwed down over the scuttles, with a mass of hammocks swinging only some five feet above the deck, the crews breathed a damp fug of their own stale exhalations and the rising vapour from wet serge slowly drying; a fug stinking of sweat, vomit and the all-pervasive reek of fuel oil. Above them in the dim electric lighting the deck-head dripped and dripped with condensation, while the thin steel plating separating them from the icy sea resounded regularly to the crashing of green water on to the forecastle.

When exhausted crews at last made landfall at Murmansk after such desolate and dangerous voyages, they found – like their predecessors of 1941–43 – no warm welcome, no chance of a jolly run ashore, as in Canada and America at the end of the North Atlantic run, but instead one of the bleakest, most poverty-stricken corners of Stalin's tyranny, and the surly face of Soviet authority. Perhaps the sourest example of the Stalinist state's hospitality to the Royal Navy during 1941–45 is offered by its refusal in 1942 to allow a medical unit (sent out with PQ18 to care ashore for wounded sailors from earlier convoys) to enter the Soviet Union, insisting that it return to Britain with the next convoy. Tovey was to write in his despatch:

> The reason for this astonishing decision by our Allies could not be discovered, but I renewed my representation for the strongest pressure to be brought to bear to induce them once more to change their minds. That British seamen, wounded while carrying supplies to Russia, should be exposed unnecessarily to the medieval treatment prevalent in Russian hospitals, was intolerable.[172]

Eventually the Soviet authorities did relent.

On 29 April 1945 the final wartime outward North Russian convoy, JW66 of 22 ships, sailed for North Russia. Powerfully escorted by the CVEs *Vindex* and *Premier*, the cruiser *Bellona* and eighteen escort ships, and with the 19th Escort Group deployed ahead to deal with waiting U-boats, it reached Kola without loss after attack by only one U-boat. The homeward RA66 suffered the very last casualty of the Arctic convoy run – the frigate *Goodall* torpedoed and sunk.

The decisive nature of the Royal Navy's Arctic victory is demonstrated in stark brevity by the statistics. Between December 1942 and May 1945 sixteen convoys made the outward voyage to North Russia, and yet in 1943 not one ton of 450,000 tons despatched was lost; in 1944 only 10,000 tons out of 1.25 million; and in 1945 10,000 tons out of 650,000.[173] Such was seapower's contribution to the Red Army's advance from the depths of European Russia to Berlin. Yet by this time seapower had done much, much more than this to aid in the destruction of the Wehrmacht. For it had been instrumental in creating a Western Front once again, where American, British and Canadian armies too could join in the work of smashing the enemy in mass battles; it had nourished the victorious march of the Allied Expeditionary Force of up to ninety divisions across France and Belgium and on into the German heartland.

PART
IV

VICTORY

24

'Neptune': Problems, Puzzles and Personalities

In October 1943 Admiral Sir Bertram Ramsay, an officer still on the retired list, entered Norfolk House, the London mansion of the Dukes of Norfolk and now the headquarters of COSSAC (Chief of Staff to Supreme Allied Commander), in St James's Square to take up the post of Allied Naval Commander, Expeditionary Force (ANCXF) for the second time. He had first been appointed in May 1942 when a 'Combined Commanders Committee' was set up to study the possibility of invading France that year in operations 'Roundup' or 'Sledge-hammer' (see above, pp. 530–1). The post had lapsed when these projects were shelved in favour of 'Operation Torch' and he became instead deputy to Andrew Cunningham as ANCXF for 'Torch'. COSSAC had been set up since then by the Casablanca Conference in January 1943, as an inter-Allied planning staff under Lieutenant-General F. E. Morgan with the title of Chief of Staff, Supreme Allied Commander (designate). His task was to produce an outline plan for the invasion of France in 1944. In August 1943 the combined Chiefs of Staff at the Quebec Conference approved this outline and instructed Morgan to get on with detailed planning and preparations for 'Operation Overlord', as it was now dubbed, with the target date of 1 May 1944.

During the Quebec Conference the then First Sea Lord, Sir Dudley Pound, recommended to the Prime Minister that Admiral Sir Charles Little, the Commander-in-Chief, Portsmouth, and at that time also the ANCXF (designate), be confirmed as ANCXF. But Churchill trenchantly objected – on this occasion with every justification – arguing that he was 'sure that Admiral Ramsay would be a far better appointment for this purpose on account not only of his natural abilities but his unique experience in conducting a great overseas descent . . .'[1] Pound reluctantly gave way, although why he should have preferred Little will never be known. Was it a pedantic belief that Ramsay, being on the Retired List, was not suitable as a C-in-C, but only as a Chief of Staff (as in 'Torch')?

In Norfolk House – elegant neo-Georgian chambers contrasting with standard-issue Whitehall desks and filing cabinets; the grand saloon now a conference room – Ramsay found himself the only one of the Allied Expeditionary Force commanders already in post. Eisenhower, the Supreme Commander, and Montgomery, C-in-C, 21st Army Group and overall land forces commander (Ramsay's opposite number), were still in the Mediterranean conducting the Italian campaign, where the Allied armies were struggling after Kesselring's troops as they retreated from Salerno towards the *Gustavstellung*. It would be several weeks before the Allied Expeditionary Air Forces Commander, Air Chief-Marshal Sir Trafford Leigh-Mallory, was even appointed. And not until January 1944 would Air Chief-Marshal Sir Arthur Tedder become Deputy Supreme Commander. Ramsay and his new Chief of Staff, Rear-Admiral G. E. Creasy, had to begin work with General Morgan in a mist of uncertainty.

Although Ramsay brought to his new task the experience and confidence acquired during the desperate improvisation of the Dunkirk evacuation and the successful mounting of 'Torch' and 'Husky', he now confronted a supreme professional challenge, for 'Neptune' (codename for the maritime first phase of 'Overlord': the whole operation of transporting the Allied Expeditionary Force across the Channel and putting it ashore on D-Day) had no precedent in terms of scale, risk and strategic importance. In the first place, it would not be another 'blue water' expedition in a secondary theatre of war like 'Torch' or 'Husky'; it would be the Anglo-Americans' one and only opportunity of re-establishing the Western Front, thereby defeating a main body of the German Army in battle and opening the way for the eventual invasion of the Third Reich. The outcome of the war was therefore to be staked on this one card. Operationally too 'Neptune' presented a far greater gamble than 'Torch' or 'Husky'. Instead of the tideless Mediterranean with its often fine weather, there would be the English Channel in all its unpredictability of wind and sea even in summer; the rise and fall of the tide and the tricky tidal streams and currents, changing from hour to hour, day to day and place to place. 'Neptune' would moreover far exceed the Mediterranean landings in sheer size and complexity, and in the consequent problems of dovetailing sea, air and land forces into a single enterprise.

Only by the efficient functioning of the vast machine on D-Day could the gamble therefore succeed. Such functioning in the face of the inevitable rule of Murphy's Law depended on the thoroughness and professional skill of the prior staff work in designing and putting together the machine. It depended on rigorous joint training of the soldiers and sailors; on the rehearsal again and again, of the landing process – and also of the complicated prior assembly of invasion forces that were scattered in ports and harbours right round the southern coasts of England.

Nor would Ramsay's problems come to an end on D-Day, for the Allied Expeditionary Force would depend on an uninterrupted seaborne flow of troops, stores, weapons, transport and fuel *en masse* for its expansion into a great field army capable of breaking out of the initial lodgement. Yet there was little prospect of immediately capturing intact a major port, let alone *ports* as in 'Torch', since the Germans had encased every such port along the Channel and North Sea coasts in reinforced concrete defences formidable alike in their density, clever tactical siting and firepower.

These stupendous problems facing the navies are sometimes ignored by some historians of the land campaign in Normandy, who commence their narratives on the beaches, almost as if all that lay between southern England and Normandy were a No Man's Land swiftly and easily traversed by the attacking armies.[2]

Nonetheless, as Ramsay was aware, a mass of crucially important preliminary work on all the operational problems had already been done before he became ANCXF in October 1943. As early as October 1941 the General Staff Intelligence section of GHQ, Home Forces, had moved into Norfolk House with the new responsibility of gathering information about the Continental coast from Den Helder in the Netherlands to the Loire, together with a zone extending thirty miles inland.[3] Later it was joined by the section of the Naval Intelligence Department concerned with German coastal defences; and early in 1942 both sections were amalgamated into the Combined Intelligence Section (CIS) of GHQ, Home Forces. After COSSAC also took up its quarters in Norfolk House in 1943 the CIS (renamed 'Theatre Intelligence Section' or TIS) continued to remain responsible for collating, updating and disseminating the Intelligence needed for the planning of a cross-Channel invasion.

To the desks of CIS had flowed since 1941 information about winds and tides from the service meteorological departments and from the Hydrographer of the Navy; about Continental airfields and airfield sites from the Air Intelligence Branch; about port capacities from the Transportation Branch of the War Office. The CIS itself had examined the advantages and disadvantages of every potential landing beach between Den Helder and the Loire, both in terms of the assault itself and of later tactical and strategic exploitation, including the relative prospects of capturing a major port.

As early as summer 1942 the CIS had been able to provide the Combined Commanders Committee with a complete dossier on the relative merits of all possible invasion shore-lines. To the Chief of Combined Operations (Vice-Admiral Lord Louis Mountbatten) and his staff the CIS dossier clearly pointed to the Bay of the Seine as the most favourable shore to assault – 50 miles of sandy beaches backed by easily accessible low-lying countryside stretching between the base of the Cotentin Peninsula in the west and the Caen area in the east. But Mountbatten's fellow members of the Combined Commanders Committee in 1942 – General Sir Bernard Paget (Commander-in-Chief, Home Forces) and Air Chief-Marshal Sir Trafford Leigh-Mallory (then Air Officer Commanding-in-Chief, Fighter Command), as well as Sir Alan Brooke, the CIGS – preferred the obvious choice from the map: the Pas de Calais, just across the narrowest part of the English Channel, within close range of United Kingdom fighter bases, and on the shortest strategic axis to the Ruhr and the heart of Germany.[4]

By April 1943, however, when the CIS had gathered together an even more comprehensive dossier on the topography and defences of the entire Channel coast of France, the Combined Commanders Committee had after all come round to the Combined Operations view that the Bay of the Seine offered the better location. Nevertheless, no formal decision was recorded; no directive issued. As a result, the newly created COSSAC found himself, in Morgan's own words, in 'an appalling quandary'.[5] From it he was rescued by the Royal Navy in the person of Admiral Mountbatten, who invited twenty generals, eleven air marshals and air commodores, and eight admirals (including five Canadians and fifteen Americans) to a conference ('Rattle') at Largs, the Combined Operations training base in Scotland. The most important participants were however Paget, Little, Leigh-Mallory and Morgan himself. The conference bent its collective mind to the task of making a final choice of invasion coast.

The Pas de Calais, despite its superficial attractions, suffered from the drawback of narrow beaches bounded by high cliffs with relatively few – and narrow – exits, so restricting the assault wave to two divisions, while the hinterland did not favour the swift build-up of an expeditionary force. Moreover road and rail communications in the region as well as the location of airfields would facilitate a German concentration and counter-stroke. In any case this stretch of coastline was for evident reasons the most densely fortified of all. And finally a landing here would, for equally obvious reasons, forfeit all hope of strategic or tactical surprise. From the naval point of view too the Pas de Calais was not a runner. Its apparent advantage of offering a short sea crossing was illusory, because the invasion forces would in any case have to be mustered from English ports as far distant as Yarmouth and Milford Haven. It offered no prospect of the early capture of a major port capable of handling the massive flow of stores and reinforcements required by a great army on the offensive, for the nearest ones, Le Havre and Antwerp, lay some 100 miles distant.

After much wearisome argument the view of Mountbatten and the Combined Operations staff carried the day. The Pas de Calais was finally sunk: the Normandy coast it was to be.[6] COSSAC could now proceed to work out – with the benefit of the CIS's invaluable dossier – the outline operational plan that was approved by the Quadrant Conference at Quebec in August 1943, and which Ramsay found awaiting him on his arrival in Norfolk House in October.

By this time the logistics conundrum fundamental to the success of 'Overlord' had also been solved – and again thanks largely to Mountbatten and his staff. The conundrum is easily stated. To expand the Allied Expeditionary Force fast enough to outweigh the flow of German reserves and enable it to break out into the interior of France demanded use of a major port. Yet there was little hope of capturing the nearest to the Bay of the Seine – Cherbourg – quickly enough; and in any case the enemy would certainly have destroyed the docks and obstructed the harbour with his customary dismal thoroughness. The German high command was indeed calculating that, with all the Channel ports fortified to the point of impregnability, the Allied invasion force would simply wither in its lodgement for want of supplies. The solution to this crucial problem was magnificently simple: the Allies would tow over the Channel two prefabricated harbours in sections and install them off the American and British invasion beaches.

It all began with limited studies of the engineering problems in designing prefabricated piers that could be erected in the open sea off a beach. On 28 April 1942 the Director of Transportation at the

War Office wrote to the Combined Development Centre to point out the potential of the so-called 'spud' system of mooring (that is, piers mounted on adjustable legs and floating up with the tide) for berthing large ships. Mountbatten's questing mind having seized on the operational possibilities of such piers, he sold the concept to the Prime Minister who, in a now famous minute of 30 May 1942 on the topic of 'piers for flat beaches', grandly directed:

> They must float up and down with the tide. The anchor problems must be mastered. The ships must have a side-flap cut in them, and a drawbridge long enough to overreach the moorings of the piers. Let me have the best solution worked out. Don't argue the matter. The difficulties will argue for themselves.[7]

By the end of September 1942 and under the aegis of Combined Operations three prototype designs were developed by the War Office Directorate of Transportation. The Directorate's own design consisted of a pierhead unit mounted on adjustable legs (the 'spud' system) and flexible steel bridges to the shore on floating steel or concrete pontoons. A second scheme by a Mr Lorys Hughes proposed steel bridges mounted on concrete caissons towed to the site and sunk on to the seabed. Finally there was the 'Swiss Roll', a floating mat bridge sponsored by the Director of Miscellaneous Weapons Development at the Admiralty, and consisting of a flexible timber and canvas mat supported on wire cables and secured to both shore and sea anchor-points. In that same month Mountbatten submitted to the Chiefs of Staff his own ideal specification: a pier one mile long that was capable of withstanding gale-force winds and berthing large coasters. Churchill, his boyish enthusiasm for imaginative inventions further roused by Mountbatten's memorandum, wrote on 26 September: 'It seems to me that we ought to have 3–4 miles of this pier tackle. It could of course be used in many places as short sections. Pray do not lightly turn this aside . . .'[8]

But thereafter impetus sagged in delays in developing and testing the three prototype systems. On 10 March 1943 Churchill was angrily minuting the Chiefs of Staff, the Chief of Combined Operations and the War Office Director of Transportation: 'This matter is being much neglected. Dilatory experiments with varying types and patterns have resulted in our having nothing. It is now nearly 6 months since I urged the construction of several miles of pier.'[9]

Despite this Prime Ministerial boot in the bottom, it was not until June 1943 that two miles of the Directorate of Transportation's design was at last ordered in preference to the others. Further trials proving satisfactory, the Chiefs of Staff on 12 July ordered four miles of pier and six pierheads (1,200 feet) for delivery in February 1944. If steel supplies permitted, the Chiefs wanted the order to be increased to ten miles of pier and fifteen pierheads. But even now it took until the autumn of 1943 finally to discard the Hughes pier, while as late as the beginning of 1944 and despite unfavourable trial reports an order was placed for two and a half miles of 'Swiss Roll'.

Yet the original intention behind these developments had been that the piers were to be erected in invasion anchorages open to the sea, as in 'Torch' or 'Husky'. It was not until 26 February 1943 that the Admiralty Director of Miscellaneous Weapons Development suggested to the War Office Director of Transportation that artificial breakwaters might be used to protect such an anchorage. During the summer two alternative designs were tested – the 'Bubble' breakwater, where a curtain of air bubbles rising from a submerged pipe was supposed to destroy the rotary motion of water particles and so damp the waves; and the 'Lilo', compartmented canvas bags filled with air and anchored so as to extend fourteen feet below the water and eight feet above, and at an angle to the sea. The 'Lilo' was supposed to yield to the pressure of the waves on its seaward side and so damp the transmission of the wave motion past it.

By the end of October 1943 these ingenious fancies had been abandoned in favour of Admiralty-sponsored cruciform hollow steel structures, each 198 feet long and 25 feet high, dubbed 'Bombardons'. Despite misgivings on the part of the Army as to whether in gale-whipped seas the Bombardons would protect or demolish the piers, an order was placed for 75, later raised to 115 and then reduced again to 93. Meanwhile, Combined Operations had gone its own way and built a prototype concrete caisson ('Hippo') to be sunk on the seabed.

It was Captain John Hughes-Hallett, RN, of Mountbatten's staff, whose mind first soared beyond mere technical development of piers and breakwaters to conceive the all-embracing idea of artificial harbours.[10] Mountbatten took the idea up and became its dynamic and successful impresario in high places, with the result that on 4 August 1943 General Morgan (COSSAC) informed the Chiefs of Staff that two artificial harbours were indispensable to 'Overlord'. The Chiefs forthwith decided to proceed with planning and developing the harbours (codenamed 'Mulberries'); a decision ratified by the Combined Chiefs of Staff at the Quadrant Conference at Quebec. The conference also set up an Anglo-American 'Combined Committee' to recommend a general specification for the Mulberries; it reported on

2 September 1943 calling for a minimum total throughput of supplies (excluding motor transport) of 12,000 tons per day – 5,000 in the American port and 7,000 in the British. The harbours would have to function for 90 days.

In both harbours a deep-water breakwater parallel to the beach capable of coping with mean high water tides would be needed. The American harbour would also require two side breakwaters in shallow water; the British an extension eastwards into shallow waters of the deep-water barrier and a further shallow-water breakwater running inshore. All this would demand 10,000 feet of deep-water breakwater 40 to 50 feet deep, and 13,000 feet of shallow-water breakwater averaging 25 feet deep. The committee also decided that concrete caissons, as under development by Combined Operations since 1942, should form the main breakwaters and that Britain would have to build them. Four days later the Chiefs of Staff instructed the War Office to supervise construction of the caissons, now codenamed 'Phoenix', and by the end of September 147 were on order in six different sizes, the work being sub-contracted by the Ministry of Supply to 24 firms.

But now the development of the Mulberries ran into the same kind of bureaucratic demarcation dispute that had bedevilled the design of an effective anti-submarine mortar (see above, pp. 256 and 588–9). Thus far, by a traditional division of engineering responsibility, the Admiralty had overseen most of the breakwater work and the War Office the piers, with Combined Operations acting as liaison link and nursery of ideas. At this point, Combined Operations suggested that a clear-cut management structure was needed to run the complete Mulberry project as now adopted. Unfortunately neither the Admiralty nor the War Office would accept the other as project leader, nor relinquish its traditional prerogatives. A civilian coordinator without executive powers, Sir Harold Wernher, was therefore appointed to try to resolve differences and agree divisions of responsibility. But the War Office and the Admiralty fiercely pursued their trade-union style battle as to who should do what into January 1944. In fact Ramsay himself forcefully entered the dispute in December 1943, asserting that the Admiralty was the responsible body; according to him, the Army said where they wanted the artificial harbours, and the Navy provided them. Such development work as the Army had done, Ramsay argued, took the form of a sub-contract from the Navy. Hardly surprisingly, the War Office stoutly repudiated this interpretation. It took a meeting held by COSSAC on 15 December and a final decision by the Chiefs of Staff on 3 January 1944 to settle the matter – in favour of the Admiralty, which was charged with drawing up the final plan for the Mulberries.[11]

The Mulberries were not the only imaginative answer to 'Overlord's' supply problems to be already well in hand by the time Ramsay took up his duties as ANCXF. Modern mechanised armies – especially the American, with its lavish scales of motor transport – gulped petroleum fuel. How was it to be delivered to the shores of Normandy without the use of a large port's oil terminal? Once again the simple but bold answer was provided by an ingenious mind in Combined Operations Headquarters,[12] when in spring 1942 Commander Thomas Hussey, RN, suggested to Mountbatten that a petroleum pipeline could be laid across the bed of the English Channel. Mountbatten, in his valuable role as marketing man for original ideas, passed Hussey's suggestion on to Geoffrey Lloyd, the Minister of Fuel, who in turn handed it to his experts, who soon produced the technical answers.

Mr A. C. Hartley of the Anglo-Iranian Oil Company proposed a pipeline like a submarine telegraph cable with the copper and gutta-percha core omitted; a trial order was placed with the British (originally German) firm of Siemens; and soon the HAIS Cable (Hartley, Anglo-Iranian, Siemens) had been successfully laid and tested in the Thames. By December 1942 a trial line had been laid by cable ship across the widest part of the Bristol Channel, and by 1 June 1943 Lloyd was able to report to Churchill that motor spirit had been continuously pumped across for two and a half months. By this time too an alternative technical solution, the HAMEL pipe (from its inventors, H. A. Hammick, Chief Engineer of the Iraq Petroleum Company, and B. J. E. Ellis, the Chief Oilfields Engineer of the Burmah Oil Company) had been tested. It consisted of a 3-inch welded steel pipe capable of being wound on to a rotating drum 50 feet in diameter mounted on a hopper barge.

In June 1943 Lloyd ordered the manufacture of both these versions of 'Pluto' (Pipe Line Under the Ocean). Responsibility for laying the pipelines would fall to the Admiralty, and so one of the more unusual branches of the Royal Navy to come under Ramsay's command was 'Force Pluto': one hundred officers and one thousand sailors from the Merchant Marine now serving beneath the White Ensign.

'Pluto' also comprised two further ingenious, though less ambitious, schemes which inspired greater confidence in the Army that they would actually work on the day than the cross-Channel pipelines. 'Tombola' consisted of a 6-inch pipeline up to 3,000 feet long to be laid on the seabed from storage tanks on the invasion shore to buoyed flexible connections to seaward which would be picked up by discharging tankers; 'Amethea' was a similar concept based on a 10-inch steel pipe towed from England and laid in places where the shore was unsuitable for 'Tombola'. The installation of these systems too would be the task of the Royal Navy's Force Pluto. Mulberry and Pluto stand as twin triumphs of the British genius for improvisation and adaptation using essentially 'low technology' components, materials and engineering methods. Nevertheless the two projects – and especially all the components of the Mulberries such as breakwaters, pierheads and piers – constituted a colossal manufacturing task to be undertaken in haste by a country already stretched to the limit.

Meanwhile the Commanders-in-Chief of the naval commands in southern England – Plymouth, Portsmouth and the Nore – had been busy preparing the elaborate infrastructure necessary for training the 'Overlord' forces and then launching them across the Channel, as well as running the actual training programmes. As Admiral Sir Charles Little, C-in-C, Portsmouth, put it in his later report on 'Neptune': 'Rome was not built in a day, and so it has been with our work of preparation . . . Broadly speaking the whole Command became involved in the preparations, many of the older establishments performing extraneous services without interfering with continuity of training . . .'[13] Early in 1942, in the little harbours of southern England, round from Yarmouth and Lowestoft in East Anglia to Fowey and Falmouth in Cornwall, the work was begun of laying down hards for landing craft and building Nissen-hutted camps for their joint-service complements and the training units. The churning of the cement-mixers preceded the rumble of landing-craft diesels; the cries of workmen, the shouts of petty officers; the clatter of hammers and the clang of corrugated iron anticipated the rattle and roar of practice small arms and ordnance.

In 1943 new repair and maintenance shops for landing craft followed; more amphibious training bases – especially in Plymouth Command after it learned in June that all the assault forces within its boundary would be American. In the words of Admiral Sir Charles Leatham, the C-in-C, Plymouth: 'From the summer of 1943, S.W. England became an American training area.'[14] American naval bases were opened at the principal ports of the Command, and the United States Navy took over its landing craft maintenance and repair centres. Between 11 October and 24 December 1943 alone the Stars and Stripes were hoisted over six new amphibious bases in this region of estuaries and fishing ports, tiny green fields and tumbled cliffs whence settlers of New England had set sail for America three centuries before, which now teemed with the soldiers and sailors of the mighty nation founded by the settlers. In November the British Cabinet requisitioned Slapton Sands in Start Bay, Devon, and its hinterland as an important American assault training area, and by 1 January 1944 it was ready for use. 'To be suddenly evacuated from their homes and means of livelihood at short notice,' wrote Admiral Leatham, 'was not a pleasant prospect for the inhabitants, but they took it in good part, realising their sacrifice was a necessary contribution to the success of the Second Front.'[15] But such requisitioning and enforced evacuation – and the cheerful acceptance of it – had long been common enough in the coastal areas of wartime Britain.

Even after Ramsay took up his new appointment as ANCXF the Commanders-in-Chief of the area naval commands retained their customary responsibilities, and continued to provide the 'Neptune' forces with administrative services and logistical support, especially with regard to infrastructure such as new hards and training centres. Only when the 'Neptune' armada was about to put to sea would Ramsay, as ANCXF, assume command. By this division of responsibility the Admiralty left Ramsay free to concentrate on all the complexities, human as well as technical, of the 'Neptune' operation itself; a task he was all too soon to find more than enough to keep him busy.

After his experiences in 'Torch' and 'Husky' Ramsay was absolutely clear in his mind as to the fundamental principle that must guide him. He laid it down that autumn of 1943 in a lecture which he wrote on 'Combined Operations' but which, on security grounds, he was not allowed by the Admiralty to deliver:

> It is important that the military plan for the subsequent land campaign should be worked out first, and that the assaults should be solely designed to position our forces for the commencement of this. A sound military plan subsequent to the assaults must be the basis of the whole operational plan. There is a danger that administrative considerations may cause the adoption of an assault plan solely based on them, which, while appearing essentially sound, will not give effect to the military requirements for the land battle later on ... it must always be remembered that the guiding rule must be the operational plan first, and the administrative plan later, rather than the other way round. Once the Army have decided how they wish to fight the land battle it is necessary to examine how the troops can best be put ashore to give effect to the Army plan. In general it is the responsibility of the Navy to land the Army as they require, but as the plan develops Naval considerations will arise which must be discussed and agreed upon ...[16]

Yet in the existing military plan for 'Overlord' there was a basic flaw. Because of the then probable limit of available military forces and landing craft lift, COSSAC had been originally instructed by the Combined Chiefs of Staff to plan on the basis of a three-division assault only. Morgan himself was well aware that an assault in this strength, with a front of only some 30 miles, had little chance of winning a secure lodgement in the face of German resistance, but he proved unable to win consent for an assault in greater strength. At a meeting in Algiers on 27 December 1943 to discuss the COSSAC plan, Eisenhower, Montgomery and Bedell Smith all agreed that three divisions were indeed not enough; that at least five were required in the first assault wave.[17] Montgomery omits to mention this consensus in his memoirs, characteristically claiming all credit for himself for seeing the need to widen the front of assault.[18]

On 2 January 1944 – 'two months too late', in Ramsay's opinion[19] – Montgomery flew into London to begin his customary 'Military Messiah' act on taking over a new command, and two days later Ramsay and Montgomery held their first meeting on 'Overlord' in Norfolk House. 'Monty is being perfectly sensible,' Ramsay wrote to his wife in Scotland, '& is creating a good impression.'[20] That night they dined together at Claridge's, and had 'a full and free discussion of things & found ourselves in complete agreement. I always find him [Montgomery] easy & amenable . . .'[21]

The two men on whose intimate professional cooperation the success of 'Overlord' primarily depended had forged a mutual respect during the planning of 'Husky'. They shared a 'big business' attitude to the mounting of great operations of modern war – a belief in careful, elaborate preplanning so that as little as possible was left to chance. They also shared a belief in employing the greatest possible strength as an insurance against the unexpected setback. Montgomery had paid Ramsay the high compliment that 'you understand us soldiers and know more about the land battle than any other sailor'.[22] Yet personally they could not have been more different – the fox-muzzled English general of Anglo-Irish descent, all egotism and wiry tensions; the Scots admiral with his broad, open features, a man imbued with the spirit of allied teamwork, a man commonsensical, steady, but a stout fighter for what he believed to be right, and a stickler for protocol and punctilio – 'ritualistic' was Eisenhower's word for it[23] – in the stiffest tradition of the Royal Navy.

Ramsay was well aware that Montgomery could set back their common purpose by upsetting colleagues or superiors in his blindness to other men's susceptibilities, and he sought in the coming months to steer Montgomery clear of the shoals. In order to forge the closest possible personal links with his colleague, Ramsay moved into the same mess in Latymer Court, a block of flats near Montgomery's headquarters in St Paul's School, Hammersmith, West London. 'He is not the ideal messmate, Monty,' he confided to his wife, 'as he apparently must always lead the stage, which gets a bit boring. But he is almost always interesting. He & I get on well together & he listens to my advice & generally acts on it.'[24]

On 5 January 1944 the struggle for an 'Overlord' plan that would be a sound operation of war began, and life for the ANCXF immediately became 'both hectic and exhausting'.[25] That day Montgomery made a formal presentation in Norfolk House of his initial proposal to increase the three division assault plus one division afloat in reserve under the COSSAC plan to four divisions plus one in reserve. 'Monty has struck out a new line of action,' Ramsay wrote to his wife, 'and it is my part to keep him within bounds. This requires accurate statement of fact & clear reasoning because much of it is of a nature which must curb his ambitions. He skates lightly over what I know to be dangerous or impossible ice and it's all got to be carefully reasoned . . .'[26]

Nonetheless, true to Ramsay's principle that the Navy must meet the needs of the Army's battle if it possibly could, he accepted Montgomery's additions, although pointing out 'the cost of what it implied & that the bill must be met by the Admlty [sic] for increased forces or it would not be possible. We then drew up a directive given to ourselves as from the Supreme Comdr [sic]. This was for a 4 Div assault & 1 in reserve.'[27] Next day Ramsay presented the new proposal to the First Sea Lord and Chief of Naval Staff, Admiral Sir Andrew Cunningham, and other members of the Naval Staff and pointed out the implications for the size of the assault shipping lift, 'which were considerable'.[28] Cunningham, never a man for difficulties, was (noted Ramsay in his diary) 'favourable to the proposals, & the consensus of opinion was that additional requirements could be met'.[29] These amounted to no fewer than 216 landing craft, 54 assault ships, three cruisers, 27 destroyers and many more smaller vessels.[30]

Yet there was a crucial proviso. The Allies did not possess in the European theatre enough landing craft to cover the requirements of the enlarged 'Overlord' plan as well as further landings along the Italian coast after the Anzio operation (then in preparation) and the Americans' cherished project of a two-division landing on the French Riviera ('Anvil') to take place simultaneously with 'Overlord'. Admiral 'Ernie' King, however, would not look kindly on any suggestion that his island-hopping war against Japan should yield up landing craft for

'Overlord'. Although the British were already seeking to persuade the Americans to drop 'Anvil' for the sake of retaining amphibious capacity in Italy, Cunningham pointed out to his colleagues that it was by no means certain that 'Anvil' *would* be abandoned, and as Ramsay recorded his words, 'without that we should not be able to carry out the whole new plan'.[31] This same day of Ramsay's discussions with the First Sea Lord, COSSAC formally recommended to the Chiefs of Staff that 'Anvil' be abandoned and the landing craft reallocated to 'Overlord': 'In view of the shortness of time available in which to complete planning, I request the early concurrence of the Combined Chiefs of Staff to this proposal.'[32]

Ramsay and the Naval Staff now proceeded urgently to examine all the naval implications (and not merely extra shipping lift and warships) of Montgomery's proposal. These implications, in Ramsay's words, proved 'very extensive, & absolutely devastating to progress in planning, in which direction we are already badly adrift. The staff are a bit frantic about it.'[33] But worse was to come on 8 January:

> Monty came to see me at 0930 & put up a proposition for an increased width of assault, including a departure from what had been proposed at our previous meeting on 5th January. This was not unexpected as I felt certain that (as in Egypt) he would not reach a decision on a final plan without several false starts. I promised to investigate the implications of his proposal & give him an answer . . . he should have, but didn't, put the same proposition to L.M. [Leigh-Mallory], as it largely affects the air forces.[34]

Montgomery's 'increased width of assault' now embraced a 50-mile front from Cabourg, east of the River Orne, to Varreville on the eastern coast of the Cotentin Peninsula, within reach of Cherbourg: this meant five divisions landing together instead of four plus one in reserve. It disturbed Ramsay that Montgomery would not pay sufficient attention to the naval problems involved although these were 'forcibly' put by himself.[35]

On 12 January, Ramsay, Leigh-Mallory and Montgomery took part in a large conference at 21st Army Group Headquarters in St Paul's School which included the commanding generals of the 1st United States Army and 2nd British Army and corresponding air force officers. The purpose of the conference was to settle the joint questions of the size of the assault wave and the width of the front, the key to all future planning as well as to the ultimate success of 'Overlord'. Montgomery did not help by stage-managing the seating arrangements in order, in Ramsay's words, 'to imply that Monty was the supreme commander & L.M. & myself subsidiary to him, which was absurd as we are not in the least . . .'[36]

Ramsay forthrightly told the conference that the implications for the five-division assault were 'very serious' from his point of view as ANCXF and that 'it could not be recommended whereas the 4 Div & 1 staggered could. As however the 5 div assault was so important from the army pt [sic] of view, I was prepared to agree to it, provided the additional naval forces and lift were provided . . .'

By now he felt deep and growing anxiety about the whole prospect for 'Neptune'/'Overlord', especially in view of the continued absence of Eisenhower as Supreme Commander, not due to arrive from Washington until 16 January. On the night before Eisenhower's arrival Ramsay confided his misgivings to his diary:

> Monty has come down firmly with request for 5 Div assault. I have agreed, subject to necessary lift *and* naval forces for Bombardment, Minesweeping & escort being available. In doing so I am under no delusions as to the complexity of the naval operations entailed by this requirement & as to the extent to which success will be a gamble with fortune. The weather both for air and surface participation could of itself mar success. The Mine menace is very real, and the degree of training of the thousands of craft will be unknown until a late date. The capacity of the beaches & their suitability for receiving the craft & ships of all kinds is also largely guesswork. The making of the artificial harbours is also in the realm of fairyland & may or may not be a practical proposition. We now await information from Chiefs of Staff whether we are to get the extra lift or not. Until then we just cannot plan on any firm foundation.[37]

Nor was he cheered by his first meeting with the Supreme Commander two days later:

> He was pleasant as usual. He is obviously keen that Anvil should not be cancelled but agrees that Overlord must be increased. Like everyone else on the highest plane he wants to have his cake and eat it. I assured him that the two things couldn't go together & the only means of making Overlord go properly was to cancel Anvil.[38]

Nonetheless, on 23 January Eisenhower did signal the Combined Chiefs of Staff to say that while the 'ideal would be to mount a five-division Overlord assault and a three-division Anvil simultaneously', he would accept 'as a last resort' a one-division 'Anvil' to serve merely as a threat. He would also accept a postponement of 'Overlord' for a month 'if I could then be sure of obtaining the required strength [in assault shipping] . . .'[39] Although the Supreme

Commander too asked for a speedy decision, his signal proved only the first salvo in yet another protracted inter-Allied battle over grand-strategic priorities. For although the British Chiefs of Staff promptly responded by advocating that 'Anvil' be cancelled altogether and 'Overlord' postponed by a month, the Joint Chiefs of Staff in Washington refused to countenance either proposal. They merely offered three extra landing ships and 57 extra landing craft for 'Overlord', which addition they reckoned would enable a five-division assault to be lifted – given 95 per cent serviceability and more economical loading. The JCS's reply 'has driven everybody mad', wrote Ramsay in his diary, 'as it consists of a series of questions bearing upon the figures we were working to . . . *Just* what we did *not* want as it starts a cross Atlantic game of ball . . .'[40]

Between 29 January and 3 February the Prime Minister and the Chiefs of Staff discussed their next play in the trans-Atlantic ball game, finally seeking to persuade the Americans that 'Anvil' should be cancelled as much for the sake of the Italian campaign as of 'Overlord'; not an argument likely to appeal to men such as General Marshall. The Joint Chiefs would only concede that 'Overlord' should in fact be postponed until the first week of June in order to gain an extra month's British production of landing craft; but they stubbornly insisted that 'Anvil' must take place and at the same time as 'Overlord'. Thus in different ways the Mediterranean theatre continued to distract Washington and London alike, and to threaten to divert amphibious strength from the Allies' true *Schwerpunkt*, 'Overlord'.

Meanwhile those responsible for planning 'Overlord' could only pursue their course 'uneasily', in Ramsay's word. 'It is outrageous,' he noted in his diary on 4 February, 'that we should still be unable to issue a firm plan.'[41]

At British request an Anglo-American conference opened on 13 February in London to try to settle this fundamental question of assault shipping lift. The American Joint Chiefs declined to attend in person because they were themselves in the midst of a grand conference on American strategy in the Pacific. Eisenhower therefore represented the United States, together with two members of the Washington planning staffs, General J. E. Hull and Rear Admiral C. M. Cooke, as his advisers. After Ramsay had presented an outline of his naval proposals, Hull and Cooke argued the Washington view that the British were asking for a greater lift than was really needed, 'forgetting,' wrote Ramsay, 'that we have to load tactically to assault a strongly defended coast & any arithmetical calculation is bound to be impractical operationally'.[42] The meeting thus turned on technicalities about load capacities, tactical loading, and probable rates of service-ability; it ended in a compromise by which the Americans offered some extra lift from their own production and the British accepted that a five-division 'Overlord' could be managed with a smaller lift than they had originally asked for. This compromise would make it possible to leave a lift in the Mediterranean for two or three divisions. The compromise infuriated Ramsay, the more so since he was forced to accept it because Montgomery had already surrendered to American pressure – 'an iniquitous thing to do'.[43]

The new decision compelled Ramsay and his staff to go through 'a series of contortions' in order to adjust their operational planning to the reduced lift. He warned the Allied Supreme Commander during a meeting of AEF Commanders-in-Chief: '. . . I would like to make it clear that the reduction agreed to will inevitably add to the complexity of what are already ultra-complex naval operations & as such is not welcome . . .'[44]

On 25 February – the weeks towards D-Day were slipping away – the British and Americans agreed that a final decision over 'Anvil' should be postponed until 20 March. They did now decide, however, that unless the Combined Chiefs of Staff concluded on 20 March that it could take place after all, only sufficient lift for one division would thereafter remain in the Mediterranean, all the surplus assault shipping being brought back to Britain for 'Overlord'. Thus the question of the total lift to be available for 'Overlord', so crucial to the planning of 'already ultra-complex naval operations' was to be left hanging for nearly another month without final answer. No wonder Ramsay groaned in his diary on 22 February that this was 'highly unsatisfactory'.[45]

In the meantime the debate and the lobbying went on. Gradually Eisenhower himself came to accept that 'Anvil' must be cancelled as an operation simultaneous with 'Overlord' because, as he signalled the Joint Chiefs on 9 March, 'we actually have, in sight, on a reasonably assured basis, fewer LST's [Landing Ships Tank] than we considered our minimum requirement for a successful OVERLORD operation. The uncertainty is having a marked effect on everyone responsible for planning and executing Operation OVERLORD.'[46]

This signal, which bears all the signs of Ramsay's advice,[47] pointed out that theoretical calculations of lift did not take into account the needs of tactical loading for assault on a strongly defended beach. Eisenhower went on to remark that it seemed to him 'that all except ourselves [in SHAEF] take it for granted that the actual assault will be successful and relatively easy whereas we feel that it will be extremely difficult and hazardous'.[48] He therefore pleaded with the JCS that the 'minimum requisite lift and flexibility for OVERLORD' made it 'inevitable' to draw on shipping so far hypothecated for a possible 'Anvil'. 'This being the case, I think it is the gravest possible mistake to allow demands for ANVIL to militate against the main effort even in the matter of time and certainty of planning.'[49]

Still Washington refused to give a prompt and satisfactory answer, and a fortnight later Eisenhower was urgently signalling General Marshall 'for eyes only' to insist that 'Anvil' must be abandoned for the sake of a badly needed 'bit of margin and more flexibility for Overlord'.[50]

It was only on 24 March, now barely more than two months to the new D-Day target of 1 June, that after yet further urging by Eisenhower and the British Chiefs of Staff the JCS finally consented to the postponement of 'Anvil' until July,[51] so that most of 'Anvil's' ration of assault shipping could in the meantime be returned to Britain for 'Overlord'.

Yet shipping lift did not pose the only question of naval resources to drag on for weeks without decision because of Washington's obduracy – or rather, Admiral Ernest King's obduracy. In view of the strength – still increasing – of German shore batteries in their concrete casemates commanding the invasion beaches, Ramsay wanted his bombarding forces to be enlarged by one battleship, seven cruisers and fourteen destroyers to a total of six battleships or monitors, 25 cruisers and 56 destroyers: 'a huge force but not great in respect for the issues at stake',[52] although even the First Sea Lord, Admiral Sir Andrew Cunningham, had felt that Ramsay's demands exceeded what was necessary, and told the Prime Minister so.[53] Ramsay himself recognised that 'the Royal Navy can't possibly meet this bill & it can only be provided by the U.S., as indeed is only right and proper'.[54]

For the Royal Navy – like every part of Britain's war effort – had now bumped up against the limits imposed by the British population of only 45 million, a third of that of the United States or Soviet Russia, and half that of Greater Germany. By October 1943 the Navy had swelled from its complement of 127,000 officers and men at the outbreak of war to some 750,000, together with over 55,000 Wrens (Women's Royal Naval Service). The Navy's slice of industrial resources, including shipbuilding, accounted for 900,000 workers.[55] 'Overlord' itself was expected to require a further 35,000 sailors and 10,000 Wrens. On top of all this there were all the new escort carriers to be manned as well as the fast-expanding Fleet Air Arm, while the technical revolution in the Royal Navy since 1939 had called for far greater numbers of electrical and radar personnel in ships' companies. And this many-faceted expansion of the Navy necessarily carried with it an ever bigger training effort, demanding in turn yet more manpower.

At the end of 1943, after a merciless review of ships and naval establishments, the Admiralty had decided on drastic measures – measures which were only possible because of the end of the Italian threat, the defeat of the Atlantic U-boats in the spring and the two-to-one superiority now enjoyed by the United States Navy over the Imperial Japanese Navy. The four unmodernised Great War battleships *Resolution*, *Ramillies*, *Revenge* and *Malaya* were to be laid up; so too were five of the 'C' and 'D' class cruisers dating from the end of that war, and 40 old destroyers. However, even these measures could not solve the Royal Navy's manning crisis, and soldiers and airmen found themselves in navy blue serge and being introduced to the mysteries of the sea service.[56]

In any case Britain lacked both the money and the shipyard resources to expand the Royal Navy as the United States Navy was expanding. At the end of 1942 the naval staff had prepared proposals for 'a correctly balanced Navy' in order to guide future building policy. The report called for 22 fleet carriers, nineteen light fleet carriers, 83 escort carriers, nine battleships, 50 cruisers, 191 destroyers, 300 submarines and 50 fleet oilers; a pattern that reflected the declining importance of battleship and cruiser in comparison with carrier-borne aviation.[57] In spite of its eloquent strategic and operational justification of this ambitious shopping list, the report was no more than fantasy, harking back to the nineteenth century when Britain had been the richest and industrially most successful country in the world as well as the world's greatest seapower; it was quite irrelevant to the present wartime reality of a bankrupt second-rank nation. Two and a half years later, at the end of the European war, the Royal Navy's strength in ships of these categories in commission was only to amount to six fleet carriers, four light fleet carriers, some 30 escort carriers, five battleships, some 40 cruisers, 108 fleet destroyers and some 120 submarines.[58]

So it was that the Royal Navy could not meet Ramsay's enlarged bill for naval forces in 'Neptune' on top of its remaining commitments in the Mediterranean, the Eastern Fleet in the Indian Ocean, the Arctic convoys and all its other duties in the war against Germany. The bill would have indeed to be met by the new mistress of the seas, the United States Navy. But it took a month after Ramsay's request was forwarded to the Joint Chiefs of Staff in Washington before Admiral King boxed his compass and offered to send three battleships, two cruisers and 34 destroyers: a more powerful force than he had been asked for.[59]

All this time, and under a pall of anxiety about the shipping lift, that essential key to the entire enterprise, Ramsay and his staff had been at full stretch in their efforts to solve 'Neptune's' operational problems and work out their detailed plans. Although Ramsay consulted frequently with the Supreme Commander and with Leigh-Mallory, the Expeditionary Air Forces Commander, it was with his opposite number as land force commander, General Montgomery of 21st Army Group, that he needed to work most closely. By and large their relationship worked well, not least because of Ramsay's guiding principle that the Navy's task was to enable the Army to win the land battle. But their methods differed sharply. Whereas Ramsay immersed himself in the transaction of business, Montgomery spent much time away from London inspecting troops, and left even participation in important meetings (such as some of those on the landing craft lift) to his Chief of Staff, the invaluable 'Freddie' de Guingand. 'It really is quite wrong,' Ramsay confided to his diary on 17 February in a moment of irritation, 'that he [Montgomery] should take no part in these high policy negotiations. His knowledge of the technique of the operation is very small and he leaves everything to Freddie & his staff, with whom, in consequence I have to negotiate. He does *no* work at all.'[60]

Of Rear Admiral Alan Kirk, the American admiral in command of the Western Task Force which would put ashore and support the 1st American Army, Ramsay as ANCXF did not entertain a high opinion, regarding him privately as a fuss-pot and a whinger, and too much under the influence of his Chief of Staff, Rear Admiral A. D. Struble. Ramsay recorded in January how Kirk, having been satisfied with the latest telegram to Washington over landing craft, came to see him 'wearing his discontented face'; and Ramsay added: 'as usual after Struble has been at him, he entirely changes ground'.[61] Ramsay's judgment of Kirk was not to soften as the strains of organising 'Neptune' grew more severe. At the beginning of May he characterised as 'hysterical' two letters from Kirk on the topics of salvage craft and the threat from E-boats: 'He has quite lost his sense of proportion besides being rather offensively rude. My opinion of him decreases steadily. He is not a big enough man to hold the position he does.'[62]

But then Ramsay, whose standards were rigorous in the quietest of times, was also to have his doubts about Rear-Admiral Sir Philip Vian, the commander of the Eastern Task Force charged with landing the British 2nd Army, whom he had personally asked the First Sea Lord to appoint.[63] During a long discussion with Vian on 3 March about his functions, Vian struck Ramsay 'as being a little helpless & requires to be given so much guidance on matters which I feel he could work out for himself. In fact I feel that I am organising his part of the show as well as my own, which gives me unnecessary additional work to do. I don't think he uses his Staff enough.'[64] It has to be said that Vian, a man of notoriously dark and difficult nature, had only accepted the post with reluctance and out of a sense of necessity.[65] However, the ANCXF's judgments were not always so critical. He found Admiral Harold Stark, the US naval representative in Britain since 1941, 'a shrewd old man';[66] the newly arrived (in March) Rear Admiral D. P. Moon, who was to command Force U ('Utah' beach), 'a fine type of U.S. officer. Efficient & alert. He should do well . . .'[67]

No great military enterprise can be immune from friction caused by individual human personality, least of all one so vast and intricate as 'Neptune'. What is remarkable in such a joint undertaking between two Allies – and is unprecedented in the history of alliances – is how relatively unimportant were such incidental gratings of personality. It is no less remarkable that they were never based on nationality. This melding of British and Americans into a common command structure – more, a single team – is rightly ascribed to Eisenhower's determination that it should be so, and his skill in bringing it about. Yet the task of planning 'Neptune' and 'Overlord', so daunting and so urgent, imposed its own discipline and provided its own drive towards unity. Nor, thanks to the patient acquisition and collation of Intelligence about the enemy, could anyone concerned with planning the invasion fail to recognise that what lay ahead must be, in Eisenhower's words, 'extremely difficult and hazardous'.

From Ultra decrypts – including a telegram home from the Japanese ambassador in Berlin in November 1943 passing on the complete order of battle of the German Army in the West as given him in a briefing by General Blumentritt, Chief of Staff to the C-in-C, West[68] – the Joint Intelligence Committee in January 1944 was able to give an estimate of the German forces that could confront the Allies on D-Day and after. It reckoned that the Luftwaffe in the West could number 2,530 aircraft, and be able to fly 1,750 sorties on D-Day against embarkation ports in England, the 'Neptune' armada on passage and the beaches. The German Army in the West could muster 45 divisions, including twelve high-quality attack formations. By D-Day evening one SS panzer division and one infantry division could have moved into place opposite the Allied lodgement; by D +

2, two panzer divisions, one panzer-grenadier, two SS divisions and one infantry field division, plus elements of two coastal defence divisions – some six in all. By D + 7 the total could be up to more than nine divisions, including four panzer and two panzer-grenadier.[69] These were the intimidating figures which clinched the decision to enlarge the 'Overlord' assault from three to five divisions, with a 50-mile front stretching from the River Dives (east of Caen) to Varreville at the base of the Cotentin Peninsula, with all that this implied for the two navies.

Month by month through the spring of 1944 Sigint, Army 'Y' radio intercept Intelligence and secret agents continued closely to monitor the ebb and flow of German divisions in the West according to the degree of pressure being exerted by the Red Army on the Eastern Front. By the end of March it had become alarmingly clear that the enemy was moving formations nearer the coast – most of them in the Pas de Calais but also some into Normandy and Brittany. A month later the JIC was putting the total number of German divisions in the West at 53, rising to 55 by D-Day. This included eight panzer or panzer-grenadier divisions and fourteen high quality infantry field divisions.[70] The JIC now conjectured that from D-Day evening to D + 1 the 'Overlord' forces would face two panzer divisions, one infantry field division and four coastal defence divisions; and that by D + 3 to D + 7 the total would have risen to no fewer than seven panzer and seven infantry field divisions, as well as the four coastal defence divisions.[71]

These constantly updated calculations determined not only the initial necessity for the Allies to land five divisions on D-Day, but also the essential pace and scale with which the follow-up formations flowed into the lodgement. On 1 February the 'Initial Joint Plan' for 'Neptune' issued by Eisenhower (giving the broad framework for detailed planning by the air, sea and land commanders) therefore set a target of nine follow-up divisions by D + 3 and twenty by D + 14.[72] And this target in turn determined the scale of shipping lift that Ramsay believed 'Neptune' would require, and which Eisenhower had by the end of March at last successfully obtained. It also gave the measure of the problems of scheduling and routing the cross-Channel traffic on and after D-Day that must be solved by the ANCXF and his staff.

Intelligence also forewarned the ANCXF about the dangers that the 'Neptune' armada on D-Day and the follow-up forces later would face while at sea. As always the German Navy Home Waters Enigma served as a marvellous window into enemy secrets, for a new key was broken by GC and CS at Bletchley Park in March 1944. 'Y' stations along the English coast eavesdropped on German radio-telephone traffic and also began to pick up easily decoded ship-to-ship tactical signals called 'PP'.[73] This electronic watch was supplemented by constant surveillance by photo-reconnaissance aircraft of enemy naval movements and bases along the French coast.

The least of Ramsay's concerns lay in the remaining serviceable ships of the German surface fleet: the pocket battleships *Scheer* and *Lützow*, the 8-inch cruisers *Hipper* and *Prinz Eugen* and the light cruisers *Leipzig, Köln, Nürnberg* and *Emden*. All of them were currently stationed in the Baltic in support of the German Army on the Eastern Front. On 10 May the British and American Joint Intelligence Committee did produce a 'worst case' scenario in which the heavier German ships would move to Norway and try to divert Allied warships from 'Neptune' by threatening to break out into the Atlantic, while the light cruisers raided convoys along the east coast of England. Four days later Ramsay, his staff and Vian met to discuss the alternative contingency of the German surface fleet making a dash into the Channel. 'P. Vian shall have the command of the forces I shall concentrate to deal with them = 2 BB [battleships], 8 Cr [sic] & 20 DD [destroyers]. It would be a glorious thing to wipe out the German fleet . . .'[74] However, an Operational Intelligence Centre report appreciated that westward sorties by the German surface fleet would depend on the military situation in the Baltic; and in the event that was where the German ships stayed, except for four heavy 'Z' class destroyers based in Brest.

The U-boats and E-boats, almost invulnerable from air or sea bombardment while within their concrete pens in their base ports, were another matter. In particular Ultra decrypts had revealed that when at the end of January a Luftwaffe aircraft falsely reported that some 200 to 300 landing craft were heading for the Gironde estuary, U-boat Command had ordered U-boats as far off as Rockall to close on the threatened area at utmost speed and ignoring all hazards.[75] At the beginning of March (when ANCXF and his staff were entering their most hectic planning period) the Operational Intelligence Centre was gloomily reckoning that no fewer than 75 500-ton U-boats could be deployed on the western flank of the cross-Channel invasion traffic by D-Day + 4 or 5.[76]

Nevertheless Ramsay appreciated that 'Neptune's' worst hazard while on passage lay in minefields, destructive and invisible obstacles waiting in ambush beneath the innocently empty surface of the sea, and which if undetected and unswept could disrupt the finely timed movements of the assault forces. On 21 February the Operational Intelligence Centre first gave warning that the enemy had begun to lay a major deep-water barrier in the Bay of the Seine. In March 'PP' decrypts revealed that an experimental inshore minefield had been laid off the little port of Ouistreham on what was to be the left flank of the British 2nd Army's landing area. But by early April, when Ramsay and his staff were busy drafting the final naval orders for 'Neptune', the OIC was still unable to give the location of inshore fields with any precision. Ramsay was particularly worried about the question of ensuring clear passage for the warships that were to provide fire support to the assaulting troops. On 24 March after a long discussion with Vian about the problems of minesweeping, Ramsay wrote in his diary:

> It is a most complicated operation & however we looked at it we could find no satisfactory solution of how best to sweep the channels of the faster groups & bombarding ships. In the end I decided that the only way out was to find 2 more flotillas made up from existing flotillas & to employ them to sweep the cruisers through to their bombarding positions. There is no doubt that the mine is our greatest obstacle to success, and if we manage to reach the enemy coast without becoming disorganised & suffering serious loss we shall be fortunate.[77]

The problem was the more perplexing because the OIC found difficulty in distinguishing inshore minelaying from the simultaneous erection of submerged beach obstacles. In February 1944 Field-Marshal von Rundstedt, the German C-in-C, West, told the press that Allied landing forces would run into a wide zone of fixed obstacles as well as mines.[78] British photo-reconnaissance confirmed from 20 February onwards that, beginning with the Bay of the Seine, these obstacles were sprouting on every beach in France and Belgium suitable for a landing. If this belt were widened from the present limit of 100 metres below the high-water mark down to the low-water mark, it would render the Allies' selection of H-Hour even more difficult than it already was. Effective counter-measures therefore depended on exact information about the obstacles themselves, and the physical characteristics and gradients of the beaches. Although by April an accurate enough picture had emerged from aerial photo-reconnaissance of the beaches at all states of tide, it had needed COPP (Combined Operations Pilotage Parties) to bring back samples of sand and shingle, as well as data about tidal flows and the widespread inundations carried out by the enemy behind key sectors of coastline, especially in the American area of assault.

One particularly valuable reconnaissance, enabling a mock stretch of German sea and shore defences to be constructed later on the Norfolk coast for experiment and training, was carried out by a force including two midget submarines, or X-Craft. The C-in-C, Portsmouth, Admiral Sir Charles Little, described their feats as a 'sustained and impudent reconnaissance under the very nose of the enemy'.[79] The sorties proved as uncomfortable as they were dangerous, as the force commander, Lieutenant-Commander H. N. C. Willmott, RN, described in his report:

It was found desirable for the naval officer on watch on the casing to be able to lift his head above water for breathing purposes. He is strapped to the induction pipe, and has a bar to which he clings, with fervour, while floating on his front like a paper streamer on the bosom of the ocean, which has submerged the rest of the craft beneath him. Legs are liable to injury. There is a vacancy in the complement for an intelligent merman to fill this role.[80]

Human daring and advanced electronic and photographic technology would continue up to the eve of D-Day to feed SHAEF and its commanders with ever more abundant information about the enemy's evolving defence and deployment. But it was the Intelligence already at hand up to April that had to guide them in framing the plans for 'Neptune'/'Overlord'. For Ramsay and his staff in particular the issue by Eisenhower on 1 February 1944 of his 'Initial Joint Plan' served as the signal to accelerate their work to utmost speed – exhaustive operational studies and discussions; meetings that took in at one time or another the Prime Minister and all the senior Allied sea, land and air commanders, including the commanders-in-chief of the Royal Navy's Home commands. In Ramsay's words

The Naval problem that had to be faced can be briefly summarized as, first, the breaking of the strong initial crust of the coast defences by assault, together with the landing of the fighting army formations; and, secondly, to commence, and continue without a pause for five or six weeks, their reinforcements at as high a rate as possible. The first required the co-ordination of the movement of thousands of ships and landing craft and aircraft, and then of the firepower; the second the co-ordination of the activities of hundreds of thousands of men and women of all services, both in the United Kingdom and off the French coast, marshalling, loading, sailing, unloading and returning at least eight ship convoys a day, in addition to 10 or 12 landing craft groups. Considerations of time and space did not permit the use of any unexpected manoeuvre to confuse the enemy; we had simply to drive ahead in great strength and to ensure that the organisation was as efficient as it could be, as the time factor was all important.[81]

On 2 March Ramsay issued the Naval Plan for 'Neptune', the comprehensive solution to all these problems and the blueprint for the next colossal task of preparing detailed operation orders. The round of meetings, of visits to training centres and exercises, spun faster. When Ramsay was in his room in Norfolk House he found himself beset by a 'queue of people waiting to see me, headed by Creasy [his Chief of Staff]'; and all of them seemed to have 'an insoluble difficulty to present to me'.[82] He wrote to his wife in Scotland on 2 April: 'Life is a great rush, & I am near up to date. Perhaps there is a lot in Monty's method of never reading anything or attending to any details but concentrating on main essentials . . .'[83] As it was, he acknowledged that his own mind was 'obsessed with current & future operations. How relieved I shall be when things are over and either one will be feeling frightfully bucked or we are back behind where we started from. One hopes & believes all will be abundantly well.'[84]

Yet in the midst of all this effort and strain came marvellous encouragement – a letter from Their Lordships of the Admiralty dated 30 March 1944 to tell him that he had been restored to the active list of flag officers of the Royal Navy, and in the rank of admiral. His pride and pleasure were however tempered by the circumstances of his reinstatement. As he confided to his wife, 'Everyone says how splendid of the Admiralty to reinstate me & acknowledge an error, little knowing that it had nothing really to do with them or rather that unless the P.M. had made a move about it, they would never have acted in the matter.'[85]

Outwardly he bore the stress well. 'One could not have worked for a more considerate or more patient master,' recalled his meteorological adviser, Captain J. Fleming, RN. 'Calm and unhurried in his duties, friendly and kindly in his personal relations, he welded us into a team . . .'[86] Inwardly the stress was beginning to tell – a repeatedly upset stomach; a 'muck sweat' while trying to prepare his hour-long briefing on the naval side of 'Neptune' to a grand two-day conference, 'Thunderclap', which opened at 21st Army Group headquarters in St Paul's School on 7 April.

'Thunderclap' began with an hour and a half long exposition of the land battle plan by Montgomery; the battle it was Ramsay's task to serve: 'The intention is to assault simultaneously: immediately north of the Carentan estuary and between the Carentan estuary and the

River Orne with the object of securing as a base for further operations a lodgement area which will include airfield sites and the port of Cherbourg.'[87]

Montgomery reckoned that by D + 5 the enemy could have concentrated six 'panzer type' divisions against the lodgement, by which time the Allies should have landed 15 divisions: 'The enemy build-up can become *considerable* from D + 4 onwards; obviously therefore we must put all our energies into the fight and get such a good situation in the first few days that the enemy can do nothing against us.'[88]

Therefore (and this reflects the intimate cooperation between Ramsay and Montgomery and their staffs):

> The general principle on which the build-up has been planned is to land on the continent the maximum number of fighting formations in the first few days . . . Flexibility has been introduced at the earliest possible moment so that the priority of fighting formations . . . can be varied to suit operational conditions as they develop . . .[89]

Montgomery's address was followed by Ramsay and Leigh-Mallory on the naval and air plans, and in the afternoon by detailed descriptions of the American 1st Army and British 2nd Army plans by Generals Omar Bradley and Sir Miles Dempsey. 'Thunderclap' ended at 1345 next day with the Allied master plan for 'Neptune'/'Overlord' finally settled and approved.

Now came the task of issuing the actual operation orders. 'Things have reached the intense stage of getting orders into print,' Ramsay wrote to his wife on 11 April, '& all the staff are stretched beyond the limit . . .'[90] It hardly helped that Creasy, his Chief of Staff, was suffering from back trouble and likely to go sick.[91] Nonetheless, thanks to a final sustained burst of work by a production line of typewriters driven by a team of Wren typists, 'Operation Neptune – Naval Orders (Short Title: ON)' went to press on 10 April 1944.[92] The introduction stated:

> This is probably the largest and most complicated operation ever undertaken and involves the movement of over 4,000 ships and craft of all types in the first three days. The Operation Orders are therefore necessarily voluminous.

This was no exaggeration. 'ON' comprised 22 parts covering every conceivable aspect of the operation, and numbered 579 pages even without the numerous appendices giving even more intricate detail. But on top of 'ON' there was also 'ONAD' (Operation Neptune

Administrative Orders) and 'ONCO' (the Communications Orders), bringing the total package to more than 1,000 pages of foolscap print. It constituted a remarkable achievement for a Navy that had been so very late in fully adopting a staff system. It was, after all, only nine years previously that Ramsay, the principal architect of the 'Neptune' plans, had retired from the Navy in the face of the then Commander-in-Chief Home Fleet's refusal to allow him to function properly as a Chief of Staff; a retirement which the Admiralty, siding with the C-in-C and his obsolete 'one-man-band' style of command, had been happy to accept.

Yet 'Operation Neptune – Naval Orders', taken together with Ramsay's preceding Naval Plan, constitute much more than a remarkable achievement in terms of just the Royal Navy's own history. In scope and thoroughness, in the complexity and scale of the problems solved, they eclipse the renowned performances of the German General Staff from 1866 onwards. They stand to this day as a never surpassed masterpiece of planning and staff work.

'A Never Surpassed Masterpiece of Planning'

The object of Operation Neptune is to carry out an operation from the United Kingdom to secure a lodgement on the Continent from which further operations can be developed. This lodgement area must contain sufficient port facilities to maintain a force of 26 to 30 divisions and enable this force to be augmented by follow-up formations at the rate of three to five divisions in a month.[1]

So began the introductory opening section and summary (ON1) of 'Operation Neptune – Naval Orders'. It defined the task of the Allied navies as 'The safe and timely arrival of the assault forces at their beaches, the cover of their landings, and subsequently the support and maintenance and the rapid build-up of our forces ashore', emphasising that this was 'a combined British and U.S. undertaking by all services of both nations'. ON1 went on to restate command responsibilities. Under Eisenhower as Supreme Commander were three equal sea, land and air Commanders-in-Chief: Ramsay (ANCXF), Montgomery (C-in-C, 21st Army Group), and Leigh-Mallory (C-in-C, Allied Expeditionary Air Forces). The ANCXF 'will exercise general command and control over the naval forces other than those providing distant cover . . . He will exercise direct command within an "assault area" off the French coast.' The Cs-in-C, naval home commands, would continue to carry out their normal functions of command and administrative support except within the assault areas.

Under ANCXF the two naval task force commanders, Rear Admiral Kirk (Western Task Force = NCWTF) and Rear-Admiral Vian

(Eastern Task Force = NCETF) would 'initially exercise command of their forces [i.e., for training and rehearsal] and later operational control within the assault area'.[2] Each task force was divided into naval forces corresponding to the assault waves of the British 2nd and American 1st Armies which it was their role to put ashore and support. In Kirk's Western Task Force, Force U ('Utah' beach at the base of the Cotentin Peninsula; the westernmost Allied landing; 4th US Infantry Division) was commanded by Rear Admiral D. P. Moon, USN; Force O ('Omaha' beach to the eastwards; 1st and 29th US Infantry Divisions) by Rear Admiral J. L. Hall, USN. In Vian's Eastern Task Force, Force G ('Gold' beach, ten miles east of 'Omaha'; 50th British Infantry Division) was under the command of Commodore C. E. Douglas-Pennant, RN; Force J ('Juno' beach, on 'Gold's' eastern flank; 3rd Canadian Division) under the command of Commodore G. N. Oliver, RN; Force S ('Sword' beach, the easternmost Allied landing; 3rd British Infantry Division) under the command of Rear-Admiral A. G. Talbot, RN. The seven follow-up divisions to land on the second tide of D-Day (2nd, 9th, 29th and 90th US Infantry; 49th, 51st British Infantry and 7th Armoured) were the responsibility of Forces B (Commodore C. D. Edgar, USN) and L (Rear-Admiral W. E. Parry).

Having set the scene in 'ON1', Ramsay's orders, section by section, tackled each phase or facet of 'Neptune' chronologically, starting with minelaying operations off enemy ports from the Baltic to the Bay of Biscay from D − 45 onwards by the Royal Navy and Royal Air Force Bomber Command (ON2), and with naval diversions with air support against the Pas de Calais and elsewhere around the time of D-Day (ON3). These diversions formed part of an elaborate plan ('Fortitude') to hoax the enemy into believing that the Allies were in fact to land in the Pas de Calais, and at a later date than D-Day. A signal net had been set up in Kent to simulate the traffic of a '1st American Army Group' under the command of General Patton,[3] and feed German Intelligence with appropriate clues about this bogus formation and its preparations to invade the Pas de Calais. Thanks to Ultra it was possible for SHAEF to monitor just how successful the hoax was proving, especially in terms of the relative weight of deployment of German divisions north of the Seine and south of it.[4] In Ramsay's own retrospective judgment:

Had the enemy not been deceived by our cover plan and the latent threat to the Pas de Calais, it would have been possible for him to have built up his forces against us at a rate at least equal to that of which we were capable with the craft and shipping at our disposal, assuming optimum conditions on our part and minimum turn-round times . . .[5]

ON4 dealt with the mammoth business of loading and assembling the 4,000 vessel-strong D-Day Armada and the immediate follow-up forces and supplies in comprehensive detail, complete with tables and 'Mickey Mouse' diagrams. The five assault forces were to assemble and load – together with their escorts and minesweepers – in south-coast ports from Plymouth round to Newhaven; the two follow-up forces in Felixstowe on the east coast, in the Thames, and in south-western ports to the west of Plymouth. The first build-up groups – and Ramsay reckoned the build-up plan to be of 'unique and major importance' – were to be brought together and pre-loaded in the Bristol Channel (American) and the Thames (British). The naval covering forces charged with protecting the flanks of 'Neptune' were to assemble in the Bristol Channel and the Thames; the heavy bombardment forces in the Clyde and Belfast Loch, except for one battleship and two monitors stationed in the south. All the varied ships, craft and equipment needed for maintenance services off the French coast after D-Day were to be slotted into ports from Falmouth to Harwich; the unwieldy components of the Mulberries were to be brought together in anchorages between Portland and Felixstowe, but clear of other shipping. ON4 laid down that the supply ships on which the logistics of the Allied Expeditionary Force would completely depend in Normandy were to start loading on D − 21: 89 of them in the Thames (33 of which were to sail to the Solent when loaded); 24 at Grimsby up on the east coast, later removed to Southend in the Thames Estuary; 104 in the Bristol Channel ports, of which 22 were then to sail to the Solent. It had been a jigsaw puzzle in which the pieces seemed larger and more numerous than the vacant spaces on the board; and yet the ingenuity of the planners had now found a place for all.

The deployment at sea of the naval covering forces was laid down in ON5. Distant cover outside the English Channel would be provided by the Commanders-in-Chief, Home Fleet, Western Approaches and Plymouth, under Admiralty direction. Should U-boats enter the Channel the Admiralty would probably transfer some support groups to the ANCXF. Close cover against German destroyers, E-boats and R-boats (motor minesweepers) would be the responsibility of the Cs-in-C, naval home commands: Plymouth, with eight British and four US destroyers; Portsmouth with four British destroyers and four frigates; Dover with four destroyers. All three commands would also have at their disposal coastal forces such as MTBs and motor launches equipped to lay smoke screens. The two 'Neptune' naval task force commanders would in addition deploy their own protective light forces.

In ON6 Ramsay gave orders for overcoming the German minefields, and especially the barrier known to have been laid from about latitude 50°N to within seven to ten miles of the Normandy coast. Although to the south of it lay a coastal channel left clear by the enemy for his own use, and which the 'Neptune' plan counted on for the final deployment of the assault and bombarding forces, even this might be mined at the last moment. Inshore mining also had to be taken into account. After much thought and long discussion with Vian and Kirk, Ramsay formulated a minesweeping plan in four main phases, of which the first would amount to the largest single minesweeping operation of the war.[6] Under his direct control two channels, each two miles wide, were to be swept simultaneously through the main German barrier for each of the five assault forces. One fleet mine-sweeping flotilla would be employed for each channel, giving a total of 255 vessels. The swept channels were to be marked by Dan buoys (small buoys bearing a flag or light on a pole) at one-mile intervals along both of their sides. In phase two, which would be carried out under the command of the task force commanders, a British inshore minesweeping flotilla would precede each bombardment group on D-Day in order to locate or, if necessary, sweep clear areas and anchorages close inshore. In phase three, the approach channels were to be widened to give more sea-room, while phase four provided for the sweeping of any mines laid after the Allied landings had taken place. Ramsay's orders emphasised that 'good navigation on the part of the Fleet minesweepers is of the utmost importance', and laid it down that they must keep to their sweeping courses even if 'heavily engaged', because the assault forces following the minesweepers relied 'solely on them for safety'.

The exact positions of all channels and areas to be swept were specified later in ON17, which also detailed swept routes across the Channel to the northern limit of the German mine barrier. From the permanently swept channels along the south coast of England four special channels were to be swept and marked with light buoys converging southwards to 'Position Z', a circle five miles in radius centred on 50° 25'N, 0° 58'W, some fifteen miles south-east of St Catherine's Head, Isle of Wight. 'Position Z' formed the entrance lobby, as it were, to 'The Spout' down which all 'Neptune' vessels would pass to the Normandy coasts. The Spout itself, as far as the northern limit of the German mine barrier, would consist of eight designated routes, not all of which would be swept unless there was evidence of minelaying.

In all, the minesweeping orders provided for a programme of as many as 76 'serials', each to be put in hand by order of the task force commanders as soon as the previous one had been completed.

Admiral Kirk, who along with other American flag officers criticised Ramsay in general for laying down the 'Neptune' plans in too much detail rather than devolving the work to commanders of task forces, was to acknowledge:

> It can be said without fear of contradiction that minesweeping was the keystone of the arch of this operation. All of the waters were suitable for mining, and minesweeping plans of unprecedented complexity were required. The performance of the minesweepers can only be described as magnificent . . .[7]

The bulk of these minesweepers was provided by the Royal Navy even in the Western Task Force area of operations; a heavy burden. At Kirk's request a British officer, Commander J. G. B. Temple, RN, was appointed Commander, Minesweeping West, with the USS *Chimo* as his headquarters ship. His opposite number, Captain, Minesweeping East, was Captain R. B. Jennings, RN.[8] In addition ANCXF would deploy a reserve force of minesweepers for work with the Mulberries, for escort duties on D-Day and to relieve the task force sweepers. Because it was so important that the swept channels through the mine barrier be clearly marked, the small Dan buoys were to be replaced between D-Day and D + 1 by large ocean light buoys laid by the Royal Navy and Trinity House (the institution responsible for lighthouses, lightships and light buoys).[9]

Next, in ON7, came Ramsay's orders to the task and assault forces for the 'approach march' from British ports to the touchdown on the Normandy beaches at H-Hour. On receipt of his signal 'Carry out operation', the Cs-in-C, naval Home commands, were to sail the invasion forces within their areas. The X-Craft X20 and X23, serving as markers for Forces J and S in the British sector, were to leave Portsmouth probably about sunset on D − 3, be towed as far as possible, and arrive off the beaches early in daylight on D − 1. The northern approaches to the swept channels were to be marked by motor launches and by radio beacons laid by the launches. Other launches were to mark the route over which American airborne divisions were to fly to land behind the German defences in the

Carentan area. Once the assault forces had entered the swept channels smoke was not to be used during the night hours, and nor were navigation lights except in an emergency and then only dimmed.

Ramsay was much concerned about the danger of friend firing on friend if vessels were sighted out of their expected positions; an eventuality all too probable in view of what he called in ON7 the 'stress of weather ... and general unhandiness of many of the units ...' He sought to reassure the recipients of his orders that 'The chances are that an unrecognised ship or object sighted in the Channel is friendly'; and he instructed that fire was not to be opened on ships by day unless clearly recognised as hostile. By night only the escorts on the outer flanks were to be permitted to open fire, and then only in an outward direction after a prior challenge. Assault shipping was ordered not to leave the swept channels if it came under enemy surface attack, but to keep driving ahead for the shore, leaving the escorts (whose orders, complete with escort diagrams, were given in ON15) to tackle the threat.

The standard procedure in the final approach and landing of each assault force took the form of sixteen carefully timed stages, ranging from H-Hour − 120 minutes (arrival at the lowering points of the first landing ship [tank] group loaded with amphibious tanks) to H − 60 (bombarding ships open fire), H − 10 (first group of rocket-equipped LCTs open fire), H − 7½ (amphibious tanks touch down on the beach) and to H-Hour itself, the infantry assault. At H + 30, assault landing craft would bring in the first infantry reserves and the obstacle clearance units; between H + 75 and H + 105 it would be the turn of LCTs with self-propelled artillery and priority motor transport to touch down.[10] The assault, ordered the ANCXF, was to be 'pressed home with relentless vigour and determination, regardless of loss or difficulty'.

ON7 also briefed recipients that fighter patrols would be flown over the assault forces on passage and on the beaches, and that they would be controlled by GCI (Ground Coastal Interception) from England and by Fighter Direction Ships with Forces O, S and G; later by ground stations.

In ON8 Ramsay turned to the bombardment forces whose task was 'to assist in ensuring the safe and timely arrival of our forces by the engagement of hostile coast defences, and to support the assault and subsequent operations ashore'. Their firepower was weighty indeed – in Kirk's Western Task Force, three battleships (all American), one British monitor, nine cruisers (of which two were American and two French; the rest British), and 25 destroyers (21 American, three

British and one Dutch); in Vian's all Royal Navy Eastern Task Force, two battleships, one monitor, eleven cruisers and 40 destroyers, plus one battleship (HMS *Nelson* in Portsmouth) and one cruiser in reserve. The bombardment forces were divided into five groups each allotted to an assault force.

It had not proved easy to agree with 21st Army Group and the Allied air forces on arrangements for an integrated air and naval bombardment. Montgomery had claimed that it was for the Army to determine the type and quantity of fire support, but Ramsay had firmly and successfully insisted that, although the fire plan itself should be jointly settled, the 'prime responsibility for calculating the type and quantity of fire support required until the beaches are captured, and for deciding upon its application must rest with the Navy, because the Navy bears the responsibility for the safe arrival of the assault convoys'.[11] The Royal Air Force and the United States Army Air Force, for their part, declined to commit themselves until late as to the weight of bombing they would provide or as to the times relative to sunrise on D-Day when the bombers should operate – hardly helpful.[12] Nevertheless a coordinated bombardment plan was finally framed by which, as ON8 described in detail, certain German batteries were to be bombed in the run-up to D-Day, others were to be attacked by Bomber Command heavy bombers the very night before D-Day, and six more batteries in key tactical positions were to be hit by medium bombers soon after daylight on D-Day itself. Starting at H − 45, heavy and medium bombers would also deliver a total of 4,200 tons of bombs on the enemy beach defences, after which the guns of the warships would take over.

In the case of the German coastal defence batteries, ON8 allocated targets to ships according to an elaborate fire plan based on photo-reconnaissance data. Bombarding warships were not to open fire before daylight except as an emergency, but wait until the assault convoys had come within range of enemy guns and spotter aircraft had arrived overhead. Fire was to be continued until the target batteries had been silenced or captured. A similar fire plan had been drawn up for the close support of the assault forces as they attacked the enemy beach defences. ON8 defined the object of close support bombardment as 'To neutralise defences and demoralise the defenders preparatory to the final assault'. Concrete bunkers were to be engaged with armour-piercing shell from as close inshore as possible. Battleships, monitors and cruisers were ordered to support thereafter the armies' advances inland by bombarding enemy troops and positions by day and night.

The fall of shot on D-Day was to be monitored by Forward Observers, Bombardment, on shore with the troops, by shore fire-control parties, and by single-seat fighter patrols. These latter, numbering 104 Mustangs and Spitfires, would work in pairs, one spotting and the other acting as escort. Further aerial spotting would also be provided after the landings by light aircraft such as Austers or Piper Cubs normally employed as spotters for the armies' artillery.

'It is in the rapid follow-up of reserves and on the swift unloading of stores that the attack relies for its impetus which alone can sustain it and give it complete success.'[13] With these words began ON9, the orders to task and assault forces for the rest of D-Day after H-Hour, and which detailed the English ports to which ships and craft must return from the beaches for reloading. This stress on the need for speed and impetus applied no less to ON10, dealing with follow-up forces: Force L (British) was to be sailed in five groups by the C-in-C, Nore, and Force B (American) in three groups by C-in-C, Plymouth. Since all LSTs could not discharge on the second tide of D-Day, some of them, so ordered ON10, would have to arrive on the third tide with the first of the build-up convoys.

Next, in ON11, Ramsay briefed his commanders about the air plan, an absolutely crucial aspect of the entire 'Neptune'/'Overlord' operation. For the Allies had always accepted that it would be impossible to launch an invasion of France until and unless the Allied air forces enjoyed mastery of the air over the Channel and the Normandy coast. By the time Ramsay and his staff were drafting 'Operation Neptune – Naval Orders', this mastery had in fact been won, and the two air forces had begun to concentrate their heavy bombers under SCAEF direction against the French transportation network. Yet these things had only come to pass in the teeth of the bomber chieftains' doctrinaire opposition.

By decision of the Washington Conference in May 1943, the Allied heavy bomber forces were to give high priority to destroying the Luftwaffe's fighter force and the German aircraft industry.[14] But by January 1944 this 'Operation Pointblank' had failed of its purpose. Air Marshal Sir Arthur Harris's Bomber Command had suffered unsustainable losses at the hands of enemy night-fighters without decisive effect on German industry or morale.[15] The United States 8th Air Force had done its best in daylight raids to demolish enemy ball-bearing and aircraft factories by precision bombing, but German aircraft production had continued to climb. By the beginning of 1944 the 8th Air Force too was suffering from such an appalling rate of loss as to constitute a strategic defeat as decisive as that of Bomber Command.

Then, in January 1944, a new phase of the 8th Air Force's offensive opened, with its fleets of Flying Fortresses and Liberators now escorted all the way to the target by long-range Merlin-engined Mustang fighters. The Luftwaffe, compelled to give battle in defence of the Reich, was rapidly gutted of combat effectiveness by the Mustangs – above all, through attrition of irreplaceable highly trained and experienced pilots. By April 1944 the Luftwaffe in France had been reduced to a wasted invalid. Thus mastery of the air over the Channel had been won in the skies of Germany – although not by means of the heavy bomber itself wrecking German aircraft production, but instead its fighter escort killing German pilots.[16] This was why Ramsay's ON11 was able to contrast the 5,886 Allied bombers and fighters to be operational on D-Day (3,612 American and 2,274 British) with an estimated Luftwaffe strength in the West of 1,515 aircraft, of which only some 590 were likely to be available for close support against the 'Neptune' forces.

Nevertheless the early months of planning for 'Neptune'/'Overlord' also saw another 'battle of the air', rather like that in 1942 over VLR aircraft for the Battle of the Atlantic. Eisenhower and his air commanders (Air Chief-Marshal Sir Arthur Tedder, his deputy, and Air Marshal Sir Trafford Leigh-Mallory, the C-in-C, Allied Expeditionary Air Force) wanted both Bomber Command and the 8th Air Force to be placed under SCAEF direction for an offensive to smash the French transportation network, so that German reserve divisions moving to the invasion front would be slowed up by a morass of wrecked railways, destroyed bridges and cratered road junctions. It eventually took a decision by the American and British governments in March to overcome the stubborn reluctance of the bomber chieftains, Harris and General Carl Spaatz (C-in-C, 8th Air Force) to give up their attacks on Germany in favour of the so-called 'Transportation Plan', and at the same time yield control of their commands to Eisenhower.[17] Henceforward Bomber Command in particular was vigorously to devote itself to French marshalling yards and similar targets, with an effect similar to hobnailed boots trampling over a child's toy railway. The accuracy and destructiveness of these attacks made their own ironic comment on Harris's inveterate belief that his aircraft could not and should not attack targets smaller than cities. The Allied tactical air forces – under Leigh-Mallory's command – also joined in the 'Transportation Plan', striking at road and rail traffic on the move.

Although the ultimate success of 'Neptune'/'Overlord', especially in the key matter of the relative rates of Allied and German military build-up in Normandy after D-Day, depended so much on this sustained air offensive deep into France, the air forces would also directly serve the Allied navies and armies on D-Day itself: the heavy bombers as part of the combined bombardment plan (ON8; see above, p. 786), and the tactical air forces as air cover. Leigh-Mallory was to deploy five squadrons of day fighters over the cross-Channel 'Neptune' routes and another ten (half at a time) over the beaches. According to ON12 ('Air Defence') three Fighter Direction Centres installed in converted landing ships (tank) would direct the fighters against incoming enemy air strikes. If these FDCs were knocked out, their role would be taken over by four appropriately equipped warships.

In this refined system of fast-reacting cooperation between the Navy and the Air Force and the similar system now perfected between Army and Air Force lies another irony. Had not the British air staff before the war and during its opening years viewed the very idea of a 'tactical air force' taking part in the Navy's or the Army's battles as heresy? It had taken much pressure from the Army and the Royal Navy, as well as the bitter lessons taught by the Luftwaffe in 1940–42 gradually to break down the Air Staff's doctrinal insistence on the 'independence' and 'unity' of airpower, although in the field – especially in North Africa – the Royal Air Force itself had contributed greatly to the development of the advanced technical and command systems for air/sea and air/land cooperation that were to be deployed on D-Day. In this process Air Chief-Marshal Sir Arthur Tedder's own enlightened advocacy since his time as AOC-in-C, Middle East, had been of crucial importance (the very title 'tactical air force' was his invention).

Coastal Command had of course always provided an exception to the Air Staff's cult of 'independent airpower', although even here it had taken some two years to overcome mutual suspicions and differences of operational opinion between it and the Royal Navy. But by 1944 they had matured the closest of professional partnerships. It helped that Admiral Ramsay personally got on well with present Air Officer Commanding-in-Chief, Air Marshal Sir Sholto Douglas. There was no question that Coastal Command would full-heartedly serve the Allied navies during 'Neptune'. It was to concentrate its effort, as ON11 explained, in the south-western approaches in order to put the 'cork in the bottle' and thereby prevent the U-boats passing through from Biscay to attack the 'Neptune' convoys. The Command hoped to maintain a 30-minute 'density' of cover in order either to catch U-boats on the surface or force them to remain submerged and so exhaust their batteries. Under the direction of Coastal Command the Fleet Air Arm would fly cover in the western and eastern exits of the Channel against U-boat or E-boat incursions. The Fleet Air Arm and Coastal Command would jointly fly night and dawn/dusk sweeps with Albacores, Swordfish and Beaufighters against enemy shipping and warships.

Also included in ON11 was a summary of Allied plans for airborne landings – the British 6th Airborne Division east of the River Orne on the night before D-Day in order to secure the Allies' eastern flank; the United States 82nd and 101st Airborne Divisions behind the German defenders at the base of the Cotentin Peninsula.

These briefings on the air and air-defence plans concluded ON's coverage of the opening phase of 'Neptune' – its mounting and launching. Next, in ON13, began the orders for the build-up phase which Ramsay had characterised in his earlier Naval Plan as 'of unique and major importance',[18] for the armies' ability to retain and expand their lodgement in Normandy depended entirely on the rate at which the navies could bring in stores, fuel, ammunition, weapons, transport and reserve formations. In the first few days especially very large numbers of convoys would have to rotate between England and France according to exact scheduling and routing – all under the operational direction of the ANCXF.

At the English end, responsibility for loading and despatching ships would lie with the Cs-in-C, naval area commands. To assist them, combined service handling agencies were to be set up: at Portsmouth a 'Build-up Control Organisation' (BUCO) to adjust the movements of ships and craft of all types and their military loads as needed; in the Nore, Portsmouth and Plymouth commands 'Turn Round Controls' (TURCOs) to speed the reloading and return of vessels to Normandy, using designated ports from the Thames to the Bristol Channel. Each convoy was code-lettered by country and place of departure, nature of cargo and its number in order of sailing; for example, 'ETM1' stood for 'England, Thames, Motor Transport Convoy No. 1'. On D + 1 and D + 2 because of the density of traffic the convoys were to traverse the Channel strictly according to the routes and times laid down in ON13. All Ramsay's orders for the loading, sailing and unloading of different kinds of vessel during the first few days reiterated the urgent need for 'sustained movement'.

Later, when the swept channels had been widened, ships were to be despatched as soon as they were ready and make the best speed on passage possible. No fewer than eight build-up convoys a day would then continue to run. Their reception off the Normandy coast, and despatch when empty back to England, were to be controlled by two officers stationed to seaward of each task force area, 'Captain, Southbound Sailings' and 'Captain, Northbound Sailings'. The unloading itself would be in the hands of a Senior Officer, Ferry Craft (SOFC) on each beach, working with the Principal Beach Master and Beach Group Commander.[19] In this build-up stage there would also be installed a complete salvage organisation ashore under the Chief Salvage Officer (Commander T. McKenzie, RNVR, seconded from Metal Industries Ltd) on ANCXF's staff. To help keep flowing the movement of vessels Ramsay's orders set up two other agencies: 'Control Organisation for Repair' (COREP) and a Tug Organisation (COTUG). The latter was particularly important because the ANCXF was anxious lest there should not be enough tugs to meet 'Neptune's' colossal need for them.

And then in ON14 came instructions for organising on D-Day and afterwards the traffic of an astonishing regatta of ancillary vessels: depot and repair ships; salvage and wreck disposal vessels; explosives carriers; rescue tugs; colliers, oilers and water tankers; telephone cable-laying vessels; despatch boats; ammunition barges; American naval pontoons to create sunken causeways; smoke-projector trawlers; ships for evacuation of casualties; air/sea rescue craft; a swarm of Royal Army Service Corps and Royal Engineers small craft; anti-aircraft ships for defence of the Mulberry harbours; mooring vessels for the components of the Mulberries.

Indeed, the transport and installation of the Mulberries – some 400 units totalling 1½ million tons – presented a colossal undertaking in itself. It merited an entire part (ON16) of 'Operation Neptune – Naval Orders'. When Ramsay had first seen 'Phoenix' concrete caissons, each 400 feet long and 2,000 to 6,000 tons displacement, at the beginning of February, he found them 'even more formidable and abortion-like than I anticipated. They will be the devil to tow into position & get round the coast.'[20] According to ON16, the process would demand 35 heavy tows daily for more than a fortnight, and a total of 158 tugs and 10,000 men. To take complete charge of this 'devil' of a task, Rear-Admiral W. G. Tennant (who as a Captain, RN, had been in command of the Dunkirk beaches in 1940) had been appointed to Ramsay's staff in January 1944.[21]

Tennant immediately doubted whether the Phoenix breakwaters could withstand even a moderate gale. Moreover, since it would be nearly three weeks before all had been towed over and put in place, he thought that in any case some other kind of shelter must be immediately provided for small craft off the beaches. He therefore proposed that obsolete ships should be sunk stem to stern as break-waters. The Prime Minister approved; 55 old merchant ships and four redundant warships were to be prepared as blockships (codename: 'Corncobs') to be scuttled to form five shelters (one in each of the five assault areas, including the two Mulberries) codenamed 'Gooseberries'.

ON16 emphasised that the Mulberry, 'an artificial harbour erected primarily for the landing of stores off the enemy beaches', was essential to the success of 'Neptune'; and laid down that Mulberry 'A' (American) at St Laurent and 'B' (British) at Arromanches were to be completed by D + 18. The breakwaters were to enclose a harbour two miles long by one mile wide; as big as Dover. The outermost breakwaters were to consist of 25 of the 200-feet-long steel 'Bombar-dons' moored end to end in ten fathoms, giving shelter to eight big ships of up to 25 feet draught. Next were to come 30 to 40 coasters at anchor; nearest the shore (but first to be installed) and sunk in up to two and a half fathoms would be the 'Gooseberries' (each made up of twelve 'Corncobs'), as shelters for landing craft. The 'Gooseberries' were to be all sunk in place by D + 3.

Within this triple shelter each Mulberry would be equipped with a large floating pierhead on the 'spud' system for stores coasters drawing up to seventeen feet, and other pierheads for unloading motor trans-port from landing ships (tank) and landing craft (tank). The pierheads were to be linked to the shore by floating piers (some seven miles of them in all). The combined system of floating pierheads and piers was codenamed 'Whales'. In the British Mulberry, stated ON16, the Royal Navy would be responsible for putting the breakwaters in place and the Army the 'Whales' (though these were to be delivered to the Army by the Navy). In the American Mulberry, the United States Navy would carry sole executive responsibility for the entire undertaking, although with the assistance of the United States Army.

The assembling of all these cumbersome novelties in British ports and their movement across the Channel supplied yet another of the brain-heating puzzles solved by ANCXF's staff. The 'Gooseberry' blockships were to assemble in Scottish ports and proceed to Nor-mandy under their own steam (except for one old French cruiser on tow); the 'Phoenix' caissons were to be assembled in Selsey, Dunge-ness and the Thames (with a final 'park' established off Selsey); the 'Bombardons' at Portland; and the 158 British and American tugs between the Thames and Portland. Towage of Mulberry units – at about three knots – was to begin in the forenoon of D-Day, using a reserved channel down 'The Spout' and through the main German mine barrier; it would continue according to a strict timetable of sailings over the following seventeen days. Survey units would mark the positions of the Mulberry components with buoys before mooring units under the direction of officers, dubbed 'Planters', put the components in place as ordered by control officers located in five HQ ships. ON16 remarked that 'Good seamanship and teamwork' would be essential; a classic of naval understatement.

Once in place the Mulberries were for administrative purposes to constitute 'ports operated by a N.O.I.C. [Naval Officer In Charge]' under the appropriate task force commander. Their daily handling capacities would amount to 5,600 tons and 1,400 vehicles in the American Mulberry and 6,000 tons and 1,250 vehicles in the British. They would have their own anti-aircraft defences mounted on the Phoenixes and Gooseberries in addition to anti-aircraft ships. Barrage balloons would be flown at 1,000 feet. All that was missing in ON16's instructions in order to make each Mulberry the complete port at war was a prefabricated dockside pub.

In striking contrast ON18 (for ON17, swept channels, see above, p. 784) simply provided compendious navigational and meteorological information – another necessary key to 'Neptune's' success. It listed the charts to be issued to ships, and stated that all landing-craft skippers were to receive a shoreline sketch prepared by the United States Navy and a 'Small Ship Folio' of useful information. ON18 also provided comprehensive astronomical data all tabulated for the period 1 June to 4 July 1944, including moonrise, moonset, sunrise and sunset on 5 and 6 June. An appendix on tidal data covered the times and heights of high and low water along the assault beaches (including Arromanches on 5 and 6 June) and also the tidal streams, although it warned that the latter were based on French predictions and might prove inaccurate. ON18 further provided a brief on the 'Neptune' meteorological organisation, with offices at the head-quarters of ANCXF in England, the Flag Officer, British Assault Area, and in certain French ports after capture. The ANCXF, it noted, would issue special weather forecasts daily.

Next, in ON19, were laid down how naval command responsibilities for the assault areas were to evolve as the Allied armies consolidated their lodgement. In the British assault area the Naval Commander, Eastern Task Force himself (Vian) was to exercise direct operational command during the initial phase, assisted by a Rear-Admiral, Administration (Rear-Admiral J. W. Rivett-Carnac). Once the lodge-ment was secure and naval headquarters and communications nets had been set up ashore, NCETF would hand over command to a Flag Officer, British Assault Area (FOBAA: Rivett-Carnac in a new role). Each British landing area, Sword, Juno and Gold, was to be self-contained under its Naval Officer In Charge (NOIC) with regard to beach and repair organisations, salvage and fire-fighting. A depot ship organisation under a Commander, Depot Ship, based in the Mulberry harbour, was to be set up to look after such needs as accommodation for the crews of ferry craft.

In the American assault area, and in accordance with United States Navy procedures, operational command in the initial phase would lie with the Commanders, Omaha and Utah beaches (under the authority of the Naval Commander, Western Task Force: Kirk). The Commander of Force O would also be responsible for Mulberry 'A'. Once the United States Army was solidly established ashore, the NCWTF would withdraw one landing area commander, leaving the other in overall control. In the third phase the second commander too would be withdrawn and naval responsibilities in the American area would be devolved to a Commander Service Force.

ON19 also dealt in detail with procedures for opening captured ports; in the first instance, the nine small fishing or yachting harbours along the immediate invasion coast. But ON19 also looked ahead to the capture of Cherbourg and even further afield to those other major ports from St Nazaire to Dieppe which would fall into Allied hands after the eventual breakout of the armies from the Normandy lodgement. It specified the sequence of operations to be followed in clearing a port, from the first arrival of a Navy/Army reconnaissance party to the work of the main port party (there were to be four of them, all Royal Navy), and of specialist units such as would be needed to deal with underwater explosive devices or undertake salvage work – not forgetting a hydrographical party for sounding and marking channels and obstructions.

In ON20 were listed no fewer than seventeen 'Mickey Mouse' diagrams plotting the intricate web of all movements of the Neptune Armada from H − 24 hours to D + 3.

'Force Pluto,' began ON21, 'consists of ships and craft which, in cooperation with the Army and the Ministry of Fuel and Power, provides means of supplying petrol to the Army on the far shore.' Having described the HAIS and HAMEL systems (see above, pp. 761–2), it instructed that ten such cross-Channel pipelines were to be laid from Sandown Bay to Querqueville near Cherbourg: the first on D + 20 and the tenth on D + 75, so giving a maximum throughput of 2,500 tons of fuel per day. With regard to 'Tombola' and 'Amethea' (the pipelines between buoyed connections for tankers to seaward and storage tanks on shore), four discharge points were to be operating off Port en Bessin by D + 18. Each line would be capable of discharging 150 tons of fuel per hour. The entire 'Pluto' operation was to be carried out under the direction of the SNO (Senior Naval Officer), Pluto, Captain J. F. Hutchings, RN, in the corvette *Campanula*. The 'Pluto' craft and equipment were to assemble at Southampton (the Pluto depot), Milford Haven, London River and Exmouth.

'Operation Neptune – Naval Orders' concluded its encyclopaedic coverage with a glossary in ON22 of all the terms and acronyms employed: five pages of initials standing for different types of ships and craft both British and American; six pages of terms and definitions; three and a half pages of British abbreviations and their American equivalents.

ON thus added up to a formidable package for its recipients to digest, especially when ONAD and ONCO were included as well. However, only a limited number of 'Need-to-know' officers were authorised to open the orders immediately on receipt. The problems would arise when all the remaining thousands of officers would open them before D-Day upon being ordered to do so. In May the Commander-in-Chief, Home Fleet, Admiral Sir Bruce Fraser, was to signal Ramsay with suggestions 'to avoid consternation and possible outcry from ships when these and other orders are opened by them . . .'[22] Ramsay himself confessed afterwards that he had been 'gravely concerned at the problems likely to arise in smaller vessels when, shortly before D-day, not only my orders but in addition the orders of the Task Force and lower commanders would be opened'.[23] In the event, oral briefings were arranged for all subordinate commanders before they began to read their orders, and they were advised only to study the sections of ON relating to their own tasks.

Had Ramsay preplanned 'Neptune' from the top in too great a detail? Certainly Kirk and his fellow American admirals believed so on the basis of US Navy practice and experience in the Pacific, although it must be said that landings on Pacific islands were weekend boating trips in comparison with 'Neptune's' scale and complication. In retrospect Ramsay himself had no doubts, writing in his official report:

The very considerable detail to which A.N.C.X.F.'s operation orders descended . . . was foreign to the practice of the U.S. Navy, where the orders of the higher levels of command are largely confined to the definition of tasks and the issuing of directives. Despite their frank criticisms, before and after the operation, it is still believed that the large size of the operation orders was unavoidable . . . The attack had to be made on a narrow front and the ports and anchorages in the Isle of Wight area were jointly used by the British and the U.S. Coordination could only therefore be achieved on the highest command level.[24]

'Neptune', like its smaller precursors 'Torch' and 'Husky', had no precedent as an exercise in seapower. From the decisive battles of the sailing era to the Royal Navy's fights with the Italian Fleet and the German heavy ships in the present war or the United States Navy's victory over the Japanese Combined Fleet at Midway in 1942, the outcome of a great naval encounter had always been determined at the time by the weather, by luck and by the orders of the opposing admirals. In 'Neptune', by contrast, the commanding admiral's orders written two months beforehand provide a detailed history of the operation as it actually took place. 'Operation Neptune – Naval Orders' constitute a painstaking and brilliantly successful exercise in operational predetermination; and it is this that lends all 22 parts of 'ON' their outstanding interest and importance.

Yet their completion and issue did not conclude the labours of the ANCXF and his staff or assuage his own anxieties. Key questions had still to be settled, such as the final choice of D-Day and H-Hour. Fresh problems continued to rear ahead like uncharted rocks. Personal relationships grew frayed with strain. The pace of preparation relentlessly quickened.

For all their comprehensive forethought, Ramsay's orders depended for successful fulfilment on the combined training of the soldiers and sailors of the 'Neptune' assault forces. Ramsay and Vian were agreed that five to six months offered the ideal time for an assault force to work up to maximum efficiency, but the reality did not always match the ideal. In the Eastern Task Force, Force S ('Sword' beach) had been based on Inverness in Scotland, since October 1943, but for three months had lacked slipways or docks for underwater repairs. Although it began work with the 3rd (British) Infantry Division in December, it could not carry out assault and live firing exercises until March because of restrictions on its training area. In April it moved with its division to the Portsmouth area.

Force G ('Gold' beach) was not formed until March 1944, being a result of the decision to widen the front of the D-Day assault from three divisions to five. It trained with the 50th (British) Infantry Division in the Portland–Poole area until the end of April when it was transferred to the Southampton–Solent area. Its headquarters ship, HMS *Bulolo*, did not return from the Anzio operation until mid-April and, because extra communications equipment had to be installed, she was not available for training until the final 'dress rehearsal' in the first week of May.[25]

Force J ('Juno' beach), however, had been training and exercising with the 3rd Canadian Division in the Isle of Wight since it had returned from the Mediterranean in September 1943. Of the American assault forces, Force U ('Utah' beach) was another belated creation as a result of the widening of the front, and so did not start training until March; even in mid-April it still lacked some of its units.[26]

Therefore although all five Allied assault forces were now training rigorously by day and by night, in good weather and foul, Ramsay was by no means always heartened by what he saw on his visits to exercises. On 27 April he and Montgomery watched the first day of 'Exercise Tiger', the final rehearsal by Admiral Moon's Force U at Slapton Sands in Devon. Because of a signals muddle over postponing the start only two companies of infantry landed after the warships had carried out their bombardment. The exercise, wrote Ramsay in his diary, was 'a flop' with 'much to criticise', especially 'the lack of senior naval officers on the beach to take charge and supervise'.[27] But after the flop came outright tragedy, for at 0020 next morning eight landing craft (tank) and two pontoons of Force U escorted by the corvette HMS *Azalea* were jumped fifteen miles off Portland Bill by a swarm of E-boats, who sank two of the LCTs and damaged a third in an encounter of utter confusion and blind firing into the night. The American casualties amounted to 638 killed (many of them much-needed engineers) and 89 wounded.[28] Here was a cruel reminder that the enemy too would have his part to play in 'Neptune'; a reminder also of the price that would be paid on D-Day for error or misfortune.

On 29 April Ramsay moved to his operational headquarters in Southwick House, a mansion seven miles north of Portsmouth. Eisenhower's command post and Montgomery's Tactical Headquarters had been installed in a sprawl of caravans and huts in the park. In the first week of May the final rehearsals of the rest of the assault forces ('Exercise Fabius') took place. Ramsay observed Forces S, G and J go ashore, and this time was 'very favourably impressed by all that I saw . . .'[29]

But he was far less impressed with the situation prevailing over the components of the Mulberries. By 1 May it had become plain that production was falling behind schedule. Nor was this all. Transport of the 'Phoenix' concrete caissons was presenting special problems.

When in mid-April a 'Phoenix' had been accidentally stranded on a sand bank, it had taken a salvage vessel a week to refloat it, so boding ill for cross-Channel towage to Normandy. There was a more general problem. After construction the 'Phoenixes' were filled with sea water and sunk in order to save berthing space. When they needed to be moved they therefore had to be pumped out in order to regain buoyancy. Regrettably the pumping gear supplied by the War Office (responsible for production of the 'Phoenixes') proved 'totally ineffective'.[30] In order to pump them out even the London Fire Brigade's Thames fire-fighting tenders had to be mobilised. In any case, as Ramsay sourly noted in his report later, the 'Phoenixes' and also the 'Whales' (another War Office production responsibility) were 'in no state to be towed, nor was towing gear provided. All the riggers in Chatham Dockyard were put on to this at high pressure to make good the deficiency. This shows how essential it is for the Admiralty to be concerned at the outset of any seagoing project.'[31]

This still left unsolved the other basic headache with the Mulberries – the shortage of tugs to tow the components to Normandy. As late as 31 May only 48 out of 72 large tugs (allocated to 'Whales' and 'Phoenixes') and four out of 44 small tugs had become available. Ramsay therefore gave the Mulberries overriding priority for tugs and appointed Captain E. J. Moran, USNR, as 'Tug Controller' of the total 'Neptune' pool of 200 tugs.[32]

All this time the picture presented by Allied Intelligence sources of the German beach and coastal defences and the enemy's deployment of sea and land forces kept altering, with consequent need to adjust 'Neptune' plans. It was especially important to establish the exact location and nature of the latest beach and underwater obstacles (as uncovered at low tide) in order to select the best phase of tide for clearing them – which in turn would determine H-Hour, about which many were the anguished discussions. Then, at the end of April, a new technique of low-level oblique-angle photo-reconnaissance with a moving camera enabled American Mustangs to bring back pictures which told Ramsay and his colleagues exactly what they needed to know.[33]

On 1–2 May he, Eisenhower, Tedder, Montgomery and Leigh-Mallory met at 'Widewings' (codename for Eisenhower's residence in Bushey Park, West London) finally to 'settle the relationship between H-hour and obstacles', with the result, as Ramsay noted in his diary, 'that my revised dates and timing were accepted . . .'[34] The obstacles were to be dealt with 'dry shod', that is, in less than two feet of water, which fixed H-Hour as three hours before high water on any given beach. D-Day was provisionally fixed for 5 June, that and the 6th being the earliest acceptable dates from the naval point of view in terms of phases of the moon, although, as Ramsay told his colleagues, the 7th would serve in case of extreme necessity.

On 9 May Ramsay formally notified Eisenhower that the naval plan would be 'frozen' at 0900 on the 12th.[35] By now the pace of work and the approach of D-Day were beginning to tell on the 61-year-old ANCXF, his staff and his fellow commanders. After one meeting Ramsay recorded that Vian and Hall had been 'sticky', and Vian in particular 'most irritating', his attitude 'one of criticism'.[36] Ramsay confided to his wife on 11 May:

> There are so many pitfalls and in an allied operation there are bound to be jealousies. Kirk is being troublesome & stupid & pompous & though I've been very patient with him & with all the Americans, most of whom are excellent in every way, one can never be certain things will continue to go well when people's nerves are strung up.[37]

In the last week of the month Ramsay's Chief of Staff, Creasy, finally went sick with his bad back:

> . At this hour it is not a good situation. Luckily most people are standing up pretty well . . . I have my better & less good days . . . I suppose that it is only to be expected when one is head of a big concern that when everything goes wrong or when they have moans, people must put it on my shoulders. One ought to be a hard, ruthless callous character I'm sure, as it would be so much easier to deal ruthlessly with people . . .[38]

On 30 May Admiral Vian, CETF, went down with quinsy, putting his fitness to command on D-Day in doubt.

Fortunately the First Sea Lord's country home was at Bishop's Waltham, not far from Southwick House, and Ramsay visited him whenever he could, to find like others before him that morally 'A.B.C.' was worth a battle-squadron. He wrote to his wife after dining one night with Cunningham: 'He was in good form & nothing seems to concern him which is a wonderful attitude!'[39]

On 25 May all holders of 'Operation Neptune – Naval Orders' were ordered to open them. Three days later D-Day was notified to them as 5 June, along with the H-Hour relating to their particular beach.[40] Although thousands of Allied officers now shared these tremendous secrets, no leak occurred, while so complete was the Allied air forces' domination over the Luftwaffe that the enemy could glean little information by air reconnaissance about the colossal concourse of naval and military power gathering along the southern coasts of England. Every suitable stretch of water was now crammed with shipping and craft. How crammed is recounted by C-in-C, Portsmouth, in his report:

> It is a commonplace expression to say that an anchorage is 'full of ships', but in the case of the East and West Solent, with an available area of approximately 22 square miles in which to anchor ships, it was literally true. On 18 May, the Admiralty offered the C-in-C Portsmouth the services of H.M.S. *Tyne* [10,850 tons displacement; destroyer depot ship], but it was only possible to accept her because H.M.S. *Warspite* was not being sent to Portsmouth till D-Day, which gave us one berth in hand.[41]

Inland from these anchorages and harbours now boarded over with vessels were concentrated 37 Allied divisions, ten of them armoured,[42] filling up the countryside so that Southern England could truly be described as one vast encampment; the Expeditionary Force's thousands upon thousands of vehicles, tanks and guns ranged *en masse* along roads turned into parking lots. A Cabinet Committee chaired by the Prime Minister made sure that everything the Supreme Allied Commander asked of British society would be granted.[43] In these last days of May 1944 a muscle of gigantic power, years in development, was tautening in a final contraction before it struck its blow.

For the Royal Navy and the British Merchant Marine, 'Operation Neptune' marked the consummation and reward of all their endeavour since 1939. The invasion armies' supplies would be carried to the pierheads of the Mulberry harbours by the coasters which, during four and a half previous years of war, had plied in convoy between the harbours of Britain, an essential part of the United Kingdom's overloaded transport system. These humble ships, escorted by the Royal Navy's oldest destroyers and by armed trawlers, had constantly braved the marauding Junkers or Heinkel bombers and more recently U-boats redeployed from the Atlantic. The minesweepers which, crewed by 'Hostilities Only' officers and men or by fishermen, month in, month out, in all weathers had kept British coastal waters clear of the magnetic mines scattered by German aircraft – they too would have their valuable role in 'Neptune'. The small craft of the Royal Navy's Coastal Forces – motor torpedo boats and motor gunboats also often manned by the RNVR – which had helped to protect coastal convoys, had skirmished with enemy E-boats, and attacked enemy shipping in the Channel and North Sea – would be laying mines and covering the invasion armada against German light forces.

Then again, it was thanks to the destruction of the *Graf Spee*, the *Bismarck* and the *Scharnhorst* by the Royal Navy's battleships and cruisers, and the Fleet Air Arm's crippling of the *Tirpitz*, that the enemy no longer possessed a surface fleet capable of posing a serious threat on D-Day. But, most of all, 'Operation Neptune' represented the ultimate reward for the hard-won victory by the Royal Navy, by Royal Air Force Coastal Command and by their Canadian and American sister services over the U-boat in the Atlantic in May 1943. This victory alone had enabled Britain herself to survive and thereafter serve as the Anglo-American base for the invasion; it alone had made it possible to transport by sea to that base an American expeditionary force of twenty divisions.

In the event the victory in the Atlantic had proved final even though Dönitz and the Admiralty alike had expected the U-boat offensive to resume in the autumn of 1943 with renewed ferocity. Dönitz had pinned his hopes on new technology – the acoustic torpedo (thwarted in the event by a towed decoy), a radar detector called 'Hagenuk' (it failed of its purpose), a radar decoy called 'Aphrodite' (no more successful), and the fitting of U-boats with armour and quadruple 20mm flak guns against air attack.[44] But in September and October 1943 his fresh offensive had been smashed by close cooperation between surface escorts, Very Long Range aircraft and the aircraft of the escort carriers. In October alone Dönitz lost 23 U-boats in the North Atlantic.[45] Even top-loading his Type VIIC boats with so much armour and anti-aircraft armament that they rolled 30° continuously in rough weather availed him nothing; nor did the laying of radar decoys ('Thetis') at 25-mile intervals across the Bay of Biscay. In January 1944 he lost nine U-boats in the Atlantic; in February he lost twelve, and in March another twelve.[46] Six of those lost in January and February were sunk by Captain F. J. Walker, RN, most renowned of all escort group commanders, whose total wartime bag came to twenty U-boats thanks to a personal technique of the 'creeping attack'. He once remorselessly hunted a victim for 38 hours.[47]

For 1944–45 Dönitz had cherished hopes of a new technological generation of U-boats, no longer 'submersibles' but true underwater vessels – the 1,600-ton Type XXI and the 850-ton Type XXIII with streamlined hulls and very powerful electric motors driven by a new kind of battery which together gave them underwater speeds of 18 knots for one and a half hours or some 12 knots for as long as ten hours. Also under development was a similarly streamlined boat designed by Dr Walter, powered by a hydrogen peroxide-fuelled turbine which could attain the astounding underwater speed of 25 knots.[48] These were performances which would destroy the whole basis of current Allied anti-submarine deployments and hunting tactics. The standard Type VIIC U-boats as well as the new designs were being fitted with the 'Schnorchel', a vertical pipe containing air inlet and exhaust outlet so that they could use their diesels under water and so avoid surfacing to recharge their batteries.[49]

Yet to bring the Type XXIs and XXIIIs, to say nothing of the Walter boats, into series production took time. All the complex working drawings for construction were ready by mid-November 1943. A month later a wooden mock-up of a Type XXI had been built. In spring 1944 the first four experimental boats were commissioned for trials; and on 26 May contracts were placed for 100 of the 850-ton Type XIIIs for delivery in 1945.[50] As for Schnorchel-equipped standard Type VIIC U-boats, only nine were based on Biscay ports by D-Day,[51] even though the original Dutch invention dated back to 1927. It was only after his defeat of May 1943 in the Battle of the Atlantic that Dönitz woke up to the Schnorchel's possibilities, and only in July that he won Hitler's sanction for its mass production – a year, two years, too late, especially under the flail of Allied bombing even if that were more disruptive than devastating.[52]

By the time 'Neptune' preparations were getting under way at the beginning of 1944 Dönitz had finally come to abandon all thoughts of retrieving the lost Battle of the Atlantic that year: 'All we could now hope to do was to fight a delaying action . . . and continue to tie down forces of the enemy.'[53] So it was that in the months before D-Day the Allies were able to run convoys between North America and Britain comprising as many as 100 ships each, which allowed the Royal Navy to strip escort groups and escort carriers from the Atlantic for the protection of the western flank of 'Neptune'. Here was a final dividend from the victory in 1943 over Dönitz's wolf packs; another aspect of 'Operation Neptune' as the crown and climax of previous endeavour.

From 20 May onwards Allied Intelligence formulated its final updates of German strength and deployment by land, sea and air opposite 'Neptune'. On 25 May the Joint Intelligence Committee (employing Operational Intelligence Centre figures) guesstimated that by D-Day there could be 70 of the Type VIIC U-boats based on Biscay ports, and perhaps ten or more from the Atlantic in the western and central English Channel; that by D + 2 the number in the Channel might climb to 45, and by D + 5 to 60.[54] Uncertainty remained about German intentions for these U-boats. How far would they be launched against the 'Neptune' armada on D-Day and how far against the follow-up convoys? No chances could be taken: the Admiralty redeployed its anti-submarine forces in order to strengthen the protection of 'Neptune's' western flank, and Coastal Command did likewise, thanks to the willing cooperation of the AOC-in-C, Air Marshal Sir Sholto Douglas:[55]

> Coastal Command [wrote Ramsay in his later report] threw themselves into the preparations for 'Neptune' with as much enthusiasm as any unit in the Allied Expedition, and I personally and the whole Naval Expeditionary Force are deeply indebted to them for the efficiency of the measures they adopted which was reflected by the very small scale of U-boat attack which eventuated.[56]

On 31 May the OIC was able to define the exact limits of the mine-free water in the Bay of the Seine and near Le Havre where the 'Neptune' bombardment and assault forces were to deploy. An Ultra decrypt of a signal in the 'Offizier' Enigma key had enabled Allied aircraft and MTBs to intercept and cut up a German minelaying force on 23 May to the north of the previously supposed southern limit of the main mine barrier, inflicting such losses as to put an end to any further minelaying. The interception in itself thus served to amend the British estimate of the barrier's extent. But it was the frenzy of 'PP' signals after the encounter specifying safe courses home for the surviving German vessels which yielded to Allied cryptographers the precise limits of mine-free waters.[57] At the same period other decrypts, together with photo-reconnaissance pictures, enabled the OIC to assure ANCXF and his staff that there was no evidence that ground-mines had been laid inshore of the main mine barrier.[58]

With regard to the Luftwaffe, the final OIC appreciation of 25 May put its total first-line strength against 'Neptune' on D-Day at 900 aircraft, with reinforcements of 530 arriving by D + 4;[59] a shrunken total indeed compared with the January estimates of a total strength of 2,530 and 1,750 D-Day sorties; a measure of the crushing victory won over Germany by the 8th Air Force's Mustangs (see above, p. 789). The OIC reckoned that the Luftwaffe's sorties against 'Neptune' from dawn on D-Day to D + 1 could amount to 1,150 to 1,250, but that 'in view of the low morale and operational efficiency of the G.A.F. [German Air Force]' such a scale of effort might not be reached in the face of Allied mastery of the air.[60]

The German Army in the West was, however, another matter – and it was the German Army whose defence of the coastline and whose panzer counter-strokes presented the greatest danger to the success of 'Neptune', especially in the precarious first few days after the Allied land forces had been put ashore. Monitoring of the movement and deployment of German divisions in France by Sigint and by secret agents worryingly showed that powerful formations were beginning to gather on the flanks of the intended Allied lodgement. By 22 May the Joint Intelligence Committee was even wondering whether the enemy had guessed that the Le Havre–Cherbourg area would be 'a likely, and perhaps the main point of assault'.[61] The 21st Panzer Division was somewhere near Caen, a key objective of the British 2nd Army, though unfortunately its exact whereabouts were unknown, while an Ultra decrypt revealed that the Germans were reinforcing the Cotentin Peninsula, in the American assault area.[62]

On 26 May – ten days to go to D-Day as then fixed – Ramsay noted in his diary: 'Disturbing features of Overlord have arisen in the strengthening of German Divisions in the Neptune area, particularly opposite the west flank of the Americans. This makes their task very much more difficult & particularly that of their Airborne Divs [sic] & may necessitate a change of plan.'[63] It did – and that meant selecting new dropping and landing zones and flying-in routes over the sea, which led Admiral Moon strenuously to object to troop-carriers flying in the vicinity of his ships[64] for fear of confusion of identity and consequent firing on friendly aircraft. Here were more unwelcome problems needing to be sorted out at the last moment.

In its final appreciation of 25 May the Operational Intelligence Centre put the total strength of the German Army in the West on D-Day at 62 divisions, of which ten would be panzer or panzer-grenadier and fourteen infantry field. In the forenoon of D-Day the Allied assault forces could encounter three coastal defence (static low establishment) divisions and one infantry field division (352nd; exact whereabouts unknown). By last light the whole of 21st Panzer could be engaged, plus elements of 12th SS Panzer. On D + 1, two more panzer divisions could be present. Between D + 17 and D + 25, the period judged most likely for a classic German counter-stroke in depth, no fewer than ten or eleven panzer or panzer-grenadier divisions, thirteen infantry field divisions and eight 'low establishment' divisions could have been concentrated.[65] These were formidable (and as the event proved, closely accurate) numbers. They showed how narrow must be the margin between victory and defeat for the Allied armies – how critical therefore the performance of the navies in landing and building up those armies on D-Day and after.

On 27 May the 'slow ahead' for 'Operation Neptune' was signalled by the imposing of restrictions on air attack on surface ships in the

Channel to the west of a line from the North Foreland to Walcheren Fort near Dunkirk except by Coastal Command. From now onwards the huge 'Neptune' machine would gradually, inexorably, gather way according to plan. On 28 May Allied minelaying operations off enemy bases were completed five days ahead of schedule, the mines accounting eventually for sixteen enemy vessels sunk and 37 damaged.[66] Two days later Ramsay was briefing Vice-Admiral Glennie (the new Vice-Admiral, Destroyers) on his role, should he have to take the place of the quinsy-stricken Vian.[67] Now that the countdown to D-Day had begun, Ramsay himself could record:

> Things are becoming a little more calm & a distinct lull in our activities is noticeable today. I took the occasion to address the Wrens of the Secretariat, amounting to about 60, & thank them for their hard & good work. Only a few days to go & everyone is thankful for that.[68]

On 31 May the Royal Navy laid ten underwater sonic buoys to mark the edge of the enemy mine barrier in the assault approach channels ('Operation Enthrone'). The buoys were laid dead to come alive on D − 1 in order to guide the motor launches which would act as marker boats enabling the minesweepers to start their work from the precisely correct positions. On this day also began the whole colossal operation of loading the assault shipping and concentrating it into assault convoys. All too soon came the first symptoms of Clausewitzian 'friction' in the functioning of a military machine. In Forces S ('Sword' beach) and J ('Juno'), both of them British, loading fell behind schedule because of a shortage of experienced military loading personnel, and in the case of Force J also because it proved difficult to back heavy trailers down the Southampton hards at low states of tide.[69]

On 1 June Ramsay assumed operational command over the 'Neptune' forces and the sea area of the English Channel. One of his first tasks was successfully to persuade the Prime Minister and King George VI that they should not go over to France with the assault forces on D-Day as they wished, because the risk was 'unacceptable'.[70] Churchill's eagerness did him credit, though hardly his commonsense: after all, 'Neptune' constituted the consummation of his war too; and, ever a man for the sound of guns, he itched to be at sea under the White Ensign to witness it.

In the evening of 2 June the first of the bombardment forces steamed out of the Clyde and headed south; and the midget submarines X23 and X20 were towed out of Portsmouth towards the French shore. By now in all the ports and estuaries of southern England, on quayside and on hard, the bustle of loading was reaching a fury of physical effort and mental concentration, of roaring engines and crashing gears, of shouted orders and curses of impatience and irritation. However, as Commodore Oliver (Force J) remarked in his report, 'the knowledge that they were "off at last" acted as a great incentive'.[71] To Ramsay 'who was not feeling at all fit today'[72] it was one relief that Vian was making a good recovery.

The ANCXF spent 3 June watching the loading at Gosport, Portsmouth and Shoreham, only to be dismayed at the blunder committed by the 50th (British) Infantry Division at Gosport, where tank landing craft were

> . . . being much overloaded, resulting in TLCs being too low in the water, with a risk of grounding too far out & thus drowning vehicles on their way out . . . [the Army's] one idea was to cram as many vehicles into ships & craft & as much into each vehicle as possible, without regard to the disastrous results which must ensue.[73]

He therefore made a signal to all 'Neptune' forces ordering that correct draughts must not be exceeded.

In the evening the weather chart was, in Ramsay's laconic word, 'unpromising';[74] unpromising enough indeed to raise the possibility of having to postpone the landings. Yet if Force U ('Utah' beach), sailing from the West Country ports of Dartmouth, Brixham and Salcombe, were to reach its assault area on time on the present D-Day of 5 June, its departure could not be delayed. At 2130 Eisenhower met his commanders-in-chief to consider whether or not to postpone; he decided, so wrote Ramsay later that night in his diary, 'to order the operation to proceed, in *spite* of a bad weather forecast. This was only done because Ike was over impressed with the frightful results of postponement . . .'[75] In fact the possibility of postponement had been written into Ramsay's naval orders, and all the 'Neptune' forces knew what they had to do in such an event. A further meeting was arranged for 0415 next morning, 4 June. In the meantime Force U put to sea according to its existing instructions.

Punctually at 0415 on 4 June, a deceptively calm and lovely morning, the Supreme Commander and his senior subordinates met as arranged to consider the latest weather report, 'which was *bad*,' wrote Ramsay in his diary,

> . . . The low cloud predicted would prohibit use of Airborne Troops, prohibit majority of air action, including air spotting. The sea conditions were unpromising but not prohibitive. I pointed out that we had only

accepted a daylight assault on the understanding that our overwhelming air & naval bombardment would be available to overcome the enemy coast & beach defences. S.A.C. decided therefore to postpone assault for 24 hours. Forces U & O would have started and must be recalled. The weather got progressively worse after midday ... as the day went on and the forecast became more fully justified.[76]

The order to postpone D-Day until 6 June was issued from SHAEF at 0515 – just about the time when the midget submarines X20 (Lieutenant K. R. Hudspeth, RANVR) and X23 (Lieutenant G. B. Honour, RNVR) arrived on station off the Normandy coast, the tiny advanced guard of a vast armada. From ANCXF's headquarters signals were made to the convoys already at sea to put back; and to divert the 'Corncob' blockships for the Mulberry harbours into Poole Bay to await the new departure time.

Unfortunately Group U2A of Force U, consisting of 128 landing craft crammed with American troops and their equipment, four escorts and a rescue tug missed the signal of recall. At 0900 they were 25 miles south of the Isle of Wight and still chugging southwards for Normandy and – as they believed – battle. The C-in-C, Portsmouth, thereupon sent two destroyers at utmost speed to catch them up and turn them back before they were detected by enemy radar. Ordered to shelter in Weymouth Bay and there refuel, Group U2A struggled all day to make to the westward against a Force 5 to 6 west-south-west wind and a nastily short, steep sea on the port bow. It was after midnight on 4–5 June before any of the group's clumsy landing craft came to anchor, and for the chilled, tired and seasick soldiers a voyage that had begun in apprehension of death ended in futility and anti-climax.

At 2100 on 4 June there opened another and perhaps even more fraught commanders' conference chaired by Eisenhower, as a gale of wind rattled the sash windows of the library in Southwick House and rain squalls splattered against the panes.

A postponement of one more day, [wrote Ramsay in his later report], e.g., till 7th June would, in the event, have proved disastrous owing to conditions of sea off the beaches. The problems arising out of postponement of 12 or 14 days to the next suitable period [of moon and tide] are too appalling even to contemplate.[77]

No record was taken of this meeting, and recollections differ as to its outcome. According to Montgomery, a final decision was put off until another meeting at 0400 next morning, in view of the continuing unfavourable weather forecasts.[78] But in fact the meteorologists were predicting that a gap would occur in the windy and overcast weather by the forenoon of Tuesday 6 June.[79] Ramsay himself recorded in his diary after the meeting that 'the weather prophets were more optimistic & we decided to continue the operation as ordered . . .'[80]

So certain was he that the great decision *had* been made, even though he recognised that it meant taking 'a big chance',[81] that he forthwith issued the necessary naval orders,[82] including the final fixing of H-Hours – Sword and Gold beaches 0725; Juno right wing 0735; Juno left wing 0745; Omaha and Utah 0630, by American wish about an hour earlier than the British landings.

At 0415 on the 5th Eisenhower and his commanders conferred yet again. 'This time,' recorded Ramsay, 'the prophets came in smiling, conditions having shown considerable improvement.'[83]

It was therefore decided to let things be & proceed. The wind was still fresh & it is clear that forces will have an uncomfortable initial journey, improving as the day proceeds. Thus has been made the vital and crucial decision to stage & start this great enterprise which will, I hope, be the immediate means of bringing about the downfall of German fighting power & Nazi oppression & an early cessation of hostilities. I am under no delusions as to the risk involved in this most difficult of all operations & the critical period at around H-hour if when initial flights are held up success will be in the balance. We must trust in our invisible assets [a reference to the 'Fortitude' deception plan?] to tip the balance in our favour & to allow the landings to proceed without interruption. We shall require all the help that God can give us & I cannot believe that this will not be forthcoming.

26

'This Great Enterprise':
'Operation Neptune'

At 0900 on 5 June the force commander of Force S, Rear-Admiral
A. G. Talbot, made the flag signal from his flagship HMS *Largs*:
'Good luck: drive on' (he kept it flying until he himself sailed in the
evening); and the first landing craft (tank) put to sea from the Solent
and Spithead.[1] Soon the landing crafts' flat bows were butting into a
short, steep sea, the wind west-south-west Force 5 on the Beaufort
scale: sixteen to twenty nautical miles per hour, causing (according to
the definition) 'large waves to begin to form; the white crests become
more and more extensive'.[2] For the British, American and Canadian
soldiers voyaging to war packed with full kit into these vessels, it was
going to be a day and a night of harsh physical discomfort as well as
mental stress – the heave of seasickness mirroring the heave of
apprehension at the prospect of battle and mutilation or death.

Throughout the day the log-jams of shipping of all descriptions,
fast and slow, in the estuaries and harbours of southern England
gradually broke up and cleared as the 'Neptune' armada sailed in due
sequence according to Ramsay's orders. The coastal waters from
Cornwall to Kent filled with traffic forming into assault and follow-up
convoys and converging from west and east towards 'Position Z', the
concentration area south of the Isle of Wight already dubbed 'Piccadilly Circus'. Some 2,700 vessels (not counting the 1,897 smaller
landing craft carried in the landing ships) were on the move, ranging
from battleships of over 30,000 tons displacement to Thames barges

on tow and making their hazardous début on the open sea. No fewer than 195,000 sailors, navy and merchant marine, more than half of them British, manned this invasion fleet with its cargo of some 130,000 soldiers, 12,000 vehicles, 2,000 tanks and nearly 10,000 tons of stores.[3]

Thanks to ANCXF and his staff's meticulous scheduling and 'Mickey Mouse' diagrams the forward movement of the assault convoys through 'Piccadilly Circus' and southwards down the ten designated channels of 'The Spout' was accomplished without muddle or delay. Admiral Vian, CETF, sailed from Spithead at 1630 in his flagship HMS *Scylla* (5,450 tons displacement, Captain T. M. Brownrigg, RN), and for the next few hours watched the passing of this huge procession into 'The Spout'. In early evening the minesweepers began sweeping the ten two-mile wide approach channels through the German mine barrier, marking the boundaries with Dan buoys as they went. Despite the west-south-west wind and a 2½-knot tidal stream running dead abeam, which compelled some vessels to make as much as 40° allowance in order to keep a true course, the assault forces followed the minesweepers on through the night hours with few errors of navigation.

And still the enemy had not stirred. The only Allied casualties had been the minesweeper USS *Osprey* sunk and the destroyer HMS *Wrestler* and a landing craft damaged by mines, and some 50 smaller craft swamped by the rough seas. That long day of mass movement had passed without attack by German aircraft or U-boat or E-boat. Ramsay, waiting in his headquarters at Southwick House for news, could hardly believe their luck:

> There was an air of unreality [he wrote in his report] during the passage of the assault force across the Channel curiously similar to that on $D - 1$ in 'Husky' as our forces approached Sicily. The achievement of strategical surprise was always hoped for in 'Neptune' but was by no means certain, whereas that of tactical surprise had always seemed extremely unlikely. As our forces approached the French coast without a murmur from the enemy or from their own radio the realisation that once again almost complete tactical surprise had been achieved slowly dawned.[4]

The German command had in fact been blinded – in the first place by the inability of the Luftwaffe to maintain constant or comprehensive surveillance of Allied shipping concentrations and movements during the past weeks, and secondly by lack of accurate forecasts of weather conditions for several days ahead, now that the German weather ships had been swept from the Atlantic. Noting the immediately unfavourable state of wind, sea and cloud in the Channel and Biscay on 4 June but ignorant that an interval of better weather was on its way for the 6th and after, the German Navy's Group West pronounced on the 4th that 'at the present moment a major invasion cannot be assumed imminent'.[5] The C-in-C of Army Group B, responsible for the defence of France between the Seine and the Loire, Field-Marshal Rommel, was himself absent in his home town in Germany for his wife's birthday. Nor did coastal radars pick up the advancing armada, thanks to Bomber Command (again in the tactical role) having knocked out several stations, including the one on Cap Barfleur commanding the western flank of the approaches to the Bay of the Seine; and thanks also to electronic jamming which had blinded the station at Arromanches and others.

That night the German coastal defence divisions (many of the soldiers being non-Germans such as ex-Russian prisoners) and the gunners of the batteries behind the beaches took to their bunks in their deep shelters in customary peace of mind, while those on watch and peering into the darkness to seaward saw as usual nothing but the faint gleam of waves.

At midnight Bomber Command shattered this German tranquillity with the first of the 5,000 tons of bombs that were going to be dropped by 1,056 aircraft during the next five hours on to ten of the most powerful and tactically important German batteries. Soon after midnight the British 6th Airborne Division began to land by glider and parachute east of the River Orne, with the objective (successfully accomplished) of capturing the bridges over the River Orne and the Caen Canal in order to secure the left flank of 'Sword' assault force from counter-attack. At 0130 the American 82nd and 101st Airborne Divisions began to land in the south of the Cotentin Peninsula behind the German defences along Utah beach. Yet it was not until 0300, when some large ships were sighted, dark shapes against the moon-glow, off Port en Bessin, that Group West realised that an Allied invasion, if not *the* Allied invasion, was about to take place, and signalled orders accordingly.

In the meantime the 'Neptune' assault convoys had been following astern of the minesweepers through the German mine barrier, the wind now north-north-westerly: for the sailors a night of tense navigation by the dim lights of the Dan buoys; for the soldiers in closed-up ships or landing craft amid the smells of diesel oil, vomit and the sweat of men afraid, an uneasy night of fitful sleep. On debouching from the southern exits of the swept channels the assault forces spread out to their lowering or bombarding positions along the courses laid

(Top, left) 'Bouncy bonhomie consorted with a high professionalism. . . .' Admiral Sir James Somerville – Flag Officer, Force H, 1940–42; Commander-in-Chief, Eastern Fleet, 1942–44. (Crown) *(Top, right)* 'Harwood lacked the sheer ruthless powers of leadership of his predecessor.' Admiral Sir Henry Harwood, who replaced Cunningham as Commander-in-Chief, Mediterranean Fleet, in May 1942, is pictured

here in 1939 when, as a Commodore, he commanded the three British cruisers which defeated the pocket battleship *Admiral Graf Spee*. (Hulton) *(Below)* 'A man of notoriously dark and difficult nature. . . .' Admiral Sir Philip Vian *(left)*, victor of the second Battle of Sirte, March 1942, Naval Commander, Eastern Task Force, in 'Operation Neptune', June 1944; commanded Pacific Fleet's aircraft carriers, 1945. (Hulton)

(Top, left) 'A belief in careful, elaborate pre-planning so that as little as possible was left to chance.' Admiral Sir Bertram Ramsay. As Vice-Admiral, Dover, he commanded 'Operation Dynamo' (the Dunkirk evacuation) in 1940, and, as Naval Commander Allied Expeditionary Force, planned and carried out 'Operation Neptune', the D-Day landings in Normandy on 6 June 1944, the most complex combined operation ever. (IWM) (Top, right) 'A man of calm and massive presence.' Rear Admiral H. Kent Hewitt, United States Navy, commander of the Western Naval Task Force in 'Operation Torch', 1942; the Western Task Force in 'Operation Husky', Sicily, July 1943, and 'Operation Avalanche' (Salerno) in September 1943. (IWM) (Below) 'Some 2,700 vessels were on the move. . . .' Landing craft on passage down 'The Spout' towards the Normandy beaches, June 1944. (Crown)

(Above) 'The transport and installation of the Mulberries presented a colossal undertaking in itself.' The 'Mulberry' artificial harbour at Arromanches, as large as Dover, showing floating pierhead and pier and, in the foreground, the 'Corncob' breakwater of scuttled old ships. (Crown) *(Below)* '. . . a chaos of wrecked equipment, corpses and wounded. . . .' Omaha Beach, where poor American joint army-navy planning and an ineffective naval bombardment led to an initial repulse on D-Day, 6 June 1944. (Hulton)

(Above) 'The wonderful little DUKWs, manned by Royal Army Service Corps men, wallowed like hippopotami between the coasters and the shore.' DUKW amphibious trucks in the British 'Mulberry' harbour at Arromanches. (Hulton) (Below) '. . . an immeasurably more destructive force than U-boats or E-boats or mines. . . .' The Arromanches 'Mulberry' harbour after the great gale of 19–22 June 1944, showing damage to piers and other components. (Crown)

down in ANCXF's orders. Ahead could be seen the flash of bomb explosions, the glow of fires and the sparkle of German anti-aircraft fire as Bomber Command did its work.

Responsibility for planning the final deployments and the actual assault landings had lain with the commanders of the two naval task forces, their subordinate commanders of Forces U, O, J, G and S, and all their military opposite numbers. In the Western Task Force American procedures were followed; in the Eastern, British. The United States command chose to locate its lowering positions some eleven miles off shore as against some seven to eight miles out for the British, in order that their 'attack transports' (landing ships infantry) might be out of range of German heavy shore batteries. Ramsay regarded this as a needless precaution, given the weight of Allied counter-bombardment available to suppress the enemy guns.[6] The decision meant that the American assault divisions would take some three hours to reach the beaches, against two for the British, so necessitating much earlier lowering and despatch. Moreover, the US command had also elected to make its H-Hour 0630, an hour before the British, so demanding an even earlier start to the run-in. It was therefore shortly after 0230, full darkness, when the Western Task Force began hoisting out landing craft, followed by the Eastern Task Force at 0530, in the growing light of morning.

The amphibious warfare pioneers of the 1920s and 1930s could not have imagined that their paper schemes and few experimental craft would lead to a landing fleet of the size and astonishing variety now massed in the Bay of the Seine. The sea-going vessels comprised six headquarters ships of 7,000 to 8,000 tons, each of them draped with radio aerials; 55 landing ships (infantry) (converted passenger ships) of 3,100 to 14,000 tons; six specialised landing ships (dock) and (repair); 236 landing ships (tank), ugly, utilitarian 4,000 tonners with bow ramps, and carrying up to 60 tanks and 300 soldiers; 248 landing craft (infantry), up to 160 feet long and taking some 200 soldiers, and in some cases converted to serve as tactical headquarters craft off the beaches; and 837 landing craft (tank), carrying up to eleven vehicles and 55 soldiers, plus others adapted for special purposes such as the 29 landing craft (flak) and the 36 landing craft (rocket). And then there were all the small craft carried in the ships and now lowered by davit into the water for the run-in – 502 landing craft (assault), carrying 30 soldiers and their kit, some being equipped to clear beach obstacles; 464 landing craft (mechanised), to supply a ship-to-shore ferry service for armoured vehicles and motor transport; 189 landing craft (personnel) carrying 22 soldiers, but also sometimes converted for special roles, in this case smoke-laying or survey work; 121 landing craft (support), equipped with machine-guns and smoke-projectors; and the invaluable 'Duck' (DUKW), the 2½-ton, six-wheeled amphibious truck carrying 25 fully equipped soldiers, and capable of 6.4 mph in water and up to 50 mph on land.[7]

At 0430 on 6 June 1944 Forces U and O, the first assault forces to be despatched, began to heave and bump over choppy seas towards the coast some eleven miles distant. For the Western and Eastern Task Forces it marked the start of what was afterwards to become the most often and most minutely described day in the history of warfare, except perhaps for the Battle of Waterloo.[8]

While the bombarding force supporting Force S, on the extreme left of the Allied line, was deploying on station, the enemy made his one and only attempt – by E-boats – to attack the 'Neptune' armada at sea before the landings could take place. Two torpedoes passed harmlessly between HMS *Warspite* and HMS *Ramillies*, but a third hit the destroyer HNorMS *Svenner* under the boiler room, breaking her back. Although she sank quickly, most of her company were safely picked up. Another torpedo was seen driving straight for the headquarters ship *Largs*, flagship of Force S, and she had to put her engines emergency full astern to evade it. *Warspite* fired back with her 15-inch and 4-inch guns, crumpling up one E-boat which sank by the stern. The remainder of the flotilla retired behind a smoke screen.[9]

At 0500 the X-Craft X20 and X23 three miles off Juno and Sword beaches began flashing their green lights to seaward to guide the approach of the British and Canadian assault waves. The two X-Craft had been waiting offshore for 76 hours, 64 of them lying on the bottom, a gruelling experience for their five-men crews (including two COPP officers); their mission, as Ramsay paid tribute in his report, a feat of 'great skill and endurance ... Their reports of proceedings, which were a masterpiece of understatement, read like the deck log of a surface ship in peacetime; and not of a very small and vulnerable submarine carrying out a hazardous operation in time of war.'[10]

At 0530, light enough now for aircraft to spot for the warships' guns, the Royal Navy's broadsides crashed out against German shore batteries along the Eastern Task Force front. The Western Task Force did not however open fire until 0550, even though H-Hour for the American 1st Army was one hour earlier than for the British 2nd Army. For Admiral Kirk had opted for a preliminary bombardment lasting only 30 to 40 minutes instead of the two hours preferred by

Ramsay and Vian, hoping thereby to gain the advantage of surprise; he was to be keenly disappointed.

Off Sword beach, on the left of the Allied invasion front, the Great War veterans HMS *Warspite* and *Ramillies* and the brand-new monitor HMS *Roberts* threw salvo after salvo of 15-inch shells at the enemy shore batteries between the rivers Orne and Seine.[11] HMS *Warspite* was present with one boiler room and one turret still out of action as a result of being hit by a FX-1400 radio-controlled bomb at Salerno; *Ramillies* because she and her sister ship *Revenge* had been reprieved from the laying-up planned in late 1943. Further west along the Sword sector the cruisers HMS *Danae*, *Frobisher* and *Arethusa*, and the Polish cruiser *Dragon* bombarded gun positions astride the River Orne and behind the beaches. In Juno and Gold sectors the cruisers HMS *Ajax* (of River Plate fame), *Argonaut*, *Emerald*, *Orion*, *Belfast* and *Diadem*, and the Dutch gunboat HNLMS *Flores* concentrated their fire on seven tactically important shore batteries.

In the Western Task Force the 14-inch battleships USS *Texas* and *Arkansas*, the cruisers FS *Montcalm* and *Georges Leygues*, and HMS *Glasgow* carried out forty-minute bombardments along Omaha beach against German positions round the little harbour of Port en Bessin, beach defences and a major German heavy battery at Pointe du Hoc. On the far right of the Allied line, Utah beach, the 14-inch battleship *Nevada*, the 15-inch monitor HMS *Erebus*, and the cruisers USS *Tuscaloosa* and *Quincy*, HMS *Hawkins*, *Enterprise* and *Black Prince*, and the Dutch gunboat HNLMS *Soemba* sought to knock out or suppress German batteries extending from St Martin de Varreville northwards to Cap Barfleur. When the assault waves began to near the shore it was the turn of the destroyers – 57 in all – to blast the German bunkers behind the beaches with close-range low-trajectory fire. Never before had such a weight of fire been put down by warships before a landing.

The Allied air forces had also been joining in again. A little before 0600, half an hour before H-Hour for the Americans, 269 Martin Marauder medium bombers of the US 9th Air Force flew in under the 2,000-foot cloud base to launch an accurate attack on German positions behind Utah beach. Next 329 Liberators and Flying Fortresses of the 8th Air Force dropped 1,285 tons of bombs through the cloud in an attempt to obliterate the enemy defences behind Omaha beach. Yet this impressive tonnage fell harmlessly in the fields beyond, owing to a mistaken decision to delay the timing of the blind, instrument-guided, drop for 30 seconds for fear of hitting the American assault waves as they neared the shore.[12] In the British sector, over 1,000 Flying Fortresses and Liberators of the 8th Air Force also bombed from above the clouds, again relying on the guidance of pathfinders fixing the moment of release by instrument. Most of the 3,000 tons of bombs simply made craters in Norman pastures, although some damage was usefully done to German defences.

From this colossal and cumulative delivery of explosive from sea and air the German coastal defence batteries and defensive positions emerged largely unscathed even though the defenders themselves had been badly shaken and their communications disrupted. This was a tribute to the effectiveness of reinforced concrete up to seven feet thick under piled earth and gun embrasures angled to enfilade the beaches and inshore waters rather than towards the open sea.[13] The Western Task Force's fire also proved far less damaging than that of the Eastern Task Force. This was partly because it was spread evenly along the coast instead of being concentrated on key enemy positions; partly because the targets proved difficult to identify because of the lie of the shoreline; and partly because some American warships had been firing at German gun-flashes some 100 feet above the actual guns.[14] In any event, as Kirk and his fellow American admirals agreed afterwards, a bombardment of forty minutes was far too brief.[15]

Thus the Allies' hope that the warships and bombers would have crushed the defence before the attackers reached it was to prove vain, just like the comparable hope entertained by Sir Douglas Haig and his generals with regard to preliminary bombardment before the Battle of the Somme in 1916.

At 0630, preceded by a final storm from rocket-launchers mounted in adapted landing craft, Forces U and O put down the 4th US Infantry Division on Utah beach and a regimental combat team (brigade group) each from the 1st and 29th US Infantry Divisions on Omaha beach. In the case of Utah at the base of the Cotentin Peninsula (and lying to the north of the estuary of the River Vire) the troops came ashore on the wrong beach, a mile south-east of the correct one; an error due to the loss of guide vessels and the veiling of the low shoreline by haze and the smoke of explosions. It proved a lucky mistake, for this stretch of coast was less strongly defended. The 4th Infantry Division pushed fast inland on to high ground and by evening had established a firm lodgement five miles deep close to elements of the 82nd Airborne. By the end of D-Day Admiral Moon's Force U had landed 21,328 soldiers, 1,742 vehicles and 1,695 tons of stores. It had been a copybook operation.[16]

But on Omaha beach, between Vierville (inclusive) in the west to just short of Port en Bessin, Admiral Hall's Force O and the two regimental combat teams from the 1st and 29th Divisions proved not so fortunate.[17] Riding the eleven miles into this more exposed north-facing coast the assault formations had suffered much more from wind and waves than the relatively sheltered Force U. Out of 32 amphibious tanks launched at sea to spearhead the assault, all but five foundered. Thirty-two out of 50 howitzers to be landed to support the infantry attack went down in swamped 'Ducks'. Many landing craft also foundered, including – disastrously – those equipped for clearing beach obstacles.

As a result, the dense belts of obstacles ('Rommel's asparagus') installed thanks to Field-Marshal Rommel's ingenuity and energy here did their job well – not least because the Americans had declined to use the tanks especially adapted by the British for smashing paths through obstacles and minefields by means of rotating chain flails. Despite the extra time available for clearing obstacles during low states of tide because of the earlier H-Hour chosen by the American command, only a few paths could be opened through them before the water rose and covered them again. Thus unable to reach the shore, the waves of landing craft began to jam up to seaward, their orderly organisation and sequence disintegrating into a formless mass. Those troops who did manage to reach the beaches now found themselves pinned down before high bluffs and a concrete sea-wall supposed to have been demolished by the air and naval bombardment but actually largely intact.

For on Omaha beach the preliminary bombardment had proved the least effective of anywhere. The USS *Texas* had fired 250 rounds of 14-inch shell at the commanding battery on Pointe du Hoc to the west of the beach, but in vain, because, as US Rangers discovered when they occupied the battery later after a stiff fight, the enemy had shifted the guns to another position. The landing craft (rocket) fired too early, their projectiles falling short of the German beach defences. Trapped now without artillery support between the high water mark and the sea-wall or the bluffs, the hapless forward elements of the 1st and 29th Divisions were raked with German artillery, mortar and small arms fire. The beach became a chaos of wrecked equipment, corpses and wounded: a scene of paralysing terror only redeemed by individual acts of initiative and bravery. Offshore in the milling mass of landing craft, the confusion and leaderlessness among the American bluejackets and seasick soldiers verged on panic.

All in all Omaha beach that forenoon of D-Day offered exactly the scene of disastrous repulse which Rommel had hoped to arrange for the entire Allied Expeditionary Force. It reflected the lack of training and experience of the crews of the 'control vessels' responsible for directing the landing craft.[18] It also reflected poor joint planning and staff work on the part of Rear Admiral Hall and Force O and his opposite number, Major-General L. T. Gerow, and the US V Corps.[19] If a panzer or panzer-grenadier division had been present or within striking distance rather than the static 716th Infantry Division (lacking any transport at all) and some elements of the 252nd Infantry Division, Omaha beach could easily have seen a repetition of the dismal opening phase of the American landing at Salerno, if not an outright catastrophe. As it was, by the afternoon the mass of landing craft offshore had been sorted back into assault formation and more gaps cleared through the obstacles. With the American forces ashore now growing steadily stronger, German resistance weakened, not least because of close-range fire by destroyers. By the end of D-Day troops of the 1st and 29th US Infantry Divisions had gained a firm lodgement after all, even though it was barely a mile deep and five miles wide.

In the Eastern Task Force area the three assault forces completed their much shorter runs-in without losing formation despite the short, steep sea: a tribute to the conning of the unhandy landing craft. On the flanks of the landing craft groups as they headed for the shore steamed the big fleet destroyers, their 4.7-inch guns constantly engaging enemy batteries of defences behind the beaches. Ahead of them the smaller 'Hunts' moved as close inshore as possible to support the assault with fire from their 4-inch guns. Rocket-firing Typhoons of the 2nd Tactical Air Force ranged low along the coast beyond, blasting German positions. About 45 minutes before touchdown sixteen landing craft (gun) opened furious close-range fire on the actual beach defences with their 4.7-inch, 6-pounder and 2-pounder armaments. Fifteen minutes later the bombardment mounted to its climax when 22 landing craft (rocket) launched flights of 5-inch rockets at the rate of a thousand per craft per minute and a half.

'The air,' wrote Rear-Admiral Talbot (Force S) in his report, 'was full of bombers and fighters, and of the noise and smoke of our bombardments. The enemy was obviously stunned by the sheer weight of support we were meting out.'[20] And certainly German artillery fire on the vast, sprawling gift of a target of landing ships, warships and massed columns of landing craft was everywhere sporadic and ineffective. There was, however, a good reason for this, as the assault forces discovered later.

As the first landing craft neared the beaches, their crews could see the waves breaking against the German beach obstacles in fountains of white spume. Beyond lay the low shoreline of dunes overhung by thick palls of smoke and dust: a scene much resembling the Dunkirk beaches in 1940. But now the bombs and shells were British, and the Royal Navy was landing the British Army in France, not rescuing it.

In Gold sector, ten miles east of Omaha, the 50th (Northumbrian) Division landed by Force G (Commodore C. E. Douglas-Pennant flying his broad pendant in the HQ ship HMS *Bulolo*) quickly ran into trouble.[21] In the centre of the sector (Jig beach) amphibious tanks could not be launched to spearhead the assault because of the rough sea; instead they were put ashore directly from their landing craft (tank), but behind instead of ahead of the obstacle clearance parties. Ten other tanks were landed late, and in any event all but one were soon knocked out. The enemy's destruction of a shore radio-link made it impossible for the troops to call in the fire of the warships as arranged. The leading infantry therefore had to attack without fire support against a vigorous defence by units of the 915th and 736th Infantry Divisions, supported by accurate enfilade fire from shore batteries. Here as everywhere else the enemy had angled the embrasures of his concrete gun emplacements towards the beaches instead of out to sea.

This cardinal fact had not been revealed by interpretation of photo-reconnaissance pictures. It largely nullified the impact of the naval bombardment designed by the 'Neptune' fire-plan to destroy or suppress shore batteries firing out to sea. Against the blind seaward faces of thick concrete, naval gunfire could do little. As Ramsay was to remark in his report: 'One of the striking intelligence lessons of the operation was that no Staff is complete without the services of a photographic interpreter ... *At the last moment* [author's emphasis] the services of a Photographic Interpretation Officer were lent to A.N.C.X.F. and his work proved invaluable.'[22]

This was not the sum of the travails on Jig beach. The clearance parties found the tide higher than expected, and had to wait for it to fall before they could begin their work. In any case the 'Rommel's asparagus' along most of this sector was particularly formidable – no fewer than 2,500 of them along three and a half miles of shore, many fitted with fuzed mines or shells. By the time the tide rose again the clearance parties had only managed to open one gap. Reserve battalions of the 50th Division found getting ashore on Jig a hard and hazardous business; many craft were damaged.

Fortunately elsewhere along the Gold sector the landings started better. In the west (Item beach) flail tanks (equipped with rotating

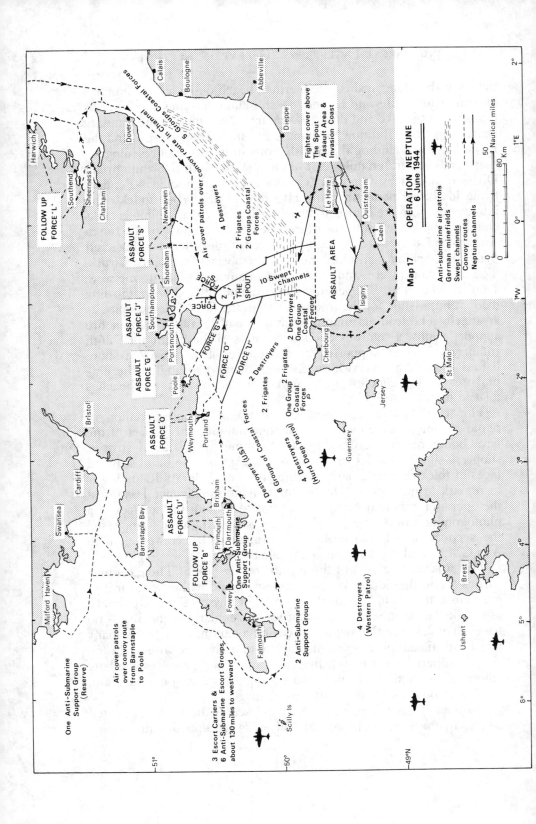

OPERATION NEPTUNE
6 June 1944

Map 17

Anti-submarine air patrols
German minefields
Swept channels
Convoy routes
Neptune channels

Nautical miles

Km

ASSAULT AREA

Fighter cover above
The Spout
Assault Area &
Invasion Coast

FORCE S
FORCE J
FORCE G
FORCE O
FORCE U
FORCE Z

THE SPOUT

10 Swept channels

2 Destroyers
One Group Coastal Forces

One Group 2 Frigates
Coastal Forces

2 Frigates

2 Destroyers

4 Groups of Coastal forces

4 Destroyers (US)

4 Destroyers
(Hurd Deep Patrol)

2 Frigates
2 Groups Coastal Forces

4 Destroyers

Air cover patrols over convoy route in Channel

5 Groups Coastal Forces

FOLLOW UP FORCE "L"

ASSAULT FORCE "S"

ASSAULT FORCE "J"

ASSAULT FORCE "G"

ASSAULT FORCE "O"

ASSAULT FORCE "U"

FOLLOW UP FORCE "B"

One Anti-Submarine Support Group

2 Anti-Submarine Support Groups

3 Escort Carriers & 6 Anti-Submarine Escort Groups, about 130 miles to westward

4 Destroyers (Western Patrol)

One Anti-Submarine Support Group (Reserve)

Air cover patrols over convoy route from Barnstaple to Poole

Harwich
Southend
Sheerness
Chatham
Dover
Newhaven
Shoreham
Southampton
Portsmouth
Poole
Portland
Weymouth
Brixham
Dartmouth
Plymouth
Fowey
Falmouth
Barnstaple Bay
Swansea
Milford Haven
Cardiff
Bristol
Scilly Is

Calais
Boulogne
Abbeville
Dieppe
Le Havre
Ouistreham
Caen
Isigny
Cherbourg
St. Malo
Jersey
Guernsey
Brest
Ushant

51°
50°
49°N
2°W
1°W
0°
1°E
2°

chains to explode mines or demolish obstacles) and armoured bulldozers landed punctually and began to smash gaps through the
obstacles for the first assault wave. But a second wave landing further
westwards later had trouble getting through intact obstacles. By the
time No. 47 Marine Commando tried to get ashore on this same
beach the obstacles had been submerged again by the returning tide.
The Commandos lost three out of five landing craft together with
vital radio kit. Meanwhile on Gold's eastern beach (King), flail tanks
together with successful work by obstacle clearance parties and naval
gunfire called in by Forward Observers Bombardment all enabled the
50th Division's 69th Brigade to land without problems and fight their
way inland, albeit against some tenacious resistance. By early afternoon
the Division's two reserve brigades had also landed. By midnight on
D-Day its lodgement extended westwards to include Arromanches,
future site of Mulberry 'B', and inland to within a mile of Bayeux,
which it had however failed to take as required by Montgomery's
master plan.

On Juno beach in the centre of the British front (lying between La
Rivière and St Aubin-sur-Mer) Force J (Commodore G. N. Oliver,
flying his broad pendant in the HQ ship HMS *Hilary*) and the 3rd
Canadian Division faced the additional barrier of an off-shore reef,
exposed at low tide.[23] The only gap, a mile wide, lay opposite the
little harbour of Courseulles. In this gap the enemy had concentrated
his strongest defences of the sector – beach obstacles, dense barbed-
wire belts, minefields, houses strengthened as strong points, concrete
gun emplacements commanding the harbour entrance. Partly in order
to make sure that the tide had risen high enough to give the landing
craft clearance over the reefs, it was decided to delay H-Hour on
Juno by ten minutes. This, coupled with the delayed arrival of some
landing craft (including those carrying flail tanks), meant that the
rising tide had already begun to engulf the German beach obstacles
by the time the assault forces reached the shore. Instead of being able
to disembark forward of them and clear them 'dry shod' as planned,
the assault forces found themselves landing among the obstacles. With
skill and determination the crews of the smaller landing craft sought
to weave their way through; the big landing craft (tank) simply
bludgeoned ahead. All too soon the tide covered the obstacles
altogether, so halting the work of the clearance parties. An officer of
the Royal Canadian Naval Reserve describes how after two out of five
landing craft under his command had been holed by mines attached
to posts or by mortar bombs, and their complements of soldiers
rescued . . .

... Another explosion holed L.C.A. 1137 and stove in the starboard bow. All troops were cleared from the craft without casualties. All troops had been disembarked from L.C.A. 1138 and the craft was about to leave the beach when a wave lifted it on to an obstruction. The explosion which followed ripped the bottom out of the craft ... the boat officer in the craft suffered several shrapnel wounds in his legs, a fracture of the right fibula and slight head injuries. All troops were discharged from L.C.A. 1151 without loss ... I ordered the crews of the sunken craft to embark for return passage to the ship. By this time there was a cleared channel through the obstructions ... but as we were leaving, an approaching L.C.T. forced us to alter course. An obstruction ripped out the bottom of L.C.A. 1151. The crews then transferred to an L.C.T. and were eventually brought back to the ship.[24]

This was the kind of operational reality against which no planning, however thorough, could provide. Ninety out of 306 landing craft employed by Force J that forenoon were lost or damaged. And except on one of the Juno beaches the amphibious tanks launched at sea failed to arrive on the shore before the infantry whose assault they were supposed to spearhead.

Once again the enemy reserved his fire for that moment of scrambling confusion after landing when the assault forces were at their most vulnerable. On all three Juno beaches it was only after hard fights that the assault forces eventually managed to escape from this killing ground by advancing inland. By the close of D-Day the 3rd Canadian Division and part of the 51st (Highland) Division, the Juno follow-up formation, held a lodgement up to six miles deep, extending from the left flank of 50th Division (Gold sector) through Villons les Buissons to the right flank of No. 48 Royal Marine Commando in Langrune-sur-Mer.

On Sword beach to the east of Juno, extending from Lion-sur-Mer to Ouistreham at the mouth of the Caen Canal inclusive, Force S (Rear-Admiral A. G. Talbot, flying his flag in the HQ ship HMS *Largs*) and the British 3rd Infantry Division confronted perhaps the most crucial task of all the 'Neptune' forces on D-Day.[25] According to Montgomery's military plan, the 3rd Division was to take the city of Caen, eight miles from the coast, and secure bridgeheads over the River Orne. Caen was needed as a bastion to secure the left flank of the entire Allied lodgement against German strategic reserves coming in from northern or central France. It was also needed as the launching point for a further British advance to occupy the good airfield country southwards towards Falaise. The 21st Panzer Division was somewhere in the Caen area, though its exact whereabouts were not known.

Montgomery therefore planned (as he hoped) an initial onslaught on the coast defences in overwhelming strength. All three brigades of the 3rd Division were to land in succession on a single Sword beach ('Queen') on a one-brigade front of barely more than two miles in width between Lion-sur-Mer and the little seaside resort of La Brèche (inclusive). Once a gap was blown in the German defence the 185th Infantry Brigade with an armoured regiment under command was to thrust swiftly into Caen.

Along this flat and duny shore and its coast road sprinkled with holiday villas Rommel had installed the 736th Infantry Division in the usual cunning defence system. Lion-sur-Mer and La Brèche had been transformed into formidable strong-points, their guns raking the beaches in between them. These beaches had been thickly planted with the standard obstacles, and their exits inland barred by a wilderness of mines, barbed wire, tank traps and machine-gunners and mortar crews in fox-holes. On the high ground of the Périers Ridge some three miles inland lay two powerful subterranean defence complexes which commanded the entire sweep of the coast from St Aubin round through Ouistreham to the Caen Canal north of Caen. And on Sword as on all the other 'Neptune' beaches on D-Day the state of wind and tide served greatly to enhance the effectiveness of 'Rommel's asparagus'.

Covered by the fire of the destroyers from as close inshore as possible, the 3rd Division's leading brigade, the 8th, began to land on time. Of 34 out of 40 amphibious tanks launched at sea all but two safely reached the beach; the remaining six landed from landing craft. However, German 88mm anti-tank guns which had held their fire during the run-in quickly knocked out ten tanks amid the surf. By this time the planned landing sequence had already gone astray, for the tanks had come ashore after instead of in advance of the infantry, the assault engineers and the clearance teams. The brisk west-north-west wind swept the tide in so fast that the clearance parties only had time to open one passage through the obstacles before these became submerged. On Queen beach as on others the landing craft therefore had to manoeuvre or butt their way ashore. That the 8th Brigade was nevertheless able to land and deploy was yet another tribute to the cool nerve, presence of mind and seamanlike skill under fire displayed by the crews of the landing craft, mostly Royal Marine or Royal Naval Volunteer Reserve.

But now came the task of breaking out of the fifteen-yard-wide strip of sand left between the rising sea and the coast defences – a strip swept by enfilade fire from La Brèche. Not until past 1000, after three hours of fighting, did this strongpoint fall. Meanwhile, just as Rommel intended, the beach obstacles and the defences barring the beach exits together choked the flow of assault troops, follow-up troops and stores into and out of the beach. To clear the exits under fire here proved a particularly hard job for the engineers, and for a whole hour the armoured regiment (the Staffordshire Yeomanry) that was supposed to lead the advance on Caen remained stuck fast on the shore. So tightly jammed were tanks, guns and transport in the ten-yard-wide strip now remaining between sea and dunes that it was hard to manoeuvre to reach the exits even when these had been eventually cleared. When at last inland beyond these exits the armour still found itself jammed nose to tail on the few available routes.[26]

By the mid-forenoon Montgomery's timetable had gone well astray, even though on the left of the 3rd Division front Ouistreham had been successfully cleared. On the right of Queen beach No. 41 Royal Marine Commando had failed to take Lion-sur-Mer; and at the end of the day a gap was still to remain between it and No. 48 Commando in Langrune (Juno beach). Much more serious, the main attack by 3rd Division, the centre, on Caen had been fatally compromised by the mishaps and confusions on the beach. Not until 1230 did 185th Brigade begin its southward advance – without the armour. Not until 1400 did the Brigade's leading elements approach the Périers Ridge and the powerful field fortification on it which barred the way to Caen. Not until around 1600 had it bypassed this position (which did not fall until 2000) and reached Biéville, four miles north of Caen. But by this time the 21st Panzer had arrived. The British advance sputtered out in a brisk action with German tanks. Caen was not to fall for another month.[27]

While the armies were everywhere struggling to get on and then off the beaches, the navies and tactical air forces had been putting down an immense weight of high-explosive on the defenders, whose reports were movingly eloquent about the distress thus caused them. Nonetheless, the evidence suggests that the effect of the naval fire support did not match its weight. Sometimes the communication links between spotting fighters and the ships broke down; sometimes lack of suitable observation posts for Forward Observers, Bombardment, or loss of FOBs in action equally left the guns without guidance. Then again, as the Naval Commander, Force J, pointed out in his report, 'the extremely fluid state of the battle . . . often left the HQ ship and bombarding ships in doubt as to the position of our own troops and with which [state] the general standard of communications between F.O.B.s and firing ships was not always able to compete'.[28]

The skill with which the Germans concealed their guns and hoaxed spotters with false flashes, coupled with the adroitness with which they switched positions, likewise lessened the effectiveness of naval gunfire.[29]

At the end of D-Day the Allied Expeditionary Force had won four firm but shallow and isolated footholds, the gap opposite 21st Panzer between the 50th Division on Juno and the 3rd Division on Sword being particularly vulnerable. This was far short of Montgomery's D-Day objective of a continuous lodgement from the east of the River Orne to the River Vire up to ten miles deep and including Caen and Bayeux, with a second lodgement north of the Vire reaching half way across the Cotentin Peninsula. However, despite the hazards and hard fighting of the day Allied casualties proved remarkably light. The British airborne and seaborne forces suffered about 3,300 killed, wounded and missing; the Canadians about 1,000; the Americans some 6,000.[30] The Royal Navy alone had had 258 landing craft sunk or damaged by the combination of rough seas and German obstacles.[31]

On balance therefore D-Day had proved a solid success when it might well have resulted in the total disaster imagined by General Eisenhower when he drafted on 5 June for use in such a contingency a communiqué announcing that the invasion had failed and that he had withdrawn the Allied forces.[32] As Admiral Sir Bertram Ramsay, Naval Commander, Allied Expeditionary Force, justly summed it up in his official report, 'the outstanding fact was that, despite the unfavourable weather, in every main essential the plan was carried out as written'.[33]

But all still turned on whether the two navies – above all, the Royal Navy – could enable the armies to build up their strength fast enough to repel the German panzer counter-strokes that must surely come.

The follow-up forces 'B' (American) and 'L' (British: 7th Armoured Division for the Caen sector) arrived as planned on the second tide of D-Day and safely disembarked. Nonetheless the muddle and wreckage on the beaches and the hindering effects of wind and rough seas meant that the whole process of landing stores and equipment was, as Ramsay glumly noted, '24 hours adrift'.[34] While the armies were fighting their way inland the naval beach parties and their military equivalents had already begun working valiantly to sort out the mess. The army beach groups set about clearing wreckage and organising the beaches into base areas complete with stores dumps, field dressing stations and all-weather roadways. The naval beach parties swung into their role of managing the flow of landing craft to and from the

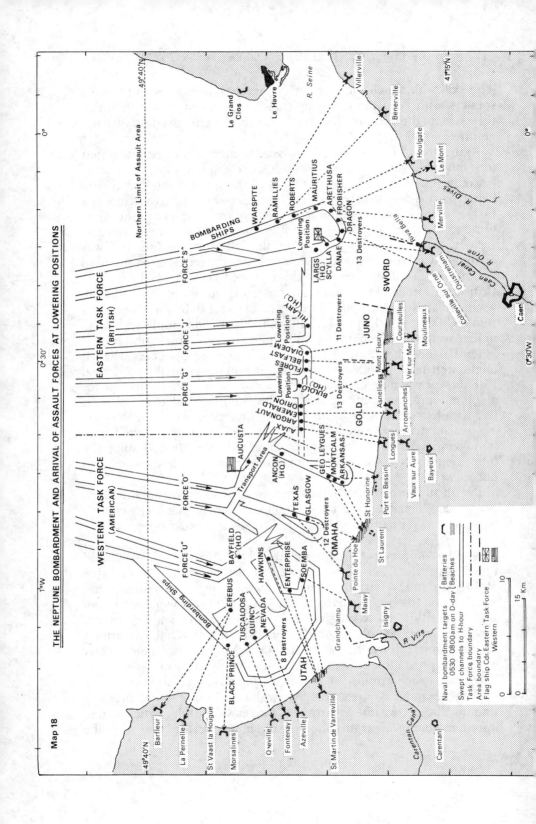

Map 18

THE NEPTUNE BOMBARDMENT AND ARRIVAL OF ASSAULT FORCES AT LOWERING POSITIONS

beaches, so that the follow-up and build-up forces and the huge tonnages of stores and equipment could move smoothly into the lodgements. For this purpose Forces S, J and G each deployed a beach party of four officers, six petty officers and 67 ratings, as well as a signals unit numbering thirty.[35] Despite all the congestion, despite the steep waves breaking along the shore, the Royal Navy and the Merchant Marine landed over 75,000 soldiers, over 6,000 vehicles (including nearly 1,000 tanks) and over 4,000 tons of stores in the British sector during D-Day.[36]

In the course of the day Admiral Vian, NCETF, had visited each of the British beaches to assess the problems for himself. His flagship HMS *Scylla* had added her eight 4.5-inch guns to the bombardment of the German defenders of Sword and Gold. That evening he held a meeting of his three force commanders in *Scylla* off Juno beach to coordinate measures to defend the mass of shipping and landing craft against German E-boat or U-boat attack or enemy mining during the night and the nights to follow. Minesweepers were to be anchored at half-mile intervals in a cordon parallel to the shore and some six miles from it. Inshore of this cordon a patrol line of MTBs and destroyers was to be deployed. On the eastern flank the cordon was to be brought shorewards into shallow water just beyond the River Orne by landing craft (support) anchored two hundred yards apart, the so-called 'Trout Line'. Vian's flagship would be anchored on this flank as extra support. Out to sea the approach channels from 'The Spout' were to be patrolled by more destroyers and MTBs. Close defence of the offshore anchorages would be the responsibility of each force commander. The United States Navy, for its part, preferred to do without such a fixed cordon of ships in the Western Task Force area and rely instead entirely on roving patrols.

In the forenoon of 7 June Admiral Ramsay (flying his flag in the minelayer HMS *Apollo*) and General Eisenhower crossed the Channel to monitor the state of the battle for themselves. They had spent D-Day itself in that nerve-twisting limbo of impotence peculiar to high commanders when they have launched their forces into action and can do nothing more but wait for news. When at 1145 on the 7th HMS *Apollo* anchored off Omaha beach Ramsay was dismayed by 'the scene of great confusion' that met his eye:

The blockships had just arrived & were hanging about awaiting someone to tell them what to do. L.S.T.s & ships & craft of all sizes anchored anywhere. No L.S.T.s unloading, the beaches littered with stranded craft and no traffic going on between beach & ships. *Augusta* was anchored 1½ miles from shore & other bombarding ships firing. But a complete absence of activity prevailed. Kirk & Bradley came over & discussed the situation & did nothing to relieve my anxiety. Situation a little better than yesterday but bridgehead still very shallow . . .[37]

A huge backlog of ships and craft built up in the next three days off Omaha, partly because of the bottleneck on the beaches caused by wreckage, but partly also because of the arthritically bureaucratic nature of the joint US Navy and Army arrangements for handling the inflow of supplies and reinforcements.[38] Finally Ramsay with Scots commonsense ordered that such pedantic adherence to set procedures for establishing priorities for unloading should be abandoned. He told the responsible American naval officer instead to 'empty the ships and the priorities will take care of themselves'.[39] So it proved: within 36 hours the backlog had cleared, and Omaha was on its way to becoming the busiest of all the 'Neptune' beaches.

After his discouraging visit to Omaha in the forenoon of 7 June Ramsay was glad to find Commodore Douglas-Pennant (Force G) off Gold beach 'in excellent form' and reporting that 'everything was fine' except for a lag of about twelve hours in landing vehicles and stores because of the weather. In a letter next day to his wife Ramsay wrote that Douglas-Pennant 'cheered me up a lot'.[40] But Vian, whom Ramsay met along with Commodore Oliver (Force J) off Juno beach, 'was looking tired & was a bit querulous, but that is hardly surprising in view of the fact that he is only just recovering from Quinzy [sic] & had been up 2 days & nights under considerable strain. Oliver was in good shape & his beach going well, after trouble owing to the weather . . .'[41] Ramsay was further reassured when Montgomery came aboard *Apollo* to give 'a quite cheerful description of the land battle'.[42] No less heartening to Ramsay was the spectacle from his flagship of the Allied (but overwhelmingly British) seapower in the Channel that was now sustaining and strengthening the Expeditionary Force's lodgements. 'The sea between here & there,' he wrote to his wife, 'was packed with returning craft who'd emptied their loads on the beach, craft who were going over . . .'[43]

Among this traffic were the first convoys of the strangest floating objects ever to go to sea – the unwieldy steel Bombardons and huge 'Phoenix' concrete caissons slowly wallowing across under tow to form the breakwaters of the Mulberry harbours. Next day the components of the 'Whale' piers and pierheads joined the procession. On 9 June, when the work of surveying the Mulberry sites was well under way, the first 'Phoenixes' were sunk in place. This proved no simple task.

After their flooding valves had been opened the 'Phoenixes' took at least half an hour to settle on the seabed. During that time their thousands of tons had to be held in place by tugs against the pull of a 2½ knot tidal stream and the push of the wind on their towering sides. Next day the 'Gooseberry' breakwaters were completed by the scuttling of the last of the 'Corncob' blockships by means of explosive charges. The 'Gooseberries' immediately provided very welcome shelter for the unloading of vessels on the beaches.[44]

According to Ramsay's 'Operation Neptune – Naval Orders' no small vessel was to 'dry out' (i.e., become beached with the fall of tide) for fear of breaking their backs. But so serious had become the backlog of landing craft (tank) and coasters waiting off shore for their turn to be discharged that on 7 June Ramsay instructed that they should all be beached. Left high and dry for unloading straight on to the sand as the tide receded, they were floated off again on the next tide. Soon the discharging of vessels and their return to England for fresh cargoes settled into a smooth and accelerating rhythm thanks to the efforts of the inter-service beach organisations. In his report as ANCXF Admiral Ramsay was to pay them high tribute:

> . . . What they achieved was really remarkable. It has been said that on the stores side alone the tonnages handled daily into France were over one-third of the normal import capacity of the United Kingdom. On an average day during the first week the following number of ships and craft arrived off the assault area:–
>   25 'Liberty' ships
>   38 coasters
>   40 L.S.T.
>   75 L.C.T.
>   9 Personnel Ships
>   20 L.C.I. (L)
> The identification, unloading, marshalling and sailing of such a volume of shipping off an open coast was a gigantic problem, which was rendered more difficult by the adverse weather . . .[45]

During the first six days of 'Operation Neptune' 326,547 men, 54,186 vehicles and 104,428 tons of stores were brought across the Channel and unloaded over the beaches.[46]

The Luftwaffe and the German Navy failed to hinder, let alone interrupt this traffic, either in these first critical days of the invasion or the weeks that followed. Their most effective means of nuisance lay in the new 'oyster' mine, which was detonated by the changes in water pressure caused by the passing of a vessel and therefore virtually impossible to sweep. On the night of 6–7 June German light craft laid a mixture of oyster and conventional mines in the western and eastern fringes of the Bay of the Seine, and from 9 June onwards the Luftwaffe too began laying mines, flying in fast and low at night. In the particularly exposed Utah sector Admiral Moon lost four destroyers and two minesweepers during the first ten days of 'Neptune' and another 25 vessels and craft damaged. Later in the month it was the Royal Navy's turn to suffer from the Luftwaffe's nightly sowing of oyster mines. Between 22 and 29 June five warships and four other vessels went down and another seven were damaged. Most of them were small ships, but Admiral Vian's own flagship HMS *Scylla* struck a mine on the 23rd, putting both engine rooms out of action. *Scylla* had to be towed back to Portsmouth, Vian transferring his flag to the HQ ship HMS *Hilary*. The minesweepers (the great majority of them from the Royal Navy) did valiant work in all weathers sweeping conventional mines, their total bag off the invasion coast in the three months after D-Day amounting to one-tenth of all the mines swept in all theatres from the beginning of the war to 6 June 1944.[47] But for the time being there was no answer to the oyster mines except to slow ships' speed to the point where the change in water pressure was too small to detonate them.

In the first week of the invasion German E-boats for their part managed to sink only three small ships, two landing ships (tank) and six smaller craft out of all that mass of shipping lying off the beaches or in transit across the Channel. Two E-boats succumbed to British mines off Barfleur in the same period, and a third was sunk by Royal Navy surface ships. Every E-boat sortie had to brave the hazard of attack by Coastal Command Beaufighters and Wellingtons; and on 13 June Beaufighters of Nos. 143 and 236 Squadrons sank three and one R-boat (motor minesweeper) off Le Touquet. At Admiral Ramsay's request Bomber Command took a hand on 14 June, sending in 325 Lancasters just before dusk to attack a mass of light craft revealed by air reconnaissance to have been concentrated in Le Havre. The 12,000-lb 'Tallboy' bombs smashed through the concrete roofs of the E-boat pens (much less thick than those of the U-boat pens) and sank thirteen boats and damaged three others. Three torpedo boats and about 40 other craft were also destroyed in the harbour. The German naval command judged this to have been 'a catastrophe', and reckoned that as a result 'the naval situation in the Seine Bay had completely altered'.[48]

On the night of 8–9 June eight ships of the 10th Destroyer Flotilla (Captain B. Jones, RN) had smashed a sortie by four ships of the

German 8th Destroyer Flotilla (Captain Baron von Bechstolsheim) west of Cherbourg. Exactly forewarned as to the enemy's course, speed and intentions by Ultra decrypts of Enigma signals,[49] Ramsay deployed the 10th Flotilla to intercept him. At 0115 radar contact was made, and ten minutes later Captain Jones's ships opened fire. There ensued a ferocious high-speed action in the dark lasting several hours. HMCS *Haida* and *Huron* chased two German destroyers westwards until they escaped in the dark, one of them so badly damaged as to be out of action for weeks. Jones's own ship HMS *Tartar* was hit by four shells round the bridge, starting a fire and bringing down the trellis foremast and radar gear. According to Captain Jones's report of proceedings, 'the conditions of fire, noise, smoke and casualties were distracting but the enemy was soon silenced'.[50] While the *Ashanti* was standing by the burning *Tartar*, whose damage looked worse than it was, the *Ashanti*'s 'Y' (radio-intercept) operator heard a German destroyer announce that he was steering 140 degrees towards the burning ship. Heading out on a reciprocal course the *Ashanti* fired four torpedoes as the two ships passed. Two of them hit home, blowing off the enemy's bow and stern. The German destroyer subsequently blew up with a 'spectacular explosion'.[51] The enemy flotilla leader was now intercepted by the two Canadian destroyers returning from their chase to the westward. Hunted down by Allied ships (the Polish destroyer *Blyskawica* was there too) and engaged ever more closely, the enemy was finally driven ashore in a flaming wreck.[52] Thus ended the attempt by the last German destroyers serviceable in Group West to attack 'Neptune' shipping.

The U-boats fared little better than the E-boats and destroyers, not least because their patrol areas and orders were throughout largely revealed to the Admiralty by Ultra.[53] In any event the density of Coastal Command patrols and surface escort groups in the western English Channel gave the U-boats little chance. It was only in the small hours of D-Day that U-boat Command ordered its anti-invasion groups in Biscay and Norway to sea – about a week too late for them to be in a position to attack the 'Neptune' armada on passage. Of nine 'Schnorchel' boats ordered out of Brest and La Pallice that morning just one finally reached her station (on 15 June) off the Isle of Wight, but even she only sank a landing craft (tank) before abandoning her mission in the face of repeated attacks by Coastal Command aircraft, and returning to Brest. On the same day, however, a 'Schnorchel' boat from Norway sank the frigate HMS *Mourne* off Land's End. Of the other eight 'Schnorchel' boats from Biscay ports, one was sunk on 10 June and two others forced to return to harbour because of damage; a fourth had to be put back because of technical defects; two more (one of them with flat batteries) entered St Peter Port, Guernsey, thereafter to return to Brest as well; and although the U-764 torpedoed the destroyer HMS *Blackwood* (who later sank while in tow), she was herself so badly damaged by the avenging counter-attack that she like her sisters made for home.[54] Of seven non-'Schnorchel' U-Boats ordered on D-Day to patrol between Start Point in Devon and the Scillies four were sunk (two of them by Coastal Command) and the remaining three forced back because of damage. The disheartened Admiral Kranke, Flag Officer, Group West, now ordered all remaining eighteen non-'Schnorchel' boats at present deployed on a patrol line in the Bay of Biscay to return to base.

In the whole of June as many as 25 U-boats were sunk in all seas, twelve of them in the Channel or the Bay of Biscay:[55] a masterful demonstration of the teamwork of Coastal Command and the Royal Navy at the zenith of its wartime evolution. Apart from the *Mourne* and the *Blackwood* and one landing craft (tank), the only success which U-boat Command could set against this gruesome writing-down of its strength were four Liberty ships torpedoed in convoy off Selsey Bill on 29 June, and even one of these successfully limped into port.[56] It was a pitiful performance for a weapons-system and a service which had come so near to winning both world wars; the last limp punch of a beaten prizefighter whose legs were already buckling.

The flow of Allied build-up formation and all their matériel into the lodgements continued to gather momentum. After ten days the strength of the Expeditionary Force had swelled to thirteen infantry divisions, three airborne and three armoured, plus abundant artillery.[57] By this time the German Army had already lost the reinforcement race, and with it all hope of driving the Allies into the sea. This was by no means only because of the failure of the German Navy and Luftwaffe to impede, let alone halt, cross-Channel traffic, or because of the Allied air forces' destruction of the French transport network. In the first critical twelve hours of the invasion the reaction of the German Army in the West itself had been paralysed because of divided command responsibilities and unresolved disputes over strategy. Rommel (C-in-C, Army Group B) wanted to post all the panzer divisions close to the coast in order to 'Dunkirk' the Allied assault forces on the beaches while they were in greatest disarray. Field-Marshal von Rundstedt (C-in-C, West) instead had urged the classic strategy of holding the armour well inland for a grand counter-stroke once the Allies had revealed their axis of advance – a strategy which in Rommel's view took no note of the power of the Allied air forces to paralyse movement. The outcome of the debate, thanks to Corporal Hitler's decision, had been a disastrous compromise. Three panzer divisions were allotted to Rommel; four others to a central reserve under Hitler's direct control. Neither Rundstedt nor Rommel enjoyed authority to commit a panzer division to battle.

In the event it was nearly 1600 on D-Day before Hitler ordered two of Rommel's panzer divisions to move up to the invasion area. Only 21st Panzer was on the spot to attack the precarious Allied lodgements. Although it cleaved its way to the coast between Juno and Sword beaches and prevented Montgomery from taking Caen, it lacked the weight to drive the British and Canadians into the sea. By the time the two panzer divisions ordered up by Hitler arrived, the German opportunity had passed. By 10 June the Allies had expanded their four beach-heads into a continuous and solidly-held lodgement from beyond the River Orne westwards to the eastern coastline of the Cotentin Peninsula. Rundstedt's war diary dolefully recorded that 'the Seventh Army [on the invasion front] is everywhere on the defensive'.[58]

In this defensive against limited Allied attacks aimed at deepening the lodgement area, the 7th Army suffered much from the broadsides of British and American battleships and cruisers (including two French cruisers) as well as the constant onslaught of the Allied tactical air forces. HMS *Ramillies* and *Warspite* carried out daily shoots with their 15-inch guns; *Rodney* and *Nelson* with their 16-inch. With corps and divisional headquarters calling down the fire on German positions and troop concentrations on their front, and aircraft monitoring the fall of shot, the salvoes from the battleships' great guns plunged accurately down with crushing moral and material effect. On 30 June German armour lying some seventeen miles south of Gold beach was astonished and disconcerted by the delivery of several tons of 16-inch high-explosive shell from the *Rodney*. In the American sector the USS *Nevada*, *Arkansas* and *Texas* were performing similar services for the US 1st Army with their 12- and 14-inch main armaments. On 11 June Rommel glumly reported to the Führer that 'the effects of heavy naval bombardment are so powerful that an operation either with infantry or armoured formations is impossible in an area commanded by this rapid fire artillery'.[59]

On 17 June troops of the American 1st Army reached the west coast of the Cotentin Peninsula, so isolating the great port of Cherbourg, which the Allies urgently needed to supplement supply across open beaches and through the two Mulberries, which were now almost complete. Two days later that existing method of supply, on which the continuance of the campaign absolutely depended, was attacked by an immeasurably more terrible destructive force than U-boats or E-boats or mines:

All Sunday, 18th June, the barometer held steady, the sea was flat, the sun shone, and the beaches had a holiday look; they were black with men and vehicles, and the masts of the landing-craft and bigger ships were like little copses growing up off shore as far as the eye could see . . .

Towards evening the barometer – how anxiously we watch that barometer – began to betray a faint tremor. It wasn't much. It wasn't anything to worry about, we told ourselves, and we went to bed.

But by 0300 on Monday morning it began to blow. We didn't get our usual dawn visit by the snooping F.W.s nor hear the Spits and the Marauders streaming over; for the cloud was down to 500 feet, the balloons were faint grey shadows overhead, and the wind was whipping up white horses on the pewter-coloured sea.

It blew all the morning and all the afternoon; but the sky seemed brighter in the north, and we told ourselves: 'It can't last. A gale can't possibly last long, in June.'

By now it was indeed a gale . . . Force 8, and stronger in the gusts. It came from the north, with a touch of east in it, and that was the worst direction, for it piled up the seas on our north-facing beaches and created the very condition which is the mariner's ancient peril and ancient dread: a lee shore, on which even great ships can meet their doom, and small ones are smashed to matchwood.

Most of ours were small ones, and they stood offshore, head to wind, riding it out. There must have been hundreds in peril there . . .

The full flood of our supplies had dried up to a trickle . . . Here and there, when the tide served, the wonderful little DUKWS, manned by R.A.S.C. [Royal Army Service Corps] men, wallowed like hippopotami between the coasters and the shore. They carried ammunition mostly . . . a priority.

In places, from time to time, a few landing-craft beached. Some broke their backs. It is terrible to watch a craft broached-to and to see the surf savage it, crunch it like a dog with a bone . . .[60]

The huge seas ripped the Bombardons from their anchorages and smashed them against the breakwaters of the Mulberry harbours; rolled and pounded 'Phoenix' caissons to pieces, especially where sunk in deep water as in the American Mulberry off St Laurent; broke up the nearly completed 'Whale' pierheads and piers and flung the segments against the ships and landing craft along the shore. Only the 'Gooseberry' shelters composed of 'Corncob' blockships stood firm against the violence and power of the waves. The American Mulberry suffered worse because the blockships had been planted from the outer ends of the breakwaters, so leaving a wide unprotected gap in the middle. It was here that the gigantic seas rampaged over the 'Phoenix' caissons and scoured under their bottoms, heaving them about as if they were mere bricks.

On Tuesday, when it blew just as hard as ever, somebody said: 'I reckon this'll be the second most famous gale to the Armada . . .'

It had blown now for forty hours; some of the ships out to sea began to get into trouble. They dragged their anchors, or their anchors carried away . . .

A destroyer hit a mine, and with her engines, steering-gear, and anchors out of action, hove ashore . . . And at dusk a big coaster, attended by frantic tugs, bore down on us, and we got a frantic signal from another ship: '*If* the vessel on your port bow is 269, she contains 3,000 tons of ammunition!' The tugs held her, held on to her all night like terriers, and she was saved.

Wednesday was the third day. Perhaps the wind was slightly less fierce; but in some ways Wednesday was the worst day, for we were all tired, the situation ashore was obviously more critical . . . And we began to get a terrible lot of flotsam and jetsam on our beaches: upturned boats, which are always a disquieting sight, lorries, a 25-pounder gun, motor bicycles, rhino ferries – and dead men.

. . . But on Wednesday evening the clouds lifted a bit and the shriek of the wind in the shrouds was less of a shriek than a long-drawn sigh. We heard a murmur in the sky that grew to a great roar and watched the Dakotas going over to bring supplies and carry back the wounded . . . And then suddenly – it was as if we saw it for the first time – the sun shone.[61]

In the three days before the gale a daily average of 34,712 men, 5,894 vehicles and 24,974 tons of stores had been landed through the Mulberry harbours and the beaches. From 19 to 22 June the daily totals dropped to 9,847 men, 2,426 vehicles and 7,350 tons of stores.[62] The build-up of the British 2nd Army alone fell three divisions behind schedule, and Montgomery was compelled to postpone his next push near Caen, due on 22 June. With the Americans now sweeping up the Cotentin Peninsula towards Cherbourg, a strong fortress as well as a port, it was desperately urgent to sort out the aftermath of the storm and get the flow of supplies back to full spate. On 23 June Ramsay went over to Normandy to put his personal weight behind this work. Although he found the damage to the British Mulberry 'not too bad', he was dismayed by the evident exhaustion of all the men on the spot: '. . . there were many craft inactive for one reason or another & a general air of floppiness prevalent. However, Harold

[Hickling, Captain, RN, whom Ramsay had just appointed as replacement Naval Officer In Charge of the Arromanches Mulberry] will soon put that right.'[63] When Ramsay later inspected the Omaha beach and the American Mulberry with Admiral Kirk, the sight struck him as 'frightful, with so many craft ashore. Much worse than Gold beach. As for the Mulberry gooseberry [sic] it was in a frightful state . . .'[64]

Back again in England Ramsay immediately concerted emergency measures with the Cs-in-C, naval home commands. Teams of skilled men were mobilised and rushed to Normandy to help in clearing the beaches and making good damage. Extra repair ships were despatched. The existing salvage organisation was strengthened. The scene of destruction and exhaustion gave way to one of energetic effort. Stranded vessels and craft were swiftly repaired and refloated, even those left high and dry far up the shore by the storm. At the same time the inter-service beach organisations, well aware that the armies were running critically short of ammunition and other supplies, made prodigious and successful efforts to restore the unloading cycle by using every available ship and craft and (thanks to the now favourable weather) every available stretch of shore. In the first week after the gale the daily average numbers of vehicles landed was actually higher than in the week before the gale; the tonnage of stores as much as a

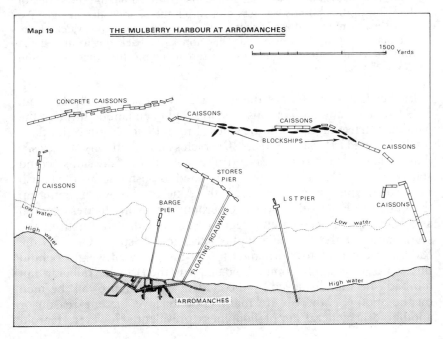

Map 19   THE MULBERRY HARBOUR AT ARROMANCHES

0   1500 Yards

CONCRETE CAISSONS

CAISSONS

CAISSONS

BLOCKSHIPS

CAISSONS

CAISSONS

STORES PIER

Low water

CAISSONS

BARGE PIER

L S T PIER

CAISSONS

High water

FLOATING ROADWAYS

Low water

High water

ARROMANCHES

third higher.[65] In the same week (on 26 June) Force Pluto brought the first of the 'Tombola' ship-to-shore pipelines into action at Port en Bessin. Thus was swiftly overcome a crisis that could have endangered the whole campaign.

On the advice of ANCXF and the American admirals Eisenhower decided that no attempt should be made to repair the wrecked Mulberry harbour at Omaha, and instead all spare components used to make good the relatively light damage to the British Mulberry and strengthen it against the winter weather. Henceforward the Americans would largely rely on pontoon piers extending off open beaches – with astonishing success, as it was to prove. On 29 June the first cargoes were discharged on to the main stores pier of the British Mulberry. When on 19 July the landing ship (tank) pier came into operation, it marked the completion of the project at long last. On that day a total of 7,000 tons of stores, the figure originally planned for the Mulberry, was unloaded. Ten days later the daily total of stores landed in the Mulberry reached a record 11,000 tons, together with nearly 4,000 men and over 400 vehicles.[66]

On 24 June Admiral Ramsay formally wound up 'Neptune' as an operation distinct from 'Overlord'. Since D-Day the Allied navies and the Merchant Marine had landed 714,000 men, 111,571 vehicles and 259,724 tons of stores.[67] When he had had the time to reflect, Ramsay was to record in his pocket diary a private 'Thought on Neptune': 'Because it all went so smoothly it may seem to some people that it was all easy & plain sailing. Nothing could be more wrong. It was excellent planning & execution . . .'[68]

Rear-Admiral J. W. Rivett-Carnac, Flag Officer, British Assault Area, hoisted his flag in a shore headquarters at Courseulles in succession to the three British assault force commanders, who returned to England during the next week. In the same period Admiral J. W. Wilkes of the United States Navy similarly took over from Rear Admirals Moon and Hall in the American assault area. The NCETF, Vice-Admiral Sir Philip Vian, returned to England on 30 June; Admiral Kirk, NCWTF, on 3 July. Two days later the millionth Allied soldier stepped ashore in France; apt and timely enough testimony to 'Neptune's' success.

The winding-up of 'Operation Neptune' signified the tremendous fact that the Western Front had now been firmly re-established – four years almost to the day after its collapse because of the French Army's capitulation. On this new Western Front was being fought a bloody struggle of attrition amid the high hedgerows of the *bocage*; a struggle in which for the time being both sides remained evenly balanced. Yet it was vital for the Allies that this should not bog down in long-term stalemate, as Hitler and his generals now hoped. Instead the limited German resources must first be ground away by attrition until only a fragile defensive crust remained, whereupon the Allied Expeditionary Force must (as envisaged in Montgomery's master plan) break out into open country and destroy the enemy in a great offensive. But this whole process depended on a continuing copious flow of tanks, guns, trucks, stores, fuel and reinforcements into the Normandy lodgement, to say nothing of all the elaborate base facilities needed by modern armies.

For the Western Allies, therefore, seapower remained as ever the midwife of victory on land.

Victory in Europe

On 26 July the German garrison commander of Cherbourg surrendered after troops of the American 1st Army had fought their way into the city. A bombardment of two coastal batteries the day before by two groups of ships under the command of Rear Admirals M. L. Deyo and C. F. Bryant of the US Navy had served to repeat yet again the ancient lesson first learnt by the Royal Navy at the siege of Havana in 1762 that naval gunfire is not particularly effective against casemated cannon ashore. The battery at Querqueville remained in action despite the attempts to silence it by a battleship (the 14-inch USS *Nevada*), four heavy cruisers (the USS *Tuscaloosa*, flying the flag of Rear Admiral Deyo, and *Quincy*, and HMS *Glasgow* and *Enterprise*) and six destroyers.[1] A second bombarding group consisting of the battleships USS *Texas* (flying the flag of Rear Admiral Bryant) and *Arkansas* and four American destroyers took on the 11-inch guns of 'Battery Hamburg'. After *Texas* had fired 206 14-inch rounds, *Arkansas* 58 12-inch and the destroyers a total of 552 5-inch, three out of the four enemy guns were still firing back.[2] Fortunately the German batteries proved equally ineffective, often straddling the Allied warships but inflicting only two hits, both on HMS *Glasgow* and neither serious.

Minesweeping and port-clearance parties immediately moved into the docks at Cherbourg to begin their work according to the procedure laid down in Ramsay's 'Operation Neptune – Naval Orders'. The overall clearance operation was directed by Commodore W. A. Sullivan, USN, who the year before had cleared the port of Naples. The bulk of the minesweepers being British, responsibility for minesweeping was given to Commander J. R. G. Temple, RN. Sullivan and

Temple faced a colossal task, as Ramsay saw for himself when he visited Cherbourg on 6 July:

> The damage is unbelievable, the place lending itself readily to demolition owing to peculiar construction of the Keys [sic]. Dry dock basins undamaged but blocked by sunken ships & craft. It will take anything up to three months to clear these wrecks, but meantime temporary measures such as landing stores in Duck & L.C.T.s & barges can be started. Later on coasters & later M/T ships . . .[3]

By 16 July over a hundred mines had been swept for the loss of three minesweepers and seven other smaller craft. Not least of the hazards thoughtfully left behind by the Germans were all manner of underwater explosive devices. These were tackled by British 'P' parties – young volunteer divers practised in the art of finding such devices in muddy waters and disarming them by finger-tip feel. Over a six-week period they explored the entire bottom of the Cherbourg docks. It therefore stands greatly to the credit of the clearance and minesweeping parties that by the beginning of August 8,500 tons of stores were being discharged in Cherbourg every day. A month later that figure would have doubled.[4]

The capture of Cherbourg opened the way for Force Pluto to begin in mid-August laying the cross-Channel oil pipeline from the Isle of Wight ('Bambi'). However, the project encountered one technical or operational setback after another and as a result no oil was pumped through until 22 September. On 3 October both types of pipe, the HAMEL and the HAIS, failed. By the beginning of November 'Bambi' had been virtually abandoned, the Minister of Fuel and Power, Gwilym Lloyd George, reporting to the Prime Minister:

> Of the four pipe-lines eventually laid from the Isle of Wight to Cherbourg, two proved defective, and the other two broke when the pumping pressure was increased from 'reduced' to 'working'. A decision was consequently made to abandon this project at least for the time being.[5]

The 'Tombola' ship-to-shore system proved the more dependable, as the British Army had always believed it would, and the quiet village of Port en Bessin became a major oil terminal.

With the occupation of the Cotentin Peninsula the Allies possessed the depth of lodgement they needed in order to build up their armies for the breakout. All the while Montgomery proceeded remorselessly with his 1917-style attrition battle with the British 2nd Army and the 1st Canadian Army (formed on 23 July). His frontal offensives forced the enemy to commit his panzer divisions piecemeal to holding the line, whereupon they were crunched up by massed air and artillery bombardment.

The German Navy could do little to help its comrades in field-grey during this mincing process amid the hedgerows of the *bocage* – only nuisance attacks against the 'Trout Line' guarding the eastern flank of Allied shipping lying off the beaches. During July no fewer than ten night-time clashes took place between frigates and MTBs of the Royal Navy and enemy E-boats, which had been reinforced to a total of twenty. New but largely ineffective marvels of German technology took to the sea – the 'Marder' 2.5-knot electrically-propelled human torpedo with a range of 35 miles; the 'Linse' radio-controlled, explosive-packed motor boat; the 'Dackel' long-range circling torpedo.[6] The total bag of these devices in July and August amounted to the destroyer HMS *Quorn*, three minesweepers, two transports, one trawler and two landing craft sunk, and the Polish-manned cruiser *Dragon*, the old cruiser HMS *Frobisher*, the repair ship *Albatross* and a minesweeper damaged. Their own losses at the hands of the Royal Navy and Royal Air Force Coastal Command came to 96 '*Marders*' out of 147 despatched on sorties, and 30 out of 60 '*Linses*'.[7]

The U-boats fared no better in their own renewed attempts to interfere with Allied cross-Channel traffic, losing seven boats to the Royal Navy and two to Coastal Command in the Channel and the Bay of Biscay between 1 July and 4 August but sinking in return only two ships.[8]

Since neither the German Navy nor the Luftwaffe (reduced to hit-and-run raids and minelaying) could choke back the flow of Allied military power into Normandy, it continued to fall to the German 7th Army and 5th Panzer Army to hold it back in battle as best they could. But by the fourth week of July they had no more reserves in hand either to patch the front or mount counter-attacks. When this was reported to Hitler along with the warning that the front must soon collapse, Hitler gave his customary absurd order to stand fast rather than retire in good time. By now six panzer divisions were deployed along the 1st Canadian Army and the British 2nd Army front; only two facing the American 1st Army. The time had come for Montgomery to launch the breakout which he had so patiently and cunningly prepared. On 25 July the American 1st Army struck south in 'Operation Cobra' against an enemy defence demoralised or obliterated by over 4,700 tons of bombs dropped by nearly 1,900 aircraft, burst through during the next two days, and poured south-westwards and then westwards into Brittany.

This sweeping American advance now had an unfortunate by-product: it revived the Prime Minister's slumbering opportunism. Hitherto he had interfered little in the strategic and tactical design of 'Neptune'/'Overlord', except to favour the sailors with advice about the high efficacy of naval gunfire against shore targets. Rather as Chairman of the 'Overlord' Preparations Committee he had constructively put his energies to serving Eisenhower's needs. Now on 4 August he proposed to Roosevelt that 'Anvil' (now renamed 'Dragoon'), the landing on the Côte d'Azur scheduled for 15 August, should after all be abandoned; this time in order to free warships and assault shipping for improvised landings at St Nazaire and other ports along the southern coast of Brittany (the Prime Minister in his memoirs however gives Bordeaux as his chosen objective).[9] Here was the gambler of the Dardanelles and Norway, of Dakar and the Aegean Islands, come to life again to vex the Allied leadership in the very climax – ironically enough – of the most carefully, most thoroughly planned and prepared combined operation ever. On 5 August Churchill convened a meeting with Eisenhower, Cunningham, Ramsay (who was 'thoroughly aggrieved & annoyed' at being hauled back from a much-needed leave),[10] and Bedell Smith, Eisenhower's Chief of Staff. The Prime Minister employed all his relentless powers of persuasion and pressure, especially on the Supreme Allied Commander, to induce them to back his proposal. 'We argued for 2½ hours,' wrote Ramsay in his diary, 'with Ike holding firm & the P.M. doing all he could to move him. I supported Ike strongly which didn't please the P.M. C.N.S. [Cunningham] supported P.M. We left off with nothing done.'[11] To his wife Ramsay reported that night that he could well have remained at home in Scotland

> . . . had it not occurred to the P.M. to think of one of his hot schemes & wanted to discuss it. Well we've discussed it and I believe killed it & so now we are no further on. When this kind of thing happens I wish we had a P.M. who left the Forces to run the war. At other times I appreciate the value of the P.M. boosting things . . .[12]

On 9 August Churchill had finally to bow before the adamant refusals of Eisenhower, the US Joint Chiefs and even Roosevelt himself to abandon 'Dragoon'; evidence of how diminished was his sway as a war-lord compared with former years.[13]

The Americans had been continuing to race on. By 6 August they had completely cut off the Brittany peninsula. On the 10th Nantes on the Loire fell, and the German troops isolated in Brittany fell back into the fortress-ports like Brest. Eisenhower now ordered the American forces to swing eastwards and then northwards to meet the British and Canadians driving down southwards, so cutting off the German armies in Normandy altogether. Hitler played into his hands by ordering his troops to launch a counter-offensive towards the west coast of the Cotentin Peninsula, with the unrealistic objective of severing the American communications. This only thrust the German head deeper into the Allied trap. By 12 August the 7th Army and 5th Panzer Army were struggling to escape as the trap closed at Falaise; a marvellous target for the Allied air forces. On 22 August the Falaise pocket was squeezed flat. The Battle of Normandy was over; the wreckage of the German defenders was retreating pell-mell towards the Low Countries and the Fatherland.

Since the Royal and United States Navies put the Allied expeditionary force ashore on D-Day, the enemy had lost 400,000 men killed, wounded and missing; 1,300 tanks; 20,000 vehicles; 500 assault guns; and 1,500 field guns. The equivalent of five panzer divisions and twenty infantry divisions had been destroyed, and the equivalent of six other panzer divisions and twelve infantry divisions badly mauled.[14] This was complete victory; victory on a scale that dwarfed the Allied successes in the Mediterranean theatre; victory on the shortest route to the enemy heartland; the first victory won by Western democracies over a great German army since 1918; victory which abundantly, triumphantly, fulfilled the object of 'Operation Neptune' as defined back in April by Admiral Ramsay on page one of his 'Naval Orders' in the soberest of staff language: '. . . to carry out an operation from the United Kingdom to secure a lodgement on the Continent from which further offensive operations can be developed . . .'

And still the unsung service of the Royal and United States Navies and the Merchant Marine continued to make it all possible. By the end of August they had landed in France the stupendous totals of 2,052,000 men, 438,461 vehicles and 3,098,259 tons of stores.[15] Yet now that its main mission was accomplished, the 'Neptune' fleet had begun to disperse. The three American battleships and HMS *Ramillies*, together with the cruisers USS *Augusta*, *Quincy* and *Tuscaloosa* had sailed to the Mediterranean along with much assault shipping to take part in the 'Dragoon' landings in the South of France on 15 August. Mounted and launched according to the well-established patterns of Mediterranean long-distance amphibious operations, 'Dragoon' encountered only light opposition. On 28 August French troops occupied Marseille, while American troops pushed on up the Rhône valley to join (on 15 September) the eastern flank of Eisenhower's armies in Alsace. This same month, with the German E-boats in the Channel now a spent force, the Admiralty withdrew from Ramsay some fifty flotilla vessels for employment as escorts to the North Russian convoys (see above, pp. 747–8), or sent as reinforcements to the Eastern Fleet.

In any case the Allied armies by their advance along the Channel coast had repaid their debt to the navies by shifting the front line for skirmishing with E-boats and other small craft from the Bay of Biscay and the English Channel to the southern North Sea. On 16 August Dönitz ordered the U-boats based on the now isolated Biscay ports to make for Norway, so finally liquidating the priceless strategic asset of direct access to the Atlantic which he had exploited to the very verge of victory in 1940–43. The vast U-boat pens lay empty now under their indestructible carapaces of concrete, at one with Roman walls and Crusader castles; prodigies of military engineering to be marvelled at by future ages. The slinking away to Norway of the Biscay boats was successfully covered by a diversionary offensive in the Channel by eight U-boats, which sank six merchantmen, the Canadian corvette *Regina*, a minesweeper and a landing craft (infantry). Nonetheless the month of August 1944 signalled yet another massacre of U-boats at the hands of the Royal Navy and Coastal Command, twelve being destroyed in the Bay of Biscay and another four in the Channel.[16]

At the beginning of September it seemed for a heady moment as though the Allied armies' pursuit could roll straight on into the heart of Germany. Eisenhower wanted this pursuit to be conducted by both his army groups – Montgomery's 21st and General Omar Bradley's 12th. Montgomery argued instead for a single concentrated thrust north of the Ardennes by his own Army Group (augmented by American divisions) aimed at the Ruhr industrial area. But the acrimonious debate turned entirely on the question of logistics. The Allied lines of communication to their United Kingdom base still ran through the Normandy beaches and the British Mulberry harbour, although Cherbourg was beginning to be of some help. On 13 September 1944, after consulting Admiral Ramsay, Montgomery and Bradley, Eisenhower issued a directive for the next stage of the campaign in which he sombrely stated:

Our port position is such that a stretch of a week or ten days of bad weather in the Channel – a condition that is growing increasingly probable as the summer recedes – would paralyse our activities and so make the

maintenance of our forces exceedingly difficult, even in defensive roles
. . . without improved communications speedy and prolonged advance by
our forces, adequate in strength and depending on bulk oil, ammunition
and transport, is not a feasible operation . . .[17]

In his judgment therefore '. . . the object we must now attain, one
which has been foreseen as essential from the very inception of the
OVERLORD plan, is the gaining of deep water ports to support major
forces in an invasion of Germany'. And above all this meant ports
north of the Seine, in order to shorten overstretched land communications. Thus final victory on the Western Front – the march of
Anglo-American armies to meet the Red Army in the heart of the
Reich – depended just as much as 'Overlord' on solving a basic
problem of a Continental campaign reliant on sea-communications:
that of adequate port capacity. Hitler and the German high command
understood this perfectly. This was why the German garrisons now
isolated in strongly fortified ports along the French Atlantic and
Channel coasts had been ordered to hold out to the last; this was why,
as the Allies had already discovered to their dismay in Cherbourg,
ingeniously comprehensive schemes of sabotage and mining had been
prepared against the day when resistance must cease.

The Channel ferry ports, Boulogne, Calais, Dunkirk and Ostend,
had all been invested by Canadian troops between 6 and 8 September,
but of them only Ostend fell without delay. Boulogne held out until
22 September; Calais until 1 October; Dunkirk until the end of the
war. At Boulogne Royal Navy port-clearance parties found 26 sunken
ships blocking the harbour entrance; it was not until mid-October
that a channel had been opened and the wrecked cranes and cratered
quays sufficiently cleared to permit five coasters to berth.[18] In Ostend
the clearance parties found the basins and harbour entrance fouled
by fourteen sunken ships, many of the quays totally demolished, and
others partly so. It was a tribute to the efforts of the clearance parties
that the first coasters crept their way in to Ostend on 25 September,
and that by the end of the month 1,000 tons of stores were being
unloaded each day. Yet it took until mid-November completely to
clear and widen a channel into the harbour; until the end of November
for daily discharges to rise to 5,000 tons.[19] No quick solution in
the Channel ports, then, to Eisenhower's acute supply crisis at the
beginning of September.

Of the three great deep-water ports along the Channel and North
Sea coasts of France and Belgium, Le Havre was the first to fall, on
12 September, to the 50th and 51st British Infantry Divisions after

the Royal Air Force had stunned and demoralised the defenders by dropping 9,500 tons of bombs in the previous seven days, and HMS *Warspite* (patched up again after being mined in July in the Thames) and the monitor HMS *Erebus* had helped things along with 15-inch shells. Royal Navy port-clearance parties immediately moved into the port to begin their work, but the enemy had carried out his blocking, booby-trapping and demolition with such thoroughness that Le Havre was not to be fully operational until mid-October.[20] On 19 September Brest, in the west of Brittany, surrendered after a bitterly fought siege of 40 days which cost the American 3rd Army more than 10,000 men killed and wounded.[21] Here a culminating bombardment by massed artillery supplemented by that ubiquitous and ever-useful old warrior, HMS *Warspite*, did the trick. In the original 'Overlord' planning high hopes had been entertained of Brest as a supply port, but in the event the prize went to the German demolition parties. So colossal was the problem presented by all the sunken blockships and the lavish sowing of oyster pressure mines that no attempt to clear Brest was made until 1945.[22]

In all the circumstances it was therefore extraordinarily fortunate that Antwerp fell to the British 11th Armoured Division on 4 September. Here was the ideal deep-water port, located conveniently close in the rear of Montgomery's 21st Army Group. There was however a snag. It lay 80 miles up the Scheldt from the North Sea, and the Germans held bridgeheads on the south bank of the river as well as the Dutch islands of South Beveland and Walcheren to the north. As Admiral Ramsay wrote in his diary, 'Antwerp is useless until the Scheldt Estuary is cleared of the enemy.'[23]

On the day before Antwerp fell Ramsay therefore signalled SHAEF 'For Action', with copies to 21st Army Group, the Admiralty and the C-in-C Nore, to warn:

It is essential that if Antwerp and Rotterdam [the latter in fact not to fall until the end of the war] are to be opened quickly enemy must be prevented from
(i) Carrying out demolitions and blocking in ports
(ii) Mining and blocking Scheldt . . .

2. Both Antwerp and Rotterdam are highly vulnerable to mining and blocking. If enemy succeeds in these operations the time it will take to open ports cannot be estimated.
3. It will be necessary for coastal batteries to be captured before approach channels to the river routes can be established.[24]

Eisenhower himself immediately hauled in this warning. When next day he signalled Montgomery to turn down the Field-Marshal's strategy of concentrating on the Ruhr and insist instead on his own 'broad front' step-by-step offensive, he remarked: 'While we are advancing we will be opening the ports of Havre and Antwerp, which are essential to sustain a powerful thrust into Germany . . .'[25] Moreover the Supreme Commander was repeatedly to allude to the importance of opening Antwerp during the ensuing debate with Montgomery over future strategy.[26] In a key strategic directive of 13 September after conferences with Montgomery, Bradley and Admiral Ramsay, he specifically instructed that while the Allied armies advanced into Germany, 'Northern Group Armies [i.e., Montgomery] must secure the approaches to Antwerp or Rotterdam quickly . . .'[27] Montgomery's own orders next day, defining the Allied objective as the Ruhr, certainly did observe that 'on the way to it we want the ports of Antwerp and Rotterdam . . .', but they placed the clearance of Antwerp second to an offensive by the 2nd Army across the Maas and Lower Rhine.[28] The orders instructed the 1st Canadian Army first of all to capture Boulogne and Calais, and only then to direct 'its whole energies' towards 'operations designed to enable full use to be made of the port of Antwerp . . .'[29]

Neglecting therefore the overriding importance to the Allied campaign of first clearing the Scheldt, Montgomery chose instead to embark (with Eisenhower's acquiescence, be it said) on 'Operation Market Garden', the attempt to drive across the Maas and Lower Rhine at Arnhem by landing the American 82nd and British 1st Airborne Divisions to seize the bridges while powerful ground forces bludgeoned their way north to link up with them. Between 17 and 26 September this offensive failed of its purpose, the 1st Airborne Division being virtually destroyed, never to be reconstituted.

Meanwhile Antwerp remained closed; other captured ports were only slowly, if at all, becoming usable. The Allied supply position remained hideously precarious[30] – with a long winter campaign now in the offing. For by this time the professional competence and moral resilience of the German Army had punctured the Allies' post-Normandy victory euphoria. From the first week in September onwards Allied spearheads along the whole front from the North Sea to Alsace stumbled up against the familiar screen of battlegroups. Headlong chase gave way to slow, small and painful advances in the autumn rains and mud. It became depressingly plain that the Allies now faced a long slog into 1945 – a winter campaign huge in its demands for replacements of men, weapons and equipment, for ammunition, motor and aviation fuel and stores of every kind. Yet Allied communications by land and sea were already stretched humming taut, with all parts by no means bearing an even strain.

In this new and unwelcome situation, the Allies' entire continental strategy once more turned on ships and on ports where they could unload. In particular the clearing of the Scheldt had now acquired a desperate urgency. On 5 October Admiral Ramsay, who had been becoming more and more worried in the course of the previous month about the failure to tackle this, attended a meeting at Supreme Allied Headquarters (now at Versailles, with a forward command post at Rheims) held to discuss future policy. Present were Eisenhower, Sir Alan Brooke, Tedder, Leigh-Mallory, Montgomery, Bradley and General J. L. Devers (commanding the newly constituted US 6th Army Group). According to Ramsay's diary for that day

> Monty made the startling announcement that we could take the Ruhr without Antwerp. This afforded me the cue I needed to lambast him for not having made the capture of Antwerp the immediate objective at highest priority, & I let fly with all my guns at the faulty strategy we had allowed. Our large forces were now practically grounded for lack of supply, & had we now got Antwerp and not the [Arnhem] corridor we should be in a far better position for launching the knock-out blow . . . I got approving looks from Tedder & Bedell Smith, and both of these, together with CIGS, told me after the meeting that I had spoken their thoughts & that it was high time someone expressed them . . .[31]

Three days later came fresh trouble on the supply front: the Channel gales struck again at the Normandy beaches and the Mulberry harbour, and even caused damage to the harbour of Cherbourg. Ramsay was therefore the more relieved to understand that Montgomery's plan for 21st Army Group

> . . . has been modified to give greater priority to Canadian army at expense of 2nd army, so as to concentrate on capture of entrances to Antwerp & of confluences of Rotterdam & the Dutch Islands. I feel sure that this is due to my address at the recent C-in-Cs meeting & the intervention of C.I.G.S. who backed my remarks & told me he intended to speak to Monty. I regard this as a major achievement. The administrative position of the armies is undoubtedly bad & Ike & SHAEF are properly fussed – as they should be.[32]

Ramsay congratulated himself too soon: Montgomery's fresh orders next day still placed the clearing of the Scheldt third in priority among tasks for his Army Group.[33] An infuriated Eisenhower signalled

Montgomery that the reduction in the flow of supplies through the Mulberry and Cherbourg because of the gale 're-emphasises the supreme importance of Antwerp':

> . . . I must repeat that we are now squarely up against the situation which has been anticipated for months and our intake into the Continent will not repeat not support our battle. Unless we have Antwerp producing by the middle of November our entire operations will come to a standstill. I must emphasise that, of all our operations on our entire front from Switzerland to the Channel, I consider Antwerp of first importance . . .[34]

Despite this and a later broadside from the Supreme Commander it was not until 16 October that Montgomery at last unequivocally ordered:

> 1. The free use of the port of Antwerp is vital to the Allied cause, and we must be able to use the port soon.
> 2. Operations destined to open the port will therefore be given complete priority over all other offensive operations in 21 Army Group, without any qualification whatsoever . . .[35]

Thus did the commander of the 21st Army Group finally acknowledge the crucial importance of seaborne supply up the Scheldt and through Antwerp – six weeks late.[36]

Meanwhile, with the main offensive to clear the Scheldt still yet to begin, Eisenhower himself was more than ever glad that he had insisted on 'Operation Dragoon' against all pressure, and now enjoyed the use of Marseille and Toulon, by this time together handling some 13,000 tons of stores a day.[37]

The Dutch islands of South Beveland and Walcheren which commanded the Scheldt from the north were defended by the 70th ('stomach trouble') Infantry Division, all men with gastric disorders and requiring special rations – a mark of the German Army's dearth of manpower after three and a half years of gutting on the Russian Front.[38] Yet they were to fight with skill and determination. The coming campaign was to prove a tough struggle along muddy dykes and across wastes of water.

Admiral Ramsay and Lieutenant-General G. C. Simonds, commanding the 2nd Canadian Corps, jointly planned the campaign as a combination of frontal attacks overland along the dykes linking the islands to each other and to the mainland and landings from the Royal Navy's landing craft to turn the enemy's defences.[39] On 24–26 October 1944 a Canadian infantry brigade assaulted the South

Beveland isthmus, a hard fight. On the 26th the Royal Navy ferried units of the British 52nd Division across the eight-mile-wide estuary of the Scheldt in a little armada of amphibious craft to land on South Beveland's southern shore behind the defenders, opposite the Canadians. Nonetheless, it still took five days of water-logged combat to clear the enemy out of the island.

On 31 October was opened the attack on the neighbouring island of Walcheren; a place of ill-omen because a British expeditionary force had died there of malaria ('Walcheren fever') in 1807 during the Napoleonic Wars in a particularly futile exercise in maritime strategy. Once again Ramsay and Simonds coupled direct overland attack with a seaborne outflanking movement. Bomber Command having smashed breaches in the sea-dykes, Walcheren was now merely a rim of land flooded in the middle. On 31 October Canadian troops began fighting their way westwards along the narrow causeway from South Beveland to Walcheren; by 2 November they had secured a precarious bridgehead at the Walcheren end. The day before, and following heavy air and artillery attack on enemy batteries, the Royal Navy had landed an assault force at Flushing in the south of the island and another at Westkappelle in the extreme west. It took the Flushing assault force four days of battle, building by building, to clear the town and its docks.

Ramsay and Simonds had designed the Westkappelle landing as a miniature repetition of the assaults on D-Day. Firstly, a bombarding squadron consisting of HMS *Warspite* (in the last shoot of her distinguished service since Jutland) and the monitors *Erebus* and *Roberts* hammered the German coastal batteries with 15-inch salvoes; then massed artillery at Breskens on the south bank of the Scheldt joined in; and finally, as the assault waves headed for the shore, 27 landing craft armed with guns or rockets, together with rocket-firing Typhoon aircraft, smothered the enemy beach defences at close range with explosive. Despite the loss of twenty landing craft to enemy shells and the usual kind of snags and hold-ups on beaching under accurate artillery and machine-gun fire, the leading assault waves (Royal Marine and Inter-Allied Commandos) soon overran the shore batteries and secured beach-heads. Now began a step-by-step advance outwards from Westkappelle along the rim of dyke leading round the north and south of the island. But on 3 November Ramsay and the Royal Navy again exploited the mobility of seapower, this time by landing two British infantry brigades on the eastern shore of Walcheren in order to outflank the German defence penning the Canadians into their bridgehead at the end of the causeway from South Beveland. Five days later the commander of the 70th Division surrendered with his 2,000 remaining soldiers.

Both banks of the Scheldt were finally clear of German troops. But now came the formidable job of sweeping 80 miles of estuary and river. To accomplish it Ramsay deployed more than ten squadrons of minesweepers working from both ends under the command of Captain H. G. Hopper, RN (Captain Minesweeping, Sheerness). At the cost of one vessel sunk with all hands and after a total of 267 mines had been swept, Hopper's minesweepers completed their task on 26 November, a week under the estimate.[40] That day three coasters reached Antwerp. On 28 November the first convoy of nineteen Liberty ships came alongside the quays. Antwerp was at last open for business, no fewer than 60 days after Allied troops first captured it.[41]

By this time too Le Havre and the Channel ports had been cleared and opened, and the second Pluto pipeline ('Dumbo') successfully laid between Dungeness and Boulogne, pumping through 600 tons of petroleum a day by the beginning of December. By March 1945 (with eleven pipelines laid), a daily average of over 3,000 tons would be pumped through Dumbo.[42]

So the Allied Expeditionary Force's supply crisis passed. From November 1944 onwards through the winter and into the spring of 1945 seapower and sea-communications would feed the armies on the Western Front with all they needed, first to defeat the German counter-stroke in the Ardennes in December; then to chew their way forward to the Rhine in a new series of attrition battles; and finally to burst over the Rhine in April 1945 in the climactic offensive of the German war. In that month, 1,341,610 tons of stores were discharged through Antwerp (some two-thirds for the United States armies) and 288,809 tons of 'POL' (petrol, oil, lubricants); 91,505 tons of stores for 21st Army Group through Ostend, and 4,893 through Calais and Boulogne. Through Le Havre and Rouen for the American armies came 406,146 tons of stores and 144,721 tons of 'POL'; through Cherbourg and minor Normandy ports 228,585 tons of stores and 161,045 tons of 'POL'; and through Mediterranean French ports 484,631 tons of stores and 153,871 tons of 'POL'.[43] Such was the staggering arithmetic of the service rendered by seapower to victory in the decisive theatre of war.

Yet it is convincing proof of the cost-effectiveness in shipping of a Continental strategy based on short cross-Channel sea routes compared with long-distance 'blue water' strategy that the average deadweight tonnage of deep-sea cargo vessels required between the beginning of June and the end of December 1944 to support the

Western Front amounted to only about 17 per cent of that required in the summer of 1942 to supply the Middle East, Persian Gulf and India.[44] There is even more striking proof: whereas an average total of one million deadweight tons of shipping supported a maximum of 90 divisions on the Western Front, nearly *seven million* tons allotted to the Mediterranean theatre supported a maximum of only 27 divisions on the Italian front.[45]

Throughout the winter of 1944–45 and on into the spring the German Navy did its best to relieve the mounting pressure on the German Army on the Western Front by attacking the dense traffic of shipping from southern England to Antwerp and the Channel ports. From their Dutch bases the E-boats sneaked out on more than 350 sorties to lay mines or torpedo the unwary. 'Small Battle Units' – one- and two-man human torpedoes, 'Linse' remote-controlled explosive motor boats, the new 'Hecht' and 'Seehund' midget submarines – braved the hazards of the open sea and the watchful Allied patrols on the surface and in the air. But once again the E-boats and the 'Small Battle Units' proved no more than nuisance. From January 1945 to the end of the war they sank only 47 Allied ships totalling 108,213 tons, the bulk of these falling victim to E-boats.[46]

It was the U-boat that caused the Admiralty much greater concern, for new German technology and new patterns of deployment had largely mastered the Royal Navy's and Coastal Command's hitherto successful hunting devices and tactical methods.[47] Thanks to the 'Schnorchel' the U-boat had no longer to surface by day or night to recharge her batteries, so denying airborne 10cm radars a target. In any event U-boats were now fitted with metric band radar search receivers on their Schnorchel tubes which could give warning of 10cm radar signals if close enough. Because U-boat Command was now deploying its boats widely spread on individual missions, there was no need for the dense radio traffic necessary for controlling 'wolf-pack' operations, and in any case U-boats had little opportunity for radio-signalling now that they spent so much time submerged.

As a result of these developments neither Ultra nor HF/DF, key instruments of victory in the Battle of the Atlantic, were any longer of much use. And the U-boats' new favourite hunting ground lay in the inshore waters round the British Isles, rather than the high seas; here they could hide from sonar under the temperature layers created by tidal streams and river estuaries, or among the wrecks that strewed the bottom of these waters. The enemy had ushered in an entirely novel phase of submarine warfare, foreshadowing the techniques of the coming age of the nuclear submarine, and the Admiralty found itself baffled. As the First Sea Lord explained to the C-in-C, Mediterranean, on 1 September 1944:

The submarines and the Oyster mines have been giving us considerable trouble. Curiously, we thought that if and when the submarines came into the Channel from the Atlantic, they would be easy to kill. Just the contrary was the case. Our escort groups had to learn a completely new technique as the submarines developed the habit of lying on the bottom and it was difficult to distinguish them from wrecks. However they have all cleared out now as they cannot work any longer from the Biscay ports ... 44 essayed channel operations against the OVERLORD supply routes and of these 23, we think, have been sunk. They are now clustering round our coasts on the trade routes and will not be easy to deal with. They are so dispersed that it is actually taking a greater effort than when they went about in packs in the Atlantic.[48]

On 19 January 1945, when writing in much the same vein to the C-in-C, Home Fleet, the First Sea Lord gloomily added that the scientists 'have not yet caught up, and the air is 90 per cent out of the picture'[49] – meaning, that is, in terms of actual U-boat kills. In the meantime, and while new sonar techniques and hunting tactics were being evolved, the Royal Navy and Coastal Command could only attempt a blanket suppression of the U-boats by sheer numbers of ships and aircraft and density of patrolling, supplemented by extensive deep minefields in the Channel and Irish Sea. Western Approaches Command deployed 37 escort groups (fourteen of them from the Royal Canadian Navy), and the naval home commands a total of five destroyer flotillas, plus the Rosyth Escort Force – in all 426 destroyers, frigates, corvettes and sloops. By February 1945 no fewer than 528 aircraft out of Coastal Command's total strength of 793 were flying on anti-submarine duties.[50] This immense effort certainly succeeded in keeping shipping losses in British home waters down to fourteen merchantmen between September and December 1944, and in destroying in return 37 U-boats (including those sunk in the Arctic).[51] Yet this rate of destruction was lower in proportion to the total U-boat fleet than in 1940 and 1941.[52] At the beginning of 1945 the war of the U-boat therefore lay in stalemate, neither side being able to inflict decisive loss.

Yet Dönitz nonetheless cherished bright hopes of breaking this stalemate and unleashing a new and this time victorious U-boat offensive – not only in British home waters, but also in the Atlantic. Thanks to the resourcefulness of Albert Speer, Reichsminister for armaments, U-boat production had risen steeply through 1944 even in the face of Allied bombing. In January 1945 as many as thirty boats were commissioned; in March the U-boat arm reached its wartime peak of 459 boats.[53] Even worse from the British Admiralty's point of view, almost all the boats now being completed were the formidable new Type XXIs and Type XXIIIs, streamlined harbingers of the future. The 1,600-ton Type XXI could cruise as far as the Pacific without refuelling and reach a sprinting speed when deeply submerged of 16 to 17 knots on her electric motors; as fast as most Allied convoy escort vessels such as the British River class frigates or Castle class corvettes. Moreover, during a pursuit at this speed the noise caused by water rushing and bubbling along the pursuer's own hull would deafen his sonars. When dived to maximum depth under attack the Type XXI could cruise for nearly 300 miles at 6 knots on her electric motors, as against barely 100 miles and 2 knots by the VIIC U-boats of the Battle of the Atlantic. The anti-submarine forces' existing operational arithmetic of search and kill would thus be rendered null and void: whereas the area unit in searching for a traditional U-boat had been 31,400 square miles, it would be 282,000 square miles for the Type XXI.[54]

In sum, the Allied navies had no ready technical or operational answers to the Type XXI, about whose development and rate of production the Admiralty were kept depressingly well informed by Sigint and photo-reconnaissance.[55] On 18 December 1944 the Admiralty estimated that 95 Type XXIs were now under construction and 35 already completed.[56] A month later the First Sea Lord was warning the Chiefs of Staff that a new Battle of the Atlantic might be opened by the high-speed U-boats in February or March: '. . . the enemy may be able to maintain about 70, increasing to over 90, U-boats on patrol compared with about 60 during the height of the U-boat campaign in the Spring of 1943 . . .'[57] Given optimum morale in the U-boat crews and maximum numbers of U-boats on patrol, the First Sea Lord reckoned that 'merchant shipping losses of the order of 70 rising to 90 ships a month may possibly be expected compared with 60 a month during the spring of 1943 . . .' Such a scale of loss during the first half of 1945, he went on, 'may well prejudice the maintenance of our forces in Europe . . .'

From this second and potentially catastrophic Battle of the Atlantic, the Royal, Royal Canadian and United States Navies were in fact saved by the Allied armies on the Western Front and by the British and American heavy bomber forces – further repayment of their debt to seapower for making their own operations possible; a telling illustration of how sea, land and air operations can each promote the success of the others. For the advance of the Allied armies to the German frontier in the autumn of 1944 had served to push the German air-defence radars back from the Atlantic and the Channel coasts into the Reich itself, so giving the German fighters only very short warning of the approaching of bomber formations: a crippling handicap to an already enfeebled force. At the same time the ground stations for the bombers' navigational and target-finding devices such as H2S could be brought forward from southern England to the edge of German territory, so greatly extending the range at which accurate bombing was possible. The by-product of the Allied armies' conquests in 1944 was therefore a triumphant relaunching that autumn of the strategic air offensive against the German industrial machine; this time devastating in its accuracy against key targets such as petrol-from-coal plants, and only weakly resisted by the Luftwaffe.

Particularly effective was the so-called 'Transportation Plan', under which the Allied bomber forces progressively cut the German transport network – roads, rail, canals – to pieces, thus in the end paralysing industrial production. U-boat construction was especially vulnerable because it depended on shifting prefabricated hull sections up to 27 feet long and 25 feet high, weighing 150 tons, along the wide German canals to their points of assembly. In September 1944 Bomber Command blew the aqueduct on the Dortmund–Ems canal near Münster; in November it returned to blow it again after it had been painstakingly repaired. In November also the Command emptied the vital Mittelland canal, and emptied it again in January 1945. Neither canal carried any further traffic for the rest of the war. That month, Otto Merker, Speer's director of U-boat production, told him that ship-building had been 'especially hard hit by the various stoppages of canal navigation' and that they must switch to rail transportation;[58] an absurd suggestion in view of the current wrecking of the railways too. By March 1945 U-boat completions of all types had dropped to only ten.

As well as these industrial delays to production affecting the Type XXI and Type XXIII there were the inevitable technical teething troubles in newly completed U-boats to be overcome; crews to be trained in their operation. Dönitz sourly sums up the cumulative consequences for his hopes of a fresh Battle of the Atlantic: 'On account of the delays caused by the ever-increasing weight of the Allied air-raids on Germany, the first boats of the new Type XXIII were not commissioned until February, while the first Type XXI did not become operational until April 1945.'[59]

But by February Nazi Germany was already being fast squeezed to death between remorseless offensives by the Allied armies on the Western Front and the Red Army on the Eastern Front. By the end of the month the Anglo-Americans were nearing the Rhine along its entire length; the Russians were on the Oder barely sixty miles from Berlin. By April, when the first Type XXI U-boats became operational, the Western Allies were everywhere over the Rhine and racing forward against disintegrating resistance; on the 18th Field-Marshal Model and 325,000 soldiers cut off in the Ruhr surrendered. On the Eastern Front the Red Army smashed through the last German defence along the Oder and on the 25th completed the encirclement of Berlin. That same day American and Russian advanced guards linked up at Torgau on the Elbe, splitting what was left of the Reich into two. Thus did the armies in the most direct possible fashion put an end to Dönitz's hopes that his new U-boats might still win the war for Germany.

Yet his existing boats fought on. In April 1945 no fewer than 44 of them put to sea, including the first Type XXI (U-2511). The last weeks of the conflict saw as furious a struggle as ever between U-boats and Allied escorts and aircraft. The anti-submarine forces deployed their latest armoury – the British Squid mortar; the American aerial acoustic torpedo (codename 'Mark 24 Mine') which homed in on the sound of cavitation caused by a U-boat's propeller; the new 'retro-bomb' (a 36lb Hedgehog bomb fired *astern* by an aircraft over-flying at a height of 200 feet a submerged submarine located by the American 'Magnetic Anomaly Detector'); American 'Sono' buoys dropped into the water to transmit the sound of a U-boat by radio to patrolling aircraft. In the air, rocket-firing Typhoons of the 2nd Tactical Air Force based in Germany joined Coastal Command Mosquitos and Beaufighters in attacking U-boats which rashly remained on the surface to fight it out with their anti-aircraft armament, and sank no fewer than 27 U-boats in the last five weeks of the war.[60] British and American heavy bombers accounted for another eighteen boats in their home bases.[61] Between 1 January and 8 May U-boat losses from all causes amounted to 151, of which 36 fell victim to the Royal Navy and/or the Fleet Air Arm, twelve to the United States Navy (mostly in the Atlantic or off the east coast of America), and three to the Royal Canadian Navy.[62] Yet in the same period this death-ride of the U-boats only achieved total sinkings of 46 merchant ships of 281,716 tons – an average of only 70,000 tons a month, barely a seventh of the 1942 average.[63]

On 30 April, while the surviving ships' companies of the German Navy were still steadfastly doing their duty, their Führer shot himself in his bunker next to the shattered Reichschancellery in a Berlin now virtually totally in the hands of the Red Army. In accordance with Hitler's political testament, Grand Admiral Dönitz now succeeded him as head of a Nazi state with just a week to run; an accolade from the Führer to the unwaveringly loyal commander who had so nearly won the war for him against the Western Allies.

At 1830 on 4 May a German delegation to Field-Marshal Montgomery's tactical headquarters sat at a trestle table in a tent pitched on Lüneburg Heath and signed an 'Instrument of Surrender', to take effect at 0800 on 5 May

> ... of all German armed forces in Holland, in northwest Germany including the Friesian Islands and Heligoland and all the other islands, in Schleswig-Holstein, and in Denmark, to the C-in-C 21 Army Group. This to include all naval ships in these areas. These forces to lay down their arms and to surrender unconditionally.[64]

This was Britain's special moment of victory over Nazi Germany – a victory delivered in the end by armies, but armies which themselves had been delivered to the field of battle largely by the Royal Navy; a victory ultimately born of the Royal Navy's successful struggle to keep the sea-lanes to the British Isles open. Hence it was entirely apt that the German delegation should be led by the Commander-in-Chief of the German Navy, General-Admiral von Friedeburg; and that Montgomery should receive them beneath a Union Flag, also the flag flown at the main by an Admiral of the Fleet.

At 0241 on 7 May 1945 at Eisenhower's advanced headquarters in Rheims, General Alfred Jodl, Chief of Staff of the Armed Forces High Command (OKW), signed the unconditional surrender of all German forces by sea, land and air everywhere. At Russian insistence this surrender was formally ratified in Berlin next day, the German signatories this time being Field-Marshal Keitel, General Stumpf (C-in-C of the Luftwaffe), and once again General-Admiral von Friedeburg. Sadly, however, the British admiral who by his efficiency, common sense, tact and team spirit had done more than anyone except Eisenhower himself to enable 'Operation Neptune'/'Overlord' to succeed was not present at these ceremonies to witness the fulfilment of his endeavour. For Sir Bertram Ramsay had been tragically killed on 2 January 1945 when his aircraft crashed on take-off from a snow-covered airfield in France. He was replaced as ANCXF by Vice-Admiral Sir Harold Burrough.

At the end of this war there was no German fleet left to be conducted into a British base with studied drama by the Royal Navy. Of major surface ships, only the cruisers *Prinz Eugen* and *Nürnberg* surrendered intact, in Copenhagen. Bombing had destroyed the pocket battleships *Scheer* and *Lützow* in Kiel, the cruiser *Emden* in Swinemünde and *Köln* in Wilhelmshaven. The cruiser *Seydlitz* had been scuttled in Königsberg in East Prussia and the *Hipper* in Kiel. The Russians took over the wreck of the *Gneisenau* at Gotenhafen (Gdynia) and the uncompleted aircraft carrier *Graf Zeppelin* at Stettin. The badly damaged cruiser *Leipzig* fell into British hands in Denmark.

The humiliation of mass surrender was thus reserved for the U-boats, who were ordered by an Admiralty signal at noon on 8 May to surface, report their positions and sail to designated British ports. Two hundred and twenty-one boats chose to scuttle themselves in harbour or at sea rather than surrender, including 82 Type XXIs and twenty XXIIIs. This latter figure shows by what a narrow margin the final victory of the Allied armies had averted a major onslaught at sea to which British and American anti-submarine technology would have had no immediate answer. All four experimental Walter boats (hydrogen-peroxide fuelled) so far in commission were also scuttled.[65] In the course of the next month 150 U-boats, among them seventeen Type XXIIIs and one Type XXI, sailed under escort to British anchorages. Above their swastika flags blazed the White Ensign in token of the Royal Navy's victory in the hardest war of its four centuries of history.[66]

For the second time in 25 years and because of the follies of British policy in the 1920s and 1930s, the Royal Navy had had to fight the U-boat and a German fleet of formidable ships. It had had to do so while also contending – because of those same follies – with the Italian and Japanese Navies, and when irreparably weakened by pre-war disarmament. To wage war against such odds had cost the Navy in casualties nearly one tenth of its total wartime strength of some 800,000 men and women – 50,860 killed, 14,685 wounded and 7,401 taken prisoner.[67] The British Merchant Marine, staunch shipmate of the Royal Navy throughout the worst of the storm, the very sinew of Britain's survival and victory – it too had paid dearly, with 30,248 crewmen drowned or killed in action. Royal Air Force Coastal Command, the Royal Canadian Air Force and Allied maritime air forces had lost 1,515 aircraft by enemy action, and suffered 8,874 aircrew killed and another 2,601 wounded.[68]

So once more the Royal Navy (this time in partnership with the Royal Air Force) had 'kept England's wall that is the sea', and with it the cause of liberty. And for all the importance of technology and tactics, of staff work and strategy, the Royal Navy had prevailed because its officers and bluejackets, 'Hostilities Only' as much as RN, RNR and RNVR, were throughout animated by the spirit of Nelson's last order flying amid the gunsmoke of Trafalgar: 'Engage the enemy more closely.'

Now the German prong of the triple threat – the only one of the three that had directly menaced the independence of the United Kingdom – lay broken. But there still remained the third prong. Before a bankrupt Britain could concentrate on the enormous task of restoring her lost prosperity, there had to be finished off that other war, the war with Japan in defence of the British imperial legacy in the East.

28

To Restore an Empire

The strategic anatomy of the Japanese war stood in total contrast to that of the German war. Whereas Germany was a continental power which could only be decisively defeated on land, Japan was an island power much like Britain; and like Britain she depended on the sea communications to move and supply her far-off garrisons and expeditionary forces, to bring home raw materials and fuel on which her war industries depended. In this essentially maritime conflict, the *Schwerpunkt* or main thrustline of the Allied counter-offensive lay along the direct route westward across the Central Pacific from Pearl Harbor to the Philippines, and then north via the island of Okinawa to Japan itself. This thrustline, in which each stage was measured in thousands of miles of blue Pacific water, was the equivalent of the 'Neptune–Overlord' thrustline across the Channel to France and then overland into Germany. But unlike 'Neptune–Overlord', which were truly Allied operations under an integrated Anglo-American command, the Pacific was a purely American sphere, jealously guarded as such by Admiral Ernest King, COMINCH and Chief of Naval Operations, and waged by Admiral C. W. Nimitz's Pacific Fleet.

The American strategic counter-offensive began once Japan's own initial march of conquest had been halted by the United States Navy in the Battles of the Coral Sea on 4–8 May 1942 and Midway on 4–5 June. The Battle of the Coral Sea (south of the Solomon Islands) afforded the first example in naval history of a decisive naval action in which the main surface forces never sighted each other, and the outcome turned entirely on carrier strikes. Though both sides lost a carrier (the USS *Lexington* and the Japanese *Shoho*), the battle ended

[860]

in a strategic defeat for the Japanese, for they abandoned their objective of landing an expedition on the south coast of New Guinea in order to consummate their occupation of the island.[1] The victory in the Coral Sea ended the direct threat to Australia and opened the way to the eventual clearing of New Guinea by Australian and American troops. It served as the necessary prelude to a ferocious struggle by land and sea for the Solomon Islands, in turn the first stage in General Douglas MacArthur's island-hopping campaign in the South-West Pacific during 1942–44 towards the Philippines.

Fought a month after the Coral Sea, the Battle of Midway in a single encounter swung the fortunes of the Pacific war against Japan, and so changed the course of history. Admiral Isoruku Yamamoto, the Commander-in-Chief of the Japanese Combined Fleet and the planner of the strike on Pearl Harbor, committed seven battleships, four fleet carriers (with over 300 aircraft), twelve heavy cruisers and many destroyers in support of a landing on the American island of Midway, 1,135 miles north-west of Pearl Harbor. By occupying Midway Yamamoto intended to entice the remaining ships of the US Pacific Fleet, and in particular the fleet carriers that had escaped him on 7 December 1941, into an ambush where they could be annihilated by overwhelming numbers. But the American Command was not taken by surprise as Yamamoto hoped, for they had been forewarned by decrypts of the Japanese JN25 naval cypher employing the equivalent of the Enigma machine. In good time to meet Yamamoto before the attack on Midway could take place Admiral Nimitz deployed his only three available fleet carriers (with some 230 aircraft) although, owing to the massacre in Pearl Harbor on 7 December 1941, entirely without battleship support. In a confused and ferocious three-day battle in which luck as well as skill favoured the Americans, Yamamoto lost four fleet carriers to Nimitz's one (USS *Yorktown*). Even though Yamamoto still enjoyed a superiority of seven battleships (including the 70,000-ton, 18-inch-gun *Yamato*) to none, he broke off the Midway operation and retired. Midway signalled the moment of the total eclipse of the battleship by the aircraft carrier after four centuries of dominance of naval warfare; an eclipse that had begun to cast its shadow in November 1941 with the Fleet Air Arm's strike on the Italian Fleet in Taranto.[2]

Her catastrophic defeat in the Battle of Midway forced Japan ineluctably on to the strategic defensive in the Pacific. From now on the Imperial Japanese Navy could only fight tenaciously against ever swelling American might in ships and maritime airpower while the task forces of the US Pacific Fleet and the landing forces of the US

Army and Marine Corps fought their way island by island, year by year, westwards across the central Pacific towards the Philippines and Japan.

During the years 1942–44 Britain and the Royal Navy played virtually no part in this Pacific war, although the carrier *Victorious* was lent to the US Navy in the south-west Pacific area for a time in 1942 when the Americans were so short of carriers, and ships of the Royal Australian and Royal New Zealand Navies served with distinction in the same area. The dominions of Australia and New Zealand, the source of so much anxiety to the pre-war Admiralty, no longer remained a direct British concern, for they passed in a strategic sense from the British Empire into the American when Britain haplessly reneged on her long-standing promise to send a great fleet to Singapore to protect them. Britain's sphere of responsibility in the war against Japan was restricted to the Indian Ocean and the Bay of Bengal. In May 1942 the Japanese had finally driven British forces out of Burma into the Indian state of Assam. Britain's immediate concern now lay, therefore, with the defence of India; no longer the 'jewel in the Crown' of Empire, but an economic and strategic burden which the British government wished to dump after the war if it could only reach a deal with Indian political leaders in negotiations already in progress.

In the meantime, and using India as a main base, the British hoped eventually to reconquer Burma and thereafter Malaya and Singapore. Yet even if and when these ultimate objectives had been attained, the Royal Navy and British Empire land forces would still be some 2,400 miles distant from the decisive theatre where the war against Japan must finally be won – the seas between the Philippines and the Japanese home islands. Thus the British effort in Burma and South-East Asia could never be more than peripheral in importance, leading to a strategic cul-de-sac; the equivalent of the Mediterranean campaign in the German war.

In the wake of the destruction of Force Z (HMS *Prince of Wales* and *Repulse*) on 8 December 1941 and the surrender of Singapore on 15 February 1942 the Admiralty had cobbled together a new Eastern Fleet based on Ceylon and commanded by Admiral Sir James Somerville, formerly Flag Officer, Force H, in the Mediterranean and no stranger to operations against great odds. Count the ships and Somerville's command looked – certainly to the Prime Minister – like a formidable enough fleet: five battleships, three aircraft carriers, seven cruisers and sixteen destroyers.[3] But judge the combat-worthiness of the ships and aircraft, the state of training of the crews and their ability to work together as a fleet unit, and the picture became very different. Of Somerville's battleships four were the 'R' class: *Resolution*, *Ramillies*, *Revenge* and *Royal Sovereign*; floating museums of Great War naval technology preserved intact by inter-war economies in defence expenditure. His fifth battleship, *Warspite*, another Great War veteran but reconstructed in 1934–37, had just returned to service after having battle damage off Crete repaired in America. Somerville's two fleet carriers, *Indomitable* and *Formidable*, were certainly modern ships, but they and his light carrier *Hermes* only embarked a combined total of some 57 strike aircraft and 36 fighters, all of them inferior in performance to Japanese aircraft. Most of Somerville's cruisers were also out-of-date.

The state of his fleet depressed even Somerville, an admiral temperamentally robust enough. In February 1942, on his way out to Ceylon, he wrote privately: 'My old Battleboats are in various states of disrepair & I've not a ship at present that approaches what I should call a proper standard of fighting efficiency . . .'[4] He also found his Fleet Air Arm crews well below the standard of his old Mediterranean carrier *Ark Royal*. 'The fact is,' he wrote at the beginning of March, 'that until I get this odd collection of boats together & train them up they aren't worth much . . .'[5]

In April 1942, just after Somerville had arrived in Ceylon with this 'odd collection of boats' and a month before the Battle of the Coral Sea, Admiral Nagumo, with four of the fast carriers employed in the Pearl Harbor strike and four battleships, lashed out across the Indian Ocean with the aim of destroying, neutralising or cowing the new British Eastern Fleet. Somerville prudently kept his 'R' class battleships well out of Nagumo's way while trying – though unsuccessfully – to close the Japanese at night with his carriers in order to launch air strikes. Thanks to Somerville's evasive tactics Nagumo only succeeded in sinking the old carrier *Hermes* and the cruisers *Cornwall* and *Dorsetshire*, although much damage was done by Japanese aircraft to shore installations at Colombo and by Japanese warships to merchant traffic in the Bay of Bengal. Nonetheless Nagumo had achieved his strategic objects, for the Admiralty now ordered Somerville to pull his vulnerable fleet back some 3,000 miles to Kilindini on the East African coast, 'a small narrow winding harbour', Somerville described it to his wife, 'with thick green jungly stuff each side . . . It's a very snug harbour but too congested for my party . . .'[6]

For Somerville the two years that followed were a time of gnawing frustration because the state of his fleet prohibited bold offensive strokes. Of his carrier aircraft only the American Martlet fighter impressed him as 'undoubtedly good'.[7] The Fulmar was 'no match for the Japanese Zero fighter'; the Albacore and Swordfish were 'too slow for day strikes'.[8] All in all he judged his carrier striking force at present to be 'a very poor thing'.[9] Somerville was not only constrained by his fleet's lack of battle-worthiness but also by its short range. He bitterly recorded during Nagumo's April 1942 raid that the Japanese ships 'have tremendous endurance while my old battleboats & destroyers have none . . .'[10] For want of a fleet train to refuel and replenish his ships at sea (an American novelty which the Royal Navy had yet to develop) he had to resort to a secret shore base at Addu Atoll (in the south of the Maldive Islands) whenever he undertook distant sorties across the Indian Ocean. For the ships' companies Addu offered a landfall as starkly unpleasant as either Iceland or Kola; but at the opposite extreme: 'The heat is simply indescribable,' Somerville wrote to his wife, 'a burning, torturing sort of heat from which there is no escape . . .'[11]

Thus Somerville could only hope, in his own words, 'to create diversions and false scents, since I am now the poor fox'.[12] His main task now lay in guarding the vital sea route up the east coast of Africa to the Red Sea and Egypt, on which the campaign in the Western Desert in 1942 so completely depended. The one major British maritime offensive operation in eastern waters in 1942 was in fact mounted from the United Kingdom, and was directed not against the Japanese but the Vichy French. For the Vichy French island colony of Madagascar commanded the convoy routes from Britain to the Middle East and India via the Mozambique Channel (lying between Madagascar and the east coast of Africa). In London it was feared that Japan might well decide to include the island in her current wave of conquest. The decision was therefore taken in principle on 7 March to forestall her – and in particular, as the Prime Minister put it to the Prime Minister of South Africa, 'to storm and occupy Diego Suarez' – the port and naval base at the north-eastern point of the island.[13] Planning now began.

This time a joint expedition with General de Gaulle's Free French forces was ruled out; the memory of Dakar in 1940 still stung. The speed and efficiency with which the all-British venture ('Operation Ironclad') was planned and organised demonstrates how much had been learned from the fumblings and bumblings of Norway and indeed Dakar, not least thanks to the work of Combined Operations on the techniques and equipment needed for assault landings. On 14 March 1942 the Chiefs of Staff submitted their outline proposals; on

18 March the final decision was made to go ahead; on the 19th the Admiralty signalled to all concerned the make-up of the naval forces and announced the appointment of Rear-Admiral E. N. Syfret (Flag Officer, Force H) as Combined Commander-in-Chief. On 13 March (actually the day before the COS submitted their plan), and on 23 March the motor transport and stores ships sailed with convoys OS22 and OS23 for Durban. The landing force itself – five assault ships carrying a Royal Marine Commando and three infantry brigade groups under Major-General R. G. Sturges, Royal Marines – sailed with the regular Durban convoy WS17. Early on 1 April Syfret put to sea from Gibraltar with the battleship *Malaya*, the cruiser *Hermione* and five destroyers, plus corvettes and minesweepers.

The mounting of 'Ironclad' no less serves as a remarkable demonstration of the flexibility and long reach of seapower. The objective lay some 9,000 miles from the United Kingdom, while the naval task force had to be put together by major reshuffling of resources. In order that Syfret could take Force H with him, ships had to be sent from the Home Fleet to fill the gap at Gibraltar – and those ships in turn had to be replaced temporarily by the United States Navy.

On 22 April, with his strength now augmented by the carrier *Illustrious*, the cruiser *Devonshire* and four more destroyers, Syfret reached Durban, where he transferred his flag to HMS *Ramillies* (from the Eastern Fleet at Kilindini).

Now followed a week of final planning in conjunction with Somerville (who released the carrier *Indomitable* to Syfret in order to strengthen the close air support for the landings), General Sturges and the South African government. On 25 April the first (slow) of two convoys sailed from Durban for Madagascar; on the 28th the second (fast). But only on 1 May did the executive order arrive from London that 'Ironclad' was to be launched on 5 May, so making the last-minute tactical arrangements more of a scramble than was comfortable. At 1500 on the 4th, on the signal 'proceed in execution of previous orders',[14] the task forces had begun to head for their deployment positions. For Captain R. D. Oliver in the *Devonshire* the coming night proved a nerve-twanging experience, responsible as he was for shepherding no fewer than 34 ships, including several large liners, through reefs which the French judged too difficult to navigate at night. But the only casualty was the corvette *Auricula*, sunk by a mine. At 0330 on 5 May the landing forces anchored at the lowering positions for the three assault beaches. Barely seven weeks had elapsed since the COS submitted their first outline for the expedition.

The British tactical plan for taking Diego Suarez exemplified the principle of the 'indirect approach'. The town and the neighbouring naval base of Antsirane lay deep inside a landlocked bay of irregular shape, the only entrance from the open sea being a narrow gut (the Orija Pass) to the eastwards, commanded by coastal defence batteries. Near the port and the naval base were more such batteries. The British command therefore decided to kick down Diego Suarez's back door by landing on the western coast of the island, which was separated by the width of a narrow peninsula from the port and the naval base, and then advancing eastwards inland.

After the cruiser *Hermione* had distracted the defenders' attention in the opposite direction by a night-time display of pyrotechnics off the entrance to Diego Suarez Bay and carrier aircraft had struck at the airport and at shipping in the harbour, the landing forces went ashore at 0430 away to the west against little or no opposition from a weak and surprised defence. They pushed on inland to cover the ten or twelve miles to Diego Suarez and Antsirane while behind them the anchorage filled with ships and the beaches with stores. By 1700 No. 5 Royal Marine Commando, on the northerly of the two axes of advance, had occupied the peninsula jutting into Diego Suarez bay on which the town itself was situated: complete success.

To the south, however, the Army's brigade groups came up against French defences covering the rear of the naval base of Antsirane. At General Sturges's request the Royal Navy agreed to land a party behind the French position. The destroyer *Anthony* (Lieutenant-Commander J. M. Hodges) embarked 50 of the *Ramillies*'s Royal Marines under Captain M. Price, RM, and at around 2000 on 6 May steamed at high speed and in rough seas straight through the Orija Pass, trading salvoes with French batteries as she did so. Now came the problem of getting alongside the quay at Antsirane in the dark in a strange harbour and in the face of a strong wind blowing off the shore. Despite setbacks Commander Hodges finally managed to hold his ship's stern to the quay long enough for the Royal Marines to swarm ashore – another small victory for cool nerves and superb seamanship. To Captain Price's little party now quickly surrendered the commandant of the naval base as well as an *embarras de richesse* of other French personnel.

At 1040 on the 7th Admiral Syfret with the *Ramillies, Devonshire* and *Hermione* and four destroyers began shelling the shore batteries commanding the Orija Pass, but ceased fire after only ten minutes on learning that the French defence had collapsed. At 1630 the British task force steamed triumphantly along swept channels into the great bay of Diego Suarez. 'Ironclad' had turned out to be an exemplary

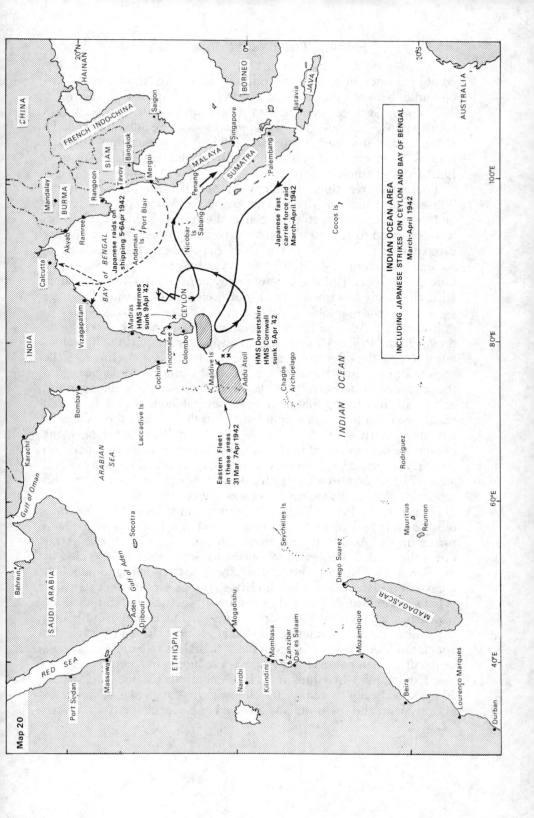

Map 20

INDIAN OCEAN AREA

INCLUDING JAPANESE STRIKES ON CEYLON AND BAY OF BENGAL
March–April 1942

Japanese raids on shipping 5-6Apr 1942

Japanese fast carrier force raid March–April 1942

HMS Hermes sunk 9Apl '42

HMS Dorsetshire HMS Cornwall sunk 5Apr '42

Eastern Fleet in these areas 31Mar 7Apr 1942

20°N

HAINAN

CHINA

FRENCH INDO-CHINA

Saigon

SIAM

Bangkok

BURMA

Mandalay

Rangoon

Akyab

Ramree

Tavoy

Mergui

BAY of BENGAL

Andaman Is

Port Blair

Nicobar Is

Sabang

Penang

MALAYA

Singapore

SUMATRA

Palembang

BORNEO

0°

Batavia

JAVA

AUSTRALIA

20°S

Calcutta

Vizagapatam

Madras

INDIA

CEYLON

Trincomalee

Colombo

Cochin

Maldive Is

Addu Atoll

Chagos Archipelago

Cocos Is

INDIAN OCEAN

Bombay

Laccadive Is

ARABIAN SEA

Karachi

Gulf of Oman

Bahrein

SAUDI ARABIA

RED SEA

Port Sudan

Massawa

Aden

Gulf of Aden

Djibouti

ETHIOPIA

Socotra

Mogadishu

Nairobi

Kilindini

Mombasa

Zanzibar

Dar es Salaam

Mozambique

Beira

Lourenço Marques

Durban

MADAGASCAR

Diego Suarez

Seychelles Is

Mauritius

Réunion

Rodriguez

100°E

80°E

60°E

40°E

combined operation, not least on account of the 'most cordial' co-operation between the services, as Syfret put it in his later report.[15]

The most serious casualties to the task force occurred three weeks later, when a Japanese midget submarine successfully attacked the *Ramillies* and a tanker in the bay, sinking the tanker and inflicting serious damage on the battleship, although she was able to steam to Durban after emergency repairs.

There still remained in Vichy French control the rest of the 900-mile coastline of Madagascar facing the Mozambique Channel and its dense convoy traffic. Since the Vichy French authorities were resolved to resist rather than surrender at discretion, a further campaign had to be mounted from September 1942 onwards to subdue the whole island. On 5 November the surrender of the Governor-General of the colony finally concluded a venture which Churchill justly described in his favourite eighteenth-century language as 'a model for amphibious descents'.[16]

In contrast, Admiral Sir James Somerville, C-in-C, Eastern Fleet, provoked the Prime Minister's keen displeasure because of his reluctance to take the offensive against the Japanese Navy. In July 1942 he minuted to the First Lord of the Admiralty and the First Sea Lord that Somerville had two 'first-class carriers' as well as the *Warspite*, and yet he 'has been doing nothing for several months, and we cannot really keep this fleet idle indefinitely'.[17] In the autumn the Admiralty cut the Eastern Fleet down to one carrier and two battleships, the remainder being needed in the Mediterranean to support 'Operation Torch'. In spring 1943 Somerville lost his sole remaining carrier and another battleship, so reducing his fleet to cruisers and destroyers and rendering the Indian Ocean a strategic backwater.

However, the Prime Minister was even more keenly and continuously dissatisfied with the performance of the British Empire land forces on the Assam–Burma front. An offensive by the 14th Army down the Arakan Peninsula of Burma in September 1942 (aided by the Royal Navy's light forces along the coast) ended ignominiously eight months later with the beaten British troops back on their startline. What Churchill angrily called 'the welter of inefficiency and lassitude which has characterised our operations on the Indian front'[18] cost Wavell his job as Commander-in-Chief in India. Instead Wavell was appointed Viceroy, with the even more thankless role of negotiating a deal with Indian politicians over post-war Indian independence. The new Commander-in-Chief in India, General Sir Claude Auchinleck, all too soon began to weary Churchill with his catalogues of shortages of every kind and the problems involved in constructing from scratch road and rail communications up from Bengal to the Burma front. Just as when Auchinleck was C-in-C, Middle East, in 1942, his military realism struck the Prime Minister as want of an offensive spirit.

In August 1943 the 'Quadrant' summit conference in Quebec approved Churchill's final answer to the problem of 'lassitude' in British operations in the East – the appointment of the young and dashing Lord Louis Mountbatten (in the rank of Acting Admiral) as Supreme Allied Commander of a new South-East Asia Command responsible for all operations by sea, land and air in India, Burma, Ceylon, Siam, Sumatra and Malaya. Although much senior to him in all but acting rank, Somerville now became Mountbatten's naval commander, the equivalent of Cunningham in 'Torch' and Ramsay in 'Husky', although he also remained responsible to the Admiralty as C-in-C, Eastern Fleet: an uneasy dual role.

At first Somerville welcomed Mountbatten's advent as bringing energy and leadership to the Indian scene of fusty imperial pomp and tropical torpor epitomised for Somerville himself by a brief stay with the Viceroy, then Lord Linlithgow, in Delhi: 'The Viceroy's house appeared to be three times the size of Buckingham Palace with an army of black bearers in scarlet and gold uniforms littering every passage ... You could easily drown yourself in the baths, and the plumbing is late Victorian ...'[19]

But all too soon Somerville's feelings towards Mountbatten soured into disillusionment. A protracted quarrel opened between them; one fomented by certain members of their staffs. For Mountbatten, a man rivalling Nelson in his hunger for admiration and surpassing him in appetite for personal aggrandisement, chose to run South-East Asia Command on authoritarian lines similar to MacArthur's style in the South-West Pacific. He and his eventually enormous war staff handed down operational plans for the land, sea and air Cs-in-C tamely to carry out; a sad contrast to Eisenhower's system whereby the Supreme Commander, with only a tiny staff of his own, acted as chairman of a committee of Cs-in-C, who with their own staffs remained responsible for planning. Moreover it was Mountbatten's mistaken belief – or contention – that the three British Chiefs of Staff in London had each orally granted him total authority over the land, air and sea Cs-in-C in South-East Asia, even to the sacking of them if he so decided. After the war this contention was specifically repudiated by Brooke and Portal, and pronounced by Cunningham (as Dudley Pound's successor as First Sea Lord) as being in Pound's case in the last degree unlikely.[20]

Mountbatten's assumption of dictatorial authority and his assertion of a right to almost royal courtesies when visiting ships of the Eastern Fleet clashed ever more sharply with Somerville's over touchy sense of his independence as a C-in-C responsible to the Admiralty. As 1943 turned to 1944 the First Sea Lord found himself the recipient of Somerville's copious complaints about the Supreme Commander's Caesar-like pretensions. The upper echelon of SEAC was not a happy ship; hardly a help to efficiency and morale.[21]

Despite Mountbatten's undoubted energy and eagerness to take the offensive, he could not for a long time prevail over the lack of resources which had bedevilled his predecessors. By land and sea the war in South-East Asia remained from 1943 far into 1944 in a true tropical doldrum. In April 1943 a long-debated project ('Anakim'), first mooted a year earlier by Wavell in a fit of over-optimism for an amphibious landing at Rangoon to take the Japanese in Burma in the rear, had to be postponed *sine die* because forthcoming Mediterranean operations would swallow up landing craft and naval forces. Churchill's own cherished project for 1944, a landing in Sumatra ('Operation Culverin'), likewise succumbed to lack of landing craft (needed for 'Neptune' as well as the Mediterranean), and to the opposition of the Chiefs of Staff and the Americans.[22] Meanwhile, the stalemate on the Burma front was broken only by the 14th Army's resounding defeat of a local Japanese offensive in the Arakan in February–March 1944, and by Major-General Orde Wingate's 'long range penetration' offensive behind the enemy front in northern Burma in the same period, which ended in the almost complete destruction of his four brigades of élite troops.[23]

At sea the only exception to the operational doldrums in the Indian Ocean and Bay of Bengal in early 1944 was provided by British and enemy submarines. In February and March German and Japanese U-boats mounted a fresh offensive against Allied merchant shipping along the route between Africa and India, compelling Somerville to restore convoy as best he could while starved of surface and air escorts. For want of air cover the troopship *Khedive Ismail* was torpedoed and sunk on 12 February off the Maldive Islands even though actually in a convoy. The packed vessel foundered in just two minutes with the loss of 1,300 lives, including Wrens, ATS (Auxiliary Territorial Service, the Army equivalent of the Wrens) and nursing sisters. It was scant consolation for so heavy a loss that the destroyers HMS *Petard* and *Paladin* promptly destroyed the attacker.

For British submarines the problem lay in a lack of worthwhile targets, for Japanese traffic in the waters off Burma, Malaya and the

Dutch East Indies was now largely restricted to junks. Nonetheless HMS *Tally Ho* (Lieutenant-Commander Bennington) put down the light cruiser *Kuma* (5,100 tons) off Penang on 11 January 1944; and on the 26th HMS *Templar* seriously damaged the light cruiser *Kitagami* in the same sea area. These were major wounds to the Imperial Japanese Navy in a region where its resources in surface ships had become slender because of the demands of the crisis in the Pacific.

By this time Somerville's Eastern Fleet was at last being rebuilt with ships released from European waters thanks to the Italian surrender, the crippling of the *Tirpitz* by X-Craft in September 1943 and the sinking of the *Scharnhorst* in December. On 23 January 1944 the battlecruiser *Renown* (flying the flag of Vice-Admiral Sir Arthur Power, Second-in-Command designate of the Eastern Fleet) arrived in Ceylon with the battleships *Queen Elizabeth* and *Valiant* and the fleet carrier *Illustrious*, together with cruisers, destroyers, escorts and submarines released from the Mediterranean. Power's squadron was the first instalment of the 146 ships which the Admiralty had decided to send to the Indian Ocean, including another fleet carrier, *Victorious* (she arrived in August), fourteen cruisers and 24 fleet destroyers.[24]

At long last Somerville was freed from the frustrations of enforced passivity. On 16 April 1944 he put to sea from Trincomalee with two carriers, three battleships, six cruisers and twelve destroyers, in accordance with Mountbatten's instruction to attack oil storage tanks, an airfield and the harbour installations at Sabang, an island off the north-east tip of Sumatra. It was the first time he had been able to take the offensive since hoisting his flag nearly two years before. Alongside the White Ensign in his battle-squadron flew the Stars-and-Stripes (the carrier USS *Saratoga*, on loan from the South-West Pacific area), the French tricolor (the fast battleship *Richelieu*), the Dutch tricolor (the cruiser HNLMS *Tromp* and a destroyer) and the stars of the Southern Cross of Australia and New Zealand (the cruiser HMNZS *Gambia* and four Australian destroyers). On the 19th the attack went in – aircraft from the carriers, the heavy guns of the battleships. Three out of four oil storage tanks were set on fire, 24 Japanese aircraft destroyed on the ground and another three in the air, and the port badly knocked about, all for the loss of one fighter from the *Saratoga*.[25] When the Fleet returned to Trincomalee, it had steamed 7,000 miles.

On the fleet's return to Ceylon for replenishment the *Saratoga* was due to sail to the United States for a refit. Admiral King, the COMINCH, therefore suggested that Somerville should accompany her as far as Java in order to launch a strike from her and the *Illustrious* on the port of Sourabaya. This was done. As the air groups returned to the carriers, huge billows of black smoke towering into a tropical sky signified the total destruction of the oil refinery at Wonokromo nearby. On 18 May the USS *Saratoga* and her escort parted company with the Eastern Fleet after what Somerville in a farewell signal called 'a profitable and very happy association'.[26]

Somerville put to sea yet again on 22 July 1944 to attack Sabang, his carriers this time being the *Illustrious* and *Victorious*. At dawn three days later the carriers opened the attack with strikes on Japanese airfields. Then the great guns of the battleships smashed at the harbour installations while the cruiser HNLMS *Tromp* and British destroyers under the command of that outstanding destroyer officer Captain R. G. Onslow, RN, bombarded targets from close inshore. Onslow then took his ships in a bold run across the harbour entrance, loosing torpedoes into the harbour as he raced past. Jubilantly Somerville wrote afterwards to the First Sea Lord, Admiral Sir Andrew Cunningham:

> The party did everyone a world of good and especially some of the big ships who had not had a chance to fire their main armaments in action previously in this war ... I am sure you would have liked to have seen the Inshore Squadron going into the harbour led by Dick Onslow as it was a most inspiring sight; he used rather a broader line of bearing than I expected, and his tail seemed to be leaning up against some of the shell bursts on the targets under fire on the East side of the harbour ...[27]

From March to October 1944 the Eastern Fleet carried out eight such air strikes, the ships joining in twice by bombarding shore targets. Yet although locally damaging to the Japanese and uplifting to British morale such raids were no substitute for a major British strategic offensive in the East – especially in view of the staggering advances and colossal victories of the United States Navy and American amphibious forces in the Pacific. The month of June 1944 saw the Americans land on the three Mariana islands of Guam, Tinian and Saipan, deep in the heart of the original Japanese defensive perimeter and 'only' (in Pacific terms) 1,200 miles from the Philippines. Admiral Raymond Spruance's 5th Fleet (seven battleships, fifteen carriers with 956 aircraft, 21 cruisers and 69 destroyers) massacred the Japanese battle-fleet's attempt to interfere with the invasion in what became known as 'The Great Marianas Turkey Shoot'.[28] This Battle of the Philippine Sea cost the Japanese nearly 500 aircraft (and, more important, their irreplaceable pilots) and a fleet carrier.[29] By August the resistance by the Japanese in the last of the Mariana islands had sputtered out; the way lay open for the leap to the Philippines.

In the South-West Pacific area MacArthur's strategy of leapfrogging Japanese-held islands so that their garrisons were left isolated and impotent had by mid-summer 1944 carried him north-westwards through the Bismarck Archipelago and the Admiralty Islands. His troops had reached the western tip of New Guinea. For him too the way was now clear for an attack on the Philippines. The two American thrustlines across the Pacific had thus converged, enabling Nimitz's and MacArthur's forces mutually to support each other in the next grand phase of operations.

What form should take the British contribution (and in particular that of the Royal Navy) to the final defeat of Japan, especially after Germany had been beaten into surrender? This question provoked the bitterest of all the wartime battles between Winston Churchill and the Chiefs of Staff.

At the 'Sextant' summit conference in Cairo on 22–26 November 1943 Roosevelt and Churchill initialled a Combined Chiefs of Staff paper which stated as a 'General Concept' that 'the main effort against Japan should be made in the Pacific'.[30] According to the paper the British Eastern Fleet was therefore only to be built up to a strength sufficient to carry out operations or pose threats in South-East Asia. All other available Royal Navy ships were to be formed into a British Pacific Fleet with a main base in Australia, advanced bases in the Solomon and Bismarck Islands, and operating either with Mac-Arthur's forces towards the Philippines or with Nimitz's fleet in the central Pacific.[31] This strategy of locating the principal British naval effort against Japan in the Pacific rather than the waters off South-East Asia was enthusiastically embraced by the British Chiefs of Staff, but not by the Prime Minister. In January 1944 he disavowed the Cairo Conference CCOS paper, opting instead for 'Culverin', his pet project for invading Sumatra. In any case he was deeply sceptical about the soundness of the proposal to create a British Pacific Fleet, minuting to the War Cabinet Defence Committee that it was not yet certain that the United States Fleet needed or desired heavy British support.[32]

On 3 February 1944 the COS condemned 'Culverin' as strategically irrelevant and also scouted proposals by Mountbatten for major offensive operations across the Bay of Bengal, on the score that these would be peripheral to the decisive attack on Japan in the Pacific and – like 'Culverin' – a wasteful diversion of resources. Here was the mirror image of Marshall's objections to Brooke's 'blue water' strategy in the Mediterranean. The Chiefs of Staff argued that all available merchant shipping and warships should be concentrated in the Pacific alongside the Americans. As Brooke explained to Field-Marshal Sir John Dill, head of the British military mission in Washington, a few weeks later:

> I am quite clear in my own mind that strategically it is right for us to use all our forces in close co-operation from Australia across the Pacific in the general direction of Formosa. By operating our forces alongside of MacArthur we can pool resources at sea and in the air for various closely connected steps. Whereas by retaining our forces in the Indian Ocean we operate independently, incapable of close cooperation, with the result that operations will be more protracted.[33]

But however technically correct these strategic arguments might be, they did not answer the Prime Minister's pertinent query as to whether the Americans would want to accept a British Pacific Fleet. They did not take into account the likelihood that a British Pacific Fleet would be operationally redundant in view of the great size (still increasing) of the United States Pacific Fleet. The truth is that the Chiefs of Staff (really Brooke again) were thinking politically as much as strategically – about renewing the British link with the dominions of Australia and New Zealand; about gaining through sharing in the victory some voice in United States policy in regard to the Pacific war and later the treatment of Japan. Brooke admitted after the war:

> The first of these alternatives [operations based on India] was the easiest to stage but limited itself to the recapture of British possessions without any direct participation with American and Australian forces in the defeat of Japan. I felt that at this stage of the war it was vital that British forces should participate in direct action against Japan in the Pacific. First of all from a Commonwealth point of view to prove to Australia our willingness to fight with them for the defence of Australia as soon as the defeat of Germany rendered such action possible. Secondly, I felt it was important that we should operate with all three services alongside of the Americans in the Pacific against Japan in the final stages of the war. I therefore considered that our strategy should aim at the liberation of Burma by South East Asia Command based on India, and the deployment of new sea, land and air forces to operate with bases in Australia alongside of forces in the Pacific.[34]

But for Churchill the very attractiveness of a South-East Asia strategy lay in that it would concentrate British resources on an almost entirely British theatre of war, and lead to the reconquest of British imperial possessions – in contrast to the Pacific where Britain must remain a very junior partner and one probably surplus to military requirements.

On 13 March 1944 President Roosevelt (prompted by Churchill) wrote to the Prime Minister to say that there 'will be no specific operation in the Pacific during 1944 that would be adversely affected by the absence of a British Fleet detachment . . .'[35] And certainly Admiral King had no wish for a British Pacific Fleet, in part because of his Anglophobe suspicion of the Royal Navy, in part because he believed it would be operationally unnecessary and logistically a burden on American resources.

For logistics supplied another important thread in the argument. A main base in Australia, advanced bases in the Pacific and a fleet train would all have to be created before a British Pacific Fleet could begin to operate – a heavy financial and material burden on a bankrupt Britain. Even then American logistical support during fleet operations would almost certainly be needed. In India, on the other hand, British naval and other bases already existed; more lay within reach of recapture in Burma and Malaya. Moreover the Minister of War Transport, Lord Leathers, estimated that to support a British effort in the Pacific, 6,000 miles further to the east than the Bay of Bengal, would take two and a half times the tanker tonnage at present envisaged for South-East Asia Command, as well as an extra half million tons of cargo shipping.[36] The Prime Minister seems to have taken far more note than Brooke and his fellow Chiefs of Staff of all these extra costs involved in starting up a British Pacific strategy from scratch.[37]

The battle between the Prime Minister and the Chiefs of Staff came to a climax in March 1944 with the delivery of a massive (in every sense) Churchillian memorandum in favour of 'Culverin' in particular and the South-East Asia theatre in general, and an equally massive attempt at its rebuttal, paragraph by paragraph, by the Chiefs of Staff, plus a fresh memorandum of their own.[38] Brooke now privately feared that the Prime Minister was trying to line up the War Cabinet against the Chiefs of Staff on the question of a Pacific strategy, writing in his diary that 'it looks very serious and may well lead to the resignation of the Chiefs of Staff Committee'.[39] It was indeed as serious as that. It remained so until April when a washy compromise was reached by which there was to be a British Empire campaign (British, Australian and New Zealand sea, land, and air forces) in the Pacific based on northern Australia, but with its own thrustline through Timor–Celebes–Borneo–Saigon instead of a mere furnishing of extra strength to American operations. This so-called 'Middle Strategy'

[875]

gradually found its way to a high Whitehall shelf, not least because the Americans disliked it as doubling up MacArthur's line of advance further to the north, and because they were keen that the British should concentrate on clearing Burma in order to bring help to Chiang Kai Shek, whose corrupt and feeble Kuomintang régime American opinion persisted in regarding as a worthwhile ally.

Early in August Churchill held a three-day staff conference in London, attended by Mountbatten as well as Cabinet Ministers and the Chiefs of Staff, to try again to decide on a British strategy for the war with Japan. In regard to South-East Asia, it was agreed to launch a seaborne landing at Rangoon as soon as forces (including landing craft) could be released from the German war, with Churchill's old favourite, 'Culverin', as a fill-in during the meantime. But the conference – now Churchill too – also agreed that 'the greatest offer of naval assistance should be made at once to the US Joint Chiefs of Staff, it being impressed on them that it is our desire to share with them in the main operations against the mainland of Japan or Formosa'.[40]

By this time, of course, Nimitz had won the crushing victory of the Battle of the Philippine Sea, and the Mariana islands had all fallen into American hands. The United States had less need than ever of British assistance in the Pacific, especially naval assistance. Nevertheless at the 'Octagon' summit conference in Quebec that September the Prime Minister formally offered Roosevelt the 'British main fleet', including 'our best and most modern battleships, adequately supported by fleet aircraft carriers, escort carriers, cruisers, etc' to take part in major operations against Japan under American command.[41] Although Roosevelt accepted the offer in principle, Admiral King in a Combined Chiefs of Staff meeting next day still fought a dour rearguard action. According to the record, he stated that he was not

prepared to accept a British fleet which he could not employ or support. In principle he wished to accept a British fleet in the Pacific but it would be entirely unacceptable for the British main fleet to be employed for political reasons in the Pacific and thus necessitate the withdrawal of some of the United States Fleet.[42]

He stressed the need for a British fleet to be self-supporting; he also sought to sidetrack the employment of such a fleet away from the central Pacific to MacArthur's subsidiary area of the South-West Pacific. Eventually, after the First Sea Lord and his fellow British

(Above) 'At 1320 HMS *Prince of Wales*, flagship of Force
Z and the Eastern Fleet, capsized and sank. . . .' The
destruction of Force Z (*Prince of Wales* and battlecruiser
Repulse) on 10 December 1941 cost the Japanese only
eight aircraft. (IWM) *(Right)* Admiral Sir T.S.V. Phillips
(with, left, his Chief of Staff, Captain Palliser) 'had
never personally experienced air attack on a task force
at sea.' Phillips was appointed by the First Sea Lord to
command the Eastern Fleet after three years at a desk
as Vice Chief of Naval Staff. He went down with *Prince
of Wales*. (IWM)

(Above) '. . . thanks to their armoured decks the destruction was mostly limited to parked aircraft.' The fleet aircraft carrier HMS *Formidable* hit by a Japanese kamikaze suicide bomber during 'Operation Iceberg' (the attack on Okinawa) in 1945. (IWM) *(Below, left)* 'For the Royal Navy he entertained the underdoggish and now quite anachronistic Anglophobia so prevalent in the US Navy in the early 1920s.' Admiral Ernest J. King, Chief of Naval Operations and C-in-C, United States Fleet (COMINCH). (Hulton) *(Below, right)* Admiral Sir Bruce Fraser, C-in-C, Home Fleet, 1942–44, Eastern Fleet, 1944, and the British Pacific Fleet, 1944–46. He sank the German battlecruiser *Scharnhorst* on 26 December 1943 in an action off Norway's North Cape. (IWM)

(*Above*) 'The first refinery lost half its production; the second was put totally out of action for six months.' The British Pacific Fleet's carrier strike on oil refineries at Palembang on Sumatra, January 1945. (IWM) (*Below, left*) Admiral C. W. Nimitz, C-in-C, US Pacific Fleet, under whose command the British Pacific Fleet served in 1945 as 'Task Force 57'. (Hulton) (*Below, right*) 'On 5 March 1945, Admiral Rawlings reported his fleet for duty to Admiral Nimitz. . . .' Vice-Admiral Sir Bernard Rawlings, Second-in-Command of the British Pacific Fleet *(right)*, and deputed by Sir Bruce Fraser to command the fleet at sea, seen here with Captain T. Halsey, RN, of the *King George V.*

'In second place [after a Chinese general] signed Admiral Sir Bruce Fraser for the United Kingdom.' The ceremony of Japan's formal surrender on board USS *Missouri*, 2 September 1945. General MacArthur is on the left. (IWM)

Chiefs of Staff had exerted the heaviest possible pressure, the Combined Chiefs of Staff

(a) Agreed that the British fleet should participate in the main operations against Japan in the Pacific.
(b) Took note of the assurance of the British Chiefs of Staff that this fleet would be balanced and self-supporting . . . [43]

So after all Brooke, Cunningham and Portal had their way, even though Churchill still insisted that Britain should make her separate amphibious thrusts in South-East Asia as well – first at Rangoon and later in Malaya.

In hindsight Churchill's earlier preference for concentrating the British effort in South-East Asia alone makes by far the better politico-strategic sense. It would have enabled Britain to win her own, if peripheral, victory against Japan in her own theatre; to play a middle-sized fish in a middle-sized pond. Logistically and economically too it would have made good sense. Brooke and his colleagues' solution, which meant playing the sprat in the largest pond in the world, could only expose Britain's shrunken relative stature as a power and above all as a naval power. Brooke's thinking in fact anticipates the British illusions of the post-war era (which he was fully to share and to foster as CIGS until 1946) – those of forging the Commonwealth into a political and strategic entity, with Britain as its leader and hence a 'world power'; and of this 'world power' securing 'a place at the top table' by means of expensive military pretensions.

In the autumn of 1944 it only remained for the Admiralty to complete a fleet base in Australia; arrange for an advanced base in the Pacific; assemble and equip a fleet train; form and equip the fleet itself, and despatch it.

To settle the command structure of the British Pacific Fleet proved simple enough, requiring as it did only typewriters and paper. By agreement between the First Lord of the Admiralty, A. V. Alexander, the First Sea Lord, Cunningham, and the Prime Minister, Admiral Sir Bruce Fraser was appointed Commander-in-Chief, British Pacific Fleet, hoisting his flag in Ceylon on 22 November 1944.[44] Since 23 August he had been commanding the Eastern Fleet in succession to Somerville, who had been posted to Washington as the only available British admiral with sufficient weight of personal broadside to engage the curmudgeonly Ernie King. 'I would much sooner have command of a trawler,' wrote Somerville to Fraser in May 1944 of this impending job.[45]

Because Fraser was to take the bulk of the Eastern Fleet's strength on with him in the guise of the new Pacific Fleet, the former fleet was abolished in favour of an 'East Indies Station' commanded by Vice-Admiral Sir Arthur Power (hitherto Second-in-Command of the Eastern Fleet). The East Indies 'Fleet' would only consist of two old battleships, twenty auxiliary carriers, six cruisers, 22 destroyers and some 120 escorts.[46]

The Admiralty appointed Vice-Admiral C. S. Daniel as 'Vice-Admiral, Administration' to the new Pacific Fleet. It fell to him in collaboration with the Australian government and Navy Board to arrange for the reception of a mass of stores and equipment, including nine floating docks, to be sent out from the United Kingdom, and for the construction of all the victualling and stores sheds, ammunition depots and base workshops needed for a main fleet base – a crucial and colossal task. He was also to act as the permanent representative in Australia of the C-in-C, British Pacific Fleet, until the latter arrived in person.

'The position of the British C-in-C was I think unique,' Admiral Fraser was to write after the war of his own place in the command structure. 'Responsible to the British Admiralty for the maintenance & welfare of the Fleet & for supplies coming from 12,000 miles away. Responsible to the Australian & New Zealand Govts [sic] for shore based activities. Responsible to the American Admiral Nimitz for operations.'[47] Because of such complicated relationships Fraser decided on arrival in Australia at the end of 1944 to fly his flag ashore in Sydney, deputing his Second-in-Command, Vice-Admiral Sir Bernard Rawlings, to command the Fleet at sea.

The finding of the merchant tonnage to support the Fleet operations and bring all its supplies 12,000 miles from the United Kingdom proved a rather less simple matter than making these flag appointments. In February 1944 the Admiralty was reckoning that 95 ships totalling about one million cargo tons would be required for the fleet train – and this at a time when Britain's annual import programme was down to 24 million tons, as against a pre-war average of some 60 million.[48] It had taken the Prime Minister himself to resolve a bitter argument between the Admiralty and the Ministry of War Transport over the release of shipping for the fleet train. On 9 April 1944 he minuted:

The Fleet Train is limited by the need of getting an absolute irreducible minimum of 24 million tons of imports this year and next. All Naval and Military requirements must be subordinated to this decisive rule, without which the life and the war effort of Britain cannot be maintained. In working out your Fleet Train you must observe these requirements.

2. The priorities are as follows:
  (a) 24 million tons of imports this year and next
  (b) The Fleet Train permissible on this basis
  (c) The fighting Fleet that can be carried by the said Fleet Train . . .[49]

The tonnage of the brand-new ships allotted to the Admiralty for this purpose would be made good by the release to the Ministry of War Transport of an equivalent tonnage of merchant shipping currently in Admiralty control. But in any event the Admiralty was only going to receive 293,000 tons of shipping for its fleet train instead of its original bid for one million tons (or 1½ million if a proposed fleet train for the Indian Ocean is also included).[50]

'The fighting Fleet that can be carried by the said Fleet Train' therefore amounted in March 1945, when it first joined Nimitz's command, to two fast battleships (*King George V*, flying Rawlings's flag, and *Howe*), four fleet carriers (*Indomitable, Victorious, Indefatigable* and *Illustrious*), five cruisers (*Swiftsure, Black Prince, Argonaut, Euryalus* and HMNZS *Gambia*), and eleven destroyers (two of them Australian).[51] Designated 'Task Force 57' by Nimitz, the British Pacific Fleet was much less than half the size of its American opposite number, Task Force 58, which comprised ten fleet carriers, six light carriers, seven battleships, eighteen cruisers and fifty-eight destroyers.[52] However, the small size of the British Pacific Fleet reflected more than the limit imposed by the available fleet train. For on balance and with the exception of anti-submarine forces and escort carriers the entire Royal Navy in 1945 together constituted a weaker striking force than Task Force 58.

In 1945 Britain had in commission only six modern fleet carriers, four light fleet carriers, five modern battleships and 41 modern cruisers.[53] Except for the *Vanguard* (laid down in 1940, launched in 1944, but not completed until 1946) new battleship construction had been halted by Prime Ministerial decision in August 1940 (see above, pp. 380–1 and 437–8). Except for the *Eagle* (laid down in 1942 but also not completed until after the war) new fleet carrier building had likewise been halted. Not a single new cruiser was begun after 1941.[54] The consequence was that as a battlefleet the Royal Navy actually shrank during the war, with only five battleships in commission in 1945 as against twelve in 1939; 41 cruisers as against 52. Necessity had gone far to transform the Royal Navy into an anti-submarine force, with 39 escort carriers (though capable of fleet operations), and nearly 600 other escort ships of all kinds, as against only 101 in 1939.[55]

In contrast the United States Navy commissioned between 7 December 1941 and the end of the Second World War a total of eight new battleships, no fewer than seventeen fleet (or in American parlance 'fast') carriers, nine light carriers (one of which was sunk), 77 escort carriers (excluding those passed to the Royal Navy under Lend-Lease), thirteen heavy cruisers and 33 light cruisers.[56]

Yet even though British naval shipbuilding resources had been deliberately concentrated on anti-submarine escorts, the Royal Navy had still come to depend critically on American yards for such vessels – all 39 escort carriers; 99 frigates as against 86 from British yards; almost all landing ships (tank). Canadian shipbuilders too had helped out the Royal Navy, supplying it with some 200 vessels, including 27 corvettes, sixteen big landing craft (tank) and many minesweepers.[57]

A navy is no more than the armour and the weapons-system of seapower. The hull, providing essential buoyancy, is the national wealth. The propulsion is commercial and industrial success, which creates the national wealth. By the end of the Second German War in May 1945 British national wealth, once the greatest in the world, had given way to bankruptcy, with overseas debts exceeding reserves of gold and foreign currency by nearly fifteen times.[58] Whereas in 1870 Britain's foreign trade had nearly equalled that of France, Germany and the United States put together,[59] in 1945 her export trade had collapsed to less than one-third of the 1939 level, and her visible exports could finance no more than one-tenth of her overseas requirements.[60] Worse still, the British industrial machine, once the envied model for the rest of the world, had been revealed by the war to the government, though not to the British people at large, as out-of-date in equipment, methods and attitudes; crippled by poor management and obstructive workforces; and weak in advanced technologies. All this was especially true of shipbuilding.

Thus by 1945 the economic buoyancy which for two centuries had sustained the Royal Navy in its world mastery had been entirely lost. The technological dynamism which had once driven the expansion of British seapower had yielded to hobbling arthritis. And yet at this same time – it is a poignant paradox – the seamanship and fighting spirit of the officers and men of the Royal Navy itself had never been greater. Adversity had rescued the Navy from the arrogant complacency bequeathed by the Victorian era, and which had marred its performance in the Great War; had awoken it from the conservatism and torpor of the inter-war years; and had restored it to the bold, hardy, resourceful and highly professional service that it was in Nelson's time.

But now it was the United States Navy instead which enjoyed the buoyancy of swelling national wealth, and American seapower whose expansion was being driven by technological prowess coupled with dynamic industrial growth. However, there was another factor in this eclipsing of British world naval mastery by America – the sheer scale of America's continental economy, which would have dwarfed Britain's island economy even if Britain had managed to retain her early Victorian dynamism. For example, the British turned out 4,133 major and minor landing craft during the war; the United States 63,218.[61] In naval shipbuilding overall, Britain produced 2.4 million tons in the course of the war; the United States 8.2 million tons.[62] Add in merchant shipbuilding too and the dwarfing of the British industrial effort becomes even more apparent – 8.3 million tons of merchant vessel from British yards, but 50 million tons from American.[63]

So the era of Britain's twin commercial and maritime supremacies, each serving to promote the other, had come to an end some two centuries after it had first opened with Marlborough's victorious war against Louis XIV. Yet this was hardly evident to the British public in the splendid hour of Nazi Germany's downfall. Indeed, a full awareness of Britain's eclipse as a world power had still to sink into the minds of even her military leadership, which had just successfully promoted the creation of a British Pacific Fleet and wished thereby to resume the old burden of imperial defence with regard to Australia. In fact, the Pacific Fleet was the precursor and prototype of the post-war global navy built round the fleet carrier to which successive British governments and Boards of Admiralty were to cling until the mid 1960s, when cruel economic and political reality at last put an end to their nostalgic self-delusion, and the Royal Navy dwindled into an anti-submarine force largely deployed in the eastern Atlantic and home waters. It is no wonder, therefore, that in 1945 the people of Britain, to say nothing of their leaders, saw British seapower as still majestically riding the oceans, when in truth it was like a ship still on even keel, not yet perceptibly lower in the water, but with her bottom blown out.

On 15 March 1945 Admiral Rawlings reported his fleet for duty to Admiral Nimitz, C-in-C, US Pacific Fleet, from his 'intermediate' base at Manus in the Admiralty Islands. Constructed by the Americans out of nothing, Manus was generously allotted by them for use by the British Pacific Fleet. On its way from Ceylon the British Pacific Fleet had launched the biggest and most destructive British carrier air strike in South-East Asian waters when Rear-Admiral Sir Philip Vian – with the fleet carriers *Indomitable*, *Indefatigable*, *Victorious* and *Illustrious*, the battleship *King George V*, three cruisers and ten destroyers – attacked the oil refineries at Palembang on the Dutch island of Sumatra.[64] The first strike force – 43 American-built Avenger bombers escorted by some 80 fighters – took off at dawn on 24 January 1945, and delivered their bombs accurately on the Pladjoe refinery despite a determined Japanese fighter defence, barrage balloons and dense anti-aircraft fire. On 29 January Vian launched a second strike with 46 Avengers on the Soengei Gerong refinery. Once again funeral pyres of black smoke signalled the success of the attacks. The first refinery lost half its production; the second was put totally out of action for six months. Vian lost sixteen aircraft in action and 25 more from various other causes. He reached Fremantle in Australia on 4 February, ready for the final preparations of the British Pacific Fleet for service with the Americans.[64a]

On 19 March Sir Bernard Rawlings sailed with that fleet from Manus to Ulithi, in the Western Caroline Islands, there to join with the United States Fifth Fleet commanded by Admiral R. A. Spruance and replenish his ships again. On 23 March he put to sea on the British Pacific Fleet's first operational sortie as Task Force 57 in the Fifth Fleet.

Since the final decision had been taken at the 'Octagon' Conference in Quebec in September 1944 that a British fleet should be sent to the Pacific, Japan had suffered a further series of colossal defeats by sea and land. In Burma the British Empire 14th Army (British, Indian and African troops) under Lieutenant-General Sir William Slim had been carrying out a sustained offensive ever since December 1944, aided by operations by ships of Vice-Admiral Sir Arthur Power's East Indies Fleet along the Burmese coast of the Bay of Bengal. This was a shore of a thousand jungly islands and swampy channels and inlets ('chaungs'); a true watery maze beneath the dense overhead cover of tropical vegetation.

The mangrove swamps are filled with scorpions and mosquitoes and every kind of poisonous stinging insect. The silence of the perpetual twilight is

Map 21

THE PACIFIC THEATRE
1944-5

SAKHALIN

HOKKAIDO

SEA OF JAPAN

JAPAN

HONSHU

Kamaishi

Hitachi

Tokyo

CHINA

Hiroshima

Nagasaki

SHIKOKU

KYUSHU

Shanghai

Amami Gunto

Foochow

Sakishima Gunto

Okinawa Gunto

NANSEI SHOTO

Bonin Is

Amoy

Swatow

Hong Kong

FORMOSA

NANPO SHOTO

Iwojima

PACIFIC OCEAN

2,200 Nautical miles to Pearl Harbor

Wake I

(BRITISH TARGETS IN OPERATION ICEBERG March April 1945)

PHILIPPINES

LUZON

Manila

MINDORO

SAMAR

LEYTE

PALAWAN

MINDANAO

Guam

BRITISH PACIFIC FLEET JOINS US 5th FLEET March 1945

Ulithi

Yap

MARSHALL Is

SOUTH CHINA SEA

CELEBES SEA

Palau Is

CAROLINE Is

4 days steaming

BRITISH PACIFIC FLEET INTERMEDIATE BASE

Nauru

BORNEO

HALMAHERA

Palembang

CELEBES

CERAM

NEW GUINEA

Manus

New Ireland

New Britain

Bougainville

SOLOMON Is

JAVA SEA

Batavia

BANDA SEA

JAVA

BALI

FLORES

LOMBOK

SOEMBA

TIMOR

ARAFURA SEA

Darwin

11 days steaming Manus–Sydney

New Hebrides

New Caledonia

AUSTRALIA

Fremantle

Sydney

BRITISH PACIFIC FLEET MAIN BASE

NEW ZEALAND

120°E   135°E   150°E   165°E

45°N

30°N

15°N

0°

15°S

30°S

broken only by the creaking of mangrove roots and the splash of the most loathsome denizen of the place, the crocodiles . . .[65]

Just as along the Dalmatian coast of Yugoslavia (see above, p. 691) the Royal Navy's light forces – often commanded by RNVR officers – conducted an aggressive guerrilla war against enemy shipping. But the Navy also provided the 14th Army with its customary humdrum but supremely useful services by ferrying forward stores and reinforcements, and by putting troops ashore to cut off or hamper the Japanese retreat.

Not all such operations were small in scale. On 21 January 1945 a task force including the battleship *Queen Elizabeth*, the light cruiser *Phoebe*, the escort carrier *Ameer*, two destroyers and two sloops landed the 26th Indian Division on the big offshore island of Ramree in order to capture it as a base for further 'descents' to the southward. The landing itself successfully followed the well-established procedures, but it then took a month before the last of the Japanese garrison were killed or taken prisoner. On 26 January the Navy also successfully landed 500 Royal Marines on the neighbouring island of Cheduba. The last of all these ventures up the 'chaungs' in a climate like a steambath took place on 13 March 1945 when a brigade was lifted from Ramree to land at Letpan, halfway down the Burmese coast from the Indian border.[66]

Seven days later, away to the east in the great central plain of Burma, General Slim consummated the destruction of the defending Japanese Army in a brilliant battle of encirclement round Mandalay. The road to the capital, Rangoon, lay open; the campaign in Burma was over except for pursuit. The city was to fall on 2 May 1945 to a now redundant amphibious landing ('Dracula', successor to the aborted 'Anakim' of 1943).

In the central Pacific, the main theatre of war, during the months since the 'Octagon' Conference in Quebec, American forces had been relentlessly smashing their way nearer and nearer Japan. In October 1944 the US Pacific Fleet had won a crushing victory over the Japanese fleet in a complex, sprawling battle comprising four separate major engagements and collectively known as the Battle of Leyte Gulf. In this, the largest naval battle in history, involving no fewer than 282 ships and some 2,000 aircraft, the Japanese lost four carriers, three battleships (including the 70,000-ton *Musashi*), six heavy cruisers, three light cruisers and eight destroyers; the Americans only one light carrier, two escort carriers and three destroyers.[67] This victory, gutting Japanese naval power, opened the way to the successful invasion of the Philippines by assault forces from Nimitz's Central Pacific Command and MacArthur's South-West Pacific Command. By the beginning of March 1945 the main Philippine island, Luzon, was in American hands. By the end of March the Americans had also taken the island of Iwojima in the Bonin Islands after ferocious fighting, so giving them an airbase for attacking Japan itself.

Now it was the turn of Okinawa in the Ryukyus, last step before the Japanese home islands: 'Operation Iceberg'. The American Expeditionary Force itself numbered 1,205 vessels from battleships (ten of them) to landing craft. The covering force consisted of the two Fast Carrier Task Forces of Admiral Spruance's 5th Fleet – Admiral Marc Mitscher's Task Force 58 and Admiral Rawlings's British Pacific Fleet (Task Force 57). Mitscher's Task Force 58 was divided into four task groups each virtually as strong in carriers, battleships, cruisers and destroyers as Rawlings's entire fleet.[68] But in aircraft the disparity in strength was even greater, for Mitscher's carriers embarked 1,218 aircraft to Rawlings's 218.[69]

The disparity in average numbers of aircraft embarked per carrier does not tell the whole story of Task Force 57's inferiority in carrier aviation compared with Task Force 58. For whereas Mitscher's ships flew an operationally compatible range of reconnaissance, fighter, torpedo and dive-bomber aircraft, Rawlings's ships were equipped with a ragbag of British and American types. This in itself complicated flying operations, for the carriers were compelled to turn into the wind again and again in order to launch aircraft with different take-off requirements, and so lost speed of advance. The American-supplied aircraft – the Vought Corsair single-seater fighter (maximum speed 415 mph); the Grumman Hellcat single-seat fighter (maximum speed 380 mph); and the Grumman Avenger torpedo-bomber (maximum speed 251 mph) – were all specifically designed like Mitscher's for carrier work. So too was Rawlings's British-made Firefly fighter-reconnaissance aircraft (maximum speed 316 mph),[70] although this had at first proved another of the aircraft industry's turkeys, the prototype in 1942 being so unstable that it killed a test pilot.[71] The Firefly only reached the squadrons two years later. However, the Vickers Supermarine Seafire fighter, a fifth of Rawlings's total strength, was simply a naval version of the Spitfire, an aircraft originally designed for the short-range air defence of Great Britain operating from grass airfields. At sea in the Pacific the Seafire's lack of range restricted it to a defensive role near the carriers, while its undercarriage proved yet again unable to cope with the thudding impact of deck landings. During 'Operation Iceberg' the British Pacific Fleet lost 46 aircraft in deck landing crashes, of which 28 were Seafires – as against an estimated total of 84 Japanese aircraft destroyed in aerial combat or on the ground.[72]

The enforced reliance on the inadequate Seafire, and the fact that 167 out of the British Pacific Fleet's 218 aircraft were American (supplied under Lend-Lease), served as a further indictment of the incompetence of the British aircraft firms – Fairey and Blackburn – which had been charged since the 1920s with building for the Fleet Air Arm. But here is also reflected the continuing legacy of the Admiralty's loss of authority over maritime aviation and aircraft procurement in 1918, and of the belatedness of the restoration of its control over carrier flying operations in 1937; the legacy too of the Royal Air Force's continued management of the design and procurement of aircraft for the Fleet Air Arm even after 1937 (see above, pp. 24–6 and 38–9).

Yet the British Pacific Fleet exemplifies the backwardness of British naval technology and operational technique, the poverty of the industrial resources behind the Royal Navy, in more ways than just carrier aviation. Although all its ships – battleships, fleet carriers, cruisers, destroyers – had been designed during the late 1930s rearmament period, their boiler, engine room and propulsion technology remained of strictly Great War specification, so rendering them inefficient in performance and wasteful of fuel, and consequently slower to gain speed and of shorter endurance than American ships (see above, p. 481). Their anti-aircraft target-acquisition and fire-control systems were similarly out-of-date. According to one expert in 1978,

It may seem strange now that after some twenty-five years of design and experiment by the acknowledged experts and designers of the day in this field, there did not exist any anti-aircraft system in the fleet by the end of the war that had really any chance of destroying an enemy aircraft.[73]

The failure stemmed from the pre-war Admiralty decision not to adopt a tachymetric fire control system as in the American and German Navies (see above, pp. 46–8) which could acquire and retain a target more quickly and accurately than the scientifically more primitive and operationally laborious British system. The same expert sums up the consequences:

It is small wonder, then, that the Director Layer and Trainer were faced with an extremely difficult task in merely getting on to and keeping on target, while, for the guns to hit it, the task was virtually impossible, especially bearing in mind the very great inaccuracy of the fuzes in use.[74]

By 1945 the problem of inaccurate fuzes had certainly been solved, thanks to the supply by the Americans of radio-proximity fuzes, a radar device invented by British scientists but which Britain lacked the industrial capacity to manufacture. This did not however solve the problem of the clumsy and partly manually operated British fire-control system. The United States Navy had adopted a mechanised fire-control system, the Mark 63, for anti-aircraft fire, including a highly compact predictor. Unfortunately the Admiralty was unable to find a British firm capable of manufacturing it to the necessary close tolerances.[75] Moreover, in the American system the hydraulic machinery for training the turrets and laying the guns was remote-controlled, automatically following the predicted position of the enemy aircraft, whereas in British ships the guns were trained and elevated by operators at the mounting following pointers in receivers in front of them. The American system eliminated the potential errors inherent in such manual operation, which demanded much practice to achieve accuracy. No wonder the Superintending Scientist at the Admiralty Research Laboratory reported in July 1943 after a visit to the United States:

I am convinced that by and large, the Americans have beaten us in the field of Remote Fire Control [i.e., including remote *power* control] ... [They are] unquestionably well ahead of ourselves so far as Remote Fire Control for gun mountings is concerned, and their developments in hydraulics for this purpose are remarkable ...[76]

This scientist contrasted the 'enthusiastic engineers' who ran the American precision-engineering industries with the 'mere dogsbodies' in British firms 'to be listened to only if it suits the convenience of those in authority'. A distinguished British engineer in the field of fire control remarked that the British attitude appeared to be: 'How can we best solve this problem on a short-term basis with our existing resources'; how on the other hand the American attitude appeared to be: 'What sort of resources and facilities shall we need as a starting point for the solution of this problem?'[77] This same engineer noted that the fire-control equipment in British ships was in any event 'without exception ... dependent for its existence in one way or another on foreign made – and designed – precision machine tools! – either American or Continental, because the equivalent British type does not exist'.[78] The experts laid the blame for this British backwardness in fire control impartially on such poverty of enterprise and competence within British industry and on the purblind conservatism of the Naval Ordnance Department, which took until 1944 to accept that the Americans and Germans enjoyed better fire-control systems.[79]

However, in one major respect British ship design proved superior to American – the fleet carriers' 3-inch armour over the flight deck, which enabled them to brush off the impact of Japanese 'Kamikaze' ('Wind of Heaven') suicide attacks in the coming action off the Ryukyus. Nonetheless a penalty had to be paid for the extra weight of the armour in terms of the number of aircraft embarked, amounting to little more than half the number in an American carrier.

But it was in the replenishment of the fleet at sea during prolonged operations far from its advanced base and some 5,000 miles from its main base in Australia that the British Pacific Fleet most glaringly displayed the Royal Navy's technical backwardness.

During four years of war in the Pacific the Americans had perfected the concept of the fleet train, which was no less than a mobile advanced base complete with oil tankers, stores ships, ammunition ships, hospital ships, aircraft and ship repair vessels, floating dry-docks and tugs, all in lavish numbers; all of them purpose-built vessels crewed by the United States Navy.[80] The British Pacific Fleet's train by contrast more resembled a maritime version of the motley procession of hired carts, sutlers' waggons and camp-followers that trailed behind eighteenth-century armies.[81] Under the command of Rear-Admiral D. B. Fisher (Rear-Admiral, Fleet Train) were vessels wearing the White Ensign or the Blue Ensign of the Royal Fleet Auxiliaries, converted merchantmen wearing the Red Ensign (some of them with all-Chinese or all-Lascar crews), other merchantmen belonging to Britain's allies and wearing a colourful variety of national ensigns. The ships of the fleet train themselves varied greatly in speed, so further complicating Admiral Fisher's problem of operating his poly-glot command; and in particular he lacked enough fast tankers able to keep station with the battlefleet. Moreover, the equipment in the ships was no less improvised and inadequate. It did not help that British operational techniques for replenishing at sea were not so rapid and efficient as American.

According to Rear-Admiral Sir Philip Vian (Flag Officer, 1st Aircraft Carrier Squadron, comprising all four British fleet carriers),

> The British method of fuelling big ships at sea, which was by means of buoyant hoses trailed astern of the tanker, was primarily at fault. It was an awkward, unseaman-like business compared with the American method, in which the two ships concerned steamed along abreast of one

another a short space apart. For some reason we had failed to benefit from American experience to fit our tankers and warships with the necessary tackle to employ this method. We were to suffer for it until we did so.

Furthermore, our tankers of the Fleet Train, hastily collected and hastily fitted out, were often inexperienced and ill-equipped. The fuelling gear would become entangled, or hoses would burst. On such occasions fuelling took up to six hours longer than it should have done; and only by steaming at full speed through the night could the flying-off position be reached in time for our first day's operations.[82]

All in all it was therefore fortunate that although the deal with Admiral King had called for the British Pacific Fleet to be self-sufficient the local American logistic authorities, in the words of a signal from Admiral Fraser to the Admiralty,

> have interpreted self-sufficiency in a very liberal sense ... American authorities are most open handed in allowing the B.P.F. to draw from these [surplus] items, but this has been subject to the over-riding proviso that in doing so it has not been necessary to refer the matter to the next higher authority. Whenever it has been necessary so to refer such questions ... the request has always met with refusal.[83]

As with other of the Royal Navy's wartime weaknesses, this failure to develop the ships, techniques and tackle for replenishing task forces at sea owed itself to past clinging to outmoded professional habits of mind coupled with pre-war lack of funds. Up to the middle of the Second World War the Royal Navy had remained loyal to the Victorian logistical concept of a chain of fixed naval bases or fuelling stations along the main imperial strategic axes, such as Gibraltar, Malta, Alexandria, Aden, Bombay, Trincomalee and Singapore. It was intended that squadrons would return to such bases, or to United Kingdom bases in regard to operations in home waters, in order to replenish after sorties à la Jutland.[84] Between 1936 and 1939 an Admiralty Supply Ships Committee had certainly studied the possible need for stores and ammunition ships, recommending that some 50 vessels should be taken up from trade and converted. This was far from the concept of a complete fleet train. Yet even in the case of operations in home waters, such as the chase of the *Bismarck*, or in the northern seas, as in the Norway campaign of 1940 and the later Russian convoys, British fleet commanders had been seriously hampered by their inability to refuel and re-ammunition their ships at sea, and the consequent need to return home after only a few days' operations. The same was true of convoy operations in the Mediterranean and the Atlantic. Even the German Navy, stationing tankers and supply vessels far from German ports for the benefit of its raiders, had something to teach the Royal Navy in this regard.

Only from the middle of the war onwards did it become more and more the custom for oilers to refuel British warships in mid-Atlantic or mid-Arctic or in the course of Mediterranean convoy runs. And only at this time did the Admiralty decide to convert some existing armed merchant cruisers into repair ships. But not until summer 1943 did it reach a decision to create fleet trains as such – one for the Indian Ocean and one for the Pacific; and not until September that year did it draw up its final staff requirement for the size and composition of the trains.

By this time, of course, Britain was suffering from a desperate shortage of ships of all kinds, while her shipyards and equipment industries were choked with existing work. The whole of 1944 was spent in a struggle to find and convert the necessary vessels. Cuts had to be made accordingly in the existing naval shipbuilding and merchant-ship repair programmes. The United States helped out by supplying some of its purpose-built fleet-train ships; Canada also helped by converting other vessels. That a fleet train was cobbled together in time to support the Pacific Fleet in spring 1945 may therefore be accounted a feat of typically resourceful British improvisation, but it nevertheless represents a sad falling-off from the standards of logistical professionalism achieved by the Royal Navy in its days of greatness in the eighteenth century;[85] it demonstrates afresh that as a seapower Britain was now only the poor relation clad in darns and patches, striving to put on a brave front.

The battle for Okinawa and neighbouring islands in the Ryukyus lasted from 18 March 1945, when Mitscher's Task Force 58 began a fortnight of preliminary air strikes against enemy airfields, till 21 June, when organised Japanese resistance on Okinawa ceased. For the American armed forces it proved the bloodiest of all the Pacific battles, costing the United States Navy over 4,900 sailors killed or missing and nearly 5,000 wounded, and the Army 7,613 killed or missing, 31,807 wounded and more than 26,000 non-battle casualties.[86] The American carrier forces (including auxiliary carriers) lost 763 aircraft. Thirty ships and craft were sunk, mostly by Kamikaze attack, and 368 others damaged, including the carriers *Wasp*, *Yorktown* and *Franklin*.[87] But for the Japanese the campaign brought complete defeat and catastrophic loss – 110,000 army casualties in the land battle, over 1,500 Kamikaze aircraft and their suicidal pilots, and the last remnant of the Japanese battlefleet, the 70,000-ton battleship

Yamato. She too had been despatched on a suicide mission, for Japan was now so short of oil that she could be fuelled for an outward voyage only. Caught by American carrier aircraft on 7 April, she sank after being struck by ten torpedoes and five bombs.[88]

The key role of covering the amphibious forces during the landings and the subsequent operations against the 2,000 Japanese aircraft based in the southernmost Japanese home island of Kyushu fell to Admiral Mitscher's Task Force 58. His ships kept the sea for two and a half months, a prodigious achievement even by American standards, and they did so despite massed air attacks pressed home with suicidal desperation (quite literally so in the case of the Kamikazes). The British Pacific Fleet (Task Force 57) was allotted the subsidiary task of suppressing the Japanese airfields on the Sakashima Gunto, a group of islands to the south of Okinawa, so that they could not be used as a staging point for air reinforcements from Formosa to Okinawa.[89] Task Force 57 launched its first air strikes on 26 March and kept them up until 20 April, when it had to return to Leyte in order to replenish, replace lost or damaged aircraft, take on fresh pilots and relieve fighter wings which had reached the end of their operational tour. So far Task Force 57 had largely escaped the savage air onslaughts delivered by the Japanese against Mitscher's Task Force 58, although the *Indefatigable* was hit by a Kamikaze at the base of her 'island' (inflicting little damage) and the destroyer HMS *Ulster* was put out of action by a near-miss from a bomb and had to be towed back to Leyte by HMNZS *Gambia*. During its fortnight's absence at Leyte the British Pacific Fleet's role in 'Iceberg' was taken over by American escort carriers of the Fifth Fleet's Carrier Support Group.[90]

Task Force 57 returned to its station on 4 May for a further three weeks of action against airfields in the Sakashima Gunto and also Formosa. But this time the British ships caught the edge of the storm of Japanese air attack. The carriers *Formidable*, *Indomitable* and *Victorious* were all hit, although thanks to their armoured decks the destruction was mostly limited to parked aircraft.

As it turned out, this was the last time in the Second World War that the ships' companies of a British battle squadron would experience that routine of life while closed up for action under heavy air attack which had become so familiar in the Mediterranean and the Arctic – the donning of clean underwear and of anti-flash hoods under tin hats; the 'action breakfast' of ham roll, tea, bread and butter and marmalade; 'action pie' at midday of meat, carrots, onions, potatoes and peas encased Cornish-pasty-style between two thick crusts of pastry, and brought back to each battle station by the 'mess cook', a traditional name dating from the Nelsonian era when each mess cooked its own food. For the last time too was heard under heavy air attack the staccato banging of the pom-poms, the deeper detonation of the high-angle guns; or from bridge and battery was seen a sky thickly blotched with puffs of smoke from exploding shells and alive with enemy aircraft. The novelty now lay in that those aircraft did not always pull out of a dive at the last moment like a Stuka, but instead kept on coming until the pilot's service to his Emperor terminated in a ball of flame and exploding metal. So for the last time too in the Second World War the sick-bay staffs in a British battlesquadron had to do what they could for sailors roasted or maimed and ripped.

On 25 May 1945 Admiral Rawlings set course for Manus with the British Pacific Fleet's role in 'Operation Iceberg' completed. The Fleet had destroyed an estimated 88 Japanese aircraft in the air (including four by ships' gunfire) or on the ground, plus eight Kamikazes, but had lost in return no fewer than 134 aircraft of its own. Of these, 30 had been destroyed in combat; 23 as a result of Kamikaze hits on the carriers; and 46 in deck-landing crashes. In addition 69 aircraft had been damaged to the point of needing replacement even though ultimately repairable. Of these, fifteen had suffered damage in deck-landings; nine in Kamikaze attacks, and no fewer than 28 in an accidental fire in the *Formidable*.[91]

At Manus the British Pacific Fleet dispersed to Sydney (eleven days' steaming away) and other bases in order to refit and train for the final operations against the Japanese home islands. It would be some six weeks before it rejoined the American fleet.

More than 2,000 miles away to the south-west Vice-Admiral Sir Arthur Power's East Indies Fleet was finding it difficult to locate targets in seas now virtually emptied of Japanese warships and shipping.[92] Nevertheless, on 10 May 1945 the submarines *Statesman* and *Subtle* patrolling in the Malacca Straits sighted a Japanese heavy cruiser escorted by a destroyer. Unable to get within attacking range, the submarines reported their find to the C-in-C, who ordered an air and surface search. On the 15th an aircraft from the escort carrier *Shah* spotted the cruiser – the 10,000-ton *Haguro* – whereupon Avengers bombed and damaged her. Now five destroyers of the 26th Flotilla, *Saumarez*, *Venus*, *Vigilant*, *Virago* and *Verulam* (all of wartime construction), steamed at 27 knots to close the 85 miles between them and the *Haguro*. After searching for her along a bearing calculated from her guessed 'farthest on' position, they picked her up on their radar screens shortly after midnight, and pounced on her simultaneously from different directions in a superbly timed and executed attack. Shattered by no fewer than eight torpedoes, the *Haguro* went down in a few minutes. It could be said that the 26th Flotilla (Captain M. L. Power) had avenged HMS *Exeter*, the cruiser sunk by the Japanese in March 1942 in the Battle of the Java Sea along with her escorting destroyers.

The Royal Navy's submarines in the waters off Malaya and the Dutch East Indies found themselves reduced to the role of sharks snapping up small fry, for Japanese merchant traffic had ceased except for coasters and junks. But now and again a submarine captain was excited to see through his periscope a worthier target. On 8 June 1945 Commander A. R. Hezlet in the *Trenchant* sighted the 10,000-ton heavy cruiser *Ashigawa* in the narrow waters of the Banka Strait off Sumatra, and promptly hit her with five torpedoes. The *Ashigawa* sank in half an hour. And British midget submarines or X-Craft towed to the target area by conventional submarines repeated in Far Eastern seas their 'Boy's Own Paper' feats of daring against the *Tirpitz*.

On 31 July 1945 the XE1 (Lieutenant J. E. Smart, RNVR), towed by HMS *Sparks* (Lieutenant D. G. Kent) and XE3 (Lieutenant I. E. Fraser, RNR), towed by HMS *Stygian* (Lieutenant G. S. C. Clarabut), carried out a sortie up the Johore Strait between Malaya and Singapore island with the task of sinking two Japanese cruisers lying off the former British naval base.[93] The XE1 proved unlucky, for encounters with enemy surface craft so delayed her approach to her own designated target, the cruiser *Myoko*, that she laid her mines instead alongside the XE3's victim, the 10,000-ton *Takao*, at an anchor in shallow water. The XE3 successfully crawled along the muddy bottom of the Strait to reach her attacking station beneath the *Takao*. But now came setback and hazard. There was not enough depth to open the hatch whence the diver must exit with the limpet mines to attach to the *Takao*'s bottom. Nevertheless the diver, Leading-Seaman J. J. Magennis, managed to squeeze his way out of the partially open hatch – only to find that a thick crust of barnacles made it impossible to fix the limpets. It took him an exhausting three-quarters of an hour to scrape a clear space and successfully complete his task. As the XE3 made her escape down the Strait the *Takao* was reduced by the limpet mines to a useless wreck sitting on the seabed. Both Fraser and Magennis were awarded the Victoria Cross for this remarkable exercise in engaging the enemy more closely.

On that same day far to the north, off Saigon in Indo-China, the XE4 (Lieutenant M. H. Shean, RANVR), towed by HMS *Spearhead* (Lieutenant-Commander R. E. Youngman, RNR), found and cut the Saigon–Hong Kong and Saigon–Singapore submarine telegraph cables. Further to the north still, off Hong Kong, the XE5 (Lieutenant H. P. Westmacott), towed by HMS *Selene* (Lieutenant-Commander H. R. B. Newton), succeeded after a three-day search in thick mud in putting the Hong Kong–Singapore cable out of action too. These were the same X-Craft commanders who in 1943 had destroyed a munitions ship and a floating dock in Bergen harbour.

It was not until 16 July that the British Pacific Fleet joined Admiral Halsey's 3rd Fleet off Japan, there to serve as an extra group in his Fast Carrier Force, launching air strikes against targets in Japan itself. By this time the enemy air forces had spent themselves, and the 3rd Fleet ranged up and down the Japanese coasts at will and virtually unscathed. Admiral Rawlings's own main anxiety lay in his ramshackle fleet train, which made it difficult to keep up with Halsey's ships, and even forced him to ask the Americans to refuel three of his cruisers. Back in Sydney Admiral Fraser, the Commander-in-Chief, British Pacific Fleet, reported to the Admiralty on how Halsey 'with easy grace' was 'striking here one day and there the next, replenishing at sea and returning to harbour as the situation demands. With dogged persistence the British Pacific Fleet is keeping up . . . but it is tied by a string to Australia, and much handicapped by its few small tankers.'[94] Nonetheless the American command deliberately left the British Pacific Fleet out of a major strike on 24 July against the remaining ships of the Japanese Navy lying immobilised in Kure naval base. Halsey accepted the advice of his chief of staff that the British ships should be so excluded in order, in Halsey's words, 'to forestall a possible post-war claim by Britain that she had delivered even a part of the final blow that demolished the Japanese fleet'.[95] So much for Sir Alan Brooke and his colleagues' naïve hopes that to contribute a British Pacific Fleet would earn a share in the victory and a voice in American counsels.

On 6 and 9 August 1945 the only two atomic bombs yet manufactured were exploded above the cities of Hiroshima and Nagasaki. On the 14th Japan announced her unconditional surrender. Yet whatever the motivation or merits or demerits of the American decision to drop the atomic bombs, whatever the effect on the Japanese leadership and especially the Emperor Hirohito, the truth is that Japan was already on the point of collapse as an industrial society – incapable of prosecuting the war further. It had not been the titanic battles and famous victories of the American surface fleets and amphibious forces that had brought her to this pass, but the American submarine, which had achieved against the island seapower of Japan the war-deciding victory which had eluded Dönitz against the island seapower of Great Britain.

For the Japanese war effort, like Britain's, had been utterly dependent on seaborne imports of food, fuel-oil and raw materials – in her case, from her newly conquered empire in Malaya, the Dutch East Indies and South-East Asia. On the very day of Pearl Harbor the United States Navy was authorised to carry out unrestricted submarine warfare against Japan, using its big 1,500-ton boats with their cruising range of 12,000 miles. This submarine 'Battle of the Pacific' was to follow a pattern exactly opposite to that of the Battle of the Atlantic. Here it was the submarines which possessed radar to help them in the search for victims; the Japanese warships that were blindfolded by lack of it until late 1943 onwards. Moreover, Japan learned nothing from parallel British experience in the Atlantic. She failed to organise a proper convoy system until 1944, and even then it existed more in name than in fact. She failed to mount anything like the immense British anti-submarine operational and research effort. Even the Imperial Japanese Navy's anti-submarine tactics lacked the skill and tenacity of the Royal Navy's, and American submariners fought a successful battle against enemy escorts, sinking 41 in 1944 for the loss of only six of their own number.

In 1943 Japan lost a million more tons of shipping than she built. Whereas she needed 3 million tons to keep civilian life going in the home islands, and another 3 million to support the war, she now possessed only 5 million tons in all. In 1944 American submarines sank 2½ million tons of shipping. By March 1945 Japan had lost 88 per cent of the merchant tonnage with which she had begun the war, and her oil imports finally ceased, available stocks amounting to only one-sixth of her requirements.[96] Lack of fuel now paralysed Japanese industry and what remained of the Japanese Navy and Air Force. With imports of rice, wheat and soya at a standstill, the Japanese people themselves faced starvation.

Perhaps, therefore, the two atomic bombs were dropped in order to impress Stalin's Soviet Union (which invaded Japanese-occupied Manchuria on 8 August 1945) as much as the leaders of Japan.

At 0856 on Sunday, 2 September, 1945 – scattered morning clouds in a sky that would soon clear to summer blue – the Japanese Foreign Minister, Mamoru Shigemitsu, in the top hat and morning coat of traditional diplomacy, and the Chief of the Army General Staff, General Yoshijiro Umezu, in baggy khaki and jackboots, came aboard the battleship USS *Missouri*, flagship of the 3rd Fleet, at her mooring in Tokyo Bay to sign the formal instrument of Japan's surrender.[97] When the Japanese delegation stepped on to the *Missouri*'s quarter deck they saw before them a green baize-covered table bearing the surrender documents; they saw behind a rope barrier a watching audience of senior Allied officers and civilian dignitaries; they saw above them American bluejackets and cameramen of all nations crowding every vantage point of the battleship's superstructure. Aloft flew the five-star flag of Fleet Admiral Nimitz, Commander-in-Chief, US Pacific Fleet, along with the personal flag of General Douglas MacArthur, now the Supreme Commander, Allied Powers, for the surrender and occupation of Japan.

For several minutes the Japanese stood immobile and alone before all these hostile eyes while the *Missouri*'s chaplain gave an address over the tannoy, followed by the American national anthem played on a record – the opening scene in an occasion as dramatically stage-managed as that other humiliation of a defeated enemy nearly 27 years earlier on board HMS *Queen Elizabeth* in the November fogs of the Firth of Forth.

Then General MacArthur, Admiral Nimitz and Admiral Halsey, C-in-C, 3rd Fleet – both admirals wearing open-necked American khaki drill rather than traditional white ducks – walked forward on to the quarter deck to begin the ceremony of surrender. Flanking MacArthur as he stood at the microphone behind the table were the skeletal figures of the American General Wainwright, who had surrendered the Philippines in 1942, and the British General Percival, who had surrendered Singapore. Both had been flown to Tokyo from a prison camp in Manchuria. Firstly MacArthur made a short but flowery speech expressing his 'earnest hope of all mankind that from this solemn occasion a better world shall emerge out of the blood and carnage of the past'.[98] Then he gestured to Shigemitsu to approach and seat himself on the opposite side of the table. At 0904 Shigemitsu signed the instrument of surrender, followed by General Umezu. MacArthur thereupon put his own signature on the document of acceptance of the surrender on behalf of all the Allied powers. Fleet Admiral Nimitz signed next. Then came the turn of the representatives of America's Allies, with a Chinese general in first place. In second place signed Admiral Sir Bruce Fraser for the United Kingdom; in third, a Soviet general; in fourth, General Sir Thomas Blamey for Australia; and thereafter the Canadian, French, Dutch and New Zealand representatives.

The signing done, MacArthur proclaimed: 'These proceedings are now closed.' The Second World War was formally over. The Japanese delegation left the *Missouri* to the twittering of the bosuns' pipes. At 0925, 450 carrier aircraft and hundreds of United States Army Air Force aircraft thundered over the flagship and the surrounding fleet of 258 Allied (overwhelmingly American) vessels from battleships to landing craft anchored in the bay.

Yet the British Pacific Fleet was not present in this mighty array – only a squadron composed of HMS *Duke of York* (flying the flag of Admiral Sir Bruce Fraser, who had steamed up from Australia for the occasion), HMS *King George V*, HMS *Indefatigable*, the cruisers HMS *Newfoundland* and HMNZS *Gambia*, and ten destroyers (two of them Australian). For when, on 14 August, the Japanese government had announced its acceptance of the Allied terms of unconditional surrender, the British Pacific Fleet had been about to return to Sydney at the end of its second tour of duty, and no extra tankers were available to keep it on station in Japanese waters. For want of just three fast fleet oilers Admiral Fraser had had no alternative but to order the main body of his Fleet south as already arranged. The warships themselves could easily have kept going – on VJ-Day the *King George V* had steamed for 52 days without once stopping her engines. To the bitter disappointment of the officers and men of the Fleet only a token force was left with Halsey to serve as a British presence.[99]

And even the victorious culmination of Churchill's preferred Indian Ocean and South-West Asia strategy, Britain's own war against Japan, had been relegated to anti-climax by order of MacArthur in his capacity as Supreme Commander, Allied Powers. For on 19 August, when the entire East Indies Fleet together with landing forces was steaming for Penang in Malaya and for Singapore, MacArthur instructed that no landings or formal surrenders of Japanese forces were to take place until after the completion of his own grand ceremony on board the *Missouri*.[100] A similar prohibition applied to a squadron detached by Admiral Fraser from the British Pacific Fleet to Hong Kong.[101]

In Tokyo Bay on that evening of 2 September 1945 Admiral Halsey went aboard HMS *Duke of York* at Admiral Fraser's invitation to witness the ceremony of 'Sunset' conducted with all the Royal Navy's traditional precision and pageantry. 'Massed bands of all the British ships played splendid martial music and a hymn,' wrote an American eyewitness to his wife. 'The flags of all the signatory Allies were flying from the signal yards, and all were slowly lowered in unison during the sunset hymn' – which was 'The Day Thou Gavest, Lord is Ended'.[102]

The 'Amen' fell away on the evening air. In His Majesty's ships, so few amidst that immense American fleet, the White Ensign was gathered in.

Sunset.

APPENDIXES

APPENDIX A

Abbreviations

AA = anti-aircraft
ABDA = American, British, Dutch, Australian
ABE Committee = Assessors on Bomb versus Battleship Experiments Committee
ACI = Atlantic Convoy Instructions
ACNS(H) = Assistant Chief of Naval Staff (Home)
AEAF = Allied Expeditionary Air Force
AEF = Allied Expeditionary Force
AFHQ = Allied Forces Headquarters
AI = Air Intelligence
ANCXF = Allied Naval Commander, Expeditionary Force
ASV = Air-to-Surface Vessel radar
ATS = Auxiliary Territorial Service

BEF = British Expeditionary Force
BLO = Bombardment Liaison Officer
BST = British Summer Time
BUCO = Build-up Control Organisation

CAM = Catapult Aircraft Merchant ship
CCOS = Combined Chiefs of Staff
CETF = Commander, Eastern Task Force
CIC = Combined Intelligence Committee
CID = Committee of Imperial Defence
CIGM = Chief Inspector of Gun Mountings
CIGS = Chief of the Imperial General Staff

CNO = Chief of Naval Operations
CNTF = Central Naval Task Force
COMINCH = Commander-in-Chief, United States Fleet
COPP = Combined Operations Pilotage Parties
COREP = Control Organisation for Repair
COS = Chief(s) of Staff
COSSAC = Chief of Staff to the Supreme Allied Commander
COTUG = Control Organisation for Tugs
CTC = Combined Training Centre
CVE = Escort Aircraft Carrier

DNI = Director of Naval Intelligence
DNO = Director of Naval Ordnance
DTM = Director of Torpedoes and Mines
DUKW = 'Duck' amphibious truck (D = 1942, year of origin, the fourth year of war; U = Utility; K = Front-wheel drive; W = Six-wheeled.)

E-boat = German fast torpedo boat
ENTF = Eastern Naval Task Force

FAT = Feder-Apparat Torpedo
FDC = Fighter Direction Centre
FDS = Fighter Direction Ship
FOB = Forward Observer, Bombardment
FOBAA = Flag Officer, British Assault Area
FOO = Forward Observation Officer
FS = French Ship

GC and CS = Government Code and Cypher School (Bletchley Park or 'Ultra')
GCI = Ground Coastal Interception
GHQ = General Headquarters
G/R = General Reconnaissance

HA = High Angle
HACS = High Angle Control System
HF/DF = High Frequency Direction Finding
HMAS = His Majesty's Australian Ship
HMCS = His Majesty's Canadian Ship
HMNZS = His Majesty's New Zealand Ship
HMS = His Majesty's Ship

[901]

HNLMS = Her Netherlands Majesty's Ship
HNorMS = His Norwegian Majesty's Ship
HON = 'Husky Naval Orders'

ISTDC = Inter-Service Training and Development Centre

JCS = Joint Chiefs of Staff
JIC = Joint Intelligence Committee

LCA = Landing Craft (Assault)
LCI = Landing Craft (Infantry)
LCM = Landing Craft (Mechanised)
LCS = Landing Craft (Support)
LCT = Landing Craft (Tank)
LSI = Landing Ships (Infantry)
LSI(L) = Landing Ships Infantry (Large)

MAC = Merchant Aircraft Carrier
ME = Middle East
MI = Military Intelligence
MTB = Motor Torpedo Boat

NCETF = Naval Commander, Eastern Task Force
NCWTF = Naval Commander, Western Task Force
NID = Naval Intelligence Department
NOIC = Naval Officer in Charge

OB = Ordnance Board
OIC = Operational Intelligence Centre
OKH = Oberkommando des Heeres (German Army High Command)
OKM = Oberkommando der Kriegsmarine (German Naval High Command)
OKW = Oberkommando der Wehrmacht (German Armed Forces High Command)
ON = 'Operation Neptune – Naval Orders'
ONAD = 'Operation Neptune – Administrative Orders'
ONCO = 'Operation Neptune – Communication Orders'

PLUTO = Pipe Line Under The Ocean
POL = Petrol, Oil, Lubricants
PP = German ship-to-ship signals

PR = Photographic Reconnaissance
PRU = Photographic Reconnaissance Unit

R and D = Research and Development
RASC = Royal Army Service Corps
R-boat = German motor minesweeper
RM = Royal Marines
RN = Royal Navy
RNorN = Royal Norwegian Navy
RNR = Royal Naval Reserve
RNVR = Royal Naval Volunteer Reserve

SCAEF = Supreme Commander, Allied Expeditionary Force
SHAEF = Supreme Headquarters, Allied Expeditionary Force
Sigint = Signals Intelligence
SIS = Secret Intelligence Service
SOFC = Senior Officer, Ferry Craft

TIS = Theatre Intelligence Section
TON = 'Torch Naval Orders'
TRE = Telecommunications Research Establishment
TURCO = Turn Round Control

U-boat = German submarine (*Unterseeboot*)
USN = United States Navy
USNR = United States Naval Reserve

VCNS = Vice Chief of Naval Staff
VHF = Very High Frequency
VLR = Very Long Range

WAAF = Women's Auxiliary Air Force
WRNS (Wrens) = Women's Royal Naval Service

Y Service = interception of radio signals

APPENDIX B

Notes to Text

Prologue – 1918: *'The German Ensign Will Be Hauled Down At Sunset'* (pages 1–16)

1. See Buist Papers, Churchill Archives Centre, BUIST 1/4.
2. Ibid; see also W. S. Chalmers, *The Life and Letters of David, Earl Beatty*, London, Hodder and Stoughton, 1951, p. 349. The account of the German internment is drawn from Chalmers, op cit, pp. 342–9; S. W. Roskill, *Admiral of the Fleet Earl Beatty; The Last Naval Hero: An Intimate Biography*, New York, Atheneum, 1981, pp. 276–80.
3. Ibid, p. 273.
4. Ibid.
5. Ibid, p. 275.
6. Arthur J. Marder, *From the Dreadnought to Scapa Flow; The Royal Navy in the Fisher Era, 1904–1919*, Vol II, *The War Years: To the Eve of Jutland*, London, Oxford University Press, 1965, p. 4.
7. Correlli Barnett, *The Swordbearers*, second edition, London, Hodder and Stoughton, 1987, p. 181.
8. Roskill, *Beatty*, op cit, p. 166.
9. Ibid, p. 160 and footnote.
10. See Marder, op cit, Vol III, *Jutland And After, May 1916–December 1916*, London, Oxford University Press, 1966, pp. 166–74; Roskill, *Beatty*, op cit, pp. 186–92, 254; see also Barnett, op cit, pp. 181–94.
11. Barnett, op cit, p. 187.
12. Roskill, *Beatty*, op cit, pp. 186–7.
13. Barnett, op cit, p. 188.
14. See Roskill, *Beatty*, op cit, p. 63; Dr J. T. Sumida (ed), *The Pollen Papers*, Publication of the Navy Records Society, Vol 124, London,

George Allen and Unwin for The Navy Records Society, 1984, especially Dr Sumida's General Introduction, pp. 1–7.

15. Sumida, op cit, pp. 194–236; Dreyer Papers, Churchill Archives Centre, Cambridge, DRYR 2/1, 2/2.

16. Roskill, *Beatty*, op cit, p. 185.

17. Ibid, pp. 152–4, 180–1; Marder, op cit, Vol III, pp. 41–3, 148–54.

18. See Papers of Admiral Sir Reginald Hall, Churchill Archives Centre, HALL; Denniston Papers, DENN 1/1–4, 2/1.

19. Quoted in Correlli Barnett, *The Great War*, London, Park Lane Press, 1979, p. 106.

20. See Marder, op cit, Vol IV, *1917: Year of Crisis*, pp. 134–5, 150–2.

21. Marder, op cit, Vol IV, Chapters V–VII, especially pp. 104–6, 108–9, 112–65.

22. See Roskill (ed), *The Naval Air Service*, Vol I, London, The Navy Records Society, 1969, *passim*, but especially pp. 484–6, 545, 639–41, 651, 658–63.

23. Ibid, Vol I, Appendix I, p. 747.

24. Marder, op cit, pp. 3–24; Roskill, *The Naval Air Service*, op cit, Vol I, pp. xi–xvii.

25. Marder, op cit, p. 11.

26. Roskill, *The Naval Air Service*, op cit, Vol I, pp. 740–4.

27. Report by Squadron-Commander C. L'E. Malone, Commanding HMS *Ben-My-Chree*, to the Director of the Air Department, 14 August 1915; AIR 1/665, reproduced in Roskill, *The Naval Air Service*, op cit, Vol I, pp. 221–3; see also Marder, op cit, pp. 19–21.

28. Letter No 3343/H.F.0022 of 11 September 1917 from Admiral Sir David Beatty, C-in-C, Grand Fleet, to the Admiralty, entitled 'Considerations of an Attack by Torpedo Planes on the High Seas Fleet', in Adm 1/8486, reproduced in Roskill, *The Naval Air Service*, op cit, Vol I, p. 541.

29. Second Report of the Committee on Air Organisation and Home Defence against Air Raids, 17 August 1917, CAB 24/22, reproduced in Roskill, *The Naval Air Service*, op cit, Vol I, p. 512.

30. Ibid.

31. Letter from Geddes to Lord Weir, Secretary of State for the Air Force, 22 May 1918, in ADM 116/1805, reproduced in Roskill, *The Naval Air Service*, op cit, Vol I, pp. 670–1.

32. Roskill, *Naval Policy Between the Wars*, Vol 1, *The Period of Anglo-American Antagonism 1919–1929*, London, Collins, 1968, p. 71.

33. CAB 32/3, Pt I, E-10, quoted in Correlli Barnett, *The Collapse of British Power*, London, Eyre Methuen, 1972, paperback edition, Alan Sutton, 1984, p. 252.

34. CAB 27/627, COS 928, 'The Situation in the Far East', 18 June 1939.

35. Ibid.

Part I: Britannia Lets the Trident Slip

1. *Dreams of Peace and the Shrinking Navy, 1918–1931* (pages 19–28)

1. Paul M. Kennedy, *The Rise and Fall of British Naval Mastery*, London, Allen Lane, 1976, p. 260.
2. Roskill, *Naval Policy Between the Wars*, op cit, Vol I, Appendix D, p. 586.
3. First Interim Report of the Committee on National Expenditure, Cmd 1581. See Roskill, *Naval Policy Between the Wars*, op cit, Vol I, pp. 230–3.
4. Ibid, p. 221.
5. CAB 32/46, Documents and Stenographic Notes of the Imperial Conference, 1926, E-9; For the course of the Washington Conference, see CAB 30/1A, 1B, 9–10, 11–13, 15–16, 26, 31; Roskill, *Naval Policy Between the Wars*, op cit, Vol 1, Chap VIII; and for a summary, Barnett, *The Collapse of British Power*, op cit, pp. 263–74.
6. See Barnett, *The Collapse of British Power*, op cit, pp. 20–68, 274–8, 282–98, on the nature and impact of romantic internationalism on British total strategy in the 1920s.
7. Cited in CAB 27/626, FP (36)2, Memorandum by Sir Maurice Hankey for the Cabinet Committee on Foreign Policy, dated 1 May 1936, summarising the history of deliberations on the proposal for a League of Nations, 1916–19. The Admiralty memorandum was dated 23 December 1918.
8. Barnett, *The Collapse of British Power*, op cit, p. 275.
9. CAB 27/407, CP 195 (29): for the history of the Singapore base, see Barnett, *The Collapse of British Power*, op cit, pp. 279–82, 288; Paul Haggie, *Britannia at Bay; The Defence of the British Empire against Japan 1931–1941*, Oxford, Clarendon Press, 1981, pp. 1–24; Roskill, *Naval Policy Between the Wars*, op cit, Vol I, passim.
10. CAB 29/117, LNC(29)5.
11. Oscar Parkes, *British Battleships: 'Warrior' 1860 to 'Vanguard' 1950; A History of Design, Construction and Armament*, London, Seeley Service, 1970, pp. 566, 612 and 614–15.
12. Cf S. W. Roskill, 'A Sailor's Ditty Box', unpublished personal memoir in the Churchill Archives Centre.
13. Bernard Ireland, *The Rise and Fall of the Aircraft Carrier*, London and New York, Marshall Cavendish, 1979, p. 23; Roskill, *Naval Policy Between the Wars*, op cit, Vol I, pp. 496–7, 528.
14. Ireland, op cit.
15. See Till, 'Airpower and the Battleship' in Bryan Ranft (ed), *Technical Change and British Naval Policy 1860–1939*, London, Hodder and Stoughton, 1977, pp. 110–20; Roskill, *Naval Policy Between the Wars*, op cit, Vol I, pp. 113–16.

16. Roskill, *Naval Policy Between the Wars*, op cit, Vol I, pp. 223–5.
17. The Balfour Enquiry, 1921; the Geddes Committee, 1921; the Balfour Committee, 1923; the Salisbury Committee, 1923; the Colwyn Committee, 1925.
18. See Roskill, *Naval Policy Between the Wars*, op cit, Vol I, Chapters VI, X and XV for detailed accounts of these transactions.
19. Sir William James, *Admiral Sir William Fisher*, London, Macmillan, 1943, p. 124.
20. S. W. Roskill, 'A Sailor's Ditty Box', op cit.
21. Ibid.
22. Report to the Committee of Imperial Defence Sub-Committee on Preparations for the League Disarmament Conference, CAB 27/476, CDC(31)2.
23. Ibid.
24. Ibid.

2. *The Triple Threat and Belated Rearmament, 1932–1939* (pages 29–56)

1. CAB 53/22, COS 295.
2. Ibid.
3. Ibid.
4. CAB 53/23, COS 310.
5. Ibid.
6. Ibid.
7. Ibid.
8. Roskill, *Naval Policy Between the Wars*, op cit, Vol II, p. 306.
9. See Roskill, ibid, pp. 306–9 for an account of the negotiations.
10. CAB 16/123, DRC 37.
11. CAB 53/25, COS 392.
12. Roskill, *Naval Policy Between the Wars*, op cit, Vol II, p. 261.
13. CAB 53/25, COS 392.
14. CAB 23/83 11(36).
15. CAB 27/606, MF(36)1.
16. CAB 53/30, COS 560.
17. See David Reynolds, *The Creation of the Anglo-American Alliance 1937–1941: A Study in Competitive Co-operation*, London, Europa Publications, 1981, Chapters 1 and 2; Christopher Thorne, *Allies of a Kind: The United States, Great Britain and the War Against Japan, 1941–1945*, London, Hamish Hamilton, 1978.
18. CAB 29/159, AFC1.
19. Barnett, *The Collapse of British Power*, op cit, pp. 217–18.
20. See ibid, Part IV, 'An Imperial Commonwealth', for a detailed account of these transactions between 1921 and 1937.
21. Ibid, p. 231; Roskill, *Naval Policy Between the Wars*, op cit, Vol. II, pp. 435–6.

22. CAB 16/209 SAC 2.
23. See Barnett, *The Collapse of British Power*, op cit, pp. 386–439 for an analysis of the reasons for the delay in commencing British rearmament, and especially the role of public opinion in 1933–35.
24. CAB 16/112, DPR(DR)9, 12 February 1936.
25. See Roskill, *Naval Policy Between the Wars*, op cit, Vol II, pp. 217 and 326–7; N. H. Gibbs, *Grand Strategy*, Vol I, *Rearmament Policy*, London, HMSO, 1976, pp. 332–55.
26. CAB 16/112 DRC 37; Gibbs, op cit, pp. 334–5.
27. Meeting of the DPRC, 21 October 1937, in CAB 16/137, DPR 44.
28. Nineteenth, 20th, 22nd and 25th Admiralty reports to the DPRC, January, February, May and December 1938, CAB 16/142, DPR 244 and 249; CAB 16/143, DPR 271 and 293.
29. Meetings of the DPRC, 18 March, 22 April and 29 April 1937, in CAB 16/137, DPR 36, 38 and 39.
30. Twelfth report by the Admiralty to the DPRC, April 1937, in CAB 16/141, DPR 194.
31. Sixteenth report by the Admiralty to the DPRC, October 1937, CAB 16/142, DPR 224.
32. Fifth report of the Admiralty to the DPRC, October 1936, in CAB 16/142, DPR 129.
33. See Barnett, *The Audit of War*, London, Macmillan, 1986, Chapter Seven, for a detailed account of aircraft production during the rearmament period 1936–39.
34. Eighteenth report by the Air Ministry to the DPRC, for November 1937, CAB 16/142, DPR 236.
35. M. M. Postan, D. Hay and J. D. Scott, *Design and Development of Weapons*, London, HMSO and Longmans, Green, 1964, p. 136: CAB 16/137, DPR 40, meeting of the DPRC on 24 June 1937.
36. Postan, Hay and Scott, op cit, p. 137.
37. Ibid, pp. 134–5.
38. See John Terraine, *The Right of the Line: The Royal Air Force in the European War 1939–1945*, London, Hodder and Stoughton, 1985, pp. 30–5.
39. See Roskill, *Naval Policy Between the Wars*, op cit, Vol II, Chapter XIII for an account of the whole matter.
40. CAB 24/270, CP 199(37), 21 July 1937.
41. See Roskill, *Naval Policy Between the Wars*, op cit, Vol II, pp. 408–11.
42. Ibid, Vol 1, p. 542.
43. Hideo Takubo, article 'To Fight a Losing Battle; Yamamoto Isoruku and the Pacific War', in *The East*, Vol VII, No 3, March 1971, p. 59.
44. Ireland, *The Rise and Fall of the Aircraft Carrier*, op cit, pp. 25–9; Admiral of the Fleet Lord Hill-Norton and John Dekker, *Sea Power*, London, Faber and Faber, 1982, p. 62; H. T. Lenton and J. J. Colledge, *Warships of World War II*, London, Ian Allan, 1964, pp. 61–3.

45. See Parkes, *British Battleships*, op cit, pp. 663–9; Roskill, *Naval Policy Between the Wars*, op cit, Vol II, pp. 279–80, 326–9, 671; Eric Grove, Christopher Chant, David Lyon, Hugh Lyon, *The Hardware of World War II*, Galley Press, London, 1984, pp. 186–7, 146–7.
46. Parkes, op cit, pp. 663–9.
47. Ibid, pp. 569–76, 614–17, 648–9.
48. Grove, Chant, Lyon and Lyon, op cit, pp. 188–95; Lenton and Colledge, op cit, pp. 39–48.
49. Edgar J. March, *British Destroyers 1892–1953*, London, Seeley Service, 1966, p. 287.
50. Ibid, pp. 322–8.
51. Ibid, p. 335.
52. David Henry, 'British Submarine Policy, 1918–1939', in Ranft, *Technical Change and British Naval Policy 1860–1939*, op cit, especially pp. 102–8.
53. 'Notes for the 1937 Naval Estimates', 26 February 1937, quoted by Henry, in Ranft, op cit; see also Willem Hackmann, *Seek and Strike; Sonar, Antisubmarine Warfare and the Royal Navy 1914–54*, London, HMSO, 1984, Chapter V, especially pp. 125–34.
54. Ranft, op cit, p. 100.
55. C. B. A. Behrens, *Merchant Shipping and the Demands of War*, London, HMSO and Longmans, Green, 1955, pp. 37–8.
56. Ranft, op cit, p. 102.
57. Roskill, 'A Sailor's Ditty Box', op cit.
58. ABE 63, in CAB 16/179, cited in Roskill, *Naval Policy Between the Wars*, op cit, Vol II, p. 420.
59. Ibid.
60. Postan, Hay and Scott, op cit, p. 435.
61. Ibid, p. 457.
62. Roskill, *Naval Policy Between the Wars*, op cit, Vol II, p. 333.
63. Roskill quotation from ibid, p. 334. For the incapability of the British armaments and engineering firms to manufacture the tachymetric system, and possible consequent pressure on the Admiralty, see letter from Rear-Admiral M. W. St. L. Searle, to Captain Roskill, 1 May 1979 in Roskill Papers, Churchill Archive Centre, ROSK 7/29; see also the present work, Chapter 28, pp. 886–8, below and relevant documentary source references.
64. Roskill, *Naval Policy Between the Wars*, op cit, Vol II, p. 333; see also Rear-Admiral M. W. St. L. Searle, unpublished paper, 'The Air Threat and the Home Fleet at the Outbreak of War, 3rd September, 1939' in ROSK 4/11.
65. Ibid.
66. Roskill, *Naval Policy Between the Wars*, op cit, Vol II, p. 453.
67. See A. Wells, 'Naval Intelligence in an era of technical change' in Ranft, op cit, pp. 136–7; Denniston Papers, Churchill Archives Centre,

DENN 1/4; F. H. Hinsley with E. E. Thomas, C. F. G. Ransom and R. C. Knight, *British Intelligence in the Second World War*, Vol I, London, HMSO, 1979, Chapter 2, especially pp. 50–3, 62–3.

68. Wells, in Ranft, op cit, pp. 133–41.
69. Terraine, op cit, pp. 70 and 223.
70. Lieutenant-Commander Sir Godfrey Style in a letter of 5 January 1979 to Captain S. W. Roskill, in ROSK 7/210.
71. Ibid.
72. Roskill, *Naval Policy Between the Wars*, op cit, Vol II, p. 462.
73. Admiral Sir John Kelly, in ROSK 5/125; see also Admiral J. H. Godfrey, 'Memoirs', pp. 299–300, Churchill Archives Centre, GDFY.
74. Letter from Captain S. W. Roskill to Admiral Crutchley, 23 July 1975, in ROSK 7/210.
75. Letter of July 1936, in the Chatfield MSS, CHT/4/6, copy in ROSK 7/210.
76. Admiral Sir Victor Crutchley in a letter to Captain S. W. Roskill, 29 July 1979, in ROSK 7/210.
77. Admiral Sir Angus Cunninghame-Graham to Captain S. W. Roskill, 16 December 1979, in ROSK 7/210.
78. Undated letter in ROSK 5/124.
79. Commander Robert Bower, in a letter to Captain S. W. Roskill, 8 March 1970, in ROSK 5/125.
80. See Barnett, *The Collapse of British Power*, op cit, pp. 550–2; R. P. Shay Jr, *British Rearmament in the 1930s: Politics and Profits*, Princeton, the Princeton University Press, 1977, Chapter VII; G. C. Peden, *British Rearmament and the Treasury 1932–1939*, Edinburgh, Scottish Academic Press, 1979, Chapters IV and V; see also CAB 27/648, Committee on Defence Programmes and Acceleration, appointed by the Cabinet on 26 October 1938, especially its Report, CP 247(38).
81. CAB 27/648, CP 247(38).
82. CP 234(38).
83. Roskill, *Naval Policy Between the Wars*, op cit, Vol II, pp. 458–9.
84. Ibid, p. 461.
85. Ibid, p. 431.
86. Roskill, *The War at Sea 1939–1945*, Vol I, *The Defensive*, London HMSO, 1954, p. 25.
87. Ibid, p. 2.
88. Roskill, *Naval Policy Between the Wars*, op cit, Vol II, p. 483.

3. *'Winston Is Back'* (pages 57–96)

1. Winston S. Churchill, *The Second World War*, Vol I, *The Gathering Storm*, London, Cassell, 1948, pp. 320–1.
2. Admiral of the Fleet Lord Fraser of North Cape, 'Churchill and the Navy', in Sir James Marchant (ed), *Winston Spencer Churchill;*

Servant of the Crown and Commonwealth, London, Cassell, 1954, pp. 78–9.

3. Churchill, op cit, Vol I, p. 321.
4. Admiral Sir Geoffrey Dickens, in undated letter to S. W. Roskill in ROSK 5/124.
5. Admiral of the Fleet Lord Cunningham of Hyndhope, *A Sailor's Odyssey*, London, Hutchinson, 1951, pp. 583–4.
6. ROSK 4/124, letter from Admiral Sir William Davis to Captain Roskill, 20 October 1961.
7. Ibid.
8. Captain G. R. G. Allen, quoted in Arthur Marder, 'Winston is Back: Churchill at the Admiralty 1939–40' in *The English Historical Review*, Supplement 5, London, Longman, 1972, p. 2.
9. Roskill, *War at Sea*, op cit, Vol I, p. 61.
10. Ibid, pp. 53–8; and Appendix G; Admiral K. Dönitz, *Memoirs: Ten Years and Twenty Days*, London, Weidenfeld and Nicolson, 1958, Chapter 5; Cajus Bekker, *Hitler's Naval War*, London, Macdonald, 1974, pp. 26–35.
11. Dönitz, op cit, p. 47.
12. Roskill, *The War at Sea*, op cit, Vol I, p. 60; Elke C. Weale, John A. Weale and Richard Barker, *Combat Aircraft of World War Two*, London, Bracken Books, 1985, p. 114.
13. Roskill, *The War at Sea*, op cit, Vol I, Appendix E, pp. 582–5.
14. Ibid.
15. Ibid, p. 51, Table 3.
16. Figures from ROSK4/73; Roskill, *The War at Sea*, op cit, Vol I, Appendix D and E, pp. 577–87.
17. All ROSK 4/73.
18. ROSK 4/7; Postan, Hay and Scott, *Design and Development of Weapons*, op cit, *passim*.
19. ROSK 4/7; Terraine, *The Right of the Line*, op cit, p. 70, Note 2.
20. Weale, Weale and Barker, op cit, p. 192.
21. Air Historical Branch Monograph II/117/1(B), p. 56, quoted in Terraine, op cit, p. 100; see Terraine, op cit, pp. 98–100 for an account of these operations.
22. Terraine, op cit, p. 100.
23. Ibid, pp. 95–100.
24. Churchill, op cit, Vol I, p. 331.
25. Roskill, *The War at Sea*, op cit, Vol I, pp. 103–4; Dönitz, op cit, pp. 54–9: Peter Padfield, *Dönitz: the Last Führer*, London, Victor Gollancz, 1984, pp. 190–207.
26. Roskill, *The War at Sea*, op cit, Vol I, pp. 92–4.
27. Ibid, p. 106. All statistics of merchant shipping losses in the present work are drawn from Roskill, *War at Sea*, op cit. The Naval Historical Branch are currently engaged in a complete re-examination of the data.

28. Ibid, Table 4, p. 67.
29. Ibid.
30. Cf British Strategic Memorandum to the Anglo-French Staff Conversations, April 1939, CAB 29/159, AFC 7; evidence of Sir Alan Barlow, Under-Secretary at the Treasury, to the Strategical Appreciation Committee, April 1939, CAB 16/209, SAC 4; C. Webster and N. Frankland, *The Strategic Air Offensive Against Germany 1939–1945*, Vol I, *Preparation*, London, HMSO, 1961, pp. 271–84.
31. ROSK 4/92, TSD/FDS/X.280/49, Memorandum to Captain Roskill; Roskill, *War at Sea*, op. cit Vol I, pp. 105–6; Dönitz, op cit, pp. 55–6; Bekker, op cit, p. 21.
32. Martin Gilbert, *Winston S. Churchill 1939–41*, Vol VI, *Finest Hour, 1939–41*, London, Book Club Associates, 1983, p. 37.
33. ROSK 4/49, Rear-Admiral T. V. Briggs, unpublished account entitled 'The First Air Attack on a Fleet at Sea: "Where is the Ark Royal?"' As a Lieutenant-Commander, Briggs was *Ark Royal*'s gunnery officer at the time.
34. Ibid.
35. Ibid.
36. See Roskill, *War at Sea*, op cit, Vol I, p. 179.
37. Ibid, pp. 73–6.
38. Cited in Gilbert, op cit, Vol VI, p. 62.
39. ROSK 4/49.
40. Roskill, *War at Sea*, op cit, Vol I, p. 80.
41. Ibid, pp. 80–1.
42. NID 24/X.11a/46 in ROSK 4/49. The following account of the action between *Rawalpindi* and the two German battleships is drawn from the Naval Intelligence Department's translation of *Scharnhorst*'s log in ibid.
43. HMS *Newcastle*'s log for November 1939 in ADM 53/109923.
44. Roskill, *War at Sea*, op cit, Vol I, p. 87.
45. Vice-Admiral F. Ruge, *Sea Warfare 1939–1945*, London, Cassell, 1957, pp. 38–9.
46. Roskill, *War at Sea*, op cit, Vol I, p. 114.
47. Churchill, op cit, Vol I, p. 405.
48. Ibid.
49. Ibid, p. 407.
50. Roskill, *War at Sea*, op cit, Vol I, pp. 113–17.
51. Despatch of Rear-Admiral Sir Henry Harwood, KCB, OBE, to the Lords Commissioners of the Admiralty, 30 December 1939; published in the Supplement to the London Gazette of Tuesday, 17 June 1947.
52. Ibid.
53. Ibid; Roskill, *War at Sea*, op cit, Vol I, p. 118.
54. Despatch of Sir Henry Harwood, op cit.

55. Ibid.
56. Ibid.
57. Report in ROSK 4/84.
58. Cf accounts by Commander Kurt Diggins, Lt-Cmdr Günter Schiebusch, Captain Jürgen Wattenberg, Commander F. W. Rasenack, cited in E. Millington-Drake (ed), *The Drama of Graf Spee and the Battle of the River Plate; a Documentary Anthology: 1914–1964*, London, Peter Davies, 1964, pp. 227–30. The account of the action of 13 December 1939 is drawn from ibid; Despatch of Sir Henry Harwood, op cit; Roskill, *War at Sea*, op cit, Vol I, pp. 118–20.
59. Admiral Sir Guy Grantham, memorandum of 19 August 1966, to Arthur Marder, cited in Marder, 'Winston is Back', op cit, p. 30.
60. Despatch of Sir Henry Harwood, op cit.
61. See Millington-Drake, op cit, Part VII for the events and decisions of the aftermath of the action.
62. Quoted in ibid, p. 368.
63. CAB 65/2, WM88(39)2 and WM90(39)8.
64. ROSK 4/43. The general account of the mining campaigns of 1939–40 is based on ADM 186/799, Naval Staff History, *Home Waters and the Atlantic*, Vol I, *September 1939–April 1940*, Chapter VIII; Roskill, *War at Sea*, op cit, Vol I, pp. 96–102, 123–8.
65. ROSK 4/43: Letter No. 704, 29 August 1953, from Commander M. G. Saunders, Foreign Documents Section, Cabinet Office Historical Section, to Captain S. W. Roskill.
66. Postan, Hay and Scott, *Design and Development of Weapons*, op cit, p. 443.
67. ROSK 4/43, letter from Saunders to Roskill, op cit.
68. See ADM 186/799 Naval Staff History, *Home Waters*, op cit, Chapter VIII.
69. ADM 199/299, comments by Churchill on a 'Most Secret' Memorandum from Pound of 3 December 1939.
70. Cited in Marder, 'Winston is Back', op cit, p. 31; see also Gilbert, op cit, pp. 26–7.
71. Pound to Forbes, 15 September 1939, copy in ROSK 4/49.
72. Ibid.
73. ROSK 4/49 photocopy of letter from Pound to Forbes, 20 January 1940.
74. ADM 205/4, Note marked 'Most Secret' and 'To be passed round only in a box' 'Notes on "C"'.
75. Ibid.
76. ADM 205/4, Note of 20 September 1939.
77. Marder, 'Winston is Back', op cit, p. 32.
78. Cited in ibid, p. 33.
79. Ibid, p. 36.
80. See Roskill, *Churchill and the Admirals*, London, Collins, 1977, p. 94, and Footnote 8.

4. 'A Very Hazardous Affair': Norway, 1939–1940 (pages 97–118)

1. ADM 205/3, 'Norway and Sweden'; Memorandum for the War Cabinet, 23 September 1939.
2. Cited in Marder, 'Winston is Back: Churchill at the Admiralty 1939–40', op cit, p. 39.
3. CAB 65/2, 116(39)4. See also ADM 205/2, First Lord's Personal Minute to First Sea Lord on Swedish iron-ore traffic and on mining the Leads, 27 November 1939.
4. CAB 66/4, WP(39)162, 'Norway – Iron-Ore Traffic', 16 December 1939.
5. Ibid.
6. CAB 65/2, 111(39)6.
7. J. R. M. Butler, Grand Strategy, Vol II, September 1939–June 1941, London, HMSO, 1957, p. 100.
8. Gilbert, Winston S. Churchill, op cit, Vol VI, pp. 108–9. See also Churchill's own notes of 22 December 1939 for use in Cabinet, in ADM 116/4471.
9. CAB 66/4, WP(39)179: Military Implications of a Policy aimed at stopping the export of Swedish iron ore to Germany.
10. CAB 66/4, WP(40)5; Scandinavia: Report of the Chiefs of Staff Committee.
11. CAB 65/11, 2(40)1; 3 January 1940, Confidential Annexe.
12. CAB 65/11, 1(40)1; 2 January 1940.
13. CAB 65/11, 10(40)1, Confidential Annexe.
14. CAB 80/7, COS 218.
15. Cf the CIGS, on 19 February, on how the land forces once ashore, 'would be quite capable of looking after themselves' against German air attack (CAB 79/3, COS No. 34, 19 February 1940); the Chief of Air Staff on the acceptability of the 'considerable risks' for the sake of the great advantages to be won (CAB 65/11, 45(40)1, Confidential Annexe).
16. See General Sir David Fraser, And We Shall Shock Them: The British Army in the Second World War, London, Hodder and Stoughton, 1983, pp. 31–2, 36–7, 41; J. L. Moulton, The Norwegian Campaign: A Study of Warfare in Three Dimensions, London, Eyre and Spottiswoode, 1966, pp. 49–50.
17. Chartwell Papers CHAR 19/3 Churchill Archives Centre, a Note on the War in 1940, 25 December 1939, sent to Pound, cited in Martin Gilbert, op cit, Vol VI, p. 112.
18. CAB 65/11, 46(40)9.
19. CAB 65/12, 66(40)2.
20. CAB 65/12, 68(40)4.
21. For the evolution of German plans, see Butler, op cit, pp. 104–5, 114–15, 124–5; Moulton, op cit, pp. 61–8.
22. Quoted in Moulton, op cit, p. 65.

23. Bekker, *Hitler's Naval War*, op cit, pp. 98–9.
24. F. H. Hinsley, *British Intelligence in the Second World War*, op cit, Vol I, p. 116. The account which follows of Allied Intelligence in regard to 'Weserübung' is drawn from this work, pp. 116–25.
25. The account of British Intelligence failures which follows is based on Hinsley, op cit, Vol I, pp. 116–25.
26. Ibid, p. 123.
27. Ibid.
28. Ibid, p. 125.
29. Gilbert, op cit, Vol VI, p. 199.
30. CAB 65/12, 77(40)2, Confidential Annexe.
31. CAB 79/85, COS meeting No. 60, 20 March 1940.
32. Roskill, *War at Sea*, op cit, Vol I, p. 157.
33. Ibid.
34. Transcript of Edwards's contemporary diary in ROSK 4/75.
35. Ibid.
36. Ibid.
37. Roskill, *War at Sea*, op cit, Vol I, p. 159.
38. Ibid.
39. ROSK 4/50, letter from Lieutenant-Commander Godfrey Style, who as Flag-Lieutenant handled Forbes's operational and cypher signals, to Captain Roskill, 10 March 1979.
40. Ibid.
41. The account of *Glowworm*'s action is based on Roskill, *War at Sea*, op cit, Vol I, pp. 158–60; Moulton, op cit, pp. 76–7; Bekker, op cit, p. 100.
42. Roskill, *War at Sea*, op cit, Vol I, p. 160.
43. ROSK 4/76, letter from Vice-Admiral W. J. Whitworth to Dr Denny of the Cabinet Office Historical Section, 5 June 1950.
44. Roskill, *War at Sea*, op cit, Vol I, p. 170.
45. Ibid, p. 171.
46. ROSK 4/76, letter to Captain Roskill, 19 June 1951.
47. ROSK 4/75, Edwards's diary.
48. Roskill, *War at Sea*, op cit, Vol I, p. 174.
49. This account of Warburton-Lee's attack is based on Roskill, *War at Sea*, op cit, Vol I, pp. 174–5; Moulton, op cit, pp. 110–13; Bekker, op cit, pp. 117–18.
50. Moulton, op cit, pp. 108–9; Bekker, op cit, pp. 115–17.
51. CAB 65/6, 85(40), 8.30 am, 9 April.
52. Ibid.

5. *A Churchillian Disaster: Norway, 1940* (pages 119–139)

1. Roskill, *War at Sea*, op cit, Vol I, p. 178.
2. Ibid.
3. Moulton, *The Norwegian Campaign*, op cit, p. 148.

4. CAB 83/3, MC(40)18, 10 April 1940.
5. CAB 65/12, 87(40)5, 88(40)5, 90(40)3, Confidential Annexes.
6. Ibid.
7. CAB 65/5, 92(40).
8. CAB 65/12, 91(40)3, Confidential Annexe.
9. CAB 65/12, 92(40)5, Confidential Annexe.
10. CAB 83/3, MC(40)23.
11. ROSK 4/75.
12. Letter of 15 April 1940 to King George V, Royal Archives, cited in Gilbert, *Winston S. Churchill*, op cit, Vol VI, p. 243.
13. *The Rise and Fall of the German Air Force (1939 to 1945)*, Air Ministry, London, 1948, p. 63.
14. ROSK 4/75.
15. Terraine, *The Right of the Line*, op cit, pp. 116–17; ROSK 4/75.
16. CHAR 19/2, Churchill Archives Centre, quoted in Gilbert, op cit, Vol VI, p. 251.
17. Ibid.
18. ADM 199/1929, 'Most Secret, Most Immediate', 1350, 17 April 1940.
19. Gilbert, op cit, Vol VI, p. 251.
20. ADM 199/1929.
21. CAB 65/6, 98(40).
22. ROSK 4/75, 'Notes on Allied Operations in the Narvik Area'.
23. Ibid.
24. Moulton, op cit, p. 168; Fraser, *And We Shall Shock Them*, op cit, pp. 38–40.
25. Letter from Colonel Beckwith to Major-General Moulton, Moulton, op cit, p. 174, Footnote 1.
26. Signal at 1157 on 14 April, cited in ROSK 4/75.
27. Signal cited in ibid.
28. Ibid.
29. CAB 83/3, MC40(27).
30. Roskill, *War at Sea*, op cit, Vol I, p. 186.
31. CAB 79/85, COS No. 87, Confidential Annexe.
32. Moulton, op cit, pp. 205–6.
33. ROSK 4/75.
34. CAB 82/3, MC(40)35; see also CAB 79/85, COS No. 98, 26 April 1940; CAB 65/12, 105(40)2, 27 April 1940.
35. Moulton, op cit, pp. 209–10.
36. Roskill, *War at Sea*, op cit, Vol I, p. 189.
37. A. Carton de Wiart, *Happy Odyssey*, London, Jonathan Cape, 1950, p. 174.
38. Admiral of the Fleet Sir Philip Vian, *Action This Day: War Memoirs of Admiral of the Fleet Sir Philip Vian*, London, Muller, 1960, p. 47.
39. Moulton, op cit, pp. 211–12; Roskill, *War at Sea*, op cit, Vol I, pp. 189–90.

40. ROSK 4/75. Even in the first month of the war Forbes was writing to Pound that he had 'a sort of bare feeling' every time he went to sea 'as I never seem to have any cruisers and very few destroyers to screen the big ships'. Signal of 27 September 1939 in ADM 205/2.
41. Moulton, op cit, pp. 224, 229.
42. ROSK 4/75.
43. Ibid.
44. ADM 199/1929, 'Most Secret'.
45. CAB 65/13, 135(40)9, Confidential Annexe.
46. Moulton, op cit, p. 249.
47. Roskill, *War at Sea*, Vol I, pp. 197–8.
48. See Hinsley, op cit, Vol I, pp. 141–2.
49. Ibid.
50. ROSK 4/77, letter from Rear-Admiral A. S. Bolt to Captain Roskill, 18 December 1979.
51. ROSK 4/76; Captain G. A. (Hank) Rotherham, *It's Really Quite Safe*, Belleville, Ontario, 1985, p. 147.
52. ADM 199/478, ERD/219.
53. Account of the sinking of the *Glorious* based on ROSK 4/76 and 77; ADM 199/478, account compiled by Commander J. E. Broome (captain of HMS *Veteran*, which picked up survivors) from evidence of survivors of the sunk ships; and report of 3 July 1940 to the First Sea Lord on the sinking of *Glorious*, including a summary of the Court of Enquiry. The Leading Signalman who read *Glorious*'s signal to *Ark Royal* was in *Diana*, commanded by Commander E. G. Le Geyt, who on 15 September 1968 wrote the account of the exchange of signals on the back of a note in ADM 199/478 to the VCNS, dated 20 June 1940, on a different topic altogether; Bekker, *Hitler's Naval War*, op cit, pp. 155–61.
54. Rotherham, op cit, pp. 142–6.
55. Moulton, op cit, p. 258.
56. Ibid, p. 260.
57. Roskill, *War at Sea*, op cit, Vol I, p. 198.

6. *'Operation Dynamo': the Dunkirk Evacuation* (pages 140–167)

1. Roskill, *War at Sea*, op cit, Vol I, pp. 210–11.
2. Churchill Archives Centre, Ramsay Papers RMSY 8/5: Report on 'Operation Dynamo', Dover Despatch A. 14/0/876/40 of 18 June 1940, by Flag Officer Commanding Dover. The account of 'Dynamo' which follows is based on this despatch and on David Divine's superb book *The Nine Days of Dunkirk*, London, Faber and Faber, 1959, except where otherwise cited.
3. RMSY 8/10.
4. Ibid.
5. Ibid.

6. RMSY 8/5.
7. Ibid.
8. RMSY 8/10.
9. Ibid.
10. Cited in Divine, op cit, pp. 150–1.
11. Ibid, pp. 154–5.
12. Ibid, p. 155.
13. Ibid, p. 172.
14. Ibid, p. 176.
15. RMSY 8/10.
16. Divine, op cit, p. 181.
17. Ibid, p. 184.
18. Ibid, p. 186.
19. RMSY 8/5.
20. Divine, op cit, p. 144.
21. Cited in ibid, p. 145.
22. RMSY 8/5.
23. Terraine, *The Right of the Line*, op cit, p. 157.
24. Ibid.
25. RMSY 8/5.
26. Divine, op cit, p. 204.
27. RMSY 8/5.
28. Ibid.
29. Ibid.
30. Ibid.
31. Ibid.
32. Ibid.
33. Ibid.
34. Ibid.
35. Cited in Divine, op cit, p. 221.
36. RMSY 8/5, List of ships which took part in 'Operation Dynamo', 25 October 1940.
37. RMSY 8/5.
38. RMSY 8/10.
39. Cited in Divine, op cit, p. 115.
40. Quoted in Gilbert, *Winston S. Churchill*, op cit, Vol VI, p. 464.
41. Ibid.
42. Roskill, *War at Sea*, op cit, Vol I, pp. 231–2.
43. Ibid, p. 239.
44. Ibid, Appendix H, pp. 593–7.
45. Behrens, *Merchant Shipping and the Demands of War*, op cit, p. 109.
46. Ibid, Footnote 3.
47. Ibid, Appendices XXXII, p. 242 and XLIX, p. 295.
48. CAB 66/11, WP40(40)324.

Part II: Storm Force

7. *The Wall of England* (pages 171–206)

1. Somerville Papers, Churchill Archives Centre, SMVL 7/19, Report of the proceedings of Force H, 28 June–4 July 1940.
2. ADM 205/6.
3. Signal cited in Gilbert, *Winston S. Churchill*, op cit, Vol VI, pp. 632–3.
4. ADM 205/4.
5. CAB 65/7, 176(40).
6. Ibid.
7. CAB 65/13, 179(40)3, Confidential Annexe.
8. Ibid.
9. Ibid.
10. Hinsley, *British Intelligence in the Second World War*, op cit, Vol I, pp. 150–3.
11. Roskill, *War at Sea*, op cit, Vol I, pp. 240–1.
12. CAB 65/13, 184(40)5.
13. ADM 205/6.
14. Cited in Roskill, *Churchill and the Admirals*, op cit, p. 151.
15. Ibid, p. 154.
16. Roskill, *War at Sea*, op cit, Vol I, p. 243; Gilbert, op cit, Vol VI, p. 629.
17. PREM 3/179/1.
18. SMVL 7/19.
19. Ibid.
20. Cited in Somerville's report on 'Catapult', SMVL 7/19.
21. CAB 65/14, 192(40); Roskill, *Churchill and the Admirals*, op cit, pp. 157–8.
22. In SMVL 7/19.
23. Cited in Gilbert, op cit, Vol VI, p. 634.
24. Ibid.
25. SMVL 7/19.
26. Ibid.
27. Hinsley, op cit, Vol I, p. 153.
28. Report of Operations by Commanding Officer, HMS *Hood*, to Vice-Admiral commanding Force H, No. 0130/T, 5 July in SMVL 7/19.
29. Report of Operations by Commanding Officer, HMS *Resolution* to Vice-Admiral commanding Force H, 4 July 1940 in ibid.
30. Quoted by Somerville in his own report, in ibid.
31. Ibid.
32. *Resolution*'s report in ibid.
33. Ibid.
34. Gilbert, op cit, Vol VI, p. 52.
35. See David Reynolds, *The Creation of the Anglo-American Alliance 1937–41; A Study in Competitive Co-operation*, op cit, Chapter 3.

36. Roskill, *War at Sea*, op cit, Vol I, p. 112.
37. CAB 66/7, WP(40)168.
38. Cited in Reynolds, op cit, p. 114.
39. See Reynolds, op cit, Chapters 4 and 5, especially pp. 121–31; also James R. Leutze, *Bargaining for Supremacy: Anglo-American Naval Relations 1937–1941*, Chapel Hill, North Carolina, 1977, Chapters 6–8.
40. ROSK 4/94, letter to Vice-Admiral Sir Geoffrey Blake, ACNS (Foreign), 28 October 1940.
41. Cited in Correlli Barnett, *Bonaparte*, London, Allen and Unwin, 1978, p. 98.
42. CAB 66/7, WP(40)168.
43. CAB 66/7, WP(40)169, 26 May 1940.
44. See Terraine, *The Right of the Line*, op cit, Chapters 16–25, for a magnificent and detailed account of the Battle of Britain.
45. Roskill, *War at Sea*, op cit, Vol I, p. 249 and Appendix Q, p. 614.
46. Dönitz, *Memoirs: Ten Years and Twenty Days*, op cit, p. 114.
47. Cited in Roskill, *War at Sea*, op cit, Vol I, pp. 248–9.
48. Ibid, pp. 250–1.
49. Ibid, p. 252.
50. Ibid, p. 258.
51. The summary of Intelligence during the invasion summer and autumn which follows is based on Hinsley, op cit, Vol I, pp. 161–3, 172–6, 183–9.
52. Ibid, p. 175.
53. Ibid, pp. 188–9.
54. Roskill, *War at Sea*, op cit, Vol I, p. 257.
55. Ibid, but see CAB 69/1, [Defence Committee (Operations)] 39(40).
56. Ibid.
57. Dönitz, op cit, pp. 111–12.
58. Ibid.
59. Ibid.
60. Ibid, pp. 91–7.
61. Ibid, p. 102.
62. Roskill, *War at Sea*, op cit, Vol I, pp. 349–50.
63. Ibid.
64. Dönitz, op cit, p. 105.
65. Roskill, *War at Sea*, op cit, Vol I, p. 350.
66. Cited in Dönitz, op cit, p. 108.
67. Roskill, *War at Sea*, op cit, Vol I, p. 351.
68. Ibid, pp. 351–2.
69. Ibid, pp. 277–80.
70. Ibid, p. 289.
71. AHB/II/117/3(A)i, p. 209.
72. Terraine, op cit, p. 242.
73. Ibid, pp. 232–3.

74. Ibid.
75. ABH/II/3(B) ii, p. 3.
76. Roskill, *War at Sea*, Vol I, Appendix R, Table I, p. 616.
77. Ibid, Table II, p. 617.
78. Gilbert, op cit, Vol VI, p. 936.
79. Butler, *Grand Strategy*, op cit, Vol II, p. 258.
80. Minute to Ismay, 5 June 1940, cited in Gilbert, op cit, Vol VI, pp. 472–3.
81. Arthur Marder, *Operation 'Menace': The Dakar Expedition and the Dudley North Affair*, London, OUP, 1976, p. 11. The following account of 'Menace' is based on Marder, op cit, John Williams, *The Guns of Dakar: September 1940*, London, Heinemann, 1976; Gilbert, op cit, Vol VI, *passim*, and Hinsley, op cit, Vol 1, pp. 149–58.
82. Marder, *Operation 'Menace'*, op cit, pp. 16–17.
83. Ibid, p. 21.
84. Letter from Commander T. C. Crease to Marder, 22 November 1973, cited in ibid, p. 57.
85. Ibid, p. 36.
86. Hinsley, op cit, Vol I, pp. 154–8.
87. Ibid, p. 155.
88. Marder, op cit, pp. 104–5.
89. Ibid, pp. 118–19.
90. Ibid, p. 128.
91. Ibid, p. 141.
92. Ibid, p. 148.
93. Ibid, p. 159.
94. James Leutze (ed), *The London Observer; The Journal of General Raymond E. Lee 1940–1941*, London, Hutchinson, 1972, p. 71.

8. *'Blue Water Strategy': The Mediterranean, 1940* (pages 207–250)

1. CAB 53/21, COS 560, Annual Review for 1937.
2. Ibid.
3. CAB 29/159, AFC 1, British Strategic Memorandum to Anglo-French Staff Talks.
4. CAB 27/625, FP(36)51, meeting of the Cabinet Foreign Policy Committee, 13 June 1939.
5. CAB 29/159, AFC 1.
6. Major I. S. O. Playfair with Commander G. M. S. Stitt, RN, Brigadier C. J. C. Molony, Air Vice-Marshal S. E. Toomer, *The Mediterranean and Middle East*, Vol I, *The Early Successes Against Italy (to May 1941)*, London, HMSO, 1954, p. 47.
7. Ibid, p. 84.
8. Signal 2330/16/6/40 to C-in-C, Mediterranean Fleet.
9. CAB 79/5, COS 40, 183rd meeting, Min 3.

10. Ibid.
11. ROSK 4/67.
12. CAB 80/13, COS (40) 469 (JP).
13. Ibid.
14. CAB 79/5, COS (40) 185th meeting, Min. 3.
15. Cunningham, *A Sailor's Odyssey*, op cit, pp. 241–2.
16. CAB 80/13, Annexe to COS (40) 521.
17. Cited in Winston S. Churchill, *The World Crisis: The Eastern Front*, Thornton Butterworth, London, 1931, p. 271.
18. Churchill, *The Second World War*, op cit, Vol II, p. 385, message of August 1940.
19. Letter of 13 July 1940, photocopy in ROSK 4/64. The account of this sortie to Malta is based on Cunningham's report to the Admiralty of 29 January 1941, Narrative, Fleet Operations – Period 7th to 13th July 1940, in ADM 199/1048, War History Case 7952, Naval Operations in the Mediterranean 1940.
20. Cunningham, *A Sailor's Odyssey*, op cit, p. 262.
21. Ibid.
22. ROSK 4/64, photocopy of letter from Cunningham to Pound, 3 August 1940.
23. Cunningham, op cit, p. 259.
24. Photocopy of letter of 13 July 1940, ROSK 4/64; account of action off Calabria is based on Cunningham's Despatch, supplement to the London Gazette No. 38273, 1948.
25. Photocopy of letter of 13 July 1940, ROSK 4/64.
26. Ibid.
27. Ibid.
28. Lenton and Colledge, *Warships of World War II*, op cit, p. 39.
29. Photocopy of letter of 13 July 1940, ROSK 4/64.
30. Ibid.
31. Roskill, *War at Sea*, op cit, Vol I, Appendix H, p. 293; Cunningham, *A Sailor's Odyssey*, op cit, p. 234.
32. Hinsley, *British Intelligence in the Second World War*, op cit, Vol I, p. 199.
33. Ibid, p. 209.
34. ROSK 4/64, Cunningham's letter to Pound, 13 July 1940; Hinsley, op cit, Vol I, p. 209.
35. ROSK 4/64.
36. Hinsley, op cit, Vol I, pp. 206–7, 210–11.
37. ADM 223/89 Section II, quoted in Hinsley, op cit, Vol I, p. 211.
38. Hinsley, op cit, Vol I, pp. 207–8.
39. Roskill, *War at Sea*, op cit, Vol I, p. 307.
40. Hinsley, op cit, Vol I, pp. 211–12.
41. ADM 186/800, p. 61, quoted in Hinsley, op cit, Vol I, p. 212.
42. Photocopy of letter from Cunningham to Pound, 3 August 1940 in ROSK 4/64.

43. ROSK 4/64, letter to Pound, 13 July 1940.
44. Cited in Oliver Warner, *Cunningham of Hyndhope: Admiral of the Fleet*, London, John Murray, 1967, p. 90.
45. Cunningham, op cit, p. 203.
46. Warner, op cit, p. 93.
47. Ibid, p. 75.
48. Quoted in ibid, p. 111.
49. Admiral Sir Geoffrey Oliver, quoted in ibid, p. 62.
50. Quoted in ibid, p. 110.
51. Cited in ibid, p. 107.
52. Ibid, p. 62.
53. Ibid, p. 24.
54. Commander G. N., later Admiral Sir Geoffrey, Oliver, quoted in Warner, op cit, p. 63.
55. Captain G. N. Brewer, quoted in Warner, op cit, p. 51. Cunningham's second principle is a version of Nelson's 'Duty is the great business of a sea officer' – letter to his wife, 4 May 1786.
56. Playfair, op cit, Vol I, pp. 119–21.
57. Ibid, pp. 154–5; SMVL 3/22.
58. 13 July 1940, SMVL 3/22.
59. Ibid.
60. Personal letter from Vice-Admiral Sir Geoffrey Blake to First Sea Lord, December 1940, ROSK 4/40.
61. SMVL 7/3. Report of Proceedings of Force H for the Period 30 August 1940 to 3 September 1940, p. 1.
62. Ibid.
63. Ibid.
64. Ibid.
65. The account of Cunningham's operations in 'Hats' is based on the orders, signals and reports, plus the C-in-C's own report dated 14 January 1941, contained in ADM 199/1049, War History Case 7953, Naval Operations September–December 1940, except where otherwise cited.
66. Cunningham, *A Sailor's Odyssey*, op cit, p. 273.
67. Midshipman Terence Lewin, unpublished journal.
68. ROSK 4/64, photocopy of letter to Pound of 19 August 1940.
69. Ibid.
70. Playfair, op cit, Vol I, p. 204.
71. Ibid.
72. Gilbert, *Winston S. Churchill*, op cit, Vol VI, p. 772.
73. Playfair, op cit, Vol I, p. 190, Footnote 1.
74. Ibid, p. 191.
75. CAB 69/11, DO(40), 25th meeting, 12 August 1940.
76. Playfair, op cit, Vol I, pp. 245–7.
77. Ibid, p. 248.
78. SMVL 7/4. Report of Proceedings of Force H for the Period 11th September 1940, to 14th September 1940.

79. Roskill, *Churchill and the Admirals*, op cit, p. 163, Footnote.
80. For full analyses, though with differing interpretations, of 'the Dudley North affair', see Roskill, *Churchill and the Admirals*, op cit, pp. 159–67; Marder, *Operation 'Menace'*, op cit, pp. 193–264; see also the Dudley North Papers in the Churchill Archives Centre, NRTH 1/4; see ADM 205/11 for the First Sea Lord's dockets on the affair.
81. Lenton and Colledge, op cit, p. 36.
82. Ibid, p. 44.
83. Except where otherwise cited, the account of Somerville's part in 'Collar' is based on his report, dated 18 December 1940, on 'The Action Between British and Italian Forces on 27 November 1940' in ADM 199/1049; and Battle Summary No. 9, 'Action off Cape Spartivento', 27th November 1940, in ADM 234/325.
84. Ibid.
85. See SMVL 3/22, letters from Somerville to his wife, 28 and 29 November 1940.
86. ADM 1/19177, Churchill to A. V. Alexander, the First Lord of the Admiralty, 20 July 1940.
87. SMVL 3/22, letter of 16 November to his wife.
88. See Record of Court of Enquiry into the loss of the Hurricanes in ADM 199/1048, Case 6183.
89. SMVL 3/22, letter of 18 November to his wife.
90. Ibid: quoted in letter from Somerville to his wife, 8 December 1940.
91. Cunningham, op cit, p. 293.
92. Ibid, p. 294.
93. Ibid, p. 273.
94. Lenton and Colledge, op cit, p. 61.
95. The account of the Taranto Operation is based on ADM 234/325, Battle Summary No. 10 – Mediterranean Operations, 4 to 14 November 1940, Air Attack on Taranto, 11 November 1940, dated 1943; ADM 199/1048 War History Case 7952; Playfair, op cit, Vol I, pp. 236–7; Roskill, *War at Sea*, op cit, Vol I, pp. 300–1; P. K. Kemp, *Fleet Air Arm*, London, Herbert Jenkins, 1954, pp. 124–7; J. Winton, *Air Power at Sea 1939–45*, London, Sidgwick and Jackson, 1976, pp. 24–6; D. Newton and A. Cecil Hampshire, *Taranto*, London, William Kimber, 1969, *passim*.
96. Cunningham, op cit, p. 285.
97. Quoted in Winton, op cit, p. 24.
98. Weale, Weale and Barker, *Combat Aircraft of World War Two*, op cit, p. 138.
99. Winton, op cit, p. 25.
100. Newton and Hampshire, op cit. pp. 140–1.
101. See ADM 199/1048, War History Case 7952, Naval Operations in the Mediterranean 1940, for technical details of British torpedoes and the damage to Italian ships.

102. Cunningham, op cit, p. 286.
103. For a succinct account of O'Connor's campaign, see Correlli Barnett, *The Desert Generals*, 2nd edition, London, Allen and Unwin, and Pan Books, 1983; John Baynes, *The Forgotten Victor: General Sir Richard O'Connor, KT, GCB, DSO, MC*, London, Brassey's Defence Publications, 1989.

9. *'Grey Water Strategy': The Atlantic, 1941* (pages 251–277)

1. The Battle of the Atlantic; Directive by the Minister of Defence, 6 March 1941. Printed in full as Appendix O in Roskill, *War at Sea*, op cit, Vol I, p. 609.
2. Grove, Chant, Lyon and Lyon, *The Hardware of World War II*, op cit, p. 149.
3. Roskill, *War at Sea*, op cit, Vol I, p. 462.
4. Dönitz, *Memoirs: Ten Years and Twenty Days*, op cit, pp. 131–40.
5. ADM 205/7, File No. 7.
6. Ibid.
7. Ibid.
8. ADM 234/578, Naval Staff History, Second World War, *Defeat of the Enemy Attack on Shipping 1939–1945: A Study of Policy and Operations*, Vol IA, Text and Appendices, p. 63.
9. Ibid.
10. Ibid, p. 64.
11. Ibid, pp. 18–19.
12. Ibid, p. 65.
13. Postan, Hay and Scott, *Design and Development of Weapons*, op cit, pp. 390–2; ADM 234/578, p. 68.
14. ADM 234/578, p. 67.
15. ADM 205/7, File No. 7.
16. ADM 234/578, p. 74.
17. Ibid; see Chapter 15 below, for a full account of the state of long-range aircraft in 1942.
18. ADM 234/578, p. 68.
19. Quoted in Terraine, *The Right of the Line*, op cit, p. 404.
20. ADM 234/578, p. 34; Roskill, *War at Sea*, op cit, Vol I, p. 361.
21. Padfield, *Dönitz; the Last Führer*, op cit, p. 230.
22. Roskill, *War at Sea*, op cit, Vol I, p. 362.
23. The account of 1941 operations in the Battle of the Atlantic is based on ADM 234/578; ADM 186/802, German Naval History, *The U-boat War in the Atlantic*, Vol I; and Roskill, *War at Sea*, op cit, Vol I, Chapter XXI.
24. Roskill, *War at Sea*, op cit, Vol I, p. 452.
25. Ibid.
26. ADM 234/578, p. 69.

27. ADM 205/7, File No. 7, letter of 16 April 1941.

28. Roskill, *War at Sea*, op cit, Vol I, p. 464, Table 14.

29. Cited in J. M. A. Gwyer, *Grand Strategy*, Vol III, Part I, p. 12, London, HMSO, 1964; cited previous statistics on shipping position from ibid, p. 9.

30. Cited in Correlli Barnett, *The Great War*, London, The Park Lane Press, 1979, p. 106.

31. The account that follows is based on Hinsley, *British Intelligence in the Second World War*, op cit, Vol I, pp. 336–9, and Vol II, pp. 163–74.

32. Dönitz, op cit, pp. 141–2.

33. Padfield, op cit, p. 229.

34. ADM 205/7, File No. 7, C-in-C, Western Approaches, Correspondence with First Sea Lord, December 1940 to November 1941.

35. Hinsley, op cit, Vol II, Appendix 9, p. 681.

36. Ibid, p. 682.

37. Ibid, p. 173.

38. Roskill, *War at Sea*, op cit, Vol I, p. 47.

39. ADM 234/578, p. 73.

40. See Reynolds, *The Creation of the Anglo-American Alliance, 1937–1941*, op cit, Chapter Eight, and Gilbert, *Winston S. Churchill*, op cit, Vol VI, *passim*, for accounts of the developing political and strategic relationship between the US and UK in 1940–41.

41. ADM 205/7, File No. 7, Memorandum from Commander Goodenough, Plans Division, Naval Staff, to VCNS and First Sea Lord, 8 April 1941.

42. Cited in Reynolds, op cit, p. 214.

43. Ibid, p. 215.

44. Ibid, p. 216.

45. ADM 234/578, pp. 80–1; Roskill, *War at Sea*, op cit, Vol I, p. 471.

46. Roskill, *War at Sea*, op cit, Vol I, p. 472.

47. Ibid, p. 473.

48. Lenton and Colledge, *Warships of World War II*, op cit, p. 255.

49. Weale, Weale and Barker, *Combat Aircraft of World War Two*, op cit, p. 200.

50. Dönitz, op cit, p. 181.

51. CAB 81/1.

52. Roskill, *War at Sea*, op cit, Vol I, p. 615, Appendix R.

53. Cf John Terraine's use of this traditional phrase in the title of his book on the Royal Air Force in the European War.

54. Dönitz, op cit, p. 182.

10. *'The* Bismarck *Must Be Sunk at All Costs'* (pages 278–316)

1. Bekker, *Hitler's Naval War*, op cit, p. 211.

2. Quoted in ibid, p. 216.

3. Quoted in Baron Burkhard von Müllenheim-Rechberg, *Battleship*

Bismarck, A Survivor's Story, translated by Jack Sweetman, London, The Bodley Head, 1980, p. 57.

4. Ibid.

5. Ibid.

6. Bekker, op cit, p. 218.

7. Ibid, p. 219.

8. See Ludovic Kennedy, *Pursuit: The Chase and Sinking of the Bismarck*, London, Collins, 1974, p. 30.

9. Müllenheim-Rechberg, op cit, p. 27.

10. Parkes, *British Battleships: 'Warrior' 1860 to 'Vanguard' 1950; A History of Design, Construction and Armament*, op cit, p. 671.

11. Technical description of *Bismarck* drawn from ibid, p. 671; Grove, Chant, Lyon and Lyon, *The Hardware of World War II*, op cit, pp. 146–7; Mullenheim-Rechberg, op cit, pp. 21–8. These authorities do not always agree on details of dimensions, thickness of armour, etc.

12. Quoted in Ludovic Kennedy, op cit. Except where otherwise cited the following account of the pursuit of the *Bismarck* is based on this excellent and highly readable book; on ADM 234/322 Battle Summary No. 5, 'The Chase and Sinking of the German battleship "Bismarck", May 23–27, 1941, according to information up to November 1948' (especially in regard to timings); Müllenheim-Rechberg, op cit; Roskill, *War at Sea*, op cit, Vol I, Chapter XIX.

13. Exchange cited in Müllenheim-Rechberg, op cit, p. 78.

14. Hinsley, *British Intelligence in the Second World War*, op cit, Vol I, pp. 339–41.

15. Ibid, p. 341.

16. Ludovic Kennedy, op cit, p. 41.

17. G. A. Rotherham, *It's Really Quite Safe*, op cit, p. 198.

18. Quoted in ADM 234/322.

19. Cunningham, *A Sailor's Odyssey*, op cit, p. 280.

20. Ludovic Kennedy, op cit, p. 38.

21. Quoted in Roskill, *Churchill and the Admirals*, op cit, p. 121.

22. ADM 234/322.

23. Ludovic Kennedy, op cit, p. 68.

24. Ibid, p. 71.

25. Admiral Sir Ralph Edwards to Captain S. W. Roskill, 3 May, no year given, in ROSK 4/17.

26. See Correlli Barnett, *The Swordbearers*, op cit, pp. 144–7; Marder, *From the Dreadnought to Scapa Flow*, op cit, Vol II, *Jutland and After*, London, Oxford University Press, 1966, pp. 57–60, and Chart No. 4.

27. See Roskill, *War at Sea*, op cit, Vol I, p. 402.

28. Admiral Sir Ralph Edwards to S. W. Roskill, 3 May, year undated, in ROSK 4/17.

29. ADM 234/322.

30. ROSK 4/17, letter to S. W. Roskill.

31. ROSK 4/17, copy of a letter from Captain Colin McMullen, RN, in 1941 as a *Prince of Wales*'s gunnery control officer, to Ludovic Kennedy, undated. See also letter to S. W. Roskill in same file from McMullen, 29 May 1979.
32. Naval Staff Battle Summary in ADM 234/322.
33. See letter from John W. Wilkinson, one-time Chief Designer at Vickers-Armstrong, to S. W. Roskill, dated 1965, in ROSK 4/17.
34. Ludovic Kennedy, op cit, pp. 99–100; Müllenheim-Rechberg, op cit, pp. 116–18.
35. Cited in Ludovic Kennedy, op cit, p. 102.
36. Ibid, p. 54.
37. ADM 234/322.
38. ADM 234/509, The sinking of the *Bismarck*, 27th May 1941 – Official Despatches.
39. Ibid.
40. Ibid.
41. Ibid.
42. Ludovic Kennedy, op cit, p. 108.
43. ROSK 4/17, letter from Admiral of the Fleet Lord Tovey to S. W. Roskill, 14 December 1961.
44. Ludovic Kennedy, op cit, p. 103.
45. ROSK 4/17; note by Admiral Sir William Davis.
46. Ibid.
47. ROSK 4/17, Tovey to S. W. Roskill, 1 January 1962.
48. ADM 234/322.
49. ADM 234/509.
50. Hinsley, op cit, Vol 1, p. 342.
51. ROSK 4/17, Note by Admiral Sir William Davis.
52. The account of 25 May is based on ADM 234/322; SMVL 7/9 No. 448/17; Hinsley, op cit, Vol I, pp. 342–5; Ludovic Kennedy, op cit, pp. 130–2; Roskill, *War at Sea*, op cit, Vol I, pp. 410–11.
53. SMVL 7/9, No. 448/17.
54. Ibid.
55. Ibid.
56. Quoted in Müllenheim-Rechberg, op cit, p. 147.
57. Ibid.
58. Ibid, p. 148.
59. Ibid, p. 149.
60. Ibid, p. 148.
61. SMVL 7/9, No. 448/17.
62. Ibid.
63. Ludovic Kennedy, op cit, pp. 151–2.
64. SMVL 7/9, No. 448/17.
65. Note by Admiral Sir William Davis in ROSK 4/17.
66. Ibid.

67. ADM 234/322.
68. SMVL 7/9 No. 448/17.
69. Ludovic Kennedy, op cit, p. 164.
70. SMVL 7/9, No. 448/17.
71. ADM 234/509.
72. Müllenheim-Rechberg, op cit, p. 186.
73. ADM 234/322.
74. SMVL 7/9, No. 448/17.
75. Cited in Ludovic Kennedy, op cit, p. 182.
76. Ibid, p. 200.
77. ADM 234/322.
78. Müllenheim-Rechberg, op cit, p. 196.
79. Quoted in ibid.
80. Ludovic Kennedy, op cit, p. 205.
81. Figures from Müllenheim-Rechberg, op cit, p. 243.
82. ADM 234/322.
83. SMVL 7/9, No. 448/170.
84. ADM 234/509.
85. ADM 234/322.
86. Ibid.
87. ROSK 4/17, First Sea Lord to C-in-C, Home Fleet, 1137B/27/5/41; text confirmed to Captain S. W. Roskill by the Cabinet Office Historical Section; authorship admitted by Churchill in *The Second World War*, Vol III, London, Cassell, 1964, p. 282.
88. ROSK 4/17, Tovey to Captain S. W. Roskill, 20 November 1954.
89. See ADM 234/324, 'Disguised Raiders 1940–1'.
90. Hinsley, op cit, Vol I, p. 345.
91. Raeder, *Struggle for the Sea*, London, William Kimber, 1959, p. 214.

11. *Greek Prelude: The Battle of Matapan* (pages 317–345)

1. See Correlli Barnett's *The Desert Generals*, op cit, pp. 44–64, for an account of the latter stages of O'Connor's campaign.
2. ROSK 4/64, photocopy.
3. The following account of British Intelligence in relation to German forward moves in the Balkans and Mediterranean, December 1940–January 1941 is based on Hinsley, *British Intelligence in the Second World War*, op cit, Vol I, Chapters 11 and 12.
4. Playfair, *The Mediterranean and the Middle East*, op cit, Vol I, p. 315.
5. Hinsley, op cit, Vol I, p. 385.
6. Lenton and Colledge, *Warships of World War II*, op cit, p. 46.
7. The account of the attack on *Illustrious* is based on ADM 186/801, Naval Staff Narrative, Mediterranean; November 1940–December 1941; CAB 106/346, Despatches re Mediterranean Convoy Operations January 1941–August 1942; Playfair, op cit, Vol I,

pp. 311–28; Cunningham, *A Sailor's Odyssey*, op cit, pp. 301–9: ROSK 4/64.

8. Cunningham, op cit, p. 303.
9. Ibid.
10. ROSK 4/64, photocopy of letter of 18 January 1941.
11. Cunningham, op cit, p. 303.
12. The following account of the bombardment of Genoa on 9 February 1941 is based on ADM 186/797, BS No. 7, 'The Bombardment of Genoa 9 February 1941'.
13. ADM 186/797.
14. Playfair op cit, Vol I, p. 325; Gilbert, *Winston S. Churchill*, op cit, Vol VI, p. 1001.
15. ROSK 4/64, photocopy of letter of 18 January 1941.
16. Gilbert, op cit, Vol VI, p. 987.
17. Ibid.
18. Ibid, p. 1001.
19. Ibid.
20. See Cunningham, op cit, p. 316; ROSK 4/64, photocopy of letter from Cunningham to First Sea Lord, 11 March 1941.
21. Terraine, *Right of the Line*, op cit, p. 331.
22. CAB 105/1, 0/34651m 10/1.
23. Ibid, 9972(M.O.5) 11/1.
24. Ibid. Wavell's signal says 'Benghazi' even though O'Connor's victory was at Beda Fomm.
25. CAB 69/2, DO(41)7th, 10 February 1941.
26. Ibid.
27. CAB 69/2, DO(41)8th, 11 February 1941.
28. CAB 80/25, COS (41)83.
29. CAB 69/2, DO(41)8th, 11 February 1941, Confidential Annexe.
30. CAB 105/2, Hist (B)2 (Final) No. 8. Telegram of 14 February 1941 from Cs-in-C to Chiefs of Staff (transmitted by HQ RAF Middle East to Air Ministry for onward distribution). The following quotation from the signal by Admiral Cunningham to the Admiralty on the same date is taken from ibid, No. 6.
31. Ibid.
32. CAB 69/2, DO(41)7.
33. Cited in Gilbert, op cit, Vol VI, p. 1013.
34. Ibid.
35. Eden.
36. Hinsley, op cit, Vol I, p. 361.
37. CAB 80/57 COS(41)43(0) (Revise) Policy in the Mediterranean and Middle East, 24 February 1941.
38. Ibid. General R. H. Haining, VCIGS, signed in Dill's place.
39. CAB 65/21 WM(41) 20th, Confidential Annexe.
40. Ibid.

41. CAB 65/21, WM(41) 21st Minute 2, Confidential Annexe.
42. Cunningham, op cit, p. 318.
43. CAB 79/9, COS (41) 82nd, 4 March 1941.
44. Ibid.
45. CAB 65/22, WM(41) 24th, Confidential Annexe.
46. CAB 79/9, COS(41) 90th, Annexe 1.
47. CAB 69/2, DO(41)9th, 5 March 1941, Confidential Annexe.
48. Ibid.
49. CAB 65/22, WM (41)26, Confidential Annexe.
50. ROSK 4/64, photocopy of letter of 11 March 1941.
51. Ibid.
52. See Hinsley, op cit, Vol I, pp. 403–5 for an account of Intelligence prior to the Battle of Matapan.
53. Cunningham, op cit, p. 326.
54. The following account of the Battle of Matapan is based on ADM 186/795, Naval Staff History: Battle Summary No. 44, The Battle of Cape Matapan, 28th March 1941; Cunningham, op cit, pp. 325–36; Playfair, op cit, Vol II, pp. 61–70; S. W. C. Pack, *The Battle of Matapan*, London Batsford, 1961. Unless otherwise stated, all courses and timings are from ADM 186/795.
55. Obituary of Rear-Admiral Fisher in the *Daily Telegraph*, 22 April 1988.
56. Vice-Admiral Sir Geoffrey Barnard, then fleet gunnery officer, quoted in Pack, op cit, p. 39.
57. Cunningham, op cit, p. 328.
58. Ibid, p. 327.
59. Ibid, p. 327.
60. Quoted in Pack, op cit, p. 93.
61. Weale, Weale and Barker, *Combat Aircraft of World War Two*, op cit, pp. 139–40.
62. ADM 186/795, Appendix G.
63. ADM 186/795.
64. Cunningham, op cit, p. 329.
65. Quoted in Pack, op cit, p. 111.
66. Ibid.
67. Ibid.
68. Quoted in Pack, op cit, p. 115.
69. ADM 186/795.
70. ADM 186/795, Appendix D.
71. Cunningham, op cit, p. 331.
72. Quoted in Pack, op cit, p. 132.
73. Ibid.
74. Ibid.
75. Cunningham, op cit, p. 331.
76. Ibid, p. 332.
77. ADM 186/795.

78. Cited in Pack, op cit, p. 118.
79. Cunningham, op cit, p. 332.
80. Ibid, p. 333.

12. *Catastrophe in the Mediterranean, 1941* (pages 346–377)

1. Playfair, *The Mediterranean and the Middle East*, op cit, Vol II, *The Germans Come to the Aid of their Ally (1941)*, p. 83.
2. The account of 'Demon' is based on Playfair, op cit, Vol II, pp. 93–106; Cunningham, *A Sailor's Odyssey*, op cit, pp. 352–9.
3. Cunningham, op cit. p. 354.
4. Ibid, p. 356.
5. Ibid, p. 357.
6. Playfair, op cit, Vol II, p. 104, Note.
7. Hinsley, *British Intelligence in the Second World War*, op cit, Vol I, p. 416.
8. Gilbert, *Winston S. Churchill*, op cit, Vol VI, p. 1072; CAB 65/22, WM(41)44, Minute 2, Confidential Annexe.
9. Quoted in Playfair, op cit, Vol II, p. 125.
10. Ibid.
11. Gilbert, op cit, Vol VI, p. 1076.
12. Playfair, op cit, Vol II, p. 129.
13. Hinsley, op cit, Vol I, p. 419.
14. ADM 234/320. Battle Summary No. 4, Naval Operations of the Battle of Crete, 20th May to 1st June 1941 (1952).
15. Gilbert, op cit, Vol VI, p. 1078.
16. Cunningham, op cit, p. 366.
17. The account of naval operations in the Crete Campaign is based on ADM 234/320, BS No. 4; Cunningham, op cit, Chapter XXIX; Playfair, op cit, Vol II, Chapter VII. All details of timings, positions and courses are drawn from ADM 234/320.
18. Cunningham, op cit, pp. 336–7.
19. Ibid, p. 370.
20. ADM 234/320.
21. Cunningham, op cit, p. 371.
22. ADM 234/320.
23. Cunningham, op cit, p. 372.
24. Ibid, p. 373.
25. ADM 234/320; Cunningham, op cit, p. 374.
26. Cunningham, op cit, p. 374.
27. Ibid, pp. 374–5.
28. ADM 234/320.
29. Ibid.
30. Cunningham, op cit, p. 375.
31. Ibid, pp. 375–6; ADM 234/320.
32. ADM 234/320.

33. For the land battle for Crete, see Playfair, op cit, Vol II, Chapter VII; I. McD. G. Stewart, *The Struggle for Crete 20 May–1 June 1941; A Story of Lost Opportunity*, London, OUP, 1966; John Hale Spencer, *Battle for Crete*, London, Heinemann, 1962.
34. ADM 234/320, p. 28.
35. ADM 234/320.
36. Ibid.
37. Ibid.
38. Ibid, p. 33.
39. Cunningham, op cit, p. 384.
40. ADM 234/320.
41. Ibid.
42. Cited in ibid, p. 33, Footnote 4.
43. ADM 234/320, Appendices A and D.
44. ROSK 4/65.
45. Cited in Gilbert, op cit, p. 1072.
46. ROSK 4/64, signal 0059/15/4/41.
47. Ibid.
48. Cunningham, op cit, p. 342.
49. Ibid.
50. Ibid, p. 343.
51. Ibid, p. 347.
52. ADM 186/797, BS No. 19, The Bombardment of Tripoli, 21 April 1941.
53. Ibid.
54. Cunningham, op cit, p. 348.
55. Ibid, p. 350.
56. Ibid, p. 351.
57. See CAB 106/346, Despatches on Mediterranean Convoy Operations January 1941–August 1942; Playfair, op cit, Vol II, p. 453; Cunningham, op cit, pp. 360–3.
58. Cunningham, op cit, p. 363.
59. Playfair, op cit, Vol II, pp. 269–70.
60. Ibid, p. 281.
61. Ibid.
62. ROSK 4/66.
63. Cunningham, op cit, p. 414.
64. Ibid.
65. Ibid, p. 412.
66. The following account of the loss of *Ark Royal* is based on ADM 234/508, BR 2055, Technical Report of Loss and Damage to H.M.S. ARK ROYAL (1942).
67. Ibid.
68. Ibid.
69. Ibid.

70. Ibid.
71. Ibid.
72. Ibid.
73. Ibid.
74. Cited in Cunningham, op cit, p. 423.
75. Ibid, p. 424.
76. Ibid.
77. Ibid.
78. Ibid, p. 433.
79. ROSK 4/63. Figures supplied to Captain Roskill by Historical Section, TSD, Admiralty, February 1952.

13. *The Sinking of HMS* Prince of Wales *and* Repulse (pages 378 –426)

1. ROSK 4/79, brief prepared in Cabinet Office Historical Section for Captain Roskill as official naval historian on 'Political Decisions relating to the Sending of the *Prince of Wales* and the *Repulse* to the Far East'.
2. Ibid.
3. CAB 79/24, COS (41) 25th.
4. CAB 32/9, E-8 and E-9, cited by C. Barnett in *The Collapse of British Power*, op cit, p. 279.
5. ADM 205/7, File No. 4.
6. See Correlli Barnett, *The Audit of War*, op cit, Chapter Six, for an analysis based on wartime official investigations.
7. ADM 205/7, File No. 4.
8. ADM 205/5.
9. Ibid, memorandum from the First Sea Lord to the First Lord, January 1940; First Sea Lord to the Controller, 3 February 1940; Admiralty Memorandum to the War Cabinet, February 1940.
10. Ibid, notes by First Sea Lord and Director of Plans for a Board Meeting on 5 September 1940.
11. Postan, Hay and Scott, *Design and Development of Weapons*, op cit, p. 63.
12. Ibid, p. 61, Table 6.
13. ROSK 4/79.
14. CAB 32/128, E(PD)(37)5, cited in Barnett, *The Collapse of British Power*, op cit, p. 441.
15. For the mid-war economic balance sheet of Empire, see Hancock and Gowing, *British War Economy*, London, HMSO and Longmans, Green, 1949, *passim*; Behrens, *Merchant Shipping and the Demands of War*, op cit, Chapter IX, especially Appendix XXXIX, p. 248; S. Woodburn Kirby, *The War Against Japan*, Vol I, *The Loss of Singapore*, London, HMSO, 1957, p. 477, Appendix I; Barnett, *The Collapse of British Power*, op cit, p. 132.
16. The following account of Anglo-American diplomacy towards Japan

and strategic discussions in 1940–41 is based on Reynolds, *The Creation of the Anglo-American Alliance*, op cit, pp. 132–44, 204–5, and Chapter Nine; Paul Haggie, *Britannia at Bay: The Defence of the British Empire Against Japan*, op cit, pp. 171–208; Christopher Thorne, *Allies of a Kind; The United States, Great Britain and the War Against Japan 1941–1945*, op cit, Part One, Chapters Two and Three.

17. Cited in Barnett, *The Collapse of British Power*, op cit, p. 301.
18. CAB 66/10, WP(40)302, 31 July 1940.
19. Cited in Haggie, op cit, p. 189.
20. Cited in ibid, p. 191; see also Gilbert, *Winston S. Churchill*, op cit, Vol VI, pp. 1044–7.
21. Cited in Haggie, op cit, p. 193.
22. CAB 80/27, COS 230, 11 April 1941.
23. CAB 80/28, COS 365, 10 June 1941.
24. Reynolds, op cit, p. 238; there is a brief, too brief, mention in Gilbert, op cit, Vol VI, p. 1160.
25. Reynolds, op cit, p. 239.
26. Cited in Haggie, op cit, pp. 202–3.
27. Reynolds, op cit, p. 225.
28. See S. Woodburn Kirby, op cit, Vol I, Map 21, opposite p. 374.
29. CAB 53/21, COS Appreciation of the Far East Situation, 28 May 1937.
30. Ibid.
31. Ibid.
32. CAB 66/10, WP(40)302, 31 July 1940, The Situation in the Far East in the event of Japanese Intervention against us.
33. Churchill to Ismay, 10 September 1940, in Churchill *The Second World War*, op cit, Vol II, *Their Finest Hour*, pp. 591–2.
34. Churchill, *The Second World War*, op cit, Vol III, *The Grand Alliance*, p. 565.
35. Ibid, Vol IV, *The Hinge of Fate*, p. 43.
36. See Woodburn Kirby, op cit, Vol I, pp. 162–5.
37. The following account of the debates leading to the despatch of the *Prince of Wales* and *Repulse* to Singapore and their subsequent operations is based on ROSK 4/79, brief prepared for Captain Roskill as official historian on 'Political Decisions relating to the Sending of the *Prince of Wales* and the *Repulse* to the Far East', and M.0251/42, 'Loss of H.M. Ships *Prince of Wales* and *Repulse* on 10th December 1941; Narrative of Operations of Force Z', being a report by the Director of Plans and the D.D.D.(F) dated 20 January 1942; ADM 234/330, Naval Staff History, B.S. No. 14 (Revised), 'Loss of His Majesty's Ships *Prince of Wales* and *Repulse*, 10th December 1941' (1955).
38. ROSK 4/79, M.0251/42.
39. ADM 205/6, memorandum by First Sea Lord to First Lord, 1 August 1940, on 'Re-Distribution of the Fleet in the event of war with Japan'.
40. CAB 79/24, COS(41) 360th.

41. ADM 205/10, 25 August 1941.
42. Ibid.
43. Ibid, 26 August 1941.
44. Ibid, 28 August 1941.
45. Ibid, 29 August 1941.
46. Ibid.
47. Ibid.
48. Ibid.
49. CAB 69/2, DO(41) 65th.
50. Ibid.
51. Ibid.
52. Ibid.
53. Ibid.
54. ROSK 4/79, photocopy of letter of 17 October 1941.
55. CAB 69/2, DO(41) 65th.
56. Ibid.
57. ROSK 4/79, photocopy of letter of 17 October 1941.
58. CAB 79/24, COS(41) 360th, 20 October 1941.
59. Ibid.
60. ROSK 4/79, note by Captain Roskill.
61. Churchill Archives Centre, A. V. Alexander Papers, AVAR 5/6/16.
62. ROSK 4/79, copy of note to the First Sea Lord on 15 September 1941.
63. CAB 79/24, COS(51) 360th.
64. Ibid.
65. ROSK 4/79, note by Captain Roskill. Information about Duff Cooper's and Churchill's role in Brooke-Popham's signal supplied to the author by a Foreign Office official in Malaya at the time.
66. CAB 79/24, COS(41) 360th.
67. Ibid.
68. CAB 69/8, DO(41) 66th.
69. ROSK 4/79, copy by Captain Roskill of signal 2023/20/10/41.
70. See Roberta Wohlstetter, *Pearl Harbor: Warning and Decision*, Stanford, California, Stanford University Press, 1962, Chapter 3, especially pp. 170–86.
71. Ibid, passim, especially Chapter 5 and pp. 393–96.
72. Ibid, p. 211.
73. Cf Hinsley, *British Intelligence in the Second World War*, op cit, Vol II, pp. 75–7.
74. Reynolds, op cit, p. 240; Woodburn Kirby, op cit, pp. 89–90.
75. Woodburn Kirby, op cit, pp. 95–6.
76. See ROSK 4/79, Brief prepared for Captain Roskill on 'Political Decisions, etc'.
77. ROSK 4/79, copy of letter to Mrs Barker.
78. ROSK 4/79, photocopy of letter of 30 January 1943.
79. AVAR 5/6/16, undated handwritten letter from First Sea Lord to First Lord.

80. ADM 234/330, p. 2, Footnote 2: message 1648a, 21 October 1941.
81. See ADM 234/330, p. 2, on this point.
82. ADM 205/10.
83. ADM 234/330, Appendix D, p. 24.
84. Ibid.
85. Ibid.
86. Ibid.
87. Ibid.
88. Geoffrey Brooke, *Alarm Starboard: A remarkable true story of the war at sea*, Cambridge, Patrick Stephens, 1982, p. 90.
89. Ibid, p. 91.
90. ADM 234/330, Appendix D.
91. Ibid.
92. Ibid.
93. Brooke, op cit, p. 93.
94. Roskill, *War at Sea*, op cit, Vol I, p. 561.
95. Ibid, p. 562.
96. Reynolds, op cit, p. 246.
97. ROSK 4/79.
98. Richard Pool, *Course for Disaster: From Scapa Flow to the River Kwai*, London, Leo Cooper, 1987, p. 55.
99. Ibid.
100. Brooke, op cit, p. 94.
101. ADM 234/330, p. 7. The following narrative of the sortie of Force Z is based on this, and on ROSK 4/79, M.0251/42.
102. ADM 234/330, p. 8, Footnote 1.
103. ROSK 4/79, photocopy of letter to Mrs Barker, 25 February 1943.
104. ADM 234/330, p. 8.
105. Ibid, p. 10.
106. Ibid, p. 8.
107. Ibid.
108. Pool, op cit, p. 56.
109. Ibid.
110. Cited in Pool, op cit, p. 57 and Brooke, op cit, p. 97.
111. ADM 234/330, Appendix D(I), p. 31.
112. ADM 205/5, carbon copy of memorandum of 25 August 1940, unsigned and without initials, but almost certainly drafted by Phillips as VCNS, as the style of the advocacy indicates.
113. Somerville and Lord Cork both had no doubt about Phillips's role; see SMVL 3/22, letters from Somerville to his wife, 16 and 18 November 1940; Roskill, *Churchill and the Admirals*, op cit, p. 170.
114. ADM 234/330, Appendix D(I).
115. Pool, op cit, p. 58.
116. Weale, Weale and Barker, *Combat Aircraft of World War Two*, op cit, p. 169.

117. ADM 234/330, p. 11.
118. ROSK 4/79, photocopy of letter of 29 January 1942 in Cunningham papers.
119. ROSK 4/79, M.0251/42; Michael Goodenough, when 4th Sea Lord, to Captain Roskill, 8 May 1951.
120. ROSK 4/79.
121. Pool, op cit, p. 59.
122. The following account of the sinking of Force Z on 10 December 1941 is based on ADM 234/330.
123. Ibid, p. 18.
124. Lenton and Colledge, *Warships of World War II*, op cit, pp. 18 and 22.
125. Cited in ADM 234/330, p. 13.
126. ROSK 4/79, letter from Admiral Sir William Davis to Captain Roskill, 12 January 1979.
127. Ibid.
128. Pool, op cit, p. 64.
129. Ibid, p. 65.
130. Cited in ADM 234/330, p. 17, Footnote 1.
131. Pool, op cit, p. 66.
132. ADM 234/330, p. 17.
133. Ibid.
134. Ibid.
135. Brooke, op cit, p. 107.
136. Ibid, p. 108.
137. ROSK 4/79, M.0251/42.
138. ADM 234/330, Appendix F.
139. Roskill, *War at Sea*, op cit, Vol I, p. 417.
140. Pool, op cit, p. 67.
141. AVAR 5/7/8.
142. Gilbert, *Winston S. Churchill*, op cit, Vol VII, *Road to Victory*, London, Heinemann, 1986, pp. 5–6; Woodburn Kirby, op cit, Vol I, pp. 254–62.
143. AVAR 5/7/8.
144. For the Battle of the Java Sea, see Woodburn Kirby, op cit, Vol I, pp. 438–43; Roskill, *War at Sea*, op cit, Vol II, pp. 13–18.
145. CAB 16/209, SAC 1.
146. Cited in Gilbert, op cit, Vol VII, p. 1274.

Part III: The Long Voyage Home

14. 'If We Lose the War at Sea, We Lose the War' (pages 429–457)

1. Roskill, *War at Sea*, op cit, Vol III, Part II, Appendix I, pp. 439–46.
2. See Terraine, *The Right of the Line*, op cit, pp. 70–115, 251–89, 459–81.
3. See Barnett, *The Audit of War*, op cit, Chapter Nine.

4. See Fraser, *And We Shall Shock Them: The British Army in the Second World War*, op cit, pp. 24–212.
5. Gwyer, *Grand Strategy*, op cit, Vol III, Part I, pp. 357–8.
6. Churchill, *The Second World War*, op cit, Vol IV, p. 176.
7. Gwyer, op cit, p. 359.
8. Ibid.
9. Ibid, pp. 364–5.
10. Ibid, p. 398.
11. Cmd 6332: *Agreements between the Prime Minister and the President of the United States of America*, cited in Behrens, *Merchant Shipping and the Demands of Wars*, op cit, pp. 287–8.
12. Roskill, *War at Sea*, op cit, Vol II, p. 115.
13. Cited in ibid, p. 43.
14. Cf Roskill 5/10, Paper for First Sea Lord by Admiral Sir Geoffrey Blake, 'Air Support for Naval Forces', 17 February 1942.
15. Roskill, *War at Sea*, op cit, Vol II, p. 92.
16. J. A. Turner, *Administration of the Navy Department in World War II*, U.S. Department of the Navy, Washington, 1959, p. 879.
17. Cited in Butler, *Grand Strategy*, op cit, Vol III, part II, p. 502.
18. Postan, Hay and Scott, *Design and Development of Weapons*, op cit, p. 289.
19. Ibid, pp. 269–90.
20. Ibid.
21. See Barnett, *The Audit of War*, op cit, Chapter Six.
22. Postan, Hay and Scott, op cit, pp. 294–5.
23. Roskill, *War at Sea*, op cit, Vol I, Appendix R, p. 618, Table 2.
24. Behrens, op cit, p. 252 and Footnote 1.
25. Ibid.
26. See analysis in Behrens, op cit, pp. 284–5.
27. Ibid, p. 284.
28. An average of 1.5 to 2 million deadweight tons over the twelve months: Behrens, op cit, p. 291.
29. Behrens, op cit, pp. 276–7.
30. CAB 69/4, DO(42)23, 5 March 1942.
31. Dönitz, *Memoirs: Ten Years and Twenty Days*, op cit, p. 182.
32. Ibid, p. 197.
33. Ibid.
34. Roskill, *War at Sea*, op cit, Vol II, p. 96.
35. Ibid.
36. ROSK 5/10.
37. ADM 205/18.
38. Cited in Roskill, *War at Sea*, op cit, Vol II, p. 97.
39. Churchill, *The Second World War*, op cit, Vol IV, p. 103.
40. Roskill, *War at Sea*, op cit, Vol II, p. 97.
41. Cited in ADM 234/578, Naval Staff History, Second World War: *The*

Defeat of the Enemy Attack on Shipping 1939–1945; A Study of Policy and Operations, Vol 1A (Text and Appendices), Historical Section, Admiralty, 1957, p. 86.

42. S. E. Morison, *History of United States Naval Operations in World War II*, Vol I, *The Battle of the Atlantic, September 1939–May 1943*, Boston, Little, Brown, 1947, p. 143.
43. Ibid.
44. Dönitz, op cit, p. 220.
45. Ibid, p. 221.
46. Ibid, pp. 221–2.
47. Hinsley, *British Intelligence in the Second World War*, op cit, Vol II, pp. 176–7.
48. The following account of the passage of *Scharnhorst* and *Gneisenau* is based on RMSY 8/16 in the Churchill Archives Centre, a dossier of relevant signals and of subsequent reports by the principal British participants, including Vice-Admiral Ramsay's own report as V-A, Dover, to the Admiralty, No. 145/211. F/42 of 16 February 1942; and ADM 186/803, BR 1736 (7) (48), BS No. 11, The Passage of the *Scharnhorst, Gneisenau* and *Prinz Eugen* Through the English Channel, 12 February 1942 (1948), and A.F.O.P. 228/49, containing additional material.
49. ADM 186/803.
50. Hinsley, op cit, Vol II, p. 179, Footnote.
51. Ibid, pp. 179–80.
52. RMSY 8/16, signal 1252/3/2/42 to all Cs-in-C.
53. Ibid.
54. ADM 186/803.
55. Ibid.
56. See RMSY 8/16, signal to the Admiralty, DF355, 11 February 1942. All the relevant signals are contained in this file.
57. RMSY 8/16, signal, 11 February 1942.
58. Hinsley, op cit, Vol II, pp. 182–3.
59. ADM 186/803, p. 5, Footnote 1 and p. 6, Footnote 2.
60. Ibid.
61. Ibid, p. 7.
62. RMSY 8/16.
63. RMSY 8/16. No. 145/211. F/42. See also sources cited in Footnote 64.
64. See RMSY 8/16, Report by Lieutenant-Commander E. N. Pumphrey, RN, Senior Officer, H.M.M.T.B.s, dated 13 February 1942; Enclosure No. 3 to Dover letter No. 145/211, F/42; Report by Lieutenant (T).D. J. Long, Senior Officer M.T.B.s 32, 71 and 18, 12 February 1942.
65. RMSY 8/14. Enclosure No. 2 to Dover letter of 16.2.42 No. 145/211. F/42, Report by Wing-Commander J. Constable-Roberts, Air Staff Officer to Flag Officer Commanding, Dover.

66. Dover No. 145/211, F/42, dated 16 February 1942.
67. Ibid; Reports by Wing-Commander T. P. Gleave, RAF, Commanding RAF Manston; by Sub-Lieutenant Lee, RN, Observer, Swordfish, W.5983. Report from Intelligence Officer, Manston, on interrogation of survivors from 825 Squadron.
68. Weale, Weale and Barker, *Combat Aircraft of World War Two*, op cit, pp. 138 and 169.
69. Rotherham, *It's Really Quite Safe*, op cit, pp. 205–6.
70. ADM 186/203, p. 14.
71. Bekker, *Hitler's Naval War*, op cit, p. 234.
72. Lenton and Colledge, *Warships of World War II*, op cit, pp. 81–8; Bekker, op cit, Appendix I, p. 370.
73. Ibid.
74. *The Times*: leading article of 14 February 1942.
75. Cmd 6775: 'Report of the Board of Enquiry appointed to enquire into the circumstances in which the German Battle Cruisers *Scharnhorst* and *Gneisenau* and Cruiser *Prinz Eugen* proceeded from Brest to Germany on February 12th 1942, and on the operations undertaken to prevent this movement.'
76. Ibid.
77. Roskill, *War at Sea*, op cit, Vol I, Appendix R, p. 618, Table II; Vol II, Appendix O, p. 486, Table II.
78. The following summary is based on Hinsley, op cit, Vol 2, pp. 176–9 and 228–33.
79. See ibid, Appendix 1, Part (i), p. 636.
80. Ibid, Appendix 9, p. 682.
81. Cited in ibid, Vol 2, p. 230.
82. Roskill, *War at Sea*, op cit, Vol II, p. 199.

15. *'The Battle of the Air', 1942* (pages 458–490)

1. Cited in Terraine, *The Right of the Line*, op cit, p. 413.
2. CAB 69/4, DO(42)14.
3. CAB 69/4, DO(42)15, 'Bombing Policy', 14 February 1942.
4. Cited in Terraine, op cit, p. 418.
5. Ibid.
6. Ibid, p. 419.
7. CAB 69/4, DO(42)23.
8. Ibid.
9. Ibid.
10. Ibid.
11. Ibid.
12. CAB 69/4, DO(42)24, 8 March 1942.
13. Ibid.
14. Ibid.

15. CAB 69/4, DO(42) 8th, Minute 1.
16. Ibid.
17. Ibid.
18. Ibid.
19. CAB 69/4, DO(42)34, 'Air forces: Cooperation with the Army and Navy'; the paper was in response to the First Sea Lord's memorandum DO(42)23 in CAB 69/4, and COS (42)164, of 10 March 1942 by the CIGS, entitled 'Army Air Requirements', in CAB 80/35.
20. CAB 69/4, DO(42)34.
21. Ibid.
22. Ibid.
23. Ibid.
24. See ADM 205/15, 19, 22A, and 25, 27, 28, *passim*.
25. CAB 66/30, WP(42)483.
26. Cited in C. Webster and N. Frankland, *The Strategic Air Offensive Against Germany 1939–1945*, op cit, Vol I, Parts 1, 2 and 3, pp. 330–3.
27. Ibid, p. 334.
28. CAB 69/4, DO(42)47, The Bombing of Germany. Report by Mr Justice Singleton, 20 May 1942.
29. Ibid.
30. Ibid.
31. Webster and Frankland, op cit, Vol I, p. 479, and Footnote 1, also Annexe V.
32. Roskill, *War at Sea*, op cit, Vol II, Appendix O, p. 386, Table II.
33. ADM 205/15, Part 4.
34. ADM 234/578, Appendix 11, p. 8.
35. Ibid.
36. Ibid.
37. Ibid.
38. CAB 79/20, COS(42), 180th Minute 12.
39. Ibid.
40. CAB 80/64, COS(42), 183(O), 23 June 1942.
41. Ibid.
42. Ibid.
43. Roskill, *War at Sea*, op cit, Vol II, Appendix O, p. 486, Table II.
44. CAB 79/21, COS(42), 188th, 24 June 1942.
45. CAB 80/37, COS (42)332, General Policy for the Employment of Air Forces.
46. Ibid.
47. CAB 80/37, COS (42)341, 14 July 1942, Provision of Long-Range Aircraft for Anti-Submarine Patrols, memorandum by CAS.
48. Ibid.
49. CAB 80/64, COS(42)204(O), 18 July 1942.
50. CAB 80/64, COS(42)172(O) 'Air Against the Sea'.

51. CAB 65/31, WM(42) 111th, Minute 2, Confidential Annexe.
52. Cited in Terraine, op cit, p. 425.
53. Ibid.
54. Ibid, p. 426.
55. CAB 66/26, WP(42)311, A Review of the War Position. Note by the Prime Minister.
56. Ibid.
57. Ibid.
58. Ibid.
59. CAB 66/28, WP(42)374 and WP(42)399.
60. CAB 66/30, WP(42)481.
61. ADM 205/24, The Anti-Submarine War.
62. Ibid.
63. CAB 70/5, DO(S)(42)88.
64. Ibid.
65. Ibid.
66. ADM 205/26.
67. Ibid.
68. CAB 66/30, WP(42)483, 24 October 1942.
69. CAB 80/65, COS(42)345(O)(Final).
70. CAB 80/65, COS(42)379(O), 'An Estimate of the Effects of an Anglo-American Bomber Offensive Against Germany'.
71. CAB 80/65, COS(42)393(O), 15 November 1942, Note by the First Sea Lord: 'Implications of the Policy on Estimating the Effects of an Anglo-American Bomber Offensive against Germany'.
72. Cf ADM 205/27, exchange of letters between the First Sea Lord and the Prime Minister, 10–19 December 1942.
73. CAB 86/2, AU(42) 3rd.
74. ADM 205/27, Notes for the Prime Minister's meeting by the First Sea Lord, 13 November 1942.
75. Ibid.
76. Ibid.
77. Ibid.
78. Ibid.
79. Ibid.
80. Ibid.
81. ADM 205/21, reviews dated 23 December 1942.
82. Roskill, *War at Sea*, op cit, Vol II, Appendix O, p. 486, Table II.
83. Ibid.
84. See CAB 86/2, AU(42) 3rd.
85. ROSK 5/12.
86. CAB 86/2, AU(42) 5th.
87. Roskill, *War at Sea*, op cit, Vol II, Appendix O, pp. 485–6, Tables I and II.
88. Behrens, *Merchant Shipping and the Demands of War*, op cit, p. 316.

89. ADM 234/578, p. 104, ADM 234/384, p. 103.
90. Terraine, op cit, pp. 404–6.
91. In AIR 41/47, Vol III, p. 83.
92. Ibid.
93. BT 28/377, Report on Vickers-Armstrong (Aircraft) Ltd, Weybridge; cited in Barnett, *The Audit of War*, op cit, p. 154.
94. AIR 41/47, Vol III, p. 83.
95. Ibid, p. 84.
96. ROSK 5/12, photocopy of paper by Joubert to the First Sea Lord, 27 September 1942, 'The Anti-Submarine War'.
97. Ibid.
98. Webster and Frankland, op cit, Vol I, p. 481; see also ADM 234/578.
99. Webster and Frankland, op cit.
100. Cited in Padfield, *Dönitz: the Last Führer*, op cit, pp. 249–50.
101. Ibid; ADM 234/578, p. 104, cites a similar note by Dönitz which it dates to 21 August.
102. ADM 234/578, p. 106.
103. Ibid.
104. See AVIA 10/104; Barnett, *The Audit of War*, op cit, Chapter 9; Postan, Hay and Scott, *Design and Development of Weapons*, op cit, pp. 378–9.
105. CAB 66/27, WP(42)352, August 1942.
106. ROSK 5/10, Notes by First Sea Lord, 13 November 1942.
107. ADM 205/15, Part 4, Memorandum to the First Sea Lord, 24 June 1942, annotated by him; see also ADM 234/578, p. 23.
108. ADM 234/578.
109. Ibid, pp. 18–19.
110. Ibid.
111. Ibid, p. 89.
112. Churchill Archives Centre, Maclean Papers, MCLN 2/1, Report by Captain I. G. Maclean, RN, entitled 'Trends in Naval Propulsion Machinery', 7 July 1946; MCLN 2/3 Report by Rear-Admiral I. G. Maclean, Deputy Engineer-in-Chief of the Fleet, 'Maritime Supremacy: the State of the British Marine Engineering Industry', April 1955; see also Grove, Chant, Lyon and Lyon, *The Hardware of World War II*, op cit, p. 196 and p. 215; Edgar J. March, *British Destroyers; A History of Development, 1892–1953*, op cit, pp. 322, 341, 354 and 500. The boiler pressures of British Second World destroyers, at 300 psi, represented only a small advance on the 250 psi reached at the end of the Great War.
113. ADM 234/578, p. 33.
114. Ibid, p. 25.
115. Ibid, p. 34.
116. Ibid, p. 105.
117. Ibid, p. 105.
118. ADM 205/23.

119. Lenton and Colledge, *Warships of World War II*, op cit, pp. 85–6, 104–5.
120. Ibid, p. 201.
121. The following account of Escort Unit B6's battle together with all quotations is drawn from ADM 234/370, BR 1736(45) BS No. 51, Naval Staff History, Second World War, *Convoy and Anti-Submarine Warfare Reports*. No. 4. *Passage of Convoy S.C.104 – October 1942*, Report of Proceedings on Convoy SC104 by Commanding Officer HMS FAME covering the period 9th–19th October 1942; including Report from Commanding Officer HMS VISCOUNT, reporting Attacks on Two U-boats and Movements of VISCOUNT when ordered to Proceed Independently; Report Received from the Commanding Officer, HNORMS POTENTILLA.
122. Roskill, *War at Sea*, op cit, Vol II, p. 213.
123. Ibid, Appendix O, p. 485, Table I.
124. Behrens, op cit, Appendix XLVI, p. 283.

16. *The Verdun of Maritime War: Malta, 1942* (pages 491–526)

1. Hinsley, *British Intelligence in the Second World War*, op cit, Vol II, p. 349.
2. ADM 205/14, minutes of 16 and 17 June 1942.
3. Cunningham, *A Sailor's Odyssey*, op cit, p. 442.
4. Ibid, p. 443.
5. ADM 234/353, Naval Staff History, B.S. No. 32, Malta Convoys (1945), based on war diaries and operational reports.
6. Quoted in Playfair, *The Mediterranean and the Middle East*, op cit, Vol III, Part II, p. 451.
7. Ibid.
8. See Nigel Hamilton, *Monty: The Making of a General 1887–1942*, London, Hamish Hamilton, 1981, pp. 745–6; Barnett, *The Desert Generals*, op cit, p. 272.
9. Cf Torres Vedras and Masséna's enforced retreat from Portugal, 1810–11.
10. Butler, *Grand Strategy*, op cit, Vol III, Part II, p. 445.
11. ROSK 5/95, photocopy of letter to Vice-Chief of the Naval Staff, 9 January 1942.
12. Ibid.
13. Ibid.
14. See Terraine, *The Right of the Line*, op cit, pp. 343–4.
15. ROSK 5/95, letter of 9 January 1942.
16. Cunningham, op cit, p. 442.
17. Ibid, pp. 442–3.
18. The following account of Operation MG1 is based on ADM 234/353, B.S. No. 32.
19. Ibid, p. 4.

20. Hinsley, op cit, Vol II, p. 347.
21. ADM 234/353, B.S. No. 32, p. 5.
22. Ibid.
23. Quoted in ibid, p. 9.
24. Ibid.
25. Cited in ibid, p. 7.
26. Ibid.
27. Cunningham, op cit, p. 452.
28. Vian, *Action This Day*, op cit, p. 90.
29. Cited in ADM 234/353, p. 13.
30. Minute reproduced as frontispiece in Vian's memoirs.
31. Vian, op cit, p. 92.
32. Cited in ADM 234/353, p. 12.
33. Cunningham, op cit, p. 457.
34. Ibid, p. 459.
35. Grove, Chant, Lyon and Lyon, *The Hardware of World War II*, op cit, p. 202.
36. Cited in Roskill, *War at Sea*, op cit, Vol II, p. 61.
37. The following account of 'Operation Harpoon' is based on ADM 234/353, unless otherwise stated.
38. Ibid, p. 18.
39. Ibid.
40. Staff Minute M.08465/42, cited in ibid, p. 20.
41. Ibid.
42. Ibid, p. 21.
43. See Roskill, *Churchill and the Admirals*, op cit, p. 189.
44. Ibid.
45. The following account of 'Operation Vigorous' is based on ADM 234/353, unless otherwise stated.
46. Ibid, p. 27.
47. ROSK 5/95, letter to S. W. Roskill, 28 November 1954.
48. Ibid.
49. Ibid.
50. ADM 234/353, p. 29.
51. Ibid, p. 28.
52. Ibid, p. 29.
53. Quoted in ibid, pp. 32–3.
54. Quoted in ibid, p. 33.
55. Lenton and Colledge, *Warships of World War II*, op cit, p. 41.
56. Quoted in ADM 234/353, p. 33.
57. Quoted in ibid, pp. 33–4.
58. Ibid.
59. Weale, Weale and Barker, *Combat Aircraft of World War Two*, op cit, p. 161.
60. ADM 234/353, p. 34.

61. ROSK 5/95, letter to S. W. Roskill, 28 November 1954.
62. Ibid: letters to S. W. Roskill of 6 and 16 November 1954.
63. ROSK 5/97, letter to S. W. Roskill, 22 November 1957.
64. Quoted in Barnett, *The Desert Generals*, op cit, p. 194.
65. Lampton Burn, *Down Ramps; Saga of the 8th Armada*, London, Carroll and Nicholson, 1948, p. 57.
66. ROSK 5/99, photocopy of letter of 18 November 1942.
67. See Hinsley, *British Intelligence in the Second World War*, op cit, Vol II, pp. 380, 392–3, 395–7, 403–5.
68. Playfair, *The Mediterranean and the Middle East*, op cit, Vol IV, *The Destruction of the Axis Forces in Africa*, pp. 9–10, Footnotes 1 and 2, p. 15.
69. Behrens, *Merchant Shipping and the Demands of War*, op cit, Appendix L, p. 296.
70. See ibid, Chapter XIII, for an analysis of the shipping and import problem in 1942.
71. The following account of 'Operation Pedestal' is based on ADM 234/353, unless otherwise stated.
72. Ibid, p. 39.
73. Weale, Weale and Barker, op cit, p. 159.
74. Ibid, p. 134.
75. ADM 234/353, p. 42.
76. Ibid, p. 45.
77. Ibid.
78. Cited in Roskill, *War at Sea*, op cit, Vol 2, p. 308.
79. See Martin van Crefeld, *Supplying War*, Cambridge, Cambridge University Press, 1977, Chapter 6.
80. Ibid.
81. Ibid.
82. Ibid, pp. 198–9.
83. Ibid.
84. Ibid, p. 199.

17. *Grand Strategy for a Maritime Alliance – I* (pages 527–536)

1. Michael Howard, *Grand Strategy*, Vol IV, London, HMSO, 1972, p. xv.
2. Ibid, p. xvi.
3. Ibid.
4. Ibid.
5. Ibid.
6. For a running historical analysis of the 'Continental' school of strategy versus the 'blue water' school since Elizabeth I, see C. Barnett, *Britain and Her Army 1509–1970*, London, Allen Lane, 1970.
7. Basil Liddell Hart, *The British Way in Warfare*, London, Faber, 1932.
8. CAB 69/4, DO(42) 10th on 14 April 1942.

9. Fraser, *And We Shall Shock Them: The British Army in the Second World War*, op cit, p. 249.
10. Howard, op cit, Vol IV, p. xvii.
11. Gilbert, *Winston S. Churchill*, op cit, Vol VII, pp. 100–1.
12. See Gwyer, *Grand Strategy*, op cit, Vol II, Part I, p. 327.
13. Ibid, pp. 364–5.
14. Fraser, op cit, p. 256.
15. Howard, op cit, Vol IV, pp. xvii–xix.
16. Cited in Gwyer, op cit, Vol II, Part II, p. 627.
17. Gilbert, op cit, Vol VII, p. 143.
18. Ibid, p. 144.
19. Gwyer, op cit, Vol II, Part II, pp. 632–3.
20. Howard, op cit, Vol IV, p. xx.
21. Ibid.
22. Fraser, op cit, p. 258.
23. Howard, op cit, Vol IV, p. xxi.
24. Ibid, p. xxii.
25. See ibid, p. xxiii for the text.
26. Ibid.
27. Ibid, pp. xxiv–xxv.
28. Ibid.

18. *'A Quite Desperate Undertaking': 'Operation Torch'* (pages 537–572)

1. Lenton and Colledge, *Warships of World War II*, op cit, p. 46.
2. ROSK 8/21, photocopy of a letter from Cunningham to Admiral Sir Bertram Ramsay, 3 November 1942.
3. Ibid.
4. Alfred D. Chandler (editor), *The Papers of Dwight David Eisenhower. The War Years: I*, Baltimore and London, the Johns Hopkins Press, 1970, p. 577.
5. Cited in Cunningham, *A Sailor's Odyssey*, op cit, p. 493.
6. Ibid, p. 577.
7. Ibid, p. 466.
8. Ibid.
9. Ibid, p. 469.
10. See RMSY 8/18.
11. The following account of the development of combined operations from the 1920s to 1942 is based on L. E. H. Maund, *Assault from the Sea*, London, Methuen, 1949, Chapters I–III, VI, VII; Bernard Fergusson, *The Watery Maze: The Story of Combined Operations*, London, Collins, 1961, Chapters I–VII.
12. N. Hamilton, *Monty: the Making of a General*, op cit, p. 286.
13. Maund, op cit, p. 8.
14. Ibid, p. 9.

15. Ibid, pp. 9–16.
16. Ibid, p. 68.
17. RMSY 8/22.
18. Philip Ziegler, *Mountbatten*, London, Collins, 1985, p. 175.
19. Ibid, p. 170.
20. Ibid.
21. Postan, Hay and Scott, *Design and Development of Weapons*, op cit, p. 285.
22. Maund, op cit, pp. 82–3.
23. Lenton and Colledge, op cit, p. 585.
24. Samuel Eliot Morison, *History of United States Naval Operations in World War II*, Vol II, *Operations in North African Waters, October 1942–June 1943*, Boston, Little, Brown, 1960, p. 24.
25. Ibid, p. 20.
26. Butler, *Grand Strategy*, op cit, Vol III, Part II, p. 641.
27. Ibid.
28. See Ziegler, op cit, pp. 192–6; and Hamilton's lame attempt to excuse Montgomery, partly by blackening Mountbatten, in Hamilton, op cit, Chapter 16.
29. See Maund, op cit, pp. 114–15; Fergusson, op cit, Chapter VII.
30. Chandler (ed), op cit, Vol I, p. 526.
31. Cited in Howard, *Grand Strategy*, Vol IV, Appendix II, pp. 600–1.
32. Ibid, p. 119.
33. Chandler (ed), op cit, Vol I, p. 461.
34. Cited in Howard, op cit, Vol IV, p. 126.
35. Ibid, p. 128.
36. Ibid.
37. Ibid, p. 130.
38. Ibid, p. 136.
39. Chandler (ed), op cit, Vol I, p. 464, Footnote 1.
40. Ibid, p. 556.
41. Eisenhower to Marshall, 12 September 1942, in ibid.
42. Roskill, *War at Sea*, op cit, Vol II, p. 319, Table 25; Morison, op cit, Vol II, pp. 36–40.
43. Eisenhower's directive to Hewitt, 13 October 1942, cited in full in Chandler (ed), op cit, Vol 1, pp. 611–12.
44. Playfair, *The Mediterranean and the Middle East*, op cit, Vol IV, p. 140.
45. ADM 234/359, BS No. 38, 'Operation Torch'; Invasion of North Africa, November 1942 to February 1943, (1948).
46. Lenton and Colledge, op cit, p. 68.
47. Ibid, p. 58.
48. Ibid, p. 282.
49. Ibid.
50. Ibid, p. 25.
51. RMSY 8/21, photocopy of letter of 12 November 1942 to Ramsay.

52. Behrens, *Merchant Shipping and the Demands of War*, op cit, p. 312.
53. Ibid, Chapter XIII, but especially p. 308.
54. The following account of 'Torch' is based on ADM 234/359 unless otherwise stated.
55. Roskill, *War at Sea*, op cit, Vol II, p. 318, and Map 32, facing p. 317.
56. Ibid, p. 317.
57. Ibid.
58. Dönitz, *Memoirs: Ten Years and Twenty Days*, op cit, p. 279.
59. RMSY 8/21, letter of 3 November 1942.
60. Dönitz, op cit, p. 279.
61. RMSY 8/21, letter of 3 November 1942.
62. Ibid.
63. Ibid.
64. Ibid.
65. Chandler (ed), op cit, Vol I, p. 651.
66. RMSY 8/21, letter of 3 November 1942.
67. ADM 234/359.
68. Ibid.
69. Morison, op cit, Vol II, p. 50.
70. Playfair, op cit, Vol IV, p. 116; ADM 234/359.
71. Hinsley, *British Intelligence in the Second World War*, op cit, Vol II, p. 487.
72. Ibid, p. 481.
73. Chandler (ed), op cit, Vol II, p. 667.
74. The following account of the Algiers landings is based on ADM 234/359; Playfair, op cit, Vol IV, pp. 138–46; Roskill, *War at Sea*, op cit, Vol II, pp. 324–5.
75. Playfair, op cit, Vol IV, Map 18, facing p. 141.
76. ADM 234/359.
77. Playfair, op cit, Vol IV, Map 18, facing p. 141.
78. Ibid.
79. Playfair, op cit, Vol IV, Map 19, facing p. 147. The following account of the Oran landings is based on ADM 234/359; Playfair, Vol IV, pp. 146–50; Roskill, *War at Sea*, op cit, Vol II, pp. 325–8.
80. ADM 234/359.
81. Ibid.
82. Playfair, op cit, Vol IV, Map 19, facing p. 147.
83. Weale, Weale and Barker, *Combat Aircraft of World War Two*, op cit, p. 91.
84. RMSY 8/21, letter of 12 November 1942.
85. See Morison, op cit, Vol I, Chapters II–VII.
86. Ibid, p. 90.
87. Playfair, op cit, Vol IV, p. 163.
88. RMSY 8/21, letter of 21 November 1942.
89. RMSY 8/21, letter of 12 November 1942.

90. Playfair, op cit, Vol IV, pp. 156–7.
91. Hinsley, op cit, Vol II, p. 493.
92. Chandler (ed), op cit, Vol I, letter to Marshall of 20 October 1942.
93. RMSY 8/21, letter to Ramsay, 12 November 1942.
94. RMSY 8/21, letter to Ramsay, 4 December 1942.
95. Behrens, op cit, p. 312.
96. Ibid and Appendix LII, p. 323.
97. Ibid.
98. ADM 234/359, Appendices D and D2, pp. 92–3.
99. Behrens, op cit, Appendix LII, p. 323.
100. Martin Blumenson, *Rommel's Last Victory*, London, Allen and Unwin, 1968, p. 54.
101. Roskill, *War at Sea*, op cit, Vol II, Appendix O, p. 486, Table 2.
102. See Behrens, op cit, Chapter XIV.

19. *'The Battle of the Atlantic Is Getting Harder'* (pages 573–613)

1. Roskill, *War at Sea*, op cit, Vol II, Appendix O, p. 486.
2. ADM 234/578, p. 90.
3. Roskill, *War at Sea*, op cit, Vol II, Appendix O, p. 486.
4. Ibid.
5. ADM 205/20.
6. Ibid, 1 October 1942.
7. Cited in ADM 234/578, p. 91.
8. ADM 205.
9. Ibid.
10. See C. Barnett, *The Audit of War*, op cit, Chapter 6, but especially pp. 116–19.
11. Postan, Hay and Scott, *Design and Development of Weapons*, op cit, p. 62; Roskill *War at Sea*, op cit, Vol II, Appendix O, p. 486.
12. Postan, Hay and Scott, op cit, pp. 62 and 300.
13. Behrens, *Merchant Shipping and the Demands of War*, op cit, pp. 366–7.
14. Dönitz, *Memoirs: Ten Years and Twenty Days*, op cit, p. 296.
15. ADM 234/578, p. 90.
16. Behrens, op cit, p. 363.
17. The following account of the balance of the Sigint struggle at the turn of 1942 and 1943 is based on Hinsley, *British Intelligence in the Second World War*, op cit, Vol 2, Chapter 26.
18. Ibid, p. 547.
19. Roskill, *War at Sea*, op cit, Vol II, p. 378.
20. Hinsley, op cit, Vol II, p. 548.
21. Ibid, Appendix 9, p. 682.
22. Ibid, p. 552.
23. Ibid, Appendix 9, p. 682.
24. Ibid, p. 552; Roskill, *War at Sea*, op cit, Vol II, p. 475.

25. Hinsley, op cit, Vol II, pp. 553–4.
26. Ibid, p. 551.
27. Roskill, op cit, Vol II, p. 364.
28. ROSK 5/132A, unpublished memoir by Admiral G. C. Cunninghame-Grahame, 'Random Recollections of Hitler's War'.
29. Ibid.
30. Bowen Papers, Churchill Archive Centre, EGBN 3/4, 'The Radar Battle of the Bay of Biscay', by A. C. B. Lovell, PhD, in the Telecommunications Research Establishment journal for July 1945, but written in 1944.
31. Ibid. See also EGBN 2/4, unpublished Technical Monographs in Wartime Research and Development in the Ministry of Aircraft Production: A.S.V. (The Detection of Surface Vessels by Airborne Radar); Chief Writer: R. A. Smith, TRE (Telecommunications Research Establishment).
32. See Barnett, *The Audit of War*, op cit, Chapter 9 for an account of radio and radar production based on Cabinet and departmental records; also ROSK 5/132A, EGBN 2/4 and 3/4; Postan, Hay and Scott, op cit, pp. 403–13, 428–30, 452–8.
33. See Barnett, *The Audit of War*, op cit, pp. 172–6.
34. ROSK 5/1, Captain S. W. Roskill, letter to Rear-Admiral W. J. M. McClure, 27 July 1979.
35. See Barnett, *Audit of War*, op cit, p. 169.
36. EGBN 3/4.
37. Ibid.
38. Ibid.
39. See Terraine, *The Right of the Line*, op cit, p. 437.
40. EGBN 3/4.
41. Ibid.
42. ADM 234/241, Anti-U-Boat Operations.
43. All ibid, p. 86.
44. Lenton and Colledge, *Warships of World War II*, op cit, p. 68.
45. Ibid.
46. ADM 234/241; ADM 205/30, Admiralty Review of Proceedings of the Anti-U-Boat Warfare Committee, 20 August 1943.
47. See Bernard Ireland, *The Rise and Fall of the Aircraft Carrier*, p. 60; ADM 234/241.
48. ROSK 5/24, Admiralty Review of Proceedings of the Anti-U-Boat Warfare Committee, 20 August 1943.
49. M. 054165/43 in ROSK 5/3.
50. Ibid.
51. ROSK 5/3, C.C.S. 335, 3 September 1943, 'Employment of CVEs in Offensive Action Against U-Boats'.
52. Ibid.
53. ADM 234/241, Appendix 4; ADM 205/30, Admiralty Review of

Proceedings of Cabinet Anti-U-Boat Warfare Committee, 20 August 1943.

54. ADM 205/30, Admiralty Review of Proceedings of Cabinet Anti-U-Boat Warfare Committee.
55. Postan, Hay and Scott, op cit, pp. 294–5.
56. ADM 234/241, p. 94.
57. Lenton and Colledge, op cit, pp. 172–4, 225–32.
58. Postan, Hay and Scott, op cit, p. 292.
59. Ibid, p. 292.
60. Dönitz, op cit, p. 95.
61. Ibid, p. 97.
62. Goodeve Papers, Churchill Archives Centre, GOEV 3/1, Most Secret Memorandum, Responsibility in Development Work; shallow-setting Depth-Charges, September 1942.
63. ROSK 5/25; GOEV 3/1.
64. ADM 205/30, Admiralty Review of Proceedings of Anti-U-Boat Warfare Committee; Terraine, op cit, pp. 430–3, 445.
65. Ibid.
66. The scientists included Edward (later Sir Edward) Bullard of HMS *Osprey* (the Anti-Submarine Warfare Establishment), Charles (later Sir Charles) Goodeve, FRS, then a Commander in the RNVR, serving in the new Admiralty Anti-Aircraft Weapons and Devices Department; Richard Keynes of the Admiralty Anti-Submarine Warfare Establishment (all future Fellows of the Royal Society). The service officers included Captain G. H. Oswald, RN (Department of Naval Ordnance); Captain G. O. C. Davies, RN of the Anti-Aircraft Weapons and Devices Department, Goodeve's superior; Major Jefferies of MD 1; Commander R. H. Stokes Rees of the Fort Halsted Experimental Establishment; and Colonel L. V. Blacker, inventor of the Spigot Mortar. For the development of the Hedgehog, see ROSK 4/14, Memorandum by Captain G. H. Oswald; GOEV 3/1, account by Sir Charles Goodeve.
67. ROSK 4/14.
68. GOEV 3/1.
69. Anthony Watts, *The U-Boat Hunters*, London, Macdonald and Jane, 1976, caption, p. 141.
70. Keynes Papers, Churchill Archives Centre, KEYN/1, letter from R. D. Keynes to the Director Scientific Research and Development Department, 26 August 1942, with reference to early 1940.
71. Ibid.
72. Captain Oswald in ROSK 4/14.
73. Ibid.
74. GOEV 3/1.
75. See Anthony Watts, op cit, pp. 139–43, for a technical description.
76. Ibid, p. 144.

77. Roskill, *War at Sea*, op cit, Vol I, p. 359; Watts, op cit, pp. 172–3.
78. ADM 205/30, Admiralty Review of Proceedings of Anti-U-Boat Warfare Committee; Watts, op cit, pp. 173–4.
79. Watts, op cit, pp. 174–5.
80. Ibid, pp. 175–6; ADM 205/30, Admiralty Review of Proceedings of Anti-U-Boat Warfare Committee.
81. ADM 205/30, Admiralty Review of Proceedings of Anti-U-Boat Warfare Committee.
82. ROSK 5/25, photocopy of letter from Rear-Admiral C. D. Howard-Johnston to J. D. Brown of the Naval Historical Branch, 23 February 1980.
83. Ibid.
84. ADM 234/578, p. 106.
85. Roskill, *War at Sea*, op cit, Vol II, p. 371.
86. Ibid; ADM 234/578.
87. Cited in Hinsley, op cit, Vol II, p. 557.
88. Ibid.
89. Dönitz, op cit, p. 317.
90. ADM 234/578; unless otherwise cited the following account in this chapter of the Battle of the Atlantic January–May 1943 is based on ADM 234/578.
91. Hinsley, op cit, Vol II, p. 558.
92. ADM 234/578.
93. Hinsley, op cit, Vol II, p. 559.
94. Ibid; ADM 234/578.
95. Dönitz, op cit, p. 322.
96. Cited in Roskill, *War at Sea*, op cit, Vol II, p. 357.
97. Hinsley, op cit, Vol II, pp. 560–1.
98. Roskill, *War at Sea*, op cit, Vol II, p. 357.
99. Dönitz, op cit, p. 325.
100. Hinsley, op cit, Vol II, p. 561.
101. Roskill, *War at Sea*, op cit, Vol II, p. 358.
102. ADM 234/578.
103. See Roskill, *War at Sea*, op cit, Vol II, p. 365.
104. Cited in Dönitz, op cit, p. 327.
105. Ibid.
106. Cited in Hinsley, op cit, Vol II, p. 563; see Roskill, *War at Sea*, op cit, Vol II, pp. 365–6, and Terraine, op cit, pp. 443–4.
107. CAB 86/3, AU(43)90.
108. CAB 65/37, 42(43), Confidential Annexe.
109. ADM 234/578.
110. ROSK 5/3, Report to Vice-Admiral, Aircraft Carriers, Home Fleet, 31 March 1943.
111. Roskill, *War at Sea*, op cit, Vol II, p. 372.
112. Ibid, Appendix K, p. 475.

113. Ibid; Grove, Chant, Lyon and Lyon, *The Hardware of World War II*, op cit, pp. 149–51.
114. Hinsley, op cit, Vol II, p. 568.
115. Ibid, p. 569.
116. Ibid.
117. Ibid.
118. Roskill, *War at Sea*, op cit, Vol II, p. 372.
119. Cited in ibid.
120. Ibid and Appendix J, p. 470, Table I.
121. Hinsley, op cit, Vol II, p. 569.
122. Ibid.
123. Cf Roskill, *War at Sea*, op cit, Vol II, Map 40.
124. ADM 234/358, p. 96.
125. Ibid.
126. Ibid.
127. Ibid.
128. ADM 234/578, p. 95.
129. Ibid, p. 107.
130. EGBN 3/4.
131. ADM 205/30; Terraine, op cit, p. 446.
132. Dönitz, op cit, p. 343.
133. Hinsley, op cit, Vol II, p. 570.
134. Lenton and Colledge, op cit, p. 115; Edgar J. March, *British Destroyers, A History of Development 1892–1953*, op cit, Chapter 15.
135. Lenton and Colledge, op cit, p. 100.
136. Ibid, p. 225.
137. Ibid, p. 170.
138. Cited in Roskill, *War at Sea*, op cit, Vol II, p. 374.
139. Lenton and Colledge, op cit, p. 86.
140. Hinsley, op cit, Vol II, p. 570.
141. Ibid.
142. Lenton and Colledge, op cit, p. 240.
143. Roskill, *War at Sea*, op cit, Vol II, pp. 375–6.
144. Hinsley, op cit, Vol II, p. 571.
145. ADM 234/578.
146. Hinsley, op cit, Vol II, p. 571.
147. ADM 234/578, pp. 94 and 96.
148. Cited in ADM 234/578, p. 93.
149. Dönitz, op cit, pp. 312–13.
150. Ibid, p. 269.
151. Ibid, p. 326.
152. Cited in ADM 234/578, p. 97.
153. Ibid.
154. ADM 234/578, p. 97.
155. See Behrens, op cit, p. 372, Chapter XVIII and XIX, especially pp. 411–12.

20. *Grand Strategy for a Maritime Alliance – II* (pages 614–626)

1. Churchill, *The Second World War*, op cit, Vol IV, *The Hinge of Fate*, London, Cassell, 1951, pp. 604–5.
2. Hinsley, *British Intelligence in the Second World War*, op cit, Vol II, pp. 454–60.
3. Roskill, *War at Sea*, op cit, Vol II, p. 341.
4. Cunningham, *A Sailor's Odyssey*, op cit, p. 517.
5. Howard, *Grand Strategy*, op cit, Vol IV, pp. xxiv–xxv.
6. CAB 66/30, WP(42)483, 24 October 1942.
7. CAB 80/65, COS(42)345(O)(Final), 30 October 1942; CAB 79/24, COS(42) 304th, 30 October 1942.
8. Howard, op cit, Vol IV, pp. 208–9.
9. Ibid.
10. CAB 80/66, COS(42)429(O), 3 December 1942.
11. CAB 80/66, COS(42)452(O), 13 December 1942.
12. CAB 80/66, JP(42) 1005, 12 December 1942.
13. CAB 80/66, COS(42)452(O), 12 December 1942.
14. Ibid.
15. CAB 79/58, COS(42) 198th(O), 16 December 1942.
16. Ibid.
17. Ibid.
18. CAB 80/66, COS(42)485(O), 29 December 1942.
19. CAB 80/66, COS(42)466(O)(Final); CAB 69/4, DO(42) 20th, 29 December 1942.
20. Behrens, *Merchant Shipping and the Demands of War*, op cit, p. 331; see also pp. 319–22.
21. Printed in full as Appendix III(B) in Howard, op cit, Vol IV, pp. 614–16.
22. Ibid.
23. Fraser, *And We Shall Shock Them: the British Army in the Second World War*, op cit, p. 321.
24. Howard, op cit, Vol IV, p. 252.
25. Gilbert, *Winston S. Churchill*, op cit, Vol VII, p. 253.
26. Howard, op cit, Vol IV, p. 254.
27. Ibid.
28. Ibid.
29. Ibid, p. 294.
30. Cited in full in Howard, op cit, Vol IV, Appendix III(D), pp. 621–2.
31. Cunningham, op cit, p. 520.
32. ROSK 5/102, photocopy of letter of 15 March 1943.
33. Cunningham, op cit, p. 529.

21. *The Invasion of Sicily: 'Operation Husky'* (pages 627–656)

1. See ROSK 5/102, photocopy of letter from Cunningham to First Sea Lord, 15 March 1943; ROSK 5/99, letter from Cunningham to Captain

S. W. Roskill, 12 November 1953; Roskill *War at Sea*, op cit, Vol II, pp. 435–7.

2. ROSK 5/99, letter of 12 November 1953 to Captain Roskill.
3. Cited in Carlo D'Este, *Bitter Victory, The Battle for Sicily July–August 1943*, London, Collins, 1988, p. 113.
4. Chandler (ed), *The Papers of Dwight D. Eisenhower*, op cit, Vol II, pp. 1046–7.
5. D'Este, op cit, p. 86.
6. Ibid, p. 87.
7. Cited in D'Este, op cit, p. 82.
8. Ibid, p. 112.
9. RMSY 8/23. The extracts from Ramsay's letters to his wife cited by Rear-Admiral W. S. Chalmers in his biography of Ramsay, *Full Cycle, The Biography of Admiral Sir Bertram Home Ramsay*, London, Hodder and Stoughton, 1959, cannot be relied upon, because Chalmers edited the extracts without indicating that he had sometimes omitted important material in their midst.
10. Ibid.
11. Ibid.
12. Ibid, letter of 14 April 1943.
13. Ibid.
14. Ibid.
15. Howard, *Grand Strategy*, op cit, Vol IV, p. 365.
16. RMSY 8/23, letter to his wife, 28 April 1943.
17. ROSK 5/98, photocopy of letter to the First Sea Lord, 28 April 1943.
18. ROSK 5/102, photocopy of No. 1 (Med)00358/R, 1 January 1944, covering reports on the invasion of Sicily.
19. ROSK 5/98, photocopy of letter.
20. Ibid.
21. RMSY 8/23, letter of 6 May 1943.
22. Letter to First Sea Lord, 8 May 1943, quoted in Cunningham, *A Sailor's Odyssey*, op cit, p. 538.
23. RMSY 8/23, letter to his wife, 10 May 1943.
24. Hinsley, *British Intelligence in the Second World War*, op cit, Vol III, Part 1, pp. 71–2.
25. ROSK 5/102, Royal Naval Staff College Course, Greenwich: Course No. 5, 1948. OPERATION HUSKY II – Execution. Phase IV, by Commander E. V. St J. Morgan, para 3.
26. ROSK 5/102, photocopy of covering letter to General Eisenhower by Admiral Sir Andrew Cunningham, enclosing reports on the invasion of Sicily, No. 1/Med/00358/R, 1 January 1944.
27. Ibid.
28. ROSK 5/105, photocopy of letter to First Sea Lord, 5 August 1943.
29. Ibid.
30. ROSK 5/102, OPERATION HUSKY I – Preparation. Phase III, by

Commander E. V. St J. Morgan, Royal Naval Staff College, Greenwich: Course No. 5, 1948, paras 12–13.
31. ROSK 5/102, photocopy of letter to Eisenhower, 1 January 1944.
32. Ibid.
33. ROSK 5/102, Morgan, op cit, I, PHASE III, para 27.
34. ADM 199/860, Husky Naval Orders.
35. Hinsley, op cit, Vol III, Part 1, pp. 78–9.
36. ADM 199/860, Husky Naval Orders.
37. Maund, *Assault from the Sea*, op cit, p. 256.
38. ROSK 5/102, letter of 1 January 1944.
39. Hinsley, op cit, Vol III, Part 1, p. 76.
40. See D'Este, op cit, pp. 213–16.
41. Terraine, *The Right of the Line*, op cit, p. 566.
42. RMSY 8/23, letter of 11 July 1943.
43. RMSY 8/23, letter to his wife of 28 May 1943.
44. RMSY 8/23, letter of 11 July 1943.
45. Morgan, op cit, I, paras 16–20; II, paras 26–7.
46. Hinsley, op cit, Vol III, Part 1, p. 75.
47. Ibid, p. 76.
48. Ibid, p. 83.
49. Howard, op cit, Vol IV, p. 361.
50. Hinsley, op cit, Vol III, Part 1, pp. 76–80.
51. Morgan, op cit, II, para 10.
52. Ibid, para 11.
53. ROSK 5/102, letter from Cunningham to Eisenhower, 1 January 1944.
54. See D'Este, op cit, Chapters 12 and 13.
55. ROSK 5/102, letter to Eisenhower, 1 January 1944; see also Hinsley, op cit, Vol 3, Part 1, p. 86, Footnote 1.
56. Hinsley, op cit, Vol III, Part 1, p. 86.
57. ROSK 5/102, letter of 1 January 1944.
58. Ibid.
59. RMSY 8/23, letter from Ramsay to his wife 11 July 1943.
60. Ibid.
61. Morgan, op cit, II, para 23.
62. Ibid; see also D'Este, op cit, Chapter 15.
63. Howard, op cit, Vol IV, p. 468.
64. Cunningham, op cit, p. 537.
65. Ibid, p. 553.
66. Roskill, *War at Sea*, op cit, Vol III, Part I, p. 139.
67. Ibid.
68. D'Este, op cit, pp. 301–5; Terraine, op cit, pp. 574–7, 578–9.
69. Terraine, op cit, pp. 574–5.
70. Cited in Roskill, *War at Sea*, op cit, Part I, p. 115.
71. ROSK 5/105, photocopy of letter to First Sea Lord, 5 August 1943.
72. See D'Este, op cit, p. 301.
73. ROSK 5/102, letter of 1 January 1944.

74. Ibid.
75. D'Este, op cit, p. 514.
76. Ibid.
77. Hinsley, op cit, Vol III, Part 1, pp. 95–9.
78. Roskill, *War at Sea*, op cit, Vol III, Part I, p. 149.
79. D'Este, op cit, p. 502.
80. Ibid; see also Roskill, *War at Sea*, op cit, Vol III, Part I, Map 11, facing p. 145.
81. Roskill, *War at Sea*, op cit, Vol III, Part I, p. 150.
82. See D'Este, op cit, Appendix I, p. 607.
83. Ibid, Appendix E, p. 597.
84. Ibid, Appendix I, p. 609.
85. Alexander Werth, *Russia at War, 1941–1945*, London, Barrie and Rockcliff, 1964, p. 683.
86. Howard, op cit, Vol IV, p. 419.
87. CAB 84/53, JP(43)99 (Final), 3 May 1943.
88. Howard, op cit, Vol IV, p. 417.
89. Ibid, pp. 417–18.
90. Ibid, p. 415.
91. Ibid.
92. Ibid.
93. Ibid, pp. 415–16.
94. Ibid, p. 419.
95. Ibid, p. 421.
96. Ibid, p. 422.
97. Ibid, p. 428.
98. Ibid, p. 431.
99. Ibid.
100. Printed in full in Howard, op cit, Vol IV, Appendix VI(C), pp. 660–7.
101. Ibid.
102. Ibid.
103. CAB 84/53, JP(43)99(Final), 3 May 1943.
104. Churchill, *The Second World War*, op cit, Vol IV, p. 630.
105. Howard, op cit, Vol IV, p. 498.
106. Ibid.
107. 13 July, cited in ibid, p. 502.
108. Ibid.
109. Ibid, p. 503.
110. Ibid.
111. Ibid, p. 564.

22. *'Some Underbelly; Some Softest Part': The Mediterranean, 1943–1945* (pages 657–692)

1. ADM 234/358, BR 1736(36) BS No. 37, The Invasion of Italy: Landing at Salerno ('Avalanche') (Naval Operations), 9th September 1943

(1946). The following account of the invasion of Italy is based on this Naval Staff History unless otherwise stated.

2. Ibid, p. 5.
3. Howard, *Grand Strategy*, op cit, Vol IV, p. 506.
4. Ibid.
5. Ibid.
6. Lenton and Colledge, *Warships of World War II*, op cit, p. 69.
7. ROSK 5/105, photocopy of letter of 5 August 1943.
8. ADM 234/358, p. 11.
9. Ibid, p. 13.
10. Ibid.
11. Cited in ibid, p. 14.
12. Hinsley, *British Intelligence in the Second World War*, op cit, Vol III, Part 1, p. 391 and Footnote 1.
13. ADM 234/358.
14. ROSK 5/105, note by Captain Roskill of fleet strength as of 1 October 1943.
15. Behrens, *Merchant Shipping and the Demands of War*, op cit, p. 391 and Footnote 1.
16. ADM 234/358.
17. See Howard, op cit, Vol IV, Chapter XXVII, for a lucid account of the Italian surrender negotiations.
18. ROSK 5/105, photocopy of letter of 5 August 1943.
19. ADM 234/358.
20. ADM 234/358, p. 17.
21. Ibid.
22. ROSK 5/105, photocopy of letter of 26 August 1943.
23. Ibid.
24. Ibid.
25. ADM 234/358, p. 18.
26. Ibid.
27. ADM 234/358; there is no mention in Hinsley, op cit, Vol 3, Part 1.
28. Cited in ADM 234/358, p. 17.
29. Lenton and Colledge, op cit, p. 64.
30. All ADM 234/358.
31. The following account of naval operations during 'Avalanche' is based on ADM 234/358, from which all otherwise unattributed quotations are drawn.
32. Hinsley, op cit, Vol III, Part 1, p. 110.
33. Roskill, *War at Sea*, op cit, Vol III, Part I, p. 168, Footnote 1; Robert Cecil (ed), *Hitler's War Machine*, London, Leisure Books, 1975, pp. 193, 209.
34. Hinsley, op cit, Vol III, Part 1, p. 111.
35. Roskill, *War at Sea*, op cit, Vol III, Part 1, p. 169.
36. Cunningham, *A Sailor's Odyssey*, op cit, p. 563.

37. Ibid.
38. Ibid, p. 565.
39. Roskill, *War at Sea*, op cit, Vol III, Part 1, Appendix H, pp. 382–5.
40. RMSY 8/22, lecture on Combined Operations, September 1943.
41. See Dominick Graham and Shelford Bidwell, *Tug of War; The Battle for Italy, 1943–1945*, London, Hodder and Stoughton, 1986, Chapters 3–6, for a first-class account of the Battle of Salerno.
42. Ibid, pp. 53–4.
43. Ibid.
44. Ibid, p. 43.
45. Ibid, p. 53.
46. Ibid.
47. Ibid, pp. 50–1.
48. ADM 234/358.
49. Lenton and Colledge, op cit, p. 24.
50. See Graham and Bidwell, op cit, pp. 61–7.
51. Weale, Weale and Barker, *Combat Aircraft of World War Two*, op cit, p. 149.
52. ROSK 5/105, Admiral Sir Geoffrey Oliver, 'Some Notes on the Project to Shorten the Front at Salerno, September, 1943', for Captain Roskill, dated 20 January 1953.
53. Graham and Bidwell, op cit, pp. 78–9.
54. ROSK 5/105, notes cited.
55. Ibid.
56. Ibid.
57. 'The Allied Navies at Salerno', article in the *US Naval Institute Proceedings*, Vol 79, No. 9, September 1953, p. 972.
58. Graham and Bidwell, op cit, p. 97.
59. Ibid, pp. 103–6.
60. See Graham and Bidwell, op cit, p. 106.
61. Cunningham, op cit, p. 575.
62. Gilbert, *Winston S. Churchill*, op cit, Vol VII, p. 502.
63. See Howard, op cit, Vol IV, pp. 61, 198, 213, 227, 232–3, 252, 377, 381–3.
64. Cited in ibid, p. 382.
65. Ibid, p. 489.
66. Ibid.
67. ROSK 5/106, No. 385 of 12 August 1943, photocopy of transcript of signal in brief prepared for Captain Roskill as official naval historian.
68. Cited in Gilbert, op cit, Vol VII, p. 497.
69. See ibid, p. 497 and pp. 502–5.
70. The following account of operations in the Aegean is based on ADM 234/364, 'Aegean Operations – 7th September to 28th November 1943: British occupation and German re-occupation of KOS and LEROS', unless otherwise cited.

71. ROSK 5/106, photocopy of transcript of exchanges of signals, September and October 1943; see also ADM 234/364, Appendix E.
72. Ibid, No. 9974 of 31 September 1943.
73. Ibid, CC 315 of 28 September 1943.
74. Ibid, NAF 438, to CCOS and COS.
75. Gilbert, op cit, Vol VII, p. 520.
76. Roskill, *War at Sea*, op cit, Vol III, Part I, p. 203.
77. See Gilbert, op cit, Vol VII, pp. 527–8, 532–3, 536, 546, 559–64.
78. David Fraser, *Alanbrooke*, London, Collins, 1982, p. 366.
79. Ibid.
80. Cf Churchill's memorandum to the COS on 19 July 1943 advocating a combination of Mediterranean/Balkan offensives and a landing in Northern Norway as a substitute for 'Overlord' in 1944, cited in Gilbert, op cit, Vol VI, pp. 444–5.
81. Fraser, *Alanbrooke*, op cit, p. 373.
82. Gilbert, op cit, Vol VII, pp. 547–8.
83. Ibid, pp. 541–2; Fraser, op cit, pp. 370–1.
84. Gilbert, op cit, Vol VII, p. 563, citing CAB 80/77, Minutes of Second Plenary meeting, 24 November 1943.
85. Gilbert, op cit, Vol VII, p. 571, citing CAB 80/77, first meeting, 28 November 1943.
86. Ibid.
87. Fraser, *Alanbrooke*, op cit, p. 391.
88. Gilbert, op cit, Vol VII, pp. 611–18.
89. Ibid, p. 628.
90. The following account of naval operations in 'Shingle' is based on ADM 234/873, 'Orders, Reports and Signals relating to Operation Shingle', unless otherwise cited.
91. Roskill, *War at Sea*, op cit, Vol III, Part I, p. 304, Table 19.
92. Ibid.
93. ADM 234/873; Roskill, *War at Sea*, op cit, Vol III, Part I, p. 307.
94. Ibid, p. 30; Cecil (ed), op cit, p. 207.
95. See Graham and Bidwell, op cit, Chapters 9–13; John Ellis, *Cassino; the Hollow Victory; The Battle for Rome January–June 1944*, London, André Deutsch, 1984, passim.
96. Graham and Bidwell, op cit, p. 401.
97. Ibid.
98. Hinsley, op cit, Vol III, Part 1, p. 29.
99. Behrens, op cit, Appendix LXX (ii)A, 9, p. 455; estimate of April 1944.
100. Graham and Bidwell, op cit, p. 399.
101. Fraser, op cit, p. 429.
102. Ibid.
103. Chandler (ed), *The Papers of Dwight D. Eisenhower*, op cit, Vol IV, letter from Eisenhower to Churchill, 11 August 1944; Gilbert, op cit, Vol VII, pp. 863–80.

104. See Graham and Bidwell, op cit, Chapters 23–4; Douglas Orgill, *The Gothic Line: The Autumn Campaign in Italy 1944*, London, Heinemann, 1967, passim.

23. *'Such Desolate and Dangerous Voyages': The Arctic Convoys, 1941–1945* (pages 693–749)

1. CAB 80/65, COS(42)345(O)/(Final), 30 October 1942.
2. All figures from ROSK 5/78, 'Answers to questions put by Lord Ismay'; undated paper.
3. ADM 234/369, p. 3, Footnote 2; BS No. 22, Arctic Convoys 1941–45 (1954). Unless otherwise cited, the following account of Arctic convoy operations, 1941–45, is based on this Naval Staff History.
4. Ibid, p. 6.
5. Ibid.
6. Ibid.
7. Ibid, p. 7.
8. This account of the passage of PQ12 and QP8 is based on ibid, pp. 7–20.
9. Ibid, p. 6.
10. Hinsley, *British Intelligence in the Second World War*, op cit, Vol II, pp. 200–1.
11. Cited in ibid, p. 8.
12. Cited in ibid, p. 8.
13. See Hinsley, op cit, Vol II, pp. 205–10.
14. Ibid, p. 210.
15. Ibid.
16. ADM 234/369.
17. Ibid, p. 21.
18. Roskill, *War at Sea*, op cit, Vol II, pp. 123–4.
19. Cited in ADM 234/369, p. 21.
20. Ibid.
21. Ibid, p. 21 and Footnote 4.
22. Lenton and Colledge, *Warships of World War II*, op cit, p. 48.
23. Ibid, p. 102.
24. ADM 234/369, p. 38.
25. Ibid, p. 33.
26. Ibid, p. 133.
27. Cited in ibid, p. 34.
28. Ibid.
29. CAB 69/4, DO 42(37).
30. Cited in Gilbert, *Winston S. Churchill*, op cit, Vol VII, p. 75.
31. Lenton and Colledge, op cit, p. 44.
32. ADM 234/369.
33. Ibid.

34. Cited in Gilbert, op cit, Vol VII, p. 98.
35. Ibid.
36. Ibid.
37. Ibid, pp. 98–9.
38. ADM 234/369, p. 39, Footnote 2.
39. Lenton and Colledge, op cit. p. 102.
40. Cited in ADM 234/369, p. 38.
41. Ibid, p. 39, Footnote 1.
42. Cited in ibid, p. 46.
43. ADM 205/19.
44. ADM 234/369, p. 47, Footnote 3.
45. Cited in ibid, p. 48, Footnote 3.
46. Report of proceedings, cited in ibid, p. 49.
47. Cited in ibid, p. 50.
48. Ibid.
49. Ibid.
50. Cited in ibid, p. 51.
51. Ibid.
52. ADM 234/369, p. 54 citing *London Gazette*, 17 October 1950, pp. 514–15.
53. Ibid.
54. ADM 234/369; the following operational account of the fate of PQ17 is based on this Naval Staff History, pp. 53–71, except where otherwise cited.
55. Ibid.
56. Signal 1145A/ 16 March 1942, cited in ibid, p. 23, and Footnote 3.
57. Ibid.
58. ROSK 5/72, notes made from First Sea Lord's papers, Vols 14, 21, 22.
59. Ibid, p. 55.
60. Lenton and Colledge, op cit, p. 86.
61. ROSK 5/72, letter to S. W. Roskill from Vice-Admiral Sir John Hayes, November 1981.
62. ADM 234/369, p. 59, Footnote 1.
63. Ibid, Footnote 2.
64. Ibid.
65. The account of Sigint during the PQ17 operation is based on Hinsley, op cit, Vol II, pp. 214–23 and ROSK 5/72, photocopy of unpublished memoir by Vice-Admiral Sir Norman (then Commander) Denning, the OIC officer responsible for evaluating the likely operations of the German surface fleet.
66. Hinsley, op cit, Vol II, p. 214.
67. Ibid, p. 215.
68. Ibid.
69. Ibid, p. 216.

70. ROSK 5/72, Denning's memoir.
71. Ibid.
72. Ibid.
73. Ibid.
74. Ibid.
75. Ibid.
76. Ibid.
77. Ibid.
78. Ibid.
79. Ibid.
80. Ibid.
81. Ibid.
82. Ibid.
83. Ibid.
84. All cited in ADM 234/69, p. 62.
85. Ibid, p. 60.
86. Ibid.
87. Ibid.
88. Cited in ibid, p. 67.
89. Cited in ibid.
90. Hamilton's report of proceedings, cited in ibid, p. 63.
91. Cited in ibid, p. 69.
92. Ibid, Footnote 1, p. 65.
93. Ibid.
94. See Morison, *History of United States Naval Operations in World War II*, op cit, Vol I, pp. 186–92.
95. Roskill, *War at Sea*, op cit, Vol II, p. 143.
96. CAB 65/31, WM(42)101.
97. Lenton and Colledge, op cit, p. 46.
98. Prime Minister, Personal Minutes, M.294/2, 'Secret', 'Action this Day', 15 July 1942, CHAR 20/67, cited Gilbert, op cit, Vol VII, p. 147.
99. Ibid.
100. CAB 79/22, COS (42) 205th.
101. Cited in ADM 234/369, p. 73.
102. Lenton and Colledge, op cit, p. 22.
103. Ibid, p. 68.
104. Ibid, p. 46.
105. Roskill, *War at Sea*, op cit, Vol II, pp. 278–9.
106. Hinsley, op cit, Vol II, p. 213.
107. Ibid, pp. 224–5.
108. Ibid, p. 226.
109. ADM 234/369.
110. Ibid, p. 77.
111. Cited in ibid, p. 78.

112. Hinsley, op cit, Vol II, pp. 194–5, 227.
113. ADM 234/369, p. 79.
114. Ibid, p. 85.
115. Ibid, p. 83.
116. All ibid.
117. Cited in ibid, p. 103.
118. Gilbert, op cit, Vol VII, p. 365.
119. ROSK 4/17, letter of 9 September 1961 to S. W. Roskill.
120. ROSK 5/77, photocopy of 'Hush' signal to First Sea Lord, 30 June 1943.
121. Ibid.
122. Gilbert, op cit, Vol VII, p. 499.
123. Ibid.
124. ROSK 5/125, letter to S. W. Roskill from Ludovic Kennedy (then in HMS *Tartar*, one of the destroyers concerned), 9 February 1975.
125. ROSK 5/125, letter from Admiral Sir Ralph Edwards to S. W. Roskill, 4 August 1954.
126. Admiral J. H. Godfrey, cited in ROSK 5/125.
127. ROSK 4/79, photocopy of letter of 7 March 1942.
128. ROSK 4/124, letter to S. W. Roskill from Admiral Sir Ralph Edwards, 28 July 1954.
129. Churchill, *The Second World War*, op cit, Vol V, p. 146.
130. Ibid, p. 145.
131. Lenton and Colledge, op cit, p. 155.
132. ADM 234/349–50, TIRPITZ: An account of the various attacks carried out by the British Armed Forces and their effect upon the German battleship. Vol I, Report and Appendices (1948). Vol II, Evidence for Detailed Accounts of Damage. The following account of 'Operation Source' is drawn from ADM 234/347, B.S. No. 29. Attack on the *Tirpitz* by Midget Submarines, 22 September 1943; C. E. T. Warren and J. Benson, *Above Us the Waves*, London, Harrap, 1953, Chapters XIV–XVII; Hinsley, op cit, Vol III, Part 1, pp. 258–62.
133. Hinsley, op cit, Vol III, Part 1, p. 258.
134. Hinsley, op cit, Vol III, Part 1, p. 261.
135. Ibid.
136. See AIR 41/48 for a full account of the *Lützow* episode. Also Hinsley, op cit, Vol III, Part 1, pp. 256–8.
137. See AIR 41/48.
138. Terraine, *The Right of the Line*, op cit, pp. 549–58; Max Hastings, *Bomber Command*, London, Michael Joseph 1979, pp. 237–69; Webster and Frankland, *The Strategic Air Offensive Against Germany 1939–1945*, op cit, Vol II, pp. 191–211, and 268.
139. ADM 234/369, p. 108 et seq.
140. ROSK 5/77, photocopy of brief prepared for Captain Roskill by Foreign Documents Section of the Cabinet Office Historical Section;

FDS 109/56: 'Background Information on the Circumstances Leading to *Scharnhorst*'s Last Operation – source: German Naval Archives.'

141. Ibid.
142. Ibid.
143. Ibid.
144. Bekker, *Hitler's Naval War*, op cit, p. 346.
145. Ibid.
146. Ibid, p. 349.
147. ROSK 5/77, FDS 109/56.
148. Ibid.
149. Grove, Chant, Lyon and Lyon, *The Hardware of World War II*, op cit, p. 145.
150. Parkes, *British Battleships; A History of Design, Construction and Armament*, op cit, p. 663.
151. Hinsley, op cit, Vol III, Part 1, pp. 267–8.
152. Ibid, p. 266.
153. Ibid.
154. The following operational account of the destruction of the *Scharnhorst* is based on ADM 234/343, BS No. 24, Sinking of the *Scharnhorst*.
155. ROSK 5/77, photocopy of letter from Captain A. G. F. Ditcham to John Winton, 10 November 1984.
156. Ibid.
157. Ibid.
158. Hinsley, op cit, Vol III, Part 1, p. 274.
159. The following account of Fleet Air Arm attacks on the *Tirpitz* is based on ADM 234/349–50, ADM 234/345, BS No. 27, Naval Attacks on *Tirpitz*.
160. Weale, Weale and Barker, *Combat Aircraft of World War Two*, op cit, p. 140.
161. Ibid, p. 200.
162. See ROSK 5/142, photocopy of translation of German reports on F.A.A. attacks on the *Tirpitz*, prepared by the Naval Intelligence Department, January 1946.
163. Ibid.
164. See ibid, translation of German damage report giving details of damage hit by hit.
165. See ADM 234/349–50, pp. 10–13.
166. ROSK 5/142, German reports.
167. See also ADM 234/349, pp. 11–13; ADM 234/350, pp. 85–92.
168. ADM 234/369, p. 133.
169. ADM 234/369, p. 124.
170. Lenton and Colledge, op cit, p. 73.
171. ADM 234/369, p. 124.
172. Despatch quoted ADM 234/369, p. 72, Footnote 5.
173. Ibid, p. 129.

Part IV: Victory

24. *'Neptune': Problems, Puzzles and Personalities* (pages 753–780)

1. Cited in Roskill, *Churchill and the Admirals*, op cit, p. 233.
2. Cf Max Hastings, *Overlord: D-Day and the Battle of Normandy 1944*, London, Michael Joseph, 1974; Carlo D'Este, *Decision in Normandy; the Unwritten Story of Montgomery and the Allied Campaign*, London, Collins, 1983.
3. The following account of Intelligence with regard to invasion preparations up to the end of 1943 is based on Hinsley, *British Intelligence in the Second World War*, op cit, Vol III, Part 2, pp. 10–19.
4. Cf Philip Ziegler, *Mountbatten; the Official Biography*, op cit, pp. 177–9.
5. Ibid, p. 213.
6. Ibid, pp. 213–15.
7. CP 216, cited in ROSK 5/121, brief prepared for Captain Roskill as official naval historian on 'The Artificial Harbours and Breakwaters up to D-Day'. The following account of the evolution of the artificial harbours is based on this brief unless otherwise cited.
8. Quoted in ROSK 5/121, brief cited.
9. Ibid.
10. Cf Ziegler, op cit, pp. 207–8; ROSK 5/121, brief cited.
11. COS(44)1st(O), quoted in ROSK 5/121, brief cited.
12. The following account of 'Pluto' is based on ROSK 5/121, 'A Brief Account of Operation Pluto', a brief prepared for Captain Roskill.
13. ROSK 5/122, summary of Cs-in-C's reports on 'Neptune' prepared for Captain Roskill by the Naval Historical Branch.
14. Report on 'Neptune', 2865 Ply 1486 of 4.8.1944, Enclosure 2, as summarised in ROSK 5/122.
15. Ibid.
16. RMSY 8/22. Lecture on Combined Operations, written in late summer 1943, but here as re-drafted for publication in 1948 in CB.04211, 'Fighting Experience'.
17. D'Este, *Decision in Normandy*, op cit, pp. 55–6, Footnotes 2 and 3, p. 56.
18. Montgomery of Alamein, *Memoirs*, London, Collins, 1958, pp. 205, 210–12.
19. RMSY 8/26, diary for 1944.
20. RMSY 8/27A, letter of 4 January 1944.
21. Ibid.
22. Cited in Chalmers, *Full Cycle*, op cit, p. 182.
23. Chandler (editor), *The Papers of Dwight D. Eisenhower*, op cit, Vol III, p. 880 and Footnote 1.
24. RMSY 8/27A, letter to his wife, 11 January 1944. It must be repeated that the quotations from Ramsay's diary and letters in Chalmers's

biography, *Full Cycle*, are unreliable, for Chalmers confuses extracts from each source and edits out material from quotations without indicating the omissions.

25. RMSY 8/27A, letter to wife, 6 January 1944.
26. Ibid.
27. RMSY 8/26, diary for 5 January 1944.
28. Ibid, diary for 6 January 1944.
29. Ibid.
30. John Ehrman, *Grand Strategy*, Vol V, London, HMSO, 1956, p. 233.
31. RMSY 8/26, diary for 6 January 1944.
32. Ehrman, op cit, Vol V, p. 234.
33. RMSY 8/26, 7 January 1944.
34. Ibid, 8 January 1944.
35. Ibid, 10 January 1944.
36. Ibid, 12 January 1944.
37. Ibid, diary for 15 January 1944.
38. Ibid, 17 January 1944.
39. Chandler (ed), op cit, Vol III, pp. 1673–4.
40. RMSY 8/26, diary for 26 January 1944.
41. Ibid, diary for 4 February 1944.
42. Ibid, diary for 14 February 1944.
43. Ibid, diary for 21 February 1944.
44. Ibid.
45. Ibid, 22 February.
46. Chandler (ed), op cit, Vol III, p. 1763.
47. Cf RMSY 8/26, Ramsay's diary for 6 March 1944.
48. Chandler (ed), op cit, Vol III, p. 1763.
49. Ibid.
50. Ibid, signal of 20 March 1944.
51. Ehrman, op cit, Vol V, p. 247.
52. RMSY 8/26, diary for 7 March 1944.
53. Ibid, diary for 26 January 1944; ROSK 5/118, photocopy from First Sea Lord's Papers, Vol 34, statement of Naval Forces to be made available for 'Neptune', memorandum from First Sea Lord to Prime Minister, 18 March 1944.
54. RMSY 8/26, 7 March 1944.
55. All ROSK 5/121; brief on 'Neptune' prepared for Captain Roskill, and based on First Sea Lord's Papers, Vol 32.
56. ROSK 5/121, document cited.
57. ROSK 5/32, xerox of Paper P.P.O. 01014/42 of 26 December 1942, 'Naval Shipbuilding: Policy for the Present War'.
58. Roskill, *War at Sea*, op cit, Vol III, Part II, Appendix S, pp. 436–7.
59. Chandler (ed), op cit, Vol III, pp. 1723–4; ROSK 5/121.
60. RMSY 6/26, diary for 17 February 1944.
61. RMSY 8/26, diary for 14 January 1944.

62. Ibid, diary for 6 May 1944.
63. Ibid, diary for 11 January 1944.
64. Ibid, diary for 3 March 1944.
65. Ibid, 11 January 1944.
66. Ibid, diary for 8 March 1944.
67. Ibid.
68. Hinsley, op cit, Vol III, Part 2, pp. 32–3; the following account of Intelligence during the preparation of 'Neptune' is drawn from this volume, pp. 17–100, unless otherwise cited.
69. Ibid, p. 35.
70. Ibid, pp. 76–7.
71. Ibid, p. 77.
72. Ibid, p. 38.
73. Ibid, p. 92.
74. RMSY 8/26, diary for 14 May 1944.
75. Hinsley, op cit, Vol III, Part 2, p. 50.
76. Ibid, p. 96.
77. RMSY 8/26, diary for 24 March 1944.
78. Hinsley, op cit, Vol III, Part 2, p. 88.
79. ROSK 5/120.
80. Ibid.
81. ANCXF's Report, Vol I, p. 5, cited in ADM 234/366, BS No. 39, Operation 'Neptune'; landings in Normandy, June, 1944 (1947), p. 13.
82. RMSY 8/27A, letter to his wife, 24 April 1944.
83. Ibid.
84. Ibid.
85. Ibid, letter of 1 May 1944.
86. Cited in Chalmers, op cit, p. 206.
87. Montgomery's speaking notes, cited in D'Este, *Decision in Normandy*, op cit, p. 74.
88. Ibid.
89. Ibid, p. 76.
90. RMSY 8/27A.
91. Ibid.
92. Ibid.

25. *'A Never Surpassed Masterpiece of Planning'* (pages 781–809)

1. The summary of 'Operation Neptune – Naval Orders' is drawn from the Orders themselves, as are all quotations unless otherwise cited. The copy consulted is held in the Naval Historical Branch.
2. Ibid.
3. See Hinsley, *British Intelligence in the Second World War*, op cit, Vol III, Part 2, pp. 47–9.
4. Ibid.

5. Report by ANCXF, Vol I, p. 94, quoted in ADM 234/366, p. 57, Footnote 2.
6. ADM 234/366, pp. 49–53.
7. ADM 234/366, p. 49, Footnote 1, citing ANCXF Report, Vol 3, p. 6.
8. Ibid, p. 51.
9. Ibid, p. 53.
10. ADM 234/366, p. 23.
11. ADM 234/366, p. 54, Footnote 1, citing ANCXF Report, Vol I, p. 28: see also RMSY 8/26, diary for 26–28 February 1944.
12. ADM 234/366, p. 54, Footnote 1.
13. 'Operation Neptune – Naval Orders', ON9.
14. Webster and Frankland, *Strategic Air Offensive Against Germany*, op cit, Vol II, pp. 22–31; Terraine, *The Right of the Line*, op cit, pp. 542–5.
15. Hastings, *Bomber Command*, op cit, pp. 261–9; Terraine, op cit, pp. 556–8.
16. See Terraine, op cit, pp. 619–20; Hastings, op cit, pp. 269–71.
17. Ehrman, *Grand Strategy*, op cit, Vol V, pp. 292–7.
18. ADM 234/366, p. 57.
19. ADM 234/366, p. 60.
20. RMSY 8/26, diary for 3 February 1944.
21. ADM 234/366, pp. 30–1.
22. ADM 234/366, p. 62, Footnote 3.
23. Ibid, p. 62, quoting ANCXF Report, Vol I, pp. 27–8.
24. ADM 234/366, p. 31, quoting ANCXF Report, Vol I, p. 28.
25. ADM 234/366, p. 64.
26. Ibid, p. 64.
27. RMSY 8/26, diary for 27 April 1944.
28. ADM 234/366, p. 65.
29. RMSY 8/26, 2 and 3 May 1944; see also ADM 234/366, p. 66.
30. ADM 234/366, p. 68.
31. Ibid, citing ANCXF Report, Vol I, pp. 6, 27.
32. Ibid, p. 68.
33. Hinsley, op cit, Vol III, Part 2, p. 89.
34. RMSY 8/26, diary for 1–2 May 1944.
35. ADM 234/366, p. 69.
36. RMSY 8/26, diary for 29 April 1944.
37. RMSY 8/27A, letter of 11 May 1944.
38. Ibid, letter to his wife 26 May 1944.
39. Ibid, letter of 29 May 1944.
40. ADM 234/366, p. 70.
41. Cited in ibid, p. 72.
42. Eisenhower, *Report by the Supreme Commander to the Combined Chiefs of Staff on the Operations in Europe of the Allied Expeditionary Force, 6 June 1944 to 8 May 1945*, London, HMSO, 1946, p. 11.
43. CAB 98/40 series: Overlord Preparations Committee and Sub-Committees.

44. See ADM 234/578, pp. 113–18; ROSK 5/24, 'U-boat AA Weapons', brief for Captain Roskill by Foreign Documents Section, Cabinet Office Historical Section, 12 May 1955.
45. ADM 234/578, p. 118.
46. Ibid.
47. Ibid, p. 121.
48. Dönitz, *Memoirs*, op cit, pp. 354, 424–5.
49. Ibid, pp. 265–6.
50. ROSK 5/19, brief for Captain Roskill on Walter U-boats by the Foreign Documents Section, Cabinet Office Historical Section, 12 May 1955.
51. Hinsley, op cit, Vol III, Part 2, p. 156.
52. Dönitz, op cit, pp. 356–7.
53. Ibid, p. 420.
54. Hinsley, op cit, Vol III, Part 2, p. 99.
55. RMSY 8/26, diary for 31 May 1944.
56. ROSK 5/121, citing ANCXF Report.
57. Hinsley, op cit, Vol III, Part 2, p. 94.
58. Ibid.
59. Ibid, Appendix 10, p. 830.
60. Ibid, p. 834.
61. Ibid, p. 81.
62. Ibid.
63. RMSY 8/26, diary for 26 May 1944.
64. ADM 234/366, p. 71, Footnote 4.
65. Ibid, p. 85.
66. ADM 234/366, p. 71, Footnote 2.
67. RMSY 8/26, diary for 30 May 1944.
68. Ibid.
69. ADM 234/366, p. 72.
70. RMSY 8/26, diary for 1 June 1944.
71. ADM 234/366, p. 72.
72. RMSY 8/26, diary for 2 June 1944.
73. RMSY 8/26, diary for 3 June 1944.
74. Ibid.
75. Ibid.
76. Ibid, 4 June 1944.
77. ADM 234/366, p. 75, citing ANCXF Report, Vol I, p. 10.
78. Montgomery, *Memoirs*, op cit, p. 248.
79. L. F. Ellis, *Victory in the West*, Vol I, London, HMSO, 1962, p. 143.
80. RMSY 8/26, diary for 4 June 1944.
81. Ibid.
82. Roskill, *War at Sea*, op cit, Vol III, Part II, pp. 39–40.
83. RMSY 8/26, diary for 5 June 1944.

26. 'This Great Enterprise': 'Operation Neptune' (pages 810–838)

1. The following account of the landing of 'Operation Neptune' on 5–6 June is based on ADM 234/366, pp. 78–105; Ellis, *Victory in the West*, op cit, Vol I, pp. 160–222; Roskill, *War at Sea*, op cit, Vol III, Part II, pp. 41–59; Morison, *History of United States Naval Operations in World War II*, op cit, Vol XI, pp. 77–153.
2. Cited in Roskill, *War at Sea*, op cit, Vol III, Part II, p. 41, Footnote 2.
3. Ellis, op cit, Vol I, pp. 222–3.
4. ADM 234/366, p. 86, citing ANCXF Report, Vol I, p. 10.
5. ROSK 5/121, brief on 'Neptune' preparations for Captain Roskill by the Naval Historical Branch.
6. ADM 234/366, p. 87, citing ANCXF Report, Vol I, p. 58.
7. ROSK 5/121, brief for Captain Roskill on preparations for D-Day, Appendix.
8. For this reason and because of prior coverage in this book of 'Operation Neptune – Naval Orders', the account of D-Day which follows is not exhaustive.
9. ROSK 5/119, photocopy of Letter of Proceedings to Rear-Admiral Commanding Second Cruiser Squadron from the Commanding Officer of HMS *Warspite*, 16 June 1944.
10. ADM 234/366, p. 74, citing ANCXF Report, Vol I, p. 11.
11. The following summary of D-Day bombardments is based on ROSK 5/119, 'Naval Bombardment in Neptune', brief prepared for Captain Roskill by the Naval Historical Branch.
12. Morison, op cit, Vol XI, p. 124.
13. ROSK 5/119, 'Naval Bombardment in Neptune'.
14. ROSK 5/119, letter to Captain Roskill by Vice-Admiral M. H. A. Kelsey, 12 September 1955. Kelsey as Captain of the *Warspite* had witnessed American shooting from aboard a US cruiser when *Warspite* was ordered to support the Americans on 7 June because they were running low on ammunition, owing to such wasteful practices as ranging with eight-gun salvoes.
15. Ellis, op cit, Vol I, p. 187, citing official reports by Kirk and Hall.
16. ADM 234/366, pp. 91–3; Morison, op cit, Vol XI, p. 102.
17. ADM 234/366, pp. 93–7; Morison, op cit, Vol XI, pp. 130–51.
18. Cf Admiral Hall's subsequent report, cited in Ellis, op cit, Vol I, p. 191.
19. See Hastings, *Overlord: D-Day and the Battle of Normandy*, op cit, pp. 90–102.
20. Cited in ADM 234/366.
21. See ibid, pp. 97–9 for Force G's D-Day operations.
22. Cited in ibid, p. 51.
23. See ADM 234/366, pp. 99–102 for operations on 'Juno'.
24. Cited in Ellis, op cit, Vol I, p. 180.
25. ADM 234/366, pp. 102–5.

26. See D'Este, *Decision in Normandy*, op cit, p. 127.
27. See ibid, Chapter 8, for an account of 3rd Division's D-Day.
28. Cited in ROSK 5/119, 'Naval Bombardment in Neptune'.
29. Ibid, citing report of the Naval Commander, Force S.
30. Ellis, op cit, Vol I, p. 22; Roskill, *War at Sea*, op cit, Vol III, Part II, p. 51.
31. Ibid.
32. Chandler (ed), *The Papers of Dwight D. Eisenhower*, op cit, Vol II, p. 1908.
33. ADM 234/366.
34. RMSY 8/26, diary for 8 June 1944.
35. ROSK 5/120, brief for Captain Roskill by the Naval Historical Branch.
36. Ellis, op cit, Vol I, p. 217.
37. RMSY 8/26, diary for 7 June 1944.
38. Morison, op cit, Vol XI, pp. 164–5.
39. Cited in ibid, p. 165.
40. RMSY 8/27A, letter of 8 June 1944.
41. Ibid.
42. RMSY 8/26, diary for 7 June 1944.
43. RMSY 8/27A, letter of 8 June 1944.
44. ADM 234/366, pp. 119–20.
45. ADM 234/366, p. 119 citing ANCXF Report, Vol I, p. 95.
46. Eisenhower, *Supreme Commander's Report*, op cit, p. 32.
47. Ibid, p. 72.
48. Cited in Hinsley, *British Intelligence in the Second World War*, Vol III, Part 3, p. 165.
49. Ibid, p. 162.
50. Cited in ROSK 5/120, Summary of account by Captain Jones, RN, commanding 10th Destroyer Flotilla, covering the night action off French coast with four German destroyers on the night of 8/9 June 1944; eyewitness information from Admiral of the Fleet Lord Lewin, then serving in HMS *Ashanti*.
51. Ibid.
52. Ibid; ADM 234/366, p. 112.
53. Hinsley, op cit, Vol III, Part 3, pp. 154–61.
54. ADM 234/366, pp. 136–7.
55. Terraine, *Business in Great Waters*, London, Leo Cooper, 1989, p. 647.
56. Ibid; ADM 234/366.
57. Ellis, op cit, Vol I, map opposite p. 262.
58. Cited in ibid.
59. Roskill, *War at Sea*, op cit, Vol III, Part II, p. 62.
60. ADM 223/163, Admiralty Weekly Intelligence Report No. 226, 'Gale off Normandy'; see ADM 234/366, pp. 139–40 for account of the gale.
61. ADM 223/163, WIR No. 226.

62. Ellis, op cit, Vol I, p. 274.
63. RMSY 8/26, diary for 23 June 1944.
64. Ibid.
65. Cf Ellis, op cit, Vol I, pp. 274 and 301.
66. ADM 234/366, pp. 141–2.
67. ADM 234/363, BS No. 49, The Campaign in North-West Europe, June 1944–May 1945 (1952), p. 3.
68. RMSY 8/26, diary for 30 July 1944.

27. *Victory in Europe* (pages 839–859)

1. Morison, *History of United States Naval Operations in World War II*, op cit, Vol XI, pp. 198–205.
2. Ibid, pp. 205–10.
3. RMSY 8/26, diary for 6 July 1944.
4. Morison, op cit, Vol XI, p. 218.
5. Cited in ROSK 5/121, A Brief Account of Operation Pluto.
6. See Roskill, *War at Sea*, op cit, Vol III, Part II, Appendix W, p. 454 for details.
7. ADM 234/363, B.S. No. 49, pp. 5–11.
8. Roskill, *War at Sea*, op cit, Vol III, Part II, pp. 126–8.
9. Churchill, *The Second World War*, op cit, Vol VI, p. 61.
10. RMSY 8/27A, letter to his wife, 5 August 1944.
11. RMSY 8/26, diary for 5 August 1944.
12. RMSY 8/27A.
13. See Gilbert, *Winston S. Churchill*, op cit, Vol VII, pp. 875–81; Chandler (ed), *The Papers of Dwight D. Eisenhower*, op cit, Vol IV, pp. 2055–6.
14. Chandler (ed), op cit, Vol IV, p. 2103, letter from Eisenhower to Combined Chiefs of Staff, 30 August 1944.
15. Ellis, *Victory in the West*, op cit, Vol I, p. 478.
16. Roskill, *War at Sea*, op cit, Vol III, Part II, pp. 130–4.
17. Chandler (ed), op cit, Vol IV, p. 2136.
18. Ellis, op cit, Vol II, p. 132.
19. Ibid.
20. ADM 234/363, pp. 33–4.
21. Ibid, pp. 21–2.
22. Ibid.
23. RMSY 8/26, diary for 4 September 1944.
24. Cited in Ellis, op cit, Vol II, p. 5.
25. Chandler (ed), op cit, Vol IV, p. 2130.
26. See Ellis, op cit, Vol II, pp. 9–10, 16–19, 23, 25–7.
27. Ibid, p. 25.
28. Ibid, p. 27.
29. Ibid.
30. See ibid, pp. 133 and 135.
31. RMSY 8/26, diary for 5 October 1944.

32. Ibid, 8 October 1944.
33. Ellis, op cit, Vol II, p. 84.
34. Chandler (ed), op cit, Vol IV, p. 2215.
35. Ellis, op cit, Vol II, pp. 91–2.
36. See ibid, pp. 83–4.
37. Ibid.
38. Ibid, p. 113.
39. The following summary of the Walcheren campaign is drawn from ADM 234/363, pp. 46–53; Ellis, op cit, Vol II, pp. 113–23.
40. ADM 234/363, pp. 53–4.
41. Ellis, op cit, Vol II, p. 127.
42. Ibid, p. 135.
43. Ibid, Appendix VII, p. 408.
44. Behrens, *Merchant Shipping and the Demands of War*, op cit, p. 398 and Footnote 3.
45. Even the 'lock-up' element in the Mediterranean total came to nearly 1 million tons. Ibid, p. 391, Footnotes 1 and 2.
46. Roskill, *War at Sea*, op cit, Vol III, Part II, p. 279, Table 35.
47. See Dr Marc Milner, 'The Dawn of Modern Anti-Submarine Warfare; Allied Responses to the U-boats, 1944–5' in the *RUSI Journal*, Vol 134, No. 1, pp. 61–8, for an illuminating discussion of new technology and its effect on operations.
48. ROSK 5/118, citing First Sea Lord's papers.
49. ROSK 5/25; see also ibid, copy of letter from the First Sea Lord to the C-in-C, British Pacific Fleet, 19 January 1945.
50. Roskill, *War at Sea*, op cit, Vol III, Part II, p. 287, Table 37 and p. 289; see also ROSK 5/25, Tables I, II and III, and summary by the Cabinet Office Historical Section of escort forces as on 1 January 1945, prepared for Captain Roskill.
51. Roskill, *War at Sea*, op cit, Vol III, Part II, p. 185.
52. Dönitz, *Memoirs*, op cit, p. 425.
53. Roskill, *War at Sea*, op cit, Vol III, Part II, p. 285.
54. Milner, article cited.
55. Hinsley, *British Intelligence in the Second World War*, op cit, Vol III, Part 2, pp. 474–87.
56. Ibid, p. 481.
57. CAB 80/90, COS(45)14(O), A Forecast of the Results of the U-Boat Campaign during 1945. Memorandum by the First Sea Lord.
58. Terraine, *Business in Great Waters*, op cit, p. 655.
59. Dönitz, op cit, p. 428.
60. Roskill, *War at Sea*, op cit, Vol III, Part II, p. 301.
61. Ibid, Appendix Y, pp. 467–8.
62. Ibid.
63. Ibid, Appendix Z, pp. 477–8.
64. Ellis, op cit, Vol I, p. 339.

65. ROSK 5/19, 'Walter U-boats – Situation at the end of the War', brief prepared for Captain Roskill by Foreign Documents Section, 12 May 1955; Roskill, *War at Sea*, op cit, Vol III, Part II, pp. 302–3.
66. In 1939–45 the Royal Navy was more stretched and in danger of losing control altogether of vital sea areas, England herself in far worse peril of extinction, than even during the American War of Independence, 1778–1783.
67. Roskill, *War at Sea*, op cit, Vol III, Part II, p. 305, Footnote 2.
68. Ibid; air force figures supplied by the Air Historical Branch.

28. *To Restore an Empire* (pages 860–898)

1. See Morison, *History of United States Naval Operations in World War II*, op cit, Vol IV, pp. 3–65, for an account of the Battle of the Coral Sea.
2. See Morison, op cit, Vol IV, pp. 69–156, for an account of the Battle of Midway.
3. Roskill, *War at Sea*, op cit, Vol II, p. 23.
4. SMVL 3/27, letter to his wife, 22 February 1942.
5. Ibid, letter to his wife, 2 March 1942.
6. Ibid, letter of 13 March 1943.
7. SMVL 8/1, letter to the First Sea Lord, 11 March 1942.
8. Ibid.
9. Ibid, letter to First Sea Lord, 15 July 1942.
10. SMVL 3/27, letter to his wife, 6 April 1942.
11. Ibid.
12. Cited in Roskill, *War at Sea*, op cit, Vol II, p. 29.
13. Churchill, *The Second World War*, op cit, Vol IV, p. 202.
14. ADM 234/331, BS No. 16, Naval Operations at the Capture of Diego Suarez (Operation 'Ironclad'), May 1942 (1943). See also ROSK 5/91.
15. ADM 234/331.
16. Churchill, *The Second World War*, op cit, Vol IV, p. 202.
17. Cited in Gilbert, *Winston S. Churchill*, op cit, Vol VII, p. 146.
18. Roskill, *War at Sea*, op cit, Vol III, Part I, pp. 213–14.
19. SMVL 8/1, letter to First Sea Lord, 11 March 1943.
20. See ROSK 5/57, for Captain Roskill's postwar correspondence with Cunningham, Brooke, Portal and Mountbatten on the subject, as also for photocopies of correspondence between Somerville and Cunningham in 1943–4.
21. Ibid; but also see SMVL 8/2, letters from Somerville to First Sea Lord, 1943–4.
22. See Ehrman, *Grand Strategy*, op cit, Vol V, pp. 152–3.
23. See Shelford Bidwell, *The Chindit War: the Campaign in Burma 1944*, London, Hodder and Stoughton, 1979, *passim*.
24. ADM 234/377, Naval Staff History, Second World War: *War with*

Japan. Vol IV, The South-East Asia Operations and Central Pacific Advance (1959). See p. 203 for sinking of *Kuma* and *Kitagami*.

25. Ibid, pp. 209–11.
26. Ibid, p. 213.
27. SMVL 8/2, letter of 27 July 1944. For an account of the attack on Sabang, see ADM 234/377, pp. 215–16.
28. Morison, op cit, Vol VIII, pp. 213–319.
29. Ibid.
30. Ehrman, op cit, Vol V, p. 422.
31. Ibid, p. 424.
32. Ibid, p. 427.
33. Cited in Fraser, *Alanbrooke*, op cit, p. 412.
34. Cited in ibid, pp. 413–14.
35. Cited in Ehrman, op cit, Vol V, p. 451.
36. Ibid, p. 449.
37. Cf ibid, p. 438 and pp. 477–8.
38. Both are quoted in full in Ehrman, Vol V, pp. 441–9.
39. Cited in Fraser, op cit, p. 416.
40. See CAB 79/79, COS(44) 264th–269th (O), 8–9 August 1944. Quotation is from CAB 79/79, COS(44) 269th (O).
41. Cited in Gilbert, op cit, Vol VII, pp. 957–8.
42. The session is quoted in full in Ehrman, op cit, Vol V, pp. 520–3.
43. Ibid, p. 523.
44. See ROSK 5/129, photocopy of memorandum from First Lord to Prime Minister on 'Command and Redeployment of the Fleet in Far Eastern Waters', 25 October 1944, in First Sea Lord's papers Vol 34; and signal from Prime Minister to Prime Minister of Australia, 8 November 1944.
45. SMVL 8/A, letter of 6 May 1944.
46. ROSK 5/129, First Lord to Prime Minister: 'Command and Redeployment of the Fleet in Far Eastern Waters', 25 October 1944.
47. ROSK 5/129, Admiral of the Fleet Lord Fraser of the North Cape to Captain Roskill, 20 May 1959.
48. Ehrman, op cit, Vol V, pp. 477–8.
49. Cited in Ehrman, op cit, Vol V, pp. 477–8; see also Behrens, *Merchant Shipping and the Demands of War*, op cit, Chapter XIX.
50. Ehrman, op cit, Vol V, p. 477.
51. Roskill, *War at Sea*, op cit, Vol III, Part II, p. 343.
52. Morison, op cit, Vol XIV, Appendix 1, pp. 382–5.
53. Roskill, *War at Sea*, op cit, Vol III, Part II, Appendix S, pp. 436–7.
54. Ibid, Vol II, Appendix B, p. 449.
55. Cf ibid, Vol I, Appendix D, pp. 577–9 and Vol III, Part II, Appendix S, pp. 436–7.
56. Fleet Admiral Ernest J. King, *U.S. Navy at War 1941–45: Official Reports to the Secretary of the Navy*, Washington, United States Navy Department, 1946, Appendix B, pp. 252–7.

57. Lenton and Colledge, *Warships of World War II*, op cit, pp. 64–73; ROSK 5/25, brief prepared for Captain Roskill by the Admiralty Historical Section, 1956; H. Duncan Hall, *North American Supply*, London, HMSO and Longmans, Green, 1955, pp. 400–1.
58. Barnett, *The Audit of War*, op cit, p. 40.
59. R. C. K. Ensor, *England 1870–1914*, Oxford, Clarendon Press, 1966, p. 104.
60. Barnett, *The Audit of War*, op cit, p. 401; Hall, op cit, p. 445.
61. Hall, op cit, pp. 401 and 403.
62. Ibid, p. 424.
63. Ibid, p. 425.
64. ADM 234/377, Naval Staff History, Second World War; *War With Japan*, op cit, Vol IV, The South-East Asia Operations and Central Pacific Advance (1957), p. 19.
65. Ibid, pp. 21–2.
66. Ibid.
67. Morison, op cit, Vol XIV, Appendix I, pp. 382–5.
68. Ibid; ROSK 5/129, brief prepared for Captain Roskill on 'The Pacific April–June 1945'. See also ADM 234/379, Naval Staff History, *War with Japan*, op cit, Vol VI, Advance to Japan, when it is opened to the public in 1992.
69. Ibid.
70. Weale, Weale and Barker, *Combat Aircraft of World War Two*, op cit, pp. 141, 200, 211.
71. ADM 205/18, Memorandum by the Chief of Naval Air Services, 14 October 1942.
72. ROSK 5/129, Statistics of B.P.F. in Iceberg, taken from M. 07991/ 45 in W.H.S. 9251. See also ADM 199/555, The British Pacific Fleet in Iceberg, and ADM 234/368, BS No. 47: Naval operations in the assault and capture of Okinawa, March–June 1945, Operation 'Iceberg' (1958).
73. ROSK 7/29, the history of 'The Flyplane Electric Predictor System – A Brief Account of its History and Application', by Mr Humphrey Nelson, sent to Captain Roskill on 23 July 1978.
74. Ibid.
75. Ibid.
76. Clausen Papers, Churchill Archives Centre, CLSN 1/2, 'The American Position with Power Control for Gunnery Purposes: Report on a Visit to the US and on some matters arising', by J. M. Ford, Superintending Scientist, Admiralty Research Laboratory, July 1943.
77. Ibid; 'Impressions of a Visit to America, August and September 1944' by Hugh Clausen.
78. Ibid.
79. CLSN 1/2 and 1/3; see also letter from Captain Roskill, a radar and gunnery expert, to Rear-Admiral M. W. St L. Searle, 11 May 1978 in ROSK 7/29.

80. Cf Logistic Support Groups, Fifth Fleet, in Morison, op cit, Vol XIV, Appendix 1, pp. 386–8.
81. For a summary of the history of the British Fleet Train, see ROSK 5/129, 'The Fleet Train', a brief prepared for Captain Roskill by the Naval Historical Branch. The relevant contemporary detailed files are in ADM 199/1740–69.
82. Vian, *Action this Day*, op cit, p. 175.
83. ADM 234/118, 1319/BPF/1780/OPS, Despatch on Operations from 22 November 1944 to Middle of July 1945, dated 23 November 1945, p. 12.
84. ROSK 5/129.
85. Cf N. M. Rodger, *The Wooden World; An Anatomy of the Georgian Navy*, London, Fontana Press, 1986, *passim* but especially Chapter III.
86. Morison, op cit, Vol XIV, p. 282.
87. Ibid.
88. Ibid, chart on p. 207.
89. The following summary of 'Iceberg' is based on ROSK 5/129, 'The Pacific April–June 1945', prepared for Captain Roskill. See also ADM 234/368 and ADM 199/555.
90. Morison, op cit, Vol XIV, p. 250; Grove, Chant, Lyon and Lyon, *The Hardware of World War II*, op cit, p. 206.
91. ROSK 5/129, Note for Captain Roskill, 'Statistics of B.P.F. in Iceberg', taken from M.07991/45 in W.H.S. 9251; see also ibid, 'Statistics on B.P.F. in Iceberg', taken from C.B.3301 (draft), Chapter XV, pp. 343–4, which gives slightly different figures.
92. The summary of British surface and submarine operations in South-East Asian waters in summer 1945 is drawn from ADM 234/377, Naval Staff History, *War with Japan*, op cit, Vol IV, The South-East Asia Operations and Central Pacific Advance (1957), pp. 16–20.
93. The account of the exploits of the X-Craft at Singapore and off Saigon and Hong Kong is drawn from ADM 234/382, Naval Staff History, *Submarines*, Vol III, Operation in Far Eastern Waters, Including the Operations of Allied Submarines (1950), pp. 111–12.
94. Roskill, *War at Sea*, op cit, Vol III, Part II, p. 374.
95. Cited in ibid, p. 375.
96. ADM 234/378, Naval Staff History, *War with Japan*, op cit, Vol V, The Blockade of Japan, pp. 100, 102 and Tables 13, 13A, B and C; J. F. C. Fuller, *The Second World War 1939–45*, London, Eyre and Spottiswoode, 1962, pp. 386 and 390; B. H. Liddell Hart, *History of the Second World War*, London, Cassell, 1970, pp. 682–3.
97. The account of the surrender ceremony aboard USS *Missouri* is drawn from Morison, op cit, Vol XIV, pp. 363–70.
98. Cited in Morison, op cit, Vol XIV, p. 365.
99. Roskill, *War at Sea*, op cit, Vol III, Part II, p. 378; see also ROSK 6/58, notes from Admiral Rawlings to Captain Roskill on the draft of *War at Sea*, op cit, Vol III, Chapter VII.

100. Ibid, p. 382.
101. Ibid, p. 383.
102. Vice Admiral T. S. Wilkinson to his wife, 2 September 1945, cited in Morison, op cit, Vol XIV, p. 369. After being later widowed, she married Admiral Sir Harry Moore of the Royal Navy.

Bibliography

I UNPUBLISHED SOURCES

1. *Public Record Office*

a. Admiralty (ADM series)
ADM 1   Admiralty and Secretariat Records (selected files)
ADM 53   Ships' Logs
ADM 116   Admiralty and Secretariat Records (selected files)
ADM 186 series: Naval Staff History; Battle Summaries (BS):
ADM 186/795   BS No 44, 'The Battle of Cape Matapan, 28 March 1941'
ADM 186/797   BS No 7, 'The Bombardment of Genoa 9 February 1941'
ADM 186/797   BS No 19, 'The Bombardment of Tripoli 21 April 1941'
ADM 186/799   *Home Waters and the Atlantic*, Vol I, *September 1939–April 1940*
ADM 186/801   Naval Staff Narrative, *Mediterranean, November 1940–December 1941*
ADM 186/802   German Naval History, *The U-boat War in the Atlantic*
ADM 186/803   BS No. 11, 'The Passage of the *Scharnhorst, Gneisenau* and *Prinz Eugen* through the English Channel, 12th February 1942' (1948)
ADM 199 series   War History Cases and Papers (selected files)
ADM 205 series   First Sea Lord's Papers
ADM 234 series: Naval Staff History: Narratives and Battle Summaries:

ADM 234/118   Despatch on Operations [of the British Pacific Fleet] from 22 November 1944 to Middle of July, 1945, dated 23 November 1945

ADM 234/241   Anti-U-boat Operations

ADM 234/320   BS No 4, 'Naval Operations of the Battle of Crete, 20th May to 1st June 1941' (1952)

ADM 234/322   Battle Summary No 5, 'The Chase and Sinking of the German Battleship "Bismarck", May 23–27, 1941, according to information up to November 1948'

ADM 234/324   'Disguised Raiders 1940–1'

ADM 234/325   BS No 10, 'Mediterranean Operations, 4th to 14th November 1940. Air Attack on Taranto, 11th November 1940' (1943)

ADM 234/330   BS No 14 (Revised), 'Loss of His Majesty's Ships *Prince of Wales* and *Repulse*, 10th December 1941' (1955)

ADM 234/331   BS No 16, 'Naval Operations at the Capture of Diego Suarez (Operation "Ironclad"), May 1942' (1943)

ADM 234/345   BS No 27, 'Naval Attacks on *Tirpitz*'

ADM 234/349–50   TIRPITZ. An account of the various attacks carried out by the British Armed Forces and their effect upon the German battleship' (1948). Vol 1, Report and Appendices (1948)

ADM 234/353   BS No 32, 'Malta Convoys' (1945)

ADM 234/358   BS No 37, 'The Invasion of Italy: Landing at Salerno ("Avalanche") (Naval Operations), 9th September 1943' (1946)

ADM 234/359   BS No 38, '"Operation Torch"; Invasion of North Africa, November 1942 to February 1943'.

ADM 234/363   BS No 49, 'The Campaign in North-West Europe, June 1944–May 1945' (1952)

ADM 234/364   BS No 36, 'Aegean Operations – 7th September to 28th November 1943: British occupation and German re-occupation of KOS and LEROS'

ADM 234/366   BS No 39, 'Operation "Neptune"; Landings in Normandy, June 1944' (1947)

ADM 234/368   BS No 47, 'Naval operations in the assault and capture of Okinawa, March–June 1945, Operation "Iceberg"' (1958)

ADM 234/369   BS No 22, 'Arctic Convoys 1941–45' (1954)

ADM 234/370   BS No 51, *Convoy and Anti-Submarine Warfare Reports*, No. 4. *Passage of Convoy S.C.104 – October 1942*

ADM 234/377   Naval Staff History, Second World War: *War with Japan*. Vol IV, 'The South-East Asia Operations and Central Pacific Advance' (1959)

ADM 234/378   Naval Staff History, *War with Japan*, Vol V, 'The Blockade of Japan' (1957)

ADM 234/382   Naval Staff History, *Submarines*, Vol III, 'Operation in Far Eastern Waters, Including the Operations of Allied Submarines' (1950)

ADM 234/508   BR 2055, 'Technical Report of Loss and Damage to H.M.S. ARK ROYAL' (1942)

ADM 234/509 The sinking of the *Bismarck*, 27th May 1941: Official Despatches

ADM 234/578 *Defeat of the Enemy Attack on Shipping, 1939–1945: A Study of Policy and Operations*, Vol 1A (Text and Appendices 1957)

ADM 234/873 'Orders, Reports and Signals relating to Operation Shingle'

b. *Air Ministry (AIR series)* Air Historical Branch Narratives:

AIR 41/10 The Rise and Fall of the German Air Force

AIR 41/19 The Royal Air Force in the Maritime War, Vol VI, The Mediterranean and Red Sea

AIR 41/20 A Review of the Campaign in Norway

AIR 41/23 The Liberation of North-West Europe, Vol I

AIR 41/24 The Liberation of North-West Europe, Vol II

AIR 41/25 The Middle East Campaigns, Vol II

AIR 41/26 The Middle East Campaigns, Vol III

AIR 41/34 The Italian Campaign, Vol I

AIR 41/44 The Middle East Campaigns, Vol I

AIR 41/45 The Royal Air Force in the Maritime War, Vol I

AIR 41/46 The Royal Air Force in the Maritime War, Vol II

AIR 41/47 The Royal Air Force in the Maritime War, Vol III

AIR 41/48 The Royal Air Force in the Maritime War, Vol IV

AIR 41/52 The Sicilian Campaign, Vol I

AIR 41/58 The Italian Campaign, Vol II

AIR 41/59 The Sicilian Campaign, Vol I

AIR 41/66 The Liberation of North-West Europe, Vol III

AIR 41/67 The Liberation of North-West Europe, Vol IV

AIR 41/68 The Liberation of North-West Europe, Vol V

c. *Cabinet and Cabinet Committees (CAB series)*

CAB 16/109–12 Reports, Proceedings and Memoranda of the Defence Requirements Sub-Committee of the Committee of Imperial Defence 1933–5

CAB 16/123 Defence Policy Requirements Committee of the Cabinet 1936

CAB 16/136–144 Minutes of Meetings of the Defence Policy Requirements Committee of the Cabinet 1936–9

CAB 16/209 Strategic Appreciation Committee of the Committee of Imperial Defence 1939

CAB 23/52–100 Conclusions of the Cabinet Meetings 1926–39

CAB 24 series Cabinet Memoranda 1919–1939

CAB 27/407 Fighting Services Committee 1929–30

CAB 27/606 Mediterranean Fleet Cabinet Committee 1936

CAB 27/627 Minutes and Memoranda of the Cabinet Committee on Foreign Policy 1936–9

CAB 27/648 Defence Programmes and Their Acceleration Cabinet Committee 1938

CAB 29/117, 118 Naval Conference, London, 1930

CAB 29/159   Anglo-French Staff Conversations, London, 1939
CAB 32 series   Imperial Conferences 1921–1939
CAB 53/1–11   Committee of Imperial Defence: Meetings of the Chiefs of
Staff Committee 1929–39
CAB 53/12–54   Committee of Imperial Defence: Memoranda of the Chiefs
of Staff Committee 1923–39
CAB 65 series   Conclusions of the War Cabinet 1939–45
CAB 66 series   War Cabinet Memoranda (CP and WP series)
CAB 69 series   War Cabinet Defence Committee (Operations)
CAB 70 series   War Cabinet Defence Committee: (Supply)
CAB 79 series   Chiefs of Staff Committee: Minutes of Meetings 1939–45
CAB 80 series   Chiefs of Staff Committee: Memoranda 1939–45
CAB 81 series   Chiefs of Staff Committee: Sub-Committees 1939–45
CAB 82 series   Deputy Chiefs of Staff Committee 1939–45
CAB 83/1–5   Ministerial Committee on Military Coordination 1939–40
CAB 84 series   Joint Planning Committee
CAB 86/1   Battle of the Atlantic Committee 1941–2
CAB 86/2–7   Anti-U-Boat Warfare Committee 1942–45
CAB 98/40   'Overlord' Committee 1944
CAB 105 series   War Cabinet: Telegrams

2. *Churchill Archives Centre, Churchill College, Cambridge*

ANCG: Admiral Sir Angus Cunninghame-Graham of Gartmore: Naval
papers and memoirs
AVAR: Earl Alexander of Hillsborough: Political papers
BRME: Captain J. H. Broome: Papers on Convoy PQ17, 1942
BUIS: Commander Colin Buist, RN: Naval signals of surrender of German
fleet, 1918
CLSN: Hugh Clausen, Naval armaments engineer: technical papers and
lectures
CUNN: Admiral of the Fleet Viscount Cunningham of Hyndhope: Corre-
spondence and material from various sources for the biography by Oliver
Warner
DENM: Captain H. N. Denham: Memoirs, papers and correspondence
concerning his time as Naval Attaché in Stockholm, 1940–45
DENN: A. G. Denniston: Papers on codebreaking in Room 40 during World
War I and ID 25 in World War II
DRAX: Admiral Sir Reginald Plunkett-Ernle-Erle-Drax: Naval and political
papers
DUPO: Admiral of the Fleet Sir Dudley Pound: Letters, cuttings and notes
collected for a projected biography by Donald McLachlan
EGBN: Edward George Bowen, scientist: Papers on the development of
radar
FWCT: Commander H. J. Fawcett: Anti-submarine warfare papers

GDFY: Admiral J. H. Godfrey: Memoirs
GOEV: Sir Charles Goodeve: Papers concerning weapons development
KEYN: Professor Richard Keynes: Anti-submarine Experimental Establishment correspondence and papers on naval radar development
MANP: Admiral Sir Manley Power: Autobiography
MCLN: Rear-Admiral Ian Maclean of Pennycross: Naval Papers
MLBE: Donald McLachlan and Patrick Beesly: Material for the *History of Naval Intelligence 1939–45*, and other works on naval intelligence
NRTH: Admiral Sir Dudley North: Papers concerning his dismissal from command, Gibraltar, 1940
OLVR: Admiral Sir Geoffrey Oliver: Naval and personal papers
RMSY: Admiral Sir Bertram Ramsay: Naval and personal papers; diaries
ROSK: Captain Stephen Roskill, RN: Historical and family papers including 'A Sailor's Ditty Box', a personal memoir
SMVL: Admiral Sir James Somerville: Naval and personal papers
WDVS: Admiral Sir William Davis: Autobiography
WLLS: Admiral of the Fleet Sir Algernon Willis: Naval papers

II PUBLISHED SOURCES

Barnett, Correlli, *The Audit of War*, Macmillan, London, 1986
  Bonaparte, Allen and Unwin, London, 1978
  Britain and Her Army, 1509–1920, Allen Lane, London, 1970
  The Collapse of British Power, Eyre Methuen, London, 1972
  The Desert Generals, Allen and Unwin, London, 1983
  The Great War, Park Lane Press, London, 1979
  The Swordbearers, Hodder and Stoughton, London, 1987
Baynes, John, *The Forgotten Victor; General Sir Richard O'Connor, KT, GCB, DSO, MC*, Brassey's Defence Publications, London, 1989
Beesly, Patrick, *Very Special Intelligence: The Story of the Admiralty's Operational Intelligence Centre 1939–1945*, Hamish Hamilton, London, 1977
Behrens, C. B. A., *Merchant Shipping and the Demands of War*, HMSO, and Longmans, Green, London, 1955
Bekker, Cajus, *Hitler's Naval War*, Macdonald, London, 1974
Bidwell, Shelford, *The Chindit War: the Campaign in Burma, 1944*, Hodder and Stoughton, London, 1979
Blumenson, Martin, *Rommel's Last Victory*, Allen and Unwin, London, 1968
Brooke, Geoffrey, *Alarm Starboard: A remarkable true story of the war at sea*, Patrick Stephens, Cambridge, 1982
Burn, Lampton, *Down Ramps: Saga of the 8th Armada*, Carroll and Nicholson, London, 1948
Butler, J. R. M., *Grand Strategy*, Vol II, *September 1939–June 1941*, HMSO, London, 1957; Vol III, Part II, June *1941–August 1942*, HMSO, London, 1961
Carton de Wiart, A., *Happy Odyssey*, Jonathan Cape, London, 1950

Cecil, Robert (ed), *Hitler's War Machine*, Leisure Books, London, 1975

Chalmers, Rear-Admiral W. S., *Full Cycle, The Biography of Admiral Sir Bertram Ramsay*, Hodder and Stoughton, London, 1959
  The Life and Letters of David, Earl Beatty, Hodder and Stoughton, London, 1951
  Max Horton and the Western Approaches, Hodder and Stoughton, London, 1954

Chandler, Alfred D. (ed), *The Papers of Dwight David Eisenhower, The War Years*, Vols I–IV, Johns Hopkins Press, 1970

Churchill, Winston S., *The Second World War*, Vol I, *The Gathering Storm*, Vol II, *Their Finest Hour*, Vol III, *The Grand Alliance*, Vol IV, *The Hinge of Fate*, Cassell, London, 1948–54
  The World Crisis: The Eastern Front, Thornton Butterworth, London, 1931

Cunningham, Admiral of the Fleet Lord, *A Sailor's Odyssey*, Hutchinson, London, 1957

Cunninghame-Graham, Angus, *Random Naval Recollections, 1905–51.* Famedram Publishers, Gartochan, 1979.

D'Este, Carlo, *Bitter Victory, The Battle for Sicily, July–August 1943*, Collins, London, 1988
  Decision in Normandy; the Unwritten Story of Montgomery and the Allied Campaign, Collins, London, 1983

Divine, David, *The Nine Days of Dunkirk*, Faber and Faber, London, 1959

Dönitz, Admiral Karl, *Memoirs: Ten Years and Twenty Days*, Weidenfeld and Nicolson, London, 1959

Ehrman, John, *Grand Strategy*, Vol V, *August 1943–September 1944*, HMSO, London, 1956

Eisenhower, Dwight D., *Crusade in Europe*, HMSO, London, 1945
  Supreme Commander's Report, HMSO, London, 1946

Ellis, John, *Cassino: the Hollow Victory; the Battle for Rome, January–June 1944*, André Deutsch, London, 1948

Ellis, L. F., *Victory in the West*, HMSO, London, 1962

Ensor, R. C. K., *England 1870–1914*, Clarendon Press, Oxford, 1966

Fergusson, Bernard, *The Watery Maze: The Story of Combined Operations*, Collins, London, 1961

Fraser, David, *Alanbrooke*, Collins, London, 1982
  And We Shall Shock Them: The British Army in the Second World War, Hodder and Stoughton, London, 1983

Fuller, J. F. C., *The Second World War, 1939–45*, Eyre and Spottiswoode, London, 1962

Gibbs, N. H., *Grand Strategy*, Vol I, *Rearmament Policy*, HMSO, London, 1976

Gilbert, Martin, *Winston S. Churchill*, Vol VI, *Finest Hour, 1939–41*, Book Club Associates, London, 1983; Vol VII, *Road to Victory 1941–45*, Heinemann, London, 1986

Graham, Dominick and Bidwell, Shelford, *Tug of War; The Battle for Italy, 1943–1945*, Hodder and Stoughton, London, 1986

Grove, Eric, Chant, Christopher, Lyon, David and Lyon, Hugh, *The Hardware of World War II*, Galley Press, London, 1984

Gwyer, J. M. A., *Grand Strategy*, Vol III, Part I, *June 1941–August 1942*, HMSO, London, 1964

Hackmann, Willem, *Seek and Strike; Sonar Antisubmarine Warfare and the Royal Navy, 1914–54*, HMSO, London, 1984

Haggie, Paul, *Britannia at Bay; The Defence of the British Empire against Japan, 1931–1941*, Clarendon Press, Oxford, 1981

Hall, H. Duncan, *North American Supply*, HMSO and Longmans, Green, London, 1955

Hamilton, Nigel, *Monty: the Making of a General, 1887–1942*, Hamish Hamilton, London, 1981; Monty: Master of the Battlefield, 1942–1944, Hamish Hamilton, London, 1983; Monty: The Field-Marshal, 1944–1976, Hamish Hamilton, London, 1986

Hancock, W. K. and Gowing, M. M., *British War Economy*, HMSO and Longmans, Green, London, 1949

Hardy, Hilbert, *The Minesweepers' Victory: A Silent Service of the Royal Navy*, Keydex, Weybridge, 1976.

Hastings, Max, *Bomber Command*, Michael Joseph, London, 1979
Overlord; D-Day and the Battle of Normandy, 1944, Michael Joseph, London, 1984

Hill-Norton, Admiral of the Fleet Lord, and Dekker, John, *Sea Power*, Faber and Faber, London, 1982

Hinsley, F. H., with Thomas, E. E., Ransom, C. F. G. and Knight, R. C., *British Intelligence in the Second World War. Its Influence on Strategy and Operations* (3 Vols) (Vol III Part Two by F. H. Hinsley with E. E. Thomas, C. A. G. Simkins and C. F. G. Ransom), HMSO, London, 1979–1984

Howard, Michael, *Grand Strategy*, Vol IV, *August 1942–September 1943*, HMSO, London, 1972

Ireland, Bernard, *The Rise and Fall of the Aircraft Carrier*, Marshall Cavendish, London, 1979

James, Sir William, *Admiral Sir William Fisher*, Macmillan, London, 1943

Kemp, P. K., *Fleet Air Arm*, Herbert Jenkins, London, 1954

Kennedy, Ludovic, *Pursuit: The Chase and Sinking of the Bismarck*, Collins, London, 1974

Kennedy, Paul M., *The Rise and Fall of British Naval Mastery*, Allen Lane, London, 1976

King, Fleet Admiral Ernest J., *U.S. Navy at War, 1941–45: Official Reports to the Secretary of the Navy*, United States Navy Department, 1946

Lenton, H. T., and College, J. J., *Warships of World War II*, Ian Allan, London, 1964

Leutze, James R., *Bargaining for Supremacy: Anglo-American Naval Relations, 1937–41*, Capel Hill, North Carolina, 1977
(ed), *The London Observer: The Journal of General Raymond E. Lee, 1940–41*, Hutchinson, London, 1972

Liddell Hart, B. H., *The British Way in Warfare*, Faber and Faber, London, 1932
  History of the Second World War, Cassell, London, 1970
March, Edgar J., *British Destroyers: A History of Development, 1892–1953*, Seeley Service, London, 1966
Marchant, Sir James (ed), *Winston Spencer Churchill, Servant of the Crown and Commonwealth*, Cassell, London, 1954
Marder, Arthur J., *From the Dreadnought to Scapa Flow; The Royal Navy in the Fisher Era, 1904–1919*, Vol III, *The War Years: To the Eve of Jutland*, Vol IV, *Jutland and After*, Oxford University Press, 1965
  Operation 'Menace': The Dakar Expedition and the Dudley North Affair, Oxford University Press, 1976
  'Winston is Back: Churchill at the Admiralty, 1939–40' in *The English Historical Review*, Supplement 5, Longmans, London, 1972
Maund, L. E. H., *Assault from the Sea*, Methuen, London, 1949.
McLachlan, Donald, *Room 39: Naval Intelligence in Action 1939–45*, Weidenfeld and Nicolson, London, 1968
Millington-Drake, E. (ed), *The Drama of the Graf Spee and the Battle of the River Plate: a Documentary Anthology: 1914–1964*, Peter Davies, London, 1964
Milner, Marc, *North Atlantic Run: The Royal Canadian Navy and the Battle of the Convoys*, University of Toronto Press, Toronto, 1985
Montgomery of Alamein, *Memoirs*, Collins, London, 1958
Morison, Samuel Eliot, *History of United States Naval Operations in World War II*, Vol I, *The Battle of the Atlantic, September 1939–May 1943*, Vol II, *Operations in North African Waters, October 1942–June 1943*, Little, Brown, Boston, 1960, Vol XI, *The Invasion of France and Germany 1944–1945* (1957), Vol XIV, *Victory in the Pacific 1945* (1960)
Moulton, J. L., *The Norwegian Campaign: A Study of Warfare in Three Dimensions*, Eyre and Spottiswoode, London, 1966
Müllenheim-Rechberg, Baron Burkhard von, *Battleship Bismarck: A Survivor's Story*, transl. Jack Sweetman, The Bodley Head, London, 1980
Newton, Don, and Hampshire, A. Cecil, *Taranto*, William Kimber, London, 1969
Orgill, Douglas, *The Gothic Line: The Autumn Campaign in Italy, 1944*, Heinemann, London, 1967
Pack, S. W. C., *The Battle of Matapan*, Batsford, London, 1961
Padfield, Peter, *Dönitz: the Last Führer*, Victor Gollancz, London, 1984
Parkes, Oscar, *British Battleships: 'Warrior' 1860 to 'Vanguard' 1950; A History of Design, Construction and Armament*, Seeley Service, London, 1970
Peden, G. C., *British Rearmament and the Treasury, 1932–1939*, Scottish Academic Press, Edinburgh, 1979
Playfair, Major-General I. S. O., *The Mediterranean and the Middle East*, Vol I, with Commander G. M. S. Stitt, RN, Brigadier C. J. C. Molony and Air Vice-Marshal S. E. Toomer, *The Early Successes against Italy (to May 1941)*; Vol II, with Captain F. C. Flynn, RN, Brigadier C. J. C. Molony and Air

Vice-Marshal S. E. Toomer, 'The Germans come to the aid of their Ally' (1941), Vol III, with Captain F. C. Flynn, RN, Brigadier C. J. C. Malony and Group-Captain T. P. Gleave, British Fortunes Reach Their Lowest Ebb, September 1941 to September 1942; Vol IV, with Brigadier C. J. C. Molony, Captain F. C. Flynn, RN, and Group-Captain T. P. Gleave, The Destruction of the Axis Forces in Africa, HMSO, London, 1954.

Pool, Richard, Course for Disaster: From Scapa Flow to the River Kwai, Leo Cooper, London, 1987

Postan, M. M., Hay, D. and Scott, J. D., Design and Development of Weapons, HMSO and Longmans, Green, London, 1964

Pugh, Philip, The Cost of Seapower; The Influence of Money on Naval Affairs from 1815 to the Present Day, Conway Maritime Press, London, 1986

Raeder, Admiral, Struggle for the Sea, William Kimber, London, 1959

Ranft, Bryan (ed.), Technical Change and British Naval Policy, 1860–1939, Hodder and Stoughton, London, 1977

Reynolds, David, The Creation of the Anglo-American Alliance, 1937–1941: A Study in Competitive Co-operation, Europa Publications, London, 1981

Rodger, N. M., The Wooden World; An Anatomy of the Georgian Navy, Fontana, London, 1989

Rohwer, Jürgen, The Critical Convoy Battles of March 1943, Ian Allan, London, 1977

Roskill, S. W., Admiral of the Fleet Earl Beatty; The Last Naval Hero: An Intimate Biography, Athenaeum, New York, 1981
Churchill and the Admirals, Collins, London, 1977
Naval Policy Between the Wars, Vol I, The Period of Anglo-American Antagonism, 1919–1929, Collins, London, 1968, Vol II, The Period of Reluctant Rearmament, 1981
The War at Sea, 1939–1945, Vol I, The Defensive, HMSO, London, 1954; Vol II, The Period of Balance, HMSO, London, 1956; Vol III, The Offensive, Part I, 1st June 1943–31st May 1944, HMSO, London, 1960; Part II, 1st June 1944–14th August 1945, HMSO, London, 1961
(ed), The Naval Air Service, The Naval Records Society, London, 1969

Rotherham, G. A., It's Really Quite Safe, Belville, Ontario, 1985

Ruge, Vice-Admiral F., Sea Warfare, 1939–1945, Cassell, London, 1957

Shay, R. P., Jr, British Rearmament in the 1930s. Politics and Profits, Princeton University Press, 1977

Sumida, Dr J. T. (ed), The Pollen Papers, George Allen and Unwin for The Naval Records Society, London, 1984

Spencer, John Hale, Battle for Crete, Heinemann, London, 1962

Stewart, I. Mc. D. G., The Struggle for Crete, 20 May–1 June 1941: A Story of Lost Opportunity, Oxford University Press, 1966

Tedder, Marshal of the Royal Air Force, Lord, With Prejudice, Cassell, London, 1966

Terraine, John, Business in Great Waters, Leo Cooper, London, 1989
The Right of the Line: The Royal Air Force in the European War, 1939–1945, Hodder and Stoughton, London, 1985

Thorne, Christopher, *Allies of a Kind; The United States, Great Britain and the War Against Japan, 1941–1945*, Hamish Hamilton, London, 1978

Turner, J. A., *Administration of the Navy Department in World War II*, US Department of the Navy, 1959

Van Crefeld, Martin, *Supplying War*, Cambridge University Press, 1977

Vian, Admiral Sir Philip, *Action this Day: the War Memoirs of Sir Philip Vian*, Frederick Muller, London, 1960

Waddington, C. H. *Operational Research in World War II: Operational Research against the U-boat*. Elek Science, London, 1973.

Warner, Oliver, *Cunningham of Hyndhope: Admiral of the Fleet*, John Murray, London, 1967

Warren, C. E. T., and Benson, J., *Above Us the Waves*, Harrap, London, 1953

Watts, Anthony, *The U-Boat Hunters*, Macdonald and Jane's, London, 1976

Weale, Elke C., Weale, John A. and Barker, Richard, *Combat Aircraft of World War Two*, Bracken Books, London, 1985

Webster, C. and Frankland, N., *The Strategic Air Offensive Against Germany, 1939–1945*, Vol I, *Preparations*; Vol II, *Encounter*; Vol III, *Victory*; Vol IV, *Annexes and Appendices*, HMSO, London, 1961

Werth, Alexander, *Russia at War, 1941–1945*, Barrie and Rockliff, London, 1964

Williams, John, *The Guns of Dakar: September 1940*, Heinemann, London, 1976

Winton, J., *Air Power at Sea, 1939–45*, Sidgwick and Jackson, London, 1976

Wohlstetter, Roberta, *Pearl Harbor: Warning and Decision*, Stanford University Press, California, 1962

Woodburn Kirby, S., *The War against Japan*, Vol I, *The Loss of Singapore*, HMSO, London, 1957

Ziegler, Philip, *Mountbatten*, Collins, London, 1985

RUSI Journal, Vol 134, No 1, Marc Milner, 'The Dawn of Modern Anti-Submarine Warfare; Allied Responses to the U-boats, 1944–5'

Telecommunications Research Establishment Journal, July 1945, A. C. B. Lovell, 'The Radar Battle of the Bay of Biscay'

Index

Beatty, Admiral Sir David – *cont.*
 1926 Imperial Conference, 22; and
 Singapore naval base, 23; leadership
 qualities of, 50
Beaverbrook, Lord (Minister of Aircraft
 Production): proposes handing
 Coastal Command to the Navy, 199;
 questions impact on shipping
 resources of sustaining Greek
 campaign, 330
Bechstolsheim, Captain Baron von (8th
 Destroyer Flotilla), 831
Beda Fomm, Italian Army cut off at, 317,
 318, 326
Bedouin, HMS (destroyer): attacks Italian
 cruisers, 507–8; sunk, 710
Belfast, HMS (cruiser) (1939), 43, 741, 815;
 damaged by magnetic mine, 91; and
 action against *Scharnhorst*, 742–3; in
 'Operation Neptune', 815
Belgium: supplies craft for 'Operation
 Dynamo', 146
Bell, Captain F. S. (*Exeter*), 83, 85
Bell, Captain L. H., 408; describes Admiral
 Phillips's strategy, 410; and Japanese
 attack on *Prince of Wales*, 415
Bellona, HMS (cruiser), 748
Benghazi, 214, 317, 326; bombardment of,
 368; blockading of, 374, 375
Ben-My-Chree, HMS (seaplane carrier), 11
Ben-My-Chree, SS: refuses to return to
 Dunkirk, 159–60
Benn, Captain W. G., 70
Bennington, Lt-Cmdr (*Tally Ho*), 871
Bergamini, Admiral, 669
Bergen, Norway, 99, 101; convoys from, 67;
 Allied plans to seize, 100, 102, 107;
 German troops head for, 104; and take,
 112; Forbes proposes attack on, 113;
 Königsberg sunk at, 117; Allied plans
 to recapture, 118; *Bismarck* calls at,
 285
Berlin, Battle of, 738
Bermuda, 27
Bermuda, HMS (cruiser), 559
Bernhardstellung (Bernhard Line), 680
Berwick, HMS (cruiser), 241; in Force F, 79;
 in 'Operation Wilfred', 107; sails for
 Norway, 129; in hunt for *Admiral
 Scheer*, 197; joins Atlantic service, 238,
 239; in action against *Admiral Hipper*,
 243; and Arctic convoys, 697
Béthouart, General, 134
Beveziers (French submarine), 205
Bey, Admiral Erich, 739; and *Scharnhorst*'s
 sortie, 740, 741, 742, 744

Bickford, Lt-Cmdr E. O. B. (*Salmon*):
 damages two battlecruisers, 90
Bideford, HMS (sloop), 149
Bidwell, Brigadier Shelford, 689
Birmingham, HMS (cruiser), 128; and
 evacuations from Norway, 130;
 ordered to refuel, 284; searches for
 Bismarck, 287, 300; bombed, 513
Biscayne, USS (headquarters ship), 677, 687
Bismarck (battleship), 253, 394, 696, 802;
 outmoded armour protection of, 42,
 283; sets out on 'Operation
 Rheinübung', 278, 279, 283;
 description of, 281–2; Lütjens fails to
 oil, 284–5; calls at Bergen, 285; the
 search for, 286–8; sighted, 289, 290,
 291; ships' deployment, 292; in action,
 293–5; efforts to intercept, 299–304;
 Lütjens's demoralising speech to crew,
 305, 311; located by Coastal
 Command, 306; strike force from *Ark
 Royal* hits, 308–9; ship damaged,
 309–10; final engagement, 312–14;
 sinking of, 314, 316
Bison (French destroyer), 131, 132
Bisset, Captain A. W. La T. (*Formidable*), 337;
 as Rear-Admiral, in 'Avalanche', 667;
 and surrender of Italian Fleet, 668, 669
Biter, HMS (escort carrier), 583, 585; in
 'Operation Torch', 553, 555, 565; and
 escort carrier support groups, 600, 603,
 609
Bizerta, 569, 667; Allied armies take, 626,
 634; 'Husky' convoys from, 637
Blackburn Botha aircraft: operational failure
 of, 64–5
Blackburn Aircraft Ltd: production
 problems with Skuas, 38; and Bothas,
 64–5
Black Prince, HMS (cruiser), 815; in Pacific
 Fleet, 879
Black Swan escort sloops, 585
Blackwood, HMS (destroyer), 832
Blagrove, Rear-Admiral H. E. C., 71
Blake, Admiral Sir Geoffrey (2nd-in-
 Command, Mediterranean Fleet), 50
Blake, Robert, 50
Blenheim aircraft, 65
Blenkhorn, Petty-Officer, 338
Blücher (cruiser), 112
'blue water' strategy, 165; Britain resorts to
 in Mediterranean and Middle East after
 fall of France, 165; heavy investment in
 shipping and warships required for,
 165–6, 236; implications of for Royal
 Navy, 167; traditional 'British way of